C000005662

Ramsay's

Catalogue of

BRITISH DIECAST
MODEL TOYS

TENTH EDITION

SWAPMEET

PUBLICATIONS

Swapmeet Publications
PO Box 47, Felixstowe, Suffolk, IP11 9HE
Phone (01394) 670700, Fax: (01394) 670730
Web site: www.swapmeet.co.uk
E-mail: info@swapmeet.co.uk

Swapmeet Toys and Models Ltd., t/a Swapmeet Publications
Reg. No. 1715966. Reg. Office: 36 Rembrandt Way, Bury St Edmunds, Suffolk. Directors: E. J. Ramsay, S. E. Ramsay, Co. Sec. M. J. Ramsay, BA.

Originator and Editor
John Ramsay

Technical Editor
John King

1st Edition published 1983
2nd Edition published 1986
3rd Edition published 1988
3rd Edition Update published 1989
4th Edition published 1991
5th Edition published 1993
6th Edition published 1995
7th Edition published 1997
8th Edition published 1999
9th Edition published 2001
10th Edition published 2003

ISBN 09528352 – 8 – 2

Book designed by John King.
Origination by Swapmeet Publications, Felixstowe.
Printed by Norwich Colour Print Ltd.

Models featured on the front cover are: a 1958 Dinky Toys 923 Big Bedford Van 'Heinz' (with tomato ketchup bottle decal) on its original box (sold by Vectis Auctions Ltd), and a French Dinky Toys 1453E Citroën Présidentielle with its 1977 presentation box. (sold by Collectoys, France).

Contents

CONTENTS continued

Acknowledgements

The Editor would like to express appreciation to the following collectors, traders, auctioneers and manufacturers, who very kindly took the time and trouble to provide updating information and photographs about new entries and colour variations, etc.

John Kinchen, Hampshire
David Cooke, Norwich
Derek Barratt, Norwich
Bruce Hoy, Queensland, Australia
Brian Goodall and Simon Smith,
  Vectis Auctions Ltd, Stockton-on-Tees
Hugo Marsh, Christie's Model Auctions
Neil-John Leonard,
  Lacy Scott & Knight Model Auctions,
  Bury St Edmunds

Glen Butler, Wallis & Wallis
  Auctioneers, Lewes, Sussex
Barry Potter of Barry Potter Auctions
Hans-Peter Brüggemann, Bremen
Robert Newson, Wood Green, London
Mike and Sue Richardson, Windsor
Simon Welham, Shenfield, Essex
Andrew Rimmer, Thame, Oxon.
Mr A.D. Wheeler-Osman,
  Southampton
Philip Hill, Maidstone
Anthony F. Sweatman, Coventry
J.S. Ross, Edinburgh
John Rhodes, Emsworth, Hants.
James H. Ingham, Preston
Peter Gibson, Orpington
Herbert Bell, Greenwood,
  Western Australia

Mr Boxall, Arundel, Sussex
C.J. Bates, Newcastle-under Lyme
Andy Woodall, Bury St Edmunds
Bernard Houssard, Brussels, Belgium
Edwina Farrow (by e-mail)
Pierre A. Blanc (by e-mail)
Phillipe Salmon, Collectoys,
  Bourges, France
Andrew Hilton and Nigel Mynheer,
  Special Auction Services, Midgham
Vincent Espinasse, France
Horace Dunkley, Stamford, Lincs.
Nigel Cooper, Basingstoke
Trevor Bannister, Seaford
Leigh Gotch, Bonhams Auctioneers
Kevin McGimpsey (MICA),
  Deeside, Flintshire

Introduction

Welcome to the 10th Edition of the 'British Diecast Model Toys Catalogue' which incorporates the greatest change in its format since the first edition was published in 1983.

As from this edition, the Catalogue will specialise in providing comprehensive information on model toys produced during the 20th century up until 1983.

In addition, to satisfy the changing market requirements for up to date and accurate information, the Catalogue will in future be available on a greatly improved annual basis. This development in the Catalogue's format reflects the great changes in the market place which have occurred since it was first published twenty years ago.

Today's market is an exciting and fast-moving environment with far greater opportunities than ever before, both for the trade and the collector. With the ever-growing availability of the Internet, today's market place is truly worldwide with twenty-four hour, round-the-clock online auctions taking place. Traditional specialist auction houses are also maintaining a constant (and in some cases, increasing) flow of models through their salerooms.

The poor performance of the stockmarket in the 1990s has forced people to seek alternative investments. Consequently, there has been a marked increase in the buying of good quality model toys (mostly from specialist auctions) for investment purposes, and with it has come an unprecedented rise in the value of rare models.

Today's traders and keen collectors have in turn matched the change in the market by becoming more specialist and demanding. Present day manufacturers have established a new collecting market and have produced for it a tremendous and seemingly endless range of products to offer the public. Consequently, the need has never been stronger for an up to date and reliable Catalogue that provides specialist information on the truly collectable model variations along with fully-researched, accurate price information.

The Catalogue has therefore changed its format to meet the demands of today's collector of important diecast models from the past. Regrettably, it will no longer be possible to provide listings of 'modern' diecasts, i.e., those produced since 1983. Their sheer volume of production and rate of issue make them incompatible with our intended format of providing specialist information on variations and up to date price guidance. Collectors of present-day products are however amply catered for by the manufacturers and by various collector clubs. Information on all of these is given in this Catalogue.

The space vacated by 'modern' diecasts has provided us with an excellent opportunity to include a new and comprehensive listing of French Meccano Dinky Toys, which we know will fill a large market gap. In addition, we have expanded the English Dinky Toys listing of Trade Boxes and have included a first listing of Nicky Toys plus a new Britains listing by James Opie. Finally, there are comprehensive Auction Price Results (including a useful selection of British tinplate sales) which we believe will help underpin the price guidance throughout the Catalogue.

We trust that the new format will meet with your requirements and as always we welcome your suggestions as to how it may be further improved.

Based on the findings of the Market Surveys undertaken since 1983 virtually all the models have been given a 'Market Price Range'. The price gap between the lower and higher figures indicates the likely price range a collector should expect to pay for the model.

Models qualifying for a price at the top end of the range could include:

- Boxed models where both the model and the box are in pristine condition,
- A scarce or unusual colour
- An unusual component such as special wheels
- A model with pristine decals where this is unusual
- A model in an unusual or special box
- A model priced by a trader who disagrees with the price range quoted in the Catalogue (which is only a guide).

PRICES FOR MODELS IN LESS THAN MINT BOXED CONDITION

Many boxed models seen for sale fail to match up to the exacting standards on which the Market Price Range has been based, having slight model or box damage. In these instances models may be priced at 50% to 60% of the Market Price Range shown, and this is particularly relevant when a model is common. Boxed models with considerable damage or models lacking their original box will be priced much lower.

Note: It cannot be over-emphasised that irrespective of the price guidance provided by this Catalogue, collectors should not always expect to see prices asked within the price ranges shown. Traders will ask a price based on their trading requirements and will NOT be governed by any figures shown in this Catalogue, nor could they be reasonably expected to do so.

MODELS NOT GIVEN A 'MARKET PRICE RANGE'

It has not been possible to give every model a price range and these exceptions are as follows:

NPP   No Price Possible
This is shown alongside models never encountered in the survey or about which there is doubt as to their actual issue, even though a model may have been pictured in a catalogue. Readers will appreciate that unlike postage stamps or coins, no birth records are available in respect of all the die-cast models designed or issued.

NGPP   No Grading Possible at Present
Price grading may not be possible at present because:
i) The model or gift set is particularly rare and has not come to market in recent times. Consequently, no price grading has been shown as the Compiler believes that to attempt one would be carrying rarity and value assessment into the realms of pure guesswork. As and when information becomes available concerning these rarities it will be included in the Catalogue.
ii) The model may have been recently introduced or announced in the model press or in a manufacturer's own literature, but a price has not yet been suggested or communicated to us.

GSP   Gift Set Price
If a model forms part of a Set (and is not available separately) the price range will be shown against the entry in the relevant Gift Set section and will refer to the complete set.

DESCRIPTION OF MODEL COLOURS

The descriptions of the various colours used to describe model colour variations have been derived from the following sources:
i)   Manufacturers colour descriptions.
ii) Colours commonly used and known to refer to certain models over a period of many years
iii) Colours which we in consultation with the trade or specialist collectors decide most closely describes a previously unrecorded genuine colour variation
iv) Colours given a model by an bonafide auction house. If this model is a previously unrecorded colour variation we will include the variation in future catalogue listings provided that:
a) The auctioneers are themselves satisfied that the model is genuine and not a repaint
b) Specialist dealers and collectors who view the model are satisifed that the colour variation is genuine and is not a repaint.

SCARCE COLOURS AND VARIATIONS

Collectors or traders who know of other variations which they believe warrant a separate listing are invited to forward this information to the Editor together with any supporting evidence.

AUCTION PRICE REALISATIONS
Prices of common models sold are often less than the Market Price Range figures shown. In many instances, the models have been purchased by the trade who will add their own mark-up.

The condition of a model and its accompanying box does of course have a direct bearing on its value which makes accurate condition grading a matter of key importance.

Unlike other collecting hobbies such as stamps or coins, no one universal grading system is used to classify the condition of models and boxes. Nevertheless, whilst several versions exist, there are really two main systems of condition classification in the UK as follows:

1. The 'Specific Condition' Grading System
The following example is fairly typical of the types of descriptions and gradings seen on Mail Order lists.

M.........Mint AM......Almost Mint
VSC ....Very Slightly Chipped SC ....Slightly Chipped
C ....Chipped VC.......Very Chipped

If a model is described as Mint Boxed, the condition of its box is not normally separately described. However, it is expected to be in first class and as near original condition as is possible, bearing in mind the age of the model concerned.

If a box is damaged the flaws are usually separately described. This method has always seemed to work out quite well in practice, for all reputable dealers automatically offer a 'Sale or Return if not satisfied' deal to their clients, which provides the necessary safeguard against the misrepresentation of the model's condition. The Compiler would stress that the foregoing is only an example of a mail order condition grading system and stricter box grading definitions are known to exist.

2. The 'General Condition' Grading System
This method is often used by auctioneers although it is also to be seen used on the occasional mail order list.

(M)   Mint (E)   Excellent
(G)   Good (F)   Fair
(P)   Poor

Usually these gradings are separately applied to describe firstly the condition of the model and secondly the condition of the box. From our observations and purely for guidance purposes, we would suggest the following descriptions approximately represent the different grades.

MODEL CONDITION GRADINGS
1. MINT (M)
The model must be complete and as fresh, new and original in appearance as when first received from the manufacturers.

2. EXCELLENT (E)
The model is almost in mint condition and is only barred from that classification by having a few slight flaws, e.g., slight paintwork chipping in unimportant areas.

3. GOOD (G)
The model is in a complete and original condition and retains an overall collectable appearance despite having a few chips or rubbed paintwork.

4. FAIR (F)
The model may not be in its original state having, for example, a broken bumper, replacement radiator or windscreen, or it may have signs of metal fatigue. The paintwork may be faded, well chipped, retouched or repainted. There may be signs of rust. Unless the model is rare it is in a barely collectable condition.

5. POOR (P)
The model may be damaged, incomplete, repainted, altered, metal fatigued, or have a rusted baseplate or heavily chipped paintwork, etc. Unless the model is rare it has little real value to a collector other than as a candidate for a complete restoration or use as spares.

BOX CONDITION GRADINGS
1. MINT (M)
The box must be complete both inside and out and contain all the original packing materials, manufacturer's leaflet and box labels. It should look as fresh, new and original in appearance as when first received from the manufacturers.

2. EXCELLENT (E)
The box is in almost mint condition but is only barred from that classification by just the odd minor blemish, e.g., there may be slight damage to the display labels caused by bad storage. The original shop price label may have been carelessly removed and caused slight damage. The cover of a bubble pack may be cracked or there may be very slight soiling etc.

3. GOOD (G)
The box is complete both inside and out, and retains an overall attractive collectable appearance. Furthermore, despite showing a few signs of wear and tear, it does not appear 'tired'.

4. FAIR (F)
The box will have a 'tired' appearance and show definite signs of wear and tear. It may be incomplete and not contain the original packing materials or leaflets. In addition it may not display all the exterior identification labels or they may be torn or soiled or a box-end flap may be missing or otherwise be slightly damaged. In this condition, unless the model is particularly rare, it will not add much to the model's value.

5. POOR (P)
The box will show considerable signs of wear and tear. It will almost certainly be badly damaged, torn, incomplete or heavily soiled and in this condition, unless it is very rare, is of little value to a collector.

Model and Box Valuation Guidelines

The research has produced the following comparative price information concerning the values of both unboxed models and separate boxes in the various condition classifications.

The guidelines have been based on the 'General Condition' grading system as described in the previous section. The percentage value ranges are designed to reflect the relatively higher values of the rarer models and boxes.

UNBOXED MODEL CLASSIFICATION	% VALUE OF MINT BOXED MODEL
Mint	50% - 60%
Excellent	40% - 50%
Good	20% - 40%
Fair	10% - 20%
Poor	0% - 10%

BOX CLASSIFICATION	%VALUE OF MINT BOXED MODEL
Mint	40% - 50%
Excellent	30% - 40%
Good	20% - 30%
Fair	10% - 20%
Poor	0% - 10%

Note: The same model may have been issued in two or more types of box (Yesteryears for example). The model in the earlier box is usually (though not always) the more valuable.

Rare Models and Sets

The exceptions to the foregoing guidelines are in respect of rare models or boxes, or models seldom found in first class condition such as some pre-war models. In these situations rarity commands a premium and the asking price or the price realised at auction will almost certainly reflect it.

Selling models to the Trade

The model value figures produced by the Price Grading system always refer to the likely *asking prices* for models.

They have been prepared solely to give collectors an idea of the amount they might reasonably expect to pay for a particular model.

The figures given are *not* intended to represent the price which will be placed on a model when it is offered for sale to a dealer. This is hardly surprising bearing in mind that the dealer is carrying all the expense of offering his customers a collecting service which costs money to maintain.

Collectors should not therefore be surprised when selling models to the trade to receive offers which may appear somewhat low in comparison with the figures shown in the Catalogue.

Dealers are always keen to replenish their stocks with quality items and will as a result normally make perfectly fair and reasonable offers for models. Indeed, depending on the particular models offered to them, the actual offer made may well at times exceed the levels indicated in the Catalogue which are only *guidelines* and not firm figures.

One last point when selling models to the trade: do get quotations from two or three dealers, especially if you have rare models to be sold.

How to use the Catalogue

Identifying models from their lettering

All lettering shown in CAPITAL LETTERS indicates the actual lettering on the model itself. It may appear in either the Model Type (vehicle) or Model Features (description) column. Similarly *lettering in Italics* indicates that it is shown on the actual model.

Abbreviations

In this 9th Edition dependence on abbreviations has been reduced to a minimum but where necessary they are used to include information concisely. An Abbreviations list is included (near the back of the book) and provides additional and helpful information.

Catalogue omissions

Accurate birth records do not exist in respect of all the die-cast models issued. Therefore whilst every effort has been made to provide comprehensive information it is inevitable that collectors will have knowledge of models which have not been included. Consequently the Compiler will be pleased to receive details of these models in order that they may be included in future editions. Naturally, supporting evidence regarding authenticity will be required.

This Catalogue has been prepared solely for use as a reference book and guide to the rarity and asking prices of die-cast model toys.

Whilst every care has been taken in compiling the Catalogue, neither the Compiler nor the publishers can accept any responsibility whatsoever for any financial loss which may occur as a result of its use.

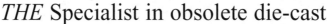

If you are really serious about buying or selling diecast models, there is only one place to visit . . .

Sandown Park

Europe's No.1 Toy Collectors Fair

Sandown Exhibition Centre, Sandown Park Racecourse, Esher, Surrey

10:30am - 4:00pm

2004 Sandown Dates

Saturday 10th January
Saturday 6th March
Saturday 31st July
Saturday 30th October

The finest 500 Stalls in Britain

Meet all the country's Top Dealers and Collectors and see the best of everything in Collectable Toys and Trains.

Sandown Park is only 5 miles from Junction 10 of the M25.
Free Parking is available for 6,000 cars.
Regular trains run from Waterloo to Esher.

Adults £4-50   Seniors £4-00   Children £2-00

Call us for a free detailed calendar of events on 01604 770025 or 01858 468459

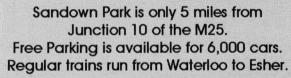

BARRY POTTER ..... *Fairs* .....

Full details also available on our website: www.barrypotterfairs.com

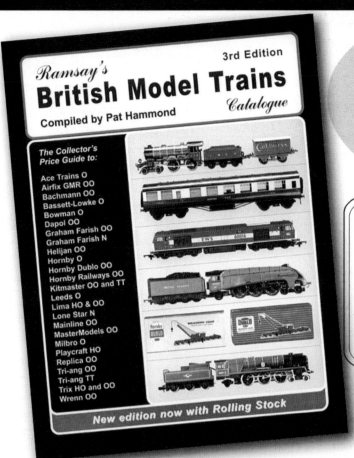

Benbros and Zebra Toys

The following history and listings of Benbros and Zebra models have been provided by Robert Newson.

Benbros was started in the late 1940s by brothers Jack and Nathan Benenson, at Walthamstow in north-east London. They first called themselves 'Benson Bros.' and made diecast toys and lead figures (some of which are marked 'Benson'). The name Benbros was adopted in 1951. One of their best known die-cast toys was a miniature coronation coach, copied from the Moko-Lesney coach. Their range of large die-cast toys was expanded during the 1950s with re-issues of various Timpo Toys, for which Benbros had acquired the dies. The miniature

'T.V. Series' was introduced in late 1954, packed in individual boxes which resembled a 1950s television set. By 1956 there were 24 models in the T.V. Series, and soon after this the packaging was changed to red and yellow 'Mighty Midget' boxes. The Mighty Midgets were available up to 1965.

The Zebra Series was introduced in the 1960s in an attempt to update the range with better features and more accurate models. However, toy production was discontinued when Benbros was taken over in 1965.

NB See the 'Miscellaneous Models' colour section for additional pictures.

Benbros 'AA' Land-Rover, **Benbros** 'AA' Motor Cycle Patrol, **Zebra Toys** No.6 'AA' Triumph Motor Cycle and Sidecar

Benbros 'Mighty Midgets' ('Qualitoys' Series) 36 'ROYAL MAIL' Land-Rover, 13 Austin Champ, 30 AEC Army Box Van

Photographs: Vectis Auctions Ltd.

Benbros 'T.V. Series' and 'Mighty Midgets'

Ref	Year(s)	Model name	Colours, features, details	Market Price Range

Most models came in a wide range of colours, so these have not been listed in the main, but full details of colours and other variations are given in the illustrated booklet 'Benbros T.V. Series & Mighty Midgets' by Robert Newson.

Ref	Model name	Colours, features, details	Market Price Range
1	Horse Drawn Hay Cart	With man and raves. Later models marked 'BENBROS'	£20-25
2	Horse Drawn Log Cart	With man and 'log', 'Made in England' under horse	£20-25
3	A.A. Motorcycle and Sidecar	With rider and separate windscreen. 'Made in England' under sidecar	£20-30
4	Stage Coach (with four horses)	'KANSAS STAGE' cast in, separate driver on some, 'BENBROS' on later models	£20-25
5	Horse Drawn Gipsy Caravan	No maker's name on model	£75-100
6	Horse Drawn Milk Cart	Milkman and horse, two separate or cast-in churns, 'BENBROS' on later models	£20-25
7	Three-wheeled Electric Milk Trolley	With milkman, 'EXPRESS DAIRY' cast in	£20-25
8	Foden Tractor and Log Trailer	With log (wood dowel)	£20-25
9	Dennis Fire Escape	Separate wheeled escape ladder	£20-25
10	Crawler Bulldozer	with rubber tracks	£15-20
11	Crawler Tractor with Hay Rake	Rubber tracks. Same basic casting as no. 10. No maker's name on model	£15-20
12	Army Scout Car	Separate or cast-in driver	£15-20
13	Austin Champ	Separate or cast-in driver	£15-20
14	Centurion Tank	with rubber tracks	£15-20
15	Vespa Scooter	With rider	£25-30
16	Streamlined Express Loco	('TV Series' only). Runs on four concealed wheels	£15-20
16	Chevrolet Nomad Station Wagon	('Mighty Midget' only). Most models have silver painted flash	£15-20
17	Crawler Tractor with Disc Harrow	Rubber tracks. Same tractor as no. 11. No maker's name on model	£15-20
18	Hudson Tourer	Same chassis as no. 16	£15-20
19	Crawler Tractor and Trailer	Rubber tracks. Same tractor as nos. 11 and 17. No maker's name on model	£15-20
20	Foden 8-wheel Flat Lorry	Early models in two-tone colours	£30-40
21	Foden 8-wheel Open Lorry	Early models in two-tone colours	£30-40
22	ERF Petrol Tanker	Similar to Matchbox 11a. No adverts or with 'Esso' transfer on one side	£30-40
23	AEC Box Van	No transfers. Open rear end	£20-25
23	Bedford Box Van	Without adverts or with 'Dunlop' transfers. Open rear end	£20-25
24	Field Gun	Solid wheels. No maker's name on model. Working firing mechanism	£10-15
25	Spyker	Similar to Charbens no. 2. Both models are marked with the maker's name	£10-15
26	1904 Vauxhall 5 hp	Same chassis as no.25. Colours observed: Silver or Yellow body, both with Black chassis; Red wheels	£10-15
27	1906 Rolls-Royce	Same chassis as no.25. Colours observed: Silver or Blue body, both with Black chassis; Red wheels	£10-15
28	Foden 8-wheel Flat Lorry with Chains	'Chains' are cast with the body; wheels may be unpainted metal or Black plastic	£20-25
29	RAC Motorcycle and Sidecar	Blue rider, separate windscreen and sidecar. 'Made in England' under sidecar, 'RAC' cast on front	£20-30
30	AEC Army Box Van	Same casting as no. 23 in Military Green paint; wheels may be painted or unpainted	£20-25
30	Bedford Army Box Van	Same casting as no. 23 in Military Green paint with red/yellow squadron transfer; wheels unpainted	£20-25
31	AEC Covered Lorry	Cast metal 'canvas' tilt, riveted in place. Colours seen: Red, Green, Metallic Blue, unpainted wheels	£20-25
31	Bedford Covered Lorry	Cast 'canvas' tilt, riveted in place. Colours seen: Red, Blue, Metallic Blue, unpainted wheels	£20-25
32	AEC Compressor Lorry	Body usually painted Yellow with unpainted metal wheels	£20-25
32	Bedford Compressor Lorry	Body usually painted Yellow with unpainted metal wheels	£20-25
33	AEC Crane Lorry	No hook cast. Colours seen: Orange, Metallic Brown, Metallic Blue, Metallic Green	£20-25
33	Bedford Crane Lorry	No hook. Colours (unpainted wheels): Green, Beige, Orange. With plastic wheels: Red, Yellow, Cream	£20-25
34	A.A. Land Rover	'AA ROAD SERVICE' cast in, open rear end. Bright or Dark Yellow; wheels may be painted or not	£30-40
35	Army Land Rover	Military-Green body and wheels (usually), open rear end, red/yellow squadron transfer on some	£15-20
36	Royal Mail Land Rover	Red body and wheels (usually), 'ROYAL MAIL E-II-R' cast in, open rear end	£20-30
37	Wolseley Six-Eighty Police Car	Black body, unpainted wheels, loud-hailers cast into roof. A little smaller than Budgie no. 5	£30-40
38	Daimler Ambulance	Similar to Matchbox 14b. Off-White (civilian) and Matt or Gloss Dark Green (military) versions	£20-25
39	Bedford Milk Float	Similar to Matchbox 29a. Orange or Red body, White crates. Wheels: White metal or Black plastic	£15-20
40	American Ford Convertible	Early issues: Light Blue or Red body with press-fit base, unpainted metal wheels	£20-25
		Later issues: Blue, Green or Silver body with rivetted base, Black plastic wheels	£20-25
41	Army Hudson Tourer	No. 18 in Military-Green, squadron transfer on some, unpainted metal wheels or Black plastic wheels	£20-25
42	Army Dispatch Motorcycle and Sidecar	Castings as nos. 3 and 29, 'Made in England' and 'AA' or 'RAC' cast on sidecar	£20-30
43-48	Bedford Articulated vehicles	Early issue tractor units are usually seen in Red, Orange or Yellow and have unpainted metal wheels. Later issue tractor units are usually seen in Blue, Beige, Green, Red or Yellow with Black plastic wheels.	
43	Bedford Articulated Box Van	Trailer colours seen: Yellow, Blue, Beige. 'Dunlop' transfers on some	£20-25
44	Bedford Articulated Crane Lorry	Yellow or Light Blue trailer with Silver plastic wheels; or Red or Cream trailer with Black plastic wheels	£20-25
NB		The box for this model is marked 'Articulated Low Loader' and has an illustration showing such a vehicle carrying a load of wooden planks. The illustrated version was not put into production.	
45	Bedford Articulated Timber Lorry	With 'log' (wood dowel); various trailer colours, unpainted metal wheels or Black or Silver plastic wheels	£20-25
46	Bedford Articulated Petrol Tanker	Various shades of Red possible, without adverts or with 'Esso' transfer on one side only	£20-30
47	Bedford Articulated Dropside Lorry	Box description: 'Articulated Waggon'. Red, Blue or Light Blue trailer, metal or Black plastic wheels	£20-25
48	Bedford Articulated Lorry with Chains	'Chains' are cast with the model. Red, Blue or Beige trailer, Silver trim on some, Black plastic wheels	£20-25
49	Karrier Bantam Bottle Lorry	Similar to Matchbox 37a. 'Drink Coca-Cola' transfers. No maker's name, Black plastic wheels	£30-40
50	RAC Land Rover	Blue body, 'RAC ROAD SERVICE' cast in, open rear	NGPP

Benbros 'Zebra Toys'

Zebra Toys were introduced in the early 1960s and were manufactured along with the existing production of large scale Benbros vehicles. Zebra Toys were packaged in distinctive black and white striped boxes. Most of the models had jewelled headlights and some also had windows and plastic interiors.

The AA and RAC Mini Vans apparently had not been introduced when toy production by Benbros came to an end in 1965. They do not appear on a trade price list dated January 1965 but a small number of these models (probably a trial run) were sold off with the remaining toy stocks and are now in the hands of collectors.

In the following list, numbers in brackets are those shown on Zebra boxes. The other numbers are cast on the models themselves. There seems to be no connection between the two numbering systems! Original retail prices (quoted in shillings and pre-decimal pence) are those given in 1964 and 1965 trade price lists. These models are rare in today's market.

Ref	Year(s)	Model name	Colours, features, details	Market Price Range
100 (16)		Foden Concrete Mixer	Red cab and chassis, Beige or Yellow barrel, 70 mm. (3s 1d)	£70-90
101 (36)		Scammell Scarab Articulated Van 'BRITISH RAILWAYS'	Maroon cab and trailer, Pale Orange or Mustard-Yellow tilt, 105 mm. (4s. 4d.)	£70-90
103 (10)		Jaguar 'E'-type	Metallic Light Green, Metallic Light Blue or Metallic Light Brown, 90 mm. (3s 0d)	£75-100
104 (30)		Routemaster Bus	Red, *'Fina Petrol goes a long way'* adverts, 111 mm. (4s. 11d.)	£100-150
106 (34)		Heinkel Bubble Car	Red or Blue body, 100 mm. (4s 4d)	£75-100
107 (27)		Daimler Ambulance	Cream body, 101 mm. (4s 1d)	£75-100
--- (20)		Bedford Cattle Transporter	Red cab and chassis, Light Brown body, 101 mm. (4s. 4d.)	£70-90
---		Lansing Bagnall Rapide 2000	Fork Lift Truck, Red body, 89 mm. (3s. 6d.)	£70-90
---		Field Gun	Dark Green, 'BENBROS' cast on model, 102 mm. (2s. 0d.)	£15-20
--- (1)		Police Patrol Motorcycle	(Triumph) 'Silver' plated, plastic rider, 'ENT 303' cast, 84 mm. (2s. 6d.)	£30-40
---		Rally Motorcycle	(Triumph) 'Silver' plated, plastic rider, 'ENT 303' cast, 84 mm. (2s. 6d.)	£30-40
--- (3)		Army Despatch Motorcycle	(Triumph) 'Silver' plated, plastic rider, 'ENT 303' cast, 84 mm. (2s. 6d.)	£30-40
--- (4)		Telegraph Boy Motorcycle	(Triumph) 'Silver' plated, plastic rider, 'ENT 303' cast, 84 mm. (2s. 6d.)	£30-40
---		'RAC' Triumph Motorcycle and Sidecar	Black bike, Blue sidecar, White fairing, plastic rider, 'ENT 303', 84 mm. (3s. 5d.)	£75-100
--- (6)		'A.A.' Triumph Motorcycle and Sidecar	Black bike, Yellow sidecar and fairing, plastic rider, 'ENT 303', 84 mm. (3s. 5d.)	£75-100
--- (60)		Austin Mini Van	'AA PATROL SERVICE', Yellow body. Opening side and rear doors	£150-200
		Austin Mini Van	'RAC', Blue body. Opening side and rear doors	£150-200

Zebra Toys

104 Routemaster Bus,

101 Scammell Scarab Articulated Van 'BRITISH RAILWAYS'

100 Foden Concrete Mixer

Photo: Vectis Auctions Ltd.

'Qualitoys' and other Benbros model vehicles

This list includes all the other vehicles in the Benbros range, mostly large scale items. Many carried the name 'Qualitoy' as well as 'Benbros', and most were individually boxed. Dating of these models is quite difficult, since there were few contemporary adverts, and the only catalogues known are trade price lists for 1964 and 1965. The Timpo re-issues were probably no earlier than 1952, and the various motorcycles were introduced in late 1955. Where a retail price is shown (in shillings and pence) the model was still available on the 1964 and 1965 price lists.

Coronation Coach with 8 horses	'ER' cast on doors, 'MADE IN ENGLAND' on drawbar. Later boxes marked 'Zebra Toys', 116 mm (3s 7d)	£30-40
State Landau with 4 horses	Two separate footmen. 'MADE IN ENGLAND' under coach. 105 mm. (3s 7d)	£30-40
Father Christmas Sleigh	With four reindeer. Metallic green or metallic blue. 110 mm. (2s 6d)	£60-80
Covered Wagon with 4 Bullocks	Re-issue of a model by L. Brooks (Toys) Ltd. (1958). Hollow-cast lead bullocks (diecast on the Brooks model). 'MADE IN ENGLAND' lengthwise under, Cloth canopy, Green wagon, Yellow wheels, cowboy. 186 mm	£60-80
Covered Wagon with 4 Horses	Same wagon as above. Canopy plain or with 'BUFFALO BILL'S COVERED WAGON' or 'CALGARY STAMPEDE COVERED WAGON' printed. Red or Green wagon (Yellow shaft) or Metallic Green or Metallic Blue (Red shaft). Yellow wheels, two barrels, metal or plastic cowboy holding whip. 186 mm. (4s 8d)	£60-80
Rickshaw with two Passengers	Pulled by Ostrich or Zulu. Shown in the Joplin book* as Crescent, but believed to be Benbros. 150 mm	£125-175
Roman Chariot with two horses	With figure. Metallic Green or Yellow with Red wheels. About 135 mm	£60-80
Horse Drawn Farm Cart and man	Re-issue of Timpo model. Light Green or Yellow cart, Brown horse	£60-80
Horse Drawn Water Wagon	Re-issue of Timpo model. Light Green wagon, Brown horse	£80-100
Horse Drawn Log Wagon with Log	Yellow with Red wheels, or Red with Yellow wheels, or Orange with Red wheels, Brown horse. 225 mm	£80-100
Stephenson's Rocket Loco and Tender	Metallic Brown or Silver plated loco. Tender metallic Green, Metallic Blue, Orange or Red. 105 mm	£30-40
Caterpillar Tractor	Copy of early Lesney model. Red or Yellow or metallic Blue, rubber tracks, 97 mm. (3s 6d)	£30-40

Caterpillar Bulldozer	Copy of early Lesney model. Red tractor with Black blade, or metallic Blue with Red or Yellow blade. Rubber tracks. 118 mm. (4s 11d)	£30-40
Caterpillar Excavator with driver	Orange (Green shovel) or metallic Blue (Red shovel), rubber tracks, Red or Green driver, 138 mm. (4s. 11d.)	£30-40
Ferguson Tractor with driver	No name on model. Yellow or Red with unpainted wheels, metallic Green or Yellow with Red wheels, Orange with Black or Blue wheels. Driver Green, Brown, Blue, Metallic Blue or Grey. 73 mm. (2s 6d)	£70-80
Ferguson Tractor with Cab and Shovel	No name on model. Red, Yellow or dark Green, unpainted wheels, Green or Brown driver. 100 mm	£70-80
Ferguson Tractor and Log Trailer	With driver and log. Tractor details as above. Red trailer (179mm) with yellow wheels. (4s 3d)	£70-80
Ferguson Tractor with Roller	With driver. No name on model. Former Timpo horse-drawn roller plus drawbar. Tractor as above, Red trailer with Yellow rollers. Trailer length 109 mm. (3s 6d)	£70-80
Ferguson Tractor with Harrow	With driver. No name on model. Former Timpo horse-drawn harrow plus drawbar. Tractor as above, Red or Yellow trailer, length about 110 mm. (3s 6d)	£70-80
Euclid Dumper Lorry	Copy of Dinky 965. Metallic Blue cab and chassis, Yellow or Orange tipper. 145mm. (5s 10d)	£50-60
Muir Hill Dumper with Driver	Orange (Green tipper, Blue wheels), Yellow (Red or Orange tipper, Blue wheels), Metallic Green (Orange tipper, Blue wheels), or Red with Yellow tipper, Black wheels, 105 mm. (3s 11d)	£40-50
A101 Army Land Rover and Field Gun	Open Land Rover has two figures cast, separate windscreen, metal wheels with rubber tyres. Field gun marked 'BENBROS', solid rubber wheels. Matt Dark Green. 111 mm. and 102 mm	£60-80
A102 Lorry with Anti-Aircraft Gun	Matt dark Green, Silver gun. 117 mm	£25-30
A103 Lorry with Radar Scanner	Matt dark Green, Silver radar dish. 117 mm	£25-30
A104 Lorry with Searchlight	Matt dark Green. 117 mm	£25-30
A105 Armoured Car and Field Gun	Dark Brownish-Green or matt dark Green. Field gun same as A101. 96 mm and 102 mm	£30-40
A106 Army AEC Lorry with Tilt	'SUNDERLAND' cast on cab sides. Dark Brownish-Green or matt dark Green, Green cloth tilt. 132 mm	£100-125
A107 Army Closed Land Rover	Casting as A101. Matt dark Green, Black roof. Opening side and rear doors. 111 mm	£40-50
A110 Army Articulated Low-Loader with Field Gun	Matt Dark Green Low-loader as no. 221, Field Gun as no. A101 but with metal hubs and rubber tyres	£30-40
220 AEC Flat Lorry with chains	'SUNDERLAND' cast on cab sides. Red cab and chassis, light Green, Blue, Beige or Metallic Green body. 130 mm. (3s 6d)	£100-125
221 Articulated Low Loader	Re-issue of Timpo model. Red or Green cab with Red, Yellow or metallic Green trailer. No name on model. 166 mm	£25-30
223 Land Rover 'Royal Mail'	Red (Black roof). 'ROYAL MAIL E-II-R' cast on sides. Opening side and rear doors, 2 figures cast inside. 111mm	£100-120
224 Articulated Tanker	Re-issue of Timpo model, no maker's name on model, 146mm (3s 6d). Red or Orange cab, Green or metallic Green or Yellow trailer, 'MOTOR OIL ESSO PETROL' transfer	£60-75
	Green cab, Red trailer, 'SHELL PETROL' label	£60-75
	Light Green cab, Red trailer, 'UNITED DAIRIES' transfer	£60-75
225 AEC Dropside Lorry	'SUNDERLAND' cast on cab sides. Red cab and chassis, light Green or Blue body. 132 mm. (3s 6d)	£75-100
226 Petrol Tanker	Re-issue of Timpo model. Red cab / chassis with Red or Yellow tank, light Green cab / chassis with Yellow tank. 'Motor Oil Esso Petrol' or 'Fina Petrol Goes a Long Way' transfer. No name on model. 117 mm. (3s 1d)	£80-100
227 AEC Flat Lorry	Re-issue of Timpo model. 'SUNDERLAND' cast on cab sides. Red cab and chassis, light Green, Blue or Cream body. 130 mm. (3s 1d)	£80-100
228 AEC Lorry with Tilt	As no.225 with plain cloth tilt. 132 mm	£75-100
Forward Control Box Van	Re-issue of Timpo model, no maker's name on model. 99 mm.	
	Green cab and chassis with light Green or Red body with 'Pickfords Removals' labels	£80-100
	Red cab, chassis and body, plain	£25-30
	Red cab and chassis, Green body, 'CHIVERS JELLIES' transfers	£80-100
Articulated Box Van	Re-issue of Timpo model, no maker's name on model. 145 mm.	
	Red or Green cab with Green, Red or Cream trailer. 'LYONS TEA' transfers.	£100-150
	Red cab with Green trailer. 'UNITED DAIRIES' transfers.	£100-150
	Light Green cab with Red or Orange trailer. 'BISHOP & SONS DEPOSITORIES LTD.' transfers	£100-150
A.A. Land Rover	Casting as A107 and 223. 'AA ROAD SERVICE' cast on sides and roof sign. Opening side and rear doors, two figures inside. Yellow with Black roof or all Yellow. 111 mm. (5s 10d)	£100-125
310 Ruston-Bucyrus 10-RB Crane	Maroon and Yellow body, dark Green chassis and jib, rubber tracks. 'BENBROS' cast underneath. (3s 6d)	£70-80
311 Ruston-Bucyrus 10-RB Excavator	Maroon and Yellow body, dark Green chassis and arms, rubber tracks. 'BENBROS' cast underneath. (3s 6d)	£70-80
AEC Lorry and Ruston-Bucyrus Crane	'SUNDERLAND' cast on cab sides. Red cab and chassis, Yellow body. Crane as no.310 with Maroon and Yellow body, dark green jib. 128 mm. (5s 10d)	£100-125
AEC Lorry with Ruston-Bucyrus Excavator	'SUNDERLAND' cast on cab sides. Red cab and chassis, Yellow body. Excavator as no.311 with Maroon and Yellow body, dark Green arms. 128 mm. (5s 10d)	£100-125
A.A. Motorcycle Patrol	Black cycle, AA badge cast on Yellow sidecar and windscreen, 'TTC147' cast on number plates. 84 mm.	
	(i) Fixed front forks, windscreen with plastic glazing, dark Brownish-Green metal rider	£75-100
	(ii) Steering front forks, windscreen with curved frame cast in place of glazing, plastic rider	£75-100
RAC Motorcycle Patrol	Black cycle, RAC badge cast on Blue sidecar and windscreen. 'TTC147' cast on number plates. Steerable front forks, windscreen with curved frame, plastic rider. 84 mm	£75-100
Solo Motorcycle with Rider	Fixed front forks, 'TTC147' cast on number plates. 84 mm.	
	(i) Police Patrol - Maroon cycle, Black metal rider	£30-40
	(ii) Telegraph Boy - Red cycle, Red metal rider	£30-40
	(iii) Army Despatch Rider - Dark Brownish-Green cycle and metal rider	£30-40
	(iv) Rally Rider - Green cycle, Blue metal rider	£30-40
Solo Motorcycle with Rider	Steerable front forks, 'TTC147' cast on number plates. Silver plated cycles with plastic riders in four versions - Police Patrol, Telegraph Boy, Army Despatch Rider and Rally. 84 mm.	£30-40
1956 Hudson Two Door Coupé	no details.	
Bedford Low-Loader	no details.	

* Reference: 'The Great Book of Hollow-Cast Figures' by Norman Joplin (New Cavendish Books).

BRITAINS MOTOR VEHICLES

by Mike Richardson

Most people are aware of the military vehicles made by Britains both before the War and after in 1/32 scale to go with their soldiers, but not so many are acquainted with the contemporary civilian models. Some of these models are only colour variations of the military versions, for example the 59F 'Four-wheeled Lorry with Driver' in the farm series is the same as 1335 'Lorry, Army, Four-wheeled type' but painted in a smart duotone colour scheme instead of khaki. Other models are only available in the civilian type, usually for the good reason that the army could not possibly have a use for a militarised version. A good example of this would be 1656 'John Cobb's Railton Wonder Car' (or 'Railton Mobil Special' as we know it!).

Britains are our oldest toy company which is still in business having been started in 1860 although the first of the famous soldiers did not appear until 1890. This still means over a hundred years continuous toy manufacture, surely a record. The motor lorry models appeared in late 1932 and were based on the Albion army lorries of the time with the familiar 'square' cab design which was to be a hallmark of the Britains lorries until the end of the decade. The range of 4, 6 and 10-wheel farm lorries are still illustrated in the 1940 catalogue. After the War the cab was brought up to date by a change to a more rounded Fordson type, not nearly so attractive.

The military ambulance was also used in civilian versions, a cream 'Corporation' and a blue 'Volunteer Corps' as alternative liveries to the khaki army one. The rarest version of this model is the red and black 'Royal Mail' van which was sold for a short time towards the end of the production run.

There are three civilian cars, a 'Two-seater Coupé' and two 'Sports Model Open Tourers' in the pre-war production. The coupé and the open sports car without driver and passenger do not have military equivalents, but when the open sports car has people in it then it is either a 'Mobile Police Car with 2 Officers'

(finished in green with black wings), or a 'Staff Car with 2 Officers' as the military offering. The occupants of the car are legless and their lower regions are covered with a tartan rug - how nice for them on cold days! After the War there was a one-piece casting version of the staff car and police car without the separate grilles of the pre-war models and these were rather plain by comparison.

The final group of models consists of the superb record cars 'Bluebird' and 'Railton Special'. These came out in the late 1930s and each is over 6 inches long. The Bluebird was produced in three versions; a) with fully detailed removable chassis, b) without this part, and c) a slightly smaller one (just over 5 inches), without underside detail. The Railton Mobil Special always had the removable chassis and was available painted silver for 1s.6d. or chrome plated for 2s.6d.

After the War two new farm tractor models appeared, a couple of Fordson Majors produced with the active co-operation of the Ford Motor Company. These are excellent models both finished in the correct shade of dark blue and with the name 'Fordson' applied to the front and sides of the radiator. One version has standard wheels but the other (rarer) one had the spiked or 'spud' wheels used on heavy ground.

All these models are to the same scale as the soldiers (1/32), but there is also a similar range in '00' gauge (1/76 scale) to go with model railways. The smaller models date mainly from the post-war era although a sports car and a fastback saloon were seen pre-war. The small scale trucks have a Fordson cab similar to the later large scale farm and army lorries.

The large scale pre-war models are very collectable and prices are consequently very high for rare items in excellent condition and with original lovely boxes. Some few years ago a batch of replicas of the coupé were made here in England so exercise care when buying this model. Spare parts are, or have been available for most of these toys to enable repairs to be carried out.

Britains No.1448 Army Staff Car with Officer and Driver   Photo: Vectis Auctions Ltd.

See colour section for additional pictures of Britains models

BRITAINS VEHICLES, GUNS and NOVELTIES, 1880 - 1916

by James Opie

Although Britains is famous for manufacturing toy soldiers, it is not so widely known that they had produced toy vehicles before they made their first soldier. In one of their catalogues pre-dating toy soldier production, there are large and small Road Rollers, and probably manufactured even before these are a much larger and cruder Road Roller and Steam Crane, mostly built of tinplate (uncatalogued), and a Rotary Railway Express (uncatalogued), which was a lead die-cast floor toy rather than a toy train. All came boxed.

Dating in all probability from 1890 or earlier, the die-cast Road Rollers can lay claim to be the earliest attributable catalogued British die-cast toys.

Item	Market Price Range
The London Road Roller c.1890 to 1895	£2,500-4,000
The Miniature Road Roller c.1890 to 1916	£750-1,000
The Rotary Railway Express c.1891 to 1894	£3,000-5,000

The next group of models, die-cast from lead alloy with steel and wire pins, springs, axles and ammunition, were the early guns and vehicles to accompany toy soldier production from 1895 to 1916. In fact, the first Britains spring gun was incorporated in a model soldier with a hollow rifle barrel and a steel spring set just behind the breech, so that a protruding piece of wire could be flicked through.

Set 28 included a three part mountain gun which loaded onto mules, set 39 was a Royal Horse Artillery set with a field gun and limber, and set 79 had the same gun as set 28, slightly modified with a wire towing eye to join to a small limber pulled by eight sailors. Set 144 used the same gun as set 39 with a modified limber as a Royal Field Artillery set. Sets 145 and 146 included a die-cast lead four wheel general purpose wagon. Sets 125 and 126 were Royal Horse Artillery sets made in a smaller size with a gun and limber, the gun from which, slightly modified without its towing hole, was also used in sets 148 and 149, and in small size second grade displays 04, 05 and 06. Perhaps the most famous gun of all, the 4.7 inch Naval Gun, was at first sold without a catalogue number. This was the gun used by H.G. Wells in his book 'Little Wars'. The field gun from set 39 was also available separately in an un-numbered box entitled 'Royal Artillery Gun'.

In 1906, Britains introduced a horse-drawn four wheel general service waggon, which was used in sets 145 and 146. In 1914, Britains produced their first civilian vehicle which was part of their standard scale figure range, the Boy Scout Trek Cart, two of which were included in both set 180 and in set 181. This would probably have been predated by the Coster's Barrow, which is almost the right scale, but produced as part of the novelty range

As the majority of these guns and vehicles came as part of sets, I will give both the price of the boxed sets and the price of the individual guns and vehicles when found separately.

Item	Market Price Range
Set 28 Mountain Artillery (oval base men), 1895-1908	£350-500
Set 28 Mountain Artillery (square base men), 1908-1916	£250-350
Mountain Artillery Gun (eight spoke wheels), 1895-1916	£30-50
Set 39 Royal Horse Artillery (shafted limber), 1896-1906	£1,500-2,000
Gun with bucket seats and Shafted Limber, 1896-1906	£250-400
Set 39 Royal Horse Artillery (centre pole limber), 1906-1916	£800-1,000
Gun and Centre Pole Limber, 1906-1916	£80-100

Item	Market Price Range
Royal Artillery Gun (boxed, no catalogue number), 1896-1916	£80-120
4.7 inch Naval Gun (boxed, no catalogue number), 1896-1916	£50-80
Set 79 Royal Navy Landing Party (oval base men), 1897-1916	£400-600
Landing Party Gun and Limber, 1897-1916	£80-100
Set 125 Royal Horse Artillery, full dress, small size, 1902-1916	£400-600
Set 126 Royal Horse Artillery, field dress, small size, 1902-1916	£600-800
Small size Gun and Limber, grey finish (from set 125), 1902-1916	£80-100
Small size Gun and Limber, khaki (from set 126), 1902-1916	£90-120
Set 144 Royal Field Artillery, bucket seats, 1906-1916	£1,000-1,500
Gun with bucket seats and Centre Pole Limber, 1906-1916	£200-300
Set 145 Royal Army Medical Corps Four Horse Ambulance Waggon, 1906-1916	£300-400
Set 146 Army Service Corps Two Horse Waggon, 1906-1916	£200-300
Four wheel General Service Waggon, 1906-1916	£50-80
Set 148 Royal Lancaster Regiment Game Set, with gun, 1907-1916	£4,000-6,000
Set 149 American Soldiers Game Set, with gun, 1907-1916	£4,000-6,000
Set 04 British Army Encampment, small size, 1910-1916	£250-400
Set 05 British Army Encampment, small size, 1910-1916	£300-500
Set 06 British Army Encampment, small size, 1910-1916	£400-600
Small size Gun, without towing hole, 1907-1916	£50-80
Set 180, Boy Scout Display with two trek carts, 1914-1916	£600-800
Set 181, large Boy Scout Display with two trek carts, 1914-1916	£2,000-3,000
Trek Cart with Boy Scout, 1914-1916	£100-150

Novelties, 1900 - 1916

Probably from around 1900 or even before, Britains produced cast alloy novelty toys. Exact dates of production are unknown. Those listed below (unboxed except where specified) were in the 1915 catalogue, but had no catalogue number quoted. The catalogue also stated 'Miscellaneous castings. Jockeys, Bicycles, Warships, Yachts, etc., in several qualities and sizes for Race Games, &c.'

Item	Market Price Range
Tea Pot, gilt, 1900-1916	£20-30
Coffee Pot, gilt, 1900-1916	£20-30
Kettle, gilt or black, 1900-1916	£20-30
Rocking Chair, 1900-1916	£30-40
Tea and Coffee Set, gilt, boxed, 1900-1916	£150-200
Saucepan, black, with lid, bright metal, 1900-1916	£30-40
Boiler with Lid, copper, gilt or black, 1900-1916	£20-30
Coal Vase with Tongs, copper, gilt or black, 1900-1916	£25-40
Watering Pot, red, 1900-1916	£20-30
Kettle on Stand, gilt, 1900-1916	£35-50
Large boxed Kitchen Set with kettles, 1900-1916	£250-400
Small boxed Kitchen Set with kettle, 1900-1916	£150-200
Baby's Chair, 1900-1916	£40-60
Push Chair, 1900-1916	£35-50
Caster's Barrow, blue or gold, 1900-1916	£40-60
Kitchen Steps, 1900-1916	£30-40
Football Association Cup, silver or gilt, 1904-1916	£600-800

An illustration from the January 1951 Britains Ltd. catalogue.

Illustration of Mechanical Unit driving No. 127F Fordson Major "Tractor.

Illustration of Mechanical Unit driving No. 128F Fordson Major Tractor.

MANUFACTURED BY W Britain IN LONDON ENGLAND

TRADE MARK

REGD No. 459993.

Britains Motor Vehicles (pre-war issues)

The models were constructed of a lead based alloy and the main body parts were hollow cast. However, parts such as wings and running boards were die-cast individually by hand. The Market Price Range figures refer to boxed models in excellent condition.

Civilian Vehicles

Ref	Model name	Colours, features, details	Price
59 F	Four-wheeled Lorry with Driver	Back and doors open, rubber tyres, 6"	£150-200
60 F	Six-wheeled Lorry with Driver	Two-tone Blue body, White cab roof, Silver radiator surround, back and doors open, White rubber tyres, 6"	£150-200
61 F	Ten-wheeled Lorry with Driver	Back and doors open, rubber tyres	£200-250
90 F	Builders Lorry	As 59 F plus builders name on side. *'DAVIS ESTATES LTD BUILDERS OF HOMES'*	£2,000-3,000
91 F	Builders Lorry	As 60 F plus builders name on side. Never seen.	NPP
92 F	Builders Lorry	As 61 F plus builders name on side. Never seen.	NPP
1398	Sports Model Open Tourer	Cream body, Black chassis and wheels, White rubber tyres, 4.25"	£750-1,000
1399	Two-Seater Coupé (fitted bumpers)	Cream body, Tan roof, wings and running-boards, Black hubs, White tyres, 4.5". (Also in other colours)	£1,000-1,250
1413	Mobile Police Car with two Officers	2-piece casting, Green body, Black wings, White tyres, 4.75". (Also in other colours)	£500-600
1470	The Royal Household Set	Coronation State Coach, King George VI plus the Queen with twelve attendants	£300-500
1513	Volunteer Corps Ambulance with Driver, Wounded Man and Stretcher	Blue body, 'AMBULANCE', Red/White cross, White tyres	£600-700
1514	Corporation Type Motor Ambulance with Driver, Wounded Man and Stretcher	Cream body, 'AMBULANCE', Red/White cross, White tyres	£700-900
1552	'ROYAL MAIL' Van with Driver	Post-Office Red body, Black bonnet, 'GR' plus crown design, White tyres	£1,600-2,000
	1924 Wembley Exhibition Locomotive	Bronze finished diecast locomotive on plinth with '1924 Wembley Exhibition' '240 tons - largest locomotive in the world'	NGPP

Military Vehicles

Early issues of lorry and truck models in the ranges 1333 - 1433 and 1641 - 1643 had 'square' cabs, (post-war issues had 'rounded' cabs).

Ref	Model name	Colours, features, details	Price
1321	Armoured Car with Gun	Military Green, solid metal wheels	£100-125
1333	Lorry, Army, Caterpillar Type with Driver	Military Green finish, rubber tyres, 6"	£150-200
1334	Four-wheeled Tipper Lorry	with Driver	£150-200
1335	Lorry, Army, Six-wheeled Type with Driver	Military Green finish, rubber tyres, 6"	£150-200
1392	Autogiro	Military Green finish, RAF roundels, pilot, three detachable rotor blades	£750-950
1432	Tender, Army, Covered, Ten-wheeled (with Driver)	Military Green finish, White rubber tyres, 6"	£150-200
1433	Tender, Army, Covered, Ten-wheeled Caterpillar Type (with Driver)	Military Green finish, White rubber tyres, 6"	£150-200
1448	Staff Car	Military Green car with 2 Staff Officers, White rubber tyres, 4"	£350-450
1641	Underslung Heavy Duty Lorry (18 wheels) with Driver	Military Green finish, 10"	£350-450
1641	Underslung Heavy Duty Lorry (18 wheels) with Driver	with 1749 Mounted Barrage Balloon Winch	£900-1,100
1642	Underslung Heavy Duty Lorry (18 wheels) with Driver	with Mounted Searchlight, Military Green finish, 10"	£350-450
1643	Underslung Heavy Duty Lorry (18 wheels) with Driver	with Mounted Anti-Aircraft Gun (small)	£350-450
1643	Underslung Heavy Duty Lorry (18 wheels) with Driver	with Mounted Anti-Aircraft Gun (large)	£600-800

Autogiro and Record Cars (1:43 scale)

Ref	Model name	Colours, features, details	Price
1392	Autogiro	Blue body, (other colours are known) including Military Green with pilot and three detachable rotor blades	£750-950
1936	Bluebird Record Car	(Napier-Campbell) Malcolm Campbell's car, lift-off body, detailed engine, White tyres	£150-175
1939	Napier Railton	John Cobb's car, '350.20 mph World Land Speed Record'	£250-300

'Circus' Series

'Mammoth Circus Roundabout'
Six horses (Black, Brown, White) plus riders, Green, Red and Yellow Carousel canopy.
Lead and card construction. Circa 1910 .... £2,000-3,000
'The Flying Trapeze' Set (No. 1141)
High wire act with balancing clown and suspended girl trapeze artiste, twirling paper parasol, wire and card winder, marbled patterned box. 1936-39 .... £2,000-3,000

'Motor and Road' Series

Ref	Model name	Colours, features, details	Price
1313	Volunteer Corps 'AMBULANCE'	Finished in Blue, with wounded man and stretcher	£300-400
2024	Light Goods Van with Driver	Various colours, 'BRITAINS LTD' logo.	£400-500
2045	Clockwork Van (c1938)	Various colours, driver, opening rear doors. In Red box with Dark Yellow picture label	£900-1,200
	NB	A boxed example of 2045 with red cab and green van body, Black 'BRITAINS' logo on White background, with driver and original clockwork key sold at the Lacy, Scott & Knight 11/97 auction for	£1,050

Britains Motor Vehicles (post-war issues)

'Farm' series

59F	19??	**Farm Tipping Lorry with Driver**, Light Green or Blue	**150-250**
127F	19??	**Fordson 'MAJOR' Tractor with Driver**, fitted with spade-end wheels	**£200-250**
128F	19??	**Fordson 'MAJOR' Tractor with Driver**, with rubber-tyred wheels	**£175-225**

The following were all supplied in cellophane fronted landscape boxes.
NB Some of the same model numbers were used twice for different models.

9520	1965-70	**Fordson Major Tractor with Driver**, cast metal wheels, plastic outset lights	**£75-85**
9526	1965-70	**Ford Super Major '5000' Tractor** with Spade End Wheels, dark blue	**£75-85**
9527	1965-70	**Ford Super Major '5000' Tractor** with rubber tyres, dark blue	**£65-75**
9529	1965-70	**Massey-Ferguson 135 Tractor** with safety cab, red/white	**£65-75**
9596	1965-70	**Ford Super Major '5000' Tractor Set**, Ford Tractor plus nine implements	**£100-150**
9630	1965-70	**Ford Super Major '5000' Tractor** with cab and Shawnee-Poole Rear Dump Set	**£85-95**
9670	1965-70	**Dumper**, red with yellow wheels and blue driver	**£20-25**
9522	1970-80	**Massey-Ferguson 595 Tractor** with safety cab, red body, silver cab	**£40-60**
9524	1970-80	**Ford 6600 Tractor**, blue/white, blue driver	**£60-70**
9526	1970-80	**Deutz DX 110 Tractor**, green/black	**£40-50**
9527	1970-80	**Fiat Half-Track Tractor**, red/black, beige driver	**£45-55**
9528	1970-80	**Fiat Tractor**, red/black	**£30-40**
9529	1970-80	**Massey-Ferguson Tractor with Cab**, dark blue/white	**£60-70**
9569	1970-80	**Unimog Tractor/Lorry**, green/yellow	**£30-40**
9570	1970-80	**Massey-Ferguson 760 Combine Harvester**, red with driver	**£100-130**
9571	1970-80	**Farm Land-Rover, 'BRITAINS FARM'**	**£30-35**
9572	1970-80	**Massey-Ferguson 595 Tractor** with Front Loader, yellow with red front loader	**£100-130**
9576	1970-80	**Farm Land-Rover**, blue with cream canopy	**£25-35**
9584	1970-80	**Ford Tractor and Front Loader**	**£45-55**

9591	1970-80	**Massey-Ferguson 595 Tractor and 2 Wheeled Trailer**, red/white tractor with green/yellow trailer	**£65-75**
9595	1970-80	**Massey-Ferguson 595 Tractor** and Front Loader, red/white	**£60-70**
9597	1970-80	**Massey-Ferguson 595 Tractor and 8 Wheeled Trailer**, red/white	**£65-75**
9515	1980-85	**Volvo BM Valmet 805 Tractor**, red/black	**£35-45**
9517	1980-85	**Massey-Ferguson MF2680 Double Rear wheeled Tractor**, red/white	**£45-55**
9518	1980-85	**Renault TX145-14 Turbo Tractor**, orange/black/white	**£30-40**
9520	1980-85	**Massey-Ferguson MF2680 Tractor**, red/white	**£40-50**
9522	1980-85	**Renault Double Rear Wheeled Tractor**, orange/white	**£40-45**
9523	1980-85	**Ford TW20 Tractor**, blue/white	**£35-45**
9525	1980-85	**Mercedes-Benz Tractor**, yellow/black	**£35-45**
9530	1980-85	**Deutz Eight Wheeled Tractor**, green/black	**£35-45**
9529	1980-85	**Massey-Ferguson MF2680 Double Rear Wheeled Tractor**, red/grey	**£45-55**
9575	1980-85	**'New Holland' Combine Harvester**, yellow	**£25-35**
9580	1980-85	**Magirus Deutz Iveco Animal Transporter**, dark blue cab, red/grey back	**£25-35**
9581	1980-85	**Unimog Breakdown Truck**, white/orange/red	**£15-25**
9582	1980-85	**Magirus Deutz Iveco Flatbed Transporter**, white cab, grey back	**£25-35**
9583	1980-85	**Magirus Deutz Iveco Tipper Truck**, yellow/black	**£20-30**
9581	1980-85	**Unimog Breakdown Truck 'Recovery Service'**	**£20-30**
9584	1980-85	**Ford Tractor** with front loader	**£40-50**
9585	1980-85	**Fiat Tractor and Vacuum Tanker**	**£40-50**
9586	1980-85	**Volvo Tractor and Trailer**	**£45-55**
9587	1980-85	**Massey-Ferguson Tractor and Rear Dump**	**£45-55**
9588	1980-85	**Ford Tractor and Rotary Manure Spreader**	**£45-55**
9589	1980-85	**Deutz Tractor and Implements Set**	**£100-125**
9591	1980-85	**Fiat Tractor and Implements Set**	**£100-125**
9596	1980-85	**Deutz Tractor and Manure Spreader**	**£45-55**
9597	1980-85	**Ford Tractor and 8 wheeled trailer**	**£50-60**
9597	1980-85	**Mercedes-Benz Tractor with Tipper Hopper**	**£40-50**
9598	1980-85	**Massey-Ferguson MF2680 Tractor and Trailer**	**£45-55**
9599	1980-85	**Farm Tractor and Implements Set**	**£100-125**

'Clockwork' series

2041		**Clockwork Unit (2-wheeled trailer)** ..'Will last 1 1/2 minutes when fully wound and capable of driving any other vehicle 20-30 feet'	**£45-55**
2045		**Clockwork Van** Finished in various colours with 'BRITAINS LTD' logo	**£500-700**

Military issues

Post-war issues of lorry and truck models in the ranges 1333 - 1433 and 1641 - 1643 had 'rounded' cabs, (pre-war issues had 'square' cabs).

1334	**Four-wheeled Tipper Lorry**	('rounded' cab) with Driver	**£150-200**
1335	**Six-wheeled Tipper Lorry**	('rounded' cab) with Driver	**£150-200**
1433	**Covered Army Truck**	('rounded' cab) Caterpillar type with Driver	**£150-200**
1448	**Staff Car**	with General and Driver	**£350-450**
1512	**Army Ambulance**	3rd version with split windscreen, driver, stretcher	**£200-250**
1791	**Motorcycle Dispatch Rider**	sold unboxed	**£25-35**
1876	**Bren Gun Carrier with Driver, Gunner and 2nd Guard**	Carden-Vickers type suspension cast-in, separate Bren gun, 3½ "	**£75-125**
1877	**Beetle Lorry and Driver**		**£65-75**
1879	**'OO' gauge Lorry with Trailer and Hydrogen Cylinders**	Military Green, solid wheels, red cylinders	**NGPP**
2150	**Centurion Tank**	Military Green	**£300-400**
2156	**Centurion Tank**	Desert Warfare finish	**£400-500**
2048	**Military Set**	1877, 2041 and 2026 Gun	**£150-175**
2150	**Centurion Tank**	Dark green finish, US star to turret	**£80-100**
2154	**Centurion Tank, Desert Warfare**	Sand colour finish. Box has illustrated label	**£225-275**

'Lilliput' Series (1:76 scale)

Manufactured under license by Horton (Toys and Games) Ltd., Reno Works, Middlesborough, England.

LV 601	**Open Sports Car**	2.25" long	**£60-70**	LV 612	**Humber 1-1/2 ton Military Truck**		**£35-45**
LV 602	**Saloon Car**	2.25" long	**£60-70**	LV 613	**Humber 1-1/2 ton Military Truck**	Covered version	**£35-45**
LV 603	**Articulated Lorry**	4" long	**£60-70**	LV 614	**Farm Trailer**		**£15-25**
LV 604	**Fordson Tractor with Driver**	1.5" long	**£35-45**	LV 615	**Saracen Armoured Vehicle**		**£15-25**
LV 605	**Milk Float and Horse** with Milkman. 2.25" long		**£45-55**	LV 616	**1fi ton Truck**		**£35-45**
LV 606	**Tumbrel Cart and Horse** with Hay Racks and Carter	2.75" long	**£35-45**	LV 617	**Civilian Ambulance**. Cream body with 'AMBULANCE' on sides, 'BRITAINS' on rubber tyres, Red plastic hubs		**£100-125**
LV 607	**Austin 3-ton Covered Military Truck**		**£35-45**	LV 618	**Army Ambulance**		**NGPP**
LV 608	**Austin 3-ton Farm Truck**		**£35-45**	LV 619	**'ROYAL MAIL' Van**		**NGPP**
LV 609	**Austin Military Champ**		**£65-75**	LV 620	**3 ton Open Truck**		**NGPP**
LV 610	**Centurion Tank**		**£35-45**				
LV 611	**Self-propelled 25-pounder Gun**		**£25-35**				

Britains

Motor Cycles 1965 - 1975

All have plastic saddles, plated engines and 'diamond' headlights, and are packed in display boxes. Market Price Range for single boxed items.......**£20-30**

9640	**Two Go-Karts**, yellow/black or red/black	
9695	**BMW with Policeman**, white with black/white rider	
9696	**BMW with Civilian**, blue with white/blue rider	
9671	**Racing Norton**, yellow with red/green rider....................................	
9674	**Chopper Trike**, yellow/gold/black	
9677	**Long Fork Chopper**, red with blue rider...	
9679	**German Army Motor Cycle**, khaki	
9680	**'Chopper' Motor Cycle**, black with pink rder	
9681	**German Army B.M.W. Combination**, khaki with two blue riders	
9682	**U.S. Army Motor Cycle**, black with khaki rider	

9683	**Drag Motor Cycle**, gold with grey rider	
9684	**Speedway Motor Cycles**, silver with black riders	
9685	**Lambretta Scooter**, red/white with blue and red riders	
9689	**Harley-Davidson**, red/white 'BUZZ' with red/blue/yellow rider	
9690	**Triumph Thunderbird 650cc**, red with blue/brown/red rider..............	
9691	**Gieves Challenger with Rider**, green with blue/brown rider	
9692	**Honda Benly 125cc**, red with black/blue/yellow rider	
9692/2	**U.S. Sheriff on Harley Davidson**, white with black/grey rider	
9693	**B.M.W. 600cc**, silver with black/blue rider	
9694	**Triumph Speed Twin with Rider**, yellow/blue with black rider	
9697	**Police Patrolman on Triumph Thunderbird**, white with black rider	
9698	**Dispatch Rider on Triumph Motor Cycle**, black, black/green rider	
9698/2	**MV-Augusta Motor Cycle**, red '7', green/yellow or white/blue rider...	
9699	**BMW Racing Combination**, red/yellow with two black riders	
9650	**Speedway Set** with four riders on motor cycles.........................**£100-125**	
9666	**Motor Cycle Boxed Set** with 3 different motor cycles...............**£80-100**	

Britains Auction Results

Britains models sold by Lacy Scott & Knight, 10 Risbygate Street, Bury St Edmunds, Suffolk.
Condition abbreviations used in their catalogues: B = Boxed, M = Mint, NM/GM = Near Mint, G = Good, F = Fair, P = Poor, R = Repainted, MF = Massey-Ferguson CF = Cellophane Fronted, U/B = Unboxed.

5F Home Farm Series Farm Wagon, blue with red lining and drover in F-G original green box with label G-M **£140**

6F Plough Set, pre war with 2 horses, ploughman/ handles/plough/yoke and link wires in B-M sepia tray box, G-M **£120**

8F Home Farm Series Horse Rake, blue with driver and brown horse in F-G green box with label, G **£80**

20F Home Farm Series Farmers Gig, green, black seat, red wheels, farmer and cream horse, original green paper covered box, single colour paper label on lid, G-M **£130**

58F model Tree, in G original straw card box with single colour printed label, G-M **£50**

Fordson Major Tractor with plough, c1960 with cast metal wheels, plastic outset lights, F U/B **£80**

127F Fordson Major Tractor, pre war, spade-lug rear wheels, dark blue, orange wheels, with driver in G green box with separate colour picture label, G-M **£310**

127F Fordson Major Tractor, post war, spudded metal wheels/driver in G green box with overlapped picture label, G-M **£190**

128F Fordson Major Tractor, rubber tyres/driver in G green box with overlapped picture label on lid, G-M **£230**

135F Disc Harrow, pre-war, navy blue in G printed picture box, M **£42**

136F Disc Tractor Roller, pre war, in original box **£80**

9520 MF Tractor with driver, M in G CF box **£70**

9522 Renault Tractor w. engine sound, c1985, in G-M clear front box, M..**£45**

9524 Ford 6600 Tractor, c1975 with adverts on box, M in G CP box **£65**

9524 Deutz 6 Tractor, c1985 clear fronted G-M box **£45**

9527 Ford 5000 Tractor, c1973, 'Steeromatic' steering, M in G-M box....**£120**

9529 MF 135, c1975 with safety cab, G-M in M box **£95**

9570 MF760 Combine Harvester, BM in landscape box **£130**

9572 MF Tractor, c1975, yellow body with red front loader in polychrome printed picture box, BM....................................**£130**

9575 'New Holland' Combine Harvester, BM in red CF box **£35**

9591 MF Tractor with Trailer, red/black in G-M clear fronted box with vac-form insert tray, M...**£95**

9606 MF 2680 with rear dump in red G CF box **£5**

9630 Ford 6600 Tractor with rear dump, issued 1973 in G-M red/black clear fronted box, M..**£75**

8711 Ferguson TE20 Tractor, 'Petite Series', BM...........................**£38**

8716 David Brown Tractor, 'Petite Series', BM............................**£30**

Farm Animals: Ayrshire bull and cow..................................**£190**
Ayrshire cow and calf...**£130**
Suffolk mare and foal...**£160**

Motorbike, 9692 US Sheriff on Harley Davidson motorbike, in G window box, G..**£25**

Britains models sold by Vectis Auctions, Fleck Way, Thornaby, Stockton-on-Tees.
Condition abbreviations used in Vectis catalogues:
M = Mint, NM = Near Mint, E = Excellent, GP = Good Plus, VG = Very Good, G = Good, F = Fair, UB = Unboxed.

MILITARY MODELS

1334 4-Wheeled Army Lorry, 2nd round nose version with tipping body, E in E box with illustrated label...........................**£190**

1335 6-Wheeled Army Lorry, 2nd version with round nose, E in F box with illustrated label....................................**£160**

1433 Covered Army Tender, 3rd version with split windscreen, VG in G box with illustrated label..................................**£230**

1448 Army Staff Car, post-war version khaki finish, officer and driver, VG in G box with illustrated label..............................**£310**

1512 Army Ambulance, 3rd version with split windscreen, driver, stretcher, dark green, red crosses on white roundels, G U/B **£260**

1641 Underslung Lorry, square nose 1st version, immediate post war, rare blue finish, VG in VG box with illustrated label...........**£660**

1641 Underslung Lorry, 2nd version, round nose cab, khaki finish, driver, G-VG U/B.........................Estimate £300-£400

2150 Centurion Tank, dark green finish, US star to turret, E U/B.........**£120**

2154 Centurion Tank, Desert Warfare, sand colour finish, E in F-G box with illustrated label...............................**£310**

Farm and Miscellaneous models
127F Fordson Major Tractor, spud wheels, GP in GP box **£110**
128F Fordson Major Tractor, rubber tyres, NM in GP box **£290**
587 Village Idiot, lime green smock, blue breeches, brown hat VG **£180**

Britains No.1879
'OO' gauge Lorry and Trailer
with Hydrogen Cylinders

Photo: Vectis Auctions Ltd.

Chad Valley

The Chad Valley company (makers of board games and wooden toys) produced tinplate toy vehicles from 1932 incorporating the year of manufacture in the registration number on the number plates.

Their first 'Wee-Kin' diecast toy vehicles were produced around 1949 and had 'CV 1949' as the registration number. They were fitted with a key-wound clockwork motor and were designed more as toys than models having generic titles like 'Open Lorry' or 'Fire Engine'. The cars issued between 1951 and 1954

as Rootes Group promotionals are much better attempts at models and were sold at Rootes Group garages as well as normal toy shops. The tractors produced from 1952 are particularly fine and well detailed models.

The years shown below indicate the periods in which Chad Valley offered them for sale though not all the toys were available for the whole of the period and some were still in the shops well after production ceased in 1956.

Ref	Year(s)	Model name	Colours, features, details	Market Price Range

Chad Valley diecast clockwork toys and model vehicles

Ref	Year(s)	Model name	Colours, features, details	Price
220	1949-53	Razor Edge Saloon	Various colours, number plates 'CV 1949', approximate scale 1:43	£140-180
221	1949-53	Traffic Control Car	Casting as 220 plus loudspeaker, 'CV 1949', approximate scale 1:43	£140-180
222	1949-53	Police Car	Casting as 220 plus loudspeaker and 'POLICE' sign, 'CV 1949', scale 1:43	£140-180
223	1949-53	Track Racer	'CV 1949' on number plates, no other details	£140-180
224	1949-53	Double Decker Bus	Red body, number plates 'CV 1949', Approximate scale 1:76	£140-180
225	1949-53	Open Lorry	Various colours, 'CV 1949' on number plates	£140-180
226	1949-53	Low-Loader	Green / Red body, 'CV 1949' on number plates, three cream-coloured packing cases	£140-180
227	1949-53	Timber Wagon	'CV 1949', body has round bosses to fit milk churns or other 'loads'	£140-180
228	1949-53	Cable Layer	Red cab, Green body, silver trim, number plates 'CV 1949'	£150-180
229	1949-53	Breakdown Lorry	Number plates 'CV 1949', no other details	£150-180
230	1949-53	Milk Float	Number plates 'CV 1949', load of eight milk churns	£150-180
231	1949-53	Fire Engine	Red body, number plates 'CV 1949'	£150-175
232	1949-53	Tower Repair Wagon	Number plates 'CV 1949', Green body and hubs	£200-250
233	1949-53	Milk Tanker	Blue body and logo, White tank, number plates 'CV 1949'	£150-175
234	1949-53	Petrol Tanker	Number plates 'CV 1949', no other details	£150-175
236	1949-53	The Hillman Minx	Grey or Metallic Dark Blue body, Rootes Group promotional, 1:43 scale	£140-180
237	1949-53	The Humber Super Snipe	Metallic Dark Green or Red body, Rootes Group promotional, 1:43 scale	£140-180
238	1949-53	The Sunbeam-Talbot	Light Blue or Metallic Dark Green, Rootes Group promotional, 1:43 scale. Base has the wording 'A Rootes Group Product' plus usual Chad Valley marks	£140-180
239	1949-53	Dust Cart	Body has tinplate sliding side panels, number plates 'CV 1949'	£140-180
240	1949-53	Commer Avenger Coach	Blue or Red body marked 'A Rootes Group Product', 1:76 scale, promotional	£200-250
242	1949-53	The Commer Hands	(6-wheel artic.), 'A Rootes Group Product', Red body with 'Commer Hands' sticker, promotional	£150-175
507	1951-54	The Humber Hawk	Metallic Dark Blue, Metallic Dark Green, or mid-Green body, Rootes Group promotional, 1:43 scale	£140-180
	1951-54	Guy Van	Dark Blue / Cream, tinplate doors, 'Lyons Ice Cream Cadby Hall London W11'	£150-200
-	1951-54	Guy Van	Red body, Blue hubs, tinplate doors, Red 'CHAD VALLEY' logo	£150-200
-	1951-54	Guy Van	Green body, tinplate doors, Yellow 'Guy Motors Ltd, Commercial Vehicle Manufacturers'	£150-200

Other issues (with or without motor)

--	1950-55	Massey Ferguson Tractor	£100-125
--	1950-55	Ford Tractor	£100-125
--	1950-55	Hillman Minx Saloon	£100-125
--	1950-55	Humber Super Snipe, blue / grey body	£90-120
--	1950-55	Guy Truck	£75-95
--	1950-55	Sunbeam Racer	£100-125
--	1950-55	Humber Hawk	£75-95
--	1950-55	Rolls-Royce Razor Edge Saloon	£75-95
--	1950-55	Routemaster London Bus	£100-125
--	1950-55	Commer Avenger Coach	£100-125
--	1950-55	Guy Truck 'LYONS ICE CREAM'	£100-125
--	1950-55	Sunbeam-Talbot Saloon, metallic pale brown	£75-95
--	1950-55	Guy Milk Tanker, blue /cream, 'MILK'	£75-95
--	1950-55	Guy Cable Lorry	£75-95
--	1950-55	Guy Petrol Tanker 'REGENT PETROL'	£100-125
--	1950-55	Guy 'FIRE' Engine	£100-125
--	1950-55	Guy Container Lorry	£75-95
	1950-55	Guy Refuse Lorry	£75-95

Chad Valley model Tractors

--	1952	Fordson Major E27N	Dark Blue body, Orange wheels, rubber tyres (2 types of tread on rear), steering, towbar with pin, clockwork wound by starting handle. Scale 1:16. Illustrated box or plain box with small label	£150-200
--	1954	Fordson Major DDN	Mid-Blue body, Orange wheels, rubber tyres, working steering, lifting bonnet, towbar/pin, hydraulic lift at rear (detachable centre arm), clockwork wound through rear hub. Scale 1:16. Illustrated box or plain box with small label	£150-200
		Static version:	As previous model but without clockwork but without clockwork operation. Illustrated box or plain box plus small label. The word 'working' is deleted from all sides of box	£150-200
		Chrome version:	Static (non-clockwork) version in chrome plate, with or without wooden plinth. Thought to be a ploughing trophy or Ford presentation model	£250-400
--	1955	Ford Dexta	Mid-Blue body, Orange wheels, radiator panels and 'Fordson Dexta', not steerable, rubber tyres, hook, 1:16. Illustrated box	£400-600
--	1955	Ferguson	Green, Red wheels, 'Ferguson' on sides, steering, hook, scale 1:16. Illustrated box inscribed 'Ferguson'. Promotional	£500-700
			Grey body, Grey wheels, hydraulic lift at rear	£600-800
--	1955	Fordson Major E27N	Red and Yellow with driver, clockwork, scale 1:43, boxed. Made under licence by 'Raybro & Sturdy Products S.A.', Johannesburg, South Africa (model marked 'Chad Valley GB')	£50-100

The introduction to the Chad Valley section was written by Sue Richardson who also provided the basic listing.
Additional listing information came from the Cecil Gibson archives and John G. Butler of Berkhampstead, Herts.

Charbens Toys

The following history and listings have been researched by Robert Newson. See the colour section for pictures.

The firm of Charbens & Co. was started around 1928 by Charles and Benjamin Reid and was based at Hornsey Road, Holloway, London N7. They made hollow-cast lead figures, and a few lead vehicles were also produced in the 1930s. After the war zinc die-casting was introduced, and some items exist in both lead and zinc versions (the latter from new dies). Zinc castings by Charbens very often have metal failure as a result of contamination from the lead that was still used extensively in the factory.

The 'Old Crocks' series of miniatures was introduced in 1955. After 1967 all vehicle models were deleted from the catalogue except for a few items included in sets with plastic figures. Production of figures was discontinued in 1973. Model numbers were allocated around 1954, so items which had already been withdrawn are not numbered. Dates of issue have been taken from catalogues or adverts, but inevitably are incomplete. Most pre-war items have 'RD' cast in, most post-war items have 'CHARBENS' cast underneath.

Ref	Year(s)	Model name	Colours, features, details	Market Price Range

Pre-war issues (part hollow-cast, part diecast construction)

Ref	Year(s)	Model name	Colours, features, details	Market Price Range
-	-	**Motorcycle Policeman**	Solid cast machine with green petrol tank	**£30-40**
-	-	**Police Motor Cycle and Sidecar**	Solid cast machine, rider and passenger in black / white uniforms, black sidecar	**£30-40**
-	-	**Soap Box Racer**	Solid cast brown base, four red wheels (six spokes), Cub Scout pushing, Cub Scout rider + another	**£200-300**
-	-	**Goat Cart with Girl**	Blue cart and girl, brown goat, yellow 6-spoke wheels	**£30-40**
-	-	**Goat Cart with Girl**	Red cart and girl, white goat, 6-spoke wheels	**£30-40**
-	-	**Road Workers Set**	Contains Horse Roller (green / orange / brown), orange / black tar boiler truck with 6-spoke wheels, plus 4 workmen, a nightwatchman, hut, brazier, 'Road up' sign, pipe and 2 barriers	**£150-180**
-	-	**Gypsy Caravan**	Blue / white caravan with white horse, yellow wheels (smaller at front) plus orange / black seated Gypsy woman with baby, standing man, linen line with washing, cooking pot	**£200-250**
-	-	**The Farm Wagon**	Green / yellow four-wheel wagon with two hay racks, brown carthorse, cream / black carter figure. In red card box with cream label	**£70-90**
-	-	**Tumbril Cart** (two wheels)	Green / yellow cart with two hay racks, brown horse, cream / black carter, cream card box	**£40-50**
-	-	**Coster Cart with Donkey**	Green / yellow cart, solid sides, grey donkey, costermonger figure (see 24 below)	**£40-50**
-	-	**Organ Grinder's Cart** (two wheels)	Brown / yellow organ, grey donkey, red monkey with mug, brown / green organ-grinder	**£70-80**
-	-	**Governor's Cart** (two wheels)	Yellow / black, cream / red or brown / black cart, 2 children, donkey, zoo-keeper figure	**£40-50**
-	-	**Milk Float** (two wheels)	Yellow / red cart with 'PURE MILK' cast in. Brown horse, milkman figure (see 25)	**£35-45**
-	-	**Milk Float** (four wheels)	Orange / white body with 'UNITED DAIRIES', 'PASTEURISED MILK' and 'CREAM' logo. 8-spoke wheels with rubber tyres, brown horse, white / blue milkman with bottle	**£150-200**
-	-	**Milk Handcart**	with 'MILK' logo and Milkman	**£150-200**
-	-	**Bread Handcart**	with 'HOVIS' logo and Delivery-man	**£150-200**
-	-	**Cape Cart** (two wheels)	Enclosed dark blue body and roof, brown horse, mid-blue figure	**£25-35**
-	-	**Tree Wagon** (four wheels)	Yellow / red log carrier, 12-spoke wheels, 4 horses, 2 white figures with poles, (see also 1)	**£70-80**
-	-	**Dairy Float** (four wheels)	Mid-blue, 'EXPRESS DAIRY', 'PURE MILK', 'BUTTER & EGGS', white shafts, brown horse, 8-spoke wheels, rubber tyres, white / blue milkman holding bottle	**£150-200**
-	-	**Coal Cart** (four wheels)	Black cart, coalman and coal sack, white / orange horse, 12-spoke wheels, 6 spare sacks	**£200-250**
-	-	**Coffee Stall**	Orange / yellow stall, silver chimney, brown / white horse, tea urn and crockery	**£70-90**
-	-	**Railway Wagon** (four wheels)	Grey / red open wagon, 'London Midland Scottish Railway' cast in, driver, white horse	**£100-150**
-	-	**Horse-Drawn Grass Cutter**	Yellow / red cutter, brown driver and horse (see also 3)	**£60-75**
-	-	**Horse-Drawn Roller**	Green / yellow roller, brown driver and horse (see also 2)	**£60-75**
-	-	**Horse-Drawn Delivery Van**	See picture in colour section	**£200-250**
-	-	**Gamekeeper with Dog**		**£50-60**
-	-	**Flower Seller**	With basket of flowers	**£50-60**
-	-	**Jack's Band**	Nine assorted musicians plus conductor	**£200-300**
-	-	**Circus Clown Set**	Clowns on Stilts, Clown on Unicycle, Clown climbing Ladder, Clown standing, Policeman clown	**£60-90**
-	-	**Circus Single Figures**	Liberty Horses, Performing Elephants, Seal with Balls, Strongman, Boxing Midgets, Acrobats, Parrot, Dog, Ringmaster	each: **£15-20**

Pre-war Motor Vehicles (all cast in lead)

6	**Petrol Tanker**. Red, blue, yellow	**£200-300**
524	**Fire Engine**. Cast-in driver, separate ladder, rubber tyres	**£150-200**
525	**Car and Caravan**. Six-light saloon car (red, green or yellow); Caravan copied from Dinky Toys 30g, yellow with orange lower half	**£200-300**
526	**Motor Van**. No details	**£100-150**
728	**Ambulance**. Man cast on rear step. Green or brown	**£150-200**
864	**Racing Car**. Pale blue, green or yellow	**£50-60**
865	**Breakdown Lorry**. No details	**£100-120**
---	**Bentley Ambulance**. Copy of Dinky Toys 24a in off-white	**£100-120**
---	**1935 Bluebird**. Blue body	**£200-300**
---	**Armoured Car**. Six wheels, brown	**£40-50**

---	**Caterpillar Tractor**. Copy of Tootsietoy but larger. 'MIMIC TOY' cast underneath	**£100-200**
---	**Tank**. Copy of Tootsietoy. 'MIMIC TOY' cast underneath. Very dark blue	**£40-50**
---	**Mack Stake Lorry**. Copy of Tootsietoy. Green and red	**£80-100**
---	**Mack Lorry with AA Gun**. Copy of Tootsietoy. Light brown, black and silver	**£100-150**
---	**Mack Searchlight Lorry**. Copy of Tootsietoy. Light brown and black	**£100-150**
---	**Mack Barrage Balloon Set**. No details. Johillco made a similar set	**£150-200**

Post-war issues (Boxed models, mostly all-diecast construction)

-	late 1940s	**Packard Saloon**. 'JAVELIN' cast under. Red or green	**£30-40**
-	late 1940s	**Petrol Tanker**. Different from the pre-war tanker. Red, Green or Blue	**£30-40**
-	late 1940s	**Station Wagon**. Tan with dark brown bonnet and wings, spare wheel at rear	**£30-40**
-	?	**Farm Tractor and Reaper**. Orange/yellow/blue/red	**£120-160**
1	1940s-60	**Horse-Drawn Log Wagon**. Yellow, red wheels, with man, two tandem horses, wooden log, cream card box	**£60-75**
2	1940s-67	**Horse-Drawn Roller**. Yellow with green or red roller, with horse and man (seated)	**£60-75**
3	1940s-67	**Horse-drawn Grass Cutter**. Yellow, red wheels, unpainted cutter, with horse and man (seated)	**£60-75**
4	1940s-67	**Horse-drawn Two-wheel Farm Wagon with Raves**. Green wagon, yellow shafts and wheels	**£60-75**
5	1940s-67	**Horse-drawn Four-wheel Farm Wagon with Raves**. Green wagon, yellow shafts and wheels	**£60-75**
6	1940s-67	**Tractor with Driver**. Red or orange with metal wheels or blue with rubber wheels	**£60-75**
7	1940s-62	**Horse-drawn Van with Man**. Blue with cream upper half, metal wheels or 'HOVIS BREAD' or 'PURE MILK' labels; or Orange with light brown upper half, rubber wheels, 'HOVIS BREAD' labels	**£100-150**
8	1940s-62	**Tipper Lorry**. Cab/tipper colours include: red/cream, blue/cream, dark green/yellow, orange/yellow	**£30-40**
9	1940s-62	**Motor Coach**. Yellow with red flash, dark red with cream flash, dark blue with green flash, light green with blue flash, beige with green flash	**£100-120**

10 to 14		**Light Vans.** Two castings known. The first was a small boxy van with no rear windows. The second (from the early 1950s) was larger and more rounded, resembling a Ford E83W, with two rear windows.	
10	1940s-60	**Royal Mail Van.** Red, second casting with black bonnet, 'ROYAL MAIL', 'G-VI-R' paper labels **£75-90**	
11	1940s-62	**'AMBULANCE'.** Cream, Red Cross on paper labels....**£75-90**	
12	1940s-62	**'Carter Paterson' Van.** Dark green, 'CARTER PATERSON' on paper labels **£75-90**	
13	1940s-60	**'Police' Van.** Dark blue, 'POLICE GR' paper labels....**£75-90**	
14	1940s-62	**Post Office Telephones Van.** Green, 'POST OFFICE TELEPHONES' on paper labels..........**£75-90**	
15	1940s-62	**Fire Engine and Wheeled Escape.** Red or orange-red, unpainted ladders, three firemen and hose **£50-60**	
16	1940s-67	**Covered Wagon with Four Horses and Driver.** Green wagon, yellow wheels, cloth canopy, metal shaft and horses ....**£50-60** Same, but Orange wagon, plastic shaft and horses **£50-60**	
17	1940s-67	**Tractor and Log Trailer with Driver.** Tractor as No.6, Trailer as No.1 but with drawbar in place of shafts **£100-150**	
18	1940s-62	**Tractor and Grass Cutter with two Drivers.** Tractor as No.6, Trailer modified from No.3 ....**£100-150**	
19	1940s-67	**Tractor and Reaper with two Drivers.** Tractor as No.6, green reaper (yellow metal blades) or light blue reaper (red plastic blades), or all plastic **£100-150**	
20	1954-67	**Mobile Crane.** Red body, green chassis, unpainted or yellow jib ....**£30-40** Orange body, light blue chassis, yellow jib **£30-40**	
21	1954-67	**Muir-Hill Dumper with Driver.** Beige or Orange with Green dumper, Orange with Yellow dumper ....**£30-40** Red with Yellow plastic dumper **£30-40**	
22	1954-67	**Travelling Zoo.** Elephant towing two cages with two lions, two polar bears, man. Red chassis, unpainted cages, yellow roofs, metal or plastic animals.....................................**£70-90** Same but orange chassis, lt. blue cages, yellow roofs....**£70-90**	
23	1955-58	**Water Pistol.** no details **£5-10**	
24	1954-55	**Costermonger's Cart.** Dark green cart, red or yellow wheels, donkey, man and basket.........................**£25-35**	
25	1955-?	**Horse-drawn Milk Cart.** Yellow with red wheels, 'PURE MILK' labels. With man and churn **£70-80**	
26	1954-62	**Armoured Car.** Green or beige, metal or rubber wheels ..**£25-35**	
27	1955-67	**Large Tractor.** Cast in two halves. Red with yellow wheels or orange with light blue wheels.........**£100-120**	
28	1954-67	**Diesel Road Roller.** Green or pale green, red wheels, unpainted flywheel **£25-35**	
29	1954-62	**Mincer.** Toy kitchen equipment, Yellow...........................**£5-10**	
30	1955	**Scammell Mechanical Horse and Trailer.** Blue with 'LNER' labels, or dark brown cab with beige trailer and 'GWR' labels.............................**£35-45**	
31	1955-62	**Articulated Low-loader with Cable Drum.** Red or green cab, yellow trailer **£35-45**	
32	1955-62	**Alfa-Romeo Racing Car.** Hollow-cast lead, red with rubber wheels **£50-75**	
33	1955-62	**Cooper-Bristol Racing Car.** Hollow-cast lead, green with rubber wheels **£50-75**	
34	1955-62	**Ferrari Racing Car.** Hollow-cast lead, blue (yellow) nose, rubber wheels **£50-75**	
35	1954-67	**Horse Log Wagon.** As No.1 but single horse.....**£50-75**	
36	1940s-55	**3-wheel Pedestrian Electric Van.** Dark blue, 'DAIRY MILK' printed on sides; milkman, crate and bottles...**£100-120** Orange, 'HOVIS' on sides, man, tray of loaves **£100-120**	
36	1957-62	**Maudslay Horse Box.** Dark red, 'HORSE TRANSPORT' printed on sides, with horse and driver.............**£100-120** Green/Red body, 'NEWMARKET HORSEBOX' **£100-120**	
36	1967	**Steam Roller Large scale.** Green body, red 12-spoke wheels, unpainted roller, black chimney **£200-300**	
37	1960-62	**Articulated Low-loader with Rocket Missile.** Dark green cab / trailer, orange / black missile launcher. No makers name on model **£70-90**	
38	1955-60	**'Shoot and Save' Money Box** Savings bank, with gun to fire coin into bank **£70-90**	
39	1955	**Telephone Kiosk** Red kiosk with opening door, unpainted telephone **£15-20**	
40	1940s-55	**Fire Engine with Ladder and Firemen.** Different from No.15. Red body, unpainted 2-part ladder.............**£70-90**	
41	1955	**Fireplace.** Dolls house item **£5-10**	
445	c1955	**'Auto Race Set'** 'Andover series'. Made only for the Flare Import Corporation, 230 Fifth Ave., New York. Contains 3 (Dinky style) racing cars, 6 mechanics, man with chequered flag. 43mm scale, hollow-cast. Card box has Formula I race scene on colour label **£300-400**	

Salco series

---	**Mickey Mouse Fire Brigade**..........................Red fire engine with unpainted ladder, 3 painted Mickey Mouse figures. All card picture box **£1,000-1,250**
---	**Mickey and Minnies' Piano** ....Cream piano with operating handle, Mickey and Minnie Mouse figures. ....Black/Blue/Yellow/White all card picture box...................**£1,000-1,250**
---	**Mickey and Minnies' Barrel Organ**.................Red organ with Yellow wheels, Mickey and Minnie Mouse figures. All card picture box **£500-700**
---	**Milk Cart with Pluto and Donald Duck** **£125-150**
---	**'Mickey and Minnie on the River'**................Green boat, 2 seats, Mickey and Minnie **£500-600**
---	**'Mickey and Donald's Garden' Set** ....Blue wheelbarrow, spade and rake. Boxed...**£500-600**
---	**Horse-drawn Brewer's Dray**.......................Light Blue dray with Yellow detachable brewery sign marked 'TOY TOWN BREWERS', ...six unpainted barrels, black bowler-hatted driver and brown horse......................**£150-200**

'Old Crocks', Military models and 'Miniature Lorries'

'OLD CROCKS' series

1	**1904 Darracq**. Dark Blue, Red or Orange, open 2-seater..............**£10-25**
2	**1904 Spyker**. Yellow 4-seater open car......................**£10-25**
3	**1914 'Old Bill' Bus**. 2-piece casting, or single casting plus separate top deck, Red or Orange **£10-25**
4	**1907 Ford Model T**. 2-piece casting, tin chassis, Dark Blue ....**£10-25** Single casting, no separate chassis, Dark Blue **£10-25**
5	**1907 Vauxhall**. Green open 2-seater **£10-25**
6	**1906 De Dion Bouton**. Light Green or Violet open 2-seater **£10-25**
7	**1898 Panhard**. Light Green or Brown 2-seater **£10-25**
8	**1906 Rolls-Royce Silver Ghost**. Silver 4-seater open car **£10-25**
9	**1903 Standard 6hp**. Dark Red or Maroon with Beige roof...........**£10-25**
10	**1902 Wolseley**. Light Blue 4-seater open car **£10-25**
11	**1908 Packard Runabout**. Light Green open 2-str........**£10-25**
12	**1905 Vauxhall Hansom Cab**, Orange / Beige **£10-25**
13	**1900 Straker Flat Steam Lorry**. Light Green, packing case ....**£10-25** **1900 Straker Lowside Steam Lorry**. Light Blue, three barrels ...**£10-25**
14	**Stephenson's 'Rocket' Locomotive**. Yellow / Black **£10-25**
15	**Tender for 'Rocket'**, colours as 14.........................**£10-25**
16	**1909 Albion**. Dark or Light Blue open truck................**£10-25**
17	**1912 Rover**. Orange 2-seater open sports car..............**£10-25**
18	**1911 Mercedes-Benz**. Dark Green open 2-seater........**£10-25**
19	**Bedford Horse-Box**. Brown, *'HORSE TRANSPORT'* cast on sides, *'H.G. IVORY'* on tailgate...............**£15-25**

20	**1910 Lanchester**. Light Blue 4-seater sports tourer.....................**£10-25**
21	**1922 Morris Cowley**. Beige 2-seater open car...........**£10-25**
22	**1900 Daimler**. Maroon 2-seater **£10-25**
23	**1904 Autocar**. Dark Blue, open 3-wheeler **£10-25**
24	**1870/80 Grenville Steam Carriage**. Green or Light Green **£10-25**
25	**1905 Napier**. Violet or Purple 2-seater racer.............**£10-25**
26	**Fire Engine and Escape**. Red or Orange...................**£10-25**
27	**Articulated Breakdown Lorry**. Dark Green cab, Light Blue trailer, Orange crane **£10-25**
28	**Mercer Runabout**. Dark Blue or Green 2-seater sports **£10-25**

MILITARY MODELS

30	**Searchlight on 4-wheel Trailer**. Green and Silver **£10-25**
31	**Twin Bofors Gun on Trailer**. Green and Silver **£10-25**
32	**Radar Scanner on Trailer**. Green and Silver **£10-25**
33	**Field Gun on Trailer**. Green and Silver.....................**£10-25**
34	**Rocket Gun on Trailer**. Green and Silver **£10-25**
35	**Armoured Car**. Green **£10-25**

'MINIATURE LORRIES' (not issued)

40	**Articulated Tanker**. Listed in 1960 catalogue ....NPP
41	**Articulated Lorry**. Listed in 1960 catalogue.............................NPP
42	**Six-wheeled Lorry**. Listed in 1960 catalogue............................NPP
43	**Six-wheeled Tanker**. Listed in 1960 catalogue..........................NPP

CORGI TOYS
PRECISION DIE-CAST SCALE MODELS
TRADE MARK REGISTERED

Post & Pkg. 1/-, 1/6 on two. 1/9 on three

150 Vanwall Racing Car
Length 3⅜" 3/2

218 Aston Martin D.B.4
Length 3⅝" 4/6

209 Riley Police Car
Length 3¾" 3/6

211S Studebaker Golden Hawk
Length 4¼" 4/6

213 Jaguar Fire Service Car
Length 3¾" 3/6

214 Ford Thunderbird
Length 4" 3/6

216 Austin A.40
Length 3⅜" 3/-

222 Renault Floride
Length 3⅝" 3/6

151 Lotus XI Racing Car
Length 3¼" 3/6

220 Chevrolet Impala
Length 4¼" 4/-

217 Fiat 800
Length 3¾" 3/6

223 Chevrolet State Patrol Car
Length 4¼" 4/6

226 Morris Mini-Minor
Length 2½" 3/4

302 M.G. "A"
Length 3½" 3/9

303 Mercedes 300SL Open
Length 3¾" 3/6

304 Mercedes Hard Top
Length 3¾" 3/6

416 R.A.C. Land Rover
Length 3¾" 3/9

DO YOU KNOW?   *East Croydon is the busiest S.R. Station, apart from London Termini*

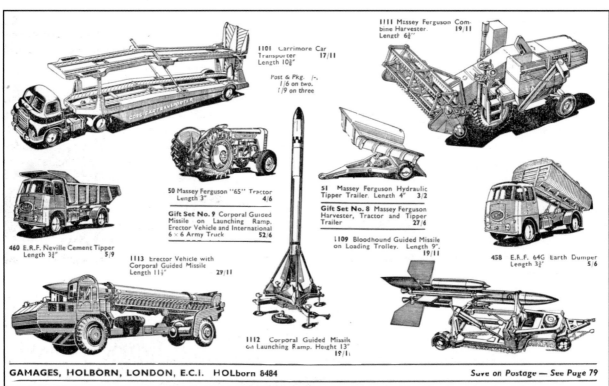

1101 Carrimore Car Transporter
Length 10⅝" 17/11

Post & Pkg. /-, 1/6 on two. 1/9 on three

1111 Massey Ferguson Combine Harvester.
Length 6⅜" 19/11

50 Massey Ferguson "65" Tractor
Length 3" 4/6

Gift Set No. 9 Corporal Guided Missile on Launching Ramp. Erector Vehicle and International 6 × 6 Army Truck 52/6

51 Massey Ferguson Hydraulic Tipper Trailer. Length 4" 3/2

Gift Set No. 8 Massey Ferguson Harvester, Tractor and Tipper Trailer 27/6

1109 Bloodhound Guided Missile on Loading Trolley. Length 9". 19/11

460 E.R.F. Neville Cement Tipper
Length 3¾" 5/9

1113 Erector Vehicle with Corporal Guided Missile
Length 11¼" 29/11

1112 Corporal Guided Missile on Launching Ramp. Height 13" 19/11

458 E.R.F. 64G Earth Dumper
Length 3¾" 5/6

GAMAGES, HOLBORN, LONDON, E.C.I. HOLborn 8484   *Save on Postage — See Page 79*

Pages from Gamages of Holborn 1961 'Model Book'

Mettoy
Corgi Toys

Corgi Toys were launched in 1956 by the Mettoy Company which had itself been founded in Northampton by Phillip Ullmann in 1933. The 'Mettoy' name was derived from the first three letters of 'Metal' plus 'toy' - the company's main product range being composed of lithographed metal toys. In 1948 Mettoy produced their first cast metal toys and called them 'Castoys'. The Castoys models contained a clockwork motor and when the first Corgi Toys models were introduced they also contained a mechanism. This, plus the introduction of window glazing, gave Corgi a competitive edge against their great rivals, Dinky Toys.

Corgi Toys were named after the Welsh breed of dogs and this logo will be found on virtually all the Corgi packaging. The models were produced in Swansea by Mettoy Playcraft Ltd., hence baseplates are marked 'Made in Gt. Britain'.

The development of the Corgi Toys product range was largely instigated by Howard Fairbairn, a Mettoy Company Director. Prior to his director appointment, he had been Head of Development at the Birmingham Aluminium Casting Co. and had considerable diecasting experience. The first truly Corgi Toys product was No.200 Ford Consul in 1956.

Corgi have always been famed for their model innovations. This was especially true when they were able to promote their models as 'The Ones With Windows'. Additionally, greater realism was achieved over time with, for example, better detailing of their wheel hubs.

Corgi introduced various model ranges which have stood the test of time. Today, virtually all the Corgi models produced in the 1950s and 1960s are highly sought after. In particular, model such as the range of 'Monte Carlo' Minis, the Gift Sets, Farm Tractors and the 'Chipperfield's Circus' subjects are very

Corgi Toys shop display card.
Photo: Vectis Auctions

collectable. In addition, television and film related models such as 'Batman', 'James Bond' and similar items fetch very high prices at auction.

In 1983, the Mettoy company went into receivership and Corgi Toys became the subject of a management buy-out. From this time, the emphasis changed from the mass-production of toy vehicles to mainly the development of authentic limited edition models aimed at adult collectors - the 'Corgi Classics' range. Regrettably these items fall outside the scope of this publication. However, collectors requiring information on Corgi Classics are recommended to join the Corgi Collectors Club (details are to be found on page 288).

The Editor wishes to thank all who have contributed to the greatly revised listings.

Market Price Range

Please note that the prices shown refer to pristine models and boxes.

Items failing to match this standard will sell for less.

Note also that boxes must still contain all their original additional contents.

Corgi Toys Identification

Often referred to as 'the ones with windows', Corgi Toys were the first manufacturer to produce models with that refinement. Some of their first models also had a mechanical motor. Spring suspension was introduced from 1959 and in 1960 the first die-cast model to have an opening bonnet. The first models were based on real cars of the period. Similarly, with the launch of the 'Corgi Major Toys' in 1959, models of real commercial vehicles were available and competed with the Dinky 'Supertoys' range.

In the 1960s Corgi produced many successful film and TV-related models. Probably the best remembered was the 'James Bond' Aston Martin which sold in huge quantities in the autumn of 1965. Indeed, such was the popularity of the model that a version was still available in 1992!

Corgi introduced many new features in the 1960s such as: jewelled headlights, opening bonnet revealing detailed engine, opening boot revealing spare, self-centering steering, ruby rear lights, etc. One particularly attractive model was the Midland Red Motorway Express Coach. The detailed interior even incorporated a toilet! Needless to say good examples of this model are highly sought after by bus collectors. Similarly the 'Chipperfields Circus' collection of models were beautifully produced and are highly prized today.

Innovations were frequent and imaginative in the 1960s. 'Golden Jacks' for instance, a built-in jacking system which enabled models to have 'Take-Off' wheels. And 'Trans-O-Lites' whereby light rays were captured and fed through prisms to illuminate the headlights. 'WhizzWheels' and the slightly larger scale of 1:42 were introduced in the 1970s.

A market strategy unique to Corgi was the launching a replica model car simultaneously with the real car. To date simultaneous launches have occurred with Austin Metro, Ford Escort, Triumph Acclaim, Ford Sierra and the MG Maestro 1600, which is a unique record. Corgi were the first die-cast manufacturers to introduce the dimensions of light, sound and movement into their models by using the micro-chip in their 'Corgitronic' range. The models 'come alive', for example by just pushing down on the rear axle or, in the case of the Road Repair Unit, by pressing the workman to activate the pneumatic drill sound. Others (like the Sonic Corgi Truck) can be operated from a remote control handset.

Mechanical. Some early Corgi Toys were produced in either the normal form or with a friction type flywheel motor. Exceptions were the sports cars and trucks which could not be converted to take the flywheel. The mechanisms were not robust and were phased out in 1959.

Boxes. July 1956 - Blue box, January 1959 - Yellow/Blue box (Two-tone cars were first to use them) December 1966 - Window box (2 square window ends) May 1973 - Angled window box (one square window end, coloured lines around box) 1980 - Yellow window box, 1987 New style Corgi logo box.

Box contents. Model boxes often contain much more than just the basic model. Prices shown in the Catalogue assume that not only is the model in pristine condition, but that it is accompanied by all the original additional contents. These can include: extra card packing, inner card or polystyrene trays, pictorial stands, plastic protectors, transit card protection intended for removal by the retailer, instruction and information leaflets, catalogues, consumables (such as unopened packets of rockets, decals, etc.). This particularly applies to some Novelty and Film/TV models, e.g., Nos. 268, 277, 497, 511, 1123, 1139, 1144 and Gift Sets 3, 10, 20 and 21. A further example relates to the early 'Blue box' models each of which should contain a concertina catalogue leaflet plus a 'Join the Corgi Club' leaflet. If original items are missing, e.g., the plastic dome protector included with 511 Chipperfields Poodle Truck or card protectors with other models, it will affect the price that a model will achieve.

Whilst every effort has been made to describe models and, where known, their accompanying contents, any further information would be welcomed.

Corgi Toys shop display item - a large representation of a Corgi Toys blue and yellow box.

Photo: Vectis Auctions Ltd.

Castoys were produced by the Mettoy Company between 1948 and 1958 and were instigated by a request from Marks and Spencers for a robust, long lasting toy. The models were made of zinc alloy and were initially advertised as 'Heavy Cast Mechanical Toys'.

Generally, they had windows, a clockwork motor and brake, plus black rubber tyres on cast hubs. Of the original issues, only two models, No. 840, the 'Eight Wheel Lorry' and 870 'Delivery Van' remained in production after 1951 and these were packaged in attractive Yellow/Red boxes which displayed a picture of the model inside. The later issues of the Delivery Van with their various attractive body designs are now rare and sought after items.

The following listing contains all the information available at present. The Editor would welcome any additional information on body colours and variations.

NB See the 'Miscellaneous Models' colour section for pictures.

Ref	Year(s)	Model name	Colours, features, details	Market Price Range

Large Scale Models 1:35

Presented in Yellow/Red endflap boxes each displaying an excellent picture of the model contained within.

Ref	Year(s)	Model name	Colours, features, details	Market Price Range
-	-	Milk Handcart	with 'MILK' logo and Milkman	£150-175
718	1956-58	Luxury Observation Coach	Metallic Blue and Gold body with Silver raised roof section and base, Red door with Brown plastic male passenger Destination board shows 'PRIVATE' and registration 'MTY 718'	£250-350
			Metallic Brown and Pink body with Silver raised roof section and radiator, with Green female passenger	£200-300
810	1948-51	Limousine	Cream, Red or Green body, 'MTY 810'	NGPP
820	1948-51	Streamline Bus	Cream, Green or Red body, clockwork mechanism, Red pressed tin seating, solid rubber wheels, unpainted chassis. Registration No 'MTY 820'	£100-200
			As previous model but with opening door and registration No 'MTY 720'	£100-200
830	1948-51	Racing Car	Light Green, 6, long approx, 'METTOY' cast in base, tinplate hollow printed wheels with motor and brake	£100-200
840	1948-58	8 Wheel Lorry	Metallic Blue cab with Grey rear body, Silver radiator and hubs	£100-200
850	1948-51	Fire Engine	Red body, Silver ladder and crank	£100-200
			Red body, Silver extending ladder, no crank	£100-200
860	1948-51	Tractor	No models seen but shown in 1951 catalogue with Yellow/Red body	£100-200
863		Ferguson TE20 Tractor and Trailer	Red/Blue tractor, Yellow trailer, Red hubs, painted plastic driver	£100-125
870	1948-51	Delivery Van	No models seen but shown in 1948 catalogue with plain Dark Blue body	£100-150
	1952-55	'EXPRESS DELIVERY'	Yellow or Blue body with Red logo and design on sides	£150-200
	1955-58	'POST OFFICE TELEPHONES'	Green body, White logo, Royal crest in Gold, Silver two part extending ladder	£200-300
	1955-58	'ROYAL MAIL'	Red body, Silver trim, Yellow logo and Royal crest, 'MTY 870'	£200-300
	1955-58	'AMBULANCE'	Cream body with Black logo on sides	£100-200
	1956-58	'BOAC'	Blue body, Silver trim, White *'Fly By BOAC'* on roof	£250-350

Small Scale Models 1:45

Ref	Year(s)	Model name	Colours, features, details	Market Price Range
---	1955-57	Soft Drinks Van	Dark red body, number plate 'CWS 300', Silver wheels, Logo on rear: 'CWS SOFT DRINKS - THIRST COME - THIRST SERVED'	£75-95

Special 1:18 scale issue for Marks and Spencer

Ref	Year(s)	Model name	Colours, features, details	Market Price Range
---	1958	'VANWALL' Racing Car	Diecast body, perspex screen, driver, 'VANWALL' transfers, 'push and go' motor in some. 'Vanwall the famous British Grand Prix Winner' cast in base.	
			i) Green body, racing number '7' or '18', no Mettoy logo on base	£200-300
			ii) French Blue body, racing number '20', no Mettoy logo on base	£200-300

The 'Miniature Numbers' series

The range of models produced between 1951 an 1954 was based on just two vehicles - the Standard Vanguard and the Rolls Royce. Models were issued in two sizes and featured a clockwork motor plus brake, adjustable steering (controlled by moving the central fog lamp sideways) and moulded grey plastic wheels. Both diecast and plastic bodies have been observed on some examples. They were packaged in attractive window boxes. The following listing has been taken from the 1951 Mettoy Catalogue and the Editor would welcome any additional information.

Ref	Year(s)	Model name	Colours, features, details	Market Price Range
502	1951	Standard Vanguard Saloon	Shown with Green body in catalogue (2 7/8 inches long)	£50-75
505	1951	Rolls-Royce Saloon	Red or Blue body, Silver trim (3 inches long)	£50-75
510	1951	Standard Vanguard Police Car	Black with White 'POLICE' logo on doors; roof siren and bell	£50-75
511	1951	Standard Vanguard Taxi	Shown in 1951 catalogue with Yellow body and Red roof rack	£50-75
512	1951	Standard Vanguard Fire Chief	Red, White 'FIRE CHIEF' on doors; single Silver ladder on roof	£50-75
602	1951	Standard Vanguard Saloon	Blue body shown in catalogue (large scale version of 502, 4 inches long)	£50-75
603	1951	Standard Vanguard Saloon	As 602 but with automatic to and fro bump feature	£50-75
605	1951	Rolls-Royce Saloon	Yellow body shown in catalogue (large scale version of 505, 4fi inches long)	£50-75
606	1951	Rolls-Royce Saloon	As 605 but with automatic to and fro bump feature	£50-75

152 B.R.M. Formula 1 Grand Prix
Racing Car

150 Vanwall Formula 1 Grand Prix
Racing Car

249 Mini-Cooper with De-Luxe
Wickerwork panels

211M Studebaker Golden Hawk
with friction motor

The photographs shown above are of Corgi Toys models sold by Vectis Auctions Ltd. and are reproduced by their kind permission.

See also 'Novelty, Film and TV-related' section.

Ref	Year(s)	Model name	Colours, features, details	Market Price Range
150	1957-61	**Vanwall Racing Car**	Green body, Silver trim, Yellow seat, flat spun hubs, racing number '3' on nose, Blue tinted screen, Blue box with leaflet	£80-90
			Same as previous model but with racing number '20' on nose and cockpit sides	£80-90
			Mid-Green body, Silver seat, '*VANWALL*' logo, clear screen, RN '1'	£80-90
			Mid-Green body, Yellow seat, small '*VANWALL*' logo, clear screen, RN '1'	£80-90
		Blue/Yellow box:	Red body, Yellow seat, large '*VANWALL*' logo, Blue tinted screen, RN '1'	£80-90
			Red body, Silver seat, small '*VANWALL*' logo, clear screen, RN '1'	£80-90
150 S	1961-65	**Vanwall Racing Car**	Red body, Silver trim, Blue/White bonnet design plus Black number '25', White driver	£80-90
150	1972-74	**Surtees TS9 Formula 1**	Metallic Purple or Metallic Blue body, 'BROOKE BOND OXO' logo, 8-spoke WhizzWheels	£20-25
			Metallic Turquoise body with cast 8-stud WhizzWheels	£15-20
	1975-76	Gift Set model:	Blue/Yellow body with '*DUCKHAMS*', (in GS 29 only)	GSP
151	1958-61	**Lotus XI Le Mans Racing Car**	Blue body, Red or Maroon seats, clear or Blue-tinted windscreen, racing numbers '1', or '3'	£140-170
			Silver body, Red seats, racing numbers '3'. Blue tinted windscreen	£100-120
			Red body, Beige seats, racing numbers '1'. Blue tinted windscreen	£200-250
151 A	1961-65	**Lotus XI Le Mans Racing Car**	Blue body, Red/White bonnet stripe, White driver, Black racing number '7'	£80-90
			Blue body, no bonnet stripe, White driver, Black racing number '7'	£80-90
			Lemon body, racing number '3', driver	£80-90
151	1974-76	**Yardley Mclaren M19A**	White body, 'YARDLEY', RN '55', 8-spoke or stud WhizzWheels	£30-35
		Gift Set model:	Same but Blue stripe on White helmet, 8-stud WhizzWheels, (GS30 only)	GSP
152	1958-61	**B.R.M. Racing Car**	Light or Dark Green body, Yellow seat, no driver, racing numbers '1', '3' or '7'. Blue box with leaflet	£80-90
	1961-65		Turquoise body, Silver trim, Union Jack on bonnet, RN's '1', '3' or '7'. Blue/Yellow box, no leaflet	£80-90
152 S	1961-65	**B.R.M. Racing Car**	Turquoise body, Silver trim, Union Jack on bonnet, racing numbers '1', '3' or '7', White driver, Blue/Yellow box, no leaflet	£80-90
152	1974-75	**Ferrari 312 B2**	Red body, 'Ferrari/Shell' logo, RN '5', White driver, Orange/Blue helmet, 8-spoke or 8-stud cast hubs	£20-25
153	1960-61	**Bluebird Record Car**	Blue body, UK and US flags on nose, metal hubs	£75-85
153 A	1961-65	**Bluebird Record Car**	Blue body, UK and US flags on nose, plastic hubs	£75-85
		variant:	Blue body with two Union Jacks on nose, Black plastic hubs	£75-85
153	1972-74	**Team Surtees TS 9B**	Red body, RN '26', Blue or Blue/White driver (Rob Walker), 8-spoke hubs	£35-40
		Gift Set issue:	Red body, '*NORRIS*' logo, (GS30 only)	GSP
154	1963-72	**Ferrari Formula 1**	Red body, Ferrari badge on bonnet, White driver, racing number '36'	£90-120
154	1974-79	**'JOHN PLAYER SPECIAL' Lotus**	Black body, Gold trim, racing number '1' or '4', drivers Emerson Fittipaldi or Ronnie Petersen.	
			'JPS' logo, Black/Red helmet, 8-stud hubs, 'Fittipaldi' on box	£25-30
			'JPS' logo, Black or Blue helmet, 'Petersen' on box	£25-30
			'JPS TEXACO' logo, Red helmet	£25-30
		Gift Set issue:	'JPS TEXACO' logo, Black helmet, (GS32 only)	GSP
		Gift Set issue:	'JPS SHELL' logo, Black/Red helmet, (GS30 only)	GSP
		Marks & Spencers issue:	No 'Corgi' on base, 'TEXACO' logo, Orange (?) helmet	GSP
155	1964-69	**Lotus Climax Racing Car**	British Racing Green body, Yellow stripe on bonnet, White driver, Blue helmet, racing number '1'	£100-130
155	1974-76	**'SHADOW' Formula 1**	Black body, 'UOP', racing number '17', driver (Jackie Collins) White/Maroon helmet	£30-35
156	1967-68	**Cooper-Maserati**	Dark Blue body, racing number '7', windscreen, White driver, Blue helmet	£40-50
156	1974-76	**Graham Hill's Shadow**	White/Red body, racing number '12', driver, '*EMBASSY RACING*'	£30-35
		Special issue:	Model in box with outer sleeve as presented at the National Sporting Club showing name 'MENU'	£300-500
158	1969-73	**Lotus Climax Racing Car**	Orange and White body, Blue driver, White helmet, Black number '8' and bonnet stripe	£35-45
158	1975-78	**Elf Tyrrell Ford F1**	Blue body, racing number '1', '*ELF*', Jackie Stewart driving	£30-35
159	1969-72	**Cooper-Maserati**	Yellow and White body with high wing, Black bonnet stripe, Blue driver, White helmet, cast wheels, Yellow racing number '3'	£35-45
159	1974-76	**Indianapolis Racing Car**	Red body, racing number '20', Patrick Eagle driving	£30-35
160	1975-78	**'HESKETH' 308 F1**	White body, 'HESKETH', Black helmet, 4-spoke or 8-stud hubs	£30-35
		Marks & Spencers issue:	White body, no 'CORGI' on some, Orange helmet	GSP
		Gift Set issue:	Yellow body, 'CORGI TEAM' logo, Orange driver (James Hunt), Black helmet, Blue belts, (GS26 only)	GSP
161	1971-73	**Santa Pod 'COMMUTER'**	Red 'Dragster' body, Chrome engine, racing number '2', WhizzWheels	£25-30
161	1977-78	**'ELF-TYRRELL' P34**	Blue and Yellow body, 'ELF' logo, Red or Blue helmet, 8-stud hubs, Yellow racing number '4'	£25-30
162	1978-79	**'ELF-TYRRELL' P34**	Blue and White body, 'FIRST NATIONAL BANK' logo, Red or Orange helmet	£25-30
		Marks & Spencers issue:	As previous model but no 'Corgi' on base, 8-stud hubs	GSP
162	1971-72	**'Quartermaster' Dragster**	Green and White body, aerofoil, driver, plastic hubs	£40-50
163	1971-73	**Santa Pod Dragster**	White body, Blue trim, Red chassis, '*GLOWORM*', driver, plastic hubs	£30-35
164	1972-73	**Ison Bros Dragster**	Yellow/Black body, 'WILD HONEY', Green tinted glass, WhizzWheels	£40-50

165	1972-74	Adams Brothers 'Drag-star'	Red/Yellow body, 4 x V-8 engines, WhizzWheels	£30-35
166	1971-74	Ford Mustang	Yellow/Green body, *'ORGAN GRINDER'*, racing number '39', driver	£30-35
167	1973-74	USA Racing Buggy	White/Red body, racing number '7', driver, US flag	£40-50
169	1974-77	'Starfighter Jet' Dragster	Blue/Silver/Red body, *'FIRESTONE'*	£30-35
170	1974-77	John Woolfe's Dragster	Blue/Yellow body, racing number '5', *'RADIO LUXEMBOURG'*, '208'	£40-50
190	1974-77	'JOHN PLAYER' Lotus	1:18 scale, Black/Gold, RN '1', driver, removable wheels, tools included in box	£35-40
191	1975-80	'TEXACO MARLBORO' F1 Mclaren	1:18 scale, White/Red, RN '5', removable wheels, tools included in box	£35-40
200	1956-61	Ford Consul	Cream, Dark or Pale Green, Tan or Dark Tan body, no suspension, leaflet with early issues	£140-180
		(First Corgi Toys model)	Blue, Light Greyish-Brown or Bright Green body, flat spun hubs	£140-180
200M	1956-59	Ford Consul	Leaflet with early issues.	
		(with flywheel motor)	Two-tone Green body, flat spun hubs	£120-150
			Green/Cream, flat spun hubs	£120-150
			Silver/Cream, flat spun hubs	£120-150
			Pale Grey over Green, flat spun hubs	£120-150
			Blue body, flat spun hubs	£120-150
			Dark Green or Bright Green, flat spun hubs	£120-150
200	1976-78	BLMC Mini 1000	Metallic Blue body, Silver roof, Red and White interior	£20-25
200A	1978-83	BLMC Mini 1000	Metallic Blue or Silver body, White or Red interior, Union Jack stripe on roof, WhizzWheels	£25-35
201	1956-61	Austin Cambridge	Pale Blue, Turquoise or Mid-Grey body, no suspension, leaflet with early issues	£120-150
			Light Grey body	£120-150
			Green/Cream	£175-225
			Two-tone Green	£120-150
			Silver over Metallic Green	£120-150
201M	1956-59	Austin Cambridge	Cream, Red, Slate Grey or Medium Grey body with motor, leaflet with early issues	£120-150
			Silver or Metallic Blue	£120-150
			Orange body, spun hubs, leaflet	£250-350
201	1970-72	The Saint's Volvo	White body, White 'Saint' logo on red label, WhizzWheels, driver, Red/Yellow 'window' box	£140-160
201	1979-82	BLMC Mini 1000	Silver body, Red interior, with or without 'TEAM CORGI' and '8'	£15-25
			As previous model but with Orange body	£15-25
			Dark Blue body without 'TEAM CORGI'	£15-25
			Dark Blue body with 'ESSO' and 'MICHELIN' labels	£15-25
202	1956-61	Morris Cowley	Bright Green or Grey body, flat hubs, no suspension, leaflet with early issues	£120-150
			Blue body, no suspension	£120-150
			Grey/Blue or Blue/Cream body	£120-150
			Pale Green/Blue or White/Blue body	£120-150
202M	1956-59	Morris Cowley	Pale Green, Medium Green or Off-White body, flywheel motor, leaflet	£120-150
			Dark Green body, spun hubs, flywheel motor, leaflet	£120-150
202	1970-72	Renault 16TS	Blue/Silver body, Yellow interior, no suspension, WhizzWheels	£25-30
203	1970-72	De Tomaso Mangusta	Metallic Dark Green, Gold stripes, racing number '1'	£20-25
203	1956-61	Vauxhall Velox	Red, Cream or Yellow body, no suspension, leaflet with early issues	£120-150
			Yellow/Red body	£200-250
203M	1956-59	Vauxhall Velox	Red body, flywheel motor, leaflet with early issues	£160-200
			Orange body, spun hubs, flywheel motor, leaflet	£250-350
203	1971-72	De Tomaso Mangusta	Green/Gold body, White interior, WhizzWheels, aerial	£20-25
			Green body, White interior, Silver base, WhizzWheels, aerial	£20-30
204	1956-61	Rover 90	Cream or Off-White body, flat hubs, leaflet with early issues	£120-150
			Light or Dark Grey body, flat hubs	£120-150
			Mid or Dark Green body, flat hubs	£120-150
			Metallic Green body, flat hubs	£120-150
			Metallic Red lower body, with Cream upper body, flat hubs	£120-150
			Metallic Cerise over Grey body	£120-150
204M	1956-59	Rover 90	Bright Mid-Green or Grey body, flat hubs, flywheel motor, leaflet	£120-160
			Mid or Dark Green body, flat hubs, flywheel motor, leaflet	£120-150
			Metallic Green body, flat hubs, flywheel motor, leaflet	£200-250
204	1972-73	Morris Mini-Minor	Dark Blue body, Lemon interior, WhizzWheels	£80-100
			Deep Blue body, Lemon interior, WhizzWheels	£200-250
			Metallic Blue body, Lemon interior, WhizzWheels	£100-125
			All-Orange body, Lemon interior, WhizzWheels	£100-125
			Orange body, Black roof, WhizzWheels	£120-150
205	1956-62	Riley Pathfinder	Red or Blue body, no suspension, flat hubs, leaflet with early issues	£120-150
205M	1956-59	Riley Pathfinder	Red body, flat hubs, flywheel motor, leaflet	£200-250
			Mid Blue body, leaflet	£200-250
			Dark Blue body, leaflet	£200-250
206	1956-59	Hillman Husky Estate	Tan or Greyish Light-Brown body, no suspension, leaflet with early issues	£100-140
			Metallic Blue and Silver body	£130-170

206M	1956-59	**Hillman Husky Estate**	Cream, Mid-Blue, Dark Blue or Grey body, flywheel motor, leaflet	£150-190
			Turquoise body, flat hubs, leaflet	£250-300
207	1957-62	**Standard Vanguard III**	White body (Red roof) or Grey body (Red roof), flat or shaped hubs, leaflet	£90-120
			Red over Green body, flat hubs	£100-140
207M	1957-59	**Standard Vanguard III**	Primrose Yellow body, flywheel motor, leaflet	£150-200
			Pale Green body, Red roof pillars, leaflet	£100-140
208	1957-60	**Jaguar 2.4 litre**	White body, flat hubs, no suspension, leaflet with early issues	£90-120
208M	1957-60	**Jaguar 2.4 litre**	Metallic Dark Blue body, flat hubs, flywheel motor, leaflet	£100-140
208 S	1960-63	**Jaguar 2.4 litre**	Lemon body, with spring suspension, flat hubs	£75-85
			Pale Lemon body, shaped spun hubs	£85-95
210	1957-60	**Citroën DS19**	Yellow body, Red roof, Grey baseplate, flat hubs, leaflet with early issues	£100-140
			Yellow body, Red roof, Silver baseplate with detailed drive shaft	£100-140
			Metallic Dark Green body, Black roof, Grey or Silver baseplate	£100-120
			As previous but with bulge to take flywheel motor. A '210M' was not produced	£120-150
210 S	1960-65	**Citroën DS19**	Red body, Lemon interior, Grey baseplate, spring suspension	£80-100
211	1958-60	**Studebaker Golden Hawk**	Blue body, Gold rear wing flashes, no suspension, flat hubs, leaflet	£90-110
			White body, Gold rear wing flashes, leaflet	£90-110
211 M		1958-59 **Studebaker Golden Hawk**		

White/Gold body, flywheel motor, no suspension, flat hubs, leaflet £125-150

211 S	1960-65	**Studebaker Golden Hawk**	Gold ('plated') body, Red interior, White flash, suspension, shaped hubs	£125-150
			Gold (painted) body, shaped hubs	£125-150
212	1958	**Road Racer**	Not released, one example known to exist	NPP
214	1959-65	**Ford Thunderbird Hardtop**	Pale Green (Cream roof) or Grey with Red roof, '1959' on rear number plate	£90-110
			Pale Green body, Cream roof, blank rear number plate	£90-110
214M	1959-60	**Ford Thunderbird Hardtop**	Pink body, Black roof, flywheel motor, '1959' on rear number plate, leaflet	£200-250
			Pale Green body, Cream roof, flywheel motor	£170-200
214 S	1962-64	**Ford Thunderbird Hardtop**	Metallic Grey/Red or Black/Red body, Lemon interior, with suspension	£90-110
215	1959-62	**Thunderbird Open Sports**	White body, Blue interior or Blue body, Silver interior, no suspension	£90-110
215 S	1962-64	**Thunderbird Open Sports**	Red body with Yellow interior and driver, with spring suspension	£90-110
216	1959-62	**Austin A40**	Two-tone Blue body, no suspension, flat hubs, leaflet with early issues	£80-100
			Red body, Black roof, flat hubs	£80-100
216M	1959-60	**Austin A40**	Red body, Black roof, flat hubs, flywheel motor, no suspension, leaflet	£120-140
			All-Red body, leaflet	£120-140
217	1960-63	**Fiat 1800 Saloon**	Light Blue body (Lemon interior); or Two tone Blue body (Lemon interior), smooth or shaped hubs	£40-50
			Light Tan body, Lemon interior	£40-50
			Mustard Yellow body, Bright Yellow interior	£80-90
218	1960-62	**Aston Martin DB4**	Red body (with or without bonnet vent), flat or shaped hubs	£65-75
	1961-62		Red body, Red interior, cast 'spoked' hubs	£75-85
			Primrose Yellow body with bonnet vent, Red interior, flat spun hubs	£80-100
			As previous model, but with cast 'criss-cross' wheels	£140-170
219	1959-63	**Plymouth Suburban Sports**	Cream with Fawn roof, Red interior	£70-80
220	1960-65	**Chevrolet Impala**	Metallic Red body, Red or Lemon interior, spun hubs, leaflet	£50-65
			Powder Blue body, Red or Lemon interior, spun hubs, leaflet	£50-65
			Pink body, Lemon interior, spun hubs	£50-65
			Sky Blue body, Red interior, spun hubs	£60-75
221	1960-63	**Chevrolet Impala Cab**	Yellow body, *'YELLOW TAXIS'*, smooth/shaped spun hubs, roof box	£55-65
222	1959-65	**Renault Floride**	Dark Red, Maroon or Lime Green body, Red, White or Yellow vac-formed interior, flat or shaped hubs, suspension	£50-60
			Metallic Blue body, Red interior, shaped hubs	£50-60
224	1961-65	**Bentley Continental**	Seats, opening boot with removable spare, steering, special lights.	
			Cream over Metallic Apple Green, Red interior, spun hubs	£100-125
			Black over Silver body, Red interior, spun hubs	£100-125
			Two-tone Green or Gold body	£100-125
			Metallic Green and White body	£100-125
			Cherry Red body, Lemon interior	£100-125
225	1961-65	**Austin 7 (Mini) Saloon**	Red body, windows, suspension, seats, steering wheel	£75-85
			Primrose-Yellow body, Red interior, flat spun hubs	£250-350
		Danish promotional:	'JENSONS', Red body, Yellow interior	£500-750
226	1960-68	**Morris Mini Minor**	Pale Blue body, Cream or Yellow interior, flat or shaped hubs	£40-45
			Red body, flat or shaped hubs	£40-45
			Sky Blue body, Red interior, flat or shaped hubs	£100-150
			Metallic Maroon body, Lemon interior, suspension, detailed cast hubs	£60-70
			Yellow body	£200-250
		Gift Set issue:	Deep Blue body, only in GS11	GSP
		NB	The Light Blue version of 226 was also supplied for a short time by a US games manufacturer as part of a table-top racing game. This version has a large drive-pin hole in the base and has 'EAST AFRICAN RALLY' stickers on the bonnet, racing number '3'. Not separately boxed	£150-250

227	1962-65	**Mini Cooper Rally**	Bright Blue body, White roof and bonnet, Red interior, spun hubs, Union Jack and chequered bonnet flags, racing numbers '1', 3' or '7'	£200-250
			As above but Bright Blue body and bonnet, White roof	£200-250
			Primrose Yellow body, White roof and bonnet, with flags and racing number '3' or '7'	£200-250
			Primrose Yellow body and bonnet, with flags and racing number '1'	£200-250
			Green body, White roof. Not seen	NGPP
228	1962-65	**Volvo P-1800**	Beige body, Red interior, spun hubs	£65-75
			Red body, Lemon interior, spun hubs	£80-100
			Pink or Dark Pink body, Lemon interior	£55-65
229	1961-66	**Chevrolet Corvair**	Mid-Blue body, Bright Yellow interior, spun hubs	£55-65
			Pale Blue body, Pale Lemon or Red interior, shaped hubs	£55-65
		Gift Set issue:	Gold body, (in 'Golden Guinea' set)	GSP
230	1962-64	**Mercedes-Benz 220 SE**	Cream (Red interior) shaped spun hubs, spare wheel in boot	£60-70
			Metallic Red body, Lemon interior, shaped spun hubs, spare wheel in boot	£60-70
			Black body, Lemon interior, shaped spun hubs, spare wheel in boot	£70-80
			Dark Blue body, Lemon interior	£60-70
231	1961-65	**Triumph Herald**	Gold top and bottom, White in centre, spun hubs, Red interior	£70-80
			Mid Blue top and bottom, White in centre, Red interior	£60-70
			All Pale Blue (other details required, please)	NGPP
232	1961-63	**Fiat 2100**	Pale Pink with Mauve roof, Lemon interior, spun hubs	£45-55
233	1962-72	**Heinkel Trojan**	Red, Blue, Orange, Pink or Lilac body, Lemon interior, spun hubs or detailed cast hubs	£60-70
			Metallic Blue, Fawn or Turquoise body, smooth spun hubs	£80-90
234	1961-65	**Ford Consul Classic**	Beige body, Pink roof, Lemon interior, or Gold body	£60-70
235	1962-66	**Oldsmobile Super 88**	Black body, White side flash, spun hubs	£60-75
			Metallic Steel Blue, White side flash, Red interior	£50-65
			Light Blue body, Red interior, White side flash, spun hubs	£60-70
236	1964-68	**'CORGI' Motor School**	(Austin A60). Light Blue body, 2 figures, 'Highway Code' leaflet, right-hand drive	£80-90
		Export issue:	Dark Blue body, left-hand drive, leaflet	£100-120
238	1962-67	**Jaguar Mk10**	All issues have spun hubs, luggage in boot. Blue/Yellow box with leaflet.	
			Pale Blue body, Red interior	£90-110
			Mid-Green body, Red interior	£90-110
			Deep Blue body, Red interior	£90-110
			Kingfisher Blue body, Lemon interior	£100-120
			Sea-Green body, Red interior	£200-300
			Metallic Steel (Blue-Grey) body, Red interior	£70-90
			Metallic Deep Blue body, Red or Lemon interior	£125-150
			Metallic Sea-Blue body, Red interior	£125-150
			Metallic Cerise body, Lemon interior	£70-90
			Metallic Silver body, Red interior	£125-150
			Metallic Green body, Red interior	£70-90
239	1963-68	**VW 1500 Karmann Ghia**	Cream (Red interior) or Red (Yellow interior) spare wheel/suitcase in boot	£50-65
			Gold body, Red or Yellow interior, spare wheel/suitcase in boot	£90-100
			Red body, White or Yellow interior, spun hubs	£60-70
			Plum body, Red interior, spun hubs	£85-95
240	1963-64	**Fiat 600 Jolly**	Metallic Light Blue body, Silver/Red canopy, Red interior, spun hubs, 2 figures	£100-125
			Metallic Dark Blue body, Red interior, two figures	£100-125
			Blue body, Red interior, spun hubs, two figures	£100-125
			Yellow body, Red interior, spun hubs, two figures	£100-125
241	1963-69	**Chrysler Ghia L64**	All have shaped spun hubs or detailed cast hubs; Corgi dog on rear shelf.	
			Metallic Blue/White or Metallic Green body, Cream interior	£30-40
			Metallic Gold, Metallic Silver Blue (Red interior), or Metallic Copper	£30-40
242	1965-66	**Ghia Fiat 600**	Orange-Yellow body, Red interior, two figures in swim gear, windscreen but no canopy	£250-350
245	1964-68	**Buick Riviera**	Metallic Gold body, Red interior, 'Trans-O-Lites', spoked hubs, towbar	£45-55
			Metallic Steel Blue (Red interior) or Metallic Greenish Blue body, towbar	£45-55
			Pale Blue body, spun or cast hubs	£55-65
246	1965-68	**Chrysler Imperial Convertible**	All issues should include driver/passenger, golf trolley in boot, Blue/Yellow box with inner packing.	
			Metallic Deep Red body, Pale Blue or Green interior, shaped spun or detailed cast hubs	£70-80
			Metallic Turquoise body, Green interior, shaped spun or detailed cast hubs	£70-80
			Metallic Blue body, Pale Blue interior, cast hubs	£110-130
			Metallic Kingfisher Blue body, Green interior, cast hubs	£175-225
247	1964-69	**Mercedes-Benz Pullman**	Metallic Maroon body, Cream interior, windscreen wipers, instruction sheet	£50-60
			Red body, Cream interior	£50-60
248	1965-67	**Chevrolet Impala**	Brown body, Cream roof/interior, Chrome side stripe, shaped spun hubs	£45-55
249	1965-69	**Morris Mini-Cooper**	Black body, Red roof, Lemon interior, wickerwork panels, spun or cast hubs	£100-120
			Blue body, Yellow interior, spun hubs	£50-60

251	1963-66	**Hillman Imp**	Metallic Blue body, Yellow interior, spun hubs, luggage	£75-85
			Metallic Bronze body with White side stripe, White interior, spun hubs, luggage	£75-85
		Danish promotional:	Light Blue body, Yellow interior, 'JENSON'S' logo, spun hubs	£300-500
252	1963-66	**Rover 2000**	Metallic Light Blue or Steel Blue body, Red interior	£65-75
			Metallic Maroon body, Red or Yellow interior	£65-75
253	1964-68	**Mercedes-Benz 220 SE**	Metallic Maroon, or Metallic Blue, luggage, spare wheel	£50-60
255	1964-68	**Motor School A60**	Dark Blue body, left-hand drive, 5 language leaflet, (USA issue of 236)	£100-125
256	1965-68	**Volkswagen 1200 Rally**	Orange body, rally number '18', 'EAST AFRICAN RALLY', steering wheel on roof, rhinoceros	£150-175
258	1965-70	**The Saint's Volvo P1800**	See 'Novelty, Film and TV-related' section.	
259	1966-69	**Citroën 'Le Dandy'**	Metallic Dark Red body with Yellow interior, wire wheels	£80-90
			Metallic Blue body, White roof and boot	£90-100
260	1969	**Renault 16 TS**	Metallic Red, Yellow interior, cast hubs	£35-45
261	1965-69	**James Bond's Aston-Martin**	Bright Gold body (metal roof), Red interior, wire wheels. With James Bond at the wheel, passenger seat ejector (with bandit figure). Accessories: envelope with 'secret instructions', spare bandit figure, self-adhesive '007' badge, (plus 'Model Car Makers to James Bond' Corgi Catalogue in earlier boxes). Blue/Yellow picture box has inner pictorial stand. From the film 'Goldfinger'	£400-500
		variant:	As previous model but the opening roof component is made of plastic	NGPP
262	1967-69	**Lincoln Continental Executive Limousine**	Metallic Gold/Black body, with picture strip for onboard 'TV set'	£125-150
			Light Blue/Tan body, with picture strip for onboard 'TV set'	£150-175
263	1966-69	**Rambler Marlin Sports**	Red body, Black roof White interior, spun or cast hubs	£50-60
		Gift Set issue:	White body, Blue roof, (in Gift Set 10)	GSP
264	1966-69	**Oldsmobile Toronado**	Metallic Medium or Dark Blue body, smooth or cast spoked hubs, retractable headlights	£35-45
269	1977-83	**James Bond Lotus Esprit**	See 'Novelty, Film and TV-related' section.	
270	1968-78	**James Bond Aston-Martin**	See 'Novelty, Film and TV-related' section.	
271	1978-92	**James Bond Aston-Martin**	See 'Novelty, Film and TV-related' section.	
272	1969-69	**Ghia Mangusta De Tomaso**	Blue/White body with Gold stripes, aerial; or Orange-Red body	£70-80
272	1981-83	**James Bond Citroën 2cv**	See 'Novelty, Film and TV-related' section.	
273	1970	**Rolls-Royce Silver Shadow**	Metallic Silver/Blue, Golden Jacks, Take-Off wheels, spare wheel	£65-75
			Pearlescent White over Grey, Blue interior, Golden Jacks, Take-Off wheels, spare wheel	£55-65
273	1982-83	**Honda Ballade 'BSM' Driving School Car**	Yellow body with Red side stripes	£25-35
274	1970-72	**Bentley 'T' Series**	Bright Pink body, Cream interior, special lights, WhizzWheels	£45-55
275	1968-70	**Rover 2000 TC**	Metallic Olive Green body, Brown or Red interior, Amber roof panel, 'Golden Jacks', spare on bootlid	£60-70
			Same as above but with White interior	£80-90
			White body, Red interior, Amber roof panel, 'Golden Jacks' wheels, spare wheel on bootlid	£100-130
			Metallic Maroon body, 'Golden Jacks' wheels, spare wheel on bootlid	£80-90
			Gold plated version	£125-150
275	1981-84	**Mini Metro**	Blue, Purple or Red body, Yellow interior, opening doors and hatchback	£10-15
			Gold body	£45-50
		'Royal Wedding' Metro	Mauve body with Silver 'Charles & Diana' crest, special Mauve box	£20-25
276	1968-72	**Oldsmobile Toronado**	Metallic Blue or Red body, Golden Jacks, cast 'Take-Off wheels'	£40-50
			Metallic Gold body, Cream interior	£40-45
			Metallic Green body, Cream interior	£40-45
			Metallic Brown body, Cream interior	£40-45
276	1982-83	**Triumph Acclaim**	Metallic Blue, Metallic Blue or Cream body, steering control	£7-10
277	1982-	**Triumph Acclaim**	'BSM' Driving School car with Yellow body, Black 'wheel' steering control on roof	£15-20
278	1982	**Triumph Acclaim Driving School Car**	Yellow body, with steering control, 'CORGI MOTOR SCHOOL' logo	£25-35
279	1980	**Rolls-Royce Corniche**	Metallic Dark Red body, opening doors/bonnet/boot, tilt seats	£20-25
280	1970-78	**Rolls-Royce Silver Shadow**	Metallic Silver upper body, Blue lower body, Brown interior, WhizzWheels	£35-40
			Metallic Blue body, Brown interior, WhizzWheels	£30-35
281	1971-72	**Rover 2000 TC**	Metallic Red body, Yellow interior, amber or clear roof, WhizzWheels	£60-75
			Lacquered Purple body, Amber roof	£80-100
281	1982-	**'DATAPOST' Metro**	Blue/White body, rally number '77', various adverts	£9-12
282	1971-74	**Mini Cooper Rally**	White/Black/Yellow, rally number '177', special lights, WhizzWheels	£55-65
283	1971-74	**DAF 'City' Car**	Red/Black body, White interior, opening doors/bonnet, WhizzWheels	£15-20
284	1970-76	**Citroën SM**	Green body, Pale Blue interior, spoked wheels	£45-55
			Metallic Cerise body, Pale Blue interior, spoked wheels	£45-55
285	1975-81	**Mercedes-Benz 240 D**	Silver, Blue, Bronze or Beige (all Metallic)	£25-35
286	1975-79	**Jaguar XJC V-12**	Blue/Black, Red/Black, Red, Pearl, Blue or Orange (all Metallic), WhizzWheels	£25-35
287	1975-78	**Citroën Dyane**	Metallic Yellow/Black, Metallic Green or Bronze, duck decal, WhizzWheels	£25-35
288	1975-79	**Minissima**	Beige/Black/White body	£25-35
289	1976-80	**VW Polo 'DBP'**	Yellow/White body, left-hand drive, WhizzWheels, (German issue)	£45-55
289	1977-81	**Volkswagen Polo**	Lime Green or Orange body	£25-35
289	1977-81	**VW Polo 'ADAC'**	As previous model but Yellow body, German issue	£35-45
290	1976-77	**Kojak Buick**	See 'Novelty, Film and TV-related' section.	
291	1977-80	**AMC Pacer**	Metallic Red body, opening doors and hatchback	£20-25

275 Rover 2000 TC
with 'Golden Jacks' and 'Take-off Wheels'

303 Roger Clark's Ford Capri
fitted with WhizzWheels

302 Hillman Hunter Rally Car with 'Golden Jacks', a
kangaroo and 18 additional transfers

513 Citroën Safari 'Alpine Rescue Car'
with St Bernard dog and handler

499 'Winter Olympics' Citroën
with tobogganist

497 'The Man From U.N.C.L.E.'s 'Thrush-Buster'
Oldsmobile in white, with
diorama packing and 'Waverley' ring

The photographs above are of Corgi Toys models sold by Vectis Auctions Ltd. and are reproduced by their kind permission.

291	1982	**Mercedes Benz 240 Rally**	Muddy Cream body, RN '5', *'EAST AFRICAN RALLY'* or *'E.A.R.'* logos £20-25
290	1977-82	**Starsky & Hutch Ford Torino** ..	See 'Novelty, Film and TV-related' section.
293	1977-80	**Renault 5 TS**	Orange, Silver or Silver/Blue body, WhizzWheels £20-25
		French issue:	Light Blue body, Dark Blue roof, 'SOS MEDICINS' £75-85
294	1980-84	**Renault 5 TS Alpine**	Black body with White stripe, opening doors and hatchback £10-15
298	1982-83	**Magnum P.I. Ferrari 308GTS**...	See 'Novelty, Film and TV-related' section.
299	1982	**Ford Sierra 2.3 Ghia**	Metallic Light Brown/Black stripe, Dark Brown or Grey interior, Brown or
			Dark Grey base. Issued in a special two-tone Blue 'Ford' box £20-25
			As previous model but Metallic Light Brown, Metallic Blue, Red or Yellow
			body, packed in White/Red 'Ford' box or normal Black/Yellow/Red box £15-20
300	1956-65	**Austin Healey 100-4**	Red with Cream interior, flat hubs, leaflet supplied with early issues £150-200
			Cream with Red interior, flat hubs, leaflet supplied with early issues £150-200
			Blue body with Cream interior £150-200
300	1970-70	**Chevrolet Corvette Stingray**.....	Lacquered-finish Bright Green, Dark Red or Green body, 'Golden Jacks' / 'Take-Off Wheels, luggage........£75-85
			Metallic Red body, Black bonnet, 'Golden Jacks' / 'Take-Off Wheels, luggage £55-65
			Metallic Green body, Black bonnet, 'Golden Jacks' / 'Take-Off Wheels, luggage £55-65
	NB		Models without box header cards contained instructions.
300	1979-82	**Ferrari 'DAYTONA'**	Green, multicoloured flash, racing number '5', opening doors £25-35
301	1956-61	**Triumph TR2**	Cream body with Red seats £150-200
			Red body with Cream seats £150-200
			Deep Green body with Cream seats £150-200
301	1970-73	**Iso Grifo 7 litre**	Metallic Blue body, Black bonnet, White interior, Silver or Black roll-bar, WhizzWheels............£30-35
301	1979-82	**Lotus Elite Racing Car**	Yellow/Red body, racing number '7', *'FERODO'* £20-25
302	1957-65	**MG 'MGA'**	Red (Cream seats) smooth or chrome spun hubs, (paint shades exist) £150-200
			Cream with Red seats £150-200
			Mid or Dark Metallic Green body (Cream or Yellow seats), smooth or shaped spun hubs £150-200
302	1969-72	**Hillman Hunter Rally**	Blue body, White roof, Matt-Black bonnet, RN '75', equipment, kangaroo,
			'Golden Jacks', transfers, toolbox, leaflet, instructions £130-160
302	1979-82	**VW Polo**	Metallic Brown/Red body, racing number '4', various adverts £20-25
303	1958-60	**Mercedes-Benz 300 SL**	White body, Blue seats, smooth hubs, Blue box £110-140
		(Open Roadster)	Blue body, White seats, smooth hubs, Blue box £80-100
			Cream body, Blue seats, smooth hubs, Blue box £80-100
	NB		Models in rare plain overprinted box, add **£20-30**.
303 S	1961-63	**Mercedes-Benz 300 SL**	White body, Yellow interior, Red bonnet stripe, racing numbers '1' to '12' £90-120
		(Open Sports)	Mid-Blue body, Yellow interior, Red bonnet stripe, racing numbers '1' to '12' £90-120
	NB		'Open Sports' models housed in 303S 'Open Roadster' boxes.
303S2	1963-64	**Mercedes-Benz 300 SL**	With driver dressed in Grey Suit, White shirt and Red bow-tie.
		(Open Sports with Driver)	White body, Yellow interior, Red bonnet stripe, racing numbers '1' to '12' £90-120
			Blue body, Yellow interior, Red bonnet stripe, racing numbers '1' to '12' £90-120
			Chrome plated body, Lemon/Brown interior, Red bonnet stripe, spoked or cast hubs, RNs '1' to '12'......£125-150
303	1970-72	**Roger Clark's Ford Capri**	White body, Black bonnet, RN '73', decal sheet, WhizzWheels £60-70
			As previous model but with Red spot hubs. Yellow/Red box with '9 transfers for you to apply!' £80-100
304	1959-61	**Mercedes-Benz 300 SL Hardtop**.	Yellow body, Red hardtop, spun hubs, no suspension £90-120
			Yellow body and hardtop, flat spun hubs £200-300
304 S	1961-63	**Mercedes-Benz 300 SL Hardtop**.	Chrome body, Red hardtop, stripe, smooth/shaped/spoked hubs, RN '3' or '7' £90-120
			White body, Red hardtop, racing number '7', shaped hubs £200-300
304	1971-72	**Chevrolet Camaro SS350**..........	Dark Blue body, White bonnet band, interior and detachable roof, special lights £30-40
305	1960-63	**Triumph TR3**	Metallic Olive Green or Cream body, Red seats, smooth or shaped hubs £110-140
305 S	1962-63	**Triumph TR3**	Light Green or Cream body, spring suspension, shaped spun hubs £150-175
305	1972-73	**Mini Marcos GT 850**	White body, Red interior, Blue/White stripes, racing number '7', WhizzWheels £30-35
306	1971-73	**Morris Marina 1.8 Coupé**	Metallic Red body, Cream interior, WhizzWheels £40-45
			Metallic Lime Green body, Cream interior, WhizzWheels £40-45
306	1980-81	**Fiat X1/9S**	Metallic Blue body with Red/Yellow bands, racing number '3' or '6' £15-20
307	1962-64	**Jaguar 'E' type**	Metallic Grey body with Red removable hard-top, spun hubs, inner packing £80-90
			Plum to Red body and hard-top, spun hubs, inner packing £90-100
307	1981-82	**Renault Turbo**..........................	Yellow/Red body, racing number '8', *'CIBIE'*, other adverts £10-15
308	1972-76	**Mini Cooper 'S'**	
		'MONTE CARLO'	Yellow body, RN '177', two spare wheels on roof-rack, WhizzWheels, (339 update) £65-75
			Gold (vacuum plated) body. Only 144 thought to exist £1,000-1,500
308	1982-82	**BMW M1**	Yellow and Black body, racing number '25', 'TEAM BMW', detailed engine £10-15
309	1962-65	**Aston Martin DB4 Competition** .	Turquoise/White body, Lemon interior, flags, spun hubs, RN '1', '3' or '7' £110-130
			Variation with spoked hubs £110-130
309	1982-	**VW 'TURBO'**	White and Orange body, racing number '14', Red decals £10-15
310	1963-67	**Chevrolet Corvette Stingray**.....	Metallic Cerise, Lemon interior, shaped hubs £40-50
			Metallic Silver body, Lemon interior, wire wheels £60-70
			Metallic Bronze body, Lemon interior £80-100

310	1982-	**'PORSCHE' 924 Turbo**	Black/Gold, opening doors and hatchback, *'GOODYEAR'*	£10-15
311	1970-72	**Ford Capri V6 3-litre**	Orange body, Gold wheels with Red hubs, Black interior	£80-90
			Fluorescent Orange body, WhizzWheels	£50-60
			Fluorescent Orange body, Red spot WhizzWheels	£70-90
			Red body, Black bonnet, Red spot WhizzWheels	£70-90
312	1964-68	**'E' type Jaguar**	Silver (vacuum plated) body, racing number '2', driver, suspension, spoked hubs	£75-85
312	1971-74	**Marcos Mantis**	Metallic Red body, White interior, spoked hubs	£20-30
312	1983-	**Ford Capri 'S'**	White, racing number '6', hinged parcel shelf, various adverts	£10-15
313	1970-73	**Ford Cortina GXL**	Metallic Blue body, Black roof, Black/White interior, Graham Hill figure, WhizzWheels	£60-70
			Bronze body, Black roof, White interior	£60-70
			Yellow body, Black roof	£150-175
			Metallic Pale Green body, Black roof, White interior	£80-90
		Promotional:	Tan body, Black roof, Red interior, left-hand drive, 'CORTINA' number plate	£250-350
314	1965-72	**Ferrari Berlinetta 250 LM**	Red body, racing number '4', wire wheels, suspension	£45-55
314	1976-79	**Fiat X1-9**	Metallic Lime Green/Black or Silver/Black body, suspension, hook	£25-35
314	1982-	**Supercat Jaguar XJS-HE**	Black body, Red or Tan interior, opening doors	£10-15
315	1964-66	**Simca 1000 Sports**	Plated Silver, Red interior, RN '8', Red/White/Blue racing stripes	£70-80
			Metallic Blue body, racing number '8', Red/White/Blue stripes	£100-120
315	1976-79	**Lotus Elite**	Red or Yellow with White seats, opening doors, suspension	£20-25
316	1963-66	**NSU Sport Prinz**	Metallic Red body, Yellow seats, spun hubs	£50-60
316	1971-73	**Ford GT 70**	Lime Green and Black body, White interior, racing number '32', (unapplied) decal sheet	£30-40
317	1964-65	**Mini Cooper 'S'** **'MONTE CARLO 1964'**	Red body, White roof, Yellow interior, racing number '37', roof spotlight	£125-150
			Red body, Pink roof variation	£175-200
318	1965	**Mini Cooper 'S'** **'MONTE CARLO 1965'**	Red body, White roof, 'AJB 44 B', racing number '52', no roof spotlight	£150-175
318	1965-67	**Lotus Elan S2 Open Top**	Metallic Steel Blue, racing number '6' or '8', driver, opening bonnet, tilt seats, 'tiger' decal, *'I'VE GOT A TIGER IN MY TANK'* logo on boot lid, Blue/Yellow box, unapplied decals	£90-110
318	1965-68	**Lotus Elan S2 Open Top**	Dark Green body, Yellow stripe with Black or Red interior (GS37)	GSP
			White body, Black interior (GS40), 'tiger' label, unapplied decals	£200-250
			Metallic Copper body, unapplied decals	£150-200
			Yellow body, Green stripe, Black interior, spun hubs	£125-150
318	1981	**Jaguar XJS**	Blue/Cream body with Red line	£15-20
318	1983		Black/Red/White body, racing number '4', 'MOTUL', *'JAGUAR'*	£15-20
319	1967-69	**Lotus Elan S2 Hardtop**	Yellow body (Green top), or Blue body (White top), shaped hubs	£90-120
			Red body, White top, cast hubs	£85-100
			Red body, Red top, cast hubs	£85-100
			Blue body, White top, cast hubs	£75-85
			Green and Yellow lift-off body	£80-100
			Red body with White top, WhizzWheels	£55-65
		NB	1967-69 boxed issues should include a sheet of self-adhesive racing numbers '1' to '12'.	
319	1973-74	**Lamborghini P400GT**	Metallic Silver body with Purple/Yellow stripes, racing number '7', WhizzWheels, fighting bull	£25-30
319	1978-81	**Jaguar XJS**	Metallic Red body, Black roof, opening doors, suspension	£15-20
320	1965-67	**Ford Mustang Fastback 2+2**	Opening doors, suspension, Corgi dog, half-open window.	
			Silver (Red interior) or Metallic Deep Blue (Cream interior) detailed cast hubs	£60-70
			Metallic Deep Blue body (Cream interior) or Light Green body (Cream interior), spoked hubs	£60-70
			Metallic Purple body, Cream interior, spoked hubs	£60-70
			Metallic Deep Yellow body, Black bonnet and interior, cast hubs	£500-750
320	1978-81	**The Saint's Jaguar XJS**	See 'Novelty, Film and TV-related' section.	
321	1965-66	**Mini Cooper 'S'** **'MONTE CARLO 1965'**	Red body, White roof, spotlight, rally number '52'.	
			317 picture box with 'No. 321' and 'MONTE CARLO WINNER' flash	£350-450
			Red body, White roof with spotlight, rally number '52'	£200-250
321	1966-67	**Mini Cooper 'S'** **'MONTE CARLO 1966'**	Red body, White roof with rally number '2' and *'TIMO MAKINEN'* and *'PAUL EASTER'* signatures, no spotlight. Box flashed with white sticker with '1966 MONTE CARLO RALLY AUTOGRAPHED MINI-COOPER 'S' in Red capital letters	£250-350
		variant:	As previous issue but in 321 pictorial box with 'RALLY' text printed in Red panel	£350-450
321	1978-81	**Porsche 924 Saloon**	Metallic Green body with hook	£40-45
			Red body	£20-25
			Metallic Light Brown body, Red interior	£60-70
322	1967-67	**Rover 2000 'MONTE CARLO'**	Metallic Maroon body, White roof, Red interior, rally number '136', rally plaques	£110-135
			As previous model but with Green interior	NGPP
			Model boxed in rare 252 box with 322 labels over the box ends	£150-200
	1967	**'INTERNATIONAL RALLY FINISH'**	White body, Black bonnet, Red interior, White/Orange label on doors with Black RN '21', cast hubs. 322 box with Red 'ROVER 2000 INTERNATIONAL RALLY FINISH' and box flash. Paint shade differences are known	£200-250

323	1965-66	**Citroën DS19**		
		'MONTE CARLO 1965'	Pale Blue with White roof, rally plaques and number '75', suspension..	£100-125
323	1974-78	**Ferrari Daytona 365 GTB/4**	White/Red/Blue body, racing number '81', opening doors	£10-15
324	1966-69	**Marcos Volvo 1800 GT**	White body with two Green stripes, Cream interior, wire wheels	£35-40
			Blue body with two White stripes, White bonnet, Blue interior, wire wheels	£40-50
	NB		Boxed models should include an unused decal sheet with racing numbers '4' and '8'.	
324	1973-75	**Ferrari Daytona Le Mans**.........	Yellow body, racing number '33', 'A.BAMFORD'	£25-35
325	1965-69	**Ford Mustang Competition**	White body with double Red stripe (Blue interior), shaped spun hubs, racing number '7',	
			detailed cast hubs, wire wheels or cast 'alloy' wheels	£80-100
			White body, double Red stripes, Gold 'alloy' wheels	£80-100
	NB		An unused sheet of four racing numbers should be enclosed with each model.	
325	1981-	**Chevrolet Caprice**......................	Metallic Light Green or Dark Green body, White-wall tyres	£20-25
			Metallic Silver over Dark Blue (US market)	£70-80
327	1967-69	**MGB GT**	Dark Red body, Blue or Yellow interior, spoked wheels, luggage	£80-95
327	1980-81	**Chevrolet Caprice Taxi**.............	Yellow body, 'THINK TWA', fare table on door	£15-20
328	1966-67	**Hillman Imp**		
		'MONTE CARLO 1966'.........	Metallic Dark Blue/White, 'FRW 306 C', rally plaques and number '107', spun hubs	£100-125
	NB		If 'HILLMAN IMP 328' Yellow/Red advertising card is with model, add **20%** to price.	
329	1973-76	**Ford Mustang Rally Car**...........	Metallic Green body, White roof, rally number '69', (391 special)	£25-30
329	1980-82	**Opel Senator**...............................	Dark Blue or Bronze body, opening doors	£15-18
			Silver body	£25-30
330	1967-69	**Porsche Carrera 6**	White body, Red bonnet and doors, racing number '60', cast hubs, Blue engine cover................	£45-50
			White body, Dark Blue bonnet and doors, racing number '60', cast hubs, Orange engine cover	£80-100
331	1974-76	**Ford Capri GT Rally**.................	White body, Black bonnet, 'TEXACO', racing number '5'	£45-55
332	1967-69	**Lancia Fulvia Zagato**	Metallic Green, Metallic Blue, or Orange, suspension, tilt seats, cast hubs	£50-60
			Yellow body, Black bonnet, cast hubs	£100-125
333	1966	**Mini Cooper 'S'**		
		'SUN - RAC Rally'.................	Red body, White roof, RN '21' and 'SUN RAC INTERNATIONAL RALLY' decals,	
			225 box with White label '1966 RAC INTERNATIONAL RALLY' in Blue, Austin grille	£200-225
			As previous model but with Morris grille	£600-900
334	1968-70	**Mini Cooper 'Magnifique'**........	Metallic Dark Blue or Green, jewelled lights, sunshine roof, Cream interior	£60-75
334	1981-	**Ford Escort 1.3 GL**...................	Blue, Green or Yellow body	£12-15
			Red body with 'AVIS' logo on roof	£25-35
335	1968-70	**Jaguar 4.2 litre 'E' type**	Metallic Dark Red body, spoked wheels, wing flap bubble pack	£80-90
			Metallic Blue body, Black interior, wing flap bubble pack	£80-90
			Orange body, Black roof, wing flap bubble pack	NGPP
336	1967-69	**James Bond Toyota 2000GI**	See 'Novelty, Film and TV-related' section.	
337	1967-69	**Chevrolet Stock Car**.................	Yellow body, Red interior, racing number '13', 'STINGRAY', suspension	£35-40
338	1968-71	**Chevrolet SS 350 Camaro**.........	Metallic Lime Green/Black (Red interior), Gold/Black or Bronze/Black, 'Golden Jacks'	£40-50
338	1980-83	**Rover 3500**................................	Metallic Blue, Red/Black or Bronze/Brown body	£15-20
339	1967-71	**Mini Cooper 'S'**		
		'MONTE CARLO 1967' ......(i)	Red body, White roof, RN '177', 2 spare wheels, shaped spun hubs, Austin grille, in	
			227 box with White flash label with '1967 MONTE-CARLO WINNER B.M.C.	
			MINI-COOPER 'S' in Red capital letters, Red '339' flash on box end	£200-300
		(ii)	As (i) but with cast detailed hubs and slight Silver detail	£200-300
		(iii)	As (i) but with shaped spun hubs and slight Silver detail	£200-300
		(iv)	As (i) but with cast detailed hubs and Morris grille	£200-300
		(v)	As (i) but in 339 picture box with winner's text in Red lettering on box front.	
			Special leaflet enclosed with each model	£200-300
		(vi)	As (i) but in 339 box with the winners text in Red panel	£200-300
340	1967-69	**Sunbeam Imp**		
		'MONTE CARLO 1967'......(i)	Metallic Blue, RN '77', spun or cast hubs, flashed 328 box with '1967 MONTE CARLO SUNBEAM IMP	
			WINNER PRODUCTION CARS UP TO 1000cc' text in Blue capitals plus model no. '340'............	£100-125
		(ii)	As (i) but in 340 pictorial box with 'winner' text printed in Red on the	
			box front plus cast detailed hubs..	£100-125
		(iii)	As (i) but Metallic Dark Blue body, cast detailed hubs, 'winner' text printed in	
			Red panel on box front..	£125-175
340	1981-84	**Rover 'TRIPLEX'**	White/Red/Blue, racing number '1', hinged parcel shelf	£15-20
341	1968-70	**Mini Marcos GT 850**	Metallic Crimson (Cream seats) or Metallic Maroon body, 'Golden Jacks' and 'Take-off' wheels....	£60-70
341	1981-82	**Chevrolet Caprice**......................	Red/White/Blue body, racing number '43', 'STP', White tyres	£10-15
342	1970-72	**Lamborghini P400 Miura**	Red body, White interior, Black plastic fighting bull figure, WhizzWheels.	
			1st type box: Blue/Yellow box has 'Revised specification' label regarding 'Take-off' wheels	£75-85
			2nd type box: Red/Yellow box with 'Revised specification' label	£40-50
			Lime Green body, Red interior, with bull figure	£40-50
342	1980-82	**'The Professionals' Ford Capri**.	See 'Novelty, Film and TV-related' section.	
343	1969-73	**Pontiac Firebird**........................	Metallic Silver/Black, Red seats, Gold/Red Take-Off wheels, Golden Jacks	£35-45
			With Red-spot WhizzWheels	£50-60
343	1980-81	**Ford Capri 3 litre**	Yellow or Silver body, Black designs, opening doors/hatchback	£30-35
344	1969-73	**Ferrari Dino Sports**	Yellow with Black doors (number '23') or Red with White doors (number '30') WhizzWheels	£40-50
			With Red-spot WhizzWheels	£50-60

345	1969	**MGC GT Competition**	Yellow body, Black bonnet, tailgate and interior, spoked wheels.	
			'MGB GT' on box overprinted 'NEW MGC' Self-adhesive numbers enclosed	**£90-120**
		Gift Set version:	Orange body, Black interior, spoked wheels. (Car Transporter Gift Set 41)	**£250-350**
345	1981-82	**Honda Prelude**	Metallic Blue, Cream/Green or Metallic Yellow body, sunshine roof	**£10-15**
346	1982-84	**Citroën 2cv**	Yellow/Black, Burgundy/Black, Red/White or Grey/Red body	**£10-15**
		German promotional:	Yellow body, Black roof, 'REISGOLD' label	**£100-120**
347	1969-74	**Chevrolet Astro Experimental** ..	Metallic Dark Blue or Green body, Red-spot WhizzWheels	**£40-50**
			As previous model but with plain WhizzWheels	**£30-40**
348	1968-69	**Mustang 'Pop Art' Stock Car** ...	Light Blue with Red/Orange 'Flower-Power' labels, racing number '20'	**£65-75**
			Light Blue body without labels	**£50-60**
348	1980-81	**'Vegas' Ford Thunderbird**	See 'Novelty, Film and TV-related' section.	
349	1967-67	**'POP ART' Morris Mini**	Red body, Lemon interior, 4 psychedelic labels, 'MOSTEST' logo, few only produced	**£1,500-2,000**
370	1982	**Ford Cobra Mustang**	White/Black/Red/Blue, 'MUSTANG', with or without tailgate stripe	**£10-15**
370	1982	**Ford Cobra Mustang**	White body, Red interior, Blue/Red design	**£10-15**
371	1970-73	**Porsche Carrera 6**	White/Red, racing number '60', plated Blue engine cover, WhizzWheels, (330 update)	**£20-25**
372	1970-72	**Lancia Fulvia Zagato**	Orange body, Black bonnet, Black interior, WhizzWheels	**£40-50**
373	1981-	**Peugeot 505**	Red body, Silver or Black lining, opening doors, suspension	**£10-15**
374	1970-76	**Jaguar 'E' type 4.2 litre**	Red or Yellow body, WhizzWheels, (2+2), (335 update)	**£50-60**
374	1973	**Jaguar 'E' type 5.3 litre**	Yellow or Metallic Yellow body 'New' on box label	**£50-60**
375	1970-72	**Toyota 2000 GT**	Metallic translucent 'candy' Blue body, White interior, WhizzWheels, (modified 336), leaflet	**£50-60**
			Metallic Purple body, White interior, Red aerial, WhizzWheels	**£45-55**
376	1970-72	**Chevrolet Corvette Stock Car** ...	Silver body, racing number '13', 'GO-GO-GO', WhizzWheels, (337 update)	**£40-50**
			Metallic Blue body, Red interior, racing number '13', WhizzWheels	**£40-50**
377	1970-72	**Marcos 3 litre**	Yellow body, Black bonnet, Black interior, WhizzWheels, (324 conversion)	**£50-60**
			White body, Grey sunroof, Whizzwheels	**£70-80**
			Metallic Blue-Green body, Black interior, bonnet decal, WhizzWheels	**£50-60**
378	1970-72	**MGC GT**	Red body, Black bonnet, interior and suitcase, WhizzWheels, (345 update)	**£60-70**
378		Gift Set issue:	Orange body, (this version in Gift Set 20)	**GSP**
378	1982-	**Ferrari 308 GTS**	Red or Black body, pop-up headlights, opening engine cover	**£20-30**
380	1970-74	**Alfa Romeo P33**	White body, Gold roll bar, Red seats, WhizzWheels, (Pininfarina)	**£25-30**
380	1983-	**'BASF' BMW M1**	Red/White, racing number '80', aerofoil, opening engine cover	**£7-10**
381	1970-76	**VW Beach Buggy**	Metallic Red/White, Blue/White, Orange/White or Red/White, 2 Maroon surfboards, WhizzWheels	**£15-20**
381	1983-	**'ELF' Renault Turbo**	Red/White/Blue, racing number '5', 'FACOM'	**£10-15**
			Blue/White, racing number '13', 'ELF'	**£10-15**
382	1970-75	**Porsche Targa 911S**	Metallic Silver-Blue body, Black roof with Gold stripe, WhizzWheels	**£25-30**
			Metallic Olive-Green body, Black roof with or without Gold stripe, WhizzWheels	**£25-30**
382	1983-	**Lotus Elite 22**	Metallic Blue body, 'Elite 22', opening doors, number plates	**£10-15**
383	1970-76	**VW 1200 'Flower Power'**	Red body with psychedelic Grenadine and Green daisy labels on bonnet and doors	**£50-60**
			Red body, Green base, White interior, no flower decals	**£25-35**
383	1970-73	**Volkswagen 1200 'ADAC'**	Yellow/Black body, 'ADAC' logo (German equivalent of 'AA')	**£70-80**
		Volkswagen 1200 'PTT'	Yellow/Black body, Red interior, 'PTT' logo, Swiss issue	**£70-80**
383	1977-78	**Volkswagen 1200 Rally**	Blue body, rally number '5', chequered roof and sides	**£10-15**
384	1978	**Volkswagen 1200 Rally**	Blue body, rally number '5', chequered stripes	**£35-45**
			As previous model but with 'CALEDONIAN AUTOMINOLOGISTS' logo	**£80-90**
			Blue body, Cream interior, WhizzWheels, '40th Anniversary 1938 - 1978'	**£140-160**
384	1970-73	**Adams Brothers Probe**	Red body, Silver base, WhizzWheels	**£30-40**
			Metallic Gold body, WhizzWheels	**£30-40**
			Green body, White interior	**£30-40**
384	1983-84	**Renault 11 GTL**	Dark Cream body, Red interior, opening doors and boot, (export issue)	**£25-30**
			Maroon or Metallic Mauve body	**£25-30**
385	1970-76	**Porsche 917**	Metallic Blue or Red body, racing number '3', cast or WhizzWheels, with leaflet	**£30-35**
386	1971-74	**Bertone Barchetta**	Yellow/Black 'RUNABOUT', aerofoil, WhizzWheels	**£20-25**
387	1970-73	**Corvette Stingray Coupé**	Metallic Blue body, Black bonnet, roof emblem, WhizzWheels	**£35-45**
			Metallic Pink body, Black bonnet, Black interior	**£35-45**
388	1970-74	**Mercedes-Benz C111**	Orange/Black body, WhizzWheels	**£20-25**
389	1971-74	**Reliant Bond 'BUG' 700 ES**	Orange body, Orange/Black 'BUG' labels, Cream interior, WhizzWheels	**£35-45**
			Lime Green body, WhizzWheels	**£65-75**
391	1972-72	**James Bond Ford Mustang**	See 'Novelty, Film and TV-related' section.	
392	1973-76	**Bertone Shake Buggy**	Pink and Green body, detailed engine, flag, WhizzWheels	**£25-30**
			Yellow body, Black or Green interior	**£25-30**
393	1972-79	**Mercedes-Benz 350 SL**	White body, Pale Blue interior with chrome, spoked wheels	**£25-30**
			Metallic Blue or Dark Blue body with chrome solid disc wheels	**£25-30**
			Metallic Green body, Brown interior	**£55-65**
394	1972-77	**Datsun 240 Z 'Safari Rally'**	'East African Safari Rally' finish: Red body, rally number '11', 'CASTROL' and 'JAPAN' logos	**£25-30**
395	1972-73	**Fire Bug**	Orange body, Whizzwheels, Red/Black or Pink/Black stripe, Yellow ladder (381 Beach Buggy)	**£20-30**
396	1973-76	**Datsun 240 Z 'US Rally'**	'US Rally' finish: Red/White body, rally number '46', 'JOHN MORTON' and 'DATSUN' logos	**£40-50**

397	1974-76	**Porsche-Audi 917-10**	White/Red body, White 'L&M' logo, racing number '6', 'CORGI', racing driver....................	£25-30
400	1974-75	**Volkswagen 1300**	Metallic Red body, 'CORGI MOTOR SCHOOL', roof steering wheel, cones	£70-80
			Metallic Blue body version	£40-50
			Metallic Blue with 'CORGI FAHR SCHULE', German issue	£100-120
401	1975-77	**Volkswagen 1300**	Same as C400 but supplied with 24 'bollards' and diorama for miniature driving practice....................	£45-55
406	1957-62	**Land Rover '109 WB'**	Yellow body, Black roof, smooth hubs, thin tyres	£70-90
			Metallic Dark Blue body, Cream roof, smooth or shaped hubs, thin or thick tyres....................	£60-70
			Green body with Tan tinplate cover, smooth hubs, thin or thick tyres	£60-70
	'ETENDARD' variant:		As previous issue but with 'ETENDARD' decals, plus Red/White/Green roundels on front wings....................	NGPP
406s	1963	**Land Rover '109 WB'**	Yellow body, Red seats, shaped hubs, suspension	£60-70
411	1976-79	**Mercedes Benz 240 D**	Orange/Black or Cream body, 'TAXI' on roof....................	£10-15
	German issue:		Black body, Red 'TAXI' roof sign, 'TAXI' on doors	£35-45
415	1976-78	**Mazda Camper**	Red body with drop-down tailboard, White caravan	£25-30
418	1960-65	**Austin FX4 Taxi**......................	Black body, 'TAXI' sign, flat or shaped hubs, no driver....................	£50-60
			Black body, 'TAXI' sign, flat or shaped hubs, 'younger' driver figure	£40-50
			Black body, 'TAXI' sign, flat or shaped hubs, 'older' driver figure	£35-45
419	1978-79	**AMC Jeep CJ-5**	Metallic Green body with White plastic top, or Metallic Dark Green body	£25-35
420	1962-66	**Ford 'Airborne' Caravan**	Ford Thames in Two-tone Green, Brown interior or Blue/Pale Grey,	
			Red interior or Blue/Green, Brown interior....................	£40-50
			Two-tone Lilac, Beige interior	£70-80
421	1977-80	**Land Rover Safari**	Orange body, Black roof rack with ladder, spare wheel	£20-25
			Red body, White roof rack with ladder, 'FOREST FIRE WARDEN' logo	£20-25
		Land Rover Workman's Bus	Yellow/Red body, no roof rack or ladder	NGPP
424	1961-65	**Ford Zephyr Estate**	Pale Blue body, Dark Blue bonnet and side flash, Lemon interior, luggage, flat or shaped spun hubs	£85-95
425	1978	**London Taxi**............................	FX4 type taxi with Black body, 'TAXI', WhizzWheels....................	£10-15
			Maroon body, Red interior, WhizzWheels	£80-100
430	1962-64	**Ford Bermuda 'TAXI'**	White body, Yellow and Red canopy	£80-90
		(Ford Thunderbird)	White body, Lime Green and Red canopy	£80-90
			White body, Blue and Red canopy	£80-90
			Metallic Blue body, Red canopy	£150-200
436	1963-65	**Citroën ID19 'SAFARI'**	Yellow body, driver and passenger, detailed interior, roof luggage, 'Wild Life Reservation' logo....................	£80-90
438	1963-77	**Land Rover 109 WB**....................	Model has plastic canopy. Earlier issues have metal towhooks (plastic later), suspension.	
			Dark Green body Grey or Tan canopy, Yellow interior, shaped hubs	£100-125
			Dark Brown body, Light Brown canopy, Red interior, shaped hubs....................	£100-125
			Metallic Green body, Olive-Green canopy, Yellow interior, shaped hubs....................	£60-80
			Metallic Green body, Olive-Green canopy, Chrome hubs	£60-80
			Metallic Green body, Olive-Green canopy, WhizzWheels	£40-60
			Red body, Brown tilt, Red interior, shaped hubs	£40-60
	'LEPRA' variant:		Metallic Green body, Tan canopy with 'LEPRA' logo, Yellow interior, shaped hubs,	
			Silver steering wheel	£400-500
			Red body, Blue canopy, (in Gift Set 19)	GSP
	Promotional:		with '10 MILLIONTH CORGI LAND ROVER' label	£50-75
440	1966-69	**Ford Consul Cortina Estate**	Metallic Dark Blue with Brown side panels, plastic golfer, caddie and trolley	£110-135
440	1979-	**Mazda Custom Pick-Up**............	Orange/Yellow/Red, US flag	£15-20
441	1979-83	**'GOLDEN EAGLE' Jeep**	Brown/Tan or Gold/White, detachable roof, spare wheel on some	£15-20
443	1963-65	**Plymouth Suburban US Mail**	Blue/White body, Red interior, 'ADDRESS YOUR MAIL CAREFULLY'....................	£65-75
445	1963-66	**Plymouth Suburban Sports**		
		Station Wagon	Pale Blue or Eggshell Blue body, Red roof, Lemon interior, Silver side stripe, spun hubs....................	£80-90
			Beige body, Tan roof	£55-65
447	1983	**'RENEGADE' 4x4 Jeep**............	Yellow body, racing number '5' (As 448 but without hood). In GS 36	GSP
448	1983	**'RENEGADE' 4x4 Jeep**............	Yellow body, Red hood, racing number '5'....................	£8-10
450	1983	**Peugeot Taxi**.........................	Beige with Blue label, '739:33:33', (French issue)....................	£30-35
451		**Ford Sierra Taxi**	Cream body	NGPP
457	1981-83	**Talbot Matra Rancho**................	Red/Black or Green/Black, opening doors and boot, tilt seats	£10-15
457	1984	**Talbot Matra Rancho**............	Orange/Black or White/Blue body, Brown seats	£20-25
475		**Citroën Safari**	See Novelty, Film and TV-related section.	
480	1965-66	**Chevrolet Impala Taxi**	Yellow body, Red roof, Chrome stripe, shaped spun hubs, roofbox, aerial....................	£100-125
			As previous model but with detailed cast wheels, roofbox, aerial	£100-125
485	1965-69	**Mini Countryman with Surfer** ..	Sea-Green body, Lemon interior, 2 surfboards on roof-rack, male figure, special leaflet....................	£160-190
			As previous model but with unpainted grille	£160-190
491	1966-69	**Ford Consul Cortina Estate**	Metallic Red body, Brown/Cream side/rear panels....................	£80-90
			Metallic Blue body, Brown/Cream side/rear panels	£80-90
			Metallic Dark Grey body, Brown/Cream side/rear panels....................	£80-90
	NB		No golf equipment issued with this model (see 440).	
497	1966-69	**'The Man From UNCLE' Car** ..	See 'Novelty, Film and TV-related' section.	
507	1969	**Chrysler Bermuda Taxi**	Shown in catalogue but not issued	NPP

317 'Monte Carlo Rally' BMC Mini-Cooper 'S'

318 Lotus Elan S2 with driver

241 Ghia L.6.4,   332 Lancia Fulvia Sport Zagato,   236 Austin A60 Motor School Car with Corgi 'Highway Code'.

The photographs above are of Corgi Toys models sold by Vectis Auctions Ltd. and are reproduced by their kind permission.

Corgi Toys 'Cars of the '50s' series   Scale 1:36

C801 82 **1957 Ford Thunderbird**, White/Tan,
   Cream/Orange or Cream/Black £15-25
	C806 83 **1956 Mercedes 300SL**,
	   Black body, Grey/Black hood £15-25
		86 White/Beige...............................£15-25
		86 Silver/Black, export model...............£15-25

C802 82 **Mercedes 300 SL**, Burgundy or
   Silver body, with suspension £15-25
   Red body, no suspension £15-25
	86 Black/Green body, Beige seats.........£15-25
	86 Red, (Cream interior), export model ...£15-25
	86 Blue body £15-25
		C815 85 **1954 Bentley 'R' type**,
		   Black or Cream body £15-25

C803 83 **1952 Jaguar XK120 Sports**,
   Red body/Black hood £15-25
	C810 83 **1957 Ford Thunderbird**,
	   White body £15-25
		86 Dark Blue and Light Blue body £15-25
		86 Cream/Brown, export model £15-25

C803/1 83 **1952 Jaguar XK120 Rally**,
   Cream body, RN '56' £15-25
   White body, rally number '56' £15-25
	84 Pink body £15-25
	87 Red body £15-25
	   Cream body, Orange roof £15-25
		White body, Black roof £15-25
		C816 85 **1956 Jaguar XK120**,
		   Red body, Black hardtop, '56' £15-25

C804 83 **Jaguar 'Coupé des Alpes'**,
   Cream/Grey RN '56' or '414' £15-25
   Same but with rear wheel 'spats' £15-25
	Black/White, Red/White interior......£15-25
	C811 84 **1954 Mercedes SL**, Silver body ...£15-25
	86 Red body £15-25
		Red body, Cream hardtop £15-25
		C819 85 **1949 Jaguar XK120**,
		   White body, Black hood, '7'............£15-25

C805 83 **1956 Mercedes 300SC**,
   Black body, Tan hood £15-25
	87 Grey body, export model £15-25
	C812 85 **1953 MG TF**, Green/Tan seats £15-25
	C813 85 **1955 MG TF**, Red/Black £15-25
		C825 85 **1957 Chevrolet Bel Air**,
		   Red body, White roof and flash........£15-25
		87 Black/White, export model £15-25

84 Maroon body £15-25
86 Beige body and hood...................£15-25
87 Grey (Black hood), export model......£15-25
	87 Cream/Red, export model..............£15-25
	C814 85 **1952 Rolls-Royce Silver Dawn**,
	   Red/Black £15-25
		C869 86 **MG TF Racing Car**, Royal Blue
		   body, Beige seats, RN '113' £15-25
		C870 86 **Jaguar XK120**, Green body, Yellow
		   seats, RN '6', export model £15-25

Corgi Classics – Cars (original issues)

ORIGINAL ISSUES. A factory fire ended production in 1969 of this original series of 'Classics' cars. Boxes are of two types: one with separate lid with coloured line-drawings printed on it and containing a separate picture of the model; and type two which has the model attached to a sliding-drawer style base in an outer box with half-flaps (similar printing to 1st type). Early issues have reference numbers '901' onwards which were changed to '9001' etc. just before release.

9001	1964-69	**1927 3-litre Bentley**	British Racing Green, racing number '3', detachable hood, driver £45-55
9002	1964-68	**1927 3-litre Bentley**	Red body, civilian driver, no racing number, detachable hood £45-55
9004	1967-69	**'WORLD OF WOOSTER'**	
		Bentley	As previous model but in Green or Red and with Jeeves and Wooster figures £100-150
9011	1964-68	**1915 Model 'T' Ford**	Black body, driver, passenger, spoked wheels, brass radiator £45-55
9012	1965-68	**Model 'T' Ford**	Version with Yellow/Black body, Black or Yellow wheels £45-55
9013	1964-69	**1915 Model 'T' Ford**	Blue/Black body, detachable hood, spare wheel, driver cranks £45-55
9014		**1915 'LYONS TEA' Van**	Appeared in 1967/68 catalogue but was not issued ....NPP
9021	1964-69	**1910 38 hp Daimler**	Red body, driver and 3 passengers, folded hood, detailed chassis £45-55
9022		**1910 38 hp Daimler**	Appeared in the 1966 catalogue but not issued ....NPP
9031	1965-68	**1910 Renault 12/16**	Lavender/Black body with carriage lamps, spoked wheels £45-55
9032	1965-69	**1910 Renault 12/16**	Same as previous model but Primrose Yellow and Black body £45-55
9041	1966-70	**1912 Rolls-Royce Silver Ghost** .	Silver and Black body, carriage lamps, spoked wheels £45-55
		variant:	Maroon body, Silver roof and bonnet £65-75

RE-INTRODUCED ISSUES. Four of the 'Classics' were re-introduced in 1985 when original tools were discovered. They have new numbers, 'SPECIAL EDITION' on their baseplates and are packed in Grey/Red boxes which do not contain a picture of the model. 13,500 of each colour were made.

C860 (9041)	1985	**1912 Rolls-Royce Silver Ghost**......................Silver, Black or Ruby Red body £15-25
C861 (9002)	1985	**1927 3-litre Bentley open top** ....British Racing Green, Black or Ruby Red body £15-25
C862 (9031)	1985	**1910 Renault 12/16**...................................Yellow, Pale Blue, Cream or Brown body £15-25
C863 (9012)	1985	**1915 Model 'T' Ford**...................................Black, Red or Blue body £15-25

Duo Packs

These packs combine standard models with (mainly) similar 'Junior' models. Launched early in 1982 in France with the name 'Les Plus de Corgi', the packs later became available in the UK in Woolworths as 'Little and Large; the Little One Free'.
See also 'Novelty, Film and TV-related' section for additional details.
All NGPP except where shown.

No.53 **Triple Pack** (1982), 'Stunt Bikes':
171 Street Bike, 172 Police Bike, 173 Café Racer....

'Les Plus de Corgi' Duo Pack range:

1352	Renault 5 (307) Metro (C275)..........**£15-25**
1353	Austin Metro.................................**£15-25**
1354	Texaco Lotus (C154) Junior 53 ....**£15-25**
1355	Talbot Matra Rancho (457)..............**£15-25**
1356	Fiat XI/9 (306) **£15-25**
1357	Golden Eagle Jeep (C441) **£15-25**
1358	Citroën 2cv.................................**£15-25**
1359	Ford Escort (334), Junior 105..........**£15-25**

**F.W. Woolworth's 'Little & Large'
Promotional Duo Pack selection:**

1352	Renault 5 (307) Metro (C275)..........**£15-25**
1353	Austin Metro.................................**£15-25**
1355	Talbot Matra Rancho (457)..............**£15-25**
1356	Fiat XI/9 (306) **£15-25**
1359	Ford Escort (334), Junior 105............**£15-25**
1363	Buck Rogers (607)......................**£50-60**
1364	Space Shuttle 'NASA' (648)............**£20-30**
1365	469 Routemaster Bus, E71 Taxi **£20-30**
1371	Volkswagen Turbo (309) **£15-25**

Other Duo Packs (most available in UK).

1360	Batmobile (267)...........................**£250-300**
1361	James Bond Aston-Martin, Silver...............................**£150-200**
1362	James Bond Lotus Esprit (269) **£150-200**
1363	Buck Rogers (607).........................**£50-60**
1364	Space Shuttle 'NASA' (648)............**£20-30**
1365	469 Routemaster Bus, E71 Taxi **£15-25**
1372	Jaguar XJS (319) **£15-25**

1372	'Magnum PI' Ferrari (298) **£80-100**
1373	Ford Capri (312) Junior 61 ....**£15-25**
1376	Starsky & Hutch Ford Torino............**£70-80**
1378	Porsche 924, Yellow **£15-25**
1380	Mercedes 240D, Metallic Grey.........**£15-25**
1381	Ferrari 308GTS, Red **£15-25**
1382	Ford Mustang (320) **£15-25**
1383	Mack Fire Pumper **£15-25**
1384	Ford Thunderbird, Cream/Orange.....**£15-25** Ford Thunderbird, Cream/Black **£15-25**
1385	Austin Metro 'DATAPOST' **£15-25**
1389	Ford Sierra (299) Junior 129............**£15-25**
1390	Porsche 924, Black **£15-25**
1393	447 Jeep and E182 Jeep **£15-25**
1394	448 Jeep and E183 Jeep **£15-25**
1395	495 Mazda, E184 Range Rover **£15-25**
1396	Space Shuttle **£15-25**
1397	BMW M1 'BASF' (380)...................**£15-25**
1401	Lotus Elite and E10 TR7 ....**£15-25**
1402	1133 Tipper plus E85 Skip Truck.....**£15-25**
1403	Mercedes Tanker, E185 Van.............**£15-25**
1405	Jaguar...**£15-25**

Corgi Toys Major Gift Set No.1 with No. 1101 Bedford 'S' type Carrimore Transporter and 4 Cars
(Picture supplied by Christie's South Kensington and used by their kind permission)

Ref	Year(s)	Model name	Colours, features, details	Market Price Range
100	1957-65	Dropside Trailer	Cream/Red or Yellow body, drawbar	£35-40
101	1958-63	Platform Trailer	Grey/Yellow or Silver/Blue or Silver/Lemon body, drawbar and axle swivel	£35-40
109	1968-69	'PENNYBURN' Trailer	Blue body, Yellow chassis	£30-35
403	1956-60	Bedford 12 cwt Van	'DAILY EXPRESS' on Dark Blue body. Blue box with leaflet	£100-130
			As previous model but Deep Blue body	£100-120
403M	1956-60	Bedford 12 cwt Van	'KLG PLUGS' on Bright Red body, flywheel motor. Blue box with leaflet	£125-150
403	1974-79	Thwaites Skip Dumper	Yellow/Green tipping body, driver, WhizzWheels	£25-35
404	1956-62	Bedford Dormobile	Cream (Blue roof on some), Turquoise, Blue, Red or Metallic Red, smooth or ribbed roof, smooth or shaped hubs. Early issues have divided windscreen. Blue box with leaflet	£80-100
			Yellow body with Blue roof	£100-120
			Yellow lower half, Blue upper half	£150-200
			All-Yellow body, with suspension	£75-85
404M	1956-60	Bedford Dormobile	Red, Metallic Red, Turquoise or Blue body, flywheel motor. Blue box with leaflet	£100-130
409	1959-65	Forward Control Jeep	Light Blue body, Red grille, smooth or shaped hubs	£60-70
405	1981	Ford Transit Milk Float	'DAIRY CREST' logo on cab doors, 'MILK MARKETING BOARD' logo on each side and 'MILK' on rear	£20-30
405	1982	Ford Transit Milk Float	'LOTTA BOTTLE' on Blue/White body, opening doors	£10-15
406	1971-75	Mercedes-Benz Unimog	Yellow/Green or Yellow/Red or Blue/Red, all with Blue interior	£25-35
407	1957-62	Smiths Karrier Bantam	'HOME SERVICES HYGIENIC MOBILE SHOP', Pale Green/Red	£75-85
408	1957-59	Bedford 'AA' Service Van	Yellow/Black, divided windscreen, smooth hubs, Blue box, leaflet	£100-120
	1958-59		Yellow/Black, undivided windscreen, smooth or shaped hubs, Blue box, leaflet	£125-150
	1959-63		Yellow/Black, undivided windscreen, shaped hubs, Blue/Yellow box, no leaflet	£125-150
	late issue:		Yellow/Black, single windscreen, ridged roof, flat spun hubs	£100-125
409	1976-77	Unimog Dumper	White/Red or Blue/Yellow body, suspension, hook	£20-30
409	1981	'ALLIS CHALMERS' Forklift	Yellow body, pallets/load/driver	£15-20
411	1958-62	Karrier Bantam Van	Yellow body, Grey plastic shutter, smooth wheels, 'LUCOZADE', Blue box	£100-120
			As previous model but with shaped wheels, Blue/Yellow box	£100-120
413	1960-64	Smiths Karrier Bantam Mobile Butchers	White/Blue van, 'FAMILY BUTCHERS', meaty decals. Blue box	£85-95
			As previous model but with suspension	£120-140
413	1976-78	Mazda Motorway Maintenance	Yellow/Black body, figure, road signs, bollards, decal sheet enclosed, (modified 478/493)	£25-35
416	1959-61	R.A.C. Land Rover	Blue body, 'RADIO RESCUE' on cab roof sign, metal canopy, smooth hubs, Blue/Yellow box	£90-110
			Blue body, no cab roof sign, 'RADIO RESCUE' on canopy, shaped hubs	£150-175
	Belgian issue:		Yellow body, Green metal canopy, 'TS RADIO' decals on doors	£250-300
416s	1962-64	R.A.C. Land Rover	Blue body, Lemon interior, suspension, 'RADIO RESCUE' on plastic canopy	£65-75
	Belgian issue:		Yellow body, Grey plastic canopy, suspension, 'TS RADIO' decals on doors	£250-300
417	1960-62	Land Rover Breakdown	Red body, Yellow tinplate canopy, spun hubs, 'BREAKDOWN SERVICE'	£70-90
417s	1963-65	Land Rover Breakdown	Red body, Yellow tinplate canopy, shaped hubs, suspension, 'BREAKDOWN SERVICE'	£65-75
421	1960-63	Bedford 12 cwt Van	'EVENING STANDARD', Black body, Silver ridged roof, undivided windscreen, flat hubs	£90-110
			'EVENING STANDARD', Black lower body, Silver upper body and ridged roof, undivided windscreen, flat hubs	£90-110
			Medium Blue body, 'AVRO BODE' logo	£250-300
422	1960-62	Bedford 12 cwt Van	'CORGI TOYS', Yellow body, Blue roof, smooth or shaped hubs	£140-160
	reversed colours:		Blue body, 'CORGI TOYS', Yellow roof, smooth wheels	£250-350
	variation:		Blue lower half with Yellow upper body, 'CORGI TOYS'	£250-350
424	1977-79	Security Van	Black/Yellow/White body, 'SECURITY', windows with grilles	£10-15
426	1962-64	Karrier Bantam Van Circus Booking Office	Red/Blue body, smooth hubs, 'Chipperfields Booking Office'	£175-200
			As previous model but with shaped hubs	£150-175
426	1978-81	Chevrolet Booking Office Van	Yellow/Red/Blue body, 'PINDER-JEAN RICHARD', two loudspeakers	£25-35
428	1963-66	Karrier Ice-Cream Van	Blue/White body, detailed chassis, salesman swivels, 'MR SOFTEE'	£150-175
431	1964-66	Volkswagen Pick-Up	Yellow body, Red or Olive-Green canopy, Red 'VW' emblem	£60-70
			Metallic Gold body, Red 'VW' emblem, Red canopy, Red interior, spun hubs	£250-350
431	1978-79	'VANATIC'	White Chevrolet van, psychedelic 'VANATIC' side labels	£15-20
432	1978-79	'VANTASTIC'	Black Chevrolet van, Orange/Red 'VANTASTIC' design	£15-20
433	1978	'VANISHING POINT'	Golden Yellow Chevrolet van with Red 'sunrise' design. Shown in 1978 catalogue but not issued	NPP

433	1962-64	**Volkswagen Delivery Van**	Red/White body, Red or Yellow interior	£60-70
		Dutch issue:	'VROOM & DREESMAN', Grey body, shaped spun wheels, promotional	£400-500
434	1962	**Volkswagen Kombi**	Metallic Pale Grey over Green body, Red interior, spun hubs	£65-75
	1963-66		Two-tone Green, Red or Yellow interior	£60-70
435	1962-63	**Karrier Bantam Van**	Blue/White/Yellow body, *'DRIVE SAFELY ON MILK'*,	£80-100
437	1979-80	**Chevrolet Van 'COCA-COLA'.**	Red body, White logo, tinted roof windows, crates	£20-25
440	1979-80	**Mazda Custom Pick-up**	Yellow body, Red roof	£15-20
441	1963-67	**Volkswagen Van**	Blue body, Lemon interior, 'Trans-o-lite' headlamps, *'CHOCOLATE TOBLERONE'*,	£75-85
443	1963-66	**Plymouth Suburban US Mail**	Blue/White body, *'ADDRESS YOUR MAIL CAREFULLY'*	£65-75
447	1965-66	**'WALLS ICE CREAM' Van**	Ford Thames van in Blue/Cream, salesman, boy, spare transfers. Blue/Yellow card box, inner base, leaflet	£200-250
450	1964-67	**Austin Mini Van**	Green body with unpainted grille, Red interior	£55-65
			Green body with painted grille, Red interior	£90-110
			Green body with Austin Countryman grille, Red interior	£90-110
		Promotional:	Metallic Green body, Grey base, Red interior, White *'FDR1.2009/17'* logo. Housed in original 450 box with club slip. Thought to be a Dutch promotional	NGPP
452	1956-63	**Commer Dropside Lorry**	Red and Cream body, (raised ridge on some cab roofs), smooth or shaped hubs	£65-75
			Blue body, Cream back	£75-85
453	1956-60	**Commer Refrigerated Van 'WALLS ICE CREAM'**	Dark Blue cab, Cream back, smooth roof, flat spun hubs	£125-175
			Light Blue cab, Cream back, cast roof, flat spun hubs	£100-125
454	1957-63	**Commer Platform Lorry**	Metallic Blue cab and chassis, Silver-Grey platform	£70-80
			Yellow cab and chassis, Silver platform	£70-80
455	1957-61	**Karrier Bantam 2-ton**	Blue, Red or Grey body, Red platform floor, smooth hubs	£70-80
		variant:	Early Mettoy issue, Red body with *'C.W.S. SOFT DRINKS'* logo on rear	£100-125
456	1960-63	**ERF 44G Dropside Lorry**	Yellow/Metallic Blue, smooth/shaped wheels	£65-75
457	1957-65	**ERF 44G Platform Lorry**	Two-tone Blue or Yellow/Blue body, smooth hubs	£65-75
458	1958-66	**E.R.F. Earth Dumper**	Red and Yellow body, 'ERF' cast-in, smooth or shaped hubs	£70-80
459	1958-60	**ERF 44G Van**	Yellow/Red, 'MOORHOUSES LEMON CHEESE'	£150-200
459	1973-78	**Raygu Rascal Roller**	Yellow/Green body, *'Road Roller'*	£15-20
460	1959-61	**E.R.F. Neville Cement Tipper**	'TUNNEL CEMENT'. Lemon cab/chassis, Silver base and metal filler caps	£30-35
			As previous version, but with Red plastic filler caps	£80-100
462	1970	**Commer Van 'CO-OP'**	White/Blue body, Blue/Yellow box	£75-85
462	1971	**Commer Van 'HAMMONDS'**	Green/Blue/White promotional model, cast hubs	£100-120
465	1963-66	**Commer Pick-Up Truck**	Red/Yellow, Yellow/Red or Green/Grey, 'Trans-O-Lites'	£50-60
466		**Commer Milk Float**	White cab, chassis and load; Blue rear roof and sides	£80-100
		Promotional issue:	As previous model but with 'CO-OP' labels. Plain card box	£80-100
470	1965-72	**Forward Control Jeep**	Blue/Grey, Mustard Yellow, Pale Green or Light Blue body, detachable canopy	£30-35
471	1965-66	**Karrier Bantam Snack Bar**	Blue/White, 'JOE'S DINER' with figure and opening hatch	£75-85
		Belgian issue:	Blue/White, 'PATATES FRITES'	£140-170
474	1965-68	**Musical 'WALLS ICE CREAM' Van**	Ford Thames van in Blue/Cream, musical movement (must function), diorama but no figures. Blue/Yellow card box	£200-250
477	1966-68	**Land Rover Breakdown**	Red, Yellow tilt, spare wheel on some, hook, WhizzWheels	£40-50
478	1965-68	**Jeep Tower Wagon**	Green, Yellow and Silver body, figure, (Forward Control)	£40-50
479	1968-71	**Commer Mobile Camera Van**	Blue/White body, shaped hubs, *'SAMUELSON FILM COMPANY LTD'*, camera and operator	£90-110
			As previous model but with cast hubs	£90-110
483	1968-72	**Dodge Tipper Truck**	White cab, Blue tipper, *'KEW FARGO'*, cast wheels	£50-60
484	1967-69	**Dodge Livestock Transporter**	Beige/Green body, *'KEW FARGO'*, 5 pigs	£30-40
486	1967-69	**'KENNEL CLUB' Truck**	White/Orange Chevrolet Impala with 'Vari-View' dachshund picture, 4 dogs	£70-80
493	1975-78	**Mazda B 1600 Pick-Up**	Blue/White or Silver/Blue body	£20-25
495	1983-	**4x4 Mazda 'OB TRUCK'**	Blue/Black, *'Corgi Cruiser'*, drop-down tailboard	£5-10
495	1985	**4x4 Mazda**	As previous model but Blue/White body, *'SURF RIDER'*	£5-10
494	1967-72	**Bedford Tipper**	Red cab/chassis, Yellow tipper	£40-50
			Red cab/chassis, Silver tipper	£90-110
			Yellow cab/chassis, Blue tipper	£110-130
			Blue cab/chassis, Yellow tipper	£130-150
508	1969-71	**Commer Minibus**	'Holiday Camp Special'. White/Orange, Green luggage, spun hubs	£70-80

Major Packs

1100	1958-63	**Bedford 'S' Carrimore**	Yellow cab, Metallic Blue low-loader trailer, smooth or shaped hubs	£120-140
		(Low-loader)	Red cab, Metallic Blue low-loader trailer, winch	£120-140
1100	1971-73	**Mack Truck**	Orange cab, Black/Orange/Silver trailer, sliding doors, jockey wheel, 'TRANS-CONTINENTAL'	£40-50
			Orange and Metallic Lime Green version	£70-80
1101	1957-62	**Bedford 'S' Carrimore**	Blue cab, Yellow transporter body, 'CORGI CAR TRANSPORTER'	£125-150
		(Transporter)	Red cab, Blue transporter body, smooth hubs	£120-140
1101	1976-81	**Mobile Crane**	Yellow/Blue body, 'Warner & Swasey'.	£25-30
1102	1958-62	**'EUCLID' TC-12 Bulldozer**	Yellow body, Pale Grey tracks. Box has inner lining	£100-125
			As previous model but with Black tracks	£100-125
			Pale Lime-Green body	£100-125
1102	1974-76	**Crane Freuhauf**	Yellow cab, Orange dumper body, 'Road Maker Construction' logo, (Berliet Dumper)	£30-35
1103	1960-65	**'EUCLID' Crawler Tractor**	Yellow or Pale Lime-Green body, Pale Grey tracks	£150-175
			As previous model but with Black tracks	£150-175
1104	1958-63	**Bedford 'S' Carrimore**	Red cab, Silver trailer, smooth hubs, operable winch, (Machinery Carrier)	£120-140
			Blue cab, Silver trailer, smooth hubs	£120-140
1104	1974-77	**Bedford 'TK' type**	Green or Metallic Green Horse Transporter, 'NEWMARKET', four horses and boy	£50-60
1105	1962-66	**Bedford 'TK' type**	Red cab, Blue/White trailer, collapsible decks, 'Corgi Car Transporter'	£150-175
1105	1976-80	**Berliet Racehorse Transporter**	Brown/White, 'NATIONAL RACING STABLES', four horses	£40-50
1106	1972-77	**Mack Container Truck 'ACL'**	Yellow/Black/White body, two Red containers with White logo	£40-50
			Promotional issue for '3M'	£120-140
1106	1984	**'CORGI' Loadlugger**	Yellow body and chassis, Red 'BIG BIN'	£10-15
1107	1963-66	**'EUCLID' with Dozer**	Yellow body, Black or Grey tracks, driver	£150-175
			Red body	£150-175
			Lime-Green body	£70-80
1107	1978-79	**Berliet Container Lorry**	Blue cab, White chassis, 2 Grey containers, 'UNITED STATES LINES'	£30-40
1108	1982	**Ford Truck 'MICHELIN'**	Blue/White articulated body, two containers	£40-50
1109	1979	**Ford Truck 'MICHELIN'**	Blue/Yellow articulated body, two containers	£40-50
1110	1959-64	**Bedford 'S' Tanker**	Red/White articulated body, detachable cab, 'MOBILGAS'	£150-175
			As previous model but with shaped spun hubs	£150-175
1110	1965-67	**Bedford 'TK' Tanker**	Blue/White articulated tanker, 'SHELL BENZEEN', Dutch model	£1,500-2,000
1110	1976-80	**'JCB' Crawler Loader**	Yellow/White body, Red working bucket, Black tracks, driver	£30-40
1110	1976-80	**'JCB' Crawler**	Yellow and White body, driver	£30-40
			Light Blue/Orange with Light Blue chassis, driver	£30-40
			Yellow body, Light Blue cab, Red bucket	£30-40
			Red body, Light Blue cab and bucket	£30-40
			Orange body, 'BLOCK CONSTRUCTION' logo	£30-40
1113	1981-86	**'HYSTER' Handler**	Yellow or Black/White main body, 'US Lines', hoist	£100-125
	1986-87		Yellow or Black/White main body, 'SEALINK', container, export model	£100-125
	1986-87		White/Dark Blue/Yellow, 'MICHELIN', container	£100-125
1114	1984	**Mercedes Gritter**	Yellow/Black body and plough, ladder	£10-15
			Yellow/Black body with Red stripes, 'MOTORWAY MAINTENANCE'	£10-15
1115	1985	**Parisienne Refuse Truck**	Green body, 'PARIS' logo, export model	£10-15
1116	1979	**Refuse Lorry**	Shelvoke and Drewry Revopak. Orange/Silver or Red/Silver body	£15-20
	1988		Blue cab, White tipper, 'BOROUGH COUNCIL'	£5-10
1117	1980-85	**'FAUN' Street-sweeper**	Orange and Yellow or All-Yellow, with operator	£15-20
1119	1983	**Mercedes Load Lugger**	Yellow/Red body, 'CORGI'	£15-20
1121	1983	**Ford Transit Tipper**	Orange/Beige body, 'CORGI', (Corgimatic)	£15-20
1126	1961-65	**Racing Car Transporter**	Metallic Dark Blue body with 'ECURIE ECOSSE' in Yellow lettering	£200-250
		later version:	with logo in Orange lettering	£100-150
			with logo in White lettering	£100-150
			with logo and raised ridges in Light Blue	£100-150
		colour variant:	Metallic Light Blue body with 'ECURIE ECOSSE' in Red lettering	£100-150
1128	1963-76	**'PRIESTMAN' Cub Shovel**	Red/Yellow body, driver	£30-35
1129	1962-65	**Bedford 'S' Tanker**	Blue/White articulated body, detachable cab, 'MILK' logo	£200-250
1131	1963-66	**Bedford 'TK' Carrimore**	Blue cab, Silver trailer, Yellow detachable rear axle unit, spun hubs, (Machinery Low Loader)	£100-120
			Blue cab, Silver trailer, Black detachable rear axle unit, spun hubs	£70-80
1132	1963-65	**Bedford 'TK' Carrimore**	Yellow cab, Red low loader trailer, spare wheels, no winch	£100-125

1137	1966-69	**Ford Articulated Truck**	Blue/Silver/Red body, 'H' series tilt-cab, 'EXPRESS SERVICES'	£80-100
1138	1966-69	**Ford Articulated Transporter** ...	Red body, Silver tilt cab, two-tone Blue transporter body, 'CORGI CARS'	£125-150
1140	1965-67	**Bedford 'TK' Petrol Tanker**	Red/Silver/White articulated body, tilting cab, 'MOBILGAS'. Box includes inner packing	£140-160
1141	1965-67	**Bedford 'TK' Milk Tanker**.......	Blue/White articulated body, tilting cab, 'MILK'	£175-200
1142	1967-74	**Holmes Wrecker Recovery Truck**	White/Red/Gold body, 2 mechanics..	£70-80
1145	1969-76	**Unimog Goose Dumper**.............	Yellow/Red body, '406'	£30-35
1146	1970-73	**Scammell Carrimore Mk.V**	Orange/White/Blue Tri-deck Transporter articulated transporter with 3 collapsible decks	£125-150
1147	1969-72	**Scammell Truck**........................	Yellow/White body, 'FERRYMASTERS INTERNATIONAL HAULIERS'	£50-60
1148	1969-72	**Scammell Carrimore Mk.IV**	Red/White car transporter body with Yellow chucks	£80-100
1150	1971-77	**Mercedes Snowplough**...............	Unimog 406 in Green/Black, 2 Red flags, Orange/Silver plough	£30-35
			Unimog 406, Yellow cab and back, Red chassis, Silver plough, 2 Red flags................................	£30-35
1151	1970	**Scammell Truck**........................	Blue/White body, 'Co-operative Society', promotional...	£120-140
1151		**Mack Tanker 'EXXON'**	Red/White body, striped window box	£60-70
1152	1971-76	**Mack Tanker 'ESSO'**................	White/Red/Blue articulated body, Gloster Saro Petrol Tanker (detachable).................................	£40-50
			As previous model but with 'EXXON' logo	£70-80
1152	1983-	**'BARRATT' Tipper**	Green/White body, tipper section tips	£5-10
1153	1973-74	**'PRIESTMAN' Crane**...............	Red/Orange body, 'Higrab'	£60-70
1153	1983-84	**'WIMPEY' Tipper Truck**........	Green/Silver body (later Yellow), tipping section tips, (Scania)	£5-10
1154	1974-76	**Priestman Crane Truck**	Yellow/Red body, Silver boom, hook	£45-55
1154	1979	**Giant Tower Crane**	Orange/Yellow crane, White body, 'BLOCK CONSTRUCTION' logo	£55-65
1155	1975-79	**'Skyscraper' Tower Crane**	Yellow/Red body, Black tracks..	£35-40
1156	1977-79	**Volvo Concrete Mixer**	Yellow/Red/Orange body, 'RAPIER'...	£30-35
1156	1980		Orange/White body, 'BLOCK CONSTRUCTION'	£30-35
1157	1976-81	**Ford Tanker 'ESSO'**	White/Red articulated body..	£25-35
1158	1976	**Ford Tanker 'EXXON'**.............	White/Black articulated body, US issue only...	£50-60
1159	1976-79	**Ford Car Transporter**	Metallic Blue/White or Metallic Green articulated body	£60-70
1160	1976-78	**Ford Tanker 'GULF'**	White/Orange articulated body	£30-40
1161	1976-78	**Ford Tanker 'ARAL'**...............	Blue/White/Black articulated body, German export model...	£50-60
1169	1982	**Ford Tanker 'GUINNESS'**.......	Red/Cream/Black articulated body	£40-50
1170	1982	**Ford Car Transporter**...............	Red/White/Yellow articulated body	£50-60

Photo: Christie's, South Kensington

Police, Fire, Ambulance and other Emergency Vehicles, etc.

See also 'Corgi Commercial Vehicles' (for breakdown recovery vehicles, etc.), and the 'Corgi Gift Sets' section.

Ref	Year(s)	Model name	Colours, features, details	Market Price Range
209	1958-61	Riley Pathfinder Police Car	Black and Silver body, bell, 'POLICE'	£100-130
213	1959-61	Jaguar Fire Chief's Car	Red body, bell, Grey aerial, roof sign, smooth spun wheels	£100-130
213s	1961-62	Jaguar Fire Chief's Car	As previous model but with suspension and shaped spun wheels	£100-130
223	1959-61	Chevrolet Impala 'State Patrol'	Black body, Silver stripe, Lemon interior, Grey aerial. Box also contains internal packing	£65-75
237	1962-66	Oldsmobile Sheriff's Car	Black body, White roof, 'COUNTY SHERIFF', clear or Blue light. Box also contains internal packing	£55-65
260	1979-81	Buick 'POLICE' Car	Metallic Blue/White body, 'CITY OF METROPOLIS', 2 flashing light bars	£30-40
284	1982-83	Mercedes-Benz 240 D	Red body, 'NOTRUF 112', flashing lights, German export model	£20-25
293	1977-80	Renault 5 TS	Metallic Orange or Two-tone Blue body, WhizzWheels	£15-25
293	1980-81	Renault 5 TS	Two-tone Blue body, roof light, 'S.O.S. MEDICINS'	£25-35
295	1982-83	Renault 5 TS Fire Chief	Red/White 'SAPEURS POMPIERS', warning lights, French export model	£15-20
297	1982-86	Ford Escort 'Panda' Car	Light or Dark Blue, White doors, Blue warning lights, 'POLICE'	£15-20
326	1980-81	Chevrolet Caprice Police Car	Black/White body, 'POLICE', suspension	£20-30
332	1980-81	Opel Doctors Car	White/Red body, 'NOTARTZ', opening doors	£30-40
339	1980	Rover 3500 Police Car	White and Red body, 'POLICE'	£20-25
373	1970-76	VW 1200 Police Car	Green and White body, Red interior, 'POLIZEI', Blue roof light, WhizzWheels	£40-50
			Black/White/Blue body, 'POLITIE', WhizzWheels	£120-140
			White body, Red interior, Blue roof light, Black 'POLICE' lettering on White decal	£50-60
			As previous model, but with White 'POLICE' lettering on Blue decal	£50-60
383	1970-73	VW 1200 'ADAC'	Yellow body, Black roof with '1341', 'ADAC STRASSENWACHT' logo on doors	£75-85
386	1987	Mercedes 'POLIZEI'	Green/White body, two Blue warning lights, German export model	£30-40
395	1972-73	Fire Bug	Orange body, Whizzwheels, Red/Black or Pink/Black stripe, Yellow ladder (381 Beach Buggy)	£20-30
402	1972-77	Ford Cortina GXL Police Car	White/Red body, 'POLICE' labels, (updated 313)	£35-45
			White/Red body, 'POLIZEI', German issue	£75-85
405	1956-60	Bedford Fire Tender 'A.F.S.'	Bright or Dark Green body, divided windscreen, Silver or Black ladder, smooth or shaped hubs. (Utilicon). Blue box with leaflet	£80-100
405M	1956-59	Bedford Fire Tender	Red body, divided windscreen, Silver or Black ladder, 'FIRE DEPT', smooth or shaped hubs, friction motor. (Utilicon). Blue box with leaflet	£120-140
405	1978-80	Chevrolet Ambulance	White/Orange, patient on stretcher and two attendants	£20-25
406	1980-81	Mercedes Bonna Ambulance	White body, Red/Black design, opening doors, stretcher, ambulancemen, 'AMBULANCE'	£15-20
		German issue:	Cream body, 'KRANKENWAGEN'	£30-40
		Danish issue:	Red/White/body, 'FALCK'	£30-40
		Swedish issue:	White/Red/Black body, 'SDL 951'	£30-40
407	1980	Mercedes Bonna Ambulance	White body, Red/Black design, opening doors, stretcher, ambulancemen, 'AMBULANCE'	£15-20
408	1957-59	Bedford 'AA' Service Van	Yellow/Black, divided windscreen, smooth hubs, Blue box, leaflet	£100-120
	1958-59		Yellow/Black, undivided windscreen, smooth or shaped hubs, Blue box, leaflet	£70-80
	1959-63		Yellow/Black, undivided windscreen, shaped hubs, Blue/Yellow box, no leaflet	£60-70
	late issue:		Yellow/Black, single windscreen, ridged roof, flat spun hubs	£70-80
412	1957-60	Bedford 'AMBULANCE'	Cream 'Utilicon' body, divided windscreen, smooth hubs. Blue box with leaflet	£100-125
			As previous model but with one-piece windscreen	£150-175
		Factory error:	A few examples of 412 were issued with 'HOME SERVICES' front labels	NGPP
412	1976-79	Mercedes Police Car	White/Black body, 'POLICE' logo, Blue roof lamp	£30-35
			Green/White body, 'POLIZEI' logo, Blue roof lamp, German	£35-45
414	1975-77	Jaguar XJ12-C	White/Blue body, 'COASTGUARD'	£10-15
416	1959-61	R.A.C. Land Rover	Blue body, 'RADIO RESCUE' on cab roof sign, metal canopy, smooth hubs, Blue/Yellow box	£100-120
			Blue body, no cab roof sign, 'RADIO RESCUE' on canopy, shaped hubs	£150-175
		Belgian issue:	Yellow body, Green metal canopy, 'TS RADIO' decals on doors	£250-300
416s	1962-64	R.A.C. Land Rover	Blue body, Lemon interior, suspension, 'RADIO RESCUE' on plastic canopy	£65-75
		Belgian issue:	Yellow body, Grey plastic canopy, suspension, 'TS RADIO' decals on doors	£250-300
416	1977-79	Buick Police Car	Blue body or Metallic Blue body, 'POLICE', two policemen	£25-30
419	1960-65	Ford Zephyr Motorway Car	White or Cream body, smooth or shaped hubs, 'POLICE', aerial, large or small roof light	£80-95
		Export issues:	with 'POLITIE' or 'RIJKS POLITIE' logo (Dutch)	£150-200
421	1977-79	Land Rover Station Wagon	Red body, White roof-rack, 'FOREST WARDEN'	£20-25
422	1977-80	Riot Police Wagon	Red/White body, number '6' and 'RIOT POLICE' on doors, water cannon	£15-20
423	1960-62	Bedford 12cwt. Tender	Red body, Black ladder, undivided windscreen, smooth or shaped hubs, 'FIRE DEPT.'	£90-110
			Red body, unpainted ladder, undivided windscreen, shaped hubs	£100-120

424	1976-79	**'SECURITY' Van**	Black/Yellow/White body, mesh windows, WhizzWheels	£10-15
428	1978-80	**Renault Police Car**	Black/White body, *'POLICE'*, aerial, warning lights, (export isssue)	£55-65
429	1978-80	**Police Jaguar XJ12-C**	White/Red/Blue body, *'POLICE'*, aerial, warning lights	£25-35
430	1978-80	**Porsche 924 'Police'**	Black/White body, *'POLICE'*, warning light	£15-20
430	1978-80	**Porsche 924 'Polizei'**	White/Green body, *'POLIZEI'*, warning light, (export isssue)	£55-65
437	1962-65	**Cadillac Superior Ambulance**	Cream over Red body, 'AMBULANCE' on side windows, Amber roof light	£80-90
	1965-68		Light Blue over White body, 'AMBULANCE' on sides, Red cross on bonnet, Red roof light	£65-75
			Metallic Red over Metallic Silver body	£65-75
439	1963-65	**Chevrolet Impala**	Red body, 'FIRE CHIEF', White stripe, aerial, Orange roof light, firemen,	
			with White painted door labels with *'FIRE DEPT'*	£60-70
			with White rectangular label on front doors *'FIRE DEPT'*	£60-70
			with round Red label on front doors *'FIRE DEPT'*	£60-70
448	1964-69	**Austin Police Mini Van**	Dark Blue body, Red interior, shaped or cast hubs, aerial, White *'POLICE'* logo,	
			policeman and dog, pictorial stand and internal support packaging	£125-150
461	1972-79	**'Police' Vigilant Range Rover**	White/Blue, warning lights, policemen, 8 *'POLICE'* emergency signs + bollards	£25-35
			White/Red body, *'LANGZAAM'*, policemen, emergency signs, Dutch model	£50-60
463	1964-66	**Commer 'AMBULANCE'**	Cream or White body, Red interior, Blue tinted windows and roof light	£90-110
464	1967-68	**Commer 'POLICE' Van**	Dark Blue, *'COUNTY POLICE'*, window bars, clear roof light, leaflet	£100-125
			As previous model but Metallic Light Blue, with Blue roof light	£100-125
			Dark Blue, window bars, Red roof light, *'CITY POLICE'*, instruction leaflet	£175-200
			Dark Blue, 'open' windows, Blue roof light, White *'POLICE'* cast into sides, with instructions	£70-90
			Deep Green body, *'POLIZEI'*, export model, opaque rear/side windows	£400-500
			Metallic Green body, *'POLIZEI'*, German issue	£150-175
			Metallic Blue body, *'SECOURS'*, French issue	£150-175
			Metallic Blue body, window bars, *'RIJKSPOLITIE'*, Dutch issue	£150-175
477	1966-67	**Land Rover Breakdown**	Red body, Yellow canopy with spotlight and 'BREAKDOWN SERVICE' logo	
			rubber (or later plastic) 'tyre' crank, shaped or cast hubs	£45-55
			As previous model but with large or small Silver crank, WhizzWheels	£35-40
481	1965-69	**Chevrolet Police Car**	White/Black body, *'POLICE PATROL'*, Red roof lights, two policemen	£90-120
482	1966-69	**Chevrolet Impala**	Red over White body, Chrome stripe, bonnet logo, Blue light, Grey aerial.	
			with rectangular *'FIRE CHIEF'* label on front doors, shaped spun wheels	£80-90
			with round label on front doors *'FIRE CHIEF'*, shaped spun wheels	£80-90
			with round label on front doors *'FIRE CHIEF'*, detailed cast wheels	£65-75
482	1974-77	**Vigilant Range Rover**	Red and White body with *'AMBULANCE'* logo	£25-30
			White body with Blue side stripe and *'AMBULANCE'* logo, stretcher and 2 ambulancemen	£25-30
483	1979	**Belgian Police Range Rover**	White body, Red stripes, warning lights, policemen, emergency signs	£75-85
484	1978-80	**AMC Pacer 'RESCUE'**	White/Orange/Black body, number '35', *'RESCUE'*	£10-15
			As previous issue but with *'SECOURS'* logo	£40-50
489	1980	**Volkswagen Polo**	White/Green body, *'POLIZEI'*, opening doors and hatchback, (export issue)	£50-55
			Variation with 'ADAC' logo, (export issue)	£50-55
490	1967-69	**Volkswagen Breakdown**	Unpainted fittings, Chrome tools, Red 'VW' emblem, Red/Yellow stripe label, two spare wheels.	
			Tan body, shaped hubs, 'BREAKDOWN SERVICE' labels	£80-90
	1968-72		As previous issue but with 'RACING CLUB' labels (in GS 12)	GSP
492	1966-70	**VW 1200 Car**	Green body, White roof, White *'POLIZEI'* on bonnet, No '18' logo	£80-100
			White body with Black *'POLIZEI'* on doors and bonnet, (Germany)	£200-250
492	1966-69	**VW European Police Car**	Dark Green body, White roof and wings, Red *'POLIZEI'*, Blue lamp	£50-60
		NB	Box should contain 'True Scale Steering' Red/Yellow cardboard roof fitting.	
			All-White body, Light Brown interior, driver, crest on doors, *'POLITIE'*, Blue lamp, Dutch model	£175-225
			All-White body, Light Brown interior, driver, crest on doors, *'POLITZIE'*, Blue lamp, Swiss model	£175-225
506	1968-69	**Sunbeam Imp 'Panda' Car**	White body, Black bonnet and roof, Blue roof light	£55-65
			White body, Black roof, 'luminous' door panels, Blue roof light	£55-65
			Light Blue body, White roof, 'luminous' door panels, Blue roof light	£55-65
509	1970-75	**Porsche 911s Targa Police Car**	White/Red body, Black roof, *'POLICE'* logo	£55-65
			White/Red body, *'POLIZEI'*, siren, warning lights	£55-65
			'RIJKSPOLITIE' export issue	£80-100
700	1974-79	**Motorway Ambulance**	White/Red body, *'ACCIDENT'*, Red Cross	£15-20
702	1975-79	**Breakdown Truck**	Red/Black, single bumper, hook, *'ACCIDENT'*	£10-15
703	1976-78	**Hi-Speed Fire Engine**	Red body, Yellow ladder, warning lights	£10-15
911	1976-80	**Air-Sea Rescue Helicopter**	Blue/Yellow body, Black 'flick-spin' rotor, *'N 428'*, operable winch	£15-20
921	1975-81	**Hughes OH-6A Helicopter**	White/Red, *'POLICE'*, *'RESCUE'*, warning lights	£15-20
921/1	1975-80	**'POLIZEI' Helicopter**	White/Blue, *'POLIZEI'*, Black 'flick-spin' rotor, operable winch, German issue	£25-30

921/2	1975-80	'POLITIE' Helicopter	White/Blue, *'POLITIE'*, Black 'flick-spin' rotor, operable winch, Dutch issue	£25-30
921/4	1975-80	'ADAC' Helicopter	Yellow body, *'D-HFFM'*, Black 'flick-spin' rotor, operable winch	£25-30
921/6	1975-80	Swiss Red Cross	Red helicopter body, Black blades, 'flick-spin' rotor, operable winch	£25-30
922	1975-78	Casualty Helicopter	Sikorsky Skycrane with Red/White body	£25-30
923	1975-78	Casualty Helicopter	Army Sikorsky Skycrane with Olive/Yellow body	£25-30
924	1977-81	Air-Sea Rescue Helicopter	Orange/Yellow/Black body, *'RESCUE'*	£25-30
927	1978-79	Surf Rescue Helicopter	Blue/White body, *'SURF RESCUE'*	£25-30
931	1979-80	Jet Ranger Helicopter	White/Red body, *'POLICE RESCUE'*, 'flick-spin' rotor, operable winch	£25-30

Major Packs (Emergency Vehicles)

1001	1980-82	HCB Angus Firestreak	Red body, Yellow ladder, 2 firemen plus equipment	£60-70
1103	1976-81	Chubb Pathfinder	Red/Silver, *'AIRPORT CRASH TRUCK'*, operable pump and siren, orange logo	£60-70
			As previous model but non-working siren, Brick-Red logo	£50-60
			Red/Silver, operable pump and siren, *'NEW YORK AIRPORT'* logo	£80-90
1118	1981-83	Chubb Pathfinder	Red body, *'AIRPORT FIRE SERVICE'*, operable water pump	£60-70
1120	1984	Dennis Fire Engine	Red body, turntable, warning lights, Yellow plastic ladder, crest design	£10-15
1126	1977-81	Dennis Fire Engine	Red/White/Yellow, turntable, ladder, 6 firemen, *'SIMON SNORKEL'*	£55-65
1127	1964-74	Bedford Fire Engine	Red/Yellow/Silver, turntable, ladder, 6 fireman, *'SIMON SNORKEL'*	£50-60
1140	1982	Ford Transit Wrecker	White/Red, *'24 Hour Service'*, operable winch, hook,	£15-20
			As previous model but logo changed to *'RELAY'*	£15-20
	1982		Red/Yellow body, *'ABSCHLEPPDEENST'*, export model	£15-20
1142	1967-74	'HOLMES WRECKER'	Red/White/Blue, Grey or Gold twin booms, ladder, 2 spare wheels	£70-80
1143	1968-80	'AMERICAN LA FRANCE'	Articulated Fire Engine in Red/White/Yellow, shaped spun or detailed cast wheels, 4-part extending ladder, 5 firemen, plain early box	£70-80
			As previous model but in later striped window box	£50-60
1144	1975-78	Berliet Wrecker Recovery	Red/White/Gold body, with Gold or Grey hoists,	£40-50
2029	1980-83	Mack Fire Engine	Red body, warning light, detachable ladder, *'HAMMOND FIRE DEPT'*	£15-25

Corgitronics and Corgimatics

These models have 'Battery-operated Micro-Chip Action'.

Ref	Year(s)	Model name	Colours, features, details	Market Price Range
1001	1982	HCB Angus Firestreak	Red/Yellow/White, *'RESCUE'*, electronic siren, on/off switch	£40-50
1002	1981	Sonic Corgi Truck Set	Yellow/White/Black/Red, *'SHELL SUPER OIL'*, *'BP OIL'*, remote control	£25-30
1002	1981	'YORKIE' Truck Set	White/Yellow/Blue/Orange, *'MILK CHOCOLATE YORKIE'*, remote control	£25-30
1003	1981	Ford Road Hog	Black, Yellow/White twirls, 2-tone horn, press-down start	£15-20
1004	1981	'Beep Beep Bus'	Red, *'BTA WELCOME TO BRITAIN'*, 2-tone horn, press-down start	£20-25
	1983		Red body with *'WELCOME TO HAMLEYS'* logo	£20-25
1005	1982	Police Land Rover	White/Red/Blue, *'POLICE'*, electronic siren, press-down start	£15-20
1006	1982	'RADIO WEST' Roadshow	*'Your Local Radio 605'*, AM radio, advertised but not issued	NPP
1006	1982	'RADIO LUXEMBOURG'	Red/White, *'RTL 208'*, AM radio, 3 loudspeakers	£25-30
1007	1982	Road Repair Unit Land Rover and Trailer	Yellow/Red/Silver, *'ROADWORKS'*, press start, road drill and sound	£25-35
1008	1982	Fire Chief's Car	Red/White/Yellow/Silver, *'FIRE DEPARTMENT'*, press-down start, siren	£15-20
1009	1983	MG Maestro 1600	Yellow/Black, press start, working front and rear lights	£15-20
			Red/Black body. Sold in Austin-Rover Group box	£20-25
1024	1983	'Beep Beep Bus'	Red, *'BTA'*, supplied exclusively to Mothercare shops	£20-25
1121	1983	Ford Transit Tipper Lorry	Orange/Black, Flashing light and working tipper	£20-25

Military and R.A.F. models

Unless described otherwise, all models in this listing are finished in Military-Green or Olive-Drab camouflage.

Ref	Year(s)	Model name	Colours, features, details	Market Price Range
350	1958-62	Thunderbird Missile	Blue, Green or Silver missile with Red tip, Air Force Blue loading trolley	£45-55
351	1958-62	RAF Land Rover	Blue body, RAF roundel, spare wheel, windows, flat spun hubs	£75-85
			As previous model but with suspension, flat spun hubs	£90-120
352	1958-62	RAF Vanguard Staff Car	Blue bodied Standard Vanguard with RAF roundel	£75-85
353	1959-61	Decca Radar Scanner	Blue/Orange, scanner rotates	£35-45
354	1964-66	Commer Military Ambulance	Military Green body, Red cross, driver	£80-100
355	1964-65	Commer Van 'MILITARY POLICE'	Military Green body, driver, Blue roof light	£80-100
356	1964-66	VW Personnel Carrier	Military Green body, Red interior, driver, Blue roof light, 'US Personnel'	£90-120
357	1964-66	Land Rover	Military Green body, Red interior, driver, White star, aerial, 'Weapons Carrier'	£120-140
358	1964-68	Oldsmobile Staff Car	Military Green body, Red interior, White star, 'HQ STAFF', driver, 3 passengers, aerial	£80-100
359	1964-66	Commer Army 'FIELD KITCHEN'	Military Green, Blue interior, US star on roof, driver/attendant	£100-125
414	1961-63	Bedford Dormobile Military Ambulance	Olive drab body, Red crosses, smooth hubs	£80-100
			As previous model but with shaped hubs and suspension	£80-100
500	1963-64	US Army Land Rover	Rare version of model 357	£150-175
900	1974-78	German Tiger MkI Tank	Brown/Green, Rubber tracks, fires shells (12 supplied) aerial, '144'	£30-40
901	1974-78	Centurion Mk.I Tank	Rubber tracks, fires shells (12 supplied) aerial, Union Jacks	£30-40
902	1974-80	American M60 A1 Tank	Rubber tracks, fires shells (12 supplied)	£30-40
903	1974-80	British Chieftain Tank	Fires shells (12 supplied) rubber tracks	£30-40
904	1974-78	German King-Tiger Tank	Rubber tracks, fires shells (12 supplied) Black crosses, 'B 34'	£30-40
905	1975-76	Russian SU100 Tank Destroyer	Grey, Fires shells (12 supplied) rubber tracks, Red Star	£30-40
906	1975-76	Saladin Armoured Car	Rubber tracks, fires shells (12 supplied) elevating gun	£30-40
907	1976-80	German Rocket Launcher	Steel Blue/Red, half-track, detachable limber, fires rockets (12)	£30-40
908	1977-80	French AMX Recovery Tank	Crane, lifting dozer blade, equipment, 3 figures	£40-50
909	1977-80	Tractor Gun and Trailer	Sand-coloured British gun and trailer, fires shells (12 supplied)	£40-50
920	1975-78	Bell Army Helicopter	Military-Green helicopter with Army markings, Black or Green rotor	£15-20
922	1975-78	Casualty Helicopter	Red/White/Yellow Sikorsky helicopter, number '3', Red crosses	£15-20
923	1975-78	Sikorsky Sky Crane	Military-Green helicopter, Red cross, 'ARMY' marking	£15-20

MAJOR PACKS - (Military and R.A.F. models)

Ref	Year(s)	Model name	Colours, features, details	Market Price Range
1106	1959-61	Karrier Decca Radar Van	Cream body, 4 Orange bands, rotating scanner, aerials, box has interior packing	£100-125
			Cream body, 5 Orange bands, rotating scanner, aerials, box has interior packing	£100-125
1108	1958-60	Bristol Bloodhound Guided Missile & Launching Ramp	Green ramp, Yellow/Red/White Guided Missile, RAF markings	£90-110
1109	1959-61	Bristol Bloodhound Guided Missile & Loading Trolley	Green ramp, Yellow/Red/White Guided Missile, RAF markings	£90-110
1112	1959-62	Corporal Guided Missile on Launching Ramp	Military-Green mechanical base, White missile, Red rubber nose cone, instruction sheet in box	£90-110
	1960-62		Same but with separately boxed 1408 Percussion Head and instructions	£90-110
1113	1959-62	Corporal Guided Missile Erector Vehicle	with lifting mechanism and Guided Missile, spare wheel	£150-200
1115	1958-61	Bristol Ferranti Bloodhound	Yellow/Red/White Guided Missile with RAF markings	£55-65
1116	1959-61	Bloodhound Launching Ramp	Military-Green launching ramp for 1115. Rotates, has lifting mechanism	£45-55
1117	1959-61	Bloodhound Loading Trolley	for use with model 1115 Military-Green, spare wheel, drawbar pivots	£45-55
1118	1959-64	International Tow Truck	Military-Green with British markings (US markings on box picture)	£100-150
			Dutch issue with Silver grille and sidelights	£100-150
			US Army issues	£100-150
1124	1960-61	Launching Ramp for Corporal Guided Missile	Military-Green, operable mechanisms, in plain 'Temporary Pack' box	£35-45
1133	1965-66	Troop Transporter	Olive International six wheeled truck, 'US 7811332 ', hook	£125-150
1134	1965-66	'US ARMY' Fuel Tanker	Olive Bedford 'S' Type Artic, US Army star, 'NO SMOKING'	£200-250
1135	1965	Heavy Equipment Transporter	Bedford Carrimore, Military Green, US Army star, driver, Red interior	£200-250

Miscellaneous Corgi models

Ref	Year(s)	Model name	Colours, features, details	Market Price Range
109	1965-68	Dolphin Cruiser	White and Blue, Red trailer, spun hubs	£70-80
171	1982-	Street Bike	Red, Silver and Black body, multicoloured swirl	£5-10
172	1982-	'POLICE' Bike	White/Black/Silver body	£5-10
173	1982-	Cafe Racer	Silver and Black racing number '26', '750 cc Class'	£5-10
450	1968-71	Lunar Bug	Red, White, Blue. Blue/Yellow window box includes inner packing	£60-70
806	1970-72	Lunar Bug	Red/White/Blue, 'Lunar Bug', windows, drop-down ramps	£65-75

Agricultural Models

Ref	Year(s)	Model name	Colours, features, details	Market Price Range
50	1959-66	**Massey-Ferguson 65 Tractor**	Red bonnet, Pale Grey or Cream chassis, Red metal or plastic hubs, metal or plastic steering wheel	£80-100
50	1974-77	**Massey Ferguson 50B Tractor**	Yellow/Black/Red body, windows	£50-60
51	1959-64	**Massey-Ferguson Tipper Trailer**	Red chassis, Yellow or Grey body, Red metal or plastic wheels	£40-45
53	1960-66	**Massey-Ferguson 65 Tractor with Shovel**	Red bonnet, Beige or Light Grey chassis, Red metal or Orange plastic hubs, operable shovel, painted or unpainted arms	£100-125
54	1974	**Massey-Ferguson Tractor with Shovel**	Yellow/Red or White/Red body	£30-35
54	1962-64	**Fordson Power Major Tractor** (Roadless Half-Tracks)	Blue body, Orange rollers and wheels, Black rubber tracks, lights in radiator grille. Plain 'early' box	£140-160
			Same but with Grey rubber tracks, lights at sides of grille, picture box	£140-160
55	1961-63	**Fordson Power Major Tractor**	Blue/Grey/Red body, Orange hubs	£100-125
			Blue/Grey/Red body, Dull Orange hubs	£140-170
55	1977	**David Brown Tractor**	Black/Red/White body, steering wheel	£35-45
56	1961-63	**Four-Furrow Plough**	Red/Brown/Yellow body	£30-35
56	1977	**Farm Tipper Trailer**	Red/Yellow or Red/White body with drop-down tailboard	£10-15
57	1963-66	**Massey Ferguson Tractor with Fork**	Red/Silver/Cream body, Red hubs, driver, steering wheel	£100-125
			Red/Silver/Cream body, Orange hubs, driver, steering wheel	£125-150
58	1965-72	**Beast Carrier**	Red, Cream and Blue body, four calves	£30-35
60	1964-71	**Fordson Power Major Tractor**	Blue body, plough lifts	£80-100
61	1964-71	**Four-Furrow Plough**	Blue/Silver body	£30-35
62	1965-72	**Ford Tipper Trailer**	Red/Yellow body with two raves	£20-25
64	1965-69	**Forward Control Jeep**	Red body, Yellow/White working conveyor, farmhand figure	£60-75
66	1966-72	**Massey-Ferguson '165' Tractor**	Red/Blue/White body, engine sound	£100-120
67	1967-72	**Ford Super Major Tractor**	Blue/White/Silver body, 'FORD 5000'	£120-140
69	1967-72	**Massey-Ferguson '165' Tractor and Shovel**	Red/Blue body, Silver shovel, figure	£125-150
71	1967-72	**Fordson Disc Harrow**	Yellow/Red/Silver body	£30-35
72	1971-73	**Ford 5000 Tractor and Towbar**	As Corgi 67 but with frame, bucket and pipes	£150-200
73	1970-73	**Massey Ferguson Tractor and Saw**	As Corgi 66 plus Yellow rotating saw	£200-250
74	1969-72	**Ford 5000 Tractor and Scoop**	As Corgi 67 plus Yellow/Silver scoop	£140-170
100	1957-61	**Dropside Trailer**	Yellow/Red body	£10-15
101	1958-61	**Platform Trailer**	Yellow/Grey or Blue/Grey body	£10-15
102	1958-59	**Rice's Pony Trailer**	Red body, Brown chassis, wire drawbar, smooth hubs, plastic pony	£50-60
			Red body, Silver chassis, wire drawbar, smooth hubs, plastic pony	£40-50
	1959-65		Red body, Black chassis, wire or cast drawbar, smooth or shaped hubs	£30-40
			Red body, Silver chassis, wire or cast drawbar, smooth or shaped hubs	£30-40
			Cream body, Red chassis, wire or cast drawbar, smooth or shaped hubs	£30-40
	1961-68		Tan/Cream body, Silver chassis, cast drawbar, shaped hubs	£30-40
112	1969-72	**Rice Beaufort Horse-Box**	Blue/White horse-box with mare and foal	£25-30
484	1967-69	**Dodge Livestock Transporter**	Beige/Green/Graphite Grey body, spun hubs, *'KEW FARGO'*, 5 pigs. Blue/Yellow card box	£60-70
			Later issue with cast hubs. Blue/Yellow window box	£60-70

Major Packs (and large Agricultural Models)   See also 'Gift Sets' section.

Ref	Year(s)	Model name	Colours, features, details	Market Price Range
1111	1959-60	**M-F Combine Harvester**	Red/Yellow, Yellow metal wheels, metal tines, box has internal packing	£100-150
1111	1960-61	**M-F '780' Combine Harvester**	Red/Yellow, Yellow metal wheels, plastic tines, box has internal packing	£100-150
	1961-64		Red/Yellow, Red plastic wheels, Yellow plastic tines, box has internal packing	£175-225
1112	1977-78	**David Brown Tractor and Combine Harvester**	Corgi 55 Tractor with Red/White/Black combine harvester	£100-150

Photo: Vectis Auctions Ltd.

Novelty, Film and TV-related models

Market Price Range: Please note that the prices shown refer to pristine models and boxes. Items failing to match this standard will sell for considerably less. Note also that boxes must contain all their original additional contents. See Corgi model identification page.

Ref	Year(s)	Model name	Colours, features, details	Market Price Range
107	1967-70	Batboat on Trailer	Black boat (tinplate fin cover) with Batman and Robin figures, gold trailer (suspension, cast wheels). Blue/yellow pictorial box also contains black accessory towing hook for attachment to Batmobile	£225-275
	1974-81		Black boat (plastic fin) with Batman and Robin figures, gold trailer (no suspension, Whizzwheels), striped window box	£140-160
201	1970-72	The Saint's Volvo	White body, White 'Saint' logo on red label, WhizzWheels, driver, Red/Yellow 'window' box	£200-225
246	1965-68	Chrysler Imperial Convertible.	All issue should include driver/passenger, golf trolley in boot, Blue/Yellow box with inner packing.	
			Metallic Deep Red body, Pale Blue or Green interior, shaped spun or detailed cast hubs	£70-80
			Metallic Turquoise body, Green interior, shaped spun or detailed cast hubs	£70-80
			Metallic Blue body, Pale Blue interior, cast hubs	£110-130
			Metallic Kingfisher Blue body, Green interior, cast hubs	£175-225
256	1965-68	Volkswagen 1200 Rally	Red body, rally number '18', 'EAST AFRICAN RALLY', steering wheel on roof, rhinoceros	£150-175
258	1965-68	The Saint's Volvo P1800	White body, Black 'Saint' logo (transfer), Red interior, driver, spun hubs, Blue/Yellow card box	£200-250
	1968-70		White body, White 'Saint' logo on Red label, Red interior, driver, cast hubs, Blue/Yellow card box	£200-250
	1968-70		As previous version but white 'Saint' logo on blue label	NGPP
	1970-71		White body, White logo on Red label, Yellow interior, WhizzWheels	£155-175
259	1979-80	Penguinmobile	White car with 'Penguin' and Red/Yellow parasol, Black/Yellow 'window' box	£35-40
260	1979-81	Superman Police Car	Blue/White body, *'CITY of METROPOLIS'*, Black/Yellow pictorial window box	£35-40
261	1965-69	James Bond's Aston-Martin	Bright Gold body (metal roof), Red interior, wire wheels. With James Bond at the wheel, passenger seat ejector (with bandit figure). Accessories: envelope with 'secret instructions', spare bandit figure, self-adhesive '007' badge, (plus 'Model Car Makers to James Bond' Corgi Catalogue in earlier boxes). Blue/Yellow picture box has inner pictorial stand. From the film 'Goldfinger'	£250-350
	variant:		As previous model but the opening roof component is made of plastic	NGPP
261	1979-81	Spiderbuggy	Red/Blue jeep body with crane, Spiderman and Green Goblin figures.	
			Black/Yellow pictorial window box	£75-100
262	1967-69	Lincoln Continental Executive Limousine	Metallic Gold/Black body, with picture strip for onboard 'TV set'	£125-150
			Light Blue/Tan body, with picture strip for onboard 'TV set'	£150-175
262	1979-80	Captain Marvel's Porsche	White with flames and stars, driver, Black/Yellow 'window' box	£35-40
263	1979-81	Captain America's Jetmobile	White/Red/Blue body, Red wheels, Black/Yellow 'window' box	£25-30
264	1979-82	Incredible Hulk Truck	Bronze Hulk in Red cage on Mazda pick-up, Black/Yellow 'window' box	£45-55
			As previous model but Hulk in Grey cage	£55-65
	NB		Dark Bronze Hulk is rare – add £10 to price.	
265	1979-82	Supermobile	Blue/Red/Silver body, Superman at the controls, moving fists'.	
			Black/Yellow pictorial 'window' box has 10 spare rockets / instruction leaflet	£40-50
266	1968-72	Chitty Chitty Bang Bang	Chrome, Brown and Red body (162 m), Red/Yellow retractable 'wings', figures of Caractacus Potts, Truly Scrumptious, a boy and a girl Pictorial Blue/Yellow 'window'box comes in two sizes	£250-300
	1992	25th Anniversary replica:	model on 'mahogany' display stand. Direct mail offer from Corgi	£60-70
266	1979-83	Spider Bike	Red/Blue motorcycle, Spiderman rider, Black wheels, Black or Red handlebars forks, Black or Blue seat and fairing, amber or clear windshield, rocket launchers.	
		Box 1:	Black/Yellow pictorial 'window' box with header card, 10 spare rockets on sprue	£80-100
		Box 2:	Black/Yellow 'window' box without header card, 10 spare rockets on sprue	£80-100
		Box 3:	Black/Red/Yellow striped 'window' box without header card, 10 spare rockets on sprue	£80-100
266	1980-82	Spider Bike	As previous model but with White wheels	£100-125
267	1966-67	Batmobile	Gloss Black body, Red 'Bat' logo on doors and on gold cast hubs, Batman and Robin figures, 'pulsating exhaust flame', sealed secret instructions concealed in box base. 12 spare rockets (Red or Yellow) attached to sprue, self-adhesive 'Batman' badge. Pictorial card box with diorama, earliest versions had 'features' leaflet within	£400-500
			As previous model but with Matt Black body	£600-800
	1967-72		Same but with towing hook cast into base. Blue/Yellow 'window' box (some in earlier card boxes)	£200-250
	1967-72		Same but with cast Silver wheels. Black/Blue/Yellow 'window' box	£250-300
	1973		As previous model but with Red WhizzWheels (with Chrome hubs) and without pulsating 'flame' effect. Blue/Yellow 'window' box with missiles and instructions	£400-600
	1974-77		As previous model but with Black WhizzWheels and without pulsating 'flame' effect. Copyright information cast in base Dark Blue/Yellow 'window' box (header card on some), spare rockets, no instruction sheet	£150-200
	1977-79		As previous casting but wider WhizzWheels, no Robin figure. Black/Red/Yellow 'window' box	£150-200
268	1978-80	Batman's Batbike	Black/Red rocket-firing motorcycle with Red or Grey Batman figure. Black and Yellow 'window' box (header card on some), spare rockets	£60-80
	1980-83		As previous versions but in Black/Red/Yellow striped 'window' box	£50-70
268	1967-72	The Green Hornet's 'Black Beauty'	Black body, Green interior, driver and Green Hornet figures, transfer on roof, spun or cast detailed hubs. Fires missiles from front, radar spinners from rear. Four of each, plus 'secret instructions' are in Blue/Yellow pictorial card box which should also include a greaseproof paper roof decal protector, and inner pictorial card	£200-300

269	1977-83	James Bond Lotus Esprit	White body, Black windows, operable fins and rocket mechanism. From the film 'The Spy Who Loved Me'. Early Black/Yellow pictorial 'window' box with plain base must contain instruction sheet and 10 spare rockets attached to sprue **£100-130**
			Later pictorial 'window' box has instructions printed on base, 10 spare rockets......................................**£90-110**
	1977		10 gold-plated versions of 269 were presented to VIPs at the film's launch. The models had special mountings and boxes...**£3,000-5,000**
270	1968-76	James Bond's Aston-Martin DB5	Silver body (slightly larger than 261). Features as 261, plus revolving number-plates and extending tyre slashers. Box must contain inner pictorial stand, James Bond leaflet, sealed 'secret instructions' packet, unused '007' lapel badge (different from 261), set of unapplied number plates and bandit figure. Variations include Gold or Silver coloured bumpers, metal or plastic spoked rear wheels.
		Box 1:	Pictorial wing-flap box. Model sits on card platform under vac-formed bubble (fragile, few made) **£300-500**
		Box 2:	Blue/Yellow 'window' box (some with card 'upstand' till 1973, few made) **£500-750**
		Box 3:	Black/Blue/Yellow striped 'window' box (1973-76)..**£250-350**
270	1977-78		As previous version but with fixed number plates, 'solid' chrome WhizzWheels, no tyre-slashers, no 'secret instructions'. Striped window box, ejectable passenger lodged in box inner **£100-130**
271	1978-81	James Bond Aston-Martin	Silver body (1:36 scale), Red interior, Gold radiator/bumpers, WhizzWheels ('spoked' detail or 'alloy racing'). Early Black/Yellow boxes had '1:36' printed on window tag, plus header card **£70-80**
			Later Black/Yellow boxes did not have the window tag **£50-60**
			Final issues were in Black/Red/Yellow striped window boxes **£40-50**
271	1990	....'MODELAUTO' promotional:	Silver body, Red interior with 2 figures, Blue logo 'National Motor Museum Holland' **£180-220**
?	1991-92	James Bond Aston-Martin	Reissue of C271 in clear plastic display box with plastic '007' badge **£20-30**
271/1		James Bond Aston-Martin	Silver body (1:36 scale), small 4-spoked wheels **£80-100**
272	1981-83	James Bond Citroën 2cv	Yellow body, opening bonnet, WhizzWheels From film 'For Your Eyes Only'.
		Box (1):	Black/Red/Yellow 'window' box with pictorial header card **£30-40**
		Box (2):	Black/Red/Yellow 'compact' box with pictorial top flap..**£30-40**
272	1981	.................Gold plated version:	(12 only produced). Strada Jewellry Certificate should be with model **£2,000-3,000**
277	1968-72	'MONKEES' Monkeemobile ...	Red body, White roof, Yellow logo, cast detailed wheels. Figures of Mike, Mickey, Davy and Pete plus red plastic 'Monkees' guitar. Blue/Yellow 'window' box **£225-275**
			As above, but without the 'Monkees' guitar..**£225-275**
			In Blue/Yellow 'window' box with clip-in cardboard header as used for shop display purposes............**£500-600**
		NB	Pre-production model with plastic engine exists.
278	1981-	Dan Dare's Car........................	Red/Yellow space vehicle. Planned but not produced ....NPP
290	1976-77	Kojak Buick	Bronze body (various shades), 4-spoke or disc type wheel hubs, 'gunfire' sound, self-adhesive 'Lieutenant' badge, figures of Kojak (no hat) and Crocker (blue jacket). Black/Yellow pictorial 'window' box..**£80-100**
	1977-80		Same but Kojak figure has a hat and Crocker has a Black jacket. 'New' tag on some boxes **£40-50**
292	1977-82	Starsky & Hutch Ford Torino .	Red body, figures of Starsky, Hutch, and a suspect. Black/Yellow pictorial 'window' box...........**£100-150**
	1986		Reissued as an export model (20,000) **£10-15**
298	1982-83	Magnum P.I. Ferrari.................	Red Ferrari 308GTS with 4-spoke or disc wheels. Black/Red/Yellow pictorial 'window' box **£20-30**
302	1969	Hillman Hunter Rally	Blue body, White roof, Matt-Black bonnet, RN '75', equipment, kangaroo, 'Golden Jacks', transfers, toolbox, leaflet, instructions...**£130-160**
320	1978-81	The Saint's Jaguar XJS	White body, standard or 'dished' WhizzWheels. Black/Yellow 'window' box (yellow or black inner) **£30-35**
336	1967-69	James Bond's Toyota 2000 GI .	White body, Red aerial, 2 figures, rocket launchers in boot. From film 'You Only Live Twice'. Diorama must have card reinforcements to protect aerial, 8 spare rockets on sprue, sealed envelope marked 'secret instructions' which also contains self-adhesive '007' badge **£250-350**
342	1980-82	'The Professionals' Ford Capri	Metallic Silver body, dished or disc hubs, figures of Cowley, Bodie, Doyle. Pictorial 'window' box **£125-150**
			As previous model but with chrome wheel hubs...**£150-175**
			Finished in Matt Silver, Dark Red interior **£125-150**
348	1968-69	Ford Mustang 'POP ART' Stock Car........	Blue body and interior, 5 psychedelic labels '20'. Not shown in catalogues **£70-80**
348	1980-81	'Vegas' Thunderbird.................	Red body with Dan Tanner figure Black/Yellow pictorial 'window' box **£60-80**
349	1967-67	'POP ART' Morris Mini	Red body, Yellow interior, 4 psychedelic labels, *MOSTEST* logo. Model not generally released or shown in catalogues, few only produced **£1,500-2,000**
383	1970-76	VW 1200 'Flower Power'	Red body with psychedelic Grenadine and Green daisy labels on bonnet and doors **£75-85**
391	1972-72	James Bond Ford Mustang Mach I	Red body, Black bonnet, White interior and base, WhizzWheels (2 types known). From film *Diamonds Are Forever'*. Red/Yellow 'window' box has '007' Red sticker.........................**£250-350**
			As previous model but with 'CORGI TOYS' shop display stand...**£250-350**
391	1972-73	'FIREBUG'	Orange body, Yellow ladder, *'FIREBUG'*, WhizzWheels..**£15-25**
423	1978-78	'ROUGH RIDER'	Yellow Chevrolet van, motorcycle side labels **£20-25**
426	1962-64	'CHIPPERFIELDS CIRCUS' Mobile Booking Office	Karrier Bantam in red and blue, with clown and circus posters, spun hubs. Blue/yellow card box **£150-175**
426	1978-80	Circus Booking Office..............	Yellow/Red Chevrolet van, 'JEAN RICHARD PINDER', WhizzWheels..**£40-60**
		NB	The 'clown's face' poster may be at the front or the rear on the nearside of the model.
428	1963-66	'Mr SOFTEE' Ice Cream Van.	Karrier van, Blue/White body, salesman swivels...**£175-225**
431	1978-79	'VANATIC'	White Chevrolet van, polychromatic side labels..**£15-20**
432	1978-79	'VANTASTIC'	Black Chevrolet, Yellow/Red design **£15-20**
433	1978	'VANISHING POINT'	Chevrolet van shown in 1978 catalogue but not issued ....NPP
434	1978-80	'CHARLIE'S ANGELS' Van ..	Pink Chevrolet Custom van, Yellow or Brown interior, 4-spoke or disc wheels. Black/Yellow pictorial 'window' box **£50-75**

435	1979-80	'SUPERMAN' Van	Metallic Silver Chevrolet 'SuperVan'. Black/Yellow pictorial 'window' box (printing variations seen)	£35-45
436	1979-80	'SPIDERVAN'	Blue Chevrolet van, 'Spiderman' design, 4-spoke or disc wheels. Black/Yellow pictorial 'window' box	£35-45
437	1979-80	'COCA COLA'	Red Chevrolet van, White design, tinted roof windows, crates	£30-35

NB Various other labels were designed for the Chevrolet 'van' series. Some prototype labels were printed but not officially used. Some of these may have found their way on to repainted van castings - they are NOT official Corgi issues. Logos include: 'Apache Patrol', 'Light Vantastic', 'Vanilla Treat', 'Cosmos', 'Columbia', 'Aquarius', 'Centaur', 'Colorama', 'Rocket Van', 'Centaur', plus four other unlettered 'psychedelic' designs.

436	1963-65	Citroën 'WILDLIFE SAFARI'	Yellow Citroën ID19, driver and passenger, detailed interior, roof luggage, 'Wild Life Reservation' logo	£70-80
440	1966-69	Ford Consul Cortina Estate	Metallic Dark Blue with Brown side panels, plastic golfer, caddie and trolley	£100-125
447	1965-66	'Walls Ice Cream' Van	Ford Thames van in Blue/Cream, salesman, boy, spare transfers. Blue/Yellow card box, inner base, leaflet	£175-225
448	1964-69	Austin Police Mini Van	Dark Blue body, Red interior, shaped or cast hubs, aerial, White 'POLICE' logo, policeman and dog, pictorial stand and internal support packaging	£115-130
450	1968-71	Lunar Bug	Red, White, Blue. Blue/Yellow window box includes inner packing	£60-70
472	1964-66	'VOTE FOR CORGI'	Corgi 438 Land Rover in Green/Yellow, Blue/Yellow card box	£75-85
474	1965-68	Musical 'Walls Ice Cream' Van	Ford Thames van in Blue/Cream, musical movement (must function), diorama but no figures. Blue/Yellow card box with packing ring and packing piece, plus unused sticker sheet	£175-250
475	1964-65	'Olympic Winter Sport'	White/Yellow Citroën Safari, '1964', roof-rack, skier, skis. Diorama 'By Special Request' box	£90-110
475	1965-68	'CORGI SKI CLUB'	Citroën Safari with Off-White body, Red roof-rack, 4 Yellow skis and 2 poles, bonnet transfer, Brown dashboard/rear seats, Green front seats	£110-130
475	1965-68	'CORGI SKI CLUB'	Citroën Safari with White body, Yellow Roof-rack, 4 Red skis and 2 poles, Green dashboard/rear seats, Brown front seats	£110-130

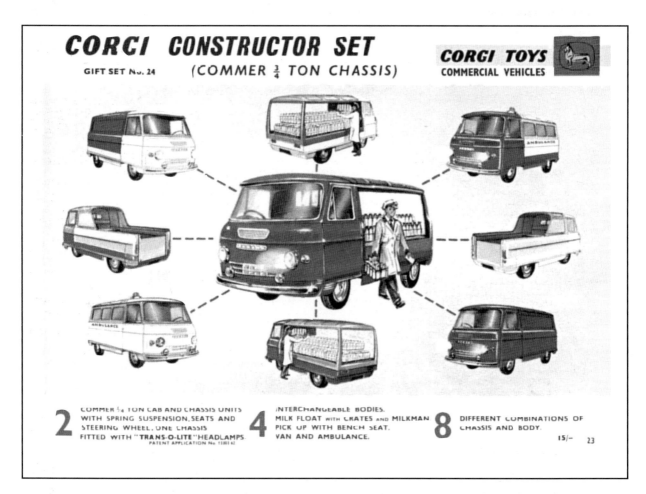

This illustration of the **Corgi Constructor Set** is taken from the 1966 Corgi catalogue.

No.	Years	Name	Description	Price
479	1967-71	Mobile Camera Van	Blue/White Commer van, spun hubs, camera/operator, 'Samuelson Film Services', equipment case	£100-125
479	1967-71		As previous model but with detailed cast hubs	£80-90
485	1965-69	Mini Countryman with Surfer	Sea-Green body, Lemon interior, 2 surfboards on roof-rack, male figure, special leaflet	£160-190
			As previous model but with unpainted grille	£160-190
486	1967-69	'KENNEL CLUB' Truck	White/Orange Chevrolet Impala with 'Vari-View' dachshund picture, 4 dogs	£50-60
487	1965-69	'CHIPPERFIELDS' Parade Vehicle	472 Land Rover in Red/Blue, 'CIRCUS IS HERE' label, chimpanzee, clown, Blue/yellow card box	£150-175
497	1966-66	'The Man From UNCLE's 'Thrush Buster'	Oldsmobile (235) with White body, cast wheels, cast spotlights, 'UNCLE' logo, gun sound, figures of Napoleon Solo and Ilya Kuriakin. Blue/Yellow pictorial card box (which must include internal packaging, roof packing, and 3-D 'Waverley' ring)	£700-900
497	1966-69		Same but Metallic Purplish-Blue body, cast or plastic spotlights	£240-280
499	1967-69	'1968 Winter Olympics'	White/Blue Citroën, 'Grenoble Olympiade', Red or Yellow roof rack, Yellow or Red skis/poles, male tobogganist, female skier. Blue/Yellow 'window' box with instruction sheet	£150-200
503	1964-70	'CHIPPERFIELDS' Giraffe Transporter	Red/Blue Bedford 'TK', cast or spun wheels, 2 giraffes. Blue/Yellow card box	£100-150
	1970-71		As previous model but larger 'stepped' front wheels	£130-170
			Window box variation	£200-300
510	1970-73	Team Manager's Car	Red Citroën, 'Tour De France', figures, spare wheels, 'Paramount'	£70-80
511	1970-71	'CHIPPERFIELDS' Poodle Truck	Blue/Red Chevrolet Impala Pick-Up, 'PERFORMING POODLES' labels, cast wheels, female trainer (Mary Chipperfield, 4 White and 2 Black poodles. Blue/Yellow 'window' box (should include a plastic dome over dogs)	£275-350
513	1970-72	Citroën 'Alpine Rescue'	White/Red car, Yellow roof-rack, St Bernard, sled, skis, male figure. Blue/Yellow 'window' box	£250-350
607	1963-68	'CHIPPERFIELDS' Elephant Cage	A Corgi Kit with Brown plastic cage and elephant parts, instruction leaflet. Blue/Yellow card box	£50-75
647	1980-83	Buck Rogers Starfighter	White/Blue, Yellow retractable wings, Wilma Dearing and Tweaky figures, Black/Yellow pictorial 'window' box, 10 spare rockets	£40-45
648	1981-82	NASA Space Shuttle	White/Black body, 'USA Satellite', opening hatch	£20-25
649	1979-82	James Bond Space Shuttle	White body (C468 casting), separate satellite (early versions retained by nylon strap). From film 'Moonraker' Larger pictorial Black/Yellow box	£50-75
681	1972	Stunt Bike	Gold body, Blue and Yellow rider, Red trolley, 'window' box, (19,000 made)	£125-150
700	1974-80	Motorway Service Ambulance	White/Red futuristic vehicle, WhizzWheels	£8-12
701	1974-80	Inter-City Mini-Bus	Orange body, Yellow labels, WhizzWheels	£8-12
801	1969-69	Noddy's Car	Yellow/Red car with dickey-seat, cast hubs, chrome bumpers. Figures of Noddy, Big-Ears, and black-faced Golly Pictorial Blue/Yellow, 'window' box	£1,000-1,500
			As previous model but Golly has Light Tan face	£750-1,000
			As previous model but Golly has Grey face	£350-500
	1969-73		As previous model but Master Tubby (light or dark brown) instead of Golly	£200-300
802	1969-72	Popeye's Paddle-Wagon	Yellow/White body, Red wings, Blue paddle covers, White or Yellow rear wheels, anchors, moving figures of Popeye, Olive Oyl, Swee'Pea, Bluto and Wimpey. Blue/Yellow pictorial 'window' box	£300-400
803	1969-72	The Beatles Submarine	Yellow/White, psychedelic design, hatches (Yellow rear, White front) open to show John, Paul, George and Ringo, pictorial window box with Blue-Green inner lining	£250-350
	1970-71		As previous model but with Red hatch covers	£300-400
	1970-71		With one red hatch and one white hatch	£500-600
804	1975-78	Noddy's Car	Red/Yellow car, no dickey-seat, no rear bumper. Figure of Noddy only. Dark Blue/Yellow pictorial 'window' box	£175-225
805	1970-71	Hardy Boys Rolls-Royce	9041 Silver Ghost casting in Red, Blue and Yellow, plated wheels. Bubble-pack of five Hardy Boys figures also contained in the Blue/Yellow 'window' box	£150-200
806	1970-72	Lunar Bug	Red/White/Blue, 'Lunar Bug', windows, drop-down ramps	£65-75
807	1971-73	Dougal's Magic Roundabout Car (based on 510 Citroën)	Yellow/Red, with Brian, Dougal and Dylan. Yellow/Blue 'window' box with decal sheet	£180-225
	1973-74		As previous model but in Black/Yellow 'window' box, with decal sheet	£130-160
808	1971-73	Basil Brush's Car	Red/Yellow car with hand-painted Basil figure, 'Laugh tapes' and soundbox are in separate printed box within pictorial Blue/Yellow 'window' box	£175-200
809	1973-73	Dick Dastardly's Car	Blue/Red/Yellow racing car with Dick and Muttley figures. Dark Blue/Yellow 'window' box	£150-175
811	1972-74	James Bond Moon Buggy	Blue/White body, Yellow WhizzWheels, Red scanner. Roof opening mechanism should be working. Blue/Yellow pictorial window box	£250-350
H851	1972-74	Magic Roundabout Train	Red/Blue, Mr Rusty and Basil in the locomotive (engine sound), Rosalie and Paul in the carriage and Dougal in the van. Blue/Yellow pictorial 'window' box with Blue nylon tow-rope	£250-300
H852	1972-74	Magic Roundabout Carousel	Red/Yellow/Blue working roundabout with Swiss musical movement playing the TV theme. Dylan, Paul, Rosalie, Florence and Basil figures. Blue/Yellow pictorial card box	£350-450
H853	1972-74	Magic Roundabout Playground	Contains a modified H852, H851 (with the figures), plus Zebedee, Dylan, four kids, see saw, park bench, 3 Blue and 3 Orange shrubs and 2 flowers. Operating carousel and track. Theme music plays when Dylan is wound up	£1,000-1,500
H859	1972-74	Mr McHenry's Trike	Red/Yellow trike and trailer, Mr McHenry and pop-up Zebedee figures, Blue and Yellow pictorial 'window' box with blue towing cord and instruction sheet	£175-225
H860-H868	1972-74	Magic Roundabout figures	Figures packed in individual clear plastic tubs: 860 Dougal, 861 Florence, 862 Zebedee, 863 Mr Rusty, 864 Brian Snail, 865 Basil, 866 Ermintrude the Cow, 868 Dylan the Rabbit	Each: £20-30
925	1976-81	Batcopter	Black body, Red 'Bat' rotors, Batman figure, operable winch, 143 mm	£65-75
926	1978-80	Stromberg Helicopter	Black body/rotors, ten spare rockets. From 'The Spy Who Loved Me'. Black/Yellow 'window' box	£60-70
927	1978-80	Chopper Squad Helicopter	White/metallic Blue Jet Ranger helicopter, operating winch. Black/Yellow pictorial 'window' box	£35-45
928	1981-82	Spidercopter	Blue/Red body, 'spider legs', retractable tongue. Black/Yellow pictorial 'window' box	£40-50
929	1979-80	'DAILY PLANET' Jetcopter	Red/White body, rocket launchers, Black/Yellow pictorial 'window' box contains 10 spare rockets	£50-60
930	1972-80	'Drax' Helicopter	White body, 'Drax' logo, ten spare rockets. From the film 'Moonraker'. Black/Yellow 'window' box	£60-70
9004	1967-69	'The World of Wooster' Bentley	Green 9002 Bentley with figures of Jeeves and Wooster, plated wheels. Bubble-packed in display base	£70-90

Marks & Spencer issues

In 1978 a series of special sets and single models were produced for sale through selected M & S stores. They were packed in attractive non-standard boxes and had unique liveries. They were not issued in great quantities.

SINGLE MODELS

8800	1979	Custom Van	No details available	£25-35
8801	1979	Spindrift Helicopter	Black body with Yellow chassis, floats and rotor blades	£25-35
8802	1979	Massey Ferguson Tractor	Red/Black body with White arms and Red shovel	£40-50
8803	1979	Buick 'FIRE CHIEF' Car	Red body with 'City Fire Department' logo on bonnet	£50-75

SMALL SETS

8000	1978	F1 Racing Set	Includes 162 'ELF' Tyrrell (Dark Blue) and 160 Hesketh F1 (White)	£75-100
8001	1978	Wings Flying Team	Includes 301 Lotus Elite (Green) and Nipper aircraft (White) on Grey trailer	£100-150
8002	1978	Motorway Police Patrol	C429 'POLICE' Jaguar (Green) and Blue Fiat X1-9	£60-80
8003	1979	Spindrift Power Boat Team	301 Ferrari Daytona (Yellow) and Yellow power boat on trailer	£60-80

MEDIUM SETS

8100	1978	Racing Team	C421 Land Rover (White with 'FORMULA' logo), 338 Rover, and 301 Lotus on trailer	£150-200
8101	1978	Wings Flying School	C421 Land Rover (Grey with 'WINGS' logo) Grey helicopter and Nipper aircraft on Grey trailer	£150-200
8102	1978	Motorway Breakdown	C429 'POLICE' Jaguar, 293 Renault 5 (Yellow) plus Berliet Wrecker with 'RESCUE BREAKDOWN SERVICES'	£100-150
8103	1979	Spindrift Power Boat Team	Includes Spindrift 301 Ferrari, Helicopter and Dinghy	£150-200

LARGE SETS

8400	1978	Grand Prix Racing	Includes 160 Hesketh (White) 162 'ELF' Tyrrell (Dark Blue) Fiat X1-9 (Blue) and Land Rover (White with 'FORMULA 1 RACING TEAM' logo)	£250-350
8401	1978	Wings Flying Club	Land Rover, Helicopter, Tipsy Nipper aircraft on trailer plus Lotus Elite	£250-300
8402	1978	Motorway Rescue	Includes 'POLICE' Jaguar, Berliet Wrecker, Renault 5 and Fiat X1-9	£250-300
8403	1979	Spindrift Power Boat Team	Includes Ferrari Daytona (Yellow) Yellow power boat on trailer, Yellow/Black helicopter, plus MF Tractor and 'RESCUE' dinghy	£250-300

Trophy Models   (Marks & Spencer special 'plated' issues)

The models were specially produced in 1961 to be sold by Marks & Spencer. The set consisted of five vacuum-plated 'gold' models taken from the existing Corgi product range, each mounted on a detachable black moulded base with a gold name label. The models were packaged in white boxes with red/grey design plus 'St Michael Trophy Models' in red. They did not sell well at the time of issue but are keenly sought after by present day collectors.

150 S	1961	**Vanwall Racing Car**	Gold vacuum-plated body, Red wheels and radiator grille	£100-200
152	1961	**BRM Racing Car**	Gold vacuum-plated body, Red wheels and radiator grille	£100-200
300	1961	**Austin-Healey Sports Car**	Gold vacuum-plated body, plastic windscreen, Red wheels and grille	£100-200
301	1961	**Triumph TR2 Sports Car**	Gold vacuum-plated body, plastic windscreen, Red wheels and grille	£100-200
302	1961	**MG 'MGA' Sports Car**	Gold vacuum-plated body, plastic windscreen, Red wheels and grille	£100-200

The 'Exploration' Range

D2022	1980	**'SCANOTRON'**	Green/Black/Yellow	£15-25
D22023	1980	**'ROCKETRON'**	Blue/Yellow, Black tracks	£15-25
D2024	1980	**'LASERTRON'**	Orange/Black/Yellow	£15-25
D2025	1980	**'MAGNETRON'**	Red/Black	£15-25

'The Muppets Show' models

D2030	1979-80	**Kermit's Car**	Yellow car with a famous Green frog, bubble-packed	£40-45
	1980-82		Same model but in Red/Yellow pictorial 'window' box	£35-40
D2031	1979-80	**Fozzie Bear's Truck**	Red/Brown/White truck, Silver or Black hooter, bubble-packed	£35-40
	1980-82		Same model but in Red/Yellow pictorial 'window' box	£30-35
D2032	1979-80	**Miss Piggy's Sport Coupé**	Pink sports car, Red or Pink dress, bubble-packed	£40-45
	1980-82		Same model but in Red/Yellow pictorial 'window' box	£35-40
D2033	1979-80	**Animal's Percussionmobile**	Red traction-engine, Yellow or Red wheels, Yellow or Black chimney, Yellow or Silver cymbal. Bubble-packed	£35-40
	1980-82		Same model but in Red/Yellow pictorial 'window' box	£30-35

Duo Packs (Film and TV-related models)

1360	1982-?	**Batmobile**	267 plus a Corgi juniors version, Black/Red/Yellow 'window' box	£150-175
1361	197?-?	**James Bond Aston-Martin**	271 plus a Corgi Juniors version, Black/Red/Yellow 'window' box	£125-150
1362	197?-?	**James Bond Lotus Esprit**	269 plus a Corgi Juniors version, Black/Red/Yellow 'window' box	£125-150
1363	1982-83	**Buck Rogers Set**	647 plus a smaller version Black/Yellow pictorial 'window' box	£50-60
1376	1982-83	**Starsky & Hutch Ford Torino**	292 plus a Corgi Juniors version	£70-80

Major Packs

Original internal packaging for securing model and accessories must all be present before model can be considered complete and therefore to achieve the best price. See Corgi model identification page.

Ref	Year(s)	Model name	Colours, features, details	Price
1121	1960-62	'CHIPPERFIELDS' Crane Truck	Red body, Raised Blue log and wheels, operable grey tinplate jib and hook, instruction leaflet. Blue/Yellow lidded box with packing	£150-200
	1963-69		Red body, raised Blue logo and wheels, operable chrome tinplate jib and hook, instruction leaflet. Blue/Yellow card box with end flaps	£150-200
1123	1961-62	'CHIPPERFIELDS' Circus Cage	Red body, Yellow chassis, smooth hubs, red diecast end and middle sliding doors, 2 plastic lions (in stapled bags), animal name decals, instruction sheet. Blue/Yellow lidded box with packing	£75-100
	1963-68		Red body, Yellow chassis, smooth or spun hubs, Blue plastic end and middle sliding doors, 4 animals (lions, tigers or polar bears in stapled bags), animal name decals. Blue/Yellow card box with end flaps	£75-100
1130	1962-70	'CHIPPERFIELDS' Horse Transporter	Bedford TK truck, Red/Blue, Green or Red 'horse-head' design at rear, cast or spun hubs, 6 Brown or Grey horses, Blue/Yellow card box with card packing around horses	£175-225
	1970-72		As previous model but with larger 'truck' wheels	£150-175
1139	1968-72	'CHIPPERFIELDS' Menagerie Transporter	Scammell Handyman MkIII, Blue/Red cab, Blue trailer with 3 plastic cages, 2 lions, 2 tigers and 2 bears. Blue/Yellow pictorial 'window' box with packing to hold animals, plus spare self-adhesive securing tape for animals	£300-400
1144	1969-72	'CHIPPERFIELDS' Crane and Cage with Rhino	Red/Blue Scammell Handyman MkIII, 'COME TO THE CIRCUS' on n/s, silver jib and hook, stepped 'truck' front wheels on some, Grey rhinoceros in plastic cage. Blue/Yellow 'window' box with pre-formed blister-pack around animals	£500-600
1163	1978-82	Human Cannon Truck	Red and Blue body, 'MARVO' figure	£30-40
1164	1980-83	Berliet 'DOLPHINARIUM'	Yellow cab, Blue trailer, Clear plastic tank, 2 dolphins, girl trainer. Black/Yellow 'window' box with header card on some	£100-150
			Yellow cab, Yellow trailer, 'window' box with header card on some	£100-150

Aircraft

Helicopters and Space Vehicles are also listed in the Emergency Vehicles, Novelty and Military Sections.

Ref	Year(s)	Model name	Colours, features, details	Market Price Range
650	1973-80	'BOAC' Concorde	White/Blue with Gold tail design, all-card box with 'BRITISH AIRWAYS', box has inner packing	£70-80
			White/Blue with Red/White/Blue tail, display stand, 'G-BBDG'	£50-60
			Version with White stripes on tail	£15-25
			Version with crown design on tail	£15-25
651	1973-81	'AIR FRANCE' Concorde	White/Blue with Gold tail design, all-card box	£70-80
			White body, Red/White/Blue tail, display stand	£40-50
652	1973-81	'JAPAN AIRLINES' Concorde	White/Red/Blue/Black, all-card box, box has inner packing	£150-200
653	1973-81	'AIR CANADA' Concorde	White/Red/Blue/Black, all-card box, box has inner packing	£150-200
1119	1960-62	HDL Hovercraft 'SR-N1'	Blue/Grey/White body, Yellow rudders and wheels (Major Pack)	£30-35
1301	1973-77	Piper Cherokee Arrow	Yellow/Black with White wings, or White/Blue, 'N 286 4 A'	£35-45
1302	1973-77	Piper Navajo	Red/White or Yellow/White, 'N 9219 Y'	£35-45
1303	1973-77	Lockheed F104A Starfighter	Silver or Camouflage with Black crosses	£35-45
1304	1973-77	Mig-21 PF	Blue or Silver, number '57', Red stars, retractable undercarriage	£25-35
1305	1973	Grumman F-11a Tiger	Blue 'NAVY', or Silver with US stars	£25-35
1306	1973-77	North American P51-D Mustang	Silver or Camouflage, Black props, US stars, moveable control surfaces	£25-35
1307	1973-77	Saab 35 X Draken	Silver or Camouflage, retractable undercarriage, Swedish markings	£35-45
1308	1973-77	BAC (or SEPCAT) Jaguar	Silver or Camouflage, retractable wheels, moveable control surfaces	£35-45
1309	1973-77	'BOAC' Concorde	Dark Blue/White, retractable wheels	£45-55
1310	1973-77	'AIR FRANCE' 'BOEING 707B'	White/Blue body, Silver wings, retractable wheels	£35-45
1311	1973-77	Messerschmitt ME410	All Silver body, Black Iron Crosses on wings and fuselage	£35-45
1312	1973-77	Boeing 727 'TWA'	White body, Silver wings, retractable wheels	£35-45
1313	1973-77	Japanese Zero-Sen A6M5	Green or Silver with Red circles, retractable wheels	£35-45
1315	1973-77	'PAN-AM' Boeing 747	White body, Silver wings, hinged nose, retractable wheels	£35-45
1315/1		'BRITISH AIRWAYS' Jumbo Boeing 747	White/Silver, Blue logo, hinged nose, retractable wheels	£45-55
1316	1973-77	McDonnell Douglas F-4c5	Phantom II in Silver or Camouflage with retractable undercarriage	£35-45
1320	1978-80	'BRITISH AIRWAYS' VC-10	White/Silver with Red tail, Blue logo, retractable wheels	£35-45
1325	1978-80	'SWISSAIR' DC-10	White/Silver with Red stripe and tail, retractable wheels	£35-45

Original internal packaging for securing models and accessories must all be present before sets can be considered complete and therefore to achieve the best price. See Corgi Toys model identification page.

Ref	Year(s)	Set name	Contents, features, details	Market Price Range
1	1957-62	**Transporter and 4 Cars**..........	1101 Blue/Yellow Bedford Carrimore Transporter plus 201 Austin Cambridge, 208 Jaguar 24, 301 Triumph TR2 (or 300 Austin-Healey) and 302 MGA, plus 2 Yellow/Black 'Corgi Toys' dummy boxes..	**£400-500**
1a	1957-62	**Transporter and 4 Cars**..........	1101 Red/Two-tone Blue Transporter, 200 Ford Consul, 201 Austin Cambridge, 204 Rover 90, 205 Riley Pathfinder, 2 Yellow 'Corgi Toys' dummy boxes.......................	**£300-400**
1b	1959-62	**Transporter and 4 Cars**..........	1101 Red/Two-tone Blue Transporter, 214 Ford Thunderbird Hardtop, 215 Ford Thunderbird Convertible, 219 Plymouth Suburban Sport, 220 Chevrolet Impala. (US issue set).................	**£350-450**
1c	1961-62	**Transporter and 4 Cars**..........	1101 Red/Two-tone Blue Transporter, 210s Citroën (or 217 Fiat 1800), 219 Plymouth Suburban Sport, 226 Mini, 305 Triumph TR3. (US issue set).................	**£350-450**
1	1966-72	**Farm Set**....................................	Ford 5000 Tractor plus 58 Beast Carrier, pictorial stand..	**£100-120**
1	1983	**Ford Sierra Set**	Ford Sierra 299 with Blue body and Blue/Cream Caravan..	**£20-30**
1/2	1985	**'London Scene'**	469 'LONDON STANDARD', Sierra Police Car and 425/1 Taxi....................................	**£15-20**
2	1958-68	**Land Rover and Pony Trailer**..	438 Land Rover (Green, Beige tin tilt) and 102 Rice Pony Trailer (Red/Black)	**£150-175**
			As previous but with All Red Land Rover...	**£175-200**
			with Light Brown Land Rover (Cream plastic tilt), Light Brown/Cream trailer....................	**£125-150**
2	1971-73	**Unimog Dumper and Shovel**	1128 Mercedes Tipper and 1145 Unimog Goose Dumper. Yellow/Blue 'window' box	**£60-70**
2	1980-81	**Construction Set**	Contains 54 Tractor, 440 Mazda, tool-box and cement mixer	**£30-35**
	1980-80	**Construction Set**	French export set containing 1110 and 1156 plus cement mixer	**£30-40**
3	1959-63	**Thunderbird Missile Set**..........	Contains 350 Thunderbird Missile and 351 Land Rover. Blue/Yellow card box	**£150-175**
3	1967-69	**Batmobile and Batboat**		
		1st issue:	267 Batmobile with 'Bat' wheels, plus 107 Batboat, in plain Blue 1st issue 'window' box with inner tray and 4 figures, instruction sheet	**£600-800**
		2nd issue:	267 Batmobile with Red wheels (without 'Bat' design), plus 107 Batboat. Yellow/Blue 'window' box should also contain unopened instruction pack	**£1,000-1,500**
	1980	3rd issue:	267 Batmobile (plain cast wheels), and 107 Batboat (WhizzWheels), two figures. Striped 'window' box should also contain instructions in unopened packet....................	**£300-400**
3	1986-88	**'British Gas' Set**	Contains Blue/White Ford Cargo Van, Ford Escort Van (2nd), plus compressor.....................	**£20-25**
4	1958-60	**Bristol Ferranti Bloodhound Guided Missile Set**	Contains: 351, 1115, 1116, 1117 (see 'Military Vehicles' section). Blue/Yellow card box	**£250-350**
4	1974-75	**Country Farm Set**	Models 50 and 62 plus hay load, boy and girl. Striped 'window' box	**£70-80**
5	1959-60	**Racing Car Set**........................	150 (Red), 151 (Blue), 152 (Green). Flat spun hubs. Yellow/Blue lift-off lid box, vac-formed inner......	**£200-250**
	1960-61	....	150 (Red), 151 (Blue with Red bonnet stripe), 152 (Green). Flat or cast spoked wheels. Yellow/Blue box with polystyrene inner tray	**£200-250**
5s	1962-63	**Racing Car Set**........................	150s (Red), 151a (Blue), 152s (Turquoise). Yellow/Blue box with 'Gift Set 5s' stickers, inner polystyrene tray	**£250-350**
5	1976-77	**Country Farm Set**	Same as Set 4 above, but minus boy, girl and hay load	**£40-50**
5	1967-72	**Agricultural Set**	484 Livestock Transporter and pigs, 438 Land Rover (no hood) 62, 69, 71, accessories 1490 skip and churns, 4 calves, farmhand and dog, 6 sacks. Box has inner pictorial stand...................	**£275-325**
6	1959-60	**'Rocket Age' Set**	Contains: 350, 351, 352, 353, 1106, 1108, 1117 (see 'Military' section).....................	**£600-800**
6	1967-69	**Cooper-Maserati Set**	Contains 490 VW Breakdown Truck plus 156 Maserati on trailer. 'Window'/flap box	**£150-175**
7	1959-64	**Tractor and Trailer Set**	Contains 50 Massey-Ferguson 65 Tractor and 51 Trailer. Yellow/Blue all-card box...............	**£200-240**
7	1968-76	**'DAKTARI' Set**........................	438 Land Rover in Green with Black Zebra stripes, spun or cast hubs. 5 figures: Paula, Dr Marsh Tracy with chimp Judy on his lap, a Tiger on the bonnet, and Clarence The Short-Sighted Lion (with spectacles!). Yellow/Blue 'window' box...............	**£200-250**
			Version with WhizzWheels. Striped box	**£100-125**
8	1959-62	**Combine Harvester, Tractor and Trailer Set**......	Contains 1111, 50 and 51	**£200-250**
8	1968-74	**'Lions of Longleat' Set**............	Land Rover with shaped hubs, keeper, 3 lions, plastic den, 3 joints of meat. Yellow/Blue 'window' box with header card and inner packing	**£200-250**
			As above but with WhizzWheels. Striped 'window' box	**£100-125**
8/2	1987	**Police Set**	Ford Sierra Police Car, 674/3 Ford Transit Breakdown Truck and 621 Ford Escort Van.............	**£30-40**
9	1959-62	**Corporal Guided Missile Set**....	Contains: 1112, 1113, 1118 (see 'Military Vehicles' section)...............................	**£300-400**
9	1968-72	**Tractor, Trailer and Shovel Set**.......................	Contains 66 Ferguson 165 Tractor with 69 Shovel and 62 Tipper Trailer with detachable raves. Yellow/Blue all-card box with inner pictorial stand...........................	**£200-250**
9	1979-82	**'RNLI' Rescue Set**..................	Land Rover and Dinghy on trailer. White, Blue, Red, Black. Striped 'window' box	**£75-95**
9		**3 Racing Minis Set**.................	Yellow, White and Blue, numbers/stripes/adverts, special Red 'Hamleys' box...................	**£90-110**
10	1968-69	**Marlin Rambler Set**	Blue/White 319 with Trailer, 2 canoes (1 with figure). Yellow/Blue box, inner packing, pictorial tray...	**£200-250**
10	1973-78	**Tank Transporter Set**	Contains 901 Centurion Mk.I Tank and 1100 Mack articulated transporter. Picture card box...............	**£100-120**
10	1982	**Jeep Set**.................................	Red 441 plus motorcycle on trailer..	**£20-25**
10	1985	**Sierra and Caravan Set**	C299 Sierra plus Pale Brown caravan with Blue/Grey strip..............................	**£25-35**
11	1960-64	**ERF Dropside and Trailer**	456 and 101 with cement and planks load. Yellow/Blue picture box with inner card stand..................	**£150-200**
			As above but with WhizzWheels	**£90-110**
11	1971-72	**London Transport Set**.............	Contains 418 Taxi, 468 *'OUTSPAN'* Bus, 226 Mini (Deep Blue), policeman on stand, Striped 'window' box with inner tray......................................	**£100-120**
	1980-82		C425 Taxi with C469 Bus *'B.T.A.'* and policeman.......................................	**£35-45**

12	1961-64	'Chipperfields Circus' Set	1121 Circus Crane Truck *CHIPPERFIELDS* and 1123 Circus Cage, plus instructions. Yellow/Blue all-card picture box **£150-175**
12	1968-71	Grand Prix Racing Set	155, 156 and 330 with 490 Volkswagen tender, 3 mechanics, 16 bollards and hay bales. Yellow/Blue 'window' box also contains cones in bag, instructions, 'Mr Retailer' card and inner polystyrene tray....**£300-400**
	1971-72	....	158, 159 and 330 (or 371) with 490 Volkswagen tender, 3 mechanics, 16 bollards and hay bales. The artwork on the box and the vac-formed base are different from previous issue **£250-300**
12	1981-	Glider and Trailer Set	345 with Trailer and Glider **£50-60**
13	1964-66	Fordson Tractor and Plough Set	Contains 60 Fordson Power Major Tractor and 61 Four Furrow Plough in Blue, Orange plastic front and rear hubs. Yellow/Blue box with inner tray **£200-250**
13	1968-72	Renault 16 Film Unit	White/Black, *'TOUR DE FRANCE'* , 'PARAMOUNT', cameraman, cyclist. Yellow/Blue box with inner tray plus plain orange card backdrop **£100-125**
13	1981-82	Tour de France 'RALEIGH' Team Car	373 Peugeot, White body, Red/Yellow 'RALEIGH' and 'TOTAL' logos, racing cycles and Manager with loudhailer **£60-70**
14	1961-64	Tower Wagon Set	409 Jeep, Yellow cradle, lamp standard and electrician. Yellow/Blue card box **£60-70**
14	1969-73	Giant 'DAKTARI' Set	Gift Set and items plus 503 and 484 transporters (spun hubs) with large and small elephants. Blue/Yellow window box with pictorial header card and inner tray **£300-400**
			Version with WhizzWheels. Striped 'window' box with pictorial header card and inner tray.................**£150-200**
15	1963-64	Silverstone Set	150s, 151a, 152s, 215s, 304s, 309, 417s, 3 buildings, plain box (no picture)............**£1,250-1,500**
	1964-66		150s, 154, 152s, 215s, 304s, 309, 417s, 3 buildings, layout shown on box **£1,250-1,500**
15	1968-77	Land Rover and Horsebox Set.	Contains 438, 112, spun hubs, mare and foal. Yellow/Blue box contains inner polystyrene tray **£100-125**
			Version with WhizzWheels. Striped 'window' box contains inner card packing **£55-75**
15	1986	'TARMAC' Motorway Set	'Motorway Maintenance' Green/Black 1128 Mercedes Tipper, Mazda Pickup and a compressor.............**£20-30**
16	1961-65	'ECURIE ECOSSE' Set	1126 Transporter with 3 individually boxed racing cars in all-card lift-off lid box with instruction leaflet and internal packing.
		i)	Metallic Dark Blue 1126 Transporter (with Orange lettering), 150 Vanwall (Red, no '25'), 151 Lotus XI (Blue, number '3'), 152 BRM (Turquoise, no '3') **£200-250**
		ii)	Metallic Dark Blue 1126 Transporter (with Yellow lettering), 150s Vanwall, 151a Lotus XI (Blue, no '7'), 152s BRM **£250-300**
	1965	....iii)	Metallic Light Blue 1126 Transporter (with Red lettering), 150s Vanwall, 152s BRM, 154 Ferrari (Red, no'36') **£200-250**
		iv)	Metallic Dark Blue 1126 Transporter (with Light Blue lettering and ridges), 150s Vanwall, 152s BRM, 154 Ferrari **£200-250**
17	1963-67	Ferrari Racing Set	438 Land Rover in Red with Green top, Red 154 Ferrari F1 on Yellow trailer. Yellow/Blue box has inner tray **£250-300**
17	1977-80	Military Set	Contains 904, 906, 920 (see 'Military Vehicles' section) **£40-50**
17	1986	'BRITISH TELECOM'	Ford Cargo Box Van, Ford Escort Van and a Compressor **£20-30**
18	1961-63	Ford Tractor and Plough Set ...	Contains 55 Fordson Power Major Tractor and 56 Four Furrow Plough in Blue/Red/Yellow. Drab Orange front and rear hubs. Yellow/Blue box with inner tray **£200-250**
18	1975-80	Emergency Gift Set	Contains 402, 481, C921 (see 'Emergency Vehicles' section) **£60-70**
18/1	?	3 Mini Racers Set	with *'CHELSEA'*, *'PARK LANE'* and *'PICADILLY'* logos **£20-30**
18/2	?	Mini Special Editions Set.........	with *'RED HOT'*, *'RITZ'* and *'JET BLACK'* logos...**£20-30**
	Note:		C18/1 and C18/2 were sold (in long 'window' boxes) exclusively by Woolworths.
19	1962-68	'CHIPPERFIELDS' Cage Set..	438 Land Rover (plastic tilt) and 607 Elephant and cage on trailer. Blue/Yellow picture box has inner card tray and additional packing **£200-250**
19		'RNLI' Set	438 Land Rover plus Orange dinghy on trailer with *'Mumbles Lifeboat'* logo **£60-70**
19	1972-77	Land Rover and Nipper Aircraft	438 Land-Rover (Blue/Orange, tinplate tilt) + trailer. Blue/Orange/Yellow plane *'23'* or Blue/Orange/White plane *'23'*. Yellow/Blue 'window' box **£60-70**
19	1973-77	'CORGI FLYING CLUB'	As previous model but Land-Rover has a plastic tilt **£45-60**
19	1979-82	Emergency Gift Set	Contains C339 and C921. Striped 'window' box **£40-60**
19	1980-82	Emergency Gift Set	Contains C339 and C931 in Red/White liveries. Striped 'window' box **£40-60**
20	1961-64	'Golden Guinea' Set	Gold-plated 224 Bentley Continental, 234 Ford Consul, 229 Chevrolet Corvair, Catalogue, 2 Accessory Packs. Inner card tray with lower card packing, outer Dark Green sleeve with window **£150-175**
20	1970-73	Tri-Deck Transporter Set........ (Scammell Handyman Mk.III)	1st issue contains 1146 Transporter with 210 'Saint's' Volvo, 311 Ford Capri, 343 Pontiac, 372 Lancia, 377 Marcos, 378 MGC GT (rare Orange version). Instruction sheet, 'Mr Retailer' transit card protector..**£500-600**
	Harrods set:		Late issue with WhizzWheels: 1146 Transporter, 382 Porsche Targa (Silver Blue), 313 Ford Cortina GXL (Bronze/Black), 201 Volvo (Orange 'Saint' label), 334 Mini (Orange) and 377 Marcos (Silver Green). Box also has instruction sheet and 'Mr Retailer' transit card protector.......**£500-600**
20	1978-80	Emergency Gift Set	Contains C429, C482, C921 (see 'Emergency Vehicles' section). Box has inner tray..........................**£35-45**
21	1962-66	ERF Dropside and Trailer	456 and 101 with milk churns and self-adhesive accessories. Yellow/Blue box with inner card stand **£225-275**
21	1969-71	'Chipperfields' Circus Set	Contains 1144 Crane and Cage, and 1139 Menagerie Transporter. Yellow/Blue box with internal packaging and 'Mr Dealer' box protector card..**£750-1,000**
21	1980-82	Superman Set...........................	Contains 260, 265 and 925, plus inner tray and plastic rockets on sprue **£100-125**
22	1962-65	Farming Set...............................	Contains 1111 M-F Combine Harvester, 406 Land-Rover and Trailer, 51 Tipping Trailer, 101 Platform Trailer, 53 M-F 65 Tractor with Shovel, 1487 Milk Churns, 1490 Skip and 3 churns, plus models in Gift Set 18 above. Lift-off lid all-card picture box with inner polystyrene tray **£500-750**

22	1980-82	**James Bond Set**	Contains 269 Lotus Esprit, 271 Aston-Martin DB5 and 649 Space Shuttle plus rockets and 2 spare bandit figures. Box has inner tray £300-400
23	1962-66	**'CHIPPERFIELDS' Set**	
		1st issue:	1121 Crane Truck, 2 x 1123 Animal Cages (2 lions, 2 polar bears), plus Gift Set 19 and 426 Booking Office. All-card lift-off lid picture box with inner polystyrene tray ..£500-750
	1964	.... 2nd issue:	as 1st issue but 503 'TK Giraffe Truck' replaces 426 Booking Office, inner polystyrene tray.............£400-600
23	1980-82	**Spiderman Set**	Contains 261 Spiderbuggy, 266 Spiderbike and 928 Spidercopter with figures, missiles on sprue. In striped 'window' box £150-200
24	1963-68	**Commer Constructor Set**	2 cab/chassis units, 4 interchangeable bodies, milkman, accessories. Yellow/Blue picture box with lift-off lid and inner polystyrene tray.............................£100-130
24	1976-78	**Mercedes and Caravan**	Contains 285 in Metallic Blue plus 490 Caravan in White. Striped 'window' box £40-50
	1979	.... colour change:	285 in Metallic Brown plus 490 Caravan in Bronze. Striped 'window' box.................£40-50
25	1963-66	**BP or Shell Garage Set**	224, 225, 229, 234 and 419 all in Blue/Yellow boxes plus: 601 Batley Garage, 602 'AA' and 'RAC' Boxes, 606 Lamp Standards (2), 608 Filling Station, 609 accessories, 1505 Figures. Plain card box with or without layout picture £1,000-1,250
25	1969-71	**Racing Car and Tender**	159 and VW Tender, 2 sets of decals in stapled bags. Blue/Yellow window box, inner plastic tray £120-140
25	1980-81	**Talbot Rancho Set**	457 plus two motorcycles on trailer £15-20
26	1971-76	**Beach Buggy Set**	381 plus Red Sailing Boat with Blue sail. Orange/Yellow 'window' box £40-50
26	1981-83	**Corgi Racing Set**	457 Talbot Matra Rancho, 160 Hesketh (Yellow), 'Corgi Racing Team' trailer......................£35-45
27	1963-72	**Priestman Shovel on Machinery Carrier**	1128 and 1131 (Bedford Machinery Carrier). Blue/Yellow box with inner tray............£225-275
27		**Emergency Set**	no details £15-20
28	1963-65	**Transporter and 4 Cars**	1105 Bedford TK Transporter with 222 Renault Floride, 230 Mercedes-Benz, 232 Fiat, 234 Ford Classic, 2 dummy 'Corgi Toys' boxes, instructions. Pictorial box, internal card packing........£400-500
28	1975-78	**Mazda B1600 Dinghy Set**	493 Mazda plus boat and trailer. Striped 'window' box £50-60
29	1963-65	**Massey-Ferguson Set**	Contains 50 Massey-Ferguson Tractor with driver and 51 Tipper Trailer - Cream/Yellow, Red plastic rear hubs. Yellow/Blue all-card box with inner tray £250-300
29	1981-82	**'CORGI' Pony Club**	Contains 441 Jeep, 112 trailer, girl on pony, 3 jumps, 3 hay bales. Striped 'window' box £55-65
29	1975-76	**'DUCKHAMS' FI Racing Set**	Surtees Racing Set with 323 Ferrari Daytona and 150 Ferrari in Blue/Yellow *'DUCKHAMS RACING TEAM'* livery. Striped 'window' box £50-75
30	1973-73	**Grand Prix Gift Set**	'Kit' versions of 151 Yardley (1501), 154 JPS (1504), 152 Surtees (1502) plus 153 Surtees (1503)? in unique Norris livery. Picture 'window' box. Mail order only £100-120
30	1979-80	**Circus Gift Set**	Land Rover and Trailer..£60-75
31	1964-68	**Buick Riviera Boat Set**	245 Buick, Red boat trailer, and Dolphin Cabin Cruiser towing lady water-skier. Pictorial sleeve box with internal packing display tray around models £125-150
31	1976-80	**Safari Land Rover Set**	C341 Land Rover with animal trailer, Warden and Lion. Box has inner polystyrene tray...................£55-65
32	1965-68	**Tractor, Shovel and Trailer Set**	Contains 54 Massey-Ferguson 65 Tractor with 69 Shovel and 62 Tipping Trailer with detachable raves - Red/Cream/Yellow. Yellow/Blue picture box with inner pictorial stand £200-250
32	1976-79	**Lotus Racing Set**	Black/Gold C301 Lotus Elite, and C154 JPS Lotus on trailer £80-100
32	1979-83	**Lotus Racing Set**	Black/Gold C301 Lotus Elite, and C154 Texaco Lotus on trailer £70-85
33	1965-68	**Tractor and Beast Carrier**	Contains 55 and 58 ....£100-125
	1968-72		Contains 67 and 58 ....£70-80
33	1980-82	**'DLRG' Rescue Set**	White/Red 421 Land Rover and boat on trailer £25-30
34	1976-79	**Tractor & Tipping Trailer**	Contains 55 and 56..£55-65
35	1964-68	**London Traffic Set**	418 Taxi with 468 *'Corgi Toys'* or *'Outspan'* Bus, policeman on stand. Yellow/Blue box, inner tray....£150-175
35	1978-79	**'CHOPPER SQUAD' Surf Boat**	Contains 927, 419, trailer, rescue boat...£30-40
36	1967-70	**Marlin Rambler Set**	Contains 263 and Boat..£45-55
36	1967-71	**Oldsmobile Toronado Set**	276 (Greenish-Blue), Chrome trailer, Yellow/Blue 'SWORDFISH' boat, 3 figures. Yellow/Blue box..£100-125
36	1983	**Off-Road Set**	447 (Dark Blue/Cream, racing number '5') plus power-boat on trailer £25-35
36	1976-78	**Tarzan Set**	Light Green 421 Land Rover and trailer, paler Green 'zebra' stripes, Tarzan, Jane, Cheetah (chimp), boy, dinghy with hunter, elephant, snake, vines, etc. Yellow/Blue 'window' box with inner pictorial backking display £250-350
37	1966-69	**'Lotus Racing Team'**	490 VW Breakdown Truck, Red trailer with cars 318, 319, 155, plus 2 sets of spare racing numbers ('5' and '9' or '4' and '8'), a 1966 illustrated checklist, a sealed pack of cones, set of bollards and a spare Lotus chassis unit. Yellow/Blue 'window' box has inner polystyrene tray.....£300-400
37	1979-80	**Fiat X-19 Set**	Fiat X-19 and Boat 'Carlsberg'..£30-40
38	1977-78	**Mini 1000 Camping Set**	Cream Mini with 2 figures, tent, barbecue in inner display stand £90-110
38	1965-67	**'1965 Monte Carlo Rally'**	318 Mini Cooper 'S', 322 Rover 2000, and 326 Citroën DS19. Monte Carlo Rally emblem on each bonnet. Yellow/Blue all-card box contains pictorial stand and inner card packing.....................£500-750
38	1980-	**Jaguar XJS Set**	319 with Powerboat on Trailer..£30-40
40	1966-69	**The Avengers Set**	John Steed's Bentley (Green body, Red wire wheels), Emma Peel's Lotus Elan (Black/White body), Steed and Emma Peel figures, 3 Black umbrellas. Yellow/Blue picture box with inner pictorial stand..£500-600
			As previous set but Bentley in Red/Black livery with Silver wire wheels.....................£400-500
40	1976-82	**Batman Gift Set**	Contains modified 107 Trailer plus 267 Batmobile (WhizzWheels) and 925 Helicopter. Striped box also contains 12 missiles on a sprue and has inner tray and card packing........................£350-450
41	1966-68	**Carrimore Car Transporter with Ford Tilt Cab**	1138 Transporter (Red/Two-tone Blue), 252 Rover 2000 (Metallic Plum), 251 Hillman Imp (Metallic Bronze), 440 Ford Cortina Estate (Metallic Blue), 204 Morris Mini-Minor (Light Blue), 321 Austin Mini Cooper 'S' (Red, RN '2', '1966 Monte Carlo Rally', with roof signatures), 249 Morris Mini Cooper 'S' (Black/Red, 'wickerwork' panels). Pictorial lift-off lid box with inner polystyrene tray. Only sold by mail order................£500-750

41	1977-81	Silver Jubilee Set	The State Landau with HRH Queen Elizabeth and Prince Phillip (and a Corgi!)	£15-20
42	1978-79	Agricultural Set	Contains 55 David Brown Tractor plus 56 Trailer, Silo and Elevator	£45-55
43	1979-80	Silo and Conveyor Set	Silo and Conveyor *CORGI HARVESTING COMPANY LTD*	£40-50
44	1978-80	Metropolitan Police Set	421 Land Rover, 112 Horsebox plus Policeman on horse. Striped 'window' box	£80-90
44	1978-80	Mounted Police Set	French issue with Policeman on horse	£75-100
45	1966	'All Winners' Set	261 James Bond's Aston-Martin, 310 Chevrolet Stingray, 324 Marcos Volvo, 325 Ford Mustang Competition, 314 Ferrari Berlinetta. 9,000 sets sold. Yellow/Blue 'window' box	£300-400
45	1978-79	Royal Canadian Police Set	RCMP Land Rover (421), Trailer (102) and 'Mountie' on horse	£85-95
46	1966-69	'All Winners' Set	264 Oldsmobile Toronado (Metallic Blue), 307 Jaguar 'E'-type (Chrome finish, RN '2', driver), 314 Ferrari Berlinetta (Red, RN '4'), 337 Chevrolet Stingray (Yellow, RN '13'), 327 MGB GT (Red/Black, suitcase). Box should contain unopened bag of cones and unused decal sheets	£225-275
46	1982	Super Karts Set	Two Karts: one Red, one Purple, with Silver/Red driver in each	NGPP
47	1966-71	Ford 5000 Tractor and Conveyor Set	Contains 67, trailer with conveyor belt, figure, accessories plus inner display card	£140-160
47	1978-80	Pony Club Set	421 Land Rover and Horsebox in Metallic Bronze, girl on pony figure	£25-30
48	1967-68	Carrimore Car Transporter with Ford Tilt Cab	1138 Transporter (Orange/Silver/Two-tone Blue) with 252 Rover 2000 (Metallic Maroon), 251 Hillman Imp, 440 Ford Cortina Estate, 180 Morris Mini Cooper 'S' (with 'wickerwork' panels), 204 Morris Mini-Minor (Metallic Maroon), 321 Mini Cooper 'S' ('1966 Monte Carlo Rally'), Red/White, RN '2'. Blue/Yellow 'window' box with inner polystyrene packing	£400-600
	1968	'SUN/RAC' variation	As previous set but 321 Mini Cooper is replaced by 333 SUN/RAC Rally Mini. Also 251 Hillman Imp is changed to Metallic Gold with White stripe and the 204 Mini Minor is now Metallic Blue with RN '21'	£500-700
48	1969	Carrimore Car Transporter with Scammell Cab	1148 Transporter (Red/White) with 378 MGB (Burnt Orange), 340 Sunbeam Imp (1967 Monte Carlo, Metallic Blue, RN '77'), 201 Saint's Volvo P1800 (White with Orange label), 180 Morris Mini Cooper 'S' (with 'wickerwork' panels), 339 Mini Cooper 'S' ('1967 Monte Carlo Rally', RN '177'), 204 Morris Mini-Minor (Metallic Maroon), plus sealed bag of cones and leaflet. Blue/Yellow 'window' box with inner polystyrene packing	£500-600
48	1978-80	'PINDER' Circus Set	Contains C426, C1163, C30, ringmaster, artistes, animals, seating, and cardboard cut-out 'Jean Richard Pinder' 'Big-Top' circus tent. Striped 'window' box	£100-125
49	1978-80	'CORGI FLYING CLUB'	Metallic Green/White Jeep (419) with Blue/White Tipsy Nipper Aircraft	£50-60
51		'100 Years of the Car' Set	3 Mercedes: C805 (White) C806 (Black) C811 (Red) (Originally for Germany)	£20-25
?	1978-80	'The Jaguar Collection'	C804 (Cream), C816 (Red), C318 (Mobil Green/White). ('UNIPART' stores)	£30-35
54	1978-80	Swiss Rega Set	Bonna Ambulance and Helicopter	£30-35
55	1978-80	Norway Emergency Set	Police Car, Breakdown Truck, Ford Transit Ambulance, 'UTRYKKNINGUSSETT'	£20-30
56	1978-80	Swedish Set	Ford Sierra 'POLIS', Bonna Ambulance	£12-18
57	1978-80	Swedish Set	Contains Volvo and Caravan	£12-18
57	1978-80	Volvo 740 and Caravan	Red Volvo, White/Red/Blue Caravan Swedish export set	£15-20
61	1978-80	Swiss 'FEUERWEHR' Set	1120 Dennis Fire Engine, Sierra 'POLITZEI', Escort Van 'NOTRUF'	£30-35
64	1965-69	FC Jeep 150 and Conveyor Belt	Jeep (409) Yellow/White Conveyor	£40-45
65	1978-80	Norway Set	Ford Transit Ambulance plus Helicopter	£20-30
67 /n	1978-80	Cyclists Sets	Sold in France, 2 Cars, 2 Bicycles. Three sets: 67/1, 67/2, 67/3	Each set: £20-30
70	1978-80	Danish 'FALCK' Set	Bonna Ambulance and Ford Breakdown Truck	£20-30
72	1978-80	Norway Set	Contains C542 plus Helicopter 'LN OSH'	£20-30
1151	1970	Scammell 'Co-op' Set	Contains 1147, 466 & 462 in Blue/White livery Promotional in brown box	£150-175
?	1967	Monte Carlo Game	Fernel Developments game with two Lavender 226 Minis, '1967 Rallye Monte Carlo' bonnet labels, RNs 1 and 4, plastic/paper winding roads, cards, dice shakers, Blue/White/Red box. Set made for the Scandinavian market	£250-350
?	1980	Construction Site Set	Contains 54 with 440 (Mazda Pick-Up)	£30-35

US EXPORT SETS. These were done exclusively for FAO Schwarz of America.

FAO-012

	c1966	'BEST IN SHOW' Animal Gift Set	Ccontains: GS2 Land-Rover with Rice's Pony Trailer, 484 Dodge Kew Fargo and 486 Chevrolet Impala 'Kennel Club'. Blue/Yellow individual card boxes, Blue/Yellow presentation box	£1,000-1,250

FAO-804

	c1968	'CIRCUS' Set	Contains: GS7 'Daktari' Set, 470 Forward Control Jeep, 1123 'Chipperfields' Circus Animal Cage and GS19 'Chipperfields Circus' Land-Rover and Elephant Cage on Trailer. Blue/Yellow individual boxes, Blue/Yellow presentation box	£1,500-1,750

469 Routemaster Bus (2nd casting) 'Mettoy Welcomes Swiss Buyers to Corgi Factory'

468 Routemaster Bus (1st casting) 'Naturally Corgi'

Photographs: Vectis Auctions Ltd.

Only models thought to have been 100% produced by Corgi have been included in the listings.

Identification of Routemaster Double-Decker Bus models

1ST CASTING, 1964 - 1975
MODEL No. 468 ONLY – CLOSED TOP MODEL

Length 114 mm, die-cast body comprised of two separate castings which make up the lower and upper decks. The castings are separated by a white plastic joint.

The baseplate is die-cast, painted grey and stamped 'Corgi Toys', 'LONDON TRANSPORT', 'ROUTEMASTER', 'MADE IN ENGLAND' plus the Patent No. 904525. The early issues had turned metal wheels with rubber tyres. These lasted until 1973 when cast metal wheels were introduced with plastic tyres and in 1974/75 WhizzWheels were seen.

Early issues also had jewelled headlights which were replaced in 1973 by the cast-in type painted silver. The decals are of the transfer printed variety and there is a board at the front only. The model has spring suspension, windows, a metal platform handrail and a driver and clippie. The interior seats are white or cream.

2ND CASTING, 1975 ONWARDS
CLOSED TOP AND OPEN TOP MODELS
MODEL Nos: C469, C470, C471'.

Length 123 mm, die-cast body comprised of two separate castings which make up the lower and upper decks. The castings are separated by a cream plastic joint for normal issues and very often by a coloured joint for 'Specials'. Until Model No. 480 was issued as an AEC Renown in 1983 the plastic baseplates were stamped 'CORGI', 'LONDON TRANSPORT', 'ROUTEMASTER' and 'MADE IN ENGLAND'. However 'LONDON TRANSPORT' and 'ROUTEMASTER' were removed from this time onwards.

The logos were originally stick-on labels followed by tampo printing in the mid-eighties. The seats were normally white or cream but other colours are used for the 'Specials' (eg. Red in the 'BRITISH DIE-CAST MODEL TOYS CATALOGUE' Special). The model has silver painted cast-in headlights, spring suspension, windows, a metal platform handrail but apart from the very early issues does not have a driver or clippie.

The wheels are of the WhizzWheel type. The early issues were of a close fitting type e.g. 'BTA', 'SWAN & EDGAR', 'DISNEYLAND'. However by the time the model was issued they had become protruding. The wheel hubs are either chrome (earlier models) or painted with plastic tyres.

Ref	Year(s)	Model name	Colours, fleetnames, details	Market Price Range

Routemaster Buses, 1964-1975, (1st casting)

Ref	Year(s)	Model name	Colours, fleetnames, details	Market Price Range
468	1964-66	'NATURALLY CORGI'	Red, London Transport, *CORGI CLASSICS*	£60-70
468	1964	'NATURALLY CORGI'	Green/Cream/Brown, (Australian) 'NEW SOUTH WALES', *CORGI CLASSICS*	£500-750
468	1966	'RED ROSE COFFEE'	Red body, driver and clippie, 1st type box, Canadian promotional	£300-400
468	1967	'OUTSPAN ORANGES'	Green/Cream/Brown body, Australian issue	£150-200
468	1967-75	'OUTSPAN ORANGES'	Red, London Transport, 10, (diecast or WhizzWheels)	£40-50
468	1968	'GAMAGES'	Red, London Transport, '10'	£150-175
468	1969	'CHURCH'S SHOES'	Red, London Transport, '10', Union Jacks	£110-130
468	1970	'MADAME TUSSAUDS'	Red, London Transport, '10'	£90-110
468	1975	'THE DESIGN CENTRE'	Red, London Transport, '10'	£50-60
468	?	'cokerchu', '2d'	Red, London Transport, promotional	£150-175

Routemaster Buses, 1975 – 1983, (2nd casting)

Ref	Year(s)	Model name	Colours, fleetnames, details	Market Price Range
C467	1977	'SELFRIDGES'	Red, London Transport, '12'. Box 1 – standard; Box 2 – 'SELFRIDGES' own	£20-25
C469	1975-76	'BTA WELCOME TO BRITAIN'	Red, London Transport, '11', driver, clippie	£15-20
C469	1976	'THE DESIGN CENTRE'	Red, London Transport, '11', driver, clippie, *Visit The Design Centre* in black or red	£110-130
C469	1977	'CADBURYS'	Orange, *Cadburys Double Decker*, on-pack offer, special box	£12-18
C469	1977	'METTOY'	Logo: 'Mettoy Welcomes Swiss Buyers to Swansea'	£250-275
C469	1979	'SELFRIDGES'	Red, London Transport, '12'. Re-issue of C467 (see above)	£20-25
C469	1979	'LEEDS PERMANENT BUILDING SOCIETY'	'LEEDS', '22'	£15-20
C469	1979	'SWAN & EDGAR'	Red, London Transport, '11'	£25-35
C469	1979	'HAMLEYS'	Red, London Transport, '11'	£15-20
C469	1980	'HAMLEYS'	Five clowns advert., '6'	£10-15
C469	1978-80	'BTA'	Red, London Transport, ('7', '11' or '12')	£10-15
C469	1982	'BLACKPOOL'	Cream/Green, 'Blackpool Illuminations', '21'	£30-40
C469	1983	'CORGI'	Logo: 'Corgi Collectors Visit'	£250-275
C469	1983	'GAMLEYS'	Red, *Toyshop Of The South*	£10-15
C469	1983	'EAGLE STAR'	White/Black, '1 Threadneedle Street'	£10-15
C469	1983	'REDGATES'	Cream/Brown (Red seats) '25'	£30-40
C469	1983	'L.T. GOLDEN JUBILEE'	Red/White/Silver, 21, *1933-1983*, (1,000)	£30-40
C469	1983	'BLACKPOOL PLEASURE BEACH'	Cream/Green, Blackpool Transport, '23', *Britain's No.1 Tourist Attraction*	£35-45
C469	1983	Open-top version:	As previous model but with open top	£50-55
C469	1983	'NORBROOK MOTORS'	Dark Blue (White seats) route '57'	£12-18
C469	1983	colour change:	As previous model but Red version	£12-18
C469	1983	'DION DION'	Dark Blue, *Saves You More* in Orange	£10-15
C469		South African issue:	has incorrect label *Saves You Money*	£15-20
C469	1983	'THORNTONS'	Brown/Cream, route '14'	£10-15
C469	1983	'MANCHESTER LIONS'	Cream, route '105BN Manchester'	£15-20
C469	1984	'NEW CORGI COMPANY'	Red, '29th March 1984', *South Wales - De Cymru*, (2,000)	£15-20
C469	?	'COBHAM BUS MUSEUM'	no details	£25-35
C470	1977	'DISNEYLAND'	Yellow Open Top, Disney characters.	£10-15
C471	1977	'SEE MORE LONDON'	Silver, '25', *The Queens Silver Jubilee London Celebrations 1977*	£10-15
C471	1977	'WOOLWORTHS'	Silver, '25', *Woolworths Welcome The World* & *Queens Silver Jubilee 1977*	£20-30
C523	1986	'BRITISH DIECAST'	Red, *British Diecast Model Toys Catalogue*	£10-15
C638	1989	'Great Book of CORGI'	Yellow/Blue, '1956-1983'. Originally only available with book	£25-35

Corgi Kits

601	1961-68	Batley 'LEOFRIC' Garage	£20-25
602	1961-66	'A.A.' and 'RAC' Telephone Boxes	£50-60
603	1961-66	Silverstone Pits	£30-40
604	1961-66	Silverstone Press Box	£50-60
605	1963-67	Silverstone Club House and Timekeepers Box	£60-70
606	1961-66	Lamp Standards (2)	£5-10
607	1963-67	Circus Elephant and Cage	£45-55
608	1963-66	'SHELL' Filling Station Building	£35-45
609	1963-66	'SHELL' Filling Station Forecourt Accessories	£25-35
610	1963-66	Metropolitan Police Box and Public Telephone Kiosk	£60-70
611	1963-66	Motel Chalet	£25-35

Spare wheels for 'Take-off Wheels' models; bubble-packed on card.

1341	1970	for **344 Ferrari Dino Sport**. Shown in 1969 catalogue but model issued with WhizzWheels	£10-15
1342	1968	for **300 Chevrolet Corvette**	£10-15
1351	1968	for **275 Rover 2000 TC**	£10-15
1352	1968	for **276 Oldsmobile Toronado**	£10-15
		for **338 Chevrolet Camaro**	£10-15
		for **343 Pontiac Firebird**. Shown in 1969 catalogue but model not issued with 'Take-off Wheels'	£10-15
1353	1970	for **342 Lamborghini P400**	£10-15
		for **302 Hillman Hunter Rally**	£10-15
1354	1970	for **273 Rolls Royce Silver Shadow**	£10-15
1361	1968	for **341 Mini Marcos GT 850**. (This was the first 'Take-Off Wheels' model)	£10-15

Corgi 'Cargoes'   Bubble-packed on card.

1485	1960	**Lorry Load - Planks**	£10-15
1486	1960	**Lorry Load - Bricks**	£10-15
1487	1960	**Lorry Load - Milk Churns**	£10-15
1488	1960	**Lorry Load - Cement**	£10-15
1490	1960	**Skip and 3 Churns**	£10-15

Figures

1501	1963-69	**Racing Drivers and Pit Mechanics** (6)	£10-15
1502	1963-69	**Silverstone Spectators** (6)	£10-15
1503	1963-69	**Race Track Officials** (6)	£10-15
1504	1963-69	**Press Officials** (6)	£10-15
1505	1963-69	**Garage Attendants** (6)	£10-15

Self-adhesive accessories

1460	1959	'A' Pack (66 items) including Tax Discs, Number Plates, 'GB' and 'Running-In' labels, etc	£10-15
1461	1959	'B' Pack (36 items) including White-wall tyre trim, 'Styla Sportsdiscs', Number Plates, etc	£10-15
1462	1959	'C' Pack (69 items) including Number Plates, Commercial & Road Fund Licences (A, B and C), 20 and 30mph Speed Limit and Trailer Plates, etc	£10-15
1463	1959	'D' Pack (100 items) including Number Plates, 'Corps Diplomatique' and 'L' Plates, Touring Pennants, etc	£10-15
1464	1961	'E' Pack (86 items) including Assorted Badges, Take-Off Wheels, Trade and Licence Plates, etc	£10-15

Spare tyre packs

1449	1970-71	New Standard 15 mm	£10-15
1450	1958-70	Standard 15 mm	£10-15
1451	1961-70	Utility Vehicles 17 mm	£10-15
1452	1961-70	Major Models 19 mm	£10-15
1453	1965-70	Mini Cars 13 mm	£10-15
1454	1967-70	Tractor wheels (Rear) 33 mm	£10-15
1455	1967-70	Tractor wheels (Front) 19 mm	£10-15
1456	1967-70	Racing wheels (Rear) 16 mm	£10-15
1457	1967-70	Racing wheels (Front) 14 mm	£10-15
1458	1967-70	Commercial (Large) 24 mm	£10-15
1459	1967-70	Commercial (Medium) 19 mm	£10-15

Miscellaneous

1401	1958-60	Service Ramp (operable)	£15-20
1445	1962	Spare Red bulb for 437 Ambulance	£2-3
1441	1963	Spare Blue bulb for 464 Police Van	£2-3
1443	1967	Red flashing bulb for 437 Ambulance	£2-3
1444	1967	Blue flashing bulb for 464 Police Van	£2-3
1445	1967	Spare bulb for 'TV' in 262 Lincoln	£2-3
1446	1970	Spare tyres for 1150 Snowplough	£2-3
1480	1959	Spare nose cone for Corporal Missile	£2-3
1497	1967	**James Bond Spares** (2 Bandits and lapel badge for 261)	£15-25
1498	1967	**James Bond Spares** (Pack of missiles for 336 Toyota)	£10-15
1499	1967	**Green Hornet Spares** (Pack of missiles and scanners for 268)	£10-15
?	1960s	**Corgi Club Badge**. Gold Corgi dog on Red background	£20-25
?	1962-64	**Corgi 'SHELL' Filling Station and Garage** in Bright Blue, Red and White, single floor, plastic 'SHELL' logo	£300-400
?	1962-64	**Corgi Garage** in Bright Blue, Yellow, Red and White, three floors, 'SKYPARK' and 'CENTRAL PARK GARAGE' logos	£300-400
?	1967	**Batmobile Accessory Pack** (sprue of missiles)	£25-35

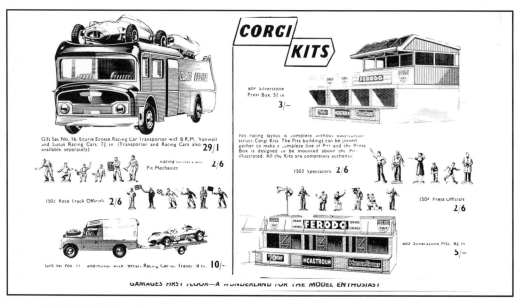

A page from an early 1960s Gamages catalogue illustrating some of the Corgi accessories that were available.

'Husky' models were introduced by Mettoy Playcraft in 1965 to compete with the Matchbox 1-75 range. These small-scale models have plenty of detail and action-features and the range includes cars, commercials, military and Film/TV specials.

The models have either a plastic or die-cast chassis together with various types of regular wheels and WhizzWheels. Models could only be obtained from 'Woolworths' stores and were only sold in blister packs. Production under the 'Husky' trade name ceased in 1969 and the range was reissued in 1970 as 'Corgi Juniors'. To facilitate this change, 'HUSKY' was removed from the baseplates which were then re-engraved 'CORGI JUNIORS'.

The models were mostly fitted with 'WhizzWheels' to enable them to be used on the 'Rocket Track' and to compete against the new Matchbox 'Superfast' range. Corgi Juniors were blister packed on blue/white card for the 'regular' issues and red/white card for the 'specials'. Each pack incorporated a 'Collectors Card' picture of the real vehicle and these could be cut out and pasted into a special collectors album.

The Market Price Range shown for 'Husky' and 'Corgi Juniors' refers only to mint condition models in unopened blister packs.

Ref	Year	Model name	Colours, features, details	Market Price Range

Husky models issued 1965-1969

Ref	Year	Model name	Colours, features, details	Market Price Range
1-a1	1965-66	Jaguar Mk.10 (small casting)	Metallic Blue, Yellow interior, Grey plastic wheels	£20-25
1-a2	1966	Jaguar Mk.10 (small casting)	Red, Yellow interior, Grey plastic wheels	£40-45
1-b1	1967	Jaguar Mk.10	Light Metallic Blue, Yellow interior, Grey plastic wheels	£20-25
1-b2	1967	Jaguar Mk.10	Blue, Yellow interior, Grey plastic wheels	£25-30
1-b3	1968	Jaguar Mk.10	Light Metallic Blue, Yellow interior, tyres	£25-30
1-b4	1968	Jaguar Mk.10	Cream, Yellow interior, tyres	£45-55
1-b5	1969	Jaguar Mk.10	Dark Blue, Yellow interior, tyres	£25-30
1-b6	1969	Jaguar Mk.10	Dark Maroon, Yellow interior, tyres	£30-35
2-a1	1965-66	Citroën Safari with Boat (small casting)	Pale Yellow, Tan boat, Grey plastic wheels	£20-25
2-b1	1967	Citroën Safari with Boat	Metallic Green, Brown boat, Yellow interior, Grey plastic wheels	£45-50
2-b2	1967	Citroën Safari with Boat	Metallic Gold, Blue boat, Yellow interior, Grey plastic wheels	£40-45
2-b3	1968-69	Citroën Safari with Boat	Metallic Gold, Blue boat, Yellow interior, tyres	£20-25
3-a1	1965-67	Mercedes 220	Pale Blue, Yellow interior, Grey plastic wheels	£15-20
3-bt	1967-68	Volkswagen Police Car	White/Black doors, smooth hubs with tyres	£25-30
3-b2	1969	Volkswagen Police Car	White/Black doors, detailed hubs with tyres	£25-30
4-a1	1965-66	Jaguar Fire Chief (small casting)	Red, chrome siren, 'Fire' labels on doors, Yellow interior, Grey plastic wheels	£25-30
4-b1	1967	Jaguar Fire Chief	Red, chrome siren, 'Fire' labels on doors, Yellow interior, Grey plastic wheels	£25-30
4-b2	1968-69	Jaguar Fire Chief	Red, chrome siren, 'Fire' labels on doors, Yellow interior, tyres	£30-35
5-a1	1965	Lancia Flaminia	Red, Yellow interior, Grey plastic wheels	£40-45
5-a2	1965-66	Lancia Flaminia	Blue, Yellow interior, Grey plastic wheels	£15-20
5-b1	1967-69	Willys Jeep	Metallic Green, Grey windshield, tyres	£15-20
5-b2	1967-69	Willys Jeep	Metallic Green, Yellow windshield, tyres	£25-30
6-a1	1965-67	Citroën Safari Ambulance	White, Red Cross, Blue warning lights, Grey plastic wheels	£20-25
6-b1	1968-69	Ferrari Berlinetta	Red, Red interior, chrome engine, tyres	£25-30
6-b2	1968-69	Ferrari Berlinetta	Maroon, Red interior, chrome engine, tyres	£25-30
7-a1	1965-66	Buick Electra	Orange-Red, Yellow interior, Grey plastic wheels	£15-20
7-b1	1967	Duple Vista 25 Coach	Green/White, tinted windows, Yellow interior, Grey plastic wheels	£20-25
7-b2	1968-69	Duple Vista 25 Coach	Green/White, tinted windows, Yellow interior, tyres	£20-25
8-a1	1965-66	Ford Thunderbird	Pink, Black open body, Yellow interior, Grey plastic wheels	£20-25
8-b1	1967	Ford Thunderbird Hardtop	Yellow, Blue detachable hard top, Yellow interior, Grey plastic wheels	£30-35
8-c1	1967-69	Tipping Farm Trailer	Yellow, Red back, tyres	£10-15
9-a1	1965-67	Buick Police Patrol	Dark Blue, Yellow interior, Red warning light, 'Police' on doors, Grey plastic wheels	£20-25
9-b1	1968-69	Cadillac Eldorado	Light Blue, Red interior, tyres	£20-25
10-a1	1965-67	Guy Warrior Coal Truck	Red, tinted windows, Grey plastic wheels	£15-20
10-a2	1968-69	Guy Warrior Coal Truck	Red, tinted windows, tyres	£20-25
11-a1	1965-67	Forward Control Land Rover	Green body (available in different shades), metal or plastic base, Brown removable tilt, rear corner windows, Grey plastic wheels	£15-20
11-a2	1968-69	Forward Control Land Rover	Metallic Green, Brown removable tilt, no rear corner windows, Grey plastic wheels	£15-20
12-a1	1965-66	Volkswagen Tower Wagon	Yellow, Red tower, Grey plastic wheels	£20-25
12-b1	1967	Ford Tower Wagon	Yellow, Red tower, Grey plastic wheels	£30-35
12-b2	1967	Ford Tower Wagon	White, Red tower, Grey plastic wheels	£15-20
12-b3	1968-69	Ford Tower Wagon	White, Red tower, tyres	£20-25
13-a1	1965-66	Guy Warrior Sand Truck	Yellow, tinted windows, Grey plastic wheels	£15-20
13-a2	1967-68	Guy Warrior Sand Truck	Blue, tinted windows, Grey plastic wheels	£15-20
13-a3	1969	Guy Warrior Sand Truck	Blue, tinted windows, tyres	£20-25
14-a1	1965-66	Guy Warrior Tanker (round tank)	Yellow, 'Shell' decals, Grey plastic wheels	£20-25
14-b1	1967	Guy Warrior Tanker (square tank)	Yellow, 'Shell' decals, Grey plastic wheels	£20-25
14-b2	1967	Guy Warrior Tanker (square tank)	White, 'Esso' decals, Grey plastic wheels	£20-25
14-b3	1968-69	Guy Warrior Tanker (square tank)	White, 'Esso' decals, tyres	£20-25
15-a1	1965-66	Volkswagen Pick Up	Turquoise, Brown removable canopy, Grey plastic wheels	£15-20
15-b1	1967-68	Studebaker Wagonaire TV Car	Yellow, tinted windows, Grey plastic wheels	£20-25
15-b2	1968	Studebaker Wagonaire TV Car	Metallic Blue, Blue tinted windows, Grey plastic wheels	£25-30
15-b3	1969	Studebaker Wagonaire TV Car	Metallic Blue, Blue tinted windows, tyres	£25-30
16-a1	1965-66	Dump Truck/Dozer	Yellow, Red back, chrome dozer, Grey plastic wheels	£15-20

16-a2	1966	**Dump Truck/Dozer**	Red, Grey back, chrome dozer, Grey plastic wheels	£20-25
17-a1	1965-66	**Guy Warrior Milk Tanker**	White, 'Milk' decals, round tank, Grey plastic wheels	£20-25
17-b1	1967	**Guy Warrior Milk Tanker**	White, 'Milk' decals, square tank, Grey plastic wheels	£20-25
17-b2	1968	**Guy Warrior Milk Tanker**	Cream, 'Milk' decals, round tank, Grey plastic wheels	£20-25
17-b3	1969	**Guy Warrior Milk Tanker**	Cream, 'Milk' decals, round tank, Grey plastic wheels	£20-25
18-a1	1965-66	**Plated Jaguar** (small casting)	Chrome, Yellow interior, Grey plastic wheels	£20-25
18-bi	1967-68	**Plated Jaguar**	Chrome, Yellow interior, Grey plastic wheels	£20-25
18-b2	1969	**Plated Jaguar**	Chrome, Yellow interior, tyres	£30-35
19-a1	1966	**Commer Walk Thro' Van**	Red, sliding Red door, Grey plastic wheels	£40-45
19-a2	1966-67	**Commer Walk Thro' Van**	Green, sliding Red door, Grey plastic wheels	£25-30
19-b1	1968-69	**Speedboat on Trailer**	Gold trailer, Red, White and Blue boat, tyres	£15-20
20-a1	1965-66	**Ford Thames Van**	Red, Yellow interior, Yellow ladder and aerial, Grey plastic wheels	£20-25
20-b1	1967	**Volkswagen 1300 with Luggage**	Tan, Yellow interior, tyres	£30-35
20-b2	1967-69	**Volkswagen 1300 with Luggage**	Blue, Yellow interior, tyres	£20-25
21-a1	1966-67	**Forward Control Military Land Rover**	Military Green, US 'star' decal on roof, Grey plastic windows	£15-20
21-b1	1968-69	**Jaguar 'E'-type 2+2**	Maroon, Yellow interior, tyres	£20-25
22-a1	1965-66	**Citroën Safari Military Ambulance**	Khaki, Red Cross on bonnet, Blue roof lights, Grey plastic wheels	£20-25
22-b1	1967-68	**Aston-Martin DB6**	Metallic Gold, Yellow interior, Grey plastic wheels	£25-30
22-b2	1968-69	**Aston-Martin DB6**	Purple, Yellow interior, tyres	£30-35
23-a1	1966-67	**Guy Army Tanker**	Khaki, US Army decals on tank, Grey plastic wheels	£15-20
23-b1	1968	**Loadmaster Shovel**	Orange, chrome shovel, Black plastic wheels	£25-30
23-b2	1968-69	**Loadmaster Shovel**	Yellow, chrome shovel, Black plastic wheels	£15-20
24-a1	1966-67	**Ford Zephyr Estate**	Blue, Yellow interior, Grey plastic wheels	£20-25
24-a2	1968-69	**Ford Zephyr Estate**	Red, Yellow interior, Grey plastic wheels	£25-30
25-a1	1966-67	**SD Refuse Van**	Light Blue, chrome back, Grey plastic wheels	£15-20
25-a2	1968	**SD Refuse Van**	Red, chrome back, Grey plastic wheels	£30-35
25-a3	1968-69	**SD Refuse Van**	Red, chrome back, tyres	£40-45
26-a1	1966-67	**Sunbeam Alpine**	Metallic Bronze, Blue removable hard top, Yellow interior, Grey plastic wheels	£25-30
26-a2	1967	**Sunbeam Alpine**	Red, Blue removable hard top, Yellow interior, Grey plastic wheels	£40-45
26-a3	1968-69	**Sunbeam Alpine**	Red, Blue removable hard top, Yellow interior, tyres	£50-55
27-a1	1966-67	**Bedford Skip Lorry**	Maroon, Grey plastic wheels	£20-25
27-a2	1967	**Bedford Skip Lorry**	Dark Green, Grey plastic wheels	£50-60
27-a3	1967	**Bedford Skip Lorry**	Orange, Grey plastic wheels	£20-25
27-a4	1968-69	**Bedford Skip Lorry**	Orange, tyres	£20-25
28-a1	1966-67	**Ford Breakdown Truck**	Blue, chrome hoist, metal jib, Grey plastic wheels	£15-20
28-a2	1968-69	**Ford Breakdown Truck**	Blue, chrome hoist, Gold jib, tyres	£20-25
29-a1	1966-67	**ERF Cement Mixer**	Yellow, Red barrel, metal chute, Grey plastic wheels	£15-20
29-a2	1968-69	**ERF Cement Mixer**	Yellow, Red barrel, metal chute, tyres	£20-25
30-a1	1966-67	**Studebaker Wagonaire Ambulance**	White, Red Cross decals, stretcher, Grey plastic Wheels	£25-30
30-a2	1968-69	**Studebaker Wagonaire Ambulance**	White, Red Cross decals, stretcher, tyres	£25-30
30-a3	1969	**Studebaker Wagonaire**	Pale Green, Green tinted windows, tyres	£35-40
31-a1	1966-67	**Oldsmobile Starfire Coupé**	Olive Green, Yellow interior, Grey plastic wheels	£15-20
31-a2	1968-69	**Oldsmobile Starfire Coupé**	Olive Green, Yellow interior, tyres	£20-25
32-a1	1966-67	**Volkswagen Luggage Elevator**	White, Yellow conveyor, Grey plastic wheels	£25-30
32-a2	1967	**Volkswagen Luggage Elevator**	White, Blue conveyor, Red belt, Grey plastic wheels	£30-35
32-a3	1968-69	**Volkswagen Luggage Elevator**	Red, Blue conveyor, Red belt, Grey plastic wheels	£35-40
33-a1	1967	**Farm Trailer and Calves**	Olive Green, tyres	£10-15
33-a2	1968-69	**Farm Trailer and Calves**	Turquoise, tyres	£10-15
34-a1	1967	**Tractor**	Red, Red exhaust, tyres	£20-25
34-a2	1968-69	**Tractor**	Red, Black exhaust, tyres	£20-25
35-a1	1967	**Ford Camper**	Yellow, chrome back, Grey plastic wheels	£20-25
35-a2	1967	**Ford Camper**	Metallic Blue, chrome back, Grey plastic wheels	£25-30
35-a3	1968-69	**Ford Camper**	Metallic Blue, chrome back, tyres	£25-30
36-a1	1967	**Simon Snorkel Fire Engine**	Red, chrome snorkel, Grey plastic wheels	£20-25
36-a2	1968-69	**Simon Snorkel Fire Engine**	Red, chrome snorkel, tyres	£20-25
37-a1	1968-69	**NSU RO80**	Metallic Blue, tyres	£25-30
38-a1	1968	**Rices Beaufort Single Horse Box**	Turquoise, tyres	£10-15
38-a2	1969	**Rices Beaufort Single Horse Box**	Metallic Green, tyres	£20-25
39-a1	1969	**Jaguar XJ6 4.2**	Yellow, Red interior, tyres	£45-55
40-a1	1969	**Ford Transit Caravan**	Red, Cream interior, White rear door, tyres	£25-35
40-a2	1969	**Ford Transit Caravan**	Lime green, Cream interior, White rear door, tyres	£25-35
41-a1	?	**Porsche Carrera 6**	Shown in catalogue but not issued	NPP
42-a	1969	**Euclid Truck**	Yellow body, Red dumper	£40-45
43-a	?	**Massey-Ferguson 3003**	no details	£40-45

Novelty, Film and TV-related models

See also following section and 'Corgi Rockets'.

1001-a1	1967	**James Bond Aston Martin DB6**	Silver, Red interior, 2 ejector figures, Grey plastic wheels	£180-200
1001-a2	1968-69	**James Bond Aston Martin DB6**	Silver, Red interior, 2 ejector figures, tyres	£180-200
1002-a1	1967-69	**Batmobile**	Black, Batman and Robin figures, tow hook, Grey plastic wheels	£150-160
1003-a1	1967-69	**Batboat**	Black boat, Red fin, Batman and Robin figures, Grey plastic wheels	£150-160
1004-a1	1968-69	**Monkeemobile**	Red, White roof, 4 figures, 'Monkees' on doors, tyres	£160-180
1005-a1	1968-69	**Man From UNCLE Car**	Blue, 3 Missiles on sprue, 2 figures, tyres	£160-175
1006-a1	1969	**Chitty Chitty Bang Bang**	Chrome, Dark Grey base, Red wings, Yellow fins, 4 figures, tyres	£120-140

Ref	Year	Model name	Colours, features, details	Market Price Range

Note: The models in this list were each accompanied by a colourful Picture Card, the lack of which could adversely affect the model's potential price.

Ref	Year	Model name	Colours, features, details	Market Price Range
1-a1	1970	Reliant TW9 Pick Up	Beige, Green tinted windows, removabte plastic front bumper, Black WhizzWheels	£20-25
1-a2	1970-72	Reliant TW9 Pick Up	Orange, Green tinted windows, removable plastic front bumper, Black WhizzWheels	£15-20
2-a1	1970	Citroën Safari with Boat	Blue, White boat, Yellow interior, tyres	£25-30
2-a2	1970	Citroën Safari with Boat	Blue, White boat, Yellow interior, Black WhizzWheels	£20-25
2-a3	1971-2	Citroën Safari with Boat	Yellow, White boat, Yellow interior, Black WhizzWheels	£15-20
2-a4	1971-2	Citroën Safari with Boat	Purple, White boat, Yellow interior, Black WhizzWheels	£15-20
3-a1	1970	Volkswagen 1300 Police Car	White, Black 'Police' sign on doors, Red interior, Blue light, tyres	£30-35
3-a2	1970	Volkswagen 1300 Police Car	White, Black 'Police' sign on doors, Red interior, Blue light, Black WhizzWheels	£20-25
3-a3	1971-72	Volkswagen 1300 Police Car	White, Black 'Police' sign on doors, Red interior, Blue light, chrome WhizzWheels	£20-25
3-a4	1971-72	Volkswagen 1300 Police Car	White, Black 'Police' sign on doors, Yellow interior, Blue tinted windows, chrome WhizzWheels	£15-20
4-a1	1970-72	Zeteor 5511 Tractor	Orange, Red base, Black chimney, Black plastic wheels	£10-15
5-a1	1970	Willys Jeep	Tan, Brown interior, Grey windshield, tyres	£15-20
5-a2	1970	Willys Jeep	Tan, Brown interior, Grey windshield, Black WhizzWheels	£10-15
5-a3	1971	Willys Jeep	Tan, Brown interior, Grey windshield, chrome WhizzWheels	£10-15
5-a4	1970	Willys Jeep	Orange, Brown interior, Grey windshield, Black WhizzWheels	£10-15
5-a5	1971	Willys Jeep	Orange, Brown interior, Grey windshield, chrome Whizzwheels	£10-15
5-a6	1971-72	Willys Jeep	Red, Yellow interior, Grey windshield, chrome WhizzWheels	£10-15
6-a1	1970	De Tomaso Mangusta	Lime Green, Green tinted windows, Black WhizzWheels	£10-15
6-a2	1970	De Tomaso Mangusta	Metallic Purple, Green tinted windows, Black WhizzWheels	£10-15
6-a3	1971-2	De Tomaso Mangusta	Metallic Purple, Green tinted windows, chrome WhizzWheels	£10-15
7-a1	1970	Duple Vista 25 Coach	Red, White, Yellow interior, Green tinted windows, tyres	£20-25
7-a2	1970	Duple Vista 25 Coach	Yellow, White, Yellow interior, Green tinted windows, Black WhizzWheels	£12-15
7-a3	1971-2	Duple Vista 25 Coach	Purple, White, Yellow interior, Green tinted windows, chrome WhizzWheels	£12-15
7-a4	1971-2	Duple Vista 25 Coach	Orange, White, Yellow interior, Green tinted windows, chrome WhizzWheels	£12-15
8-a1	1970	Tipping Farm Trailer	Blue, Orange back, tyres	£10-15
9-a1	1970	Cadillac Eldorado	Metallic Green, Red interior, Red tow hook, tyres	£25-30
9-a2	1970	Cadillac Eldorado	Metallic Green, Red interior, Red tow hook, Black WhizzWheels	£15-20
9-a3	1970	Cadillac Eldorado	White, Black bonnet, Red interior, Red tow hook, Black WhizzWheels	£15-20
9-a4	1971	Cadillac Eldorado	White, Black bonnet, Red interior, Red tow hook, chrome WhizzWheels	£15-20
9-b1	1971-72	Vigilant Range Rover	White, 'Police' decals on doors, Blue tinted windows, chrome WhizzWheels	£12-15
10-a1	1970	Guy Warrior Coal Truck	Orange, Green tinted windows, tyres	£15-20
10-b1	1971-2	Ford GT7O	Orange, Green tinted windows, Silver engine cover, chrome WhizzWheels	£10-12
11-af	1970	Austin Healey Sprite Le Mans	Red, Blue interior, Amber windows, Grey base, RN '50', sticker pack, Black WhizzWheels	£30-35
11-a2	1971	Austin Healey Sprite Le Mans	Red, Yellow interior, Amber windows, Grey base, RN '50', sticker pack, chrome WhizzWheels	£30-35
11-a3	1971-2	Austin Healey Sprite Le Mans	Red, Yellow interior, Amber windows, Black base, RN '50', sticker pack, chrome Whizzwheels	£30-35
12-a1	1970	Reliant-Ogle Scimitar GTE	White, Amber tinted windows, Yellow interior, Black WhizzWheels	£20-25
12-a2	1970	Reliant-Ogle Scimitar GTE	Metallic Blue, Amber tinted windows, Yellow interior, chrome WhizzWheels	£20-25
12-a3	1971-2	Reliant-Ogle Scimitar GTE	Matt Blue, Amber tinted windows, Yellow interior, chrome WhizzWheels	£20-25
13-a1	1970	Guy Warrior Sand Truck	Blue, Green tinted windows, tyres	£15-20
13-a2	1971-72	Guy Warrior Sand Truck	Red, Green tinted windows, chrome WhizzWheels	£12-15
14-a1	1970	Guy Warrior Tanker (square tank)	White, Green tinted windows, 'Esso' decals, tyres	£15-20
14-a2	1971-2	Guy Warrior Tanker (square tank)	White, Green tinted windows, 'Esso' decals, Black plastic base, chrome WhizzWheels	£12-15
15-a1	1970	Studebaker Wagonaire TV Car	Metallic Turquoise, Blue tinted windows, tyres	£35-40
15-a2	1970	Studebaker Wagonaire TV Car	Yellow, Blue tinted windows, Black WhizzWheels	£25-30
15-a3	1970	Studebaker Wagonaire TV Car	Metallic Lime Green, Blue tinted windows, Black WhizzWheels	£25-30
15-a4	1971-2	Studebaker Wagonaire TV Car	Metallic Lime Green, Blue tinted windows, chrome WhizzWheels	£25-30
16-a	1970-2	Land Rover Pick Up	Metallic Green, Orange tinted windows, chrome WhizzWheels	£10-12
17-af	1970	Volkswagen 1300 Beetle	Metallic Blue, Yellow interior, 'flower' decals	£45-50
17-a2	1970-72	Volkswagen 1300 Beetle	Metallic Green, Yellow interior, 'flower' decals	£20-25
18-a1			nothing issued	
19-a1	1970	Speedboat on Trailer	Blue trailer, Red,White and Blue boat, tyres	£15-20
19-a2	1970	Speedboat on Trailer	Blue trailer, Red,White and Blue boat, Black WhizzWheels	£10-15
19-a3	1971-2	Speedboat on Trailer	Blue trailer, Red,White and Blue boat, chrome WhizzWheels	£10-15
20-a1	1967	Volkswagen 1300 with Luggage	Mustard Yellow, Yellow interior, tyres	£25-30
20-a2	1967-69	Volkswagen 1300 with Luggage	Red, Yellow interior, Black WhizzWheels	£20-25
21-a1	1971-72	BVRT Vita-Min Mini Cooper S	Metallic Purple, chrome interior, Blue tinted windows, chrome WhizzWheels	£25-30
22-a1	1970	Aston-Martin DB6	Purple, Yellow interior, tyres	£45-50
22-a2	1970	Aston-Martin DB6	Metallic Olive, Yellow interior, tyres	£45-50
22-b1	1971-72	Formula 1 Grand Prix Racing Car	Yellow, Union Jack on front, White driver, chrome WhizzWheels	£12-15
23-a1	1970-2	Loadmaster Shovel	Yellow, chrome shovel, Black plastic wheels	£10-12
24-a1	1971-2	Aston-Martin DBS	Green, Black bonnet, Cream interior, chrome WhizzWheels	£20-25

25-a1	1970-72	**SD Refuse Van**	Orange, chrome back, Green tinted windows, tyres	£15-20
26-a1	1971-72	**ERF Fire Engine Water Tender**	Red, Green tinted windows and roof lights, Yellow ladder, chrome WhizzWheels	£12-15
27-a1	1970	**Bedford Skip Lorry**	Orange, Silver skip, tyres	£20-25
28-a1	1970	**Ford Breakdown Truck**	Blue, chrome hoist, Gold jib, Green tinted windows, tyres	£20-25
28-a2	1970	**Ford Breakdown Truck**	Blue, chrome hoist, Gold jib, Green tinted windows, Black WhizzWheels	£15-20
28-a3	1970	**Ford Breakdown Truck**	Turquoise, chrome hoist, Gold jib, Green tinted windows, Black WhizzWheels	£15-20
29-a1	1971-72	**Simon Snorkel Fire Engine**	Red, Yellow snorkel, Green tinted windows, chrome WhizzWheels	£12-15
30-a1	1970	**Studebaker Wagonaire Ambulance**	White, Red Cross decals, Blue windows, removable stretcher, tyres	£25-30
30-a2	1970	**Studebaker Wagonaire Ambulance**	White, Red Cross decals, Blue windows, removable stretcher, Black WhizzWheels	£20-25
30-a3	1970	**Studebaker Wagonaire Ambulance**	White, Red Cross decals, Blue windows, non-removable stretcher, Black WhizzWheels	£15-20
30-a4	1971	**Studebaker Wagonaire Ambulance**	White, Red Cross decals, Blue windows, non-removable stretcher, small chrome WhizzWheels	£15-20
30-a5	1971-72	**Studebaker Wagonaire Ambulance**	White, Red Cross decals, Blue windows, non-removable stretcher, chrome WhizzWheels	£15-20
31-a1	1970-71	**Land Rover Breakdown**	Purple, 'Wrecker Truck' labels, Gold hook, Amber windows	£12-15
31-a2	1972	**Land Rover Breakdown**	Red, 'Wrecker Truck' labels, Gold hook, Amber windows	£12-15
32-a1	1970-71	**Lotus Europa**	Metallic Green, Yellow interior and engine cover, chrome WhizzWheels	£15-20
32-a2	1972	**Lotus Europa**	Green, Yellow interior and engine cover, chrome WhizzWheels	£15-20
33-a1	1970	**Farm Trailer and Calves**	Orange, tyres	£10-15
33-b1	1970-72	**Jaguar 'E'-type Series 2**	Yellow, Red interior, chrome WhizzWheels	£12-15
34-a1	1970-72	**B.M. Volvo 400 Tractor**	Red, Yellow plastic Wheels, tyres	£15-20
35-a1	1970	**Ford Camper**	Turquoise, chrome back, Green tinted windows, tyres	£25-30
35-a2	1970-2	**Ford Camper**	Turquoise, chrome back, Green tinted windows, Black WhizzWheels	£25-30
35-a3	1970-2	**Ford Camper**	Red, Cream back, Green tinted windows, Black WhizzWheels	£20-25
36-a1	1970	**Simon Snorkel Fire Engine**	Red, chrome Snorkel, tyres	£20-25
37-a1	1970	**NSU RO80**	Metallic Blue, Silver interior, Green tinted windows, tyres	£25-30
37-a2	1970	**NSU RO80**	Metallic Mauve, Silver interior, Green tinted windows, Black WhizzWheels	£15-20
37-a3	1970	**NSU RO80**	Purple, Black bonnet, Silver interior, Green tinted windows, Black WhizzWheels	£15-20
37-a4	1971-2	**NSU RO80**	Purple, Black bonnet, Silver interior, Green tinted windows, chrome WhizzWheels	£15-20
37-a5	1971-2	**NSU RO80**	Metallic Copper, Black bonnet, Silver interior, Amber tinted windows, chrome WhizzWheels	£15-20
38-a1	1970	**Rices Beaufort Single Horse Box**	Metallic Green, horse, tyres	£15-20
38-a2	1970	**Rices Beaufort Single Horse Box**	Red, White horse, tyres	£15-20
38-a3	1970	**Rices Beaufort Single Horse Box**	Red, White horse, Black WhizzWheels	£10-15
38-a4	1971-72	**Rices Beaufort Single Horse Box**	Metallic Copper, White horse, chrome WhizzWheels	£10-15
39-a1	1970	**Jaguar XJ6 4.2**	Yellow, Red interior, tyres	£30-35
39-a2	1970	**Jaguar XJ6 4.2**	Silver, Red interior, Black Whizzwheels	£20-25
39-a3	1971-72	**Jaguar XJ6 4.2**	Silver, Red interior, chrome WhizzWheels	£20-25
39-a4	1971-72	**Jaguar XJ6 4.2**	Metallic Red, Yellow interior, chrome WhizzWheels	£20-25
39-a5	1971-72	**Jaguar XJ6 4.2**	Red, Yellow interior, chrome WhizzWheels	NGPP
4d-a1	1970	**Ford Transit Caravan**	Yellow, Blue interior, Silver rear door, tyres	£25-30
40-a2	1970	**Ford Transit Caravan**	Yellow, Cream interior, Silver rear door, Black WhizzWheels	£20-25
40-a3	1970	**Ford Transit Caravan**	Blue, Cream interior, Silver rear door, Black WhizzWheels	£20-25
40-a4	1971-72	**Ford Transit Caravan**	Blue, Cream interior, Silver rear door, chrome WhizzWheels	£20-25
40-a5	1971-72	**Ford Transit Caravan**	Metallic Pale Blue, Cream interior, Silver rear door, chrome WhizzWheels	£15-20
40-a6	1972	**Ford Transit Caravan**	Metallic Pale Blue, Cream interior, Silver rear door, Black plastic base, chrome WhizzWheels	£15-20
41-a1	1970	**Porsche Carrera 6**	White, clear canopy, RN '19', tyres	£20-25
41-a2	1970	**Porsche Carrera 6**	White, Blue tinted canopy, RN '19', Black WhizzWheels	£15-20
41-a3	1971-72	**Porsche Carrera 6**	White, Blue tinted canopy, RN '19', chrome WhizzWheels	£15-20
42-a1	1970	**Euclid Dumper**	Yellow cab, Red back, Dark Grey base, Black wheels	£15-20
42-a2	1970	**Euclid Dumper**	Red cab, Yellow back, unpainted Base, chrome WhizzWheels	£10-15
42-a3	1971-72	**Euclid Dumper**	Yellow cab, Red back, Dark Grey base, Black WhizzWheels	£10-15
42-a4	1971-72	**Euclid Dumper**	Blue cab, Silver back, Dark Grey base, chrome WhizzWheels	£10-15
42-a5	1971-72	**Euclid Dumper**	Blue Cab, Yellow back, Dark Grey base, chrome WhizzWheels	£10-15
43-a1	1970	**Massey Ferguson Tractor Shovel**	Yellow, Red interior, Black plastic wheels	£12-15
43-a2	1971-72	**Massey Ferguson Tractor Shovel**	Yellow, Red shovel and interior, Black plastic wheels	£10-15
44-a1	1970-72	**Raygo Rascal Road Roller**	Blue, Orange front, Grey roller, Grey seat and engine, Black plastic wheels	£10-12
45-a1	1970	**Mercedes 280SL**	Metallic Silver, Red interior, tyres	£30-35
45-a2	1970	**Mercedes 280SL**	Metallic Blue, Red interior, Black Whizzwheels	£20-25
45-a3	1970	**Mercedes 280SL**	Yellow, Red interior, unpainted base, Black Whizzwheels	£15-20
45-a4	1970	**Mercedes 280SL**	Yellow, Red interior, White base, Black Whizzwheels	£15-20
45-a5	1970	**Mercedes 280SL**	Red, Cream interior, Black WhizzWheels	£25-30
45-a6	1971-72	**Mercedes 280SL**	Red, Cream interior, chrome WhizzWheels	£25-30
45-a7	1971-72	**Mercedes 280SL**	Blue, Cream interior, unpainted base, chrome WhizzWheels	£20-25
46-a1	1970	**Jensen Interceptor**	Maroon, Yellow interior, Green tinted windows, unpainted base, tyres	£35-40
46-a2	1970	**Jensen Interceptor**	Maroon, Yellow interior, Green tinted windows, unpainted base, Black WhizzWheels	£25-30
46-a3	1971	**Jensen Interceptor**	Orange, Yellow interior, Green tinted windows, unpainted base, chrome WhizzWheels	£25-30
46-a4	1972	**Jensen Interceptor**	Metallic Green, Yellow interior, Green tinted windows, unpainted base, chrome WhizzWheels	£25-30
47-a1	1971-72	**Scammell Concrete Mixer**	White cab, Blue base, Red mixer, Amber windows, chrome WhizzWheels	£10-15

48-a1	1971-72	**ERF Tipper Truck**	Red cab, Silver back, unpainted base, Amber windows, chrome WhizzWheels	**£10-15**
48-a1	1971-72	**ERF Tipper Truck**	Blue cab, Orange back, unpainted base, Amber windows, chrome Whizzwheels	**£10-15**
48-a1	1971-72	**ERF Tipper Truck**	Blue cab, Orange back, Dark Grey base, Amber windows, chrome WhizzWheels	**£10-15**
48-a1	1971-72	**ERF Tipper Truck**	Blue cab, Yellow back, Dark Grey base, Amber windows, chrome WhizzWheels	**£10-15**
49-a1	1971-72	**Pininfarina Modulo**	Yellow, Red stripe, Red interior, chrome WhizzWheels	**£10-12**
50-a1	1971-72	**Ferrari 5l2s**	Metallic Red, Cream interior, unpainted base, chrome WhizzWheels	**£10-12**
51-a1	1971-72	**Porsche 917**	Gold, RN '23', chrome interior, Red base, chrome WhizzWheels	**£10-12**
52-a1	1971-72	**Adams Probe 16**	Metallic Pink,White interior, Green tinted windows, Black plastic base, chrome WhizzWheels	**£10-12**
54-a1	1971-72	**Ford Container Wagon**	Red, Yellow skip, Yellow plastic base, chrome WhizzWheels	**£10-12**
55-a1	1970-72	**Daimler Fleetline Bus**	Red, Yellow interior, 'Uniflo' adverts, chrome WhizzWheels	**£10-12**
56-a1	1970-72	**Ford Capri Fire Chief**	Red, White bonnet, 'Fire' decal on door, White interior, Blue windows, chrome WhizzWheels	**£25-30**
56-a2	1970-72	**Ford Capri Fire Chief**	As previous model but with 'Fire Chief' decal on door	**£25-30**
56-a3	1970-72	**Ford Capri Fire Chief**	All-Red, 'Fire Chief' decal on door, Yellow interior, Blue windows, chrome WhizzWheels	**£25-30**
57-a1	1970-72	**Caddy Hot Rodder**	Metallic Blue, Red interior, 'Caddy Hot Roddy' on doors, sticker pack, chrome WhizzWheels	**£12-15**
57-a2	1970-72	**Caddy Hot Rodder**	Metallic Pink, Red interior, 'Caddy Hot Roddy' on doors, sticker pack, chrome WhizzWheels	**£12-15**
58-a1	1971-72	**G.P. Beach Buggy**	Metallic Red, Cream interior, chrome WhizzWheels	**£10-12**
58-a2	1971-72	**G.P. Beach Buggy**	Metallic Red, Yellow interior, chrome WhizzWheels	**£10-12**
59-a1	1971-72	**The Futura**	Orange, Blue windows, 'Futura' on sides, Black base, sheet of stickers, chrome WhizzWheels	**£10-12**
60-a1	1971-72	**VW Double Trouble Hot Rod**	Metallic Pink, chrome interior, Green tinted windows, chrome WhizzWheels	**£12-15**
61-a1	1970-72	**Mercury Cougar Police Car**	White, Black roof, 'Sheriff', Yellow interior, Blue windows and lights, chrome WhizzWheels	**£12-15**
62-a1	1970	**Volvo P1800**	Red, Black bonnet, Yellow interior, chrome WhizzWheels	**£35-40**
62-a2	1971-72	**Volvo P1800**	Red, Black Bonnet, Blue interior, chrome WhizzWheels	**£25-30**
62-a3	1972	**Volvo P1800**	Red, Black Bonnet, Cream interior, chrome WhizzWheels	**£45-50**
63-a1	1970-72	**Ford Escort Monte Carlo Rally Car**	Metallic Blue, RN '32', Red interior, sheet of stickers, chrome WhizzWheels	**£35-40**
63-a2	1972	**Ford Escort Monte Carlo Rally Car**	Metallic Blue, RN '32', Yellow interior, sheet of stickers, chrome WhizzWheels	**£45-50**
63-a3	1972	**Ford Escort Monte Carlo Rally Car**	Metallic Blue, RN '32', Cream interior, , sheet of stickers, chrome WhizzWheels	**£45-50**
64-a1	1971-72	**Morgan Plus 8**	Yellow, Black interior, chrome WhizzWheels	**£20-25**
64-a2	1971-72	**Morgan Plus 8**	Red, RN '20' on doors, Black interior, chrome WhizzWheels	**£20-25**
65-a1	1971-72	**Bertone Carabo**	Metallic Purple, Pale Green base, White interior, Amber tinted windows, chrome WhizzWheels	**£12-15**
65-a2	1971-72	**Bertone Carabo**	Metallic Purple, Pale Green base, Orange interior, Amber tinted windows, chrome WhizzWheels	**£10-12**
67-a1	1971-72	**Ford Capri Hot Pants Dragster**	Yellow, 'Hot Pants' decal on roof, opening body, Red interior, chrome WhizzWheels	**£35-40**
70-a1	1971-72	**US Racing Buggy**	Blue, 'Stars and Stripes' on roof, White driver, chrome WhizzWheels	**£10-12**
71-a1	1971-72	**Marcos XP**	Orange, chrome interior, Amber tinted windows, chrome WhizzWheels	**£12-15**
72-a1	1971-72	**Mercedes-Benz C111**	Red, Amber tinted windows, chrome Interior, Black plastic base, chrome WhizzWheels	**£10-12**
73-a1	1971-72	**Pininfarina Alfa Romeo P33**	Blue, White interior and base, chrome WhizzWheels	**£10-12**
74-a1	1971-72	**Bertone Barchetta**	Orange, Red interior, White base, chrome WhizzWheels	**£10-12**
75-a1	1971-72	**Superstock Car**	Silver, Blue base, Union Jack on bonnet, Red interior, sticker pack, chrome WhizzWheels	**£20-25**
76-a1	1971-72	**Chevrolet Astro**	Metallic Red,Cream interior, chrome WhizzWheels	**£12-15**
77-a1	1971-72	**Bizzarrini Manta**	Pink, Cream interior, Black base, chrome WhizzWheels	**£10-12**
78-a1	1971-72	**Old MacDonalds Truck**	Red, Brown back, chrome WhizzWheels	**£25-30**
1017-a1	1971-72	**Holmes Wrecker & Towing Cradle**	Yellow cab, Red back, Amber glass, 'Auto Rescue' decals, Gold booms, Red cradle and hooks	**£100-120**

Novelty, Film and TV-related models   See also preceding section and 'Corgi Rockets'.

1001-a1	1970	**James Bond Aston-Martin DB6**	Silver, Red interior, 2 ejector figures, tyres	**£180-200**
1001-a2	1970	**James Bond Aston-Martin DB6**	Silver, Red interior, 2 ejector figures, Black WhizzWheels	**£160-180**
1001-a3	1971-72	**James Bond Aston-Martin DB6**	Silver, Red interior, 2 ejector figures, chrome WhizzWheels	**£160-180**
1002-a1	1970	**Batmobile**	Black, Batman and Robin figures, tow hook, Grey plastic wheels, 'Corgi Junior' label on base	**£150-160**
1002-a2	1970	**Batmobile**	Black, Batman and Robin figures, tow hook, Black WhizzWheels	**£150-160**
1002-a3	1971-72	**Batmobile**	Black, Batman and Robin figures, tow hook, chrome WhizzWheels	**£150-160**
1003-a1	1970	**Batboat**	Black boat, Red fin, Batman and Robin figures, GPW, 'Corgi Junior' label on base	**£140-150**
1003-a2	1970	**Batboat**	Black boat, Red fin, Batman and Robin figures, Black WhizzWheels	**£130-140**
1003-a3	1971-72	**Batboat**	Black boat, Red fin, Batman and Robin figures, chrome WhizzWheels	**£140-150**
1004-a1	1970	**Monkeemobile**	Red, White roof, 4 figures, 'Monkees' on doors, tyres, 'Corgi Junior' label on base	**£160-180**
1004-a2	1970	**Monkeemobile**	Red, White roof,4 figures, 'Monkees' on doors, tyres, 'Corgi Junior' base	**£160-180**
1004-a3	1971	**Monkeemobile**	Red, White roof, 4 figures, 'Monkees' on doors, tyres, Black WhizzWheels	**£150-160**
1005-a1	1970	**Man From UNCLE Car**	Blue, 3 missiles on sprue, 2 figures, tyres, 'Corgi Junior' label on base	**£160-175**
1006-a1	1970	**Chitty Chitty Bang Bang**	Chrome, Dark Grey base, Red wings, Yellow fins, 4 figures, tyres	**£130-140**
1006-a2	1971	**Chitty Chitty Bang Bang**	Chrome, Dark Grey base, Red wings, Yellow fins, 4 figures, Black WhizzWheels	**£120-130**
1007-a1	1971-72	**Ironsides Police Van**	Blue, 'San Francisco' logo, Ironside in back, chrome WhizzWheels	**£160-180**
1008-a1	1971-72	**Popeye's Paddle Wagon**	Yellow, Blue, Popeye with Olive and Sweet Pea, chrome WhizzWheels	**£120-130**
1010-a1	1972	**James Bond Volkswagen**	Orange, Green stripe / 'Corgi Toys' on roof, RN '5', Yellow interior, chrome WhizzWheels	**£750-1,000**
1011-a1	1971-72	**James Bond Bobsleigh**	Yellow, '007' decal, Grey plastic bumper, George Lazenby figure, Black WhizzWheels	**£500-750**
1012-a1	1971-72	**S.P.E.C.T.R.E. Bobsleigh**	Orange, 'Boars Head' decal, Grey plastic bumper, Blofleld figure, Black WhizzWheels	**£750-1,000**
1013-a1	1971-72	**Tom's Go Cart**	Yellow, Tom figure, chrome WhizzWheels	**£50-60**
1014-a1	1971-72	**Jerry's Banger**	Red, Jerry figure, chrome WhizzWheels	**£50-60**

Major Models

2001	1968-69	'HUSKY' Multi Garage............	A set of four garages (no cars), 'Husky' on base................................	£15-20
	1970-75	Corgi Juniors issue:	As previous model but with 'CORGI' logo, 'Juniors' on base................	£10-15
2002	1967-69	'HUSKY' Car Transporter	Hoynor MkII, White/Blue/Orange, detachable cab, 'Husky' on base.......	£30-40
	1970-72	Corgi Juniors issue:	As previous model but with 'CORGI' logo, 'Juniors' on base................	£25-35
2003a	1968-69	Machinery Low-Loader...........	Red/Blue/Yellow, detachable cab, drop-down ramp, 'Husky' on base	£25-35
2003b	1970-73	Corgi Juniors issue:	As previous model with metal wheels or WhizzWheels, 'Juniors' on base	£25-35
2004a	1968-69	Removals Delivery Van...........	Red or Blue cab, plated box, 'HUSKY REMOVALS', metal wheels, 'Husky' on base....	£45-55
2004b	1970-72	Corgi Juniors issue:	As previous model but 'CORGI REMOVALS', WhizzWheels, 'Juniors' base..	£20-30
2006	1970-79	Mack 'ESSO' Tanker	White body and tank, WhizzWheels, 'Juniors' on base	£10-15

Husky and Corgi Juniors Gift Sets 1968 - 1970

3001	1968-69	4 Garage Set............................	Contains 23, 27, 29, or 9, 30 or 36	£75-100
3002	1968-69	Batmobile Set...........................	1002 Batmobile and 1003 Batboat on trailer	£150-200
3002	1970	'Club Racing' Set	Juniors set of 8 racing cars inc Mini Cooper 'S' (Metallic Mauve), Ford Capri, Morgan, etc	£150-250
3003	1968-69	Car Transporter Set.................	2002 Husky Car Transporter plus 16, 26, 6-2, 21-2, 22-2, 26.............	£150-200
3004	1968-69	4 Garage Set............................	Contains 23-2, 29	£60-80
3004		James Bond 'OHMSS' Set	Contains 1004, 1001, 1011, 1012 plus un-numbered VW Beetle in Red with Black No'5' on White circle on sides. (From film 'On Her Majesty's Secret Service').......	£2000-2500
3005	1968-69	Holiday Time / Leisure Time ...	Contains 2-2, 5-2, 7-2, 15-2, 19-2, 20-2, 21-2, 35-1	£150-200
3006	1968-69	Service Station	Contains 14-c, 22-2, 28	£60-80
3007	1968-69	'HUSKY MULTIPARK'	In 1968 catalogue but not issued	NPP
3008	1968-69	Crime Busters Set....................	Contains 1001, 1002, 1003, 1005	£450-550
	1970	Corgi Juniors issue:	As previous set	£350-450
3011		Road Construction Set.............	Gift Set containing seven models..	£120-140

Husky Accessories

1561/2	1968-69	Traffic Signs........................	£20-30
1571	1968-69	Pedestrians	£10-15
1572	1968-69	Workmen.............................	£10-15
1573	1968-69	Garage Personnel	£10-15
1574	1968-69	Public Servants	£10-15
1580	1968-69	Husky Collector Case storage for 48 models............	£15-25

1585	1968-69	Husky Traveller Case opens to form Service Station (this item never seen)	NPP
2001	1968-69	'HUSKY' Multi Garage A set of four garages, (no cars) 'Husky' on base	£20-25
	1970-75	Corgi Juniors issue: As previous model but with 'CORGI' logo, 'Juniors' on base................	£10-15

Husky and Corgi Juniors Catalogues and listings

HUSKY CATALOGUES

Mettoy Playcraft (Sales) Ltd 1966	Leaflet (single fold)	Red, illustrating No.1 Jaguar Mk.10 on cover and Nos.1-29 inside. '1/9 each'	£20-25
same ref.	1966	Leaflet (Belgian issue).....	As previous leaflet but Nos.1-32 shown, printed in French....................................	£20-25
same ref.	1966	Booklet (10 pages)	Front/rear covers feature a row of garages and cars. Good pictures of 1002 Batmobile and 1001 James Bond's Aston-Martin, plus Nos.1-36	NGPP
no ref.	1967	Catalogue (24 pages)	Cover features boy with Husky vehicles and sets. Good pictures of all the rare models and Gift Sets plus accessories and models 1-41	£30-40

CORGI JUNIORS CATALOGUES

Mettoy Playcraft 1970	Catalogue (16 pages)	Blue cover with 10 models featured. Contains excellent pictures of all the rare early models including GS 3004 James Bond 'O.H.M.S.S.' Set etc.	£30-40

Qualitoys

A range of sturdy toys made up from the same basic parts. First issued in 1969 they were aimed at the pre school age group.

They were publicized as being from the 'makers of Corgi Toys' and did not form part of the Corgi range

as such. They have little collectable value at the present time.

Q701 **Pick Up Truck**..
Q702 **Side Tipper** ....
Q703 **Breakdown Truck**...

Q704 **Tower Wagon**...
Q705 **Horse Box** ....
Q706 **Giraffe Transporter** ....
Q707 **Fire Engine** ....
Q708 **Pick Up Trailer** ....

Corgi Juniors 1975 - 1983

Market Price Range - scarcer items as shown, otherwise under £15. These models are fitted with WhizzWheels.

E2	80-81	Blake's Seven Liberator...£75-100		
E3	77-81	Stromberg's Helicopter.....£25-35		
E6	79-80	'Daily Planet' Helicopter ...£15-20		
E11	79-85	Supermobile £20-30		
E17-2	79-81	Metropolis 'POLICE' Car..£25-35		
E19	80-82	Pink Panther Motorcycle...£15-20		
E20-2	79-81	Penguinmobile £20-30		
E21	77-80	Charlie's Angels Van £15-20		
E23	79-81	Batbike.............................£75-100		
E24	79-80	'SHAZAM' Thunderbolt...£40-50		
E25	79-80	'Capt. America' Porsche ...£40-50		
E32	70-74	The Saint's Jaguar XJS £65-85		
E33	79-80	'Wonderwoman's Car'.......£30-40		
E38	80-83	Jerry's Banger £15-20		
E40-2	79-81	J. Bond's Aston-Martin ...£75-125		
E41	79-81	J. Bond Space Shuttle £15-20		
E44-2	79-80	Starship Liberator.............£50-75		
E45	77-81	Starsky and Hutch Ford Gran Torino £15-20		
E49-2	81-83	Woody Woodpecker's Car £15-20		
E50	79-80	'Daily Planet' (Leyland) Van, Red or Silver £15-20		
E52-2	82-83	Scooby Doo's Vehicle £20-25		
E56	79-80	Chevrolet 'SPIDERVAN'..£20-25		
E57-2	79-80	Spiderbike £20-25		

E59-1	80-83	Tom's Cart £15-20
E60	77-79	James Bond Lotus Esprit 1: with side and rear wings ..£50-75 2: without wings; some have 'TURBO' side design.......£50-75
E64	80-82	'The Professionals' Ford Capri £15-20
E67-2	80-83	Popeye's Tugboat £15-20
E68	77-79	Kojak's Buick Regal..........£20-25
E69	76-80	Batmobile £50-75
E72-2	79-83	Jaguar XJS, Blue or Red .....NGPP Jaguar XJS, Red with White 'MOTOR SHOW' logo.......£20-30
E73	80	'DRAX' Helicopter.............£20-25
E75	77-80	Spidercopter £20-30
E78	76-81	Batcopter £30-40
E79-2	80-83	Olive Oyl's Aeroplane........£15-20
E80	79-80	'MARVEL COMICS' Van£20-25
E82-2	81-82	Yogi Bear's Jeep £20-30
E84-2	80-83	Bugs Bunny Vehicle £15-20
99	79-81	Jokermobile.......................£30-40
100	81-83	Hulk Cycle.........................£30-40
E115	81-83	James Bond 2cv Citroën £40-50
128	82-83	Fred's Flyer.......................£25-35
131	82-83	Ferrari 308GTS,

		'Magnum PI'....................£25-35
133	82-83	Buick Regal 'POLICE' Car, 'Magnum PI' £25-35
134	82-83	Barney's Buggy, Red/Orange, (The Flintstones') £25-35
E148	83-84	USS Enterprise £15-20
E149	83	Klingon Warship £15-20
E151	83	Wilma's Coupé £25-35
198	83	James Bond Citroën 2cv ...£25-35
E2009	?	James Bond 'Aerocar' ('The Man With the Golden Gun'). NB: Not a licensed product.........£200-300

GERMAN ISSUES:

E119	83	'FLUGHAFEN-FEURWEHR' Fire Engine £15-20
120	?	Leyland Van, 'Eiszeit'.......£15-20
120	83	Ice Cream Van, 'FRESHLICHE' £15-20
121	83	Chevrolet Van, 'TECHNISCHER'...........£15-20
126	82-83	Ford Transit Breakdown, 'ABSCHIEPPDIENST'....£15-20
127	82-83	'ADAC' Car £20-25

Corgi Juniors Sets

2601	Batman Triple-Pack...£175-225	
E2001	Multi Garage Complex. 4-garage complex (plastic)............£30-35	
E3001	Multi Garage and three cars...£45-55	
E3005	Leisure Time Set £100-125	
E3013	Emergency Rescue Set (Rescue Station + 3 models).........£70-85	
E3109	Agricultural Set. Contains: 2 Tractors, Land-Rover, 3 Trailers, 2 Huts £90-110	
3019/1	James Bond 'Octopussy' Set, 1983-84 ....£200-300	
E3021	Crimefighters Gift Set (E45, E60, E68, E69, E75, E78) .£200-300	
E3023	Mercedes Transporter plus 4 cars.................................£75-100	
E3024	Construction Gift Set (6 vehicles)..................................£75-100	
E3026	Emergency Gift Set (6 vehicles)....................................£75-100	
E3030	James Bond 'The Spy Who Loved Me' Gift Set, 1976-77 (E3, E60, 'Jaws' Van, Mercedes, Speedboat) £300-400	
E3040	Superman 'City of Metropil' Adventure Set £100-125	
E3071	'Growlers' 6-Car Speed Set. Ford GT70, Ferrari 312s, Marcos XP, CanAm Racer, Jaguar 'E'-type, Porsche 917..£100-150	

E3080	Batman Gift Set, 1980-82 (E20, E23, E69, E78, E99) £300-400
E3081	Superman Gift Set (E6, E11, E17, E47, E50) £125-150
E3082	James Bond 'Goldfinger' Gift Set, 1980-82, (E40, E41, E60, E73, plus 'Jaws' van).................£300-400
E3084	Cartoon Characters Set (E19, E38, E58, E67, E79) £100-125
E3100	Construction Gift Set (7 items) £75-100
E3101	Fire Gift Set (6 items)...£75-100
E3103	Emergency Gift Set (6 items) £75-100
E3105	Transporter Gift Set (Mercedes Transporter + 4 cars) £75-100
E3108	'Scoobie and His Friends' Set Contains 5 items...............£75-100
E3114	'Superheroes' Gift Set (Batman / Superman vehicles)......£100-125
E3116	'Crimefighters' Gift Set (Starsky & Hutch, James Bond and Buck Rogers vehicles)..........................£100-125
E3184	'Data Post' Set Contains 6 items.......................................£40-50

Corgi Super Juniors and Superhaulers

FORD D SERIES TRUCK (1970-75)

2002	Car Transporter, White cab, Blue lower, Red deck........£20-25 Red cab, White deck..........£40-50	
2003	Low Loader, Blue £20-25	
2004	'CORGI' Removals Van, Red cab, Silver trailer.......£40-50 Light Blue cab £40-50	
2007	Low Loader, Red cab, Blue trailer with Orange Junior digger load..............£25-35	
2012	Low Loader, Military Green with US vehicle ....NGPP	

FORD D SERIES SETS (1970-76)

3003	Car Transporter Set, White or Red cab, 5 Juniors........£40-50
3011	Low Loader Set, Red cab, plus 6 Juniors....................£50-60
3024	Low Loader Set, Blue cab, Yellow trailer (1976), 6 Juniors £50-60
3025	Car Transporter Set, Yellow cab, Orange deck (1976), 5 Juniors £30-35

MACK TRUCKS (issued 1971-75)

2006	'ESSO' Tanker, White £10-15
2010	'EXXON' Tanker, White ..£20-25
2011	'US' Army Tanker, Military Green body £20-25
2027	'RYDER RENTALS', Yellow cab + box trailer £10-15

MERCEDES TRACTOR UNITS, CAR TRANSPORTER (issued 1976)

2014/15	White cab and deck, Blue chassis £20-25
2015	White cab, Yellow deck, Red chassis £20-25
	N.B. Car Transporter Sets 3023, 3015, 3105 ....£30-35

MERCEDES TANKERS (1983-84)
Market Price Range - as shown otherwise **£10-15**. Liveries issued:

1130	'CORGI CHEMCO', Red or White cab ....
1130	'SHELL' Yellow or White cab ......
1166	'GUINNESS' ....
1167	'DUCKHAMS' ....
1167	'7 UP' £20-30

MERCEDES BOX TRAILERS (issued 1978-85)
Market Price Range as shown otherwise **£10-15**. Liveries issued:

1111	'SAFEWAY' £15-20
1129	'ASG SPEDITION' ....
1129	'CORGI' Black or White cab ....
1131	'CHRISTIAN SALVESON'.......
1137	'SOUKS SUPERMARKET' (Saudi issue) £25-30
1139	'HALLS FOOD' ....
1144	'ROYAL MAIL PARCELS' ....
1145	'YORKIE' ....
1146	'DUNLOP' ....
1166	'ARIA DAIRY' ....
1175	'INTERNATIONAL' £70-80
1175	'TI RALEIGH' ....
1176	'ZANUSSI' ....
1177	'WEETABIX' ....
1178	'MAYNARDS' ....
1202	'PICKFORDS HOMESPEED' £70-80
2028	'GERVALS DANONE' ....
2020	'BIRDS EYE' ....
---	'B. H. S.' £20-30
---	'CARTERS Lemonade'....£25-35

MERCEDES SETS

1200	'DUCKHAMS' & 'GUINNESS' Tanker plus 3 Scammells...£40-50
1403	'CORGI CHEMCO', plus Junior Van £25-30
3128	'DUCKHAMS' & 'YORKIE', plus 10 Juniors................£40-50

RECOMMENDED READING

'CORGI SUPER JUNIOR and SUPERHAULER GUIDE' provides full details plus pictures of all the variations compiled by Andy and Pat Browning, 3 Waterside Terrace, Ninn Lane, Great Chart, Ashford, Kent, TN23 3DD. Tel: (01233) 643461.

NB All the profits from this publication go to a children's charity.

Corgi Juniors Twin-Packs

Corgi Juniors bubble-packed in pairs from 1977 approximately.

2501	London Bus and Taxi	**£20-30**
2502	Land Rover Breakdown and Jaguar XJS	**£30-40**
2503	Land Rover and Horse Box	**£20-30**
2504	Land Rover Breakdown and AMC Pace Car	**£30-40**
2505	'DAILY PLANET' Van and Helicopter	**£20-30**
2506	Supermobile and Superman Van	**£50-60**
2507	Tom's Cart and Jerry's Banger	**£20-30**
2508	Popeye's Tugboat and Olive Oyl's Aeroplane	**£20-30**
2510	Formula 1 and Formula 5000 Racing Cars	**£30-40**
2511	Sting Helicopter and Scout Car	**£20-30**
2512	Space Shuttle and Star Ship 'Liberator'	**£40-50**
2513	Fire Tender and Ambulance	**£20-30**
2514	Building Set	**£25-35**
2515	Citroën and Speedboat	**£25-35**
2516	Tractor and Tipping Trailer	**£25-35**
2518	Mercedes and Caravan	**£25-35**
2519	Batmobile and Batboat	**£100-150**
2520	Rescue Set	**£30-40**
2521	James Bond Lotus and Aston-Martin DB5	**£70-80**
2522	Army Attack Set	**£30-40**
2523	Police Car and Helicopter	**£25-35**
2524	Custom Van Twin	**£25-35**
2525	Triumph TR7 and Dinghy on Trailer	**£40-50**
2526	Dumper Truck and Shovel Loader	**£25-35**
2527	'Kojak' and New York Police Helicopter	**£50-60**
2528	Starsky and Hutch Twin Pack	**£50-60**
2529	James Bond Lotus and Helicopter	**£80-100**
2530	Rescue Range Rover and Helicopter	**£30-40**
?	AMF 'Ski-daddler' Snowmobile and trailer	**£100-150**

Collectors notes

Corgi Rockets Stock Cars and Sports Cars (see page 75)

Corgi Rockets

This model range was issued between 1970 and 1972 to compete against Mattel 'Hot Wheels' and similar products. The models had 'WhizzWheels' and featured a special 'Tune-Up' system which increased the play value and speed of the virtually frictionless wheels. In addition they were very robust, being advertised as 'four times stronger' than most other diecast racers. To begin with seven Corgi Juniors were adapted as Rockets and five of those received a vacuum metallised finish. A range of accessories was also issued in the form of 'Speed Circuits' etc, and each car was provided with a special 'Golden Tune-Up Key' which released the base. The bubble-packed models are difficult to find in top condition and the prices reflect their scarcity.

Ref	Year	Model name	Colours, features, details	Market Price Range
D 901	1970-72	Aston-Martin DB-6	Metallic Deep Gold body, Green interior	£60-70
D 902	1970-72	Jaguar XJ-6	Metallic Green body, Cream interior	£80-100
D 903	1970-72	Mercedes-Benz 280 SL	Metallic Orange body, White interior	£60-70
D 904	1970-72	Porsche Carrera 6	Orange-Yellow body, Black number '19'	£60-70
D 905	1970-72	'The Saint's Volvo P1800	White body, Blue/White 'Saint' label on bonnet	£80-100
D 906	1970-72	Jensen Interceptor	Metallic Red body, Yellow interior	£60-70
			Pink / Cream body	£80-100
D 907	1970-72	Cadillac Eldorado	Metallic Copper body, White interior	£60-70
D 908	1970-72	Chevrolet Astro	Metallic Red/Black body	£40-50
D 909	1970-72	Mercedes-Benz C111	Red or Blue body, White interior	£40-50
D 910	1970-72	Beach Buggy	Orange body, Black interior	£30-40
D 911	1970-72	Marcos XP	Gold body, Chrome interior	£30-40
?	1970-72	Ford Capri	Purple body	£40-50
D 913	1970-72	Aston-Martin DBS	Metallic Blue, Yellow interior	£70-90
D 916	1970-72	Carabo Bertone	Metallic Green/Blue, Orange interior	£20-30
D 917	1970-72	Pininfarina Alfa-Romeo	Metallic Purple/White	£20-30
D 918	1970-72	Bitzzarini Manta	Metallic Dark Blue, White interior	£20-30
D 919	1970-72	'Todd Sweeney' Stock Car	Red/Purple, Yellow/Black front, RN '531'	£100-125
D 920	1970-72	'Derek Fiske' Stock Car	White/Red, Silver bonnet, Red logo, RN '304'	£100-125
D 921	1970-72	Morgan Open Sports	Metallic Red body, Black seats	£60-75
D 922	1970-72	Rally Ford Capri	Yellow body, Orange/Black stripe, RN '8'	£100-125
			Green body, Black bonnet, (GS 2 model)	£60-75
D 923	1970-72	'James Bond' Ford Escort	White body, Pale Blue stripes, racing number '7', 'JAMES BOND', White '007' and 'SPECIAL AGENT' logos (From film 'On Her Majesty's Secret Service')	£500-700
D 924	1970-72	Mercury Cougar XR7	Red body with Black roof, Yellow interior	£30-40
		'James Bond' issue:	Red/Black with Yellow side flash, interior and skis on roof rack (From film 'On Her Majesty's Secret Service')	£500-700
D 925	1970-72	'James Bond' Ford Capri	White body with Black/White check design, 2 bonnet stripes and RN '6' (From film 'On Her Majesty's Secret Service')	£500-700
D 926	1970-72	Jaguar 'Control Car'	Metallic Brown body, Red roof blade, Blue/White figures	£200-250
D 927	1970-72	Ford Escort Rally	White body, Red RN '18', 'DAILY MIRROR' labels on doors, '1970 Mexico World Cup Rally Winner'	£300-400
D 928	1970-72	Mercedes 280 SL 'SPECTRE'	Black body with Red 'SPECTRE' logo, plus boars head design	£300-400
D 930	1970-72	Bertone Barchetta	Metallic Green over White body, Red interior	£40-50
D 931	1970-72	'Old MacDonald's Truck'	Yellow cab, Brown rear, Silver engine	£100-125
D 933	1970-72	'Holmes Wrecker'	White or Blue cab, White back, 'AUTO RESCUE'	£100-125
D 937	1970-72	Mercury Cougar	Metallic Dark Green body, Yellow interior and spoiler	£20-30

Corgi Rockets Gift Sets

D 975	1970	Super Stock Gift Set 1	Contains D 905, D 919, Trailer and 3 figures	£250-350
D 976	1970	Super Stock Gift Set 2	Contains Green/Black D 922, D 920, Trailer and 3 figures	£250-350
D 977	1970	Super Stock Gift Set 3	Contains D 926, D 919, D 920 and 5 figures	£600-800

The listing above has been prepared from a Corgi Rockets 1970 catalogue. The sets themselves have not been seen and further information is required.

D 978		'OHMSS' Gift Set	Models of cars in the James Bond film 'On Her Majesty's Secret Service': D 923 and D 925 (as driven in the ice-racing scene), D 924 (as driven by 'Tracey'), D 928 (as driven by the Chief of 'SPECTRE')	£2,000-2,500

NB Male skier has red metal base, red/yellow skis and yellow poles.

Corgi Rockets Accessories

D 2051	1970	Action Speedset	One car, 'Autostart', 12 ft of track	NGPP
D 2052	1970	Super Autobatics Speedset	One car, 'Autostart', 16 ft of track plus 'leaps' etc	NGPP
D 2053	1970	Clover Leaf Special Speedset	One car, 'Autostart', track plus 'clover-leaf leaps' etc	NGPP
D 2058	1970	Race-Abatic Speedset	Two cars, 'Autostart', 2 x 16 ft of track plus 'leaps' etc	NGPP
D 2071	1970	Jetspeed Circuit	One car, 'Superbooster', 16 ft of track plus 'leaps' etc	NGPP
D 2074	1970	Triple-Leap Speed Circuit	One car, 19 ft, 6 in of track plus 'leaps' etc	NGPP
D 2075	1970	Grand Canyon Speed Circuit	One car, 12 ft of track	NGPP
D 2079	1970	World Champion Speedset	Two cars, 2 x 16 ft of track, 2 Boosters	NGPP

D 1928 **Rocketlube Tune-up Kit**	D 1936 **Space Leap**	D 1963 **Track** (16ft)	D 1977 **Lap Counter**
D 1931 **Superleap**	D 1937 **Autostart**	D 1970 **Super Booster**	D 1978 **Pitstop**
D 1934 **Autofinish**	D 1938 **Super Crossover**	D 1971 **Hairpin Tunnel**	D 1979 **Spacehanger Bend**
D 1935 **Connections** (3)	D 1945 **Adaptors** (3)	D 1976 **Quickfire Start**	

Corgi Rockets Catalogues

no ref	1969	8-page booklet	listing the first 7 issues, Green model on cover	£20-25
no ref	1970	16-page booklet	listing most issues, good pictures of rare models, sets and accessories	£30-35

Catalogues (UK Editions)

Information taken from the Cecil Gibson Archives and this Catalogue compiler's own collection of reference material.
Note: 'Concertina' leaflets were issued with models sold in the early Blue boxes.

Ref	Year	Publication	Cover features, details	Market Price Range
no ref	1956	Concertina leaflet	Blue cover, famous Corgi dog, shows first 14 models, no prices	£15-20
no ref	1956	Concertina leaflet	Blue cover with Red/Gold Corgi dog. Depicts first 14 models and shows prices of both normal and mechanical models	£20-25
50/157/K1	1957	Concertina leaflet	Blue cover with Red/Gold Corgi dog. Depicts ten models and lists the mechanical models in red	£5-10
40/257/K1	1957	Concertina leaflet	Blue cover with Red/Gold Corgi dog. Depicts ten models but does not list mechanical models	£5-10
40/257/K2	1957	Concertina leaflet	As previous leaflet but with the addition of 208	£5-10
50/557/K3	1957	Concertina leaflet	As 40/257/K2 plus 100,150, 408, 454, 'WOW! CORGI TOYS' logo	£5-10
100/1057/K3	1957	Concertina leaflet	Blue cover showing 100, 150, 207, 208, 302, 405, 408, 453, 455	£5-10
50/1057/K4	1958	Concertina leaflet	Blue cover, 'WOW! CORGI TOYS' logo. Listings include models 102, 406/7, and first 'MAJOR' toy (1101)	£15-20
50/1157/K4	1957	Concertina leaflet	Cover shows 102, 210, 406, 407, 412, 1101, 'WOW! CORGI TOYS' logo	£5-10
52/258/K5	1958	Concertina leaflet	Cover shows GS 1 and 2, 101, 211, 302, 457, 459, 1100, 1401, 1450.	£5-10
52/258/K6	1958	Concertina leaflet	As previous leaflet plus 350, 351	£5-10
300/658/K7	1958	Concertina leaflet	Shows GS 3, 151, 209, 458, 'NEW CORGI TOYS' logo and prices	£5-10
25/257/C1/UK	1957	Four-fold leaflet	'Blue box' 208 Jaguar on cover, 15 model pictures inside	£50-75
25/257/C2/UK	1957	Four-fold leaflet	As previous leaflet but with 24 model pictures	£50-75
50/1057/C3/UK	1957	Four-fold leaflet	Shows GS 1 Bedford Transporter and 6 cars on Blue/Yellow cover with details of 100, 150, 200-8, 210, 300-2, 403-8, 412, 452-5, 1101	£25-30
25/1157/C4/UK	1957	Four-fold leaflet	As previous leaflet plus 101 and 102	£25-30
no ref	1958	Four-fold leaflet	As previous leaflet plus 211 No prices, car listing or ref no	NGPP
650/858/C8	1958	Catalogue	First 'book' catalogue Cover depicts boy playing with Bloodhound Missile, many other vehicles	NGPP
no ref	1959	Four-fold leaflet	Blue cover with 'THE ROCKET AGE WITH CORGI TOYS' (issued with Rocket Age models)	£15-20
no ref	9/59	Interim leaflet	Lists 152, 50 Tractor, 350 Thunderbird, new TT van and accessories	NGPP
UK 9/59	1959	16 page Catalogue	Cover features Massey Ferguson Tractor No. 50 and BRM Racer No. 152. Agricultural and 'MAJOR' issues (No.1100 etc) are listed	£30-40
no ref	1959	Single page leaflet	Features Renault Floride plus 'STRAIGHT FROM THE MOTOR SHOW' logo	£10-15
no ref	1959	Two fold leaflet	Features 'AUTHENTIC ROCKET AGE MODELS' logo and models plus 1102 Tractor Dozer	£10-15
no ref	1960	Interim leaflet	Depicts M1 Motorway scene	£5-10
UK 9/60	1960	20 page Catalogue	Cover has motorway bridge scene and Corgi models. This catalogue was the first with listings of 'CHIPPERFIELDS' issues	£30-40
UK 9/61	1961	24 page Catalogue	Racetrack scene on cover. Listings and pictures include new Sports Cars, Express Coach and Kits	£20-25
no ref	1961	Price List	Single double-sided sheet (size as catalogue), 'Revised price list as from August 1961'. 'UK' on back	£1-2
no ref	1962	Two-fold Checklist	Leaflet front cover depicts Blue/Yellow 'CORGI TOYS' plus seven models and their features Red/Grey interior plus first check list	£15-20
C/100/62	1963	32 page Catalogue	Cover depicts schoolboy (in red cap and blazer) crossing road with Corgi dog. No catalogue date is shown on front cover	£50-75
no ref	1963	32 page Catalogue	Same cover as C/100/62 but boy's cap and blazer are Blue. '1963-64' is shown on front cover	£15-20
Playcraft Toys Ltd 1964	1964	Two-fold Checklist	Leaflet with Blue/Yellow 'Corgi Toys' design on cover featuring 241 Ghia	£15-20
Playcraft Toys Ltd 1964	1965	40 page Catalogue	Cover logos: 'CORGI TOYS', 'CORGI CLASSICS', '1965'. Contains Classics and first Routemaster in the listings	£15-20
Mettoy Playcraft (Sales) Ltd 1965	1965	Two-fold Checklist	Leaflet with six model cars from six different nations featured on the cover	£5-10
Playcraft Toys Ltd 1965	1966	40 page Catalogue	Cover depicts model 261 James Bond's Aston Martin DB5. Contents give details of special Rallye Monte Carlo issues. 'Price 3d'	£15-20
C2038/66	1966	Leaflet	Cover proudly states 'MODEL CAR MAKERS TO JAMES BOND'	£8-12
C2039/4/66	1966	Four-fold Checklist	Leaflet similar to previous with 'MODEL CAR MAKERS TO JAMES BOND'. The contents feature 1127 Simon Snorkel etc	£10-15
C2017/9/66	1967	48 page Catalogue	The cover and contents are dominated by Film and TV-related models of 'BATMAN' and 'THE AVENGERS' etc. Also contains details of a model never issued – 498 Mini Countryman	£15-20
Mettoy Playcraft (Sales) 1967	1967	Three-fold Checklist	Leaflet cover shows 'NEW' in 5 languages plus 1142 Holmes Wrecker. Listings include 1967 Monte Carlo Rally winners	£15-20
C/2017/7/67	67-68	48 page Catalogue	Model 262 Lincoln Continental makes up the covers. 'Price 6d'. 2 models shown but not issued: 9022 Daimler 38 with Hood, and 9014 Model 'T' Van 'Lyons Tea' (eventually issued as Corgi Classic C865 in Feb 1986)	£10-15
C2017/9/68	1968	48 page Catalogue	Cover features 268 'Chitty Chitty Bang Bang'. Listings include 803 'Yellow Submarine' and 'Take-off Wheels' issues	£15-20
Mettoy Playcraft (Sales) Ltd 1969	1969	Seven-fold Checklist	Leaflet has 'Concorde' model on cover plus 302 Hillman Hunter. Listings include 'Corgi Comics', 'CHIPPERFIELD' and Scammell Transporter Set No.48	£5-10
The Mettoy Co Ltd 1970	1970	48 page Catalogue	Cover depicts 388 Mercedes-Benz C111, first 'WhizzWheels' models listed	£5-10
no ref	1970	Corgi Juniors Collectors Album	28 pages. To hold cards cut from Corgi Junior bubble packs. Has details of featured models below space for card. Centre two pages have 'Corgi Toys' adverts plus articles, etc.	

1970 Mettoy Co Ltd ..1971	**Two-fold Checklist**	....Leaflet with 6 WhizzWheels models on the cover. The final 'Take-Off Wheels' issues are listed	**£5-10**
C2017 Petty			
7/71/LOI7b 1972	**48 page Catalogue**	.....Cover shows 1972 Car models. Excellent 'CORGI COMICS' pictures inside	**£5-10**
C2017 Petty			
7/71/LOI7B (2nd)......1972	**48 page Catalogue**	.....Cars across both covers	**£5-10**
no ref.........................1972	**'Corgi Juniors with**		
	WhizzWheels'	...........'© 1972 The Mettoy Company' on rear. 4 pages (A4). Includes 'Juniors Extra' section of TV models	**£5-10**
1973 Mettoy Co Ltd ..1973	**40 page Catalogue**	.....F1 Racing Cars featured on the cover. Good Racing/Rally pictures within	**£5-10**
1974 Mettoy Co Ltd ..1974	**40 page Catalogue**	.....'John Player' Lotus on cover, good Military and Aircraft pictures	**£5-10**
1975 Mettoy Co Ltd ..1975	**Three-fold leaflet**	......Helicopters, Noddy's Car, etc on the cover. Numbers given 'C' prefix	**£5-10**
1976 Mettoy Co Ltd ..1976	**Three-fold leaflet**	......First page features 'KOJAK'. Good Roadmaking and Public Services listings	**£5-10**
C2210 1977	**48 page Catalogue**	.....Silver Jubilee Coach on cover. Large section listing Corgi 'Juniors'	**£5-10**
The Mettoy Co Ltd 1978	**48 page Catalogue**	.....James Bond's Lotus on cover, 'JEAN RICHARD PINDER' models within	**£5-10**
C2250 1979	**48 page Catalogue**	.....James Bond's Space Shuttle C649 'MOONRAKER' is featured on the cover, and 'SUPERMAN' and 'THE MUPPETS' are listed inside	**£5-10**
C2270 1980	**48 page Catalogue**	.....Rover 3500 'POLICE' C339 and C1001 HCB ANGUS are the cover features. Good listings of Emergency vehicles includes foreign 'POLICE' issues	**£5-10**
C2285 1981	**32 page Catalogue**	.....'CORGI' container on cover. Listings feature Film/TV models	**£5-10**
C2337 1982	**32 page Catalogue**	....Cover features 'Gull-wing' Mercedes (C802), 'Corgitronics' within	**£5-10**
Mettoy Co PLC..........1983	**36 page Catalogue**	.....Boxed models on cover, new Mercedes and Scania trucks inside	**£5-10**
no ref.........................1984	**32 page Catalogue**	.....'CORGI '84' and boxed models on cover. Large scale '800' series cars listed. This was the last catalogue to display Corgi Dog emblem	**£3-5**
no ref.........................1985	**48 page Catalogue**	.....Cover shows new 'CORGI' trade name logo. The new 'CLASSICS' Commercials range is listed	**£3-5**

Trade Catalogues

Catalogues for trade purposes have been produced for some years and occasionally are offered for sale to collectors. No information is available on catalogues issued before 1980 but those from the 1980-90 decade tend to be in the **£5** to **£15** range.

An imaginative illustration features on the cover of this **1966 Corgi catalogue**.

Overseas Editions of Corgi Catalogues, Leaflets and Box Inserts

IDENTIFICATION of OVERSEAS CATALOGUES

The overseas editions are comprised of specially amended U.K. editions and there are many versions. They may be identified by:

- All the text being in the relevant language.
- A special reference number (but not always) e.g. 52/258/K5 AUSTRALIA.
- An adapted checklist/pricelist in the language/currency of the country concerned.
- The name of the country either on the cover, on page two, or on the checklist.
- Some complete catalogues were issued with all the text being in the language concerned, e.g. French, German, etc.
- Normally overseas editions, unlike U.K. editions, do not display the catalogue price on the cover. The exception to this rule being those issued with all the text in the language concerned.

As stated above, the overseas editions are basically the same as the U.K. editions. Similarly the catalogues, leaflets and box inserts issued in any one particular year were the same for all overseas countries. The only differences being the reference numbers, the type of language and currency shown.

The following listing of overseas editions correspond with the country by country listings and will assist collectors identify the various editions. The reference codes shown, e.g. '52/258/K5' are common to all countries with a country reference being added as required, e.g. '52/258/K5 EAST AFRICA'. The '258' part refers to the month and year of issue, i.e. Feb. 1958.

TYPES of CATALOGUES LISTED

Box Inserts - These were inserted in the early blue box issues circa 1957-1959. They have a single fold and contain a checklist with prices in the local currency, plus a few pictures of the latest models.

Catalogue Leaflets - These are large, full colour leaflets, usually listing the full range available, together with pictures plus a checklist with prices.

Catalogues - These may contain 16, 20, 32, 40 or 48 pages and are full colour booklets containing the complete current range.

Interim Leaflets - Usually a double folded leaflet issued to supplement the main catalogues. These contain six pages, plus a checklist of the latest issues.

The information contained in these listings has been obtained from Corgi archive material. Whilst many issues have been listed, we believe others exist and we would welcome any such information.

Overseas catalogues were produced in much smaller numbers than were the U.K. editions. Consequently as they seldom appear for sale, it is not possible to give their individual market prices. For guidance purposes however, some have been known to sell for prices in excess of £100. As a result the extremely rare issues such as British East Africa, West Africa, Malta, Hong Kong, etc. may be expected to attract a premium. In the circumstances all the editions have been categorised **NGPP**.

Leaflets, Box Inserts and Catalogues 1957 - 1982

1957 **Catalogue Leaflet '20/657/C2'**. Unfolded size (11" x 8 3/4"). Cover shows 1st type blue box for 208 Jaguar ....
1958 **Catalogue Leaflet '15/158/C4'**. Unfolded size (1' x 11"). 1101 Car Transporter on cover ....
1958 **Catalogue Leaflet '10/258/C5'**. Unfolded size (1' x 11"). 1101 Car Transporter on cover ....
1958 **Catalogue Leaflet '40/258/C5'**. Same as previous ....
1958 **Box Insert '52/258/K5'**. 1401 Corgi Service Ramp on cover ....
1958 **Box Insert '52/258/K6'**. 350 'Thunderbird' Guided Missile on cover ....
1958 **Box Insert '3.350/658/K7'**. 1401 Corgi Service Ramp on cover ....
1958 **Box Insert '5/658/K7'**. 458 E.R.F. Truck & 209 Police Car on cover ....
1958 **Box Insert '10/658/K7'**. Same cover as previous issue.......................
1958 **Box Insert '120/1058/K8'**. Same cover as previous issue...................
1958 **16 page Catalogue '40/1058/C8'**. Boy and large collection on cover ....
1959 **20 page Catalogue** (no ref.). Racing Car and Tractor design on cover ....
1960 **20 page Catalogue** (no ref.). Motorway picture on cover ....
1960/61 **Interim Leaflet** (no ref.). 1119 H.D.L. Hovercraft, etc. on cover ....
1961 **24 page Catalogue** (no ref.). Formula 1 Racing Cars on cover...............
1961/62 **Interim Leaflet** (no ref.). 231 Triumph Herald, etc. on cover ....
1962/63 **32 page Catalogue 'C/100/62'**. Red boy with Corgi dog on cover.......
1962/63 **Interim Leaflet** (no ref.). 224 Bentley + 304s Mercedes on cover ....
1963/64 **32 page Catalogue 'C/100/62'**. Red boy with Corgi dog on cover.......
1963/64 **40 page Catalogue** (no ref.). Blue boy with Corgi on cover ....
1964 **Interim Leaflet** (no ref.). 251 Hillman Imp, etc. on cover. 'Playcraft Toys Ltd. 1964' on checklist....................................
1964/65 **40 page Catalogue** (no ref.). 9001 1927 Bentley, etc. on front cover. 'Playcraft Toys Ltd. 1964' on rear cover ....

1965 **Interim Leaflet** (no ref.). 155 Lotus Climax Racing Car, etc. 'Mettoy playcraft (Sales) Ltd. 1965' on cover..
1965/66 **40 page Catalogue** (no ref.). 261 Aston Martin and with or without '1966' and 'Playcraft Toys Ltd. 1965' on cover ....
1966 **48 page Catalogue 'C2017/9/66'**. Batman, Avengers, 007 and Man from U.N.C.L.E. on cover ....
1967/68 **48 page Catalogue 'C2017/7/67'**. 262 Lincoln continental on front cover. 'Mettoy Playcraft (Sales) Ltd. 1967' rear cover..........
1967 **Interim Leaflet** (no ref.). 1142 'Holmes' Wrecker on cover...................
1969 **48 page Catalogue 'C2017/9/68'**. 266 Chitty Chitty Bang Bang on cover...
1969 **Catalogue Leaflet** (no ref.). Unfolded size 2'6" x 8 3/4". Concorde on front cover; 'Mettoy Playcraft (Sales) Ltd. 1969' on rear cover ....
1970 **48 page Catalogue** (no ref.). 388 Mercedes Benz C111 on cover ....
1973 **40 page Catalogue** (no ref.). 152 Ferrari 312 B2 Racing Car on cover......
1974 **40 page Catalogue 'C2107'**. 'Corgi '74' on cover................................
1974 **40 page Catalogue 'C2111'**. 'Corgi '74' on cover................................
1975 **Catalogue Leaflet** (no ref.). Unfolded. Size 2' x 8 1/2", 'Corgi 75' on cover...
1977 **48 page Catalogue 'C2211'**. 'Corgi 77' on cover ....
1977 **32 page Catalogue 'C2222'**. 'Corgi 77' on cover ....
1980/81 **48 page Catalogue 'C2275'**. Fire 'RESCUE' Vehicle plus '1980/81' on cover...
1980/81 **32 page Catalogue 'C2282'**. As previous, but no Juniors included.......
1980/81 **32 page Catalogue 'C2283'**. Same as previous ....
1981/82 **32 page Catalogue 'C2290'**. 'Corgi' Container on cover ....
1981/82 **32 page Catalogue 'C2292'**. 'Corgi' Container on cover ....

African issues

English text - local currency

BRITISH EAST AFRICA
1959 **16 page Catalogue '8/59'**. 'British East Africa 8/59' on cover, along with a tractor and racing car..
1960 **20 page Catalogue '9/60'**. 'British East Africa 9/60' on cover..........................
1962/63 **Interim Leaflet** (no ref.). 'British East Africa' on checklist ....
1961/62 **Interim Leaflet** (no ref.). 'British East Africa' on top of page two ....

EAST AFRICA
1958 **Box Insert '52/258/K5 East Africa'**. 'East Africa' on checklist.................
1965 **Interim Leaflet** (no ref.). 'East Africa' plus 'Mettoy 1965' on checklist ....
1964/65 **40 page Catalogue** (no ref.). 'East Africa 8/64' on checklist ....

KENYA, UGANDA & TANGANYIKA
1958 **Catalogue Leaflet '15/158/C3 KUT'**. 'Kenya, Uganda and Tanganyika'
1958 **Box Insert '3.350/658/K7/KEN.-UG.-TAN'**..

RHODESIA
Early Distributors: Coombe & Dewar Pty Ltd. P.O. Box 1572, Bulawayo and P.O. Box 663, Salisbury.
1961/2 **Interim Leaflet** (no ref.). 'Rhodesia' top of page two ....
1962/3 **Interim Leaflet** (no ref.). 'Rhodesia' on checklist ....
1962 **32 page Catalogue 'C/100/62'**. 'Rhodesia 1/63' on checklist. Red boy on cover ....
1964 **Interim Leaflet** (no ref.). 'Rhodesia' and 'Playcraft 1964' on checklist ....
1965 **Interim Leaflet** (no ref.). 'Rhodesia' and 'Mettoy 1965' on checklist ....

RHODESIA, ZAMBIA & MALAWI
1965/66 **40 page Catalogue** (no ref.).
'Rhodesia/Zambia/Malawi 8/65' on checklist, plus '1965' on cover...........

SOUTH AFRICA & RHODESIA
1958 **Box Insert '52/258/K5 South Africa/Rhodesia'**.
'South Africa/Rhodesia' on checklist...................
1958 **Box Insert '52/258/K6 South Africa/Rhodesia'**.
'South Africa/Rhodesia' on checklist.........................

SOUTH AFRICA
1958 **Box Insert '10/658/K7/S. Africa'**. 'S. Africa' on checklist page...................
1958/59 **16 page Catalogue '40/1058/C8/S. Africa'**. 'S. Africa' on back page.......
1961/62 **Interim Leaflet** (no ref.). 'South Africa on page two...................
1962/63 **Interim Leaflet** (no ref.). 'South Africa' on checklist.....................
1964 **Interim Leaflet** (no ref.). 'S. Africa' and
'Playcraft Toys Ltd. 1964' on checklist...................
1965 **Interim Leaflet** (no ref.). 'South Africa' and 'Mettoy 1965' on checklist.........
1966 **48 page Catalogue 'C/2017/9/66'**. 'South Africa' on checklist and cover.......
1967 **Interim Leaflet** (no ref.). 'South Africa' on cover, plus
'Mettoy, etc. 1967' on last page...................
1971 **2-fold checklist '© 1970 Mettoy Co Ltd'**. 'Corgi Toys with
WhizzWheels' plus 'Australia', 'S.Africa' and 'USA' on cover.
Checklist has prices in all three currencies...................
NB As listed under CANADA, a catalogue was issued in 1970 with a combined CANADA and SOUTH AFRICAN checklist.

Australia

Address of Corgi Club in 1959: The Secretary, Corgi Model Club (Australian Section), P.O. Box 1607, M. Melbourne C1.
1957 **Catalogue Leaflet '20/657/C2/AUS'**. Checklist dated 1.6.57.
Cover shows early 'Blue Box' with model 208...................
1958 **Box Insert '52/258/K5/Australia'**. Cover shows Model 350...................
1958 **Box Insert '52/258/K6/Australia'**. 1401 Corgi Service Ramp on cover...
1958 **Box Insert '10/658/K7/Aus'**. Cover shows Models 209 & 458...................
1959 **16 page Catalogue** (no ref.). Australia 8/59 on cover...................
1961/62 **Leaflet** (no ref.). 'Australia' on top of page two...................
1962/63 **Leaflet** (no ref.). 'Australia' on checklist...................
1967 **Leaflet** (no ref.). 'Australia' on cover...................
1971 **2-fold Checklist '© 1970 Mettoy Co Ltd'**. 'Corgi Toys with
WhizzWheels' plus 'Australia', 'S.Africa' and 'USA' on cover.
Checklist has prices in all three currencies...................

Austria

German Text. 'Kontrolliste fur den sammler'
1957 **Leaflet '20/657/C2/A'**. 'Austria' on checklist...................
1964 **Interim Leaflet** (no ref.). 'Austria' on checklist...................
1961/62 **Interim Leaflet** (no ref.). 'Austria' on top of page two...................
1964/65 **40 page Catalogue** (no ref.). 'Austria 9/64' on checklist...................
1965 **Interim Leaflet** (no ref.). 'Austria' on checklist...................

Belgium

Early distribution:
Joets Eisenmann, S.A., 111/113 Rui Masui, Bruxelles, Teleph: (02) 15.48.50.
1958 Belgian Corgi Club: M. Le Secretaire du Club Corgi, Jouets Eisenmann, 20 BD M. Lemonnier, Bruxelles.

English Text - (French Checklist). 'Liste de Contrôlle pour le Collectionneur'
1958 **Box Insert '52/258/K6/Belgium'**. 'Belgium' on checklist...................
1958 **Box Insert '5/658/K7/Belg.'**. 'Belg' on checklist...................
1967 **Leaflet** (no ref.). 'Belgium' on cover...................

English Text (Flemish Checklist). 'Kontroleer zo de Verzameling'
1966 **48 page Catalogue 'C/2017/9/66'**. 'Belgium' on cover and on checklist...
1967 **Leaflet** (no ref.). Belgium (Flemish) on cover...................

English Text (separate French and Flemish checklists)
1961/62 **Interim Leaflet** (no ref.). 'Belgium' on top of page two...................
1962/63 **Interim Leaflet** (no ref.). 'Belgium' on checklist...................
1963/64 **40 page Catalogue** (no ref.). 'Belgium 8/63' on checklist...................
1964 **Interim Leaflet** (no ref.). 'Belgium' and 'Playcraft 1964' on checklist...................
1965 **Interim Leaflet** (no ref.). 'Belgium' and 'Mettoy 1965' on checklist...................
1967 **Leaflet** (no ref.). 'Belgium' on cover...................
1967/68 **48 page Catalogue 'C/2017/7/67'**. 'Belgium (French) 1967' on
checklist...................
1967/68 **48 page Catalogue 'C2017/7/67'**. 'Belgium 8/67' on Flemish
checklist and 'Belgium (French) 8/67' on French checklist...................

1974 **40 page Catalogue** (no ref.). 'C2103 Belgium' on Flemish checklist
plus '2107' on French checklist...................

English Text (French/Flemish combined checklist)
1957 **Catalogue Leaflet '20/657/C2/B'**. 'Belgium' on checklist...................
1958 **Catalogue Leaflet '20/258/C5/B'**. 'Belgium' on checklist...................

French Text - French checklist
1958 **Box Insert '120/1058/K8/Belg'**. No. 458 E.R.F. on cover...................
1960 **20 page Catalogue** (no ref.). 'Belgium 9/60' and 'Frs.3.' - on cover...................
1961 **24 page Catalogue** (no ref.). 'Belgium 9/61' and 'Frs.3.' - on cover...................
1965/66 **40 page Catalogue** (no ref.). 'Belgium 8/65' on checklist...................

Canada

English text - local currency
1958 **Catalogue Leaflet '40/258/C5/CA'**. 'Canada' on checklist...................
1958 **Box Insert '52/258/K5/Canada'**. 'Canada' on checklist...................
1958 **Box Insert '52/258/K6/Canada'**. 'Canada' on checklist...................
1958 **Box Insert '5/658/K7/CAN'**. 'CAN' on checklist...................
1960 **20 page Catalogue 'Canada 9/60'**. 'Canada 9/60' on cover...................
1960/61 **Interim Leaflet 'Canada'**. 'Canada' on checklist...................
1961/62 **24 page Catalogue 'Canada 9/61'**. 'Canada 9/61' on cover...................
1961/62 **Interim Leaflet 'Canada'**. 'Canada' on checklist...................
1963 **32 page Catalogue 'C/100/62'**. 'Canada 1/63' on checklist...................
1964 **Interim Leaflet 'Canada'**.
'Canada' and 'Playcraft Toys Ltd. 1964' on checklist...................
1965 **Interim Leaflet 'Canada'**. 'Canada' and 'Mettoy etc. 1965' on checklist...................
1964/65 **40 page Catalogue 'Canada 9/64'**.
'Canada 9/64' on checklist plus '1965' on cover...................
1965/66 **40 page Catalogue 'Canada 8/65'**.
'Canada 8/65' on checklist plus '1966' on cover...................
1966 **48 page Catalogue 'C2017/9/60'**. 'Canada' on cover and checklist...................
1967 **Interim Leaflet 'Canada'**.
'Canada' on cover plus 'Mettoy 1967' on last page...................
1969 **7-fold Leaflet 'Canada'**. Concorde featured on cover; '8/69' on checklist.......

French Text Issue
1966 **48 page Catalogue 'C/2017/9/66'**. 'Canadian (French)' on cover...................

Combined Canadian and South African checklist
1970 **48 page Catalogue** (no ref.). 'Canada, South Africa' on checklist.
'The Mettoy Co. Ltd. 1970' on rear cover...................

Denmark

All the text in Danish
1960 **20 page Catalogue** (no ref.). 'Denmark 9/60' and '25 re' on cover...................
1961/62 **24 page Catalogue** (no ref.). 'Denmark 9/61' and '25 re' on cover...................
1977 **48 page Catalogue 'C2214'**. 'Katalog' and 'Corgi '77' on cover...................

English text - Danish checklist. 'Samlerers Kontrolliste'
1960/61 **Interim Leaflet** (no ref.). 'Denmark' on checklist...................
1961/62 **Interim Leaflet** (no ref.). 'Denmark' on page two...................
1963/64 **40 page Catalogue** (no ref.).
'Denmark 8/63' on checklist plus '1963-64' on cover...................
1964 **Interim Leaflet** (no ref.). 'Denmark' and 'Playcraft 1964' on checklist...................
1964/65 **40 page Catalogue** (no ref.).
'Denmark 9/64' on checklist plus 1965 on cover...................
1965/66 **40 page Catalogue** (no ref.).
'Denmark 8/65' on checklist plus 1966 on cover...................
1966 **48 page Catalogue 'C2017/9/66'**. 'Denmark' on cover and checklist...................
1974 **40 page Catalogue 'C2105 1974'**. Danish checklist + 'Corgi '74' on cover....
1980/81 **48 page Catalogue 'C2271'**. Danish checklist plus 1980/81 on cover...................
1981/82 **30 page Catalogue 'C2292'**. Danish checklist plus 1981-82 on cover.......

Eire

1958 **Box Insert '52/258/K6/EIRE'**. 'Eire' on checklist...................
1958 **Box Insert '5/658/K7/EIRE'**. 'Eire' on checklist...................
1960/61 **Interim Leaflet** (no ref.). 'Eire' on checklist...................
1962/63 **Interim Leaflet** (no ref.). 'Eire' on checklist...................
1964/65 **Interim Leaflet** (no ref.). 'Eire' plus 'Playcraft 1964' on checklist...................

Finland

English Text - local currency
1963/64 **40 page Catalogue** (no ref.).
'Finland 8/63' on checklist plus '1963-64' on cover...................
1965 **Interim Leaflet** (no ref.). 'Finland 6/65' and 'Mettoy 1965' on checklist.........

Corgi Toys Overseas Catalogues

France

English Text - French checklist
1961/62 **Interim Leaflet** (no ref.). 'France' on page two ....
1962/63 **Interim Leaflet** (no ref.). 'France' on checklist..
1963/64 **40 page Catalogue** (no ref.).
    'France 8/63' on checklist plus 1963-64 on cover..
1964/65 **Interim Leaflet** (no ref.). 'France' & 'Playcraft 1964' on checklist..............
1965 **Interim Leaflet** (no ref.). 'France' and 'Mettoy 1965' on checklist..............

French Text and checklist   'Liste de Controle pour le Collectioneur'.
1965 **40 page Catalogue** (no ref.).
    'France 8/65' on checklist plus 'Playcraft Toys Ltd. 1965' on rear cover .....
1968 **48 page Catalogue 'C2017/8/67'**. French text - 1968 on cover ....
1969 **48 page Catalogue 'C2017/9/68'**. French text - 1969 on cover ....
1973 **40 page Catalogue** (no ref.). French text - 1973 on cover..............................
1974 **40 page Catalogue 'C2107 1974'**. French text - 1974 on cover..............
1975 **Catalogue Leaflet** (no ref.). French text - 'Corgi '75' on cover ....
1977 **16 page Catalogue 'C2222'**. French text plus 'Corgi '77' on cover ....
1980/81 **48 page Catalogue 'C2275'**.
    French text plus 1980/81 on cover (includes Juniors) ....
1980/81 **32 page Catalogue 'C2282'**. French text plus 1980/81 on cover..............
1981/82 **32 page Catalogue 'C2290'**.
    French text plus '1981 Mettoy' on rear cover..

Holland / Netherlands

Agent for Holland: N.V.S/O, Herengracht 25, Amsterdam.

Dutch Text throughout
1959 **20 page Catalogue** (no ref.).
    'Holland 8/59' plus 'FL.O.10' on cover plus Dutch text ....
1961 **24 page Catalogue** (no ref.).
    'Holland 9/61' plus 'F.O.10' on cover plus Dutch text ....

French Text - Dutch checklist. 'Kontroleer zo de Verzameling'.
1980/81 **48 page Catalogue 'C2281'**.
    French text, Dutch checklist, plus '1980 Mettoy' on rear cover..............
1981/82 **30 page Catalogue 'C2291'**.
    French text, Dutch checklist, plus '1981 Mettoy' on rear cover..............

English Text with French and Dutch checklists
1974 **40 page Catalogue** (no ref.). 'C2107 1974' on French checklist.
    'C2103 1974' on Dutch checklist ....

English text - Dutch checklist
1957 **Catalogue Leaflet '20/657C2/NL'**. 'Holland' on checklist ....
1958 **Catalogue Leaflet '15/158/C4/H'**. 'Holland' on checklist..............
1958 **Box Insert '52/258/K5/HOLLAND'**. 'Holland' on checklist..............
1958 **Box Insert '52/258/K6/HOLLAND'**. 'Holland' on checklist..............
1958 **Box Insert '5/658/K7/HOL.'**. 'HOL' on checklist..............
1960/61 **Interim Leaflet** (no ref.). 'Holland' on checklist..............
1961/62 **Interim Leaflet** (no ref.). 'Holland' top of page two..............
1962/63 **Interim Leaflet** (no ref.). 'Holland' on checklist..............
1963/64 **40 page Catalogue** (no ref.). 'Holland 8/63' on checklist..............
1964 **Interim Leaflet** (no ref.). 'Holland' on checklist..............
1964/65 **40 page Catalogue** (no ref.). 'Holland 9/64' on checklist..............
1965 **Interim Leaflet** (no ref.). 'Holland' on checklist..............
1966 **48 page Catalogue 'C2017/9/66'**. 'Holland' on cover and checklist..............
1967 **Interim Leaflet** (no ref.). 'Holland' on cover..............
1967/68 **48 page Catalogue 'C2017/7/67'**. 'Holland 8/67' on checklist ....
1969 **48 page Catalogue 'C2017/9/68'**. 'Holland 10/68' on checklist..............
1974 **40 page Catalogue 'C2211 1974'**. Dutch text in checklist..............
1974 **40 page Catalogue** (no ref.).
    C2107 on French checklist plus C2103 on Dutch checklist..............

Hong Kong

1961 **Catalogue** (no ref.). 24 pages, 'Hong Kong 9/61' on cover..............
1961/62 **Interim Leaflet** (no ref.). 'Hong Kong' on page two ....
1963 **Catalogue 'C/100/62'**. 24 pages, 'Hong Kong 3/63' on checklist..............
1963 **Interim Leaflet** (no ref.). 'Hong Kong' on checklist..............
1964 **Interim Leaflet** (no ref.). 'Hong Kong' on checklist..............
1965/66 **40 pages** (no ref.). 'Hong Kong 8/65' on checklist..............
1966 **Catalogue 'C2017/9/66'**. 48 pages, 'Hong Kong' on cover and checklist ....

Italy

1963 Concessionairia per l'Italia: Ditta 'Guimar' via Disciplini 7, Milano (303). 'Distinta di Controllo per l'Collezzionisti'.
1958 **Box Insert '52/258/K5 ITALY'**. 'Italy' on checklist ....
1958 **Box Insert '52/258/K6 ITALY'**. 'Italy' on checklist ....
1958 **Box Insert '5/658/K7 ITALY'**. 'Italy' on checklist ....
1959 **Catalogue** (no ref.). 20 pages, 'Italy 8/59' on cover..............
1960/61 **Interim Leaflet** (no ref.). 'Italy' on checklist..............
1961 **Catalogue** (no ref.). 24 pages, 'Italy 9/61' on cover ....
1961/62 **Interim Leaflet** (no ref.). 'Italy' on page two ....
1962/63 **Interim Leaflet** (no ref.). 'Italy' on checklist..............
1963/64 **Catalogue** (no ref.). 40 pages, 'Italy 8/63' on checklist..............
1964 **Interim Leaflet** (no ref.). 'Italy' on checklist..............
1964/65 **Catalogue** (no ref.). 40 pages, 'Italy 9/64' on checklist..............
1965 **Interim Leaflet** (no ref.). 'Italy' on checklist..............
1967 **Interim Leaflet** (no ref.). 'Italy' on cover.
    'ATTENDETE OGNIMESE LE NOVITA 'CORGI'..............

1974 concessionaria per l'Italia:
Toyuro s.n.c., Via S. Vittore 45, Milano (20123).
1974 **Catalogue 'C2112 1974'**. 40 pages, 'Italia' reference on checklist..............
1980/81 **Catalogue 'C2278'**. 48 pages, Italian text throughout..............
1981/82 **Catalogue 'C2293'**. 32 pages, Italian text throughout..............

Japan

1973 **Catalogue** (no ref.). 40 pages, Japanese text throughout ....

Malta

1964 **Leaflet** (no ref.). 'Malta' on checklist ....
1964/65 **Catalogue** (no ref.). 40 pages, 'Malta 8/64' on checklist..............
1965 **Leaflet** (no ref.). 'Malta' in checklist ....

New Zealand

1964/65 **Catalogue** (no ref.). 40 pages, 'New Zealand 8/64' on checklist ....
1965 **Leaflet** (no ref.). 'New Zealand' on checklist..............
1965/66 **Catalogue** (no ref.). 40 pages, 'New Zealand 8/65' on checklist ....

Sweden

'Kontrollista för Samlaren'.
English text - Swedish checklist
1958 **Box Insert '52/258/K5/SWEDEN'**. 'Sweden' on checklist..............
1958 **Box Insert '52/258/K6/SWEDEN'**. 'Sweden' on checklist..............
1958 **Box Insert '5/658/K7/SWEDEN'**. 'Sweden' on checklist..............
1959 **Catalogue** (no ref.). 16 pages, 'Sweden 8/59' on cover..............
1960/61 **Leaflet** (no ref.). 'Sweden' on checklist..............
1961 **Catalogue** (no ref.). 24 pages, 'Sweden 9/61' on cover..............
1961/62 **Leaflet** (no ref.). 'Sweden' on page two..............
1962/63 **Leaflet** (no ref.). 'Sweden' on checklist..............
1963/64 **Catalogue** (no ref.). 40 pages, 'Sweden 8/63' on checklist..............
1964/65 **Catalogue** (no ref.). 40 pages, 'Sweden 9/64' on checklist..............
1965 **Leaflet** (no ref.). 'Sweden' on checklist..............
1966 **Catalogue** (no ref.). 40 pages, 'Sweden 6/65' on checklist..............
1966 **Catalogue 'C2017/9/66'**. 40 pages, 'Sweden' on cover and checklist..............
1967 **Leaflet** (no ref.). 'Sweden' on cover..............
1974 **Catalogue 'C2106 1974'**. 40 pages, Swedish text on checklist..............
1975 **Leaflet** (no ref.). Swedish text throughout..............
1980/81 **Catalogue 'C2277'**. 48 pages, Swedish text throughout..............

Swedish text - Norwegian checklist
1981/82 **Catalogue 'C2287'**. 32 pages, Swedish text with Norwegian checklist........

Switzerland

English Text - English/Swiss checklist
1957 **Catalogue Leaflet '20/657/C2/CH'**. 'Switzerland' on checklist ....
1958 **Box Insert '52/258/K5/Switzerland'**. Reference on checklist ....
1958 **Box Insert '52/258/K6/Switzerland'**. Reference on checklist ....
1958 **Box Insert '5/658/K7/SWITZ'**. Reference on checklist..............
1958 **Catalogue '25/1058/C8/SWITZ'**.
    16 pages, 'Switz' on checklist. New issues in French..............
1958 **Catalogue Leaflet '5/658/C5/CH'**. 'Switzerland' on checklist ....

1960/61 **Leaflet** (no ref.). 'Switzerland' on checklist ....
1961 **Catalogue** (no ref.). 24 pages, 'Switzerland 9/61' on cover ....
1961/62 **Leaflet** (no ref.). 'Switzerland' on page two ....
1962/63 **Catalogue** 'C100/62'. 32 pages, 'Switzerland 1/63' on checklist ....
1962/63 **Leaflet** (no ref.). 'Switzerland' on checklist ....
1964 **Leaflet** (no ref.). 'Switzerland' on checklist..
1964/65 **Catalogue** (no ref.). 40 pages, 'Switzerland' on checklist ....
1965 **Leaflet** (no ref.). 'Switzerland' on checklist..
1966 **Catalogue** (no ref.). 40 pages, 'Switzerland 8/65' on checklist.....................
1966 **Catalogue** 'C/2017/9/66'. 48 pages, 'Switzerland' on cover and checklist.......
1967 **Leaflet** (no ref.). 'Switzerland' on cover ....
1969 **Catalogue** 'C2017/9/68'. 48 pages, 'Switzerland 10/68' on checklist ....

United States of America

1958 Sole Distributor for U.S.A.: Reeves International Incorp., 1107 Broadway, New York 10, N.Y.
1958 **Catalogue Leaflet** '20/458/C5/U.S.A.'. 'U.S.A.' on checklist ....
1958 **Box Insert** '20/658/K7/U.S.A.'. 'U.S.A.' on checklist ....
1959 **Catalogue** 'USA 8/59'. 16 pages, pictures of tractor and racing car on cover...
1961 **Catalogue** 'USA 9/61'. 24 pages, U.S.A. 9/61' on cover ....
1961/62 **Leaflet**. 'U.S.A.' on page two ....
1962/63 **Catalogue** 'C/100/62'. 32 pages, Cover shows boy in red with
     corgi dog. 'U.S.A. 5/63' on checklist ....
1962/63 **Leaflet** 'USA 8/65'. 'U.S.A.' on checklist ....
1964 **2-fold Checklist** (no ref.). Ghia L 6.4 featured on cover.
     'USA' and '© Playcraft Toys 1964' ....
1964/65 **Catalogue** (no ref.). 40 pages, Green 9001 Bentley and
     Ghia L6.4 on cover. 'USA 8/64' on checklist ....
1965/66 **Catalogue** (no ref.). 40 pages, 'U.S.A. 8/65' on checklist.........................
1967 **Leaflet** (no ref.). 'U.S.A.' on cover ....
1968/69 **Catalogue** 'C2017/9/68'. 48 pages, Chitty-Chitty-Bang-Bang on cover.
     'USA 10/68' on checklist...
1971 **2-fold Checklist** '© 1970 Mettoy Co Ltd'. 'Corgi Toys with
     WhizzWheels' plus 'Australia', 'S.Africa' and 'USA' on cover.
     Checklist has prices in all three currencies ....

Norway

'Se dem alle 1 den nye Katalogen, Samlers Liste'.
English Text - Norwegian checklist
1961/62 **Leaflet** (no ref.). 'Norway' on page two..
1962/63 **Leaflet** (no ref.). 'Norway' on checklist ....
1964 **Leaflet** (no ref.). 'Norway' on checklist...
1964/65 **Catalogue** (no ref.). 40 pages, 'Norway 9/64' on checklist.......................
1965 **Leaflet** (no ref.). 'Norway' on checklist..
1966 **Catalogue** (no ref.). 40 pages, 'Norway 8/65' on checklist...........................
1966 **Catalogue** 'C2017/9/66'. 48 pages, 'Norway' on cover and checklist ....
1967/68 **Catalogue** 'C2017/7/67'. 48 pages, 'Norway 8/67' on checklist ....
1970 **Catalogue** (no ref.). 48 pages, 'Norway' on checklist ....
1974 **Catalogue** 'C2113'. 40 pages, Norwegian checklist ....
1980/81 **Catalogue** 'C2272'. 48 pages, Norwegian checklist ....
Norwegian text throughout
1975 **Catalogue Leaflet** (no ref.). Text plus '1975 Mettoy' ....

Portugal

'Lista de controle para o colecionador'.
English Text - Portuguese checklist.
1957 **Catalogue Leaflet** '25/257/C2/P'. 'Portugal' on checklist...............................
1960 **Leaflet** (no ref.). 'Portugal' on checklist ....
1961/62 **Leaflet** (no ref.). 'Portugal' on page two...
1962/63 **Leaflet** (no ref.). 'Portugal' on checklist ....
1963/64 **Catalogue** (no ref.). 40 pages, 'Portugal 8/63' on checklist ....
1964 **Leaflet** (no ref.). 'Portugal' on checklist ....
1967/68 **Catalogue** 'C2017/7/67'. 48 pages, 'Portugal 8/67' on checklist..................

Singapore and Malaya

1958 **Box Insert** '52/258/K5 SINGAPORE/MALAYA',
     'Singapore/Malaya' on checklist ....
1958 **Catalogue Leaflet** '10/258/C5/SM'. 'Singapore/Malaya' on checklist ....
1958 **Box Insert** '3.350/658/K7 SING.-MAL'. 'Sing.-Mal' on checklist.................
1960 **Catalogue** (no ref.). 20 pages, 'Singapore Malaya 9/60' on cover ....
1960 **Leaflet** (no ref.). 'Singapore/Malaya' on checklist ....
1961 **Catalogue** (no ref.). 24 pages, 'Singapore/Malaya 9/61' on checklist ....
1962/63 **Leaflet** (no ref.). 'Singapore/Malaya' on checklist ....
1962/63 **Catalogue** 'C/100/62'. 32 pages, 'Singapore/Malaya 2/63' on checklist......
1965 **Leaflet** (no ref.). 'Singapore/Malaya' on checklist ....

Spain

Spanish Text and checklist. 'Lista de Coleccionistas'.
1961 **Checklist**. 24 pages, 'Spanish 9/61' on cover ....

English Text - Spanish checklist "Lista de Precios para Coleccionistas"
1962 **Checklist** 'C/100/62'. 'Spanish' on checklist ....
1980/81 **Checklist** 'C2273'. Spanish text in checklist ....

International Issues 1981 - 1985

The catalogue listings are printed in English, French and German.
Catalogue 'C2293' was issued as a miniature booklet.

1965 Corgi Club addresses

Canada: ....Kleinberg Agencies 1085 St. Alexander St., Montreal'Can,
                    Quebec, Canada.
South Africa:.....PO Box 6024, Johannesburg,
U.S.A.: ....1107 Broadway, New York 10, N.Y.

Collectors notes

Shop display and 'point-of-sale' items

Ref	Year	Item	Details
no ref	1957-59	Display stand, wooden	Ten cream 'corrugated' hardboard shelves, pale blue display background with yellow/blue plastic 'CORGI TOYS' sign screwed to top of display, (30 x 29 x 12 inches).....................£150-175
no ref	1957-59	Display card/sign	Tin/cardboard, yellow/blue with gold 'dog' logo, 'Wow! Corgi Toys - The Ones With Windows'.....................................£75-100
no ref	1957-59	Display card/sign	As previous item but with 'new Corgi Major Toys - The Ones With Windows'........................£75-100
no ref	1957-59	Wooden display unit	Two shelf stand with Blue backing logo 'CORGI TOYS', 'THE ONES WITH WINDOWS', 'MODEL PERFECTION' and 'NEW' plus the early gold Corgi dog on red background £150-175
no ref	1957-59	Counter display unit	Cardboard, single model display card with Dark Blue inner display area, 'new - CORGI TOYS' logo.....£75-100
no ref	1957-59	Counter display unit	Cardboard, 2 tier unit with 'new - CORGI MAJOR TOYS' yellow/blue design...................£200-300
no ref	1957-59	Counter display unit	Cardboard, 2 tier unit, 'COLLECT CORGI TOYS' and 'new MODELS EVERY MONTH' logos in yellow/blue design.....................£200-300
no ref	1957-59	Counter display unit	Cardboard, Renault Floride (222) pictorial display card with '1959 MOTOR SHOW' and 'EARLS COURT' logos........................£200-300
no ref	1957-59	Counter display unit	Cardboard, Citroën (475) pictorial display card with 'new - THE CITROEN' and 'OLYMPIC WINTER SPORTS' logos.....................£200-300
no ref	c.1959	Display unit	Shows picture of Gift Set 8 'Combine Harvester Set'. 'At work in the field' logo £150-175
no ref	1957-67	Metal display stand	Tiered stand 75cm x 3.cm x 45cm high, three 'CORGI TOYS' and Black logos, plus three early gold Corgi dog emblems £175-200
no ref	c.1960	Window display sign	Yellow background with 'Naturally Corgi Toys' in Red and Blue, illuminated. 27" long x 8" high. (Possibly Belgian market)........................£500-700
no ref	1960-61	Window sticker	'NEW MODELS EVERY MONTH'.....................£15-20
C2034	mid 1960s	Metal display stand	Stand has 'Corgi Display C2034' on the back. No other details at present..................NGPP
no ref	1966-69	Window sticker	Window bills advertising new releases £15-20
no ref	1960-69	Oblong window sign	Glass or plastic with 'CORGI TOYS' and 'PRECISION DIE-CAST SCALE MODELS' logos plus gold Corgi 'dog' logo in blue/yellow/red design.....................£150-175
no ref	1960s	Tinplate stand	5 Grey tiers topped by 'CORGI TOYS'/Gold dog header £200-300
no ref.	1960-69	Glass display sign	Square sign, gold corgi dog on Red panel within Blue lined glass surround.....................£150-175
no ref	1961	Corgi Dog	Moulded dog standing on hind feet holding a 'CORGI CHRISTMAS CARD' £200-300
no ref	1968-83	Metal display stand	Tiered stand 75 cm x 3.5 cm c 45 cm high, with three 'CORGI TOYS' Black/Yellow logos, plus three White/Red late Corgi dog emblems £145-175
no ref	1971-73	Oblong sign	Plastic with 'CORGI' and 'TESTED BY THE CORGI TECHNOCRATS' logos plus white Corgi 'dog' logo on red square, yellow background plus 3 'Technocrats' faces £75-100
C2001/2	1963-65	Display stand, rotary	For self-selection, 7 tray unit, large 'CORGI TOYS' header sign £200-300
C2003	1963-65	Display stand, rotary	Self-selection, 4 columns, 4 compartments (45 x 30 in.), large 'CORGI TOYS' header boards.............£200-300
C2004	1963-65	Display stand, rotary	Self-selection, 4 column, 72 compartments (72 x 30 in.)........................£200-300
C2005	1963-65	Display stand, rotary	Self-selection, 2 column, 36 compartments (72 x 30 in.)........................£150-200
C2006	1963-65	Display stand, rotary	Self-selection, 2 column, 36 compartments (55 x 30 in.)........................£100-150
C2007	1963-65	Display stand, plastic	Large moulded plastic counter display to house up to 50 models, large black header display board with 'NATURALLY CORGI TOYS' on yellow/blue background, and 'JOIN THE CORGI MODEL CLUB' on display front £200-300
C2008	1960s	Display stand, revolving	Glass fronted large electric display to house 100-120 models with light and dark simulated wood panels with four 'CORGI' logos, (38 x 24 x 24 in.).....................£400-600
C2009	1957-66	Showcase, glass	Three glass shelves, three 'CORGI TOYS' logos (black/blue) plus gold Corgi 'dog' logo on red background, (20 x 15 x 9 in.) £200-300
E9051	1970s	Corgi Juniors unit	Yellow plastic (21.75 x 21.75 in.), displays 48 models, logo 'LOOK FOR WHIZZWHEELS MODELS'.....................£100-150
---	1975	Army diorama	Plastic unit for displaying tank models £140-160
---	1976	Kojak's Buick	Card counter-display unit £80-90
---	?	Window poster	Advertising new model 428 'MR SOFTEE' Ice Cream Van £60-80

NB The Editor would welcome any further information on Corgi display material.

Presentation and display material
for Corgi Toys retailers

Photo: Vectis Auctions Ltd.

Corgi Toys Numerical Index

Refer first to the Contents List (page 3) for quick guidance to main sections. Sets, for example, are not listed in this Index since that section is easily found and items in it are listed numerically. A quick check through this general (alphabetical) list may also prove helpful.

Ref.	Model	page	Ref.	Model	page	Ref.	Model	page	Ref.	Model	page
1a-1017a	Husky and Corgi Juniors	67	159	Cooper-Maserati	31	229	Chevrolet Corvair	33	C271	James Bond's Aston Martin	54
E1/2009	Corgi Juniors	73	C159	Indianapolis Car	31	230	Mercedes-Benz 220 SE	33	C272	James Bond's Citroën 2cv	54
C46	Super Kart	61	C160	Hesketh Racing Car	31	231	Triumph Herald	33	273	Rolls-Royce S. Shadow	35
50	Massey-Ferguson Tractor	53	161	Santa Pod 'Commuter'	31	232	Fiat 2100	33	274	Bentley 'T' Series	35
51	M-F Trailer	53	161	Elf-Tyrrell Project 34	31	233	Heinkel Trojan	33	275	Rover 2000 TC	35
C51	'100 Years Of The Car'	63	162	Quartermaster Dragster	31	234	Ford Classic	33	C275	Mini Metro	34
53	MF Tractor Shovel	53	C163	Santa Pod Dragster	31	235	Oldsmobile Super 88	33	C275	Royal Wedding Metro	34
54	MF Tractor Shovel	53	164	Ison 'Wild Honey'	31	236	Motor School Austin A60	33	276	Oldsmobile Toronado	35
54	Fordson Half-Track	53	165	Adams Brothers Dragster	31	237	Oldsmobile Sheriff Car	46	C276	Triumph Acclaim	54
55	Fordson Major Tractor	53	166	Ford Mustang	31	238	Jaguar Mk10	34	277	'Monkeemobile'	54
55	David Brown Tractor	53	C167	USA Racing Buggy	31	239	VW Karmann Ghia	34	C277	Triumph School Car	34
56	Four-Furrow Plough	53	C169	Starfighter Jet Dragster	31	240	Fiat 600 Jolly	34	C278	Dan Dare Car	54
56	Farm Tipper Trailer	53	C170	John Woolfe's Dragster	31	241	Chrysler Ghia L64	34	C279	Rolls-Royce Corniche	34
57	Massey-Ferguson Tractor	53	C171	Street Bike	42, 52	242	Fiat 600 Jolly	34	C279/3	Rolls-Royce	34
C57	Volvo and Caravan	63	C172	Police Bike	42	245	Buick Riviera	34	C280	Rolls-Royce Si. Shadow	34
58	Beast Carrier	53	C173	Cafe Racer	52	246	Chrysler Imperial	34	281	Rover 2000 TC	34
60	Fordson Power Major	53	190	Lotus 'John Player'	31	247	Mercedes-Benz Pullman	34	C281	Metro 'Datapost'	34
61	Four-Furrow Plough	53	191	McLaren 'Texaco Marlboro'	31	248	Chevrolet Impala	34	282	Mini-Cooper Rally	34
62	Tipper Trailer	53	200	Ford Consul	32	249	Morris Mini-Cooper	34	283	DAF 'City' Car	34
64	Conveyor on Jeep	53	201	'The Saint's Volvo	32	251	Hillman Imp	35	C284	Citroën SM	34
66	Massey Ferguson 165	53	201	Austin Cambridge	32	252	Rover 2000	35	C285	Mercedes-Benz 240 D	34
67	Ford Super Major	53	202	Morris Cowley	32	253	Mercedes-Benz 220 SE	35	C286	Jaguar XJC V-12	34
69	MF Tractor & Shovel	53	203	Vauxhall Velox	32	255	Motor School Austin A60	35	C287	Citroën Dyane	34
71	Fordson Disc Harrow	53	203	De Tomaso Mangusta	32	256	VW Safari Rally	35	C288	Minissima	34
72	Tractor and Towbar	53	204	Rover 90	32	258	The Saint's Volvo	54	289	VW Polo 'DBP'	34
73	MF Tractor & Saw	53	204	Morris Mini-Minor	32	259	Citroën 'Le Dandy'	35	C289	VW Polo	34
74	Tractor & Scoop	53	205	Riley Pathfinder	32	C259	Penguinmobile	54	C290	Kojak's Buick	54
100	Dropside Trailer	53	206	Hillman Husky	32	260	Renault R16 TS	35	C290	Bell Helicopter	59
101	Platform Trailer	53	207	Standard Vanguard III	32	260	Buick Police Car	49	291	AMC Pacer	34
102	Pony Trailer	53	208	Jaguar 24 litre	32	C260	Superman Police Car	54	C291	Mercedes 240 Rally	35
107	Batboat on Trailer	54	209	Riley Police Car	46	261	James Bond's Aston Martin	54	C292	'Starsky & Hutch'	54
109	Pennyburn Trailer	44	210	Citroën DS19	32	262	Lincoln Continental	35	293	Renault 'Medicins'	35
112	Horse Box	53	211	Studebaker Golden Hawk	32	C262	Capt. Marvel's Porsche	54	293	Renault 'Pompiers'	35
150	Vanwall	31	213	Jaguar Fire Service Car	46	263	Marlin Rambler	35	C294	Renault Alpine	35
150	Surtees TS9	31	214	Ford Thunderbird	32	C263	Capt.America Jetmobile	54	297	Ford Escort 'Police'	35
151	Lotus XI	31	215	Thunderbird Sports	32	264	Oldsmobile Toronado	35	298	Magnum PI Ferrari	54
C151	McLaren 'Yardley'	31	216	Austin A40	32	C264	Incredible Hulk Van	54	299	Ford Sierra 'Polis'	35
152	BRM Racing Car	31	217	Fiat 1800	32	C265	Supermobile	54	300	Austin-Healey 100-4	35
C152	Ferrari 312-B2	31	218	Aston Martin DB4	32	266	Chitty Bang Bang	54	300	Corvette Stingray	35
153	Bluebird Record Car	31	219	Plymouth Suburban	32	C266	Spider Bike	54	C300	Ferrari Daytona	35
153	Team Surtees	31	220	Chevrolet Impala	32	C267	Batmobile	54	301	Triumph TR2	35
154	Ferrari Formula 1	31	221	Chevrolet Cab	32	268	'Green Hornet'	54	301	Iso Grifo	35
C154	Lotus 'JPS'	31	222	Renault Floride	32	C268	Batman's Bat Bike	54	C301	Lotus Elite	35
C154	'Texaco Special'	31	223	Chevrolet 'Police'	46	269	James Bond's Lotus	54	302	MG 'MGA'	35
155	Lotus Climax	31	224	Bentley Continental	32	270	James Bond's Aston Martin	54	302	Hillman Hunter Rally	35
C155	Shadow F1 Racing Car	31	225	Austin 7 Saloon	32	271	Ghia De Tomaso Mangusta	32	C302	Volkswagen Polo	35
156	Cooper-Maserati	31	226	Morris Mini-Minor	32				303	Mercedes-Benz 300 SL	35
C156	Shadow F1 (G. Hill)	31	227	Mini-Cooper Rally	33				303	Roger Clark's Capri	35
158	Lotus Climax	31	228	Volvo P-1800	33				304	Mercedes-Benz 300 SL	35
C158	Tyrell-Ford 'Elf'	31								304	Chevrolet Camaro	35

Collectors notes

CORGI TOYS sold by Vectis Model Auctions,
Fleck Way, Thornaby, Stockton-on-Tees. TS17 9JZ

Condition abbreviations appearing in Vectis Auctions catalogues:
M = Mint, **NM** = Near Mint, **NMB** = Near Mint Boxed, **EP** = Excellent Plus,
E = Excellent, **EB** = Excellent Boxed, **GP** = Good Plus, **VG** = Very Good,
G = Good, **GB** = Good Box, **F** = Fair, **FB** = Fair Box, **P** = Poor.
Description abbreviations
WW = Whizzwheels, **RN** = Racing Number

CARS
151a Lotus Mk.Eleven Le Mans Racing Car, E in E box £90
204 Morris Mini Minor, orange, red interior, WW, NM in E box £1,160
204 Morris Mini Minor, in blue, lemon interior, WW, E in E box £100
200M Ford Consul, M in G box £140
201M Austin Cambridge, powder blue, E in G box £150
202M Morris Cowley, green, NM in G box £120
203M Vauxhall Velox, red NM in G box £100
204M Rover 90, green, E in E box £90
204 Rover 90, grey, NM in GP box £170
205M Riley Pathfinder, blue, E in G box £70
206M Hillman Husky, grey, NM in G box £170
207M Standard Vanguard, lemon-yellow, E in GP box £140
 Same in cream/red, NM in E box £130
208s Jaguar 2.4, lemon-yellow, E in E box £100
210 Citroen DS19, red, lemon interior, NM in E box £130
224 Bentley Continental, black/silver, M in NM box £110
225 Austin Seven, red, lemon interior, M in NM box £110
226 Morris Mini, maroon, NM in G box £90
236 Austin A60 School Car, blue, NM in GP box £80
238 Jaguar Mk.X, metallic green, NM in G box £100
249 Mini Cooper 'wickerwork' issue, NM in E box £90
300 Austin-Healey, red/cream, E, GP box £120
302 MGA Sports, red/cream, GP in G box £70
 Same model, cream body/seats, NM in GP box £130
317 Mini Cooper S 'Monte-Carlo Rally', RN '37', E in F box £80
318 Lotus Elan S2 ' Tiger in Tank', metallic blue, NM in G box £100
318 Lotus Elan S2, yellow, green stripe, NM in GP box £120
319 Lotus Elan Coupé, yellow/green, NM in E box £120
321 Mini Cooper S 'Monte-Carlo Rally', RN '52' NM in E box £170
322 Rover 2000, white/black, NM in G box £140
333 Mini Cooper S 'Sun Rally', NM in blue/yellow box with flash £210
339 Mini Cooper S 'Monte-Carlo Rally', RN '177', E in G box £140
510 Ciroën DS19 'Tour De France', NM in G box £120
681 Stunt Motorcycle, red/gold, NM in E box £100

COMMERCIAL VEHICLES
403 'Daily Express' Van, E in G box £90
403 'KLG Plugs' Van, E in GP box £100
406 Land Rover, blue/cream, M in GP box £160
408 Bedford 'AA' Van, early issue, E boxed £120
416 'RAC Radio Rescue' Land Rover, E in GP box £90
422 Bedford 'Corgi Toys' Van, yellow, blue roof, E in GP box £230
433 VW Van, white/red, NM in E box £110
447 Ford Thames Ice Cream Van, E in G box £140
454 Commer Platform Lorry, lemon yellow, NM in GP box £110
455 Karrier Bantam Van, blue/red, NM in GP box £120
457 ERF Platform Lorry, TT blue, NM in G box £100
462 Commer Van 'Hammonds', E in E box £120
1100 Bedford Carrimore Low Loader, red/blue, NM in G box £120
1103 Euclid Crawler Tractor, green, NM in GP box £180
1110 Bedford 'S' Type 'Mobilgas' Tanker, E in G box £150
1126 Ecurie Ecosse Transporter, E in F box £140
1129 Bedford 'S' Type 'Milk' Tanker, E in G box £160
1140 Bedford 'TK' 'Mobilgas' Tanker, E in G box £130

BUSES
468 Routemaster Bus 'Red Rose Coffee', MB £400
 Same model 'Red Rose Tea', issue £340
468 Routemaster Bus 'Corgi Classics', MB £500
468 Routemaster Bus 'Corgi Classics' & 'Outspan' logos, M, GP box ..£120
468 Routemaster Bus 'Cokerchu', E boxed £160
C469 Routemaster Bus 'Mettoy Welcomes Swiss Buyers' £260
C469 Routemaster Bus, 'Corgi Collectors Visit', M in E box £260

NOVELTY, FILM and TV-RELATED MODELS
107 Batman's Batboat on Trailer (tin) MB £240
 Same model in plastic, NM in E box £160
201 'The Saint' Volvo P1800, white, yellow interior, red bonnet label,
 WhizzWheels, MB £220
258 'The Saint' Volvo P1800, white ,red interior, white bonnet label,
 spun hubs, MB £260
258 'The Saint' Volvo P1800, white, red interior and bonnet label,
 spun hubs, EP in G box £100
261 'James Bond' Aston Martin DB5, complete with sealed secret
 instruction pack including lapel badge, folded leaflet and spare
 bandit figure, Mint model, pictorial stand and outer blue/yellow
 picture box £300
267 Batman's Batmobile, matt black, red bat hubs, instruction pack with
 lapel badge/leaflet, model NM, pictorial stand E,
 packing and outer blue/yellow box GP £700
268 'The Green Hornet' 'Black Beauty', NM inGP box £200
270 'James Bond' Aston Martin DB5, silver, red interior and tyre
 slashers, complete secret instruction pack with spare bandit
 figure/lapel badge and folded leaflet. NM in EP box £320
270 'James Bond' Aston Martin DB5, WhizzWheels issue, MB £110
277 'The Monkee's' 'Monkeemobile', M in M blue/yellow box £260
336 'James Bond' Toyota 2000 GT, instruction pack with missile on
 sprue/leaflet/lapel badge, model M inner packing, pictorial
 card and outer blue/yellow window picture box £260
391 'James Bond' Ford Mustang Mach 1, NM in NM box £240
497 'The Man from Uncle' 'Thrushbuster', blue body, cast lamps and
 hubs, Waverley ring, inner packing and pictorial stand EP,
 model EP in NM box £280
497 'The Man from Uncle' 'Thrushbuster', white body, cast lamps and
 hubs, Waverley ring, inner packing and pictorial stand M,
 model M in NM outer blue/yellow picture box £800
511 'Chipperfields Performing Poodles', Chevrolet Impala, blue,
 red cast hubs and Mary Chipperfield with poodles,
 all M in E box £280
802 'Popeye's Paddle Wagon', EP in G box £240
803 'The Beatles Submarine', red hatches, EP, inner tray M,
 outer blue/yellow window box E £280
804 'Noddy' Car with Big Ears and Tubby, NM in E box £260
805 'Hardy Boys' 1912 Rolls Royce, M in E box £150
808 'Basl Brush', Mint including laughing box, outer window box EP £130
811 'James Bond' 'Moonbuggy', EP in E box £320

AGRICULTURAL VEHICLES
50 Massey-Ferguson 65 Tractor, NM in GP box £100
53 Massey-Ferguson 65 Tractor with Shovel, GP in F box £110
54 Fordson Power Major with Roadless Halftracks, NM in G box £140
55 Fordson Power Major Tractor, blue, orange plastic hubs, NM, G box .£90
55 Fordson Power Major Tractor, blue, dull orange front and rear hubs,
 E in GP box £150
57 Massey-Ferguson 65 Tractor with Fork, red cream, orange front
 and rear hubs, EP in G box £135
57 Massey-Ferguson 65 Tractor with Fork, red including front and
 rear hubs, EP in G box £110
66 Massey-Ferguson 165 Tractor, red, grey white, EP in
 E blue/yellow card box £120
67 Ford 5000 Super Major Tractor, blue, grey driver, M including
 packing in E box £140
69 Massey-Ferguson 165 Tractor with Shovel, red, grey, white,
 NM in NM box £150
72 Ford 5000 Super Major Tractor with Trenching Bucket,
 M in E blue/yellow window box £200
73 Massey-Ferguson 165 Tractor with Saw Attachment, M in E box £120
74 Ford 5000 Super Major Tractor with Hydraulic Scoop, M, E box ...£170
1111 Massey-Ferguson 780 Combine Harvester with metal hubs and
 tines, EP in G box £100
1111 Massey-Ferguson 780 Combine Harvester with plastic hubs and
 tines, E in E box £240

MILITARY VEHICLES
352 Standard Vanguard 'RAF' Car, EP in G box £70
354 Commer 'Ambulance', M in G box £100
355 Commer 'Military Police', M in F box £90
357 Land Rover Weapons Carrier, green, red interior, MB £130
500 Land Rover 'US Army', green., lemon interior, NM in G box £130

1106 **Decca Mobile Airfield Radar**, NM in GP box...................£120
1112 **Corporal Missile on Launcher**, E in G box......................£100
1118 **International Truck**, NM in G box £100
1135 **Bedford Transporter**, M, inner tray EP, picture box G...................£190

GIFT SETS
GS3 Batman 2 piece Set, Batmobile, red wheels and Batboat, secret
    instructions, NM in NM box..................£270
GS4 Military Set, models E, M, packing E, Box G..................£270
GS5 Farming Set, models GP, NM, packing/outer box G..................£340
GS5 British Racing Cars, E, NM in G box..................£200
GS6 Racing Set, E -M in G box..................£140
GS11 ERF Lorry/Trailer, cement and plank loads, E in GP box.............£140
GS11 Same issue with Milk Churns load, E in G box..................£140
GS11 London Set, E in G box..................£170
GS15 'Silverstone' Set, yellow/blue boxed models EP, M, outer box G...£1,200
GS17 Racing Set, NM, M in GP box..................£180
GS20 Transporter Set, E, M in G box..................£360
GS22 Farming Set, GP, NM, packing and outer box G..................£540
GS23 'Chipperfields Circus' Set, models E, packing NM, box GP £440
GS25 Racing Car and Tender Set, NM, M in G box..................£170
GS25 'Shell' / 'BP' Garage Layout, NM, M, in M yellow/blue boxes
    plus layout, outer box G..................£1,500
GS31 Buick Riviera Set, models NM, inner stand E in G box..................£180
GS37 Lotus Racing Set, 3 Lotus models plus chassis are NM, plus
    'James Bond' leaflet, unapplied decals, unused cones, inner
    polystyrene packing NM, outer yellow/blue window box GP £320
GS38 Monte Carlo Rally Set, models E, NM, inner pictorial
    stand F, E in G box..................£750
GS40 Batman Set, Batmobile, Batboat and Batcopter plus missiles
    still on sprue NM in GP box..................£420
GS40 The Avengers Set, models F, GP, inner stand G (missing
    umbrellas), box F..................£290
GS46 All Winners Set, models E, NM in GP box..................£310
GS48 Transport Set, 321 Mini Cooper S 'Signatures' issue E/M, G box ..£580
GS48 Transport Set, without the above 321 model, E, M in G box..........£520
GS48 Circus 'Pinder' Set, models NM, M in F, G box..................£130

NEW US SETS - see listings
FAO102 'Best in Show' Animal Gift Set, NM in E box..................£1,200
FA08804 Circus Set, models M, outer blue/yellow
    presentation box NM..................£1,900

CORGI ROCKETS
D905 Volvo P1800 'The Saint', M on E blister card £80
D923 Ford Escort 'James Bond', M on E blister card..................£500
D924 Mercury Cougar 'James Bond', M on E blister card..................£560
D925 Ford Capri 'James Bond', M on E blister card..................£420

HUSKY MODELS
1005 'The Man from Uncle', M on E blister card..................£170

CORGI JUNIORS
1001 'James Bond' Aston Martin DB5, M on E blister card £160
1002 'Batman' Batmobile, M on E blister card..................£160
1004 'Monkeemobile', M on NM blister card..................£160
1006 'Chitty Chitty Bang Bang', M on E card..................£50
1007 'Ironsides' Van, M on E card..................£100
1008 'Popeye's Paddlewagon', NM on E card..................£130
1010 'James Bond' VW 1200, M on GP blister card..................£940
1011 'James Bond' Bobsleigh, M on E card..................£520
1012 'Spectre' Bobsleigh, M on E blister card..................£900
E2009 'James Bond' Aerocar, E in F box..................£190
E3019 'James Bond' Set 'Octopussy', two models both NM on
    GP blister card..................£170
E3021 Crimebusters Set, NM in GP box..................£120
E3030 'James Bond' Set 'Spy who loved me', NM in GP £220
E3040 'Superman' Adventure Set, NM in E box..................£120
E3080 Batman Set, NM in GP box..................£270

AIRCRAFT MODELS
652 Concorde 'Japan Airlines', EP in E box..................£100
653 Concorde 'Air Canada', NM in E box..................£130

CORGI TOYS sold by Christie's South Kensington
85 Old Brompton Road, London, SW7 3LD.
Model and Box Condition Abbreviations
M - Mint, **E** - Excellent, **VG** - Very Good, **G** - Good, **F** - Fair, **P** - Poor.

Gift Set 1 Carrimore Transporter with Four Cars,VG-E,
    inner boxes, VG-E, box G..................£540
Gift Set 3 Batmobile and Batboat, E in VG box..................£705
Gift Set 15 Silverstone Racing Layout, E, inner boxes E, set box G ...£1,057
**Gift Set 21 'Chipperfields' Circus Scammell Handyman Crane and
Menagerie Trailer**, VG-E in G box..................£705
Gift Set 23 'Chipperfields' Circus, 1st type with **Booking Office**,
    VG in F-G box..................£411
Gift Set 40 The Avengers, VG in G box..................£235
268 Routemaster Bus, 'New South Wales' livery with information slip,
    VG in G-VG box..................£587

CORGI TOYS sold by Lacy Scott & Knight,
10 Risbygate Street, Bury St Edmunds, Suffolk, IP33 3AA.
Condition Grading: B = Boxed, **D** = Damaged, **M** = Mint,
NM/GM = Near Mint, **G** = Good, **F** = Fair, **P** = Poor, **R** = Repainted.

67 Ford 5000 Super Major Tractor, M in G box..................£70
200 Ford Consul Saloon, beige, spun hubs, early blue box, M in F box......£90
201 Austin Cambridge, met. green/silver, spun dome hubs, M in G box ..£130
202 Morris Cowley Saloon, blue, spun hubs, in G original box M £130
226 Morris Mini Minor, pale blue, red interior, M, BG £85
227 Morris Mini Cooper, white, RN '7', G in G box..................£210
238 Jaguar Mk. X, rare sea green, G-M BG..................£320
407 Karrier Bantam Mobile Shop, pale duck egg blue, G-M in F-G box..£90
447 Ford Thames Ice Cream Van, M, insert F-G box G..................£180
Gift Set No.15 Silverstone Racing Set, models F-G, boxes F-G,
    overall condition F-G..................£500
Perspex Shop Display Sign, blue/yellow, Corgi dog logo, 61cms long £75

CORGI TOYS sold by Wallis & Wallis,
West Street Auction Galleries, Lewes, Sussex, BN7 2NJ
Grades of Condition, Abbreviations:
M = Mint, **VGC** = Very Good Condition, **GC** = Good Condition,
QGC = Quite Good Condition, **FC** = Fair Condition, **TT** = Two-tone.

NOVELTY, TV and FILM
107 Batboat and Trailer, tinplate fin, pictorial box,
    gold trailer with cast wheels, VGC, M..................£120
261 James Bond Aston-Martin DB5, metallic gold,
    boxed/instructions/spare figure, vehicle VGC..................£185
266 Chitty-Chitty Bang-Bang in original cloud display box, M..............£230
267 Batmobile, gloss black body, gold cast hubs, with
    figures/rockets/instructions/display insert, model VGC, M........£330
268 The Green Hornet's Black Beauty, boxed with display
    insert/packing, vehicle M..................£280
277 Monkeemobile, complete, boxed with minor wear, vehicle M............£240
336 James Bond 2000 GT with instructions/badge/rockets,
    vehicle VGC, M..................£260
447 Thames Walls Ice Cream Van, boxed, non-musical example,
    vehicle M..................£150
497 Oldsmobile Thrush Buster, metallic blue, boxed with Waverley
    ring/display insert, packing rings, vehicle M..................£230
511 Chipperfield's Performing Poodles, boxed, contents M..................£280
803 'Beatles' Yellow Submarine, red hatches, box VGC, contents M £380
1130 Chipperfields Circus Horse Transporter, box with horses still
    in packing, model VGC, M..................£95
1139 Chipperefields Menagerie, complete, boxed, minor wear,
    vehicle M..................£170

CARS and BUSES
GS37 Lotus Racing Team, complete with paperwork and traffic cones,
    box wear, contents M..................£200
440 Cortina Super Estate Car, with golfer/caddy/clubs/trolley,
    display insert, vehicle M..................£130
468 Routemaster Bus, 'New South Wales' green/cream livery with slip
    detailing NSW Transport, VGC, M..................£310
1126 Ecurie Ecosse Transporter, dark metallic blue/yellow lettering,
    boxed with packing, vehicle VGC..................£135

MILITARY
1108 Bloodhound Guided Missile, complete with nose cone in good
    condition, contents VGC..................£180

Crescent Toys Grand Prix Racing Cars
1285 B.R.M. Mk.II and 1293 Vanwall

Crescent Toys Grand Prix Racing Cars
1284 Mercedes-Benz and 1289 Gordini 2.5 litre.
Photos: Vectis Auctions

Crescent Toys

The Crescent Toy Company was founded in July 1922 by Henry G. Eagles and Arthur A. Schneider in a workshop 30 feet square at the rear of a private house at 67 De Beauvoir Crescent, Kingsland Road, London N1.

They manufactured model soldiers, cowboys, kitchen sets, etc. from lead alloy. These were hollow castings, hand painted, packed one dozen to a box, and sold to wholesalers at six shillings per dozen boxes. The small firm prospered and eventually opened up a factory in Tottenham. With the second World War came a ban on metal toys and production was changed to munitions. After the War the firm resumed making metal hollow-cast toys and in addition marketed the diecast products of a firm called DCMT (Die Casting Machine Tools Ltd).

As a consequence early post-war models had 'DCMT' cast into the underside of the body. In 1948 the firm opened a modern factory on a four-acre site at Cymcarn, a Welsh mining village near Newport, Monmouth (now Gwent) and two years later transferred all production there, maintaining only an office in

London. From this time Crescent toys made their own diecast products without 'DCMT' on them. Hence it is possible to find the same models with or without 'DCMT' cast in. Die Casting Machine Tools went their own way and from 1950 produced models under the name of 'Lone Star'.

Crescent Toys will be best remembered for their excellent ranges of military models and farm equipment but probably most of all for their superb reproductions of the racing cars of the 1950s.

The following post-war model listings have been extracted from a unique collection of original trade catalogues (1947-80) most kindly provided by Mr. J. D. Schneider, the former Managing Director of Crescent Toys Ltd. All of the original research and actual compiling of the lists was undertaken by Ray Strutt.

The Editor would also like to thank Les Perry of Rochdale for additional information.

Ref.	Year(s)	Details	MPR

EARLY POST-WAR MODELS (various colours)

Ref.	Year(s)	Details	MPR
223	1948	**Racing Car**	£25-35
422	1949	**Sports Car**	£30-40
423	1949	**Oil Lorry**	£30-40
424	1949	**Truck Lorry**	£30-40
425	1949	**Saloon Car**	£30-40
800	1947-49	**Jaguar**	£35-45
802	1947-49	**Locomotive**	£25-35
803	1947-48	**Locomotive**, Silver	£25-35
804	1948-49	**Police Car**, Black	£35-45
1221	1949	**Fire Engine**, Red body	£40-50
-		**Garages**, retailing at 1/-, 1/6, 2/6 and 4/-. Complete with Modern Pumps, Motor Cars and Garage Attendants, *'CRESCENT GARAGES'* logo.	NGPP
FC 330		**Domestic Iron and Stand**	£10-15
-		**Zulu-drawn Rickshaw**. Red/Green rickshaw, 'Zulu' with wheel attached to foot, colonial couple in tropical dress/pith helmets in rickshaw	£125-175

FARM EQUIPMENT (various colours)

Ref.	Year(s)	Details	MPR
1802	1949-60	**Tractor and Hayrake**	£65-75
1803	1967-74	**Dexta Tractor and Trailer**	£45-55
1804	1950-59	**Tractor and Disc Harrow**	£55-65
1805	1950-61	**Tractor**	£55-65
1806	1950-60	**Hayrake**	£5-10
1807	1950	**Disc Harrow**	£5-10
1808	1950-56	**Platform Trailer**	£5-10
1809	1950-56	**Ricklift Trailer**	£5-10
1809	1962-80	**Dexta Tractor**	£25-35
1810	1950-80	**Box Trailer / Farm Trailer**, (No.148 1968-74)	£15-20
1811	1950-67	**Animal Trailer / Cattle Trailer**, (No.148 1968-71)	£10-15
1811	1975-81	**Dexta Tractor and Trailer**	£15-20
1813	1950	**Timber Wagon** (Horse Drawn)	£75-95
1814	1950-60	**Plough Trailer**, (No.150 1968-71)	£10-15
1815	1950	**Hayloader**	£10-15
1816	1950	**Roller Harrow**	£5-10
1817	1950-56	**Timber Trailer**	£10-15
1818	1954-60	**Tipping Farm Wagon**	£10-15
1819	1954-55	**Large Farm Wagon**	£25-35

DIECAST ACTION TOYS (various colours)

Ref.	Year(s)	Details	MPR
1219	1954-59	**'Milking Time' Set**. 2 Milkmaids, 2 cows, calf. Card box with picture on lid	£75-95
1222	1954-59	**Builders & Decorators Truck** (red handcart), unpainted ladder and bucket, beige figure on green base. Grey card box with drawing of set	£80-100
1268	1954-59	**Mobile Space Rocket**	NGPP
1269	1954-59	**Mobile Crane**	£30-40

Ref.	Year(s)	Details	MPR
1272	1954-59	**Scammell Scarab and Box Trailer**	£70-80
1274	1954-59	**Scammell Scarab and Low Loader**	£70-80
1276	1955-59	**Scammell Scarab and Oil Tanker**	£70-80
2700	1956-60	**Western Stage Coach**	£70-80
2705	1955	**Western Stage Coach**	NGPP
-		**Scammell Scarab Set**, Mechanical Horse, Box Trailer and Low Loader	NGPP

MILITARY MODELS (All in military colours)

Ref.	Year(s)	Details	MPR
155	1960-68	**'Long Tom' Artillery Gun**	£15-20
235	1946	**Cannon**, operable	NGPP
F 355	1938	**Tank and Cannon Set**	NGPP
650	1954-59	**Military Set**: two 696 British Tanks, one 698 Scout Car, one 699 Russian Tank	NGPP
NN656/2	1938-40	**Field Gun and Gunner**	NGPP
NN692	1938-40	**Deep Sea Diver**, with equipment	NGPP
NN693	1938-40	**A.R.P. Searchlight Unit**, 3 personnel, boxed	£60-80
NN694	1938-40	**A.R.P. Rangefinder Unit**, 2 personnel, boxed	£60-80
695	1938-40	**A.R.P. First Aid Post**: a tent, two stretcher bearers and patient, Red Cross nurse	£100-125
F 695	1946	**Howitzer**, unpainted with spring and plunger, *'CRESCENT'* cast-in	£10-12
696	1954-59	**British Tank**	£30-40
698	1954-59	**Scout Car**	£20-30
699	1954-56	**Russian Tank**	£30-40
NN700	1938-40	**Royal Engineers Field Set**: Engineers (2 standing, 2 kneeling), telegraph pole, transmitter, aerial. Box has colour picture of set on lid	£100-125
701	-	**GPO Telephone Engineers Set**: 4 men, telegraph pole, hut, cart, accessories. Box has colour picture of set on lid	£120-150
702	-	**Sound Locator Unit**, operator figure, boxed	£60-80
K 703	1938-40	**Field Wireless Unit** with two Soldiers	NGPP
K 704	1938-40	**R.A.M.C. Stretcher Party**, 2 Soldiers and Patient	NGPP
1248	1957	**Field Gun**	£5-10
1249	1958-79	**18-pounder Quick-Firing Gun**	£10-15
1250	1958-80	**25-pounder Light Artillery Gun**	£10-15
1251	1958-80	**5.5" Medium Heavy Howitzer**	£10-15
1260	1976-79	**Supply Truck**	£30-40
1263	1962-80	**Saladin Armoured Scout Car**	£20-30
1264	1975-80	**Scorpion Tank**	£12-16
1265	1977-80	**M109 Self-Propelled Gun**	£12-15
1266	1978-79	**Recovery Vehicle**	£12-15
1267	1958-63	**'Corporal' Rocket and Lorry**	£50-60
1270	1958-60	**Heavy Rescue Crane**	£40-50
1271	1958-60	**Long Range Mobile Gun**	£20-30
1271	1976-80	**Artillery Force**	£15-20
2154	1962-74	**Saladin Armoured Patrol** (No.1270 1975-80)	£10-15

HISTORICAL MODELS (in Regal colours)

1300	1975-76	**Royal State Coach**....................................	**£20-30**
1301	1977-79	**Royal State Coach**, (Commemorative box)	**£20-30**
1302	1977	**Royal State Coach and Figures**....................	**£20-30**
1450	1956-60	**Medieval Catapault**................................	**£20-30**
1953	1954-60	**Coronation State Coach**	**£30-40**

Miniature 'WILD WEST' Transport

906	1956	**Stage Coach**, various colours....................	**£30-40**
907	1956	**Covered Wagon**, various colours	**£30-40**

GRAND PRIX RACING and SPORTS CARS

1284	1956-60	**Mercedes-Benz**, all-enveloping silver body, racing number '12'....................	**£90-120**
1285	1956-60	**B.R.M. Mk.II**, bright green, '7'	**£90-120**
1286	1956-60	**Ferrari**, orange-red	**£90-120**
1287	1956-60	**Connaught**, dark green, racing number '8'	**£90-120**
1288	1956-60	**Cooper-Bristol**, light blue, racing number '2'	**£90-120**
1289	1956-60	**Gordini**, French blue, racing number '14'..........	**£90-120**
1290	1956-60	**Maserati**, cherry red, racing number '3'............	**£90-120**
1291	1957-60	**Aston-Martin DB3s**, white/light blue	**£100-150**
1292	1957-60	**Jaguar 'D' type**, dark green	**£100-150**
1293	1958-60	**Vanwall**, dark green, racing number '10'.........	**£150-200**
6300	1957	**Racing Cars Set**, 1284 - 1289 in display box	NGPP
	1958-60	Same set but 1290 replaces 1284............................	NGPP

LONG VEHICLES (various colours)

1350	1975-80	**Container Truck**	**£20-25**
1351	1975-80	**Petrol Tanker**	**£20-25**
1352	1975-80	**Girder Carrying Truck**	**£20-25**
1353	1975-80	**Flat Platform Truck**	**£20-25**

'TRUKKERS' (various colours)

1360	1976-81	**Cement Mixer**......................................	**£5-20**
1361	1976-81	**Covered Truck**.....................................	**£5-20**
1362	1976-81	**Tipper Truck**......................................	**£5-20**
1363	1976-81	**Recovery Vehicle**..................................	**£5-20**
1364	1976-81	**Super Karrier**	**£5-20**

CRESCENT AIRCRAFT

O 2	1940	**Spitfire Set**. Two Spitfires with two Pilots and two Mechanics.................................	**£50-75**
Q 2	1940	**Spitfire Set**. As O 2 but new ref. no.	**£50-75**
U 2	1940	**Aircraft Set**. Five Aircraft plus three Pilots and six Groundcrew............................	**£75-100**
FC 38	1946	**Aeroplane**, Spitfire	**£5-10**
FC 89	1946	**Aeroplane**, Mosquito	**£5-10**
FC 90	1946	**Aeroplane**, Lightning, 3" x 2", US markings	**£5-10**
FC 179	1946	**Khaki Bomber**	**£5-10**
FC 372	1946	**Aeroplane**, Lightning, 4.75" x 3", US markings	**£5-10**
FC 663	1946	**North Sea Patrol**. Aeroplane with pilot and one other crew member..........................	**£20-25**

CRESCENT SHIPS

BATTLESHIPS

---		**HMS 'King George V'**. Grey hollow-cast, with main armament only, boxed........................	**£15-20**
---		Same but additional separately cast secondary armament	**£15-20**
---		**HMS 'Vanguard'**. Grey / black / white, solid, *CRESCENT* cast-in............................	**£5-7**
Q 3	1940	**Battleship Set**, Battleship plus four Sailors...........	NGPP
S 3	1940	**Warships Set**, Battleship and Destroyer plus eight Sailors	NGPP
NN 691		**HMS 'Malaya'**, grey hollow-cast, black funnels, boxed	**£15-20**

AIRCRAFT CARRIERS

-		**HMS 'Victorious'**, grey hollow-cast body, separate unpainted aircraft, boxed....................	**£20-25**
NN 667		**HMS 'Eagle'**, grey hollow-cast body, unpainted aircraft, Union Jack sticker attached to box	**£10-15**

OTHER WARSHIPS

---		**'H' or 'I' Class Destroyer**. Unpainted solid cast body, *CRESCENT* cast into bow	**£15-20**
---		**'H' or 'I' Class Destroyer**. As previous model plus three lead figures of naval personnel..	**£20-25**
---		**'V' and 'W' Class Destroyer**. Grey hollow-cast body	**£2-3**
A 34		**Gunboat**. Grey hollow cast body	**£2-3**
234		**Submarine**. Unpainted, conning tower and deck gun, 4"	**£10-15**
C 310		**'County' Class Cruiser, 'Cumberland'**, grey hollow-cast....................................	**£7-9**
K 664		**'County' Class Cruiser**, grey hollow-cast body	**£7-9**
K 665		**War Transport Ship**, grey hollow-cast body, boxed	**£15-20**

PASSENGER SHIPS

---		**'Queen Mary'**. Black / white / red, hollow-cast body, boxed	**£15-20**
---		**'Dunnottar Castle'**. Mauve / white / red, hollow-cast, boxed	**£25-30**
---		**'Athlone Castle'**. Mauve / white / red, hollow-cast, boxed	**£25-30**

'Dunnottar Castle' and 'Athlone Castle' were part of the 'Union Castle' fleet and the models were sold in souvenir boxes, probably on board.

SHIP MODEL IDENTIFICATION. Crescent Ships are of rather crude manufacture and have virtually no identifying features. Only the HMS 'Vanguard' and the 'H' or 'I' Class Destroyer are known to have *CRESCENT* cast in. A few of the early models had a little paper 'Crescent' half-moon label. Ship models were packed in cream cardboard boxes of varying quality.

MISCELLANEOUS models and sets

'Dodgem' Car	Blue version seen, other colours possible.....**£80-120**
'Tower Bridge'	Solid cast model of the famous landmark, in various colours..........................**£5-10**

'Dial 999' Police and Robbers Set. Contains black police car with loudhailer on roof and four semi-flat action figures (policeman running, policeman and dog, two fleeing villains, one with swag).
Packed in card box with black and white label **£150-175**

'Dan Dare' Set. With figures of Dan Dare, Miss Peabody, Dan Dare in spacesuit, 2 Treens (1 silver, 1 gold) + rocket and launcher.
Packed in card box **£300-400**

'Wild Animals' Set. No details ....NGPP
'Model Farm' Set. No details ....NGPP

Meccano
Dinky Toys

Dinky Toys represent by far the largest and most important of all the model collecting series – there are thousands of variations to collect. The listings are structured on a thematic basis. This enables models to be identified that much quicker and for collectors to specialise on a particular favourite theme be it cars, commercials or aircraft etc.

Today Dinky Toys are bought and sold across the world by thousands of collectors for whom there is nothing quite so rewarding as a new variation to add to their collection. It has been estimated that the value of top quality boxed models have increased by 18% in the twelve month period 2002/3. Consequently it is hardly surprising that a substantial acquisition of Dinky Toys has become a serious part of an alternative investment fund.

All of this is a very long way indeed from Frank Hornby's original vision of a range of vehicles which would complement his model railway layouts!

HISTORY OF DINKY TOYS

In 1931, Meccano Ltd introduced a series of railway station and trackside accessories to accompany their famous 'HORNBY' train sets. These 'Modelled Miniatures' were in sets numbered 1 – 22 and included railwaymen, station staff, passengers and trains. Set number 22 was comprised of six vehicles which were representative rather than replicas of actual vehicles. It was first advertised in the Meccano Magazine of December 1933.

At about this time 'Tootsie Toys' of America were introducing model vehicles into the United Kingdom and they were proving to be very popular. Consequently Meccano Ltd decided to widen their range of products and issue a comprehensive series of models to include vehicles, ships and aircraft. 'Modelled Miniatures' therefore became 'Meccano Dinky Toys' and set number 22 the first set of 'Dinky Cars'. The first 'Dinky Toys' advertisement appeared in the April 1934 edition of the Meccano Magazine. The first Dinky car produced after the change of name was 23a in April 1934. It was probably based on an early MG but was again generally representative rather than an accurate model. Set 22 cost 4/- and consisted of: 22a Sports Car, 22b Sports Coupé, 22c Motor Truck, 22d Delivery Van, 22e Tractor and 22f Tank and is today highly sought after.

The range of models produced grew quickly so that the Meccano Magazine of December 1935 was claiming that there were 200 varieties to choose from! Although the phrase 'Dinky Toys' became a household name, the actual range was of course far greater and was not limited to cars; it even included dolls house furniture. Indeed, by the time the famous Binns Road factory in Liverpool finally closed its doors in November 1979 over 1,000 different designs had been produced. Pre-war models are rare today and fetch high prices, which reflects how difficult it is to find a model in really good condition. This is because so many 1930s models were made from an unstable alloy which has tended to crystallise and disintegrate. Fortunately the post-war models do not suffer from the same problem and much of today's collecting interest is centred around the delightful models produced in the fifties and sixties with Gift Sets being particularly sought after. Most Dinky Toys boxes were made by McCorquodale in Northern Ireland.

Models produced after 1980 fall outside the scope of this book but the name lives on as follows:
In 1987 the Dinky trade name was bought by Matchbox who were at the time part of the Universal International Co. of Hong Kong. They introduced the 'Dinky Collection' in 1988 with some very fine models in a constant scale of 1:43. On the 7th May 1992 it was announced in the 'New York Times' that 'Tyco Toys Inc.' had acquired by merger the 'Universal Matchbox Group' and with it the famous 'Dinky Toys' brand name.

In 1998, Mattel bought the Matchbox brand and in 1999 disclosed that all new car models will be classified as 'Dinky Toys', including those previously included in their Matchbox Models of Yesteryear range. At the beginning of 2001 however, both of those famous names have been all but buried in favour of Mattel's 'Hot Wheels' brand since most of their products have been aimed at the US toy market.

Common Features. There are several features common to various groups of models and to avoid unnecessary repetition in the listings they are shown below. Exceptions to these general indications are noted in the listings.

'Dinky Toys', 'Meccano Ltd', or 'Meccano Dinky Toys'.
These wordings are to be found cast or stamped on the base-plate or chassis or in the case of early models without a base they are cast into the model itself. Some very early models have 'HORNBY SERIES' cast-in (e.g, those in the 22 series).

Wheel hubs. Solid one-piece wheel/tyre castings were fitted to the 'Modelled Miniatures' and first pre-war 'Dinky Toys'. They had 'Hornby' or 'Meccano' cast onto their rims and were covered in a thin colour wash or silver-plated. This casting was soon replaced with more realistic cast hubs (having a smooth convex face) fitted with white (sometimes coloured) rubber tyres. Pre-war hubs may be black, coloured or sometimes silver-plated. Post-war hubs were of the 'ridged' type having a discernible ridge simulating a hub cap. They were painted and usually fitted with black rubber tyres.

Supertoys hubs and tyres. When Supertoys were introduced in 1947 the ridged type of hub was used on the Fodens with black 'herringbone pattern' tyres, and on the Guys with smooth black tyres. Fodens graduated to the use of 'fine radial-tread' tyres first in black, later in grey, then to black again but with a more chunky 'block' tread. Supertoys later acquired plastic hubs and plastic tyres.

Hub materials. Lead was used originally for a short time, the majority of models from the mid-1930s to the early 1960s having diecast mazak hubs. Small models like motor-cycles or the 35b Racer were fitted with solid one-piece wheel/tyre moulding (white or black rubber pre-war, black post-war). In 1958/9 aluminium hubs were introduced and some models (such as 131, 178, 179, 180, 181, 182 and 290 Bus) appeared fitted with either type. Plastic hubs replaced the diecast versions on racing cars numbered 230-235 while the Austin A30 and Fiat 600 were given solid one-piece wheel/tyre plastic injection mouldings. **Speedwheels** were introduced in the 1970s and some model can be found fitted with metal wheels or Speedwheels. The former are more collectable.

Baseplates are tinplate or diecast unless described otherwise. Plastic moulded baseplates are generally restricted to a few models made after 1970. **Model Numbers** appear on many Dinky Toys baseplates but not all. The **Model Name** however appears on virtually every post-war Dinky Toy. Pre-war models usually had neither (the 38 and 39 series are exceptions having the model name on their baseplates).

Construction Materials. All models assumed to be constructed at least in part of a diecast alloy. Some pre-war models were made of a lead alloy like the 22 and 28 series plus the few odd models such as 23 a Racing Car and 23m Thunderbolt. The Blaw-Knox Bulldozer was one of the very few produced (right at the end of its production) in plastic.
Windows. Pre-war and early post-war models had tinplate or celluloid windscreens. Moulded plastic windscreens appeared in the 1950s on open car models. The first Dinky to be fitted with all-round plastic window glazing was the Austin A105 Saloon. Some models in production at the time were fitted with glazing later and may therefore be found with or without it.

Hooks were not fitted to the first Supertoys Foden models (1947). Small hooks were fitted in early 1948, the usual (larger) hook appearing in mid-1948.

Axles were all 'crimped' pre-war and on these series of models post-war: 23, 25, 29, 30, 34, 35, 36, 37, 38, 39, 40 and 280. Otherwise models had rivet-ended axles until the advent of Speedwheels. Early Guy models had tinplate clips to retain the front axles. Pre-war axles are generally thinner than post-war at 0.062mm diameter while post-war axles are 0.078mm in diameter.

Size of models (where shown) is in millimetres and refers to the longest overall measurement (usually the length). In the case of pre-war models slight inaccuracies may occur from expansion of the casting as it ages in the course of time.

The Scale of Dinky Toys was originally 1:43 (with a few exceptions). Supertoys Foden and Guy vehicles (introduced in 1947) were in a scale of 1:48 while military models issued from 1953 were smaller at 1:60. Most aircraft models before 1965 were around 1:200 and ships 1:1800. In the late 1960s and early 1970s the 1:36 scale was introduced, mostly for cars.

Dinky Numbering System. The dual/triple reference numbers used on some Dinky Toys and Supertoys (for example 409 / 521 / 921 Bedford Articulated Lorry) refers to the basic model type and casting and not to model colours. The renumbering by Meccano was an administration process to re-catalogue production of existing lines and introduce new models. New colours on existing castings which arise at about the time of renumbering are therefore coincidental with it rather than a consequence of it.

Identification of early post-war Dinky Toys cars.
Note that pre-war wheel hubs may be smooth diecast or the rare chrome ('Tootsie-Toy' type) hubs which attract a premium.

Post-war 30 Series
Circa 1946.........Open chassis with smooth black wheel hubs.
Circa 1948.........Plain chassis with ridged black wheel hubs.

36 Series
Circa 1946.........Moulded chassis with smooth black wheel hubs.
Circa 1948.........Moulded chassis with ridged black wheel hubs.

38 Series
Circa 1946........With pre-war lacquered metal base, silvered sidelights, smooth black hubs, spread spigots not rivets.
Circa 1946.........Solid steering wheels, smooth black hubs, silvered sidelights, black painted baseplate.
Circa 1947.........As above but with silver-edged windscreen.
Circa 1948-49....Open or solid steering wheel, ridged hubs, black painted baseplate.
Circa 1950.........As above but with coloured wheel hubs.

39 Series
Circa 1946.........'Gold' pre-war baseplate, smooth black wheel hubs, silver door handles and radiator cap.
Circa 1948.........Black painted baseplate, ridged black wheel hubs.
Circa 1950.........As above but with coloured wheel hubs.

Box Types Introduction

A mint condition model car without its correct box is worth but a fraction of its mint boxed equivalent. Furthermore, as model boxes made from card do not survive as well as their die-cast contents, pristine box examples are scarce and becoming scarcer. The condition of a box is of paramount importance and attention is drawn to the section in the catalogue introduction, namely: 'Classifying the Condition of Models and Boxes'.

The following listing provides collectors with a working knowledge of the range of box types issued. In addition details are given of their dates of issue, their design and of the models which used them. See also the colour sections for examples of many types of boxes.

Whilst every care has been taken in preparing the listing, other variations may exist and information on them is welcomed. Similarly, with no 'dates of birth' available the dates of issues shown are approximate and again any further information is welcomed.

Box Identification

Model colour identification marks - colour spots

These are shown on the box lid end flap and take the form of a circular colour spot. This may be either a single colour or, in the case of the later two-tone car issues, a two-tone colour spot. Colour spots were used until the early 1960s.

NB The dual numbered 234/23H box displays the **Ferrari** model name against a blue panel which matches the main body colour.

Dual numbered boxes 1953 - 1954

A new numbering system was introduced which resulted in models being issued displaying both the old and new reference numbers. The information was shown on the box end flaps as follows:

Old model number shown in red letters on either side of a larger white number set on a black oval background, e.g. 40J **161** 40J. Dual numbered boxes were only issued for a short period and may attract a premium. The numbers may be large or small.

Pre-war issues

Apart from special issues such as 23m Thunderbolt Speed Car and 23p Gardner's M.G. Record Car, individual models were sold unboxed. They were usually packaged in half-dozen retailers trade packs (see the section on Trade Packs). Models were also sold in boxed sets (see the Gift Set Section).

Post-war After the second world war models continued to be sold unboxed from trade boxes until 1953/54 when the first individual boxes were introduced. The boxes have been catalogued into three types as follows:

Type 1: Card boxes with tuck-in flaps
Type 2: Display boxes -Blister packs, rigid plastic packs,
vacuform packs and card window boxes.
Type 3: Export Issue boxes.

Type 1 1953 – 1975 All card box with tuck-in end flaps

(i) 1953- 1954 Deep yellow box with 'DINKY TOYS' in red plus the model's name and type in black. A white reference number on a black oval background is on the box end flaps but no reference number is shown on the box face. The model is pictured on the box sides but without a white shaded background. Colour spots shown on box-end flaps as applicable. Foreign language information is shown on one of the end flaps of the early issue boxes. Box in general use during the model renumbering period. Consequently, dual numbered boxes will be found. It would appear that only models 23f, g, h, j, k and n, and 40j were housed in individual boxes prior to renumbering. Please supply details of any other models housed in boxes displaying just their old reference number.

(ii) 1955 - 1956 Same as (i) but a white reference number on a black oval background is shown on the face of the box to the left of the model picture. Also as (i) but with a white reference number on a red oval background and placed either to the left or right of the model picture. Box in general use for all issues.

(iii) 1956 - 1960 Same as (ii) but model pictures are displayed against a white shadow background. In some instances only one picture. had a shadow, e.g. 171 Hudson Commodore and in others both pictures were given a shadow; e.g. 152 Austin Devon. Box in general use for all issues. Later issues display 'WITH WINDOWS', caption in a red line features box.

(iv) c1960 Deep yellow plain box with no model picture, 'DINKY TOYS' and text in red; rarely used. Colour spots shown as applicable. We believe these boxes may have been used for mail-order or possibly export purposes. The Editor would welcome any new information. Known examples: 103, 108, l09, 163 and 191.

(v) 1959–1961 Plain lighter yellow box with no model picture. It has two yellow and two red sides. 'DINKY TOYS' is shown in yellow on red sides. Colour spots shown as applicable. Models recorded: 105, 109, 131, 150, 157, 165, 169, 173. 174, 176, 178, 187, 189, 191, 192 and 230 to 235. The special issue 189 Triumph Heralds used this box.

(vi) 1960 - 1966 Yellow box with a separate red line features box placed to the right of the model picture. Colour spots still in use on early 1960s issues. Foreign language text on one box end flap and 'WITH WINDOWS' captions on box face. Models recorded: 105, 112, 113, 131, 144, 148, 155, 157, 164–167, 176–178, 181/2, 184, 186, 191-195, 197, 199, 230-235, 237, 239 and 449. Later issues without colour spots. Boxes used for some South African issues display both English and Afrikaans text.

(vii) c.1962 – 1963 Lighter yellow box similar to (v) but colour spots not in use. A scarce issue box which may attract a premium. Model recorded: 166.

(viii) 1962 – 1963 Yellow box with a red end features panel around the left side of the box. Recorded models: 113, 147 and 198.

(ix) 1962 – 1963 (?) Yellow/red box similar to previous items, but has yellow ends, yellow top and bottom panels and red side panels, the latter virtually filled with the text: 'DINKY TOYS'. Colour spots not seen. See page vii of the colour section for an illustration of this box (containing 178 Plymouth Plaza).

(x) 1963 – 1970 Yellow box with a red end features panel around the right side. The panel is bisected by the model picture and is with or without a large or small white arrow design. Models recorded: 112-114. 120, 127-130, 133-139, 140-148, 198, 240-243, 268, 273 and 274. Some South African issues used this box, e.g. 141 Vauxhall Victor Estate Car. They display both English and Afrikaans text. The rare Triumph 2000 Saloon promotional issues will be found in this box. Some have an applied white label on the box face showing the colour of the model, e.g. Olive-Cactus.

(xi) 1966 – 1969 Detailed full colour picture box with pictorial scene on two sides with 'DINKY TOYS' in red letters. Recorded issues: 133, 136, 183, 212, 214, 225 plus Hong Kong issues 57/001-57/006.

(xii) 1968 – 1974 White-fronted box with a thin yellow band across the box face. A yellow laurel leaf design on a black background is a main box feature. The white face of the box may contain features information such as '1st AGAIN' and 'SPEEDWHEELS'. Variation exists with a semi-pictorial box face (probably an export special) e.g. 176 NSU R80. Models recorded: 157, 159 165/6, 169, 174/5, 179, 183, 192, 205 and 212. NB. A variation of this box exists with a large red 'DINKY TOYS' and number to the left of the picture and no yellow band across the face, e.g. 138 Hillman Imp.

Type 2 1962 – 1980 Display boxes, Blister packs, Rigid plastic and Vacuform packs, Window boxes

(i) 1962 – 1964 Blister Card Packs used for racing cars nos. 205210. Red/yellow display card with chequered flag design.

(ii) 1967 – 1971 Rigid plastic 'see-through' case with lift-off lid. models displayed on a card base with a black 'roadway' surface. The base sides are yellow with 'DINKY TOYS' in red. Recorded issues: 110, 116, 127, 129, 131/2, 142, 152-154, 158, 161, 163/4, 168, 175, 187-189, 190, 208, 210, 213, 215, 216, 220/1 and 223/4.

(iii) 1972 – 1976 Vacuform Packs. Models displayed on a black base with a blue surface with 'DINKY TOYS' in red/white letters. The model is covered by a close fitting plastic cover. Known issues: 129, 131, 149, 168, 178 and 192 plus 1:25 issues 2214, 3162 and 2253.

(iv) 1976 – 1979 Window Box with 'see-through' cellophane front and blue and red header card with a 'DINKY DIECAST TOYS' in yellow letters. Variations exist with a model picture on the header card e.g. 112 'Purdey's TR7'. Known issues: 113, 120, 122/3/4, 128. 180, 192, 207/8, 211, 221/2/3 and 226/7.

(v) 1968 – 1969 Plastic see-through red box made in a garage shape to house 'Mini Dinky' issues.

(vi) 1979 Bubble Pack 219 'Big Cat' Jaguar.

Type 3   1966 – 1980   Export issue boxes

(i) 1966 – 1980 An all yellow card and cellophane 'see-through' display box with outward-folding ends. 'DINKY TOYS' and four diagonal stripes plus 'A MECCANO PRODUCT MADE IN ENGLAND' are in red on the box face. The box display base may be either yellow or have a black 'roadway' design.

Whilst generally used for export issues it was specifically used for the U.S. export series 'MARVELS IN MINIATURE - which appeared in red letters on the box front. Later issues listed the models on the base of the box.

A box variation exists with just 'DINKY' and 'A MECCANO PRODUCT' on the face of the box plus the model name and number. The base of the box is yellow. The box was issued with a card protection strip which stated: 'Mr DEALER PLEASE REMOVE THIS STRIP'. Models known to have been issued in this box include: 110-115, 120, 127/8, 133-138, l41/2. 151, 161, 170-172, 190, 192, 196, 215, 237, 240-243, 257/8, 57/006. **NB** We believe this box was probably used in the UK but would be grateful for confirmation.

(ii) 1966 – 1968 All gold card and cellophane 'see-through' display box with just 'DINKY' in gold letters set in a red panel on the box front plus red and black diagonal stripes. 'A MECCANO PRODUCT MADE IN ENGLAND' in black is also on the front of the box. Only used for a short time so models in these boxes often sell at a premium. The known issues are: 112, 113, 148, 193, 215, 238, 240-243, 340 and 448.

(iii) 1979 – 1980 A flat yellow box with blue end flaps. Used to house the Swiss promotional issue No. 223 Hesketh F1 Racing Car 'OLYMPUS CAMERAS'. **Export issue:** 449 has been observed in an 'all gold' box.

40 Series issues distribution, renumbering and packing

Models in the 40 Series were initially sold unboxed from retailers' trade boxes of 6 models as follows:

i)   1947-50   Plain Brown card box with lift-off lid. On the end of the lid was a Yellow label displaying the quantity, the model's name and its reference number, e.g., '6 RILEY SALOON 40a'.

ii)   1950-54   All Yellow card box with lift-off lid. The contents were printed in Black on the end of the box lid.

iii) 1954   Models renumbered. When the 40 Series models were renumbered, the final all-Yellow card boxes for six displayed both the original number and its new number, for example: '158 RILEY SALOON 40a'.

iv)   1954-60   The renumbered models were individually boxed in the first type of Yellow end-flap boxes as follows:
    a) Displaying the dual numbers for a short time, e.g., '40a 158 40a' on the end flap.
    b) Displaying just the model's new number, e.g., '158' plus the correct colour spot for the model.

Dublo Dinky Toys usually came in yellow boxes with a distinctive red band around each end. Exceptions include the 071 VW Delivery Van and 070 AEC Mercury Tanker 'SHELL-BP' shown in this picture. Also illustrated here is the box for Dinky Toys 772 British Road Signs.
Photo: Barry Potter Auctions.

Chassis types 1934 – 1950

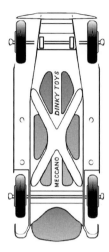
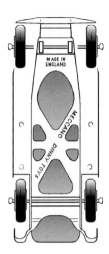
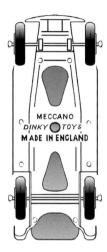
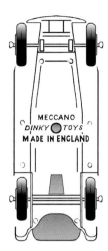
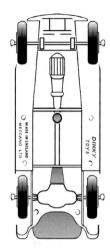

1934 - 1935
'Criss-cross' chassis
1st type
with or without
slot for spare wheel

1935 - 1936
'Criss-cross' chassis
2nd type
with or without
slot for spare wheel

1936 - 1940
Open chassis
with or without
slots for figures

1946 - 1947
Plain chassis, no
slots for figures,
hole for caravan
drawbar

1948 - 1950
'Moulded'
(detailed) chassis,
hole for caravan
drawbar

24 Series radiator grille types 1934 – 1940

1st type
1934 - 1938
With diamond shape
in centre of bumper
No radiator badge
No over-riders

2nd type
1934 - 1938
No diamond shape in
centre of bumper
No radiator badge
No over-riders

3rd type
1938 - 1940
'Bentley' style
with radiator badge
and over-riders

The first and second type grilles will be found on the both the first and second type chassis.
The later third type grille will be found with the second type chassis.

40 Series – casting and base identification

40e / 158 Standard Vanguard 1948 - 60

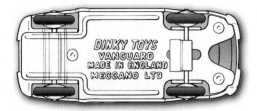

Casting with open wheel arches
(no spats) (1948 - 50)

Tinplate clip secures rear axle (1948 - 49)
Small lettering on baseplate (1948 - 53)
Baseplate has raised rails (1948 - 53)

40b / 151 Triumph 1800 Saloon 1948 - 60

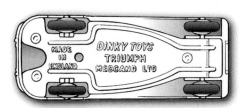

Baseplate tabs secure rear axle (1949 - 60)
Large lettering on baseplate (1954 - 60)
No raised rails on baseplate (1954 - 60)
Body casting includes rear wheel spats (1951 - 60)

Casting with rear axle pillars (1948 - 50)
Small lettering on baseplate, as illustrated (1948 - 53)
Large lettering on baseplate (not illustrated) (1954 - 60)
Two raised rails on baseplate, as illustrated (1948 - 53)
No raised rails on baseplate (not illustrated) (1954 - 60)

40f / 154 Hillman Minx 1951 - 59

1951 - 54
Small lettering on baseplate
Two raised rails on baseplate
Rear axle secured by baseplate tabs

1954 - 59
Large lettering on baseplate
No raised rails on baseplate
Rear axle secured by baseplate tabs

Market Price Range (MPR) for pre-1954 unboxed car models.
Prior to 1954, virtually all the cars were sold unboxed from retailer's trade boxes of either 6, 4 or 3 models. Consequently, all pre-1954 issues (except for 23m and 23s) have been priced as being unboxed. Post-1954 models were all boxed and have been priced accordingly. As a consequence, models which have been renumbered will be found to have two differing prices – one for the pre-1954 unboxed version and another for its boxed and renumbered successor. See also the Trade Box section for details of individual boxes and packs that were used to supply shops.

Ref	Year(s)	Model name	Colours, features, details	Market Price Range

22 Series

22a	1933-35	**Open Sports Car**	'Modelled Miniature' with 'HORNBY SERIES' cast into lead body, solid metal wheel/tyre castings (thinly painted in metallic blue, purple, green, yellow or red, or not painted at all) lead windscreen surround, tinplate radiator (grille may be same colour as body, or overpainted with the colour of the mudguards).	
			Blue body, Yellow seats and mudguards	£400-600
			Blue body, Red seats and mudguards	£400-600
			Cream body, Red seats and mudguards	£400-600
			Cream body, Green seats and mudguards	£400-600
			Cream body, Blue seats and mudguards	£400-600
			Red body, Cream or Blue seats and mudguards	£400-600
			Yellow body, Green seats and mudguards or reversed colours	£400-600
			Orange-Brown body, Cream seats and mudguards	£400-600
			Green body, Yellow seats and mudguards	£400-600
22b	1933-35	**Closed Sports Coupé**	'Modelled Miniature' with 'HORNBY SERIES' cast into lead body, solid metal wheel/tyre castings (coloured or plain, as 22a) tinplate radiator (painted in main body colour).	
			Cream body, Red roof and mudguards or Green roof and mudguards	£600-900
			Cream body, Green roof and mudguards	£600-900
			Red body, Blue roof and mudguards or reversed colours	£600-900
			Red body, Cream roof and mudguards	£600-900
			Yellow body, Green roof and mudguards	£600-900
			Orange body, Green roof and mudguards, Gold washed wheels	£600-900
			Blue body, Yellow roof and mudguards	£600-900
			Blue body, Red roof and mudguards	£600-900
22g	1935-41	**Streamline Tourer**	Model has cast steering wheel and windscreen, smooth diecast hubs which may be painted as body colour or a contrasting colour. Some have chrome hubs.	
			Body colours: Green, Maroon, Red, Light or Dark Blue, Cream, Buff or Black	£300-400
			Turquoise body, Blue hubs, White tyres	£500-750
22h	1935-41	**Streamlined Saloon**	Red, Maroon, Blue or Cream saloon version of 22g (no steering wheel). Wheels may be painted as body colour or a contrasting colour	£300-400

23 Series

23	1934-35	**Racing Car** 1st casting:	Lead body, no racing number, no driver, 0, 2, 3 or 4 exhausts stubs (without pipe), coloured tyres on some.	
		variations:	Cream or White body with either Blue, Cream, Green, Orange or Red top and nose flash	£200-300
			Yellow body with Blue upper body flash, 3 exhaust stubs	£200-300
23a	1935-41	**Racing Car** (23 re-issued)	As 1st casting but diecast body, no driver, no number, Black or White tyres, 4 exhausts.	
		variations:	White body and hubs, Blue flash and circle on nose	£200-300
			Cream body and hubs, Red top flash and circle on nose	£200-300
			Blue body, White top flash and circle on nose	£200-300
			Orange body, Green top flash and circle on nose	£200-300
			Yellow body, Dark Blue top flash and circle on nose	£200-300
			Brown body, Cream top flash	£200-300
			Silver body, Green racing number '8'	£200-300
23a		**Racing Car** 2nd casting:	With driver plus raised circles for racing numbers, 6 exhausts in fishtail.	
		colour type 1:	With minor colour sidestripes and perhaps coloured tyres,	
		colour type 2:	Broad nose flash, even width top rear flash,	
		colour type 3:	Broad flash at cockpit and pointed ends top flash, cast circle on nose.	
		variations:	(type 1) Cream body, Red stripes, number '9', ('Humbug' version)	£400-600
			(type 2) Blue with White stripes and driver, racing number '11'	£400-600
			(type 2) Yellow body, Dark Blue top flash, racing number '7' or '1'	£200-300
			(type 2) Blue body, White top flash, racing number '11', '4' or '5'	£200-300
		'Humbug' version:	(type 2) Yellow with Blue stripes, racing number '7', Silvered 'Tootsie Toy' type hubs	£750-1,000
		'Humbug' version:	(type 2) Orange with Green stripes, racing number '10', Silvered 'Tootsie Toy' type hubs	£750-1,000
			(type 3) White body, Blue nose/circle/top flash, number '2'	£200-300
			(type 3) Cream body, Red nose/circle/top flash, number '3'	£200-300
			(type 3) Red body, Cream nose/top flash, no number, no transverse ribs	£200-300
			(type 3) White body, Green nose/circle/top flash, number '6'	£200-300
			(type 3) Orange body, Green nose/circle/top flash, number '4'	£200-300
		casting variation:	With driver, raised racing number circle on nearside only, no detailed exhaust,	
			Orange body, Green nose circle, Green racing number '4'	£150-175
			Orange body, long Green upper body flash, 3 exhaust stubs, Green RN '4' or '10'	£150-175
			Yellow body, long Dark Blue upper body flash, chrome hubs	£200-250

23a	1946-52	Racing Car...............3rd casting:	With transverse body ribs, no raised circle for racing numbers, and only issued in colour type 3, with or without racing numbers. (Re-introduced in 1954 as 220).	
			Red or Red/Green body, Silver nose circle, top flash and side circle (Red RN '4'), Red hubs	£40-50
			Silver body, Red nose circle, top flash and side circle (Silver RN '4'), Red hubs	£40-50
			Red body, Cream flashes, Black hubs	£40-50
23b	1935-41	Hotchkiss Racing Car	Blue body, Dark Blue, Red or Silver flash and RN '2', '5' or '8'; or Cream (Red flash and RN '1')	£150-200
	1935-41		Yellow (Blue flash and RN '3'), Orange (Green flash and RN '6'), Green (Yellow flash and RN '5') or Turquoise (Blue flash and RN '4')	£150-200
	1946-48		Red with Silver flash and RN '5', or Silver with Red flash and RN '5'	£40-50
23c	1936-38	Mercedes Benz Racing Car	Red, Light Blue, Silver, Yellow or Light Green body with contrasting body flashes, with or without racing numbers '3', '4' or '5', driver cast-in, Black hubs, treaded tyres	£150-200
	1938-40		As previous model but with rivetted baseplate bearing information	£150-200
	1946-50	('Large Open Racing Car')	Re-issued 23c in Blue or Silver, various racing numbers	£40-50
23d	1936-38	Auto-Union Racing Car	Early pre-war issues without driver: Red, Turquoise, Pale Green, Yellow or Silver body, with or without racing numbers, clipped-in tinplate base	£150-200
	1938-41		Later pre-war issue with driver, rivetted baseplate	£150-200
	1946-50		Early post-war issue with driver: Red or Silver body, with or with RN's, Black or White tyres	£50-60
			Later post-war issue without driver	£40-50
23e	1936-38	'Speed Of The Wind' Racing Car	Red, Blue, Light Blue, Green, Yellow or Silver body, plain clipped-in tinplate base, driver, with or without racing numbers '3' or '6', Black hubs and herringbone tyres. Lead versions exist	£50-75
	1938-41		As previous model but with rivetted baseplate bearing information	£50-75
	1946-49		Red or Silver, rivetted informative baseplate, Red hubs, Grey tyres	£35-45
	1950-54	(Renumbered 221)	Silver body and hubs, plain base	£35-45
23f	1952-54	Alfa-Romeo Racing Car	Red body, White racing number '8', Red diecast hubs. (Renumered 232)	£85-95
23g	1952-54	Cooper-Bristol Racing Car	Green body, White racing number '6', Green diecast hubs. (Renumbered 233)	£75-85
23h	1953-54	Ferrari Racing Car	Blue body, Yellow nose, racing number '5' and diecast hubs. (Renumbered 234)	£85-95
23j	1953-54	H.W.M. Racing Car	Light Green body, Yellow racing number '7', Green diecast hubs. (Renumbered 235)	£85-95
23k	1953-54	Talbot-Lago Racing Car	Blue body, Yellow racing number '4', Blue diecast hubs. (Renumbered 230)	£85-95
23m	1938-41	'Thunderbolt' Speed Car	Silver body, Black detailing, Union Jacks on tail, Silver baseplate. In original Blue box dated '2-38', code: 'A2247'	£100-125
			Red body, Silver detailing	£300-400
23n	1953-54	Maserati Racing Car	Red, White flash and racing number '9', Red diecast hubs. (Renumbered 231)	£85-95
23p	1939-40	Gardner's MG Record Car	Dark Green, White flash and 'MG' logo, Union Jacks, 'MG Magnette' on lacquered unpainted tinplate baseplate, Yellow box, dated '9-39', 104 mm	£150-200
	1946-47		Dark Green, Union Jacks, no flash, 'MG Record Car' on base, not boxed	£80-100
23s	1938-40	Streamlined Racing Car	Light Green body, Dark Green detailing, lead	£100-125
			Light Blue body, Dark Blue or Silver detailing, lead	£100-125
			Orange body, lead	£100-125
			Light Green, Light Blue, Red or Orange body, mazak	£75-100
23s	1948-54	(Renumbered 222)	Light, Mid or Dark Green, or Navy Blue, Silver or Green flashes	£40-50
			Silver body with Red, Green or Blue flashes	£40-50
			Red body with Silver or Black flashes, Black base	£60-75

24 Series

Note: The rarest of the 24 Series have coloured tyres matching the body colour and a higher value can be expected.

24a	1934-40	Ambulance	See 'Fire, Police and Ambulance Vehicles' Section.	
24b	1934-38	Limousine	Types 1 or 2: criss-cross chassis. Types 1, 2 or 3: grille, no sidelights, no spare wheel, 3 side windows, 3 'stacked' parallel horizontal bonnet louvres. Blue, Black or plated 'Tootsie-Toy'type hubs.	
		..................body/chassis colours:	Maroon/Dark Maroon, Maroon/Grey, Maroon/Black, Blue/Yellow, Dark Blue/Black, Yellow/Brown	£300-500
	1937-40	............................casting change:	Same colours but no spare wheel slot, 3 parallel bonnet louvres, open chassis, 'Bentley' grille and bumper	£200-400
24c	1934-38	Town Sedan	Types 1 or 2: criss-cross chassis. Types 1, 2 or 3: grille, spare wheel, no sidelights, separate windscreen/steering wheel casting, smooth Blue, Black or plated 'Tootsie-Toy'type hubs.	
		body/chassis colours:	Green/Black, Green/Yellow, Pale Green/Red, Dark Blue/Dark Blue, Cream/Dark Blue, Cream/Black, Dark Blue/Black	£300-500
	1937-40	............................casting change:	Same colours but open chassis, no spare wheel slot, narrower boot, shorter door handles	£200-400
24d	1934-38	Vogue Saloon	Types 1 or 2: criss-cross chassis. Types 1, 2 or 3: grille, with nearside spare wheel, no sidelights. Smooth Blue, Black or plated hubs with White tyres.	
		body/chassis colours:	Blue/Dark Blue, Blue/Black, Blue/Maroon, Cream/Blue, Brown/Green, Pink/Green, Green/Blue, Red/Grey, Green/Black, Maroon/Black	£300-500
	1937-40	............................casting change:	Same colours but open chassis, higher 'domed' roofline, no spare wheel	£200-400
24e	1934-38	Super Streamlined Saloon	Types 1 or 2: criss-cross chassis. Types 1, 2 or 3: grille, no spare or sidelights, 12 bonnet louvres. Smooth Blue, Black or plated 'Tootsie-Toy' type hubs.	
		body/chassis colours:	Maroon/Black, Red/Maroon, Red/Black, Green/Maroon, Green/Blue, Red/Brown, All Maroon	£300-400
	1937-40	............................casting change:	As previous model but with 13 bonnet louvres	£300-400
24f	1934-38	Sportsmans Coupé	Criss-cross chassis, with spare wheel, no sidelights, smooth hubs. Blue/Blue, Blue/Black, Yellow/Brown, Cream/Dark Blue, Tan/Brown	£200-400
	1937-40	............................casting change:	Open chassis, higher 'domed' roofline, no spare wheel	£200-400
24g	1934-38	Sports Tourer Four-seater	Types 1 or 2: criss-cross chassis. Types 1, 2 or 3: grille, spare wheel hub cast-in, no sidelights, open tinplate windscreen, separate dashboard/steering wheel casting. Blue or Black smooth hubs or plated 'Tootsie-Toy'type hubs.	
		body/chassis colours:	Yellow/Black, Yellow/Blue, Yellow/Brown, Blue/Brown, Cream/Green, Cream/Brown, Black/Cream, Blue/Maroon	£300-500
	1937-40	............................casting change:	Open chassis, filled-in windscreen, cast impression of spare	£300-500

24h	1934-38	**Sports Tourer Two-seater**.........	Types 1 or 2: criss-cross chassis. Types 1, 2 or 3: grille, spare wheel hub cast-in, no sidelights, open tinplate windscreen, separate dashboard/steering wheel casting. Plated, Blue or Black smooth hubs.	
		body/chassis colours:	Red/Red, Green/Dark Green, Yellow/Green, Yellow/Blue, Yellow/Black, Yellow/Brown, Black/Cream, Cream/Green, Red/Green, Blue/Brown, Yellow/Purple	£400-600
	1937-40	..........................casting change:	Open chassis, filled-in windscreen, cast impression of spare	£400-600
25j	1947-48	**Jeep**	Red body, Black, Red or Blue hubs	£80-100
			Green body, Black or Red hubs	£80-100
			Aqua Blue or Sky Blue body, Black or Yellow hubs	£100-150
25y	1952-54	**Universal Jeep**...........................	Red body, Blue hubs	£80-100
		(Renumbered 405)	Red body, Red hubs	£80-100
			Dark Green body, Mid-Green hubs	£80-100
			Dark Green body, Maroon hubs	£80-100
27d	1950-54	**Land Rover**.................................	See 'Farm and Garden Models'	
27f	1950-54	**Estate Car**..................................	See 'Farm and Garden Models'	

30 Series

30a	1935-40	**Chrysler 'Airflow' Saloon**.........	No chassis, separate bumper units, lead versions exist, smooth plain or silvered hubs.	
		(Renumbered 32)	Turquoise, Maroon, Cream, Green, Purplish Blue, Red, (hubs may be any colour)	£300-400
			Rare issues with 'Tootsie-Toy' type plated chrome hubs..	£300-400
	1946		Cream or Green body, smooth hubs, White tyres	£150-200
	1946-48		As previous model but Blue, Cream or Green body (ridged hubs usually Black)...................	£130-160
30b	1935-40	**Rolls-Royce**................................	Open chassis, no sidelights, authentic radiator, smooth Black hubs or coloured hubs.	
		NB:	Models with coloured hubs attract a premium.	
	1935-40		Cream/Black, Red and Maroon, Blue/Black, Dark Blue/Black, Fawn/Black, Tan/Dark Brown, Red/Black, All Black	£300-400
			Yellow/Brown, Red/Red, Grey/Grey, Green/Light Green, Pale Green/Black	£250-350
			Light Blue body, smooth Black wheel hubs, open chassis	£250-350
			Fawn body, smooth Black wheel hubs, Black open chassis	£250-350
		hub variation:	Fawn body, ridged Silver wheel hubs, Black open chassis	£200-250
	1946		Fawn body, smooth Black hubs, Black open chassis	£90-120
		hub variation:	Fawn body, ridged Silver wheel hubs, Black open chassis	£200-250
	1946-50		Plain (closed) chassis, Violet-Blue/Black, Mid-Blue/Black, Dark Blue/Black, Light Blue/Black, Fawn/Black or Greyish-Brown/Black; all with ridged hubs	£100-125
30c	1935-40	**Daimler**	Open chassis, no sidelights, authentic radiator, smooth hubs.	
	1935-40		Cream/Black, Blue/Black, Dark Blue/Black, Yellow/Black, Fawn/Black	£200-300
			Turquoise/Black, Fawn/Black, Light Green/Black	£200-300
			Pink/Maroon, Red/Red	£175-250
			Two-tone Grey or two-tone Green	£300-500
		Wartime issue:	Pale Tan body, Black chassis and hubs	£200-250
	1945-46		Beige body, smooth black wheel hubs, open chassis	£300-400
			Green or Fawn body, open chassis, smooth or ridged hubs	£90-120
	1946-50		Plain (closed) chassis, Dark Green/Black, Cream/Black, Fawn/Black, Beige/Black, Grey/Black, Light Green/Black; all with ridged hubs	£100-150
			Medium Green body with Pale Green ridged hubs	£100-125
30d	1935-40	**Vauxhall**.....................................	Open chassis, no sidelights, spare wheel, 'egg box' or 'shield' grille.	
	1935-38		Green/Black, Blue/Black, Grey/Black, Yellow/Black, Brown/Black	£200-300
			Yellow/Brown, Cream/Brown, Tan/Brown	£200-300
			Two-tone Grey or two-tone Green	£300-400
	1938-40	.......................radiator change:	As previous model but with 'shield' grille, Black chassis	£200-300
			With 'shield' radiator and coloured chassis	£200-300
	1946		Dark Olive Green body, open chassis, smooth black hubs, White tyres	£100-125
	1946-50		Plain (closed) chassis, no spare wheel, 'shield' radiator, Green/Black, Dark Brown/Black, Maroon/Black, Yellow/Black, Grey/Black, Olive-Green/Black, Blue/Black	£100-125
		hub variation:	Dark Olive Green body, Black chassis, Silver ridged hubs, thick axles	£200-250
30e	1935-48	**Breakdown Car**..........................	See 'Commercial Vehicles' section.	
30f	1936-41	**Ambulance**..................................	See 'Emergency Vehicles' section.	
30g	1936-50	**Caravan**	See 'Accessories (Pre-War)' section.	
32	1934-35	**Chrysler 'Airflow' Saloon**.........	Maroon (lead) body, no chassis, separate bumper units	£200-250
		(Previously 30a)...........................	Maroon (diecast) body, no chassis, separate bumper units...	£200-250
34a	1935-40	**'Royal Air Mail' Service Car**	See 'Commercial Vehicles and Vans' section.	

35 Series

35a	1936-40	**Saloon Car**.................................	Some versions may have spare wheel cover in darker shade of main colour.	
			Blue, Maroon, Grey, Yellow, Red, Turquoise, Black or White solid rubber wheels	£65-75
	1946-48		Grey or Blue body (spare wheel cover not enhanced), Black rubber wheels.......................	£50-60
35az	1939-40	**Fiat 2-seater Saloon**	Red, Blue or Green, White rubber wheels, 'Simca 5' cast inside. French issue...................	£80-100
35b	1936-39	**Racer**..	Red, Silver, Yellow or Blue body, with or without driver, White solid rubber wheels, Red grille and steering wheel..	£65-75
35b	1939-54	**Midget Racer**..............................	Silver body, Red grille, Brown driver, solid Black rubber wheels only...............................	£65-75
		(Renumbered 200)........................	Silver body, Red grille, Silver driver, solid Black rubber wheels only................................	£65-75
			Green body, Black tyres	£150-175
35c	1936-40	**MG Sports Car**	Red, Pale or Dark Green, Turquoise, Blue or Maroon, Silver detailing, White solid rubber wheels..	£65-75
	1946-48		Red or Green body, Silver on radiator only, Black rubber wheels only	£40-50

35d	1938-40	**Austin 7 Car** (open tourer)..........	Wire windscreen frame, Black or White rubber wheels, Silver radiator and steering wheel, hole for driver, 50 mm. Blue, Turquoise, Grey, Lime Green, Maroon or Yellow, (Yellow may have Orange spare wheel cover) £50-60
	1946-48	....	Blue, Grey or Yellow body, Silver on radiator only, Black rubber wheels only £35-45
			Fawn body, Silver on radiator only, Black rubber wheels only £45-55

36 Series

36a	1937-41	**Armstrong-Siddeley Limousine with Driver and Footman**	Detailed chassis with slots, tinplate figures, sidelights, Black smooth hubs. Red/Dark Red, Grey/Dark Grey, Maroon/Dark Maroon, all-Maroon...............................£900-1,200
	1946	....	Grey body, Black smooth wheel hubs, Moulded chassis with or without slots, no figures.......................£100-130
36a	1947-50	**Armstrong-Siddeley**....................	(no slots or figures), moulded chassis, ridged hubs (black or coloured), plated radiator. Mid-Blue/Black, Grey/Black, Maroon/Black, Red/Maroon, Light Blue/Black, Powder Blue/Black, Saxe-Blue/Black, Olive-Green/Black, Turquoise/Black, Blue/Blue £100-175
36b	1937-41	**Bentley 2 seat Sports Coupé with Driver and Footman**	Detailed chassis with slots, tinplate figures, sidelights, smooth black hubs. Cream/Black, Yellow/Maroon, Grey/Grey £900-1,200
	1946		Light Green or Saxe Blue body, smooth black hubs, moulded chassis (slots on some), no figures...........£200-300
36b	1947-50	**Bentley**	(no slots/figures). Moulded chassis, ridged hubs, plated radiator. Green/Black, Dark Blue/Black, Light Blue/Black, Grey/Black, Fawn/Black, Light Fawn/Black £100-175
36c	1937-41	**Humber Vogue Saloon with Driver and Footman**	Detailed chassis with slots, tinplate figures, sidelights, plated radiator. Green/Dark Green, Blue/Dark Blue, all Royal Blue, smooth Black hubs..................................£900-1,200
	1946	....	Early post war issues with smooth Black hubs, moulded chassis with or without slots, no figures £100-150
36c	1947-50	**Humber Vogue**...........................	Dark Brown/Black, Blue/Black, Grey/Black, Maroon/Black, no slots or figures, ridged hubs £90-120
			Light Blue body, Black moulded chassis, ridged Black hubs, plated radiator £150-200
36d	1937-41	**Rover Streamlined Saloon with Driver and Footman**	Detailed cast chassis with slots, tinplate driver and passenger, sidelights, Black smooth hubs. Light Green body, mid-Green wings, White tyres...£900-1,200
			Red Green body, Maroon wings, White tyres...£400-600
	1946		Early post war issues with smooth Black hubs and moulded chassis with or without slots £100-150
36d	1947-50	**Rover**...	Dark, Saxe, Mid or Bright Blue/Black, Light or Mid-Green/Black, no slots or figures.....................£90-120
			Green body with Light Green hubs £100-125
			Dark Blue body, Black wings, Light Blue hubs £150-200
			Navy Blue body, Black wings, Black hubs £150-200
36e	1937-41	**British Salmson Two-seater Sports Car with Driver**	Detailed chassis, hole in seat for driver, cast Red or Green driver, Black hubs, solid windscreen, sidelights, spare wheel on some. Royal Blue/Black, Blue/Dark Blue, Black/Red, Grey/Dark Grey, Silver/Black, Red/Maroon £500-750
	1946	**British Salmson**........................	Early post war issues with smooth Black hubs, moulded chassis, no driver..£125-175
			Rare Brown issues £400-600
36e	1947-50	**British Salmson Two-seater Sports Car**	Red/Black, Light, Mid or Dark Green/Black, Fawn/Black, Mid-Blue/Black, Sky-Blue/Black or Saxe-Blue/Black, no hole in seat, tinplate windscreen, ridged hubs £90-150
			Red or Brown body, moulded chassis, ridged hubs £300-400
36f	1937-41	**British Salmson Four-seater Sports Car with Driver**	Detailed chassis, hole in seat for driver, cast driver, sidelights, Black smooth hubs and solid windscreen, cast-in spare wheel. Red/Maroon, Green/Dark Green, Grey/mid-Grey £500-750
36f	1947-50	**British Salmson Four-seater Sports Car**	Light or Mid-Green/Black, Brown/Black, Grey/Black, Fawn/Black, no hole or driver. Greenish-Grey/Black or Light Grey/Black, tinplate windscreen, ridged hubs.................................£90-150

38 Series

NB Early Post War Issues 38 and 39 Series - see the Model Identification section for details.

38a	1940-41	**Frazer Nash BMW Sports**	Red body and smooth Black hubs with Red or Maroon seats, or Light Green with Dark Green seats........£150-250
			Dark Blue body and smooth hubs, Fawn seats £150-250
			Light Grey body, Brown seats £150-250
	1946	...............................Special issue:	Dark Blue body, Light Blue seats, spread spigot not rivet, 'Hornby Series' tinplate sheet base £100-150
	1947-50	..............................Regular issues:	with Black base, Black ridged hubs, celluloid windscreen:
			Light or Dark Blue (Fawn or Grey seats)...£75-95
			Grey (Fawn, Khaki or Blue seats), Grey (Red seats and hubs) or Blue (Blue hubs) £150-200
			Light Grey (Blue seats, Black hubs), Blue with Putty seats..£150-200
38a	1950-55	....	Same as previous models but made for export only (renumbered 100) ....NGPP
38b	1940-41	**Sunbeam Talbot Sports**.............	Red (Maroon tonneau), Red or Black smooth hubs, lacquered metal base £150-200
	1946	....	Grey body, Fawn seats or Green with Dark Green tonneau, Black smooth hubs....................£300-400
	1947-49	....	Red/Maroon or Maroon/Grey, Black baseplate, Black ridged hubs £90-120
			Light Green/Green, Brown/Blue, Green/Dark Yellow, Black baseplate, Black ridged hubs £90-120
			Light Grey (Grey or Dark Blue tonneau), Black ridged hubs, Black baseplate £90-120
			Dark Grey (Grey or Light Blue tonneau), Black ridged hubs, Black baseplate £90-120
			Yellow body and ridged hubs with matt Fawn tonneau, Black painted baseplate £200-250
			Deep Yellow body and ridged hubs with Dark Green tonneau, Black base, Silver edged screen...............£200-250
			Dark Blue body, Light Grey tonneau, Black ridged hubs and baseplate...£90-120
			Light Blue body, Dark Grey tonneau, Black ridged hubs and baseplate..£90-120
			Mid-Blue body, Grey tonneau, Black ridged hubs and baseplate..£90-120
			Brown body, Blue tonneau, Silver edged screen..£150-175
		NB	All issues may have a silver-edged windscreen.
	1950		Late post war issues with coloured hubs, e.g. Yellow body, Green tonneau, Yellow ridged hubs or Red body, Maroon tonneau, Red ridged hubs, plain screen £100-150
			Red body, Dark Green tonneau, Red ridged hubs, Black baseplate £100-150
38b	1950-55	....	As previous models but made for export only (renumbered 101). ....NGPP

38c	1946	**Lagonda Sports Coupé**..............	Early post war issues with Black smooth hubs...	£100-150
	1947-50	....	Green body, Black or Dark Green seats, ridged Black hubs, Black baseplate	£90-120
			Grey body, Fawn or Maroon seats, ridged Black hubs	£90-120
			Maroon body, Dark Blue or Grey seats, ridged Black hubs, Black baseplate	£90-120
			Light Grey Mid or Dark Grey seats, ridged Black hubs	£90-120
38c	1950-55	....	As previous models but made for export only (renumbered 102)............................	£100-150
	1950	....	Late post war issues with coloured hubs, eg. Green body with Light Green hubs	£100-150
38d	1940-41	**Alvis Sports Tourer**	Green body, Black seats and hubs or Maroon body, Red seats, lacquered base	£150-175
	1946	....	Early post war issues	£100-150
	1947-50	....	Green/Dark Green, Green/Brown, Black painted baseplate	£90-120
			Green body, Black seats and hubs, Black painted baseplate	£90-120
			Green body, Black seats, Green hubs, Black painted baseplate	£90-120
			Maroon/Grey, Red hubs, Maroon/Red, Light Blue/Dark Blue, Black base.................	£100-150
			Blue/Grey, Grey/Blue, Black painted base..	£75-95
	1950	....	Late post war issues with coloured hubs, eg. Maroon body with Red hubs	£100-150
38d	1950-55	....	As previous models but made for export only (renumbered 103)..........................	NGPP
38e	1940 ?	**Triumph Dolomite**	Planned and catalogued but not issued	NPP
38e	1946	**Armstrong Siddeley Coupé**........	('Hurricane'). Early post war issues with Black smooth wheel hubs	£100-150
	1947-50	....	Grey/Deep Blue, Light Grey/Blue, Black painted baseplate	£90-120
			Light Grey/Green, Light Green/Grey or Grey/Dark Green	£90-120
			Bright Green/Grey, Red/Maroon, Cream/Blue, Black painted baseplate	£90-120
			Dark Green body and interior	£90-120
			Royal Blue body, Dark Green interior	£90-120
			Apple Green body, Dark Grey interior	£90-120
	1950	....	Light Green body, Apple Green hubs..	£200-250
			Light Green body, Grey interior, Mid-Green hubs	£200-250
			Light Grey body, Dark Green interior, Grey hubs	£200-250
			Grey body, Dark Blue interior, Red hubs	£200-250
			Grey body, Dark Blue interior, Pale or Mid-Blue hubs	£200-250
38e	1950-55	....	As previous models but made for export only (renumbered 104)...........................	£200-250
38f	1940-41	**Jaguar (SS100) Sports Car**	Khaki/Blue, Blue/Grey, Light Blue/Grey, Grey/Blue, Grey/Black,	
			Red/Maroon, Dark Brown/Black, 2 celluloid windscreens, clear lacquered baseplate..........	£150-175
	1946	....	Early post-war issues with Black smooth hubs (later issues are ridged)...................	£90-120
	1947-50	....	Light, Mid- or Dark Blue body, Grey or Putty interior, Black painted baseplate	£90-120
			Light Brown body, Blue interior, Black painted baseplate or Red body, Maroon interior.........	£90-120
			Brownish-Grey body, Black interior and ridged hubs	£100-150
			Grey body, Red interior and ridged hubs	£100-150
	1950	....	Late post-war issues with coloured hubs, e.g. Light Blue body, Putty interior (Blue hubs) or	
			Red body, Maroon interior (Red hubs), Silver-edged screens	£200-300
38f	1950-55	....	As previous models but made for export only (renumbered 105)...........................	£100-150

39 Series		See lso the 'Model Identification' and 'Wooden Prototypes' sections for further information.

39a	1939-41	**Packard Super 8 Tourer**	Light Green, Grey, Black, Yellow, Blue, Silver baseplate....................................	£300-400
	1946	....	Early post-war issues with Black smooth wheel hubs	£90-120
	1947-50	....	Dark Brown, Green or Olive-Green body, Black painted baseplate, ridged hubs	£90-120
	1950	....	Late post-war issues with coloured ridged hubs...	£200-250
39b	1939-41	**Oldsmobile 6 Sedan**	Black, Maroon, Yellow, Mid Blue, Light or Mid-Grey or Green, Silver base............	£150-200
	1946	....	Early post-war issues with Black smooth wheel hubs	£100-150
	1947-50	....	Grey, Brown, Green or Fawn body, oval baseplate supports,	
			Black painted baseplate open at rear, ridged hubs..	£90-120
			Cream body, ridged hubs	£100-125
			Violet-Blue, Black chassis, ridged hubs	£125-150
	1947-50	...........................US issue:	Light Blue body, Black ridged hubs, oval baseplate support, open rear baseplate, ridged hubs.................	£200-300
	1950	....	Late post-war issues with coloured ridged hubs	£200-250
	1952	...........................Export issue:	Beige body and hubs, oval front supports, closed rear baseplate..........................	£200-300
39bu	1950-52	**Oldsmobile Sedan** (US issue)	Cream with Dark Blue wings, Black painted baseplate	£600-800
			Cream body, Tan wings, Black painted baseplate (closed at rear), Black hubs	£800-1,000
			Tan body and hubs, oval studs, baseplate closed at rear	£600-800
			Light Blue body, Dark Blue wings, Light Blue hubs	£600-800
39c	1939-41	**Lincoln Zephyr Coupé**	Grey/Black, Yellow Red or Green body, lacquered baseplate, smooth Black hubs	£150-175
	1946	....	Early post-war issues with Black smooth wheel hubs	£100-150
	1947-50	....	Light Grey, Brown, Maroon or Red body, Black painted baseplate, ridged hubs	£90-120
	1950	....	Late post war issues with coloured ridged hubs e.g. Light 'Riley' Green with darker Green hubs	
			or Red body with Red hubs or Yellow with Green hubs.......................................	£200-400
39cu	1950-52	...........................US issue:	Red body and ridged hubs, Maroon wings, Black painted baseplate	£2,000-2,500
39cu	1950-52	...........................US issue:	Cream body and ridged hubs, Brown wings, Black painted baseplate	£700-900
39cu	1950-52	...........................US issue:	Tan with Brown wings, Black painted baseplate, Black ridged hubs	£700-900
39d	1939-41	**Buick Viceroy Saloon**	Grey, Green, Maroon, Cream or Blue, lacquered baseplate, smooth Black hubs	£150-200
	1946	....	Early post-war issues with Black smooth wheel hubs	£100-125
	1946	....	Olive body, smooth hubs	£100-125
	1947-50	....	Light or Dark Green, Maroon, Fawn, Blue, Beige or Grey body, Black base, matching ridged hubs........	£80-110
			Mustard body, Black painted baseplate, matching ridged hubs	£150-200
			Greyish-Brown body, Light Brown ridged hubs, Black painted baseplate	£140-160
			Apple Green body and matching ridged hubs	£150-200
	1950	....	Late post-war issues with coloured ridged hubs, eg. Light 'Riley' Green body with darker green	
			hubs or Brown body with Green or Yellow hubs	£200-400

39e	1939-41	**Chrysler Royal Sedan**	Black, Green, Royal Blue or Grey body, lacquered baseplate, smooth Black hubs	£100-150
			Yellow body, lacquered baseplate, Black hubs	£400-600
	1946	....	Early post-war issues with Black smooth wheel hubs	£100-125
	1947-50	....	Light Blue, Mid-Blue, Dark Blue, Light Green, Mid-Green, Dark Green or	
			Dark Grey body, Black ridged hubs and baseplate	£85-110
			As previous models but with Silvered baseplate	£250-350
			Cream body, Light Green ridged hubs, Black painted baseplate	£500-750
	1950	....	Late post-war issues with coloured ridged hubs, eg. Light 'Triumph 1800' Blue with blue hubs	£200-250
39eu	1950-52	**Chrysler Royal**.........(US issues)	Yellow with Red wings, Yellow hubs, Black baseplate, Blued axles	£1,500-2,000
			Two-tone Green body, Light Green hubs, Black baseplate, Blued axles	£1,000-1,400
39f	1939-41	**Studebaker State Commander** ..	Yellow, Green or Dark Grey body, lacquered baseplate	£200-250
	1946		Early post-war issues with Black smooth wheel hubs	£100-150
	1947-50		Yellow body, Black smooth hubs	£250-350
			Green, Olive or Maroon body, Black baseplate, ridged hubs	£85-110
			Dark Grey or Light Grey body, Black ridged hubs	£85-110
			Dark Maroon body, Black ridged hubs	£85-110
			Very Dark Blue or Navy Blue body, Black ridged hubs	£90-120
			Tan body, Black ridged hubs	£120-150
			Mid-Blue body, Black baseplate, Mid-Blue ridged hubs	£200-250
			Dark Green body, Black baseplate, ridged hubs	£120-140
	1950		Late post-war issues with coloured ridged hubs	£200-250

40 Series

See also the 'Dinky Toys Cars - Box Types' and 'Model Identification' information pages.

40a	1947-50	**Riley Saloon**...............................	Tinplate baseplate '40A' has small print and the rear wheels are retained by cast pillars.	
			Light, Mid or Dark Grey body, Black hubs	£70-80
			Light Grey body, Tan hubs	£70-80
			Mid-Green body, Black hubs	£80-100
	1950-53	...............................2nd baseplate:	Baseplate with '40A' and large print. With tow-hook aperture.	
			Dark Blue or Mid-Blue body, Black hubs	£80-100
			Grey body, Black hubs	£150-175
			Dark Green body, Black hubs	£80-100
			Cream body, Mid-Green hubs	£75-85
	1954	40a renumbered 158	Baseplate '158' has large print. No tow-hook aperture.	
158	1954-55	**Riley Saloon**...............................	Cream body, Mid-Green hubs	£100-150
			Mid-Green body with Green hubs, or Light Green body and hubs	£100-150
			Pale Green body, Mid-Green hubs	£100-150
			Dark Blue body, Mid-Blue hubs	£100-150
			Light Grey body and hubs	£100-150
40b	1948-49	**Triumph 1800 Saloon**	Small baseplate print, rear axles held by cast pillars (see diagram).	
			Light, Mid or Dark Grey body, Black or Grey hubs	£70-80
			Mid-Blue body and hubs	£100-130
			Light Blue body, Blue or Fawn hubs	£90-110
			Fawn body, Black or Fawn hubs	£80-90
			Black body, Black hubs	£400-600
	1949-54	...............................2nd baseplate:	Small print on baseplate, rear axle retained by baseplate tabs.	
			Mid or Dark Blue body, Fawn hubs, or Light Blue body and hubs	£80-90
			Fawn body, Green hubs	£80-90
	1954	40b renumbered 151	Large baseplate print.	
151	1954-59	**Triumph 1800 Saloon**	Beige body, Green hubs, or Dark Blue with Light Blue hubs	£90-110
			Light Blue body with Mid-Blue, Fawn or Grey hubs, or Mid-Blue body with Light Blue hubs	£90-110
40c	1940	**Jowett Javelin**.............................	Factory drawing exists but model not issued	NPP
40d	1949-54	**Austin (A40) Devon**	Small baseplate print, rear axle retained by the baseplate.	
			Maroon body and hubs	£80-90
			Red body, Maroon hubs	£400-600
			Light Grey-Green body and hubs or with Beige hubs	£90-110
			Light Blue body, Mid-Blue hubs, or Mid-Blue body with Light Blue hubs	£90-110
			Dark Green body, Cream hubs	£80-90
			Luminous Blue body, Mid-Blue hubs, Black baseplate	£120-140
	1954	40d renumbered 152	'DEVON' cast into underside of roof.	
152	1954-59	**Austin (A40) Devon**	Large baseplate print (see example diagrams).	
			Suede Green body and hubs, or Dark Blue body with Mid Blue hubs	£100-120
			Tan body, Suede Green hubs	£500-700
			Maroon body, Red hubs	£175-200
			Light Blue body and hubs	£400-500
			Dark Blue body, Light Blue hubs..	£130-160
			Light Green body, Mid-Green hubs, or Dark Green body with Fawn hubs	£130-160
	1956-59	...........................Two-tone issue:	Blue upper body and hubs, Yellow lower body	£200-300
	1956-59	...........................Two-tone issue:	Cerise lower body, Green upper body, Cream hubs	£200-300
40e	1948	**Standard Vanguard**	1st casting: Open rear wheel arches, small baseplate print, rear axle secured by tinplate clip.	
			Fawn body and hubs	£100-120
			Fawn body, Red hubs	£140-170
	1949-50	........................baseplate change:	Open rear wheel arches, small or large baseplate print, rear axle secured by baseplate tabs.	
			Fawn body and hubs	£70-80
			Mid-Blue body and hubs..	£80-90
			Maroon body and hubs	£80-90
			Dark Blue body, Fawn hubs	£500-600
	1950-54	..................................2nd casting:	Closed rear wheel arches, small baseplate print.	

(40e continued)   Light Blue body, Fawn hubs, or Fawn body with Fawn hubs £100-120
     1954   40e renumbered 153 .... 'VANGUARD' cast into underside of roof, large baseplate print.

153   1954-59   **Standard Vanguard**................... Mid-Blue body, Cream, Blue or Fawn hubs £100-150
             (renumbered from 40e)   Dark Blue body, Fawn hubs £200-250
                               Fawn body, Fawn hubs...£100-150
                               Cream body, Cream hubs..£100-150
                               Maroon body, Fawn hubs...£100-150
                               Maroon body, Maroon hubs...£750-1,000
                         NB   The ridge which appears on the boot of some Vanguard models is the result of worn die replacement.

40f   1951-54   **Hillman Minx** ....1st baseplate: Small baseplate print (see diagram).
                               Tan body, Fawn hubs £150-175
                               Mid-Green body, Light Green hubs £150-175
                               Light Green body and hubs £150-175
                               Light Green body, Mid-Green hubs £150-175
                               Dark Tan body, Green hubs £150-175
                               Dark Tan body, Cream hubs £150-175
                               Light Tan body, Cream hubs £150-175
                               Dark Green body, Mid-Green hubs £150-175
     1955   40f renumbered 154...................... 'HILLMAN MINX' cast into underside of roof.
154   1955   **Hillman Minx** ....2nd baseplate: Large baseplate print (see diagram).
             (renumbered from 40f)   Dark Tan body with Cream or Green hubs, or Pale Tan body with Blue or Yellow hubs £100-120
                               Light Green body and hubs, or Dark Green body with Light Green hubs.............................£175-200
                               Pale Green body with Light Green hubs, or Light Green body with Mid-Green hubs.............£175-225
                               Pale Blue lower body and hubs, Cerise upper body £200-250
                               Lime Green lower body, Cream upper body and hubs £200-250

40g   1950-54   **Morris Oxford**........................... Small baseplate print.
                               Fawn body, Grey hubs £80-100
                               Grey body and hubs £80-100
                               Green body, Light Green hubs £80-100
                               Green body, Fawn hubs £80-100
     1954   40g renumbered 159 .... Small baseplate print, 'MORRIS OXFORD' cast into underside of roof.
159   1954   **Morris Oxford**........................... Dark Green body and hubs or Green body with Light Green hubs..........................£140-175
                      Export issue: Beige body and hubs £500-800
                               Blue body, Grey hubs...£1,500-2,000
                               Fawn body, Grey or Stone hubs £120-140
                   Two-tone issue: Green upper body and hubs, Cream lower body £150-175
                   Two-tone issue: Cream upper body and hubs, Cerise lower body £150-175
                   Two-tone issue: Turquoise upper body, Cream lower body, Turquoise-Green hubs £500-700

40h   1952-54   **Austin Taxi** (FX3).........Chassis: Diecast chassis with cast-in driver and model number.
                               All-Yellow body and hubs, Black chassis ('40H'), interior and driver....................£90-120
                               All-Yellow body and hubs, Brown chassis ('40H'), interior and driver...................£150-250
                               Dark Blue body, Light Blue hubs, Black chassis ('40H'), interior and driver...........£250-350
                               Mid-Blue body and hubs, Black chassis ('40H'), interior and driver........................£400-600
     1954   40h renumbered 254
254   1956-59   **Austin Taxi** (FX3).......Two-tone: Yellow upper body and hubs, Dark Green lower body, Black chassis ('254'), interior and driver £90-120
                      Spun hubs: Black body, spun hubs, Grey chassis ('254'), interior and driver £110-130
                               Blue body, Light Blue hubs..£500-750

40j   1953-54   **Austin (A40) Somerset** .... Large print on baseplate.
                               Pale Blue body and hubs £80-100
                               Red body and hubs £80-100
                               Mid-Blue body and hubs £80-100
                               Dark Blue body, Mid-Blue hubs £80-100
     1954   40j renumbered 161 .... Large baseplate print, 'AUSTIN SOMERSET' cast into underside of roof.
161   1954   **Austin (A40) Somerset** .... Pale Blue body, Mid or Dark Blue hubs £80-100
                               Red body and hubs £80-100
     1956-59   Two-tone issue: Red lower body and hubs, Yellow upper body £200-250
     1956-59   Two-tone issue: Cream lower body and hubs, Black lower body £200-250

Models 101 onwards

101   1957-60   **Sunbeam Alpine**......................... Maroon body, Cream interior, Cream diecast hubs, Grey driver £120-140
             (touring finish)   Maroon body, Cream interior, spun hubs, Grey driver £200-300
                               Light Turquoise body, Dark Blue interior, Mid-Blue diecast hubs, Grey driver £120-140
                               Light Turquoise body, Dark Blue interior, spun hubs, Grey driver £150-175
                               Light Blue body, Blue diecast hubs £120-140
102   1957-60   **MG Midget**............................... Orange body, Red interior and diecast hubs, Grey driver £150-175
             (touring finish)   Pale Green body, Cream interior, Cream diecast hubs, Grey driver.........................£150-200
                               Late issues with spun aluminium hubs, in plain or lighter yellow boxes £250-350

103   1957-60   **Austin Healey 100** .... Red body, Grey interior, diecast hubs and driver...£175-225
             (touring finish)   Cream body, Red interior and diecast hubs, Grey driver £175-225

104   1957-60   **Aston-Martin DB3S**..................... Light Blue body, Dark Blue interior, Mid-Blue hubs, Grey driver..........................£150-200
             (touring finish)   Salmon-Pink body, Red interior and diecast hubs, Grey driver, Matt or Gloss baseplate............£150-200
105   1957-60   **Triumph TR2**............................. Grey body, Red interior and diecast hubs, Grey driver £130-160
             (touring finish)   Same, but with spun hubs and plastic steering wheel. In 'plain' printed box or late lighter yellow box....£180-240
                               Lemon Yellow body, Light Green interior, Mid-Green hubs, Grey driver £180-220
     1959-60   .... As before but with spun hubs, in 'plain' printed box with Yellow spot, or in late lighter Yellow box £250-350

106	1954-58	**Austin A90 Atlantic**	Light Blue body, Cream interior, Cream hubs	£100-120
		(Renumbered from 140a)	Light Blue body, Red interior, Red or Cream hubs	£130-160
			Light Blue body, Dark Blue interior, Cream or Dark Blue hubs...	£100-120
			Black body, Red interior and hubs, White tyres	£100-120
			Pink body, Cream interior, Cream hubs, '106' on baseplate	£100-120
		NB	Interiors may have a gloss or matt finish.	
107	1955-59	**Sunbeam Alpine**		
		(competition finish)	Pale Blue, Beige or Cream interior, Beige hubs, '26', racing driver..................................	£120-140
			Deep Pink body, Grey interior, Beige hubs, RN '34', racing driver	£120-140
		NB	See also 'Factory samples' listing at the end of this section.	
108	1955-59	**MG Midget**		
		(competition finish)	Red body, Tan interior, Red hubs, RN '24', racing driver	£150-175
			Cream body, Maroon interior, Red hubs, RN '26' or '28', racing driver	£150-175
			NB The version of 108 issued in the US is numbered 129.	
109	1955-59	**Austin-Healey 100**		
		(competition finish)	Cream body, Red interior and hubs, racing driver and racing number '22' or '23'	£150-175
			Yellow body, Blue interior and hubs, racing driver and racing number '21' or '28'...........	£150-175
110	1956-59	**Aston-Martin DB3S**		
		(competition finish)	Grey body, Blue interior and hubs, racing driver and number '20'	£150-175
			Mid-Green body, Red interior, Red ridged hubs, racing number '22' or '25'.....................	£150-175
			Light Green body, Red interior, Red ridged hubs, RN '22' or '25'....................................	£200-250
110	1966-67	**Aston-Martin DB5**	Metallic Red, Cream or Black interior, '110' on base, spoked wheels...............................£75-95	£75-95
	1967-71		Metallic Red or Blue, Cream or Black interior, plain base, spoked wheels £75-95	£75-95
		NB	See also 'Factory samples' listing at the end of this section.	
111	1956-59	**Triumph TR2 Sports Car**		
		(competition finish)	Salmon-Pink body, Blue interior and hubs, racing driver and RN '29'	£175-200
			Turquoise body, Red interior and hubs, racing driver and racing number '25'	£175-200
112	1961-66	**Austin-Healey Sprite Mk.II**	Red body, Cream interior, spun hubs, English and Afrikaans wording on box	£100-125
		South African issue:	Turquoise body, Cream interior, spun hubs, English and Afrikaans wording on box	£500-750
		South African issue:	Light or Dark Blue body, Cream interior, spun hubs, English and Afrikaans wording on box	£500-750
		South African issue:	Lilac (Pink) body, Cream interior, spun hubs, English and Afrikaans wording on box	£500-750
113	1962-69	**MG 'MGB'**	White body, Red interior, Grey plastic driver, spun hubs	£70-90
		South African issue:	Mid-Blue body, Red interior, spun hubs, English and Afrikaans wording on box	£500-750
		South African issue:	Red body, Cream interior, spun hubs, English and Afrikaans wording on box	£500-750
114	1963-71	**Triumph Spitfire**	Sports car with Blue lady driver (plastic), spun hubs, jewelled headlamps.	
	1963-66	....	Metallic Silver-Grey body, Red interior	£120-140
			Red body, Cream interior	£120-140
	1966-70	....	Metallic Gold body with Red interior and 'Tiger In Tank' on bootlid	£120-140
	1966-70	....	Metallic Gold body, without bootlid logo	£120-140
	1970-71	....	Metallic Purple body, Gold interior	£120-140
115	1965-69	**Plymouth Fury Sports**	White open body, Red interior, cast wheels, driver and passenger.....................................	£75-85
116	1966-71	**Volvo P 1800 S**	Red body, White interior, wire wheels	£60-75
			Metallic Red body, Light Blue interior, wire wheels	£80-100
120	1962-67	**Jaguar 'E' type**	Red body, detachable Black or Grey hardtop plus optional Cream or Grey folded soft-top, spun hubs	£80-100
			Metallic Blue and White, Black, Grey or Cream body, spun hubs	£80-100
			Metallic Light Blue and Black body, Cream interior, spun hubs	£600-800
122	1977-78	**Volvo 265 DL Estate**	Metallic Blue (Brown interior), or Cream with '265DL' wing badges, cast hubs	£30-35
	1979-80		Orange version without '265 DL' (made in Italy by Polistil), Brown box	£40-50
		NB	See also 'Factory samples' listing at the end of this section.	
123	1977-80	**Princess 2200 HL**	Metallic Bronze with black roof side panels, plastic wheels...	£30-35
			All White	£30-35
			White body, Blue roof	£30-35
			White body, Blue side panels	£30-35
124	1977-79	**Rolls-Royce Phantom V**	Metallic Light Blue, boot opens - bonnet does not (see 152)..	£35-45
127	1964-66	**Rolls-Royce Silver Cloud Mk.3.**	Metallic Blue or Metallic Green body, White interior, spun hubs	£65-75
	1966-69	....	Metallic Gold body, White interior, cast hubs	£55-65
	1969-72	....	Metallic Red body, White interior, cast hubs	£55-65
128	1964-67	**Mercedes-Benz 600**	Metallic Maroon body, White interior, spun hubs, three figures/luggage	£45-55
	1967-75		Metallic Maroon body, White interior, Blue base, spun hubs or Speedwheels, driver only........	£30-40
	1975-79		Metallic Blue body, White interior, driver, Speedwheels..	£30-35
129	1954?	**MG Midget** (US issue)	White body, Maroon or Red interior and tonneau, Red hubs, no driver or racing number (see 108), Yellow box with '129'	£600-800
			Red body, Tan interior and tonneau, Red hubs, no driver or racing number (see 108), Yellow box with '129'	£600-800
129	1965 -72	**Volkswagen 1300 Sedan**	Metallic Blue body, White interior, spun hubs, registration plate 'K.HK 454'	£45-55
	1972-76		Metallic Bright Blue body, White interior, plastic Speedwheels	£30-35
130	1964-66	**Ford Consul Corsair**	Red or Metallic Wine Red body, Off-White interior, spun hubs	£55-65
	1966-69		Pale Blue, Metallic Dark Grey base, Off-White interior, spun hubs	£45-55
			NB Baseplates on 130 may have rounded or dimpled rivets.	
131	1956-61	**Cadillac Eldorado**	Yellow body, Cerise interior, Grey driver, Grey or Cream diecast hubs, packing piece also in box...........	£110-140
			Salmon-Pink body, Grey interior, Grey driver, Beige diecast hubs, packing piece also in box..........	£110-140
	1962-63	....	As previous models but with spun aluminium hubs..	£130-160

131	1968-70	**Jaguar 'E'-type 2+2**..................	White body, Light Blue or Red interior, cast spoked wheels, Gold base	£80-100
	1970-75	....	Metallic Copper body, Blue interior, Gold base, cast spoked wheels or plastic wheels	£80-100
	1975-76	....	Metallic Purple body, Light Blue interior, cast spoked wheels	£80-90
	1976-77	....	Bronze body, Speedwheels...	£65-75
	1977-77	....	Metallic Red or Post Office Red body, Blue interior, Speedwheels..	£70-80

132	1955-61	**Packard Convertible**	Light Green body, Red interior and hubs, Grey driver	£110-140
			Pale Tan body, Red interior and hubs, Grey driver	£110-140
	1962-63		As previous models but with spun aluminium hubs	£130-160
132	1967-74	**Ford 40 RV**	Metallic Silver body, Red interior, spoked wheels...	£30-40
			Fluorescent Pink body, Yellow engine cover, White interior, spoked wheels	£35-45
			Metallic Light Blue body, Red or Yellow interior, spoked wheels..	£30-40
	NB		Early models have red headlight recesses.	

133	1955-60	**Cunningham C5R**....................	White body, Dark Blue stripes, Brown interior, RN '31', Blue hubs, Light Blue driver	£65-75
			Off-White body, Blue interior and driver..	£65-75
			As previous models but with spun aluminium hubs	£70-80
133	1964-66	**Ford Cortina**	Metallic Gold/White body, Red interior, spun hubs, (issued to replace 139).............................	£55-65
	1966-68		Pale Lime body, Red interior, spun hubs..	£65-75
134	1964-68	**Triumph Vitesse**...................	Metallic Aqua Blue body, White side stripe, Red interior, spun hubs.....................................	£70-85
			Metallic Aqua Blue body, White side stripe, Grey interior, spun hubs...................................	£80-90
		Indian issues:	Manufactured in India and fully licensed by Meccano. Sold as 'Dinky Toys' and not the later	
			'Nicky Toys'. Box marked 'Licenced Manufacturer & Registered User in India, S. Kumar & Co.,	
			Registered Proprietors of Trade Mark Meccano Ltd.' Model base also marked 'Licensee in India	
			S. Kumar & Co.'. Variations:	
			Green body, White flash, cast hubs, rubber tyres	£300-400
			Red body, cast hubs, rubber tyres	£300-400

135	1963-69	**Triumph 2000 Saloon**................	Red interior, Grey base, spun hubs, wipers, luggage.	
		normal colours:	Metallic Green with White roof or Metallic Blue with White roof, spun hubs.............................	£60-70
		Gift Set 118 colour:	White body, Blue roof, Red interior, spun hubs, individually boxed......................................	£110-140
		promotional colours:	Each promotional issue was packed in a standard Yellow/Red card picture box.	
			Black body, Cactus-Green or White roof	£300-500
			Blue Grey body, Black roof	£300-500
			Light Green body with Lilac roof, or Metallic Green with White roof....................................	£300-500
			Brown body, Light Green roof	£300-500
			British Racing Green, White roof	£300-500
			Red or Cherry Red body, White roof, Blue interior	£300-500
			White body, Black or Light Green or Light Grey roof, Blue interior	£300-500
			White body, Wedgewood Blue roof, Blue interior	£300-500
			Dark Green body, Cactus-Green roof...	£300-500
			Gunmetal body, Black roof, with 'Gunmetal/WD' label on box	£300-500

136	1964-65	**Vauxhall Viva**............................	White-Grey body, Red interior, spun hubs...	£50-60
	1965-68	....	Metallic Bright Blue body, Red interior, spun hubs	£45-55
	1969-73	....	Pale Metallic Blue body, Red interior, spun hubs	£40-50

| 137 | 1963-66 | **Plymouth Fury Convertible**....... | Green, Pink, Blue or Metallic Grey body, Cream hood, spun hubs.. | £70-85 |

138	1963-66	**Hillman Imp**	Metallic Silver-Green body, Red or White interior, luggage, spun hubs, cast headlamps	£75-85
	1966-68	....	Metallic Red body, luggage, spun hubs, jewelled or plastic headlamps...................................	£70-90
	1968-73	....	Metallic mid-Blue body, Red interior, luggage, spun hubs, jewelled headlamps...........................	£70-90
			As previous issue but with Blue interior, in picture box with white background	£175-225
		Late issue:	Metallic Deep Blue body, Red interior, bare metal baseplate, spun hubs	£175-225

139	1963-64	**Ford Consul Cortina**	Pale Blue body, Off-White interior, spun hubs, cast headlamps..	£55-65
	1964-65	....	Metallic Blue body, Fawn interior, spun hubs..	£65-75
		South African issue:	Bright Green body, Fawn interior, spun hubs, English and Afrikaans wording on box	£500-750
		South African issue:	Dark Green body, Fawn interior, spun hubs, English and Afrikaans wording on box........................	£800-1,100

139a	1949-54	**Ford Fordor Sedan**....................	All have small lettering on the black baseplates which may be gloss or matt.	
		(Renumbered 170)	Yellow, Red, Green or Tan body, (all with matching hubs)...	£70-90
			Green body, Yellow hubs	£70-90
			Brown body, Red hubs	£70-90
			Tan body, Maroon hubs	£70-90
			Red body, Maroon hubs	£70-90
	NB		Later issues have 'Ford Sedan' cast into underside of roof.	
139am	1950-54	**US Army Staff Car**	See 'Military Vehicles' section.	

139b	1950-54	**Hudson Commodore**	Dark Blue body, Stone roof and hubs	£70-90
		(Renumbered 171)	Dark Blue body, Tan roof and hubs...	£70-90
			Deep Cream body, Maroon roof and hubs	£70-90
			Royal Blue body, Pale Tan roof and hubs	£100-130
			Grey lower body, Light Blue roof (as 151 (40b) Triumph Renown Blue).....................................	NGPP
			Dark Blue body, Grey roof and hubs	NGPP

140a	1951-53	**Austin A90 Atlantic**	Mid-Blue body, Red interior, Cream hubs	£300-400
		(Renumbered 106)	Mid-Blue body, Dark Blue interior, Mid-Blue hubs...	£1,200-1,500
			Mid-Blue body, Maroon interior, Cream hubs...	£1,000-1,250
			Deep Blue body, Red interior and hubs	£100-120
			Red body, Maroon interior and hubs..	£1,200-1,500
			Light Blue body, Red interior, Cream hubs	£250-350

(140a continued)			Red body, Cream interior and hubs	£100-120
			Light Blue body, Red interior and hubs	£80-100
			Pink body, Cream interior and hubs	£100-120
			Black body, Red interior and hubs	£80-100
		NB	Interiors may have a gloss or matt finish.	
140b	1951-54	**Rover 75 Saloon**	Maroon body and hubs. Sold unboxed	£90-110
		(Renumbered 156)	Maroon body, Red hubs. Sold unboxed	£90-110
			Cream body and hubs. Sold unboxed	£90-110
			Cream body, Blue hubs. Supplied in dual-numbered box ('140b/156')	£140-180
			Red body, Maroon hubs. Supplied in dual-numbered box ('140b/156')	£1,000-1,250
140	1963-69	**Morris 1100**	Light Blue or Dark Blue, spun hubs	£40-50
		South African issue:	White body, Blue roof, Red interior, spun hubs, English and Afrikaans wording on box	£500-700
		South African issue:	Caramel body, Red interior, spun hubs, English and Afrikaans wording on box	£500-700
		South African issue:	Sky Blue body, Red interior, spun hubs, English and Afrikaans wording on box	£500-700
141	1963-67	**Vauxhall Victor Estate Car**	Yellow body, Blue interior, spun hubs	£45-55
	1963	South African issues:	Pink, Ivory or Yellow body, all with Blue interior, spun hubs, English and Afrikaans wording on box	£400-600
		US promotional:	Dark Red body, Blue interior, spun hubs. Paper labels with Yellow wording:	
			'LIGHTNING FASTENERS LTD', 'TECHNICAL SERVICES'	£500-750
142	1962-68	**Jaguar Mk.10**	Metallic Light Blue or Mid-Blue, Red interior, spun aluminium hubs	£40-50
	1963	South African issue:	Ivory body, spun hubs, English and Afrikaans wording on box	£500-750
		South African issue:	Green body with White roof, spun hubs, English and Afrikaans wording on box	£500-750
		South African issue:	Sky Blue body, Red interior, luggage, Cream base, spun hubs, English and Afrikaans wording on box	£800-1,100
		NB	Gold, US export issue 'see-through' window boxes. Model nos. 134, 138 and 142 housed in these boxes may attract a premium of 50%. See 'Cars - Box Types' for a complete listing.	
143	1962-67	**Ford Capri**	Turquoise body, White roof, Red interior, spun hubs	£50-60
144	1963-67	**Volkswagen 1500**	Off-White body, Red interior, luggage, spun hubs	£45-55
			Metallic Gold or Bronze body, Blue interior, luggage, spun hubs	£45-55
			Metallic Gold or Bronze body, Red interior, luggage, spun hubs	£100-125
	1963	South African issue:	Metallic Green body, spun hubs, English and Afrikaans wording on box	£500-750
		South African issue:	Caramel body, English and Afrikaans wording on box	£500-750
145	1962-67	**Singer Vogue**	Metallic Light Green body, Red interior, spun hubs	£60-75
			Yellow body, Red interior, spun hubs, Yellow steering wheel, Silver trim	£1,500-2,000
146	1963-67	**Daimler 2.5 litre V8**	Metallic Pale Green body, Red interior, spun hubs	£60-70
147	1962-69	**Cadillac '62**	Metallic Green body, Red or White interior, spun hubs	£60-75
148	1962-65	**Ford Fairlane**	(Non-metallic) Pea Green body, Cream interior, open or closed windows, spun hubs	£65-75
			As previous model but with Red interior	£100-125
	1963	South African issue:	Bright Blue body, closed windows, spun hubs, White tyres	£500-800
		South African issue:	Dark Blue body, Light Grey interior, spun hubs, no base number	£500-800
		South African issue:	Heather Grey body, Light Grey interior, spun hubs, no base number, White tyres	£500-800
	1965-67		Light Metallic Green, Pale Cream interior, open windows, spun hubs	£125-150
		US issue:	Metallic Emerald Green body, spun hubs, US issue Gold 'see-through' window box	£300-400
149	1971-75	**Citroën Dyane**	Metallic Bronze body, Black roof and interior, Speedwheels	£30-35
	1971-75		Light Grey body, Dark Grey or Black roof, suspension, Speedwheels	£25-30
150	1959-64	**Rolls-Royce Silver Wraith**	Two-tone Grey body, suspension, spun hubs, Chromed metal bumpers	£55-65
			Later issues with plastic bumpers	£50-60
		NB	The French version of 150 (French reference 551) was cast from English-made dies, was assembled in France, and has 'Made in France' on the baseplate.	
151	1954-59	**Triumph 1800 Saloon**	Beige body, Green hubs, or Dark Blue with Light Blue hubs	£90-110
		(renumbered from 40b)	Light Blue body with Mid-Blue, Fawn or Grey hubs, or Mid-Blue body with Light Blue hubs	£90-110
151	1965-69	**Vauxhall Victor 101**	Pale Yellow body, Red interior, spun hubs	£80-100
			Metallic Red body, White interior, spun hubs	£80-100
152	1954-59	**Austin (A40) Devon**	Large baseplate print (see example diagrams).	
		(renumbered from 40d)	Suede Green body and hubs	£100-130
			Dark Blue body, Mid-Blue hubs	£100-130
			Dark Blue body, Light Blue hubs	£130-160
			Light Blue body, Light Blue hubs	£400-500
			Tan body, Suede Green hubs	£500-700
			Maroon body, Red hubs	£175-200
			Light Green body, Mid-Green hubs	£100-130
			Dark Green body, Fawn hubs	£100-130
	1956-59	Two-tone issue:	Blue upper body and hubs, Orange-Yellow lower body	£250-350
	1956-59	Two-tone issue:	Pink lower body, Green upper body, Cream hubs	£250-350
152	1965-67	**Rolls-Royce Phantom V**	Navy Blue body, Beige interior, chauffeur and two passengers, spun hubs or cast hubs	£40-50
	1967-77	design change:	Very Dark Blue body, White interior with Chauffeur but no passengers, Blue base, cast hubs	£30-40

153	1954-59	**Standard Vanguard**....................	Mid-Blue body, Cream, Blue or Fawn hubs..	£150-200
		(renumbered from 40e)	Dark Blue body, Fawn hubs	£250-350
			Fawn body, Fawn hubs..	£150-200
			Cream body, Cream hubs	£150-200
			Maroon body, Fawn hubs	£150-200
			Maroon body, Maroon hubs	£750-1,000
		NB	The ridge appearing on the boot of some Vanguard models is the result of worn die replacement.	
153	1967-71	**Aston-Martin DB6**	Metallic Silver Blue body, Red interior, spoked wheels	£50-60
			Metallic Turquoise body, White interior, spoked wheels	£55-65
154	1955	**Hillman Minx** ....2nd baseplate:	Large baseplate print (see diagram).	
		(renumbered from 40f)	Dark Tan body with Cream or Green hubs, or Pale Tan body with Blue or Yellow hubs	£100-120
			Light Green body and hubs, or Dark Green body with Light Green hubs	£175-200
			Pale Green body with Light Green hubs, or Light Green body with Mid-Green hubs............	£175-225
			Pale Blue lower body and hubs, Cerise upper body	£200-250
			Lime Green lower body, Cream upper body and hubs	£200-250
154	1966-69	**Ford Taunus 17M**	Yellow body, White roof, Red interior, rounded spun hubs or cast wheels	£40-50
155	1961-66	**Ford Anglia 105E**	Turquoise or Green body, Red interior, suspension, windows, spun hubs.	£100-125
			Turquoise body, Pale Blue interior, spun hubs.	£80-100
			Very Pale Green body, Red interior, spun hubs. In mail-order box with correct spot	£350-450
		NB	Meccano issued a batch to Ford to mark the first Ford made on Merseyside on	
			8th March 1963. Some were fixed on plinths and given as souvenirs.	
	1963	.....................South African issue:	Caramel body, Red interior, spun hubs, English and Afrikaans wording on box	£500-750
		South African issue:	Off-White body, Red interior, spun hubs, English and Afrikaans wording on box	£500-750
		South African issue:	Light Blue body, Red interior, spun hubs, English and Afrikaans wording on box	£500-750
156	1954-56	**Rover 75**....................	Cream body, Cream or Light Blue hubs	£130-150
		(Renumbered from 140b)	Red body, Maroon hubs	£750-1,000
			Maroon body, Cream hubs	£130-150
	1956-59	...........................Two-tone issues:	Light Green upper body, Mid-Green lower body and hubs, treaded tyres	£150-175
			Dull two-tone Green body, Mid-Green hubs '156' to base	£300-400
			Light Green upper body, Turquoise lower body, Mid-Green hubs	£750-1,000
			Mid-Blue upper body, Cream lower body and hubs, treaded tyres	£150-175
			Dark Blue upper body, Cream lower body and hubs	£250-350
			Violet-Blue upper body, Cream lower body and hubs	£400-600
156	1968-71	**Saab 96**....................	Metallic Red or Metallic Blue body, suspension, spun hubs	£65-75
157	1954-57	**Jaguar XK120**	Yellow body, Light Yellow hubs	£125-150
			Red body, Red diecast hubs	£150-175
			White body, Fawn hubs	£125-150
			Dark Sage Green body, Beige or Fawn hubs	£150-200
	1957-59	.........................Two-tone issue:	Turquoise lower body, Cerise upper body, Red hubs	£200-250
	1957-59	.........................Two-tone issue:	Yellow lower body, Light Grey upper body and hubs	£200-250
	1959-62		Red body, spun hubs	£200-250
			Dark Sage Green body, spun hubs	£200-250
157	1968-73	**BMW 2000 Tilux**	Blue/White, Red interior, cast hubs, box has inner pictorial stand................	£55-65
			Metallic Blue with Gold upper half, pictorial box inner	£90-120
			Pale Blue body, Red interior, spun hubs	NGPP
158	1954-55	**Riley Saloon**....................	Cream body, Mid-Green hubs	£120-140
		(Renumbered from 40a)	Mid-Green body with Green hubs	£120-140
			Pale Green body, Mid-Green hubs	£120-140
			Dark Blue body, Mid-Blue hubs	£120-140
			Light Grey body and hubs..	£120-140
		NB	All the 158 Riley issues have large lettering on their baseplates.	
158	1967-70	**Rolls-Royce Silver Shadow**	Metallic Red, White interior, cast hubs	£45-55
	1970-73	....	Metallic Bright Blue, White interior, cast hubs	£55-65
			Metallic Light Blue, White interior, cast hubs..	£55-65
159	1954	**Morris Oxford**....................	Dark Green body with Mid-Green hubs, or Green body with Light Green hubs ...	£140-175
		(Renumbered from 40g)	Blue body, Grey hubs...	£1,500-2,000
			Fawn body, Grey or Stone hubs	£120-140
		Export issue:	Beige body and hubs	£500-800
		Two-tone issue:	Green upper body and hubs, Cream lower body..	£200-300
		Two-tone issue:	Cream upper body and hubs, Cerise lower body......................................	£200-300
		Two-tone issue:	Turquoise upper body, Cream lower body, Turquoise-Green hubs	£500-750
160	1958-62	**Austin A30**	Turquoise body, smooth or treaded solid grey plastic wheels	£80-100
			Pale Beige body, smooth or treaded solid grey plastic wheels.....................	£80-100
		NB	A version of the Austin A30 has been reported with spun hubs, but is not confirmed.	
160	1967-74	**Mercedes-Benz 250 SE**	Metallic Blue body, suspension, steering, working stop-lights.....................	£25-35
161	1954	**Austin (A40) Somerset**	Pale Blue body, Mid or Dark Blue hubs	£140-170
		(Renumbered from 40j)	Red body and hubs...	£140-170
	1956-59	Two-tone issue:	Red lower body and hubs, Yellow upper body	£200-300
	1956-59	Two-tone issue:	Black lower body, Cream upper body and hubs	£200-300
161	1965-69	**Ford Mustang Fastback**	White (Red seats), 'MUSTANG' decal badge on wings, chrome detailed wheels ...	£60-70
	1969-73		Yellow body, Blue seats, cast-in logo replaces decal badge	£50-60
			Orange body (without decal), Speedwheels..	£30-40

162	1956-60	**Ford Zephyr Mk.I**	Cream upper body, Dark Green lower body, Cream hubs	£80-90
			Cream upper body, Lime Green lower body, Cream hubs	£110-140
			Two-tone Blue body, Grey hubs	£80-90
		NB	Rear number plate may be plain or Silver.	
162	1966-70	**Triumph 1300**	Light Blue body, Red interior, fingertip steering, spun aluminium hubs	£65-75
163	1956-60	**Bristol 450 Coupé**	British Racing Green body, Light Green hubs, RN '27'	£70-90
163	1966-70	**Volkswagen 1600 TL**	Red or Dark Metallic Red, suspension, cast detailed hubs	£40-50
			Metallic Blue body, Speedwheels	£60-70
164	1957-60	**Vauxhall Cresta**	Maroon lower body, Cream upper body, Cream hubs	£80-100
	1957-60		Green lower body, Grey upper body, Grey hubs	£80-100
		NB	Rear number plate may be plain or Silver.	
164	1966-71	**Ford Zodiac Mk.IV**	Metallic Silver body, Red interior, Yellow or Black chassis, cast wheels	£50-60
			Pale Metallic Blue body, Yellow chassis, cast wheels	£75-85
			Metallic Copper body, Red interior, Yellow chassis, cast wheels, rigid plastic case	£50-60
165	1959-60	**Humber Hawk**	Black and Green lower body, Black roof, spun hubs	£90-110
			Maroon and Cream lower body, Maroon roof, spun hubs	£125-150
		NB	Both versions available with or without a front number plate casting.	
	1959-63		Black lower body, all Green upper body, spun hubs, with front number plate casting, in late issue lighter Yellow box with Green spot	£150-200
165	1969-76	**Ford Capri**	Metallic Green body, Orange interior, Speedwheels	£50-60
			Metallic Purple body, Orange interior, Speedwheels	£50-60
			Metallic Turquoise body, Yellow interior, Speedwheels	£60-70
166	1958-63	**Sunbeam Rapier**	Yellow lower body, Deep Cream upper body, Beige hubs	£80-90
			Yellow lower body, Deep Cream upper body, spun hubs	£90-100
			Blue lower body, Turquoise upper body, Blue hubs	£80-90
			Blue lower body, Turquoise upper body, spun hubs	£90-100
166	1967-70	**Renault R16**	Metallic Blue, suspension and fingertip steering, spun hubs	£40-50
167	1958-63	**A.C. Aceca Sports Coupé**	Grey body, Red roof, Red hubs	£80-100
			Cream body, Reddish-Maroon roof, Silver cast hubs	£100-125
			Deep Cream body, Dark Brown roof, Cream hubs	£80-100
			All Cream body, spun aluminium hubs. In lighter Yellow box with Cream spot	£100-125
			Cream body, Maroon roof, spun hubs	£100-125
			Cream body, Dark Brown roof, spun hubs	£150-175
			Grey body, Red roof, spun hubs. In plain Red/Yellow box	£100-125
168	1959-63	**Singer Gazelle Saloon**	Deep Brown lower, Cream upper body, spun aluminium hubs	£80-100
			Dark Green lower, Grey upper body, spun aluminium hubs	£80-100
			Black body, spun aluminium hubs, Silver trim	NGPP
168	1968-70	**Ford Escort**	Pale Blue or White, cast detailed hubs	£40-50
	1970-74		Metallic Red body, spun aluminium hubs	£67-75
	1974-75		Metallic Blue body, Speedwheels	£67-75
169	1958-63	**Studebaker Golden Hawk**	Light Brown body, Red rear side panel and hubs, White tyres, plain Yellow/Red box	£90-110
			As previous issue but with spun aluminium hubs, White tyres	£80-90
			Light Green body, Cream rear side panel and hubs, White tyres	£80-90
			As previous issue but with spun aluminium hubs, White tyres	£80-100
169	1967-69	**Ford Corsair 2000 E**	Silver body, Black textured roof, suspension and steering	£65-75

Models 170, 171 and 172	**Two paint schemes exist for two-colour issues on models 170, 171 and 172:**
	1: Lower colour covers wing tops and doors up to windows (generally known as 'Highline') and
	2: Lower colour extends only up to ridge on wings/doors ('Lowline').

170	1954-56	**Ford Fordor Sedan**	Brown body, Red hubs	£120-150
		(Renumbered from 139a)	Yellow body, Red hubs	£120-150
			Green body, Red hubs	£120-150
			Red body, Red hubs	£120-150
	1956-58	('Highline')	Red lower body, Cream upper body, Red hubs	£200-250
	1956-58	('Highline')	Blue lower body, Pink upper body, Blue hubs	£200-250
	1958-59	('Lowline')	Red lower body, Cream upper body, Red hubs	£150-200
	1958-59	('Lowline')	Blue lower body, Pink upper body, Blue hubs	£150-200
170m	1954-54	**Ford US Army Staff Car**	See 'Military Vehicles' section.	
170	1964-70	**Lincoln Continental**	Metallic Bronze body, White roof, Blue interior, cast wheels	£75-85
			Light Blue body, White roof, Mid-Blue interior, cast wheels	£75-85
170	1979	**Ford Granada Ghia**	Not issued, but a Metallic Silver factory publicity sample was sold by Vectis Auctions in 1999 for £470.	
171	1954-56	**Hudson Commodore Sedan**	Dark Blue body, Pale Tan roof and hubs	£90-110
		(Renumbered from 139b)	Royal Blue body, Pale Tan roof and hubs	£150-200
			Light Blue body, Pale Tan roof, Fawn hubs	£400-600
			Cream body, Dark Maroon roof and hubs	£90-110
			Cream body, Dark Maroon roof, Red hubs, large lettering on baseplate	£90-110
	1956-58	('Highline')	Turquoise lower body with Red upper body, Red hubs	£250-350
		('Highline')	Blue lower body, Red upper body, Red hubs	£250-350
		('Highline')	Blue lower body, Maroon upper body, Red hubs	£250-350
		('Highline')	Light Grey lower body with Mid-Blue upper body, Blue hubs	£250-350
	1958-59	('Lowline')	Turquoise lower body with Maroon upper body, Red hubs	£250-350
		('Lowline')	Light Grey lower body with Mid-Blue upper body, Blue hubs	£250-350

171	1965-68	**Austin 1800**.....................................	Metallic Blue or Light Blue body, Red interior, spun hubs..	£50-60
172	1954-56	**Studebaker Land Cruiser**.........	Light Green body, Mid-Green or Mid-Blue hubs..	£90-110
			Blue body, Fawn or Beige hubs..	£130-160
			Light Beige body, Cream hubs..	£250-350
	1956-58	.................................('Highline')	Beige lower body, Maroon upper body, Cream hubs..	£150-200
		('Highline')	Beige lower body, Tan upper body, Cerise hubs..	£150-200
	1958-59	.................................('Lowline')	Off-White lower body, Maroon upper body, Cream hubs..	£150-200
		('Lowline')	Cream lower body, Light Tan upper body, Cream hubs..	£150-200
172	1965-69	**Fiat 2300 Station Wagon**...........	Two-tone Blue body, Red interior, spun hubs..	£50-60
173	1958-62	**Nash Rambler Station Wagon**...	Turquoise body with Cerise flash, Grey hubs, no number on later baseplates..	£90-120
			Pink body with Blue flash, Cream hubs, no number on later baseplates..	£90-120
			As previous issues but with spun hubs, in plain Yellow/Red box without picture..	£90-120
173	1969-72	**Pontiac Parisienne**.....................	Metallic Maroon body, Lemon interior, retractable aerials, cast wheels..	£80-100
			Metallic Blue body..	£80-100
174	1958-63	**Hudson Hornet**..........................	Red lower body, Cream roof and side flash, Beige hubs, White tyres..	£70-90
			Yellow lower body, Dark Grey roof and flash, Cream hubs, White tyres..	£100-125
			Later issues with spun aluminium hubs..	£140-170
174	1969-72	**Ford Mercury Cougar**...............	Blue or Metallic Dark Blue body, cast hubs or Speedwheels..	£45-55
175	1958-61	**Hillman Minx**............................	Grey lower body, Mid-Blue upper body and cast hubs..	£100-125
			Grey lower body, Mid-Blue upper body, spun hubs..	£200-250
			Pale Brown body, Green roof and boot, Beige hubs..	£100-125
			Pale Brown body, Green roof and boot, spun hubs..	£200-250
175	1969-73	**Cadillac Eldorado**.....................	Metallic Purple body, Black roof, Orange interior, cast or Speedwheels..	£50-60
			Metallic Sea-Green body, Black roof, Orange interior, cast or Speedwheels..	£50-60
176	1958-63	**Austin A105 Saloon**...................	First Dinky Toys car to have full window glazing. Body sides have a contrasting panel line. Treaded tyres may be Black or White.	
	1958-59	....	Cream body, Navy Blue panel line, Cream hubs..	£80-95
			Pale Grey body, Red panel line, Red hubs..	£130-160
	1959-63	....	Cream body, Dark Blue roof and panel line, Cream hubs..	£90-120
			Cream body, Mid-Blue roof and panel line, Cream hubs..	£150-200
			Cream body, Mid-Blue roof and panel line, spun aluminium hubs..	£150-200
			Cream body, Mid-Blue roof (but no panel line)..	£150-200
			Pale Grey body, Red roof and panel line, Light Grey hubs..	£150-200
			Pale Grey body and roof, Red panel line, spun hubs..	£125-175
176	1969-74	**N.S.U. Ro80**..............................	Metallic Red body, spun hubs, luminous seats, working lights..	£40-50
			Metallic Blue body..	£100-150
177	1961-66	**Opel Kapitan**............................	Light Greyish-Blue body, Red interior, spun hubs..	£60-75
	1963	....................South African issue:	Mid or Dark Blue body, Red interior, spun hubs, English and Afrikaans wording on box....................	£800-1,100
		South African issue:	Caramel body, Red interior, spun hubs, English and Afrikaans wording on box..................................	£800-1,100
		South African issue:	Pale Yellow body, Red interior, spun hubs, English and Afrikaans wording on box..........................	£800-1,100
	NB		South African models should be housed in boxes with both English and Afrikaans text.	
178	1959-63	**Plymouth Plaza**..........................	Light Blue body, Dark Blue roof and side flash, spun hubs..	£100-130
			Salmon Pink body, Light Green roof and side flash, spun hubs..	£140-170
			Light Tan body, Light Green roof and side flash, matt-Black base, spun hubs..	£150-200
			Light Blue body, White roof and flash, spun hubs, Lighter Yellow box..	£175-225
			Pale Blue body, White roof and flash, spun hubs, late issue – no number on baseplate..	£140-170
178	1975-79	**Mini Clubman**............................	Bronze body, opening doors, jewelled headlights on some, Speedwheels..	£40-50
			Red body version, Speedwheels..	£100-125
179	1958-63	**Studebaker President**.................	Light Blue body, Dark Blue flash, Cream hubs, White tyres..	£90-110
			Yellow body, Blue flash and hubs, White tyres..	£90-110
			Late issues with spun hubs..	£120-150
179	1971-75	**Opel Commodore**.......................	Metallic Blue body, Black roof, suspension, Speedwheels..	£45-55
180	1958-63	**Packard Clipper**........................	Cerise upper body, Cream lower body and hubs, White tyres..	£80-100
			Orange lower body, Light Grey upper body and hubs, White tyres..	£110-130
			Late issues with spun hubs..	£110-130
180	1979-80	**Rover 3500**................................	White body, plastic chassis and wheels. Made in Hong Kong, scale 1:35..	£20-25
181	1956-70	**Volkswagen Saloon**....................	Pale Grey body, Mid-Blue hubs..	£80-100
			Blue-Grey body, Mid-Blue hubs..	£80-100
			Dark Blue body, Mid-Blue hubs..	£130-160
			RAF Blue body, Mid-Blue hubs..	£130-160
			Lime Green body, Mid-Green hubs..	£80-100
		Spun hubs issues:	Pale Grey body, spun hubs..	£90-110
			Blue-Grey body, spun hubs..	£90-110
			Pale Blue body, spun hubs, unpainted or matt or gloss black baseplate..	£90-110
			RAF Blue body, spun hubs..	£90-110
		Plastic hubs issue:	Pale Blue body, Blue plastic hubs..	£250-350
	NB		See also 'Factory samples' listing at the end of this section.	
		South African issue:	Lime Green or Pale Yellow body, Red interior, spun hubs..	£400-600
		South African issue:	Pale Blue or Metallic Blue body, Red interior, spun hubs..	£400-600
		South African issue:	Grey body, Red interior, spun hubs..	£400-600
	NB		South African models should be housed in boxes with both English and Afrikaans text.	

182	1958-66	**Porsche 356a Coupé**	Pale Blue body, Cream, Mid-Blue or spun hubs..	£80-100
			Cerise body, Cream or spun hubs..	£80-100
			Red body and hubs, in standard Yellow box (no coloured spot)..	£100-120
			Off-White body, Mid-Blue, Beige or spun hubs, with window glazing................................	£100-120
			Red body and hubs. In late issue lighter Yellow box with Red spot..................................	£250-350
			Plum Red body, spun hubs. In lighter Yellow box...	£250-350
183	1958-60	**Fiat 600**	Red body, smooth or treaded solid Grey plastic wheels...	£70-80
			Pale Green body, smooth or treaded solid Grey plastic wheels...	£70-80
183	1966-74	**Morris Mini Minor (Automatic)**	Metallic Red body, matt or gloss Black roof, White interior, spun hubs. Box should contain 'Meccano Automatic Transmission' leaflet...	£75-85
			Metallic Red body, Black roof, White interior, Speedwheels...	£60-70
			Metallic Bright Blue body, White interior, spun hubs..	£90-110
		NB	Late issues with 'Austin Cooper S' cast on boot (model 250 casting) will be found................	NGPP
			Various registration numbers will also be found, e.g., 'UVR 576D', 'MTB 21G', 'HTB 21H'.	
184	1961-65	**Volvo 122 S**	Red body, Off-White interior, spun hubs	£70-80
			Dark Red body (colour much darker than standard model), spun hubs..............................	£200-250
			Off-White body, White interior, spun hubs..	£175-200
			Cream body, Cream interior, spun hubs...	£200-225
	1962	....................South African issue:	Grey-Blue body, White interior (in box with both English and Afrikaans text)...................	£400-600
		South African issue:	Sage Green (White interior) or Pale Green (Fawn interior). (English and Afrikaans text on box).............	£400-600
185	1961-63	**Alfa Romeo 1900 Sprint**	Yellow body, Red interior, spun hubs...	£55-65
			Red body, Off-White interior, spun hubs...	£55-65
186	1961-67	**Mercedes-Benz 220 SE**	Light Blue body, Red or White interior, spun hubs..	£45-55
			Light Blue body, Yellow interior, spun hubs..	£55-65
			RAF Blue body, Cream interior, spun hubs..	£45-55
	1963	....................South African issue:	Sky Blue or Grey body. Box printed with both English and Afrikaans text.........................	£250-350
187	1959-64	**VW Karmann Ghia Coupé**	Red body, Black roof, spun hubs, White tyres, 'plain' box...	£70-90
			Green body, Cream roof, spun hubs, White tyres, 'plain' box..	£70-90
			As previous issue but in rare late issue picture box...	£100-150
187	1968-77	**De Tomaso Mangusta 5000**	Fluorescent Pink body, White panels front/rear, Black interior, cast wheels, racing number '7'	£35-40
188	1968-74	**Jensen FF**	Yellow body, Black interior, cast wheels or Speedwheels. In rigid plastic case..............	£45-55
189	1959-64	**Triumph Herald Saloon**	Pale or Light Blue roof and sides with White centre, spun aluminium hubs....................	£75-85
			Green roof and sides with White centre, spun aluminium hubs..	£75-85
		special issue:	Lilac body, spun hubs, standard box..	£200-300
		special issue:	Magenta body, spun hubs, standard box...	£200-300
		special issue:	Red lower, White upper body, spun hubs, plain printed box with Red spot.......................	£200-300
		special issue:	Greyish-Green, Pale Whitish-Green roof, spun hubs, plain box with correct colour spot.....	£200-300
		special issue:	Pinkish-Brown body with Pale Grey roof, spun hubs, standard box..................................	£200-300
		special issue:	Dark Grey body and roof, Pale Grey bonnet and boot, spun hubs, standard box..............	£200-300
		special issue:	All Red body, spun hubs, in 'plain' standard box with Red spot.......................................	£200-300
		special issue:	Very Dark Blue body, Pale Blue hubs, standard box..	£200-300
		special issue:	Very Dark Blue lower body and roof, Pale Blue mid-section, spun hubs..........................	£200-300
		special issue:	Deep Grey and White body, spun hubs...	£200-300
		special issue:	Pale Lilac body, Bluish White roof, spun hubs, in box with Blue and White spot...........	£200-300
		special issue:	Black and Pale Grey body, spun hubs..	£200-300
189	1969-76	**Lamborghini Marzal**	Green/White or Red/White, cast detailed hubs...	£25-45
			Yellow/White body, cast detailed hubs..	£40-45
	1976-78	....	Metallic Blue/White or Dark Metallic Green/White, Speedwheels...................................	£35-45
190	1970-74	**Monteverdi 375 L**	Metallic Maroon body, White interior, cast wheels or Speedwheels. In rigid plastic case	£35-45
		NB	See also 'Factory samples' listing at the end of this section.	
191	1959-64	**Dodge Royal Sedan**	Cream body with Tan flash, spun hubs, White tyres	£90-110
			Cream body, Blue flash, spun hubs, lighter Yellow box, late issue – no number on base........	£150-200
			Pale Green body with Black flash, spun hubs, White tyres..	£90-110
		NB	Casting used for 258 'USA Police Car'.	
192	1959-64	**De Soto Fireflite**	Grey body, Red roof and flash, spun aluminium hubs, White tyres.................................	£90-110
			Turquoise body, Light Tan roof and flash, spun aluminium hubs, White tyres.................	£120-140
192	1970-80	**Range Rover**	Metallic Bronze (Pale Blue interior), Yellow body (Red interior), or Black body (? interior), cast detailed or Speedwheels..................................	£25-35
		NB	See also 'Factory samples' listing at the end of this section.	
193	1961-69	**Rambler Station Wagon**	Pale Yellow body, White roof, Red interior, Black plastic roof-rack, spun hubs, standard box	£70-80
			As previous issue but with White interior. In Gold 'see-through' US export window-box	£150-175
	1962	....................South African issue:	Lilac body, Cream or Black roof, Red interior, spun hubs, English and Afrikaans wording on box........	£400-600
		South African issue:	All-Lilac body, Red interior, spun hubs, English and Afrikaans wording on box.............	£400-600
		South African issue:	Sage Green body, Red interior, spun hubs, English and Afrikaans wording on box.........	£400-600
		South African issue:	Pale Blue body, Cream roof, Red interior, spun hubs, English and Afrikaans wording on box	£400-600
		South African issue:	Dark Blue body, White roof, Red interior, spun hubs, English and Afrikaans wording on box	£400-600
		South African issue:	Light Greyish-Green body, Black roof, Red interior, spun hubs, English and Afrikaans wording on box...	£400-600
		South African issue:	All-Cream body, Red interior, spun hubs, English and Afrikaans wording on box...........	£400-600
194	1961-67	**Bentley 'S' Coupé**	Grey body, Red interior, Tan hood, Grey male driver, spun hubs, gloss black baseplate........	£70-90
			Metallic Bronze body, Cream interior, Dark Blue hood, driver, spun hubs.....................	£100-125
		NB	Late issues have plated plastic parts.	
	1962	....................South African issue:	Lime Green body, Red interior, Black hood, spun hubs..	£600-800
		South African issue:	Cream body, Red interior, Dark Cream hood, spun hubs..	£600-800

195	1961-71	**Jaguar 3.4 Mk.II**	Maroon body, White interior, spun hubs	**£70-90**
			Cream body, Red interior, spun hubs	**£70-90**
			Light Grey body, Red interior, spun hubs	**£70-90**
	1962	South African issues:	Light or Sky-Blue body, Cream or Red interior, English and Afrikaans wording on box	**£400-600**
		South African issues:	Red or Off-White body, Cream or Red interior, English and Afrikaans wording on box	**£400-600**
196	1963-70	**Holden Special Sedan**	Metallic Gold body, White roof, spun hubs. (First Dinky Toys model to have jewelled headlights)	**£55-65**
			Turquoise body, White roof, spun hubs, Grey baseplate, Off-White interior	**£55-65**
			Turquoise body, White roof, spun hubs, Silver baseplate, Red interior	**£55-65**
			Turquoise body, White roof, spun hubs, Dark Grey baseplate, Red interior	**£55-65**
	1966	South African issue:	White body, Turquoise roof	**£400-600**
197	1961-71	**Morris Mini Traveller**	White body, Yellow interior, spun hubs	**£600-800**
			White body, Red interior, spun hubs	**£90-110**
			Dark Green body, Pale Blue interior, spun hubs	**£150-175**
			Dark Green body, Yellow interior, spun hubs	**£500-700**
			Fluorescent Green body, Red interior, spun hubs, with or without front number plate	**£160-190**
			Fluorescent Pink body, Red interior, spun hubs	**£200-250**
		NB	Unlike 199, there is no 'colour change' label on the 197 box.	
198	1962-69	**Rolls-Royce Phantom V**	Metallic Cream lower body, Metallic Light Green upper body, Blue or Red interior, glossy baseplate, spun hubs, chauffeur. (First Dinky Toys model with metallic paint and opening windows)	**£75-85**
			Metallic Cream upper body, Grey lower body, Red interior, glossy baseplate, chauffeur, spun hubs	**£75-85**
			Two tone Grey body, Red interior, matt baseplate, chauffeur, spun hubs	**£75-85**
	1963	South African issue:	Dark Grey over Metallic Cream body, Red interior, English and Afrikaans wording on box	**£750-1,000**
		South African issue:	Sage Green or Two-Tone Grey, English and Afrikaans wording on box	**£750-1,000**
		South African issue:	Pale Grey body, Ivory or Grey roof, Red interior, English and Afrikaans wording on box	**£750-1,000**
		South African issue:	Lime Green body, Ivory roof, Red interior, spun hubs, English and Afrikaans wording on box	**£750-1,000**
199	1961-71	**Austin 7 Countryman**	Blue body with Yellow interior, spun hubs	**£130-160**
			Electric Blue, Blue or Blue-Grey body with Red interior and 'wood' trim, spun hubs	**£75-85**
			Fluorescent Orange body, Red interior, spun hubs. Box must have bear a small oblong label stating: 'COLOUR OF MODEL MAY DIFFER FROM ILLUSTRATION'	**£150-200**
			Deep Grey body, Red interior, Brown 'woodwork', spun hubs	**£150-200**
		Promotional issue:	Luminous Pink body, Red roof, spun hubs	**£160-190**
200	1954-57	**Midget Racer**	Silver body, Red grille, Brown driver, solid Black rubber wheels. (Renumbered from 35b)	**£65-75**
200	1971-78	**Matra 630 Le Mans**	Blue body, racing number '5', '9' or '36', Speedwheels	**£25-30**
201	1979-80	**Plymouth Stock Car**	Blue body, racing number '34', wide plastic wheels	**£35-45**
202	1971-75	**Fiat Abarth 2000**	Fluorescent Red/White body, opening doors, Speedwheels	**£20-30**
202/2	1979-80	**Customised Land Rover**	Yellow body with white crash guard. White or Black rails/aerials (344 casting)	**£25-35**
203	1979-80	**Customised Range Rover**	Black body, Yellow/Red design, White plastic chassis/crash guard	**£20-25**
204	1971-74	**Ferrari 312 P**	Metallic Red body and opening doors, Speedwheels, RN '60'	**£25-30**
			Metallic Red body, White opening doors, Speedwheels, RN '60'	**£25-30**
205	1962-64	**Talbot Lago Racing Car**	Blue, Red or Yellow plastic hubs, RN '4', blister-packed ('230' on base – see also 23k and 230)	**£250-350**
205	1968-73	**Lotus Cortina Rally**	White body, Blue interior, Red bonnet and side stripe, 'Monte Carlo' logo, RN '7', 2 aerials, cast hubs	**£70-80**
206	1962-64	**Maserati Racing Car**	Red/White body, Red or Yellow plastic hubs, blister-packed, ('231' on base – see also 23n and 231)	**£250-350**
	1962-64	late issue:	As previous model but in lighter Yellow box, (see also 23n and 231)	**£120-140**
206	1978-80	**Customised Corvette**	Red/Yellow or White/Black, plastic chassis and wide wheels	**£20-30**
207	1962-64	**Alfa-Romeo Racing Car**	Red body, Red plastic hubs, blister-packed, ('232' on base – see also 23f and 232)	**£250-350**
	1962-64	late issue:	As previous model but in lighter Yellow box. (See also 23f and 232)	**£120-140**
207	1977-80	**Triumph TR7 Rally**	White/Red/Blue, RN '8', plastic chassis and wheels, 'Leyland'	**£25-35**

Photo: Christie's

208	1962-64	**Cooper-Bristol Racing Car**.......	Dark Green, Red plastic wheel hubs, blister-packed, ('233' on base – see also 23g and 233) £250-350
		variant:	As previous model but with Green metal hubs...£150-200
	1962-64	....................................late issue:	Green body and plastic hubs, White flash and RN '6', lighter Yellow box, (see also 23f and 233)..........£100-120
208	1971-75	**VW Porsche 914**....................	Yellow body, Black interior, cast detailed wheel hubs...£25-30
		promotional:	As above, but packed in a Yellow/Red promotional card box...£70-80
	1976-80		Metallic Blue/Black body, Speedwheels..£25-30
209	1962-64	**Ferrari Racing Car**..................	Blue, Yellow triangle, Yellow plastic hubs, blister-packed, ('234' on base – see also 23h and 234)........£250-350
	1962-64	.................................late issue:	As previous model but in lighter Yellow box, (see also 23h and 234) £175-225
210	1962-65	**Vanwall Racing Car**	Green, Yellow plastic hubs, blister-packed, ('239' on base – see also 239)..................................£250-350
210	1971-73	**Alfa-Romeo 33 Tipo**	Red body, Black doors, White interior, racing number '36', cast wheels, leaflet in box £30-35
211	1975	**Triumph TR7 Sports Car**	Metallic Blue body, Union Jack badge £90-100
			Yellow body, Black bumpers and interior £90-100
			Yellow body, Grey bumpers and interior £90-100
			Red body, Black bumpers and interior £50-60
			Red body, Grey bumpers and interior £50-60
212	1965-70	**Ford Cortina Rally**	White body, Black bonnet, 'EAST AFRICAN SAFARI' and 'CASTROL' logos, Black or Red RN '8',
			spotlight, Red interior, spun hubs. In picture box...£80-100
213	1970-73	**Ford Capri Rally**	Metallic Red body, Black bonnet, Yellow interior, racing number '20', rigid plastic case £55-65
	1973-75		Bronze body, Black bonnet, spotlights, wing mirrors, Speedwheels, rigid plastic case £55-65
214	1966-69	**Hillman Imp Rally**	Dark Blue body, Red interior, 'MONTE CARLO RALLY' logo, RN '35', spun hubs, picture box £70-80
215	1965-66	**Ford GT Racing Car**	White body, Red interior, racing number '7', spun hubs..£55-65
	1966-70		White body, Red interior, racing number '7', Silver spoked wheels...£35-45
	1970-74		Metallic Green body, Gold engine, Orange/Black stripe, Yellow interior, RN '7', Silver spoked wheels......£35-45
			Metallic Green body, Silver engine, Red interior £35-45
			Metallic Green body, Dark Blue/White stripe, White interior £35-45
			Yellow or Metallic Blue, removable bonnet, Silver or Gold spoked wheels £35-45
216	1967-69	**Dino Ferrari**	Red body, Light Blue interior...£40-50
	1969-75		Metallic Blue/Black, Silver or brass spoked wheels or Speedwheels £30-40
217	1968-70	**Alfa Romeo Scarabeo OSI**	Pink body, cast spoked wheels...£30-35
	1969-74		Red, Orange or Green body, Speedwheels..£25-30
218	1969-73	**Lotus Europa**	Yellow body, Blue panels/roof, chequered flags, Gold engine...£35-45
	1973-75		Yellow/Black body or Metallic Blue body, Silver engine, Speedwheels..£30-35
219	1977-79	**Leyland Jaguar XJ-5.3**	White body, 'Leyland' decal. (Made in Hong Kong)..£35-45
219	1978-79	**'Big Cat' Jaguar**	White/Red, Black 'Big Cat' decal, (unboxed)...£35-45
			Boxed version with 'The Big Cat' logo £50-75
220	1954-56	**Small Open Racing Car**	Silver (Red hubs), or Red (Silver hubs), RN '4'. (Renumbered from 23a) £40-50
220	1970-73	**Ferrari P5**	Metallic Red body, Yellow interior, cast hubs...£25-30
	1973-75		Metallic Red body, Yellow interior, Speedwheels £25-30
221	1954-56	**'Speed Of The Wind'**	
		Racing Car	Silver diecast body with plain baseplate. (Renumbered from 23e)...£40-45
221	1969-76	**Corvette Stingray**..................	Metallic Gold body, Silver or Gold spoked wheels...£25-35
	1976-78		Red or White body, Black bonnet, opening doors, Speedwheels...£25-35
222	1954-56	**Streamlined Racing Car**	Silver body with Red, Blue or Green trim. (Renumbered from 22s)...£60-70
222	1978-80	**Hesketh 308 E**	Dark Blue or Bronze, RN '2', cast-detailed or Speedwheels...£20-30
		promotional issue:	As previous model but in 'OLYMPUS CAMERAS' box, (Swiss)...£50-75
223	1970-75	**McLaren M8A Can-Am**.............	White body, Metallic Blue engine cover, cast detailed wheels..£20-25
	1976-78		Metallic Green body, Black engine cover, White interior, Speedwheels......................................£20-25
224	1970-74	**Mercedes-Benz C111**	White body, Blue interior, cast hubs £20-25
			Metallic Dark Red body, White interior, cast hubs £20-25
225	1971-76	**Lotus F1 Racing Car**	Metallic Red body with racing number '7', inner pictorial box and stand £20-25
	1976-77		Lime-Green or Metallic Blue body with racing number '7' £20-25
226	1972-75	**Ferrari 312 B2**	Red body with racing number '5' £20-25
	1976-80		Bronze or Gold body, Black, White or Yellow rear wing, racing number '5' £20-25
227	1975-77	**Beach Buggy**.......................	Yellow/Grey, Yellow/White, Green/Grey or Pink/Black body £20-25
		....**NB**	See also 'Factory samples' listing at the end of this section.
228	1970-72	**Super Sprinter**	Blue/Silver or Blue/Orange body, suspension, Speedwheels..£20-25
230	1954-60	**Talbot Lago Racing Car**	Blue body, Yellow racing number '4', Blue diecast hubs £100-130
	1960-62		Blue body, Yellow racing number '4', spun aluminium hubs £150-175
231	1954-60	**Maserati Racing Car**	Red body, White flash and RN '9', Red diecast hubs. (See also 23n and 206) £100-130
			Red body, White flash and racing number '9', Yellow plastic hubs..£200-250
	1960-62		Red body, White flash and racing number '9', spun aluminium hubs. (See also 23n and 206) £150-175
232	1954-60	**Alfa-Romeo Racing Car**............	Red body, White racing number '8', Red diecast hubs, White racing driver. (See also 23f and 207).........£100-130
			Red body, White racing number '8', Red plastic hubs...£200-250
	1960-62		Red body, White racing number '8', spun aluminium hubs, White racing driver...............................£150-175
233	1954-60	**Cooper-Bristol Racing Car**........	Green body, White flash and RN '6', Green diecast hubs. (See also 23f and 208) £100-120
			Green body, White flash and racing number '6', Red plastic hubs £200-250
	1960-62		Green body, White flash and racing number '6', spun aluminium hubs. (See also 23f and 208)............£100-150
234	1954-60	**Ferrari Racing Car**	Blue body, Yellow nose, diecast hubs and RN '5'. (See also 23h and 209) £100-130
	1960-62		Blue body, Yellow nose and racing number '5', spun aluminium hubs. (See also 23h and 209)..............£100-150
	1962-62		Blue body, Yellow triangle on nose, RN '5', spun hubs, boxed..£300-400
			Blue body, White triangle on nose, RN '8', Blue plastic hubs..£300-400
		South African issue:	Red body, RN '36', spun hubs (as UK issue but with dimpled rivets). South African box £300-400

235	1954-60	**H.W.M. Racing Car**	Pale Green body, Yellow RN '7', Green diecast hubs. (Renumbered from 23j)	£100-130
236	1956-59	**Connaught Racing Car**	Pale Green body, Red interior, Mid-Green hubs, RN '32', White driver	£75-85
237	1957-60	**Mercedes-Benz Racing Car**	Gloss White body, Red interior, Red plastic hubs or spun hubs, Red RN '30', Yellow driver	£80-100
	1960-62		Matt White body, Red plastic hubs or spun hubs, RN '30', Blue driver	£80-100
	1962-64		Matt White body, plastic hubs, RN '30', Tan driver	£80-100
	late issue:		Matt White body, Red plastic hubs, RN '30', Blue or Yellow driver. Late issue Yellow window box	£100-130
238	1957-60	**Jaguar 'D' type**	Turquoise body, Blue interior, White driver, with or without RN '4', Blue diecast hubs	£80-100
	NB		Boxes for 238 that have a descriptive adhesive label stating 'Le Mans 1955/56/57' may attract a premium.	
	1960-62		Turquoise body, Blue interior, White driver, RN '4', spun aluminium hubs	£100-120
	1962-65		Turquoise body, Blue interior or Turquoise interior, White or Yellow driver, RN '4', Blue or Yellow plastic hubs, in plain lighter Yellow box	£130-150
239	1958-60	**Vanwall Racing Car**	Green body, Green hubs, White or Yellow driver, RN '25', '26' or '35', 'VANWALL' logo	£100-130
	1960-62		Green body, White driver, RN '35' or '26', spun aluminium hubs	£120-150
	1962-65		Green body, White or Tan driver, RN '35', Yellow plastic hubs. In lighter Yellow box	£150-175
	1962-65		Green body, Yellow driver, RN '35', Yellow plastic hubs. In lighter Yellow box	£150-175
240	1963-70	**Cooper Racing Car**	Blue body, White design, Black RN '20', spun hubs, White driver (Silver or Yellow helmet)	£40-50
241	1963-70	**Lotus Racing Car**	Green body with racing number '7' or '36', spun hubs, White driver, Silver helmet	£60-80
			Green body with racing number '24', spun hubs, driver with Red helmet	£60-80
	South African issue:		Green body with racing number '24', cast wheels, White driver with Red helmet	£250-350
242	1963-71	**Ferrari Racing Car**	Red body, RN '36', spun hubs, driver, with Silver helmet	£60-80
243	1963-71	**B.R.M. Racing Car**	Green, Yellow cowl, RN '7', spun hubs, driver with Red helmet	£60-80
	1963-71		Metallic Green, Yellow cowl, racing number '7', spun hubs	£60-80
	NB		Gold, US export issue 'see-through' window boxes. Model nos. 237 - 243 housed in these boxes may attract a premium of 50%.	
254	1956-59	**Austin Taxi** (FX3) Two-tone:	Yellow upper body and hubs, Dark Green lower body, Black chassis ('254'), interior and driver	£90-120
	Spun hubs:		Black body, spun hubs, Grey chassis ('254'), interior and driver	£110-130
			Blue body, Light Blue hubs	£500-750
260	1971-72	**VW 'Deutsche Bundespost'**	Yellow body (129 casting, 100mm), German export model	£100-150
262	1959-60	**Volkswagen 'PTT' Car**	(181 casting, 90mm, fixed doors), Yellow/Black, 'PTT', Yellow cast hubs, Swiss Post export model	£500-750
	1960-62		As previous issue but with spun aluminium hubs, Swiss export	£500-750
	1962-66		As previous issue but with plastic hubs, Swiss export	£500-750
			NOTE 262 models listed above should be in the correct French / German box with 'Auto Suisse VW' and 'Schweizer Postauto VW' on the end flap.	
	1966-68	129 casting (100mm):	Yellow/Black, opening doors, spun aluminium hubs, hard plastic case	£150-200
	1968-72		Yellow/Black, opening doors, plastic hubs, Swiss export	£100-125
	1972-76		Yellow/Black, opening doors, Speedwheels, Swiss export	£100-125
268		**Renault Dauphine Mini-cab**	See 'Public Transport' section.	
281	1968-70	**'PATHE NEWS' Camera Car**	See 'Novelty, Film and TV' section.	
340	1954-66	**Land Rover**	Mid-Green body, Light Brown interior and Green cast hubs, Tan cast driver, (renumbered from 27d)	£65-75
	1966-69		Orange body, Green interior, Red cast hubs, Tan cast driver	£75-85
			Orange body, Deep Blue interior, Red cast hubs, Tan cast driver	£75-85
	1969-71		Dark Red body, Red cast hubs, Yellow interior, Blue plastic driver	£110-140
	1971		Red body, Yellow interior, Blue plastic driver, Green or Yellow plastic hubs	£110-140
			Orange body, Dark Green interior, Blue plastic driver, Red plastic hubs	£110-140
341	1954-66	**Land-Rover Trailer**	Orange body (Red hubs), or Green body (Green hubs). (Renumbered from 27m)	£20-30
			Red body, Black plastic hubs	£150-200
			Olive-Drab body	£150-200
342	1966-72	**Austin Mini-Moke**	Metallic Green, Grey canopy with 1 or 2 windows, bubble-packed or boxed	£35-45
	1972-75		Metallic Greenish-Blue, 1 canopy window, bubble-packed or boxed	£35-45
344	1954-61	**Estate Car**	See 'Farm and Garden Models'	
344	1970-72	**Land Rover Pick-Up**	See 'Farm and Garden Models'	
370	1969-76	**Dragster Set**	Yellow/Red, driver, 'FIREBALL', 'INCH-PINCHER', starter unit	£40-50
405	1954-66	**Universal Jeep**	Red body and hubs or Green body and hubs. (Renumbered from 25y)	£80-100
	1966-67		Red body, red plastic hubs, boxed in late lighter yellow box	£100-130
	1963	South African issues:	Green body with Red hubs or Off-White body with Red hubs, English and Afrikaans wording on box	£300-400
448	1963-68	**Chevrolet El Camino Pick-Up with Trailers**	Turquoise/Cream/Red Pick-up and 2 trailers, 'Acme Trailer Hire'	£200-250
449	1961-69	**Chevrolet El Camino Pick-up**	Turquoise body, White roof, Red interior, spun hubs	£80-90
			Turquoise body, White roof, Pale Turquoise interior, spun hubs	£150-200
			Turquoise body, White roof, Lemon interior, spun hubs	£150-200
			NB Various shades of Turquoise are known to exist.	
	South African issue:		All-Turquoise body, Red interior, spun hubs	£750-1,000
	South African issue:		Cream over Caramel lower body, Red interior, spun hubs	£750-1,000
	South African issue:		Turquoise over Cream lower body, Red interior, spun hubs	£750-1,000
	South African issue:		All-Cream lower body, Red interior, spun hubs	£750-1,000
475	1964-66	**Model 'T' Ford**	Blue body, Yellow panels and wheels, driver/female passenger	£45-55
476	1967-69	**Morris Oxford** ('Bullnose')	Yellow body, Blue chassis, Fawn hood, driver	£45-55
516	1965-66	**Mercedes-Benz 230 SL**	Metallic Red, Cream roof, windows. (French issue)	£75-95
675	1954-59	**Ford US Army Staff Car**	See 'Military Vehicles' section.	
2162	1973-76	**Ford Capri**	Metallic Blue, Black roof, Black or Blue interior, 175 mm (1:25 scale, vacuform packed on card base)	£70-90
2214	1974-76	**Ford Capri Rally Car**	Red, Black roof and bonnet, RN '12', Black or Blue interior, 175 mm (1:25 scale, vacuform packed)	£80-100
2253	1974-76	**Ford Capri Police Car**	White/Orange, 'POLICE', Blue light, suspension, windows, 175 mm (1:25 scale, vacuform packed)	£80-100

Cars

Dinky Toys cars made by Meccano, Paris, France and sold in Britain

24kz	1939-40	**Peugeot Car**	Red or Blue, tinplate front bumper, rubber tyres for UK	NGPP
516		**Mercedes-Benz 230sl**	Bronze body, Cream interior	£80-100
518	1962-65	**Renault 4L**	Brown or Grey body, suspension, steering, windows, 85 mm. (French issue)	£75-95
524	1965-67	**Panhard 24c**	Dark Metallic Grey body, (French issue)	£75-95
532		**Lincoln Premiere**	Metallic Light Green body, Dark Green roof	£75-95
530	1965-66	**Citroën DS19**	Light Green body, Light Grey roof. (French issue)	£75-95
535	1962-65	**Citroën 2cv**	Blue body, suspension, steering, windows, 88 mm. (French issue)	£75-95
550	1962-65	**Chrysler Saratoga**	Pink/White body, windows, suspension, steering, 129 mm. (French issue)	£75-95
551	1959-64	**Rolls-Royce Silver Wraith**	Same as UK issue 150 'Made in France'	£75-95
553	1962-65	**Peugeot 404**	Green or White, suspension, steering, windows, 102 mm. (French issue)	£75-95
555	1962-65	**Ford Thunderbird**	White, driver, windscreen, suspension, steering, 121 mm. (French issue)	£90-110

Dinky Toys cars made in Hong Kong

Models **57-001 to 57-006** all have spun hubs, detailed end-flap picture boxes, and are in a scale of 1:42. Hong Kong made models were issued in tab-ended alternative pictorial card boxes or rare yellow 'see-through' cellophane window boxes.

57-001	1965-67	**Buick Riviera**	Light Blue body with Cream roof and Red interior, cast wheels	£80-100
57-002	1965-67	**Chevrolet Corvair Monza**	Red body, Black roof, White interior, cast wheels	£80-100
57-003	1965-67	**Chevrolet Impala**	Yellow body with White roof and Red interior, cast wheels	£80-100
		US / Canadian issue:	Yellow body with Yellow roof, cast wheels	£80-100
57-004	1965-67	**Oldsmobile Dynamic '88'**	White body, Blue roof, Red interior, cast wheels	£125-150
57-005	1965-67	**Ford Thunderbird**	Blue body with White roof, Red interior, cast wheels	£125-150
57-006	1965-67	**Nash Rambler Classic**	Light Green body with Silver roof trim, Cream interior, cast wheels	£125-150
180	1979-80	**Rover 3500**	White body with opening doors, plastic wheels	£20-25
219	1978-79	**'Big Cat' Jaguar**	White/Red, Black 'Big Cat' decal. (This model was bubble-packed or sold unboxed)	£35-45

Dinky Toys made in Italy by Polistil under licence to Dinky Tri-ang

122	1979-80	**Volvo Estate Car**	Orange body, Brown interior, plastic wheels, Brown card box	£20-30
			Cream body, Red interior, cast wheels	£20-30
243	1979-80	**Volvo 'Police' Car**	White body, Brown card box	£15-20

'Mini-Dinky' models

Models 10 – 61 inclusive were made in a scale of 1:65.
Models 94 – 99 inclusive were made in a scale of 1:130.

Mini-Dinky models were issued in 1968 and were made in Hong Kong and Holland. Each model was sold with a free red plastic garage. The cars are fitted with Flexomatic Independent Suspension. Racing cars 60 and 61 were made by Best Box of Holland (now EFSI). The models listed are illustrated in the 1968 US issued 3-page fold-out leaflet which advertised them as 'Swinging Value' at 59 cents and 69 cents. Models 94-99 Construction Vehicles are illustrated in a US issued 'Mini-Dinky' fold-out launch leaflet '1'. The Market Price Range is **£30-40** each.

10	**Ford Corsair**	Yellow or Metallic Gold	22	**Oldsmobile Toronado**	Metallic Pale Blue	57	**Chevrolet Corvair Monza Coupé** ...Red/Black
11	**Jaguar 'E' type**	Red or Metallic Maroon	23	**Rover 2000**	Blue	60	**Cooper** ...Blue '10'
12	**Corvette Stingray** ..Blue or Metallic Dark Blue		24	**Ferrari Superfast**	Red	61	**Lotus Racing Car** ...Green, '4'
13	**Ferrari 250 LM**	Red or Metallic Maroon	25	**Ford Zephyr 6**	Silver	94	**International Bulldozer** ...Yellow
14	**Chevrolet Chevy II**	Yellow or Met. Maroon	26	**Mercedes 250 SE**	White or Bronze	95	**International Skid Shovel** ...Yellow
15	**Rolls-Royce Silver Shadow**	Blue	27	**Buick Riviera**	Blue	96	**Payloader Shovel** ...White
16	**Ford Mustang** ..White, Cream or Metallic Blue		28	**Ferrari F 1**	Red, '7'	97	**Euclid R40** ...Yellow, 10 wheels
17	**Aston Martin DB6**	White	29	**Ford F 1**	White	98	**Michigan Scraper** ...Yellow
18	**Mercedes Benz 230 SL**	White/Black	30	**Volvo 1800s**	Blue	99	**Caterpillar Grader** ...Orange
19	**MGB Roadster**	Blue	31	**Volkswagen 1600TC** ..Blue or Metallic Green		-	**'Mini-Dinky' 12-Car Collector Case,**
20	**Cadillac Coupé de Ville**	Silver or White	32	**Vauxhall Cresta**	Silver or Dark Green		with models ...**£400-600**
21	**Fiat 2300 Station Wagon** ...Blue or Yellow/White		33	**Jaguar**	Red		

'Dinky Toys' issued by Airfix Products Ltd.

Issued by Airfix as 'DINKY TOYS'; made in France to 1:43 scale. Supplied in the last design of Red/Yellow/Blue 'Dinky Toys' window box with header card. They were all issued circa 1980 and all are in the Market Price Range of **£10-15**.

500	**Citroën 2cv**	Red/Orange or Green body, 'duck' motif, open roof	504	**Citroën Visa**	Red body, no decals
500	**Citroën 2cv**	Red/Orange or Green body, 'duck' motif, closed roof	505	**Peugeot 504**	Blue body with 'flame' decal on doors
501	**Fiat Strada**	Blue or Metallic Bronze body, no decals	505	**Peugeot 504**	Greenish-Gold with Black 'cougar' decal on doors
502	**BMW 530**	Purple body with 'flame' decal on doors	506	**Alfa-Sud**	Not seen	NGPP
502	**BMW 530**	Metallic Green with Black 'cougar' decal	507	**Renault 14**	Not seen	NGPP
503	**Alfetta GTV**	Red or Yellow body, Green 'clover leaf' on bonnet	508	**Ford Fiesta**	Not seen	NGPP

COUGAR Model Toys

Many of the 'Airfix Dinky Toys' appeared erratically in the early 1980s (in France, then in the UK), under the name 'Cougar Model Toys'. For information on this small range of 'budget' toys, please see the 'French Meccano Dinky Toys' chapter where they are listed at the end of the 'Cars' section.

AIRFIX – matchbox sized miniatures made in Hong Kong

Although announced in 1980, only a few seem to have appeared in the UK. Market Price Range **£10-15**.

101	**'56 Corvette**	White body with Red flash, bubble-packed	116	**'63 Corvette**	Metallic Blue body
103	**Chevette**	Yellow, 'Turbo' decal, Silver base, bubble-packed	117	**'71 Corvette**	Yellow body with 'Vette' decal
104	**Honda Accord**	Lilac body, Orange flash, Silver base, bubble-pack	119	**Ford Van**	Blue body with Orange flash
105	**Toyota Celica**	Red body, '3', Silver base, Orange bubble-pack	120	**Renegade Jeep**	Yellow/Green body, Silver base, Green packaging
106	**Datsun 280Z**	Brown body, bubble-packed	121	**Chevy Blazer**	Red body
107	**BMW Turbo**	Orange body, Black/Yellow flash, bubble-packed	122	**Sun Van**	Orange body with 'Sun Van' decal, Blue packaging
108	**Alfa Romeo**	Purple body with Yellow flash, bubble-packed	123	**Yamaha 250 MX**	Blue body with 'Yamaha' decal
110	**Stepside Pick-up**	Blue and Brown body, bubble-packed	124	**Honda MT 250**	Orange body with 'Honda' decal
110	**Camper**	Yellow and Two-tone Brown body	125	**Kawasaki Fll 250**	Red body with 'Kawasaki' decal
113	**Pick-up**	Red and Black body, '4 x 4' decal	126	**Suzuki TM 400**	Yellow/Black body with 'CCI' and 'Suzuki' decals
114	**Firebird**	Black body	129	**T-Bird Convertible**	Red and White body
115	**Camaro**	Red body with racing-number 'Z28'	130	**Chevy Convertible**	Metallic Blue and White body

Wooden prototypes, first castings and factory colour samples

These are unique items, produced as samples within the factory to aid the design and development process. Some were made for publicity and catalogue illustration purposes prior to actual volume production. Price guidance is usually not possible since they so rarely come to market in significant quantities. However, the sale in 2001 by Christie's of the Remy-Meeus Collection has enabled us to list the following:

Pre-war items

38a Frazer-Nash BMW, Blue with Grey interior, Turquoise hubs £400-500
38a Frazer-Nash BMW, (first casting), Green with Dark Green
    seats, fabricated, painted tinplate baseplate..........................£300-400
38d Alvis, (first casting), Blue with Tan seats, 'ALVIS' in
    Indian ink on base £300-400
38e Armstrong-Siddeley Coupé, (colour sample), plain Brown
    dashboard, production baseplate painted Khaki £200-300

38f Jaguar Sports Car, (wooden prototype),
    Dark Green body, 'JAGUAR' in Indian ink on base £1,200-1,500
38f Jaguar Sports Car, (1st casting), Green body, Grey seats........£800-1,000

39a Packard Sedan, (wooden prototype),
    Dark Blue with Silver windows, 'PACKARD' on base £600-800
39b Oldsmobile Six Sedan, (wooden prototype), Dark Green with Silver
    windows, 'Oldsmobile Six Sedan' in Indian ink on base.....£500-800
39c Lincoln Zephyr, (wooden prototype of saloon version, not coupé),
    unpainted, with 'Lincoln Zephyr' in pencil on base.............£500-600
39d Buick Viceroy, (wooden prototype), Maroon with Silver
    windows, 'BUICK' in pencil on base...................................£600-800
39e Chrysler Royal Sedan, (wooden prototype), Red with Silver
    windows, 'CHRYSLER' in Indian ink on base £1,400-1,700
39f Studebaker State Commander Coupé, (wooden prototype),
    Yellow Ochre with Silver windows, 'STUDEBAKER' in
    Indian ink on base...£1,500-1,750

39 Series Hupmobile, (wooden prototype), Green with Silver
    windows, 'HUPMOBILE' in Indian ink on base.
    Not issued as a production model £1,200-1,500
39 Series Luxicab, (wooden prototype), Black and Pale Yellow
    with Silver windows, 'LUXICAB' in pencil on rear spare wheel
    cover and '1st sample not approved' in pencil on base.
    Not issued as a production model £1,100-1,400
39 Series Luxicab, (wooden prototype), Black and Canary Yellow
    with Silver windows, 'LUXICAB' in pencil on rear spare
    wheel cover. Not issued as a production model £1,100-1,400

Post-war paint colour samples

38b Sunbeam-Talbot, Red body, hubs and tonneau. Tie-on label stating:
    'Approved 22 Oct 1948', plus paint code details £200-300
38e Armstrong-Siddeley Coupé, Green body, Light Grey interior,
    Green hubs. Tie-on label stating:
    'Approved 22 Oct 1948', plus paint code details £200-300
39b Oldsmobile Sedan, Beige body, Fawn hubs. Tie-on label stating:
    '1 Oct 1948', plus paint code details £300-500
39e Chrysler Royal Sedan, Cream body, Light Green hubs.
    Tie-on label stating: '1 Oct 1948', plus paint code details ..£300-500
40b Triumph 1800, Black body, Silver hubs, rear window pillars.
    Two tie-on labels stating: '30/9/48', + paint code details £500-600
40d Austin Devon, Red body, Maroon hubs. Tie-on label stamped:
    '6 Jan 1950', plus paint code details £400-600
40e Standard Vanguard, Fawn body, Fawn hubs, axle clip,
    open rear wheel arches. Tie-on label stating:
    '18 Oct 1948', plus paint code details...............................£400-600

We are also aware of the following (these were not in Christie's sale, NPP)

107 Sunbeam Alpine in Maroon with Grey interior (unfinished casting).........
107 Sunbeam Alpine in Light Blue with Cream interior (unfinished casting)..
110 Aston-Martin in Grey with Blue interior (unfinished casting)...................
111 Triumph TR2 in Pink with Blue interior ....
122 Volvo 256DL Estate in White ....
122 Volvo 256DL Estate in Red ....
122 Volvo 256DL Estate in Green ....
170 Ford Granada Ghia in Metallic Silver ....
181 Volkswagen Saloon in Pale Blue (with baseplate, 1970s) ....
181 Volkswagen Saloon in Pale Blue (with spun hubs, 1970s) ....
181 Volkswagen Saloon in Metallic Blue ....
181 Volkswagen Saloon in Turquoise ....
190 Monteverdi 375L in Metallic Gold (Copper), White interior, cast wheels.
190 Monteverdi 375L in Metallic Black, Red interior, cast wheels ....
211 Triumph TR7. Metallic Green body, Red, Grey or Green interior ....
227 Beach Buggy. Copper body, Grey hood, 'fire' design ....

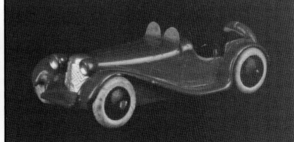

Dinky Toys wooden prototypes (pre-war):

(above) **39e Chrysler Royal Sedan**, Red with Silver windows, 'CHRYSLER' in Indian ink on base

(above right) **38f Jaguar Sports Car**, Dark Green body, 'JAGUAR' in Indian ink on base

(right) **39 Series Luxicab**, Black and Canary Yellow with Silver windows, 'LUXICAB' in pencil on rear spare wheel cover. Not issued as a production model

Photographs: Christie's, South Kensington

Commercial Vehicles Box Types Introduction

A mint condition commercial vehicle without its correct box is worth a fraction of the value of its boxed equivalent. Furthermore, as model boxes made from card do not survive as well as their die-cast contents, pristine box examples are scarce and becoming scarcer. The condition of a box is of paramount importance and attention is drawn to the section in the main catalogue introduction, namely: 'Classifying the Condition of Models and Boxes'.

The following listing provides collectors with a working knowledge of the range of box types issued. In addition details are given of their dates of issue, their design and of the models which used them. See also the colour sections for examples of many types of boxes.

Whilst every care has been taken in preparing the listing other variations no doubt exist and information on these is welcomed.

Similarly with no 'dates of birth' available the dates of issue shown are approximate and again any further information is welcomed.

Commercial Vehicles Box Identification

(See also 'Dinky Toys Trade Boxes' section).

Model Colour Identification Marks
These are shown on the box lid and label and take the form of either a circular colour spot or a capital letter, e.g. 'R' for red. A colour spot may be a single colour or in the case of the later two-tone colours models a two-tone colour spot.

'Lead-free' labels 'LF'
In the l950s the government introduced new regulations concerning the lead content of die-cast models. Consequently, to indicate that a model complied with the new regulations, a round white label with 'LF' in blue was added to box end labels for a short time. Alternatively, an 'LF' coloured ink stamp was used. (See example in the colour section.)

Model Reference Numbers
These are always shown on the box lid and label.

Dual numbered boxes c. l953 – 1954
A new numbering system was introduced which resulted in models being issued displaying both the old and new reference numbers. The information was shown in one of two ways:
(a) A black new number stamped alongside the old number
(b) A small old model number shown in red on either side of a larger black new number, e.g. 511 911 511". (See examples in the colour section). Dual numbered boxes (issued for a relatively short period) may attract a premium.

Quality Control Box Markings. 1947 – 1957
(a) Factory Checkers Marks
A quality control mark may be found on the base of the buff coloured boxes. This takes the form of a coloured ink stamp of a reference number within a circle, e.g. 'M42' or 'M19'. See the examples shown in the colour section. Stamped on the underside of the blue covered box lid may be found a similar ink stamp e.g. 'ZQ Z8'.
(b) Date Stamps
Ink stamped on the base of boxes or box lids may be found a purple date stamp relating to the date of the model's issue. Recorded examples include: 'GR950' on a (25x) orange coloured box; '10 KR 55' on a (933) blue/white stripe box; 'H656' on a (902) blue/white stripe box; 'KB956' on a (433) yellow covered box lid; '01057' on a (689) military blue/white box.
The Editor would welcome any further information on this subject.

Pre-war issues 1933 – 1939
Apart from sets (see the Gift Sets listing) commercial vehicles were sold unboxed. They were usually packaged in half-dozen retailers trade packs such as Nos. 28/1, 28/2 and 28/3 Delivery Vans.

Post-war Issues 1947 – 1979
In 1947 the first individual boxes were introduced to house the exciting new range of 'Supertoys' models. However, the small commercial vehicles continued to be sold unboxed from trade packs until 1953/54.
The boxes have been catalogued into four types as follows:
Type 1 1947-75 - Boxes with lift-off lids
Type 2 1953-75 - All card boxes with tuck-in end flaps
Type 3 1963-79 - Display boxes
Type 4 l964-64 - Export only boxes

TYPE I   1947 - 69   BOXES WITH LIFT-OFF LIDS

A 1947-49
(A-a) Brown card box with wrap around all-white label with red lettering 'DINKY SUPERTOYS' and model number shown in black. Model shown as a black/white photographic illustration, e.g., 563 Heavy Tractor.

(A-b) Brown card box with separate labels on the box top and one box end. The half red and white box labels show 'DINKY SUPERTOYS' in red. Model number is white on a black oval background. In addition the main label displays an illustration of the model and whilst the main design of the label remains constant, the position of the model does vary as follows:

(i) Facing inwards on the right side of the label.
 Models recorded using this box: 25x, 501 (1st type), 521 and 563.

(ii) Facing outwards on the left side of the label.
Models recorded using this box: 502, 503, 511, 512, 513 (all 1st types). The small separate label attached to the right side of the box lid is white with red model information text. Some labels include a line drawing of the model eg. 503 and 513.

(iii) Buff plain card box with a single 'wrap round' red and white label which covers the box lid from end to end with 'DINKY SUPERTOYS' in red on the larger Foden type box, one end of the label contains information about the model in German, French and Spanish. In addition, the model number on the top and ends is now white on a circular black background. The model picture is facing inwards from the right and the models recorded in this box to date are: 504 Tanker 1st type and 531.

(iv) As previous issue but the model picture is facing outwards from the left. Models recorded: 511, 512, 521 and 533.

B c.1950
(i) Green covered box with red and white wrap-around label. Models recorded in this box: 25x, 501, 502, 503, 504 (lst and 2nd types), 504 'MOBILGAS', 511, 512, 513 and 521. Model picture facing inwards from the right. 'DINKY SUPERTOYS' in red letters.
(ii) Orange card box with black printing, e.g., 25x Breakdown Lorry.
(iii) Orange card box with orange/white label, e.g., 25x Breakdown Lorry.

C c.1951
(i) Pale or dark blue covered box with wrap-around red and white label. Model picture facing inwards from the right with 'DINKY SUPERTOYS' logo. Models recorded: 25x, 501, 502, 503, 504 (1st and 2nd types), 505, 511, 512, 513, 514 (all issues except 'Spratts'), 521, 531/931, 532/932 and 533/933.

(ii) Pale or dark blue box with wrap-around orange and white label with 'DINKY SUPERTOYS'. Model picture facing inwards from the right front. Beneath the model picture is a black factory code, e.g. on the 522 Big Bedford lorry issue the code is '50522'. Models recorded: 25x, 504 (1st / 2nd), 511, 514 'LYONS' and 'SLUMBERLAND', 531 and 571.

(iii) Same as C(ii) but with model picture facing outwards from the left. Models recorded: 502(1st), 503 (2nd) and 512.

(iv) Same as C(ii) but with model picture facing inwards from the right front but with 'DINKY TOYS'. Models recorded: 501(1st type), 504 Tanker (1st and 2nd types), 504 'MOBILGAS', 514 'WEETABIX', 514 'SLUMBERLAND', 514'SPRATTS', 521, 522, 564, 591/991, and 917.

(v) Same as C (iv) but with model picture facing outwards from the left front. Models recorded: 502, 503 (1st types), 512, 513 (1st types).

(vi) Same as C (iv) but with model picture facing inwards from the left front. Models 505 (1st type), 532 and 581 US issue.

D c1953   (i) Blue and white striped box lid with dark blue bottom section. Box lid is white with dark blue parallel stripes. 'DINKY TOYS' logo is shown in red plus a colour picture of the model facing inwards from the right. The model number is on the left of the picture. Colour identification spots shown as appropriate on box ends. Models recorded:
409, 418, 430, 582, 511, 511/911, 512, 512/912, 513, 513/913, 521/921, 901/2/3 (2nd type),   911/12/13. 917, 921, 923 ('ketchup bottle'), 923 ('baked beans can'), 930, 931, 932/33, 941/42, 963, 980, 982, 991.

NB The 417 Leyland Comet Lorry yellow/green issue was housed in a box with a blue/yellow picture.

(ii) As D (i), but with 'DINKY SUPERTOYS' logo and with the model picture facing inwards from the right. Models recorded:
901/2/3, 905, 913, 918/9, 923, 930, 934/5/6, 942/3, 948, 954, 958, 960, 963/4, 966/7/8/9, 973, 977, 982/3/4, 986, 991, 994.

On the box side is a note stating the colour of the model which may vary from the one illustrated on the box front. This only happened when a model was issued for a short time and hence some of the rarest models were issued in this manner (e.g. 902 Foden Flat Truck in yellow/green livery was issued in box with red/green model picture; 913 Guy Flat Truck with tailboard in yellow/green livery issued in box with all-green model picture; 934 Leyland Octopus Wagon in blue and yellow livery was issued on the standard box with a yellow/green model picture but displaying a dark blue colour spot).
The Editor would welcome any further examples.

(iii) As D (ii), but with model picture facing outwards from the left. 'DINKY SUPERTOYS' logo. Model recorded No.982.

(iv) As D (ii), but with model picture facing inwards from the left. 'DINKY SUPERTOYS' logo. Model recorded No. 979.

(v) Plain blue and white striped box with no model picture on lid. A white end label 'DINKY SUPERTOYS' and the model details in blue letters. Models recorded: 920 and 923.

E   Yellow covered box lid with blue bottom section.
(i) c.1956 - 1959
On two of the box sides is a picture of the model set against a white shadow background. The top of the box lid has a 'DINKY TOYS' logo in red. Colour spots shown as appropriate. In addition white circular 'LF' (lead free) labels may be found. Models recorded: 408/9, 417, 419, 430/1/2/3, 437.
NB. The rare 408 Big Bedford Lorry in pink and cream livery was issued in this box but with the standard maroon and fawn model box picture.

(ii) Yellow covered box lid but with red side panels with pictorial scene with 'DINKY TOYS' logo in red. The box lid shows the model picture facing inwards from the right with a pictorial scene in an end panel on the left. Models recorded: 401, 408, 417, 419, 425, 430, 434, 448, 450, 925, 960, 964, 972 and 978.

(iii) Same as previous issue but with 'DINKY SUPERTOYS' logo. Models recorded: 908, 934, 935, 944, 958/9, 962, 964, 972 and 978.
NB. No. 935 Leyland Octopus with chains in the rare dark blue and grey livery was issued in the standard box with the green and grey version illustrated but with a dark blue spot displayed.

(iv) All yellow covered lid with a pictorial scene in the middle of the box lid top. 'DINKY SUPERTOYS' in red. Models recorded: 959, 987/8/9.

F   'One off' box issues with lift-off lids.

(i) Plain dark blue covered box with no picture. White label on box lid end with dark blue text. Model recorded: 982 Pullman Car Transporter in rare mid-blue livery with brownish-grey decks.

(ii) Orange covered box (c.1950) with white/orange wrap-around lid label. Models recorded: 25x Breakdown Truck and 14c Coventry Climax Fork Lift Truck.

TYPE 2   1953 - 1975
ALL CARD BOXES WITH TUCK-IN END FLAPS

A   1953 - 1964
(i) Deep yellow box with 'DINKY TOYS' in red plus the model's name and type in black. A white reference number on a black or red oval background is on the box end flaps but no reference is shown on the box face. The model is pictured on the box sides with or without a white shadow background. Colour spots shown as applicable. Foreign language information is shown on one of the box end flaps. Box used for small and medium size models, e.g., 431/432. Box in general use during the model renumbering period. Consequently dual numbered boxes will be found.
Very few boxes were issued displaying just the old type of reference number. Recorded models to date: 25d, e, f, g and 30e. In addition, 29c Bus and 29e Coach have been identified. Please send details if you have any other examples. Later issues display 'WITH WINDOWS' captions.

(ii)   Plain light yellow box with two red sides and no model picture. The 'DINKY TOYS' logo, the model type and its reference number are shown in yellow and white. Colour spots are shown as appropriate. Models recorded: 252, 413, 414 and 428 plus 070 and 071 Dublo Dinky.

(iii) 1963 - 1970
Yellow box with red end features panel around the front right side, with or without an upward pointing white arrow. Models recorded: 273, 274, 435.
(iv) 1966 - 1969
A detailed full colour picture box with 'DINKY TOYS' in red plus a pictorial scene on two sides. A yellow laurel leaf design on a black background incorporates the model number Models recorded: 280, 402, 407 'KENWOOD', 914, 923, 944/5, 959/60, 965, 970, 972 and 978.

(v) 1968 - 1974
White fronted box with a narrow yellow band across the face. The box front displays 'DINKY TOYS' in red plus the model number and type in black and white letters. A colour picture of the model is shown on two sides. Models recorded: 407, 438/9/40, 91, 917, 974, 978 and 980.

(vi) 1966 - 1970
Picture box used for large commercials with two full pictorial sides with 'DINKY TOYS' in red. The other sides are yellow and red. Models recorded: 434 'AUTO SERVICES', 914 and 945.

(vii) 1970 - 1975
Heavy card box used for heavy models e.g. 924 Centaur Dump Truck. Box has white face with a colour picture of model combined with a black band across the face and sides.

(viii)   Promotional Box Types
(a)   No. 274 'JOSEPH MASON PAINTS' Minivan. Dark red box with white letters plus an enclosed leaflet.
(b)   No. 491 Plain yellow box with red letters. 'JOBS DAIRY'.
(c)   No. 917 Mercedes-Benz LP1920 Truck with 'HENRY JOHNSON' logo. Plain white card box with no lettering
(d)   No. 940 Mercedes-Benz, 'FISONS', plain white box

TYPE 3   1963 - 1979   DISPLAY BOXES

A   1970 - 1976 Vacuform packs
Models displayed on a black card plinth with a blue surface with 'DINKY TOYS' in red and white. The model is covered by a close-fitting see-through protective plastic cover. Known examples include: 407,416, 438/9, 915, 944, 945 'ESSO' and 'LUCAS' issues.

B   1976 - 1979 Window boxes
Cellophane fronted window boxes with a dark blue and red header card giving the model's name and 'DINKY DIECAST TOYS' in yellow and white letters. Known examples include: 275, 432, 440, 451, 940, 950 and 980.
C   1963 - 1966 Fold-back lid display box
224 Commer Convertible Truck and 975 Ruston Bucyrus Excavator which also had a coloured outer box display wrapper issued for a while.

TYPE 4   1964 - 1966   EXPORT ONLY BOXES

A   1964 - 1966
An all-yellow card and cellophane 'see-through' display box.
'DINKY' plus the model type and number is shown across the box front in red letters plus 'A MECCANO PRODUCT MADE IN ENGLAND'. Box issued with a card protection strip. Known models include: 275, 434, 492, 914. A version of this box was used for the 944 'SHELL BP' tanker - see picture in the colour section, Also used for the U.S. Export Series: 'MARVELS IN MINIATURE' which is shown on the sides of the box front in red capital letters, e.g. 275, 434, 437, 448 and 965. Later issues display the range on the base of the box.

B   c.1965
Same as previous issue but all-gold box with two black and red diagonal stripes. A rare box type. Known issues include 434 and 989.

INNER BOX LININGS and MODEL SUPPORTS

To be complete a box should contain all its original model supports. The following issues all had supports or linings. In some instances top and bottom linings were included (2).
14c, 400, 561, 581, 908(2), 924, 930(3), 958, 964, 965, 967, 968, 969(2), 972, 974, 976, 977(2), 979(2), 980, 982, 983(2), 984(2), 985(2), 986, 989(2).

Identification of casting types
The 25 Series Lorries 1934 - 1950

Type 1: **(1934-36)**, 'open' chassis (usually black), tinplate radiator, no headlamps,
no front bumper, 'smooth' cast hubs (various colours) with large white tyres. 105 mm.

Type 2: **(1936-46)**, 'open' chassis (usually black), diecast radiator with headlamps but
no front bumper, 'smooth' cast hubs (various colours), with large white tyres. 105 mm.

Type 3: **(1947-48)**, 'closed' chassis (only in black), diecast radiator with headlamps but
no front bumper, 'smooth' or 'ridged' wheel hubs (only in black) ,with black tyres. 105 mm.

Type 4: **(1948-50)**, detailed moulded chassis (only in black), diecast radiator with headlamps and
with bumper, 'ridged' coloured wheel hubs with black tyres. 110 mm.

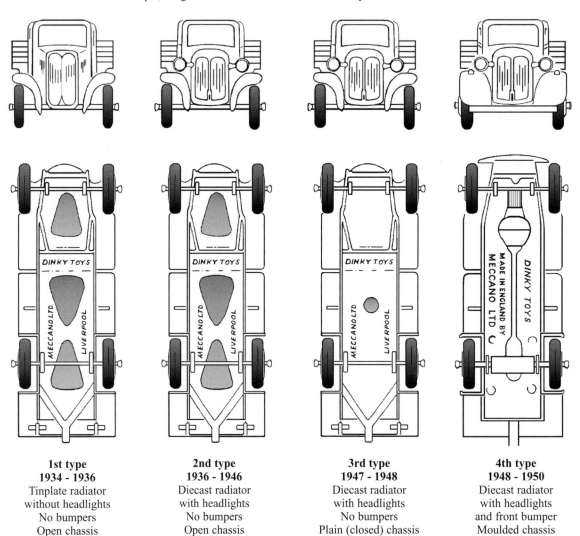

1st type	2nd type	3rd type	4th type
1934 - 1936	**1936 - 1946**	**1947 - 1948**	**1948 - 1950**
Tinplate radiator	Diecast radiator	Diecast radiator	Diecast radiator
without headlights	with headlights	with headlights	with headlights
No bumpers	No bumpers	No bumpers	and front bumper
Open chassis	Open chassis	Plain (closed) chassis	Moulded chassis

25 Series Trucks 1934-50 Wheel types The first pre-war issues have cast metal wheels followed by chrome (rare) or diecast hubs with large white tyres. The early post-war issues c.1946 have smooth hubs and large black tyres. **1947-48** issues have ridged black hubs with large black tyres. The last issues **c.1949-50** have coloured ridged hubs and attract a premium. Similarly early cast or chrome hubs also attract a premium.

Foden cab types

1947 - 1952
Foden 'DG'
(1st type) cab
Exposed radiator
Colour flashes on sides

1952 - 1964
Foden 'FG'
(2nd type) cab
Radiator behind grille
No colour flashes on sides

Guy cab types

Guy 1st type cab 1947 - 1954
Exposed radiator
No gusset at either
side of number plate

Guy 2nd type cab 1954 - 1958
Exposed radiator
With gusset at each
side of number plate

Guy Warrior cab 1958 - 1964
Radiator behind grille
Restyled front with
sidelights in wings

28 and 280 Series Delivery Vans

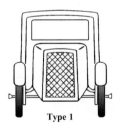
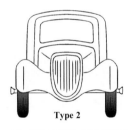

Type 1   Type 2   Type 3

Type 1: **(1933-35)**, two-piece lead body with *'HORNBY SERIES'* (early issues) or *'DINKY TOYS'* cast-in
under cab roof, tinplate radiator, no headlamps, thinly-painted coloured solid wheel/tyre castings
(some silver plated), 84 mm. (Coloured wheels tend to attract a premium to the price of the model.)
Type 2: **(1935-39)**, one-piece diecast body, cast-in shield-shaped radiator, rear wheel spats, cast smooth wheel
hubs with rubber tyres (usually white), 81 mm. All carried advertising.
Type 3: **(1939-41)**, one-piece diecast body with rear wheel spats, cast smooth wheel hubs (various colours)
with black tyres, open rear windows, 83 mm. All carried advertising.
Type 3: **(1947-54)**, one-piece diecast body with rear wheel spats, cast ridged wheel hubs (usually black) with
black tyres, filled-in rear windows, cast boss under roof , 83 mm. No advertising.

Identification of Ford Transit Van castings (not illustrated)

Type 1: **(1966-74)**, has sliding driver's door, opening hinged side door, and twin rear doors.
Type 2: **(1974-78)**, non-sliding driver's door, one side-hinged door, one top-hinged rear door.
Type 3: **(1978-80)**, as Type 2 but with a slightly longer bonnet (18 mm.)

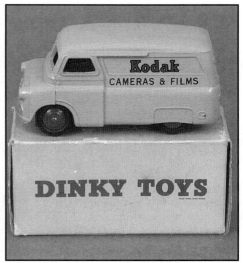

Photo: Vectis Auctions

Photo: Vectis Auctions

Photo: Christie's

Market Price Range (MPR) for pre-1954 unboxed commercial vehicle models: Prior to 1954, virtually all smaller, non-Supertoy commercial vehicle models were sold unboxed from retailer's trade boxes of either 6, 4 or 3 models. Consequently, all pre-1954 issues have been priced as being unboxed. Post-1954 models were all boxed and have been priced accordingly. As a consequence, models which have been renumbered will be found to have two differing prices – one for the pre-1954 unboxed version and another for its boxed and renumbered successor.

See also the Trade Box section for details of individual boxes and packs that were used to supply shops.

Ref	Year(s)	Model name	Colours, features, details	Market Price Range
14a	1948-54	B.E.V. Truck	Mid-Blue body with Blue hubs, Fawn driver, hook, (renumbered 400)	£30-35
			Grey body (with Blue, Grey or Red hubs), Fawn driver, hook	£30-35
14c	1949-54	Coventry Climax Fork Lift	Orange, Brown or Dark Red body, Green forks, Fawn driver, 1 packing piece, (renumbered 401)	£25-30
14z	1938-40	Three-wheel Delivery Van	'Triporteur' with Green, Red, Grey, Blue or Yellow body, Black hubs,	
			White tyres, driver is always a different colour from van, French model	NGPP

22 Series

Ref	Year(s)	Model name	Colours, features, details	Market Price Range
22c	1933-35	Motor Truck	Two-piece lead body with 'HORNBY SERIES' cast-in, tinplate radiator, diecast wheels that may be plain or may have an applied colour wash.	
			Blue cab, Red truck body	£300-400
			Blue cab, Cream or Yellow truck body, Blue wash wheels	£500-750
			Red cab, Green, Blue or Cream truck body	£300-400
			Yellow cab, Blue truck body	£300-400
22c	1935-40	Motor Truck	Orange-Red, Maroon, Green or Blue (diecast one-piece) body, open rear window, coloured diecast hubs	£125-150
			Dark Blue body, chrome hubs	£125-150
			Off-white body, Mid-Blue hubs	£125-150
	1945-47		Red, Green or Brown body, open rear window, Black diecast hubs	£60-70
	1948-50		Red, Green or Brown body, closed rear window, Black diecast hubs	£60-70
22d	1933-34	Delivery Van	Lead body, tinplate radiator, 'HORNBY SERIES' cast-in.	
			Green cab, Blue van body, Blue wash wheels, Type 1	£1,500-2,000
			Orange/Blue or Blue/Yellow body, Red wheels, no advertising, Type 1	£1,500-2,000
	1934-34		As previous models but with 'DINKY TOYS' cast-in	£400-500
	1934	Delivery Van 'MECCANO'	Orange cab and chassis, Blue van with Red/Black 'Meccano Engineering For Boys'	£2,000-2,500
22d	1934-35		Yellow body (lead), 'Meccano Engineering For Boys' in Red and Black, Type 1. Model number 22d until April 1935, (renumbered 28n)	£900-1,200

25 Series

Ref	Year(s)	Model name	Colours, features, details	Market Price Range
25a	1934-36	Wagon	Maroon, Green, Red or Blue body, Black chassis, Type 1	£300-400
	1936-40		Maroon, Green, Red or Blue body, Black or Red chassis, Type 2	£125-150
	1936-40		Blue body with Orange chassis, Type 2	£150-200
	1946		Grey, Green or Blue, Type 2, smooth hubs	£80-100
	1947-48		Grey, Green, Red, Orange, Stone or Blue body, Black chassis, Type 3	£70-80
	1948-50		Grey, Green, Light Blue or Orange body, Black chassis, Type 4	£70-80
			Cream or Red body, Black chassis, Type 4	£70-80
25b	1934-36	Covered Wagon	Blue body, Cream tilt, Black chassis, Type 1	£300-400
	1936-40		Green body, Green, Cream or Yellow tilt, Black chassis, Type 2	£140-180
			Cream/Yellow or Fawn/Cream, Black chassis, Type 2	£140-180
			Orange body, Cream tilt, Green chassis, Type 2	£150-200
	1936-40	Covered Wagon		
		'CARTER PATERSON'	Green body, Blue hubs, Green tilt, Black chassis, Type 2, 'Express Carriers London'	£300-350
		'CARTER PATERSON'	Green body, Blue hubs, Type 2, 'Special Service To The Seaside'	£400-500
		'MECCANO'	Green body, Cream tilt, Black chassis, Type 2, 'Engineering For Boys'	£300-400
			Variation with chrome hubs	£500-600
		'HORNBY TRAINS'	Fawn body, Cream tilt, Black chassis, Gold lettering, Type 2	£300-400
	1945-47	Covered Wagon	Green/Green, Grey/Light or Dark Grey, Blue/Grey, Black chassis, Type 3	£100-140
	1947-50		Green/Green, Grey/Grey, Cream/Red, Cream/Blue, Black chassis, Type 4	£100-140
			Yellow body, Blue tinplate tilt, Black ridged hubs	£300-400
25c	1934-36	Flat Truck	Dark Blue body, Black chassis, Type 1	£150-200
	1936-40		Green or Stone body, Black chassis, Type 2	£125-150
	1946		Fawn, Green or Grey body, smooth hubs, Type 2	£70-80
	1947-48		Green, Blue, Stone or Grey body, Black chassis, Type 3	£70-80
	1948-50		Green, Blue, Orange or Stone body, Type 4	£70-80
	NB		Some pre-war (1934-40) Truck issues will be found with a '20 mph' disc on the rear.	
25d	1934-35	Petrol Tank Wagon	Same chassis casting as other 25 series lorries but with hook removed.	
		(plain, unlettered)	Red body, no advertising, Black chassis, Type 1, open windows to back of cab	£500-750
		'SHELL BP'	Red body, Black chassis, Type 1	£500-750
		'SHELL'	Red body, Blue hubs, Type 1, 'SHELL LUBRICATING OIL' in Gold serif lettering	£500-750
		'ESSO'	Green body, Black chassis, Type 1	£500-750
		'POWER'	Green body, Black chassis, Type 1	£500-750
		'PRATTS'	Green body, Black chassis, Type 1	£500-750
		'CASTROL'	Green body, Black chassis, Blue hubs, Red logo, Type 1	£500-750
		'TEXACO'	Red body, Black chassis/hubs, White logo 'PETROLEUM & PRODUCTS', Type 1	£500-750
	1936-46	'PETROL'	Red body, Black chassis, Black or White lettering, Type 2	£500-750

25d Petrol Tank Wagon list continues overleaf:

25d Petrol Tank Wagon list continued from previous page:

		'SHELL BP'	Red body, Black chassis, Blue or chrome hubs, Type 2	£500-750
		'MOBILOIL'	Red body, Black chassis, Type 2	£500-750
		'TEXACO'	Red body, Black chassis, Type 2	£500-750
		'PETROL'	Green body, Black chassis, Type 2	£500-750
		'ESSO'	Green body, Black chassis, Black or Blue hubs, Gold lettering, Type 2	£500-750
		'POWER'	Green body, Black chassis, Type 2	£500-750
		'CASTROL'	Green body, Black chassis, Black or Blue hubs, Red lettering, Type 2	£500-750
		'REDLINE GLICO'	Blue body, Black chassis, Red panel, Gold lettering, Type 2	£500-750
	1945	'POOL' (Wartime)	Grey body, White chassis, Black hubs, Black lettering, Type 2	£500-750
	1945-46	'POOL' (Wartime)	Grey body, Black chassis, Type 2	£500-750
	1945-46	'PETROL' (Wartime)	Grey body, Type 2	£500-750
	1946-47	'PETROL'	Red, Orange or Green body, Black chassis, Type 3	£100-150
	1947-48	'PETROL'	Orange body, Type 4	£300-400
	1948-50	'PETROL'	Red, Light Green or Mid-Green body, Black chassis, Type 4	£70-100
	1948-?	'PETROL'	Yellow body, Black chassis, Type 4	£200-300
25e	1934-35	Tipping Wagon	Maroon/Yellow body, Black chassis, Type 1	£150-200
	1936-40		Maroon/Yellow, Brown/Turquoise or Fawn/Fawn body, Black chassis, Type 2	£100-125
			Fawn/Fawn body, Black chassis, Type 2	£100-125
	1946		Grey, Green or Fawn, Type 2	£70-80
	1947-48		Grey, Stone, Green or Yellow body, Black chassis, Type 3	£70-80
	1948-50		Grey, Stone or Brown body, Black chassis, Type 4	£70-80
	1948-50		Blue/Pink body, Black chassis, Type 4	£70-80

NB Some early post-war 25 series Trucks variations exist with smooth hubs.

25f	1934-35	Market Gardeners Lorry	Green body, Black chassis or Yellow body, Green chassis, Type 1	£150-200
	1936-40		Green or Yellow body, Black chassis, Type 2	£70-80
			Green body, Yellow chassis, Type 2	£150-200
	1945-47		Green, Grey, Stone or Yellow body, Black chassis and hubs, Type 3	£70-80
	1947-50		Green, Grey, Yellow or Red body, Black chassis and hubs, Type 4	£70-80
			Orange body, Black chassis and hubs, Type 4	£140-160
			Green or Yellow body, Black chassis, Yellow hubs, Type 4	£70-80
25g	1935-40	Trailer	Dark Blue or Green body with cast-in hook, tinplate drawbar	£35-40
	1946-47		Green, Grey, Stone, Pale Blue or Orange body, cast-in hook, tinplate drawbar	£15-20
	1947-48		Green, Stone, Pale Blue or Orange body, cast-in hook, wire drawbar	£15-20
	1948-49		Green, Stone, Pale Blue or Orange body, tinplate hook, wire drawbar	£15-20
25g	1950-54		Green or Red body with tinplate hook and wire drawbar, (renumbered 429)	£15-20

NB Most 25g Trailers have a white 'T' on a square black background, located at the rear.

25m	1948-52	Bedford End Tipper	Dark Green cab and truck body, Black hubs, crank-handle operates tipper	£60-75
	1948-54		Orange cab and truck body, Black hubs	£60-75
			Orange cab and truck body, Light Green hubs	£500-750
			Cream cab and truck body, Red hubs	£500-750
			Dark Green cab and truck body, Light Green hubs	£300-400
			Red cab, Cream back, Red cast hubs	£60-75
			Yellow cab, Mid-Blue back, Yellow cast hubs	£90-120

NB 25m was renumbered 410 in 1954. All 25m models were sold from trade packs of six.

25p	1948-54	Aveling Barford Road Roller.	Mid or Pale Green body with driver and hook, Red wheels, (renumbered 251)	£30-40
			All-Orange body, Tan driver	£150-200
25r	1948-54	Forward Control Lorry	Orange body, Black hubs	£60-70
		(renumbered 420)	Orange body, Green hubs	£75-85
			Cream body, Black hubs	£60-70
			Cream body, Blue hubs	£75-85
			Cream body, Black hubs	£75-85
			Dark Brown body, Green hubs	£75-85
			Green body, Cream hubs	£75-85
			Green body, Red hubs	£75-85
25s	1937-40	Six-wheeled Wagon	Reddish-Brown body, Cream, Brown or Grey tilt, holes in seat (but no figures)	£100-125
			Royal Blue body	£200-250
	1945-48		Brown (various shades), Green or Dark Blue body, Grey or Light Blue tilt, with or without holes for figures (but no figures)	£100-125
			Brick Red body, Grey tinplate tilt, Black hubs	£125-150
25t	1945-47	Flat Truck and Trailer	(25c Flat Truck (Type 3), and matching 25g Trailer), Green, Blue, Orange or Stone	£140-160
	1947-50		(25c Flat Truck (Type 4), and matching 25g Trailer), Green or Orange	£120-140
25v	1948-54	Bedford Refuse Wagon	Fawn body, Green opening shutters and rear door, (renumbered 252). (Trade box contains 4)	£75-85
25w	1948-54	Bedford Truck	Light Green cab, truck body and hubs. (Shades of Pale Green exist)	£60-75
		(renumbered 411)	Same as previous model, but with 'straight across' Black front mudguards	£250-350
			Dark Green cab, Light Green truck body, Light Green hubs	£300-400
			Light Green cab and truck body, Red hubs	£500-750
25x	1949-54	Commer Breakdown Lorry	'DINKY SERVICE' logo. First issues in Trade Boxes of 4, then individually in Orange card boxes.	
		(renumbered 430)	Tan cab and chassis (various shades), Light Green back, Red hubs, Black logo	£100-120
			Dark Grey cab, Violet Blue back, Red hubs, White logo	£130-150
			Dark Grey cab, Royal Blue back, Red hubs, White logo	£115-135

28 Series Delivery Vans

28a	1934	'HORNBY TRAINS'	Orange body, 'Hornby Trains' logo, 1st Type	£2,000-3,000
28a		'HORNBY TRAINS'	Yellow body, 'Hornby Trains British & Guaranteed' in Gold,	
	1934-35		Type 1, 84 mm, Blue wash wheels	£2,000-3,000
	1935-36		Type 2, 81 mm	£250-350
28a		'GOLDEN SHRED'	Cream body, 'Golden Shred Marmalade' on right hand side, 'Silver Shred Marmalade' on left hand side,	
	1936-39		Type 2, 81 mm	£2,000-3,000
	1939-41		Type 3, 83 mm	£750-1,000
28b		'PICKFORDS'	Royal Blue, 'Pickfords Removals & Storage, Over 100 Branches' in Gold,	
	1934-35		Type 1, 84 mm, Purple wash wheels	£2,000-3,000
	1935	'PICKFORDS'	Dark Blue. Late version with diecast hubs, White tyres, Type 1	£2,000-3,000
	1935-35		Type 2, 81 mm	£750-1,000
28b		'SECCOTINE'	Blue body, 'Seccotine Sticks Everything' in Gold,	
	1935-39		Type 2, 81 mm	£750-1,000
	1939-41		Type 3, 83 mm	£300-400
28c		'MANCHESTER GUARDIAN'	'The Manchester Guardian' in Gold,	
	1934-35		Black/Red body, Yellow wash wheels, Type 1	£2,000-3,000
	1935-39		Red body, Type 2	£300-400
	1939-41		Red body, Type 3	£300-400
28d		'OXO'	Blue body, 'Beef In Brief' and 'Beef At Its Best' in Gold,	
	1934-35		Type 1, Green wash wheels	£2,000-3,000
	1935-39		Type 2	£750-1,000
	1939-41		Type 3	£500-700
28e		'ENSIGN CAMERAS'	Orange body, 'ENSIGN CAMERAS' (on n/s) and 'ENSIGN LUKOS FILMS' (on o/s) in Gold,	
	1934-35		Type 1, Blue wash wheels	£2,000-3,000
28e		'FIRESTONE TYRES'	'Firestone Tyres' in Gold,	
	1934-35		White body, Type 1	£2,000-3,000
	1935-39		Blue or White body, Type 2	£750-1,000
	1939-41		Blue or White body, Type 3	£200-300
28f		'PALETHORPES'	Pale Grey-Blue body, Pink sausage decal, 'Palethorpes Royal Cambridge' on van sides, 'Palethorpes Model Factory' on rear (Red and Navy Blue transfers),	
	1934-35		Type 1, Blue wash wheels	£1,500-2,000
	1935-38		Type 2	£750-1,000
28f		'VIROL'	Yellow body, 'Give Your Child A Virol Constitution' in Black,	
	1938-39		Type 2, Blue wash wheels	£750-1,000
	1939-41		Type 3	£300-400
28g		'KODAK'	Yellow body, 'Use Kodak Film To Be Sure' in Red,	
	1934-35		Type 1, Blue wash wheels	£1,500-2,000
	1935-39		Type 2	£750-1,000
	1939-41		Type 3	£300-400
28h		'SHARPS TOFFEES'	'Sharps Toffee, Maidstone' in Gold,	
	1934-35		Black/Red body, Type 1, Yellow wash wheels	£1,500-2,000
	1935-35		Red body, Type 2	£400-500
28h		'DUNLOP'	Red body, 'Dunlop Tyres' in Gold,	
	1935-39		Type 2	£750-1,000
	1939-41		Type 3	£300-400
28k		'MARSH & BAXTER'	Dark Green body, 'Marsh's Sausages' and pig logo in Gold,	
	1934-35		Type 1, Purple or Green wash wheels	£1,500-2,000
	1935-39		Type 2	£750-1,000
	1939-41		Type 3	£500-600
28L		'CRAWFORDS'	Red body, 'Crawfords Biscuits' in Gold,	
	1934-35		Type 1, Yellow or Green wash wheels	£1,500-2,000
28m		'WAKEFIELD'S CASTROL'	Green body, 'Wakefield Castrol Motor Oil' in Red,	
	1934-35		Type 1, Yellow wash wheels	£1,500-2,000
	1935-39		Type 2	£300-400
	1939-41		Type 3	£1,500-2,000
28n		'MECCANO'	Lemon Yellow body, 'Meccano Engineering For Boys' in Red and Black,	
	1934-35		Type 1. Was 22d	£2,500-3,500
	1935-35		Type 2	£300-400
28n		'ATCO'	Green body, 'Atco Lawn Mowers Sales and Service' in Gold/Red,	
	1935-39		Type 2	£750-1,000
	1939-41		Type 3	£500-600
28p		'CRAWFORDS'	Red body, 'Crawfords Biscuits' in Gold,	
	1935-39		Type 2	£750-1,000
	1939-41		Type 3	£750-1,000
28r		'SWAN'	Black body, 'Swan Pens' and logo in Gold,	
	1936-39		Type 2	£750-1,000
	1939-41		Type 3	£200-300
28s		'FRYS'	Brown or Cream body, 'Frys Chocolate' in Gold,	
	1936-39		Type 2	£750-1,000
	1939-41		Type 3	£300-400
28t		'OVALTINE'	Red body, 'Drink Ovaltine For Health' in Gold/Black,	
	1936-39		Type 2	£750-1,000
	1939-41		Type 3	£300-400
28w		'OSRAM'	Yellow body, 'Osram Lamps - a G.E.C. Product' in Gold/Black,	
	1936-39		Type 2	£750-1,000
	1940-41		Type 3	£300-500
28x		'HOVIS'	White body, 'Hovis For Tea' in Gold/Black,	
	1936-39		Type 2	£750-1,000
	1939-41		Type 3	£300-400

28 series Delivery Vans list continues overleaf:

28 series Delivery Vans list continued from previous page:

28y		'EXIDE'	Red body, 'Exide Batteries' and 'Drydex Batteries' in Gold/Black,	
	1936-39		Type 2	£300-400
	1939-41		Type 3	£300-400
		NB	Further issues in this series were numbered 280a - 280f.	

30 Series

30e	1935-40	Breakdown Car (Crane Lorry)..	Red, Yellow, Green, Brown or Grey body, Black wings, Black or Blue smooth hubs, open rear window	£100-120
			Blue body, Dark Blue wings, Blue hubs, open rear window	£100-120
	1946-46		Red or Grey body, Black wings, open rear window, ridged hubs	£60-70
	1947-48		Red, Grey or Green body and wings, no rear window, ridged hubs	£40-50
30j	1950-54	Austin Wagon	Blue body with hook, Mid-Blue hubs	£100-120
		(renumbered 412)	Light, Medium or Dark Maroon body, Maroon or Red hubs	£100-150
			Brown body, Tan hubs	£400-500
			Dark Blue body, Mid-Blue hubs	NGPP
			Red body, Red hubs	NGPP
30m	1950-54	Rear Tipping Wagon	Maroon or Orange cab, Pale Green rear, 'Dodge' on baseplate	£60-70
		(renumbered 414)	Blue or Dark Blue cab, Grey rear	£60-70
30n	1950-54	Farm Produce Wagon	See 'Farm and Garden Models'.	
30p	1950-54	Petrol Tanker	Based on a Studebaker vehicle.	
30p	1950-51	'PETROL'	Red or Green body, cast in aluminium	£80-90
	1951-52	'PETROL'	Red or Green body, cast in mazak	£80-90
30p	1952-54	'MOBILGAS'	Red body, Blue lettering on White background, (renumbered 440)	£80-90
30pa	1952-54	'CASTROL'	Green body and hubs, some cast in aluminium, most in mazak, (renumbered 441)	£80-90
30pb	1952-54	'ESSO'	Red body and hubs, 'MOTOR OIL - ESSO - PETROL', (renumbered 442)	£80-90
30r	1951-54	Fordson Thames Flat Truck	Red or Green body with hook	£60-70
		(renumbered 422)	Brown body, Brown hubs	£60-70
			Brown body, Maroon hubs	NGPP
30s	1950-54	Austin Covered Wagon	Maroon body, Cream cover, Cream hubs, sold unboxed	£100-150
		(renumbered 413)	Dark Blue body, Light Blue cover, Light Blue hubs, sold unboxed	£300-400
			Mid-Blue body, Light Blue cover, Light Blue hubs, sold unboxed	£100-150
30v	1949-54	Electric Dairy Van 'EXPRESS DAIRY'	Cream body, Red chassis, hubs and logo, (renumbered 490)	£75-90
			Grey body, Blue chassis, hubs and logo	£75-90
30v	1949-54	Electric Dairy Van 'N.C.B.'	Cream body, Red chassis, hubs and logo, (renumbered 491)	£75-90
			Grey body, Blue chassis, hubs and logo	£75-90
30w	1952-54	Hindle-Smart Helecs	Maroon body, Maroon or Red hubs, 'British Railways', hook, trailer uncouples, (renumbered 421)	£60-70

31 Series

31	1935-35	Holland Coachcraft Van	Red, Green, Blue or Orange, 'Holland Coachcraft Registered Design', lead body	£1,000-2,000
	1935-36		Red, Blue or Orange, 'Holland Coachcraft Registered Design', diecast body	£1,000-2,000
	1935		Mid-Green body, Gold stripe, Silver advert., Chrome hubs	£1,000-2,000
	1935		Cream body with Red coachline	£1,000-2,000
		NB	A Red variant from 1935/6 was sold by Christie's in 2001 for £2,350.	
31a	1951-54	Trojan 15 cwt Van 'ESSO'	Red body, Maroon or Red hubs, (renumbered 450)	£80-90
31b	1952-54	Trojan 15 cwt Van 'DUNLOP'	Red body, Maroon or Red hubs, 'The Worlds Master Tyre', (renumbered 451)	£60-70
31c	1953-54	Trojan 15 cwt Van 'CHIVERS'	Green body and hubs, 'CHIVERS JELLIES' and design, (renumbered 452)	£60-70
31d	1953-54	Trojan 15 cwt Van 'OXO'	Mid-Blue or Violet-Blue body, Mid-Blue hubs, 'BEEFY OXO', (renumbered 453)	£250-300

33 Series

33a	1935-36	Mechanical Horse	Red, Green, Blue or Yellow body, 2.5 mm. trailer step. **NB** 1st type have long slot and chrome hubs.	£150-175
	1936-40		As previous model but trailer step is 9.5 mm. long	£125-150
	1946-?		As previous model but also in Brown, Grey or Khaki	£125-150
33b	1935-40	Flat Truck Trailer	Red, Green, Blue or Yellow body, no sides	£45-55
33c	1935-40	Open Truck Trailer	Red, Green, Blue or Yellow body with sides	£45-55
33d	1935-40	Box Van Trailer	Green tinplate body on cast chassis, no advertising	£100-150
		'HORNBY TRAINS'	Dark Blue body, 'Hornby Trains British and Guaranteed' in Gold	£125-175
		'HORNBY TRAINS'	Green body, 'Hornby Trains British and Guaranteed' in Gold	£125-175
		'MECCANO'	Green body, 'Meccano Engineering For Boys' in Red and Black	£125-175
		NB	Models 33a and 33d combined and given Ref No 33r.	£200-300
33e	1935-40	Dust Wagon Trailer	Blue or Yellow 33c (Open Trailer) with Blue tinplate top	£70-90
			Grey or Green 33c (Open Trailer) with Green or Blue tinplate top	£70-90
	1946-47		Grey or Red body with Blue tinplate top	£70-90
33f	1935-40	Petrol Tank Trailer	Green (33b) chassis/Red tank, or Red chassis/Green tank, no logo	£70-90
		'ESSO'	Green chassis/Red tank with 'ESSO' in Gold	£70-90
		'CASTROL'	Red chassis/Green tank, 'Wakefield Castrol'	£70-90
33r	1935-40	Railway Mechanical Horse and Trailer Van	33a Mechanical Horse and 33d Box Van Trailer in railway liveries. These were also available separately as 33ra and 33rd (see below).	
33r		'L.N.E.R.'	Blue and Black, 'L.N.E.R. Express Parcels Traffic'	£200-300
33r		'L.M.S.'	Maroon and Black, 'L.M.S. Express Parcels Traffic'	£200-300
33r		'G.W.R'	Brown and Cream, 'G.W.R. Express Cartage Services'	£200-300
33r		'S.R.'	Green (Cream cab roof) and Black, 'Southern Railway'	£200-300

33ra	1935-40	Mechanical Horse 'L.N.E.R.'	Blue and Black, 'L.N.E.R. 901'	£200-300
33ra		'L.M.S.'	Maroon and Black, 'L.M.S. 2246'	£200-300
33ra		'G.W.R.'	Brown and Cream, 'G.W.R. 2742'	£200-300
33ra		'S.R.'	Green (Cream roof) and Black, '3016 M'	£200-300
33rd		Railway Trailer 'L.N.E.R.'	Blue and Black, 'L.N.E.R. Express Parcels Traffic'	£200-300
33rd		'L.M.S.'	Maroon and Black, 'L.M.S. Express Parcels Traffic'	£200-300
33rd		'G.W.R.'	Brown and Cream, 'G.W.R. Express Cartage Services'	£200-300
33rd		'S.R.'	Green and Black, 'Southern Railway'	£200-300
33w	1947-54	Mechanical Horse and Open Wagon	Cab colours: Grey, Fawn, Dark or Mid-Green, Olive, Red, Brown, Blue or Yellow. Trailer colours: Grey, Fawn, Maroon, Brown, Dark or Mid-Green, Olive or Cream. (renumbered 415)	£75-95

34 Series

34a	1935-40	'ROYAL AIR MAIL SERVICE'	Blue car body with Silver lettering and Gold crest	£200-250
34b	1938-47	'ROYAL MAIL' Van	Red body, Black bonnet/wings/roof/hubs, open rear windows	£100-150
	1948-51		Red body, Black bonnet/wings/roof, Black or Red hubs, filled-in rear windows	£80-100
	1952-52		Red body/roof/hubs, Black bonnet/front wings, filled-in rear windows	£100-125
34c	1948-54	Loudspeaker Van	Fawn, Grey, Green, Brown or Blue body (280 casting) Black loudspeakers, (renumbered 392)	£60-70
			Brown, Blue or Green body (280 casting) Silver loudspeakers	£60-70
60y	1938-40	Thompson Aircraft Tender	Red with 'Shell Aviation Services' in Gold; Black or White solid rubber wheels, (renumbered 25s)	£250-350
151b	1937-40	6-wheel Covered Wagon	Gloss Green body, tinplate canopy, seat holes, spare wheel, (renumbered 25s)	£125-150
151b	1947-54	6-wheel Covered Wagon	Matt-Green or Greenish-Brown body, (export only from 1950), (renumbered 620)	£60-70
251	1954-63	Aveling Barford Road Roller	Mid or Dark Green body, Red rollers, (renumbered from 25p)	£45-55
			Lime Green or Apple Green body, Red rollers	£70-90
252	1954-60	Bedford Refuse Wagon	Fawn body, Green tinplate shutters, Red hubs, window glazing in some, (renumbered from 25v)	£125-150
	1960-63		Lime Green body, Black tinplate shutters, Cream hubs, with or without window glazing	£125-150
	1963 only		Orange cab, Light Grey back, Green tinplate shutters and diecast hubs, window glazing, Black grille	£300-350
	1964		Orange cab, Light Grey back and diecast hubs, Green plastic shutters, window glazing	£250-350
	1964-65		Bright Orange cab, Light Grey back, Green plastic shutters, Red plastic hubs, window glazing	£250-350
			As previous model but with matt-Black base	£250-350
260	1955-61	'ROYAL MAIL' Van	(Morris 'J') Red body, Black roof, Gold 'E II R' crest	£125-150
260	1971-72	Volkswagen 'DEUTSCHE BUNDESPOST'.	Yellow body (129 casting, 100mm), made for German Market	£100-150
261	1955-61	Telephone Service Van	(Morris 'Z') Olive-Green/Black, 'POST OFFICE TELEPHONES', ladder	£100-125
273	1965-70	Mini Minor Van 'R.A.C.'	Blue body, White roof, Black base, Red interior, 'ROAD SERVICE' on sides	£175-200
			As previous model but with Blue interior	£175-200
			With Red interior, Silver baseplate and redesigned rear doors	£150-175
		NB	Factory errors have resulted in some rear door logos reading 'ROAD ROAD' instead of 'ROAD SERVICE' as normal.	NGPP
274	1964-73	Mini Minor Van 'A.A.'	Yellow body, White roof, 'PATROL SERVICE', original 'entwined' logo	£100-125
			Same, but with Yellow roof, Blue interior	£100-125
			Yellow body, White roof, Red interior, 'AA SERVICE', modern 'simple' logo, Silver or Black base	£65-75
			As previous model but with Blue interior	£65-75
			With Yellow roof and Blue interior	£65-75

Note: 'AA' logo designs a) Embossed paint 'AA', b) Waterslide transfer in square recess, c) Waterslide transfer on raised panel

Rear door casting variations: a) Rear door hinge pins extend directly into chassis holes, b) Rear door hinge pins located into slots

Central base colour variations: a) Red, b) Blue, c) White

274	1970-70	'JOSEPH MASON PAINTS'	(Mini Minor Van). Promotional in special Red box with advert card. 650 issued. Maroon body, Red seats and rear van body base, roof sign, 'PAINTS' labels, spun hubs	£500-750
275	1964-66	Brinks Armoured Car	Grey/Blue, 'Brinks Security Since 1859', 2 figures, 2 crates, plastic hubs	£110-130
	1966-70		Same as previous model but no driver or crates, US packaging	£50-60
			Grey body White roof, Blue base, metal hubs, assembled in USA	NGPP
	Mexican issue:		Blue body with Grey doors and Red/White/Blue crests, plastic hubs	£750-1,000
279	1965-71	Aveling Barford Diesel Roller	Orange body, Grey engine covers, Blue or Green rollers	£150-200
	1971-80		Yellow cab, Black roof, Silver rollers	£25-35
			Yellow cab, Black roof, Black rollers	£25-35
			Yellow cab, Blue roof, Yellow square engine covers, Silver rollers	£25-35
			Yellow cab, Black roof, Yellow square engine covers, Silver rollers	£25-35
			Yellow cab, Grey Roof, Yellow square engine covers, Silver rollers	£25-35
280	1945-47	Delivery Van	Red or Blue body, Type 3, open rear windows	£50-60
	1948-54		Red or Blue body, Type 3, filled-in rear windows, no advertising	£50-60
280	1966-68	Mobile 'MIDLAND BANK'	White/Silver, Blue stripe, Gold crest, opening doors, figure	£70-80

280 Series Delivery Vans

Delivery Vans numbered 280a - 280k are an extension of the 28 series. They were supplied to shops in Trade Boxes and sold individually unboxed.

280a		'VIYELLA'	Blue body,'Viyella for the Nursery' in White and Black,	
	1937-39		Type 2	£2,000-2,500
	1939-41		Type 3	£700-950
280b		'LYONS TEA'	Dark Blue body, 'Lyons Tea Always the Best' in Red and White,	
	1937-39		Only issued as Type 2	£750-1,000

280b		'HARTLEYS JAM'	Cream body, 'Hartleys is Real Jam' in Red/Green,	
	1939-39		Type 2	£800-1,000
	1939-40		Type 3	£300-400
280c		'SHREDDED WHEAT'	Cream body, Red stripe, 'Welwyn Garden City, Herts' in Black,	
	1937-39		Type 2	£750-1,000
	1939-40		Type 3	£300-400
280d	1937-40	'BISTO'	Yellow body, 'Ah! Bisto' with logo, Type 2	£350-500
280d	1940	'BISTO'	Yellow body, wording altered to 'Bisto' with logo,	
	1938-39		Type 2, with large Bisto Kids transfer	£750-1,000
			Type 2, small Bisto Kids transfer, with pie on table	£600-800
	1939-40		Type 3, small Bisto Kids transfer with pie on table	£300-400
280e	1937-39	'ECKO'	Dark Green body, 'ECKO Radio' in Gold, Type 2	£500-750
280e		'YORKSHIRE EVENING POST'	Cream body, 'Yorkshire Evening Post - The Original Buff'	
	1938-39		Type 2	£750-1,000
	1939-39		Type 3	£600-800
280f		'MACKINTOSHS'	Red body, 'Mackintosh's Toffee' in Gold,	
	1937-39		Type 2	£750-1,000
	1939-40		Type 3	£300-400
280g	1939 ?	'BENTALLS'	Green body, Yellow upper side panels, White roof, 'Bentalls Kingston on Thames' and 'Phone Kin: 1001' in Yellow, promotional, Type 2. Two examples known	£5,000-7,500
280h	1939 ?	'MAISON de BONNETERIE'	Dark Red, 'Maison de Bonneterie, Leverancier', promotional, Type 2	£3,000-5,000
280i	1939 ?	'LIVERPOOL ECHO'	Promotional, Type 2, no other details available	£3,000-5,000
280j	1939	'FENWICK'	Apple Green body, White roof, 'Newcastle on Tyne', promotional, Type 2. Two examples known	£2,000-3,000
280k	1939	'H. G. LOOSE'	Dark Green body, 'H. G. LOOSE' on Cream panel, 'Looe' and 'Phone 123', promotional, Type 2. One example known	£2,000-3,000
343	1954-64	Farm Produce Wagon	See 'Farm and Garden Models'.	

'Convoy' Series (380-387)

Budget-priced models, having the same generic cab but with different rear body types.

380	1977-79	Skip Truck	Yellow and Orange body	£10-20
381	1977-80	Farm Wagon	Yellow and Brown body	£10-20
382	1978-80	Dumper Truck	Red body/Grey back, Red body/Black back or Yellow body/Grey back	£10-20
383	1978-80	'N.C.L.' Truck	Yellow body, 'NATIONAL CARRIERS Ltd'	£10-20
384	1977-79	Fire Rescue Wagon	Red body, White fire escape	£10-20
385	1977-79	'ROYAL MAIL' Truck	Red body	£10-20
386	1979	'AVIS' Truck	Red body. Catalogued but not issued	NPP
387	1979	'PICKFORDS' Truck	Red and Blue body. Catalogued but not issued	NPP
?	1979	'HARRODS' Truck	Khaki body	NGPP
?	1979	'POST OFFICE TELEPHONES'	Khaki body	NGPP
?	1979	'A.A.' Truck	Yellow body	NGPP
?	1979	'AMERICAN FIRE BRIGADE'	No details	NGPP
		NB	See also 687 Convoy Army Truck in the Military Vehicles section.	
390	1978	Customised Transit Van	Metallic Blue body with 'VAMPIRE' and 'flame' design, Transit van Type 3	NGPP
400	1954-60	B.E.V. Truck	Dark Blue or Mid-Blue or Grey with Blue, Grey or Red hubs, 1 packing piece, (renumbered from 14a)	£30-35
401	1954-64	Coventry Climax Fork Lift	Orange body, Green forks, Tan driver, (renumbered from 14c)	£30-35
			Red body, Green forks	£300-400
402	1966-69	Bedford 'COCA-COLA' Truck	Red cab and back, White roof, Blue interior, 'COCA-COLA', six trays of crates, Red plastic hubs	£120-150
404	1967-72	Climax Fork Lift	Red/Yellow body with 'CG4' rear logo	£25-35
			Red/Yellow front with all Red rear, plus stick-on 'CG4' label.	£20-25
	1978		Yellow body with 'Climax' on fork guide and 'TC4' on engine cover	£20-25
406	1963-66	Commer Articulated Truck	Yellow/Grey, Blue plastic hubs, Supertoy, (424 without accessories)	£90-110
407		Ford Transit Vans	See 'Commercial Vehicles Identification' pages for an explanation of casting Types 1, 2 and 3.	
	1966-69	'KENWOOD'	Blue/White, 'KENWOOD', promotional. Type 1	£50-60
	1970-71	'TELEFUSION'	White body, 'Colour TV, Telefusion'. Intended promotional not issued	NPP
	1970-75	'HERTZ'	Yellow body, 'Hertz Truck Rentals', promotional. Type 1	£50-60
	1970-73	'AVIS'	Red body, 'Avis Truck Rentals'. Kit only but not issued	NPP
		'PELTZ BADKEREI'	Blue lower body, Yellow upper half, promotional	£50-60
408	1956-63	Big Bedford Lorry (renumbered from 522 / 922)	Maroon cab, Light Tan back, Fawn or Cream hubs, (with window glazing from 1961)	£100-130
			Dark Blue cab, Yellow back, Yellow or Cream hubs	£150-175
			Pink cab, Cream back, Cream hubs	£1.500-2.000
409	1956-63	Bedford Articulated Lorry (renumbered from 521 / 921)	Deep Yellow cab and back, Black wings, Red hubs, Yellow box	£100-130
			As previous model but with window glazing. Lighter Yellow box	£150-200
410	1954-61	Bedford End Tipper Truck (renumbered from 25m)	Red cab, chassis and diecast hubs, Cream back	£200-250
			Yellow cab, chassis and diecast hubs, Mid-Blue back, window glazing	£200-250
	1962-63		Red cab, chassis and plastic hubs, Cream back, window glazing	£200-250
			Yellow cab, chassis and plastic hubs, Dark or Mid-Blue back, window glazing	£200-250
410		Bedford CF Vans		

	1972-72	'SIMPSONS'	Red/Black, 'Simpsons' and logos, Canadian promotional	£35-45
	1974	'DANISH POST'	Yellow body, 'Danish Post' emblem, Danish promotional	£35-45
	1974-75	'JOHN MENZIES'	Dark Blue body with 'John Menzies' logo, promotional	£25-30
	1974-74	'BELACO'	Brown/Black, 'Belaco Brake and Clutch Parts', promotional	£35-45
	1975-76	'M.J. HIRE'	White body, 'M.J. Hire Service', promotional	£25-30
	1975-77	'MODELLERS WORLD'	White body, 'Modellers World'. This is a Code 2 model	£25-30
	1975-75	'MARLEY TILES'	Red body with 'Marley Building' logo	£25-30
	1979	'COLLECTORS GAZETTE'	White body, 'Collectors Gazette' logo. A Code 2 model	£25-30
	1972-74	'ROYAL MAIL'	Red body with 'ROYAL MAIL' and 'E II R' crest	£15-20
	1974-80	'ROYAL MAIL'	As previous model but with raised rectangle on roof	£15-20

NB Many Code-2 issues exist (produced by John Gay) and include the following liveries:
'MOBIL', 'BN', 'HERTZ TRUCK RENTAL', 'JIMMY CARTER', 'MATRA', 'ELF',
'SILVER JUBILLEE 1952-1977', 'KLG', 'PORTAKABIN', 'WIMPEY'.

411	1954-59	Bedford Truck	Mid-Green cab, chassis, back and hubs, (renumbered from 25w)	£100-125
	1959-60		Mid-Green cab and body, Pale Green hubs, gloss base, block-tread tyres	£100-125
412	1954-60	Austin Wagon	Powder Blue body, Lemon or Dark Blue hubs, (renumbered from 30j)	£350-450
			Maroon body, Pale Red hubs	£120-140
			Dark Blue body, Mid-Blue hubs	£140-160
			Lemon Yellow body, Mid-Green or Blue hubs	£350-450
412	1974-80	Bedford CF Van 'AA'	Yellow or Lemon-Yellow body, 'AA SERVICE', headboard, plastic hubs	£15-20
413	1954-60	Austin Covered Wagon	Maroon body, Cream tinplate tilt, Cream hubs, (renumbered from 30s)	£100-150
			Maroon body and hubs, Tan tinplate tilt	£100-150
			Dark Blue body, Mid-Blue tinplate tilt, Light Blue hubs	£150-200
			Mid-Blue body, Mid-Blue tinplate tilt, Light Blue hubs	£100-150
			Red body, Light Grey tinplate tilt, Cream or Grey hubs	£300-400
			Red body, Beige tinplate tilt, Red hubs	£300-400
			Light or Mid-Blue body, Cream tinplate tilt, Lemon-Yellow hubs. Plain box	£275-325
			Red body, Grey or Beige tinplate tilt, Grey hubs	£275-325
			Maroon body, Beige tinplate tilt, Red hubs	£200-250
			Olive-drab body, (Royal Army Volunteer Reserve)	NGPP
414	1954-64	Dodge Rear Tipping Wagon	Red cab and hubs, Green back	£80-100
		(renumbered from 30s)	Orange cab and hubs, Green back; or Orange cab with Mid-Green back and hubs	£80-100
			Greyish-Blue cab, Grey back, Mid-Blue hubs	£80-100
			Mid-Blue cab and hubs, Grey back	£80-100
			Mid-Blue cab, Cream hubs, Grey back. In late issue lighter Yellow box	£100-125
			Violet-Blue cab, Grey back and hubs	£100-125
			Royal Blue cab, Grey back and hubs	£125-150

NB Early issues with or without bonnet louvres.

415	1954-59	Mechanical Horse and Wagon	(Models 33a + 33c), Blue horse/Cream trailer or Red horse/Brown trailer, (renumbered from 33w)	£125-175
		Ford Transit Vans	See 'Commercial Vehicles Identification' pages for an explanation of casting Types 1, 2 and 3.	
416	1975-78	Ford Transit Van, 'FORD'	Orange-Yellow body, cast hubs, '1,000,000 TRANSITS', Type 2, promotional	NGPP
416	1975-78	Ford Transit 'MOTORWAY'	Yellow body, 'MOTORWAY SERVICES', special lights, Type 2, with two warning boards and cones	£25-35
417	1978-79	Ford Transit 'MOTORWAY'	As previous model but Type 3 casting	£20-30
417	1956-58	Leyland Comet Lorry with Stake Body	(Stake body secured by a rivet. Yellow box. Renumbered from 531 / 931).	
			Violet Blue cab and chassis, Dark Yellow back, Mid-Blue hubs	£140-160
			Dark Blue cab and chassis, Brown back, Mid-Blue hubs	£200-300
	1958-59		Yellow cab and chassis, Pale Green back, Mid-Green hubs, Grey tyres	£300-400
418	1956-59	Leyland Comet with Hinged Tailboard	(Back of model secured by a rivet. Yellow box. Renumbered from 532 / 932).	
			Green cab and chassis, Orange back, Light Green hubs	£120-140
			Dark Blue cab and chassis, Mid-Blue back, Blue, Cream or Red hubs	£120-140
419	1956-59	Leyland Comet Cement Lorry	Yellow body and hubs, 'Portland Blue-Circle Cement', 1 packing piece, (was 533 / 933)	£110-130
420	1954-61	Forward Control Lorry	Cream body, Mid-Blue hubs	£65-75
		(renumbered from 25r)	Red body, Cream hubs	£65-75
			Red body, Mid-Green hubs	£65-75
			Pale Green body, Cream hubs	£65-75
			Pale Green body, Red hubs	£65-75
421	1955-59	Hindle Smart Helecs	Maroon body, Red hubs 'British Railways', hook, (renumbered from 30w)	£70-80
422	1954-60	Fordson Thames Flat Truck	Red body and hubs, (renumbered from 30r)	£125-150
			Bright Green body and hubs	£125-150
			Dark Green body, Mid-Green hubs. In dual-numbered box	£125-150
424	1963-66	Commer Convertible Articulated Vehicle	Primrose-Yellow cab, Silver-Grey back with Blue plastic tilt, Blue plastic hubs, plus detachable White plastic 'stake' body	£120-140
425	1964-69	Bedford TK Coal Wagon	Red body and interior, Silver chassis, Red plastic hubs, roof board 'HALL & Co.', 6 bags, scales	£100-125
428	1955-66	Large Trailer	Grey body, Red hubs, Black front axle mount, hook, (renumbered 951)	£30-35
			Grey body, Cream hubs. In late issue lighter Yellow box	£75-100
			Grey body, Mid-Blue hubs. In late issue lighter Yellow box	£75-100
	1967-71		Red body, Silver hubs, Silver front axle mount	£60-75
			Yellow body, Red hubs	£60-75
429	1954-64	Trailer	Dark Green or Red, hook, axle pivot is part of main casting, (renumbered from 25g)	£20-25

430	1954-64	**Commer Breakdown Truck**	'DINKY SERVICE' logo, operable crane, late issues have window glazing, (renumbered from 25x).	
			Tan cab, Green back with Black logo, Red hubs. Yellow or Blue/White striped box	**£100-120**
			Cream cab, Mid-Blue back with Black logo, Red hubs. Yellow box	**£450-550**
			Dark Stone cab, Blue back with Black logo, Red hubs. Yellow box	**£450-550**
			Red cab, Light Grey back with Blue logo, Mid-Blue or Red metal hubs. Yellow box	**£450-550**
			Red cab with glazing, Light Grey back with Blue logo, Blue plastic hubs. Yellow box	**£450-550**
			Red cab with glazing, Light Grey back with Blue logo, Red plastic hubs. Yellow box	**£500-750**
430	1977-80	**Johnson 2 ton Dumper**	Orange/Red body with Blue driver, Black or Orange engine	**£20-25**
431	1956-58	**Guy 4 ton Lorry** (2nd type)	Red cab/chassis, Fawn back, Red hubs, unpainted hook, (renumbered from 511 / 911)	**£200-250**
			Violet Blue cab/chassis, Mid-Blue back, Mid-Blue hubs	**£200-250**
431	1958-60	**Guy Warrior 4 ton Lorry**	Light Tan cab (no window glazing), Dark Green back, Mid-Green hubs	**£350-450**
			Light Tan cab (with window glazing), Dark Green back, Mid-Green hubs	**£350-450**
	1960-64		Red cab (with window glazing), Red chassis, Dark Green back, Red hubs	**£350-450**
432	1956-57	**Guy Flat Truck** (2nd type)	Mid-Blue cab/chassis/hook, Red flatbed, Mid-Blue hubs, (renumbered from 512 / 912)	**£200-300**
	1956-57		Red cab/chassis/hook, Mid-Blue flatbed and hubs	**£300-350**
432	1958-60	**Guy Warrior Flat Truck**	Green cab (no window glazing), Red flatbed, Red hubs	**£300-350**
	1960-64		Green cab (with window glazing), Red flatbed, Red hubs	**£300-350**
432	1976-79	**Foden Tipping Lorry**	White cab, Red chassis, Yellow rear body, (same casting as 668)	**£35-45**
433	1956-57	**Guy Flat Truck with Tailboard**	Dark Green cab/chassis/hook, Mid-Green flatbed and hubs, (renumbered from 513 / 913)	**£200-250**
		(2nd type)	Violet Blue cab/chassis/hook, Orange flatbed, Mid-Blue hubs, one packing piece in box	**£200-250**
433	--- ---	**Guy Warrior Flat Truck** **with Tailboard**	Listed in the 1958 catalogue but not issued	**NPP**
434	1964-66	**Bedford TK Crash Truck**	White body with Green flash, Dark Green hubs, 'TOP RANK Motorway Services', Red interior	**£70-85**
	1966-70		Red or Metallic Red cab, Pale Grey back, 'AUTO SERVICES', Red metal or plastic hubs	**£60-75**
		NB	Add 15% to price if in detailed picture box or with Green hubs.	
435	1964-66	**Bedford TK Tipper**	Grey cab with Blue roof, Orange back	**£90-120**
	1966-68		Yellow cab with Yellow or Black roof, Silver back, Yellow drop sides	**£90-120**
	1968-71		White cab and roof, Silver back with Blue sides	**£60-80**
			Blue cab, Orange and Grey back	**£75-100**
			Red cab, Black roof, Silver back, Red sides	**£60-80**
436	1963-69	**'ATLAS COPCO' Lorry**	Yellow body, Pale Grey interior, matt baseplate	**£50-60**
			Yellow body, Dark Blue interior, gloss baseplate	**£50-60**
			Yellow body, Black roof, Red interior, Silver/Yellow back, Blue plastic hubs	**£80-100**
437	1962-70	**Muir Hill 2WL Loader**	Red body with hook, no grille detail.	**£20-25**
			Yellow body with Red or Silver hubs	**£20-25**
	1970-78		Yellow with Red arms with hook, with or without grille detail	**£20-25**
			Orange body with Orange or Black arms	**£30-40**
438	1970-77	**Ford D800 Tipper Truck**	Metallic Red cab, Yellow tipper, Yellow or Silver hubs	**£40-45**
		(with opening doors)	Metallic Red cab, Metallic Blue tipper, Yellow plastic hubs, White interior	**£100-125**
			Orange cab, Orange or Yellow tipper, Silver hubs	**£40-45**
			Bright Red cab, Orange tipper, Silver hubs	**£40-45**
			Bright Red cab, Bright Red tipper, Silver hubs	**£40-45**
		promotional issue:	White cab, Blue back, Silver chassis, with cardboard load 'POLCARB'.	
			Packed in plain White box with folded leaflet	**£200-250**
439	1970-76	**Ford D800 Snow Plough**	Dark Metallic Blue cab, Orange tipper, Yellow plough, White hubs	**£50-70**
	1976-78		Dark Metallic Blue cab, Pale Blue tipper, Yellow plough, Silver hubs	**£50-70**
			Light Metallic Blue cab, Orange tipper, Dark Yellow plough, Silver hubs	**£50-70**
			Light Metallic Blue cab, Pale Blue tipper, Red plough	**£100-125**
			Medium Blue cab, Yellow plough, Powder Blue tipper, Silver hubs	**£50-70**
			Medium Blue cab, Yellow plough, Powder Blue tipper, Lemon hubs	**£50-60**
			Orange cab and tipper, Dark Yellow plough, Silver hubs	**£50-60**
			Orange cab, Dark Yellow tipper and plough, Silver hubs	**£50-60**
			All-Orange body, cast Silver hubs	**£50-60**
440	1977-78	**Ford D800 Tipper Truck**	Orange cab, Yellow tipper, Silver or Black chassis	**£35-40**
		(non-opening doors)	Orange cab, Orange tipper, Black chassis	**£35-40**
			Orange cab, Light Blue tipper, Black chassis	**£35-40**
			Red cab, Red Tipper, Black chassis, Silver hubs	**£35-40**
			Red cab, Orange Tipper, Silver chassis, Silver hubs	**£35-40**
			Red cab, Light Blue Tipper, Black chassis, Silver hubs	**£35-40**
			Red cab with Black roof, Red Tipper, Red hubs	**£35-40**
440	1954-58	**Petrol Tanker 'MOBILGAS'**	Red body and hubs, 'MOBILGAS' in White letters with Blue borders, (renumbered from 30p)	**£110-140**
	1958-61		Red body and hubs, 'MOBILGAS' in Blue letters on White background	**£110-140**
441	1954-60	**Petrol Tanker 'CASTROL'**	Mid-Green body and hubs, (renumbered from 30pa)	**£110-140**
442	1954-60	**Petrol Tanker 'ESSO'**	Red body and hubs, Dark Blue decal: 'ESSO MOTOR OIL - PETROL', (renumbered from 30pb)	**£110-140**
			As previous model but with Pale Blue outline decal	**£125-150**
442	1973-79	**Land Rover Breakdown Crane** .	White and Red body, 'Motorway Rescue', operable winch	**£25-30**
	1975-78		White body, Red bonnet and door panels, Blue interior, 2 Orange rooflights, Black jib, 'FALCK'	**£40-50**
			All Red body, Blue interior, Light Blue header board, Black jib, Speedwheels, 'FALCK'	**£50-60**
			All Red body, Black interior, deeper Blue header board, Black jib, Speedwheels, 'FALCK'	**£50-60**
443	1957-58	**Petrol Tanker 'NATIONAL'**	Yellow body and hubs, 'NATIONAL BENZOLE MIXTURE'	**£150-175**
448	1963-68	**Chevrolet El Camino**		

		Pick-Up with Trailers...............	Turquoise/Cream/Red Pick-up and 2 trailers, 'Acme Trailer Hire'	£225-275
449	1961-69	**Chevrolet El Camino Pick-up** ...	Turquoise body, White roof, Red interior, spun hubs	£80-90
			Turquoise body, White roof, Pale Turquoise interior, spun hubs	£150-200
			Turquoise body, White roof, Lemon interior, spun hubs	£150-200
		NB	Various shades of Turquoise are known to exist.	
		South African issue:	All-Turquoise body, spun hubs..	£300-400
		South African issue:	Cream over Chocolate Brown lower body, spun hubs	£500-750
		South African issue:	Turquoise over Cream lower body, spun hubs	£500-750
449	1977-79	**Johnston Road Sweeper**	Later version of model 451 but with cast-in (non-opening) cab doors.	
			Yellow or Lime-Green body	£30-35
			All Yellow body, promotional with 'JOHNSTON' stickers, normal box	£40-50
			All Yellow body, promotional with 'JOHNSTON' stickers, special box	£70-80
			Orange or Metallic Red cab, Metallic Green rear..	£40-50
450	1954-57	**Trojan Van 'ESSO'**	Red body, White stripe, Red or Maroon hubs, 'Esso' logo, (renumbered from 31a)	£130-160
			Maroon hub version issued in U.S.A. trade packs.	NGPP
450	1965-70	**Bedford TK Van 'CASTROL'** ..	Green/White body, Red interior, Red plastic hubs, 'CASTROL - The Masterpiece In Oils'	£90-110
451	1954-57	**Trojan Van 'DUNLOP'**	Red body and hubs, 'Dunlop The Worlds Master Tyre', (renumbered from 31b)	£125-150
451	1971-77	**Johnston Road Sweeper**	Orange cab (opening doors), White interior, Metallic Green tank	£40-50
			Yellow cab and tank, White interior..	£125-150
			Light Metallic Blue cab, White interior, Metallic Green tank	£110-130
			Metallic Green cab, White interior, Orange tank	£40-50
452	1954-57	**Trojan Van 'CHIVERS'**	Dark Green body, Mid-Green hubs, 'CHIVERS JELLIES' logo, (renumbered from 31c)	£125-150
453	1954-54	**Trojan Van 'OXO'**	Mid-Blue or Violet-Blue body, Mid-Blue hubs, White 'BEEFY OXO', (not boxed), (was 31c) ...	£250-300
454	1957-59	**Trojan Van 'CYDRAX'**	Light Green body and hubs, 'DRINK CYDRAX' logo..	£125-150
455	1957-60	**Trojan Van 'BROOKE BOND'**	Dark Red body, Red hubs, 'BROOKE BOND TEA' logo	£130-160
		promotional issue:	As previous issue with White label on roof. The Red logo states: 'Since 1924 more than 5,700 Trojan 'Little Red Vans' supplied. Replaced on a long life basis'.	
			A similar label is attached to its (normal) box.	£400-600
465	1959-59	**Morris 10 cwt Van 'CAPSTAN'**	Light Blue and Dark Blue body, Mid-Blue hubs, 'Have A CAPSTAN'	£200-250
470	1954-56	**Austin A40 Van 'SHELL-BP'** ...	Red and Green body with 'SHELL' and 'BP' decals	£120-140
470	1954	**Austin A40 Van 'OMNISPORT'**	Factory drawing exists but model not issued	NPP
471	1955-60	**Austin A40 Van 'NESTLES'**	Red body, Yellow hubs, 'NESTLES' logo	£110-140
472	1956-60	**Austin A40 Van 'RALEIGH'** ...	Dark Green body, Yellow hubs, 'RALEIGH CYCLES' decals	£110-140
480	1954-56	**Bedford CA Van 'KODAK'**	Yellow body, 'Kodak CAMERAS & FILMS' in Red and Black	£110-140
481	1955-60	**Bedford CA Van 'OVALTINE'**	Blue body with 'Ovaltine' and 'Ovaltine Biscuits' logo on Cream panel and sides	£110-140
482	1956-60	**Bedford Van 'DINKY TOYS'**...	Orange-Yellow lower body, Lemon upper body and hubs, 'Dinky Toys' in Red	£110-140
490	1954-60	**Electric Dairy Van 'EXPRESS DAIRY'**	Cream body with Red chassis, hubs and logo, (renumbered from 30v)..............................	£80-100
			Light Grey body with Blue chassis, hubs and logo	£80-100
491	1954-60	**Electric Dairy Van 'N.C.B.'**.......	Cream body with Red chassis, hubs and logo, export model, (renumbered from 30v)	£80-100
			Grey body, Blue chassis, hubs and logo, export model	£80-100
491	1960	**Electric Dairy Van 'JOB'S DAIRY'**........................	Cream/Red. 1176 made for promotional purposes (Code-2)	£120-140
492	1954-57	**Loudspeaker Van**......................	Violet-Blue, Fawn or Green body, Silver, Mid-Blue or Black hubs, Silver or Black loudspeakers, (280 casting, Type 3), (renumbered from 34c)..	£80-90
492	1964-64	**Election Mini-Van**	White body (as 273), Red interior, Orange loudspeakers, 'Vote for Somebody', figure, microphone and cable. Yellow 'see-through' box.	£125-150
501	1947-48	**Foden Diesel 8-Wheel Wagon**....	**1st type cab** with flash, spare wheel, hook on some, no tank slits in chassis, no chain-post bosses, Black 'herringbone' tyres, Supertoy.	
			Pale Grey cab and back, Red flash and hubs, Black chassis, no hook	£600-800
			Dark Blue cab, Mid-Blue back and hubs, Silver flash, Black chassis, no hook	£500-700
			Chocolate Brown cab and back, Silver flash, Brown hubs, Black chassis, no hook............	£400-500
			Red cab and back, Silver flash, Red hubs, Black chassis, no hook, (US only issue)............	£2,000-3,000
			Dark Grey cab and back, Red flash, chassis and hubs, small unpainted hook on some	£300-400
	1948-52	....	Hook and tank-slits in chassis (introduced 1948), Black 'radial tread' tyres.	
			Violet-Blue cab/chassis, Mid-Blue flash/back/hubs, small unpainted hook......................	£1,250-1,500
			Red cab/chassis/hubs, Silver flash, Fawn back, unpainted hook, slits on some................	£300-400
	1952-54	(renumbered 901)	**2nd cab**, no flash, large painted hook, Supertoy hubs, (renumbered 901).	
			Violet-Blue cab/chassis, Mid-Blue back and hubs, Grey tyres	£400-500
			Red cab/chassis, Fawn back, Red hubs, Grey tyres	£250-350
502	1947-48	**Foden Flat Truck**......................	**1st type cab** with flash, spare wheel, hook on some, no tank slits in chassis, no chain-post bosses, Black 'herringbone' tyres, Supertoy.	
			Dark Green cab and back, Silver flash, Black chassis, Dark Green hubs, no hook..............	£350-450
			Mid-Blue cab and back, Dark Blue flash/chassis/hubs, no hook	£1,250-1,500
	1948-52	....	Hook and tank-slits in chassis introduced in 1948, Black 'radial' tyres.	
			Dark Blue cab/wings/chassis, Red flash and back, Mid-Blue hubs, slits on some, small hook ...	£1,500-1,750
			Burnt Orange cab/chassis, Mid-Green flash and back, Green hubs, slits on some. In Dark Blue box showing 2nd cab model...	£450-600
	1952-52	....	**2nd cab**, no flash, large painted hook, Supertoy hubs.	
			Dark Blue cab/chassis, Red back, Mid-Blue hubs, chain-post bosses................................	£2,000-2,500
	1952-54	(renumbered 902)	Dull Orange cab/chassis, Green back and hubs, chain-post bosses..................................	£350-450
			Red cab/chassis, Green back and hubs	£350-450
			Yellow cab/chassis, Green back and hubs	£1,000-1,250

503 1947-48 **Foden Flat Truck with Tailboard** **1st type cab** with flash, spare wheel, hook on some, no tank slits in
chassis, no chain-post bosses, Black 'herringbone' tyres, Supertoy.
Red cab and flatbed, Black flash and chassis, Red hubs, no hook £1,000-1,250
Pale Grey cab and flatbed, Dark Blue flash and chassis, Blue hubs, no hook £600-800
Mid-Grey cab and flatbed, Mid-Blue chassis and hubs £600-800

1948-52 .... Hook and tank-slits in chassis introduced in 1948, Black 'radial' tyres.
Dark Green cab/chassis, Mid-Green flash/flatbed/hubs, small hook....................................£1,000-1,250
Deep Blue cab/chassis, Dull Orange flatbed, Light Blue hubs, hook, slits £600-800
Violet-Blue cab/chassis, Orange back and side flash, Mid-Blue hubs, hook, slits £750-1,000

1952-52 .... **2nd cab**, no flash, large painted hook, Supertoy hubs.
Dark Green cab/chassis, Light Green flatbed and hubs, Grey tyres, bosses £1,750-2,250
1952-56 (renumbered 903) .... Violet-Blue cab/chassis, Orange flatbed, Mid-Blue hubs, chain-post bosses £250-350
1952-53 .... Dark Orange cab/chassis, Yellow flatbed and hubs, Grey tyres, bosses £1,700-2,000
1953-54 (renumbered 903) .... Violet-Blue cab/chassis, Yellow flatbed, Mid-Blue hubs, chain-post bosses.................£500-700

504 1948-52 **Foden 14 ton Tanker** .... **1st type cab** with flash, spare wheel, tinplate tank, small hook,
no advertising, Black 'fine radial tread' tyres, Supertoy.
Dark Blue cab/chassis, Silver flash, Light Blue tank and hubs..£300-400
Dark Blue cab/chassis, Light Blue flash, tank and hubs £300-400
1948-52 .... Red cab/chassis, Silver flash, Fawn tank, Red hubs £450-550
1952-57 .... **2nd cab**, no flash, large painted hook, Supertoy hubs.
1952-52 .... Violet-Blue cab/chassis, Mid-Blue tank and hubs, Grey tyres.
Model housed in 2nd type picture box..£1,500-2,000
1952-53 .... Red cab/chassis, Fawn tank, Red hubs, Grey tyres £450-550

504 1953-54 **Foden 14 ton Tanker**
'MOBILGAS' (renumbered 941) Red cab/chassis/tank/filler caps/hubs, 'MOBILGAS', Grey tyres.
With Red 'Pegasus' logo at cab end of tank facing the cab..£350-450
Same, but with Red 'Pegasus' logo at rear of tank facing away from cab £1,500-2,000

505 1952-52 **Foden Flat Truck with Chains**.. **1st type cab** with flash, spare wheel, large hook, slits in chassis, 'dimpled' post bosses,
Black 'fine radial tread' tyres, Supertoy. Blue covered box showing 1st type cab.
Dark Green cab/chassis/flatbed, Mid-Green flash and hubs...£3,000-4,000
Maroon cab/chassis, Silver flash, Maroon flatbed and hubs £8,000-11,000
1952-54 .... **2nd cab**, no flash, large painted hook, Supertoy hubs.
Dark Green cab/chassis/flatbed, Mid-Green hubs, 'dimpled' chain-post bosses....................£250-350
Maroon cab/chassis/flatbed/hubs, 'dimpled' chain-post bosses £250-350
1954-56 (renumbered 905) .... Green cab/chassis/body, Mid-Green hubs, 'rounded' chain-post bosses £250-350
Maroon cab/chassis/body/hubs, 'rounded' chain-post bosses £250-350

511 1947-48 **Guy 4 ton Lorry**........................ **1st type cab** casting, Supertoy, spare wheel, small unpainted hook.
Green cab, back and hubs, Black chassis and wings..£200-250
Brown cab, back and hubs, Black chassis and wings £200-250
Fawn cab and back, Red chassis, wings and hubs..£200-250
Maroon cab and back, Black chassis and wings..£200-250
Grey cab, back and hubs, Red chassis and wings..£200-250
1948-52 .... **1st type cab** casting, Supertoy, large painted or unpainted hook.
Red cab/chassis/wings/ 'ridged' hubs, Fawn back £200-250
Violet-Blue cab/chassis/wings, Mid-Blue back and 'ridged' hubs £200-250
1952-54 (renumbered 911, 431) .... Red cab/chassis/wings/ 'grooved' hubs, Fawn back £200-250
Violet-Blue cab/chassis/wings, Mid-Blue back and 'grooved' hubs £200-250
1954 .... **2nd type cab**, Violet-Blue cab and chassis, Mid-Blue back and hubs...............................£250-300

512 1947-48 **Guy Flat Truck** .... **1st type cab** casting, Supertoy, spare wheel, small unpainted hook.
Maroon cab, flatbed and hubs, Black chassis and wings...£300-350
Dark Brown cab, Dark Green flatbed and hubs, Black chassis and wings £300-350
Yellow cab and flatbed, Black chassis and wings, Red hubs £450-550
Khaki cab and flatbed, Black chassis and wings, Green hubs £400-500
Grey cab and flatbed, Red chassis and wings, Red hubs £400-500
Grey cab and flatbed, Black chassis, Black hubs...£400-500
Red cab and flatbed, Black chassis, Black hubs £400-500
1948-48 .... Brown cab/chassis/wings, Green flatbed, Mid-Green 'ridged' hubs £300-350
1948-54 (renumbered 912, 432) .... **1st type cab** casting, Supertoy, small or large unpainted hook.
Dark Blue cab/chassis/wings, Red flatbed, Mid-Blue 'ridged' hubs £200-250
1949-54 .... Orange cab/chassis/wings, Green flatbed, Green 'ridged' hubs £300-400
1952-54 .... Mid-Blue cab/chassis/wings, Red flatbed, Mid-Blue 'grooved' hubs £200-250
1954 .... **2nd type cab**, Red cab and chassis, Mid-Blue back and hubs.......................................£250-350
Mid-Blue cab, chassis and hubs, Red back £200-250

513 1947-48 **Guy Flat Truck with Tailboard** **1st type cab** casting, Supertoy, spare wheel, small unpainted hook.
Green cab and flatbed, Black chassis, wings and hubs...£200-250
Dark Yellow cab and flatbed, Black chassis, wings and hubs £300-400
Dark Yellow cab and flatbed, Dark Blue chassis, wings and hubs £300-400
Grey cab and flatbed, Black chassis, wings and hubs..£200-250
Grey cab and flatbed, Dark Blue chassis, wings and hubs £500-750
1948-52 .... **1st type cab**, 'ridged' hubs, Supertoy, small or large unpainted hook.
Dark Green cab/chassis/wings, Mid-Green back and hubs, small hook £250-350
Violet-Blue cab/chassis/wings, Orange back, Mid-Blue hubs, large hook £200-250
1952-54 (renumbered 913, 433) .... **1st type cab**, Supertoy, 'grooved' hubs, large unpainted hook.
Dark Green cab/chassis/wings, Mid-Green body and hubs £250-350
Deep Blue cab/chassis/wings, Orange body, Mid-Blue hubs £200-250
Yellow cab/chassis/wings, Green hubs £750-950
1954 .... **2nd type cab**, Violet-Blue cab and chassis, Orange back, Mid-Blue hubs..................£200-250

514 Guy Vans

514	1950-52	**Guy Van 'SLUMBERLAND'**....	Red **1st type cab**/chassis/body and 'ridged' hubs, 'Slumberland Spring Interior Mattresses', spare wheel, Supertoy	**£200-300**
514	1952-52	**Guy Van 'LYONS'**	Dark Blue **1st type cab**/body, Mid-Blue 'ridged' hubs, 'Lyons Swiss Rolls', spare wheel, Supertoy	**£700-900**
			Same model but rear axle in cast mounts	**£700-900**
514	1952-52	**Guy Van 'WEETABIX'**	Yellow **1st type cab**/body, Yellow 'ridged' hubs, 'More Than a Breakfast Food', spare wheel, Supertoy	**£2,000-3,000**
	1952-54		As previous model but with Yellow 'grooved' hubs	**£2,000-3,000**
514	1953-54	**Guy Van 'SPRATTS'**	Red/Cream **1st type cab**/body, Red 'grooved' hubs,	
		(renumbered 917)	'Bonio Ovals & Dog Cakes', spare wheel, Supertoy	**£300-400**
521	1948-48	**Bedford Articulated Lorry**	Red body, Black wings, Black or Red hubs, '20' transfer, 'Supertoys' on base, Brown box	**£200-250**
	1949-50		Yellow body, Black wings, Black hubs, '20' transfer, 'Supertoys' on base. Brown box with Red/White label	**£200-250**
	1950-54	(renumbered 921, 409)	Yellow or Yellowish-Orange body, Black wings, Red hubs, '20' transfer, 'Supertoys' or 'Dinky Toys' on base. Blue box, Orange or White label	**£120-140**
522	1952-54	**Big Bedford Lorry**	Maroon cab, Fawn truck body, Fawn hubs, Supertoy	**£110-130**
		(renumbered 922, 408)	Dark Blue cab, Yellow truck body, Yellow hubs, Supertoy	**£150-175**
531	1949-54	**Leyland Comet Lorry with Stake Body**	Red cab and chassis, Yellow back and hubs, Blue box	**£175-225**
		(renumbered 931, 417)	Blue cab and chassis, Brown back, Red or Blue hubs, Blue box	**£175-225**
			Violet-Blue cab and chassis, Orange-Yellow back, Red hubs, Blue box	**£175-225**
			Yellow cab and chassis, Pale Green back, Mid-Green hubs, Grey tyres	**£300-400**
		NB Odd colours:	Be wary of colour combinations not listed. The screw fitting makes it easy to interchange the chassis and body components.	
532	1952-54	**Leyland Comet Lorry with Hinged Tailboard**	Dark Green cab and chassis, Orange back, Cream hubs, Blue box	**£120-140**
		(renumbered 932, 418)	Dark Green cab and chassis, Orange back, Green hubs, Blue box	**£120-140**
			Dark Blue cab and chassis, Mid-Blue back, Cream hubs, Blue box	**£120-140**
			Dark Blue cab and chassis, Mid-Blue back, Red hubs, Blue/White box	**£120-140**
		NB Odd colours:	Be wary of colour combinations not listed. The screw fitting makes it easy to interchange the chassis and body components.	
533	1953-54	**Leyland Comet Cement Wagon**	Yellow body and hubs, 'PORTLAND BLUE-CIRCLE CEMENT', Supertoy, (renumbered 933, 419)	**£110-130**
551	1948-54	**Trailer**	Grey body, Black hubs, hook, Supertoy	**£20-30**
		(renumbered 951)	Yellow body, Black hubs, hook, Supertoy	**£90-110**
			Green body, Black hubs, hook, Supertoy	**£90-110**
	1969-73	.............................Gift Set issue:	Red body, Grey front chassis, protruding chromed hubs. Only in Gift Set 339	GSP
561	1949-54	**Blaw Knox Bulldozer**	Red body, Green or Black rubber tracks, driver, lifting blade, Supertoy. Blue box with Orange/White label, or 'natural' card box with Red/White label, 1 packing piece	**£40-50**
561	1962-64	**Citroën Delivery Van**	Light Blue body, Red/Yellow 'CIBIE' logo, sliding door. French issue	**£60-70**
562	1948-54	**Muir Hill Dump Truck**	Yellow body, metal wheels/tyres, hook, (renumbered 962)	**£15-20**
563	1948-54	**Blaw Knox Heavy Tractor**	Red, Orange or Blue 561 without the dozer blade.	
		(renumbered 963)	Buff cardboard box has Red/White label, 1 packing piece	**£70-90**
			Dark Blue body, Mid-Blue rollers, Green rubber tracks, Beige driver. Buff box with Red/White picture label	**£200-250**
564	1952-54	**Elevator Loader**	Renumbered 964 – see that entry for details.	
571	1949-54	**Coles Mobile Crane**	Yellow and Black, operable crane, Supertoy, (renumbered 971)	**£30-40**
579	1961-63	**Simca Glaziers Lorry**	UK issue: Yellow and Green body, mirror/glass load, 'MIROITIER'	**£70-80**
		French issue:	Grey and Green body, mirror/glass load, 'SAINT GOBAIN'	**£80-90**
581	1953-54	**Horsebox**	Maroon body (cast in aluminium) 'British Railways', 2 packing pieces, (renumbered 981)	**£80-100**
581	1953-54	...................................US issue:	Maroon, 'Hire Service', 'Express Horse Van', 'Express'. Blue box has Orange/White labels with picture of US model, 2 packing pieces, (renumbered 980)	**£500-700**
581	1962-64	**Berliet Flat Truck**	Red and Grey body, 6 wheels plus spare, hook. French issue	**£70-80**
		NB	The French issues listed above have been included because they were sold in the U.K.	
582	1953-54	**Pullmore Car Transporter**	Bedford cab/chassis, aluminium trailer with 'DINKY TOYS DELIVERY SERVICE' logo on sides. Same logo on rear ramp plus '20' sign. No window glazing, 'DINKY TOYS' on baseplate, Black grille/bumper, Silver trim.	
		(renumbered 982)		
	1953-53		Light Blue cab, trailer and hubs, Fawn decks, six lower deck retaining rivets. Model only issued for very short period	**£400-600**
	1953-54		As previous model but decks may be Fawn or Grey. Four lower deck retaining rivets	**£110-140**
	1954-54		Dark Blue cab, trailer and hubs, Fawn decks, four lower deck retaining rivets.	
			Model supplied in 582/982 all Dark Blue box with White end label	**£500-750**
			Model supplied in 582/982 Blue/White striped box	**£200-300**
591	1952-54	**A.E.C. Tanker**	Red/Yellow, 'SHELL CHEMICALS LIMITED', Supertoy, (renumbered 991)	**£140-175**
620	1950-54	**6-wheel Covered Wagon**	Matt-Green or Greenish-Brown body, 'Export only' (to USA), (renumbered from 151b)	**£60-70**
752	1953-54	**Goods Yard Crane**.....................	Yellow operable crane on Blue (or Dark Blue) base (steps in some). Dark Blue box, (renumbered 973)	**£30-40**
893	1962-64	**Unic Pipe Line Transporter**	Beige articulated body, spare wheel, 6 pipes. French issue	**£90-110**
894	1962-64	**Unic Boilot Car Transporter**	Grey body, 'Dinky Toys Service Livraison'. French issue	**£100-120**

901	1954-57	**Foden 8-wheel Diesel Wagon**	**2nd type cab**, Supertoy, spare wheel, large hook.	
		(renumbered from 501)	Red cab and chassis, Fawn truck body, Red hubs	£230-350
			Violet-Blue cab and chassis, Mid-Blue truck body and hubs	£500-700
			Dark Green cab and chassis, Light Green truck body and hubs.	
			'LF' sticker on Blue/White striped box lid, '1956' stamped inside bottom of box	£5,000-7,500
902	1954-56	**Foden Flat Truck**	**2nd type cab**, Supertoy, spare wheel, large hook.	
		(renumbered from 502)	Yellow cab and chassis, Mid-Green flatbed body, Green hubs	£700-900
	1954-57		Burnt-Orange cab and chassis, Mid-Green flatbed body and hubs	£300-400
	1957-59		Dark Red cab and chassis, Green flatbed, Green hubs	
			(NB Red similar to colour of 919 Guy 'GOLDEN SHRED' van)	£1,000-1,500
			Cherry-Red cab, wings and chassis, Green flatbed body and hubs	£400-500
			Orange cab and chassis, Fawn flatbed, Mid-Green hubs	£300-400
903	1954-55	**Foden Flat Truck with Tailboard**	**2nd type cab**, Supertoy, spare wheel, large hook.	
		(renumbered from 503)	Violet-Blue cab and chassis, Yellow flatbed, Mid-Blue hubs	£350-450
			Yellow cab, chassis and flatbed, Mid-Green hubs. In box with correct colour spot	£2,000-2,500
	1954-57		Violet-Blue cab and chassis, Orange flatbed, Mid-Blue hubs	£250-350
	1957-60		Mid-Blue cab and chassis, Fawn flatbed, Mid-Blue hubs, spare wheel rivetted on	£500-600
905	1954-56	**Foden Flat Truck with Chains** ..	**2nd type cab**, Supertoy, spare wheel, large hook.	
		(renumbered from 505)	Maroon cab, chassis and flatbed, Maroon hubs, 'rounded' chain-post bosses	£250-350
	1954-58		Dark Green cab, chassis and flatbed, Mid-Green hubs, 'rounded' chain-post bosses	£200-300
	1956-57		Maroon cab, chassis and flatbed, Maroon hubs, 'rounded' chain-post bosses	£250-350
			As previous issue but with Red hubs	£350-450
	1957-64		Red cab and chassis, Grey flatbed, Red metal hubs, 'rounded' chain-post bosses	£350-450
	19??-64		Red cab and chassis, Grey flatbed, Red plastic hubs	£400-500
908	1962-66	**Mighty Antar and Transformer**	Yellow tractor unit, Light Grey trailer, Red ramp and hubs, transformer, 3 packing pieces	£350-450
911	1954-56	**Guy 4 ton Lorry**	**2nd type cab** casting, Supertoy, 'grooved' hubs, large hook.	
		(was 511, renumbered 431)	Red cab and chassis, Fawn back, Red hubs	£250-350
			Violet-Blue cab and chassis, Mid-Blue back and hubs	£250-350
			Mid-Blue cab and chassis, Mid-Blue back and hubs	£400-600
912	1954-56	**Guy Flat Truck**	**2nd type cab** casting, Supertoy, 'grooved' hubs, large hook.	
		(was 512, renumbered 432)	Orange cab and chassis, Green flatbed body and hubs	£300-400
			Mid-Blue cab and chassis, Red flatbed body, Mid-Blue hubs	£200-250
			Dark Green cab and chassis, Light Green flatbed body and hubs	£300-400
913	1954-54	**Guy Flat Truck with Tailboard**	**2nd type cab** casting, Supertoy, 'grooved' hubs, large hook.	
		(was 513, renumbered 433)	Yellow cab and chassis, Green body, Green hubs	£750-950
	1954-56		Dark Green cab and chassis, Mid-Green flatbed body and hubs.	£200-250
			Deep Blue cab and chassis, Orange flatbed body, Light Blue hubs	
			Usually in Blue/White striped box with picture of Green lorry	£200-250
			Deep Blue/Orange model in box with correct colours	£750-950
914	1965-70	**A.E.C. Articulated Lorry**	Red cab ('CIA 7392' on doors), White interior, Light Grey trailer, Red plastic hubs,	
			Green tilt 'British Road Services'	£100-120
915	1973-74	**A.E.C. with Flat Trailer**	Orange cab, White trailer, 'Truck Hire Co Liverpool'	£55-65
			Orange cab, White trailer, 'Thames Board Mills', bubble-packed. Truck carries load	
			of four Brown card tubes with 'UNILEVER' logos in Black	NGPP
			Bright Metallic Blue cab, White interior, Orange chassis, Yellow trailer	£140-160
917	1954-56	**Guy Van 'SPRATTS'**	Red **2nd type cab**, chassis and Supertoy hubs, Cream/Red van body with	
		(renumbered from 514)	'Bonio Ovals & Dog Cakes' design	£300-400
917	1968-74	**Mercedes Truck and Trailer**	Blue cab/chassis (White roof), Yellow trailers, White tilts, pictorial stand and tray	£45-55
			Blue cab/chassis (White roof), Yellow trailers, Yellow tilts, pictorial stand and tray	£55-65
			Dark Blue cab/chassis, Yellow trailers, Dark Blue tilts, pictorial stand and tray	£65-75
		'MUNSTERLAND'	Dark Green cab and trailers, White tilts, Green logo, pictorial stand and tray, promotional	£250-350
		'HENRY JOHNSON'	Dark Green body, White tilts, plain White box, promotional	£200-250
918	1955-58	**Guy Van 'EVER READY'**	Blue **1st type cab** with small square sides to front number plate (never seen)	NGPP
			Blue **2nd type cab**/body, Red 'grooved' hubs, 'Ever Ready Batteries For Life', spare wheel, Supertoy	£250-300
919	1957-58	**Guy Van 'GOLDEN SHRED'** ...	All Red **2nd type cab** and body, Yellow Supertoy hubs,	
			'Robertsons Golden Shred' and 'golly' design, spare wheel	£500-600
920	1960-61	**Guy Warrior Van 'HEINZ'**	Red cab and chassis, window glazing, Yellow van body and Supertoy hubs,	
			spare wheel, 'HEINZ 57 VARIETIES' and 'Tomato Ketchup' bottle design	£1,000-1,250
921	1954-56	**Bedford Articulated Vehicle**	Yellowish-Orange body, Black wings, Red hubs, Supertoy, (was 521, renumbered 409)	£120-140
922	1954-56	**Big Bedford Lorry**	Maroon cab, Fawn back, Fawn hubs, Supertoy, (was 522, renumbered 408)	£110-130
			Dark Blue cab, Yellow back, Yellow hubs	£150-175
923	1955-58	**Big Bedford Van 'HEINZ'**	Red cab and chassis, Yellow back and hubs, 'Heinz 57 Varieties' plus Baked Beans can, Supertoy	£300-400
	1958-59		As previous model but with 'Tomato Ketchup' bottle advertising	£1,000-1,250
924	1972-76	**Aveling Barford 'CENTAUR'** ...	Red/Yellow body, tipping dump truck	£30-40
925	1965-69	**Leyland Dump Truck**	8-wheeled Supertoy with 'SAND BALLAST GRAVEL' on tailgate.	
			White (tilting) cab and chassis, Blue cab roof, Orange diecast tipper, Mid-Blue plastic hubs	£125-150
			As previous model but with tinplate tipper in Orange, Pale Grey or Red	£125-150
930	1960-64	**Bedford Pallet-Jekta Van**	Orange and Yellow body, 'Dinky Toys' and 'Meccano', 3 pallets, 1 packing piece, Supertoy	£200-250

931	1954-56	**Leyland Comet Lorry with Stake Body**	Violet-Blue cab and chassis, Orange-Yellow back, Red hubs, Supertoy, (was 531, renumbered 417)	**£175-225**
932	1954-56	**Leyland Comet with Hinged Tailboard**	Dark Green cab and chassis, Orange back, Mid-Green hubs	**£120-140**
		(was 532, renumbered 418)	Dark Green cab and chassis, Red back, Cream hubs	**£120-140**
			Dark Blue cab and chassis, Mid-Blue back and hubs	**£120-140**
			Dark Blue cab, chassis and back, Red hubs	**£120-140**
			Dark Blue cab and chassis, Light (Powder) Blue back, Cream hubs	**£250-350**
			Red cab and chassis, Mid-Blue back and hubs	**£250-350**
		NB Odd colours:	Be wary of colour combinations not listed. The screw fitting makes it easy to interchange the chassis and body components.	
933	1954-56	**Leyland Comet Cement Wagon**	Yellow body and hubs, 'Portland Blue-Circle Cement', Supertoy, (was 533, renumbered 419)	**£110-130**
934	1956-58	**Leyland Octopus Wagon**	Yellow cab and chassis, Green truck body secured to chassis by a screw, Green band around cab (but without Yellow band above radiator), Red diecast Supertoy hubs, 1 packing piece	**£150-175**
	1958-59		As previous model but with Green diecast hubs. Body secured by rivet	**£150-175**
	1958-63		As previous model but with Yellow band immediately above radiator, Red diecast hubs, body secured by rivet	**£250-300**
	1963-64		Dark Blue cab/chassis, Pale Yellow cab band and rivetted back, Red diecast hubs. In picture box	**£1,750-2,000**
	1963-64		Dark Blue cab/chassis, Pale Yellow cab band and rivetted back, Grey plastic hubs. In picture box	**£1,750-2,000**
	1964-64		Dark Blue cab/chassis, Pale Yellow cab band and rivetted back, Red plastic hubs. In picture box	**£1,750-2,000**
935	1964-66	**Leyland Octopus Flat Truck with Chains**	6 chain-posts, 8 wheels, flatbed held by rivet, Supertoy, 1 packing piece, picture box.	
			Mid-Green cab/chassis, Pale Grey cab band and flatbed body, Red plastic hubs	**£1,250-1,500**
			Mid-Green cab/chassis, Pale Grey cab band and flatbed body, Grey plastic hubs	**£1,250-1,500**
			Blue cab/chassis, Yellow cab flash, Pale Grey flatbed and hubs	**£3,000-4,000**
936	1964-69	**Leyland 8-wheel Chassis**	Red/Silver, 'Another Leyland on Test', three '5-ton' weights	**£75-85**
940	1977-80	**Mercedes-Benz LP.1920 Truck**	White cab, Pale Grey cover, Red chassis, hubs and interior	**£35-45**
			As above but with Black interior and White hubs	**£40-50**
		'HALB UND HALB'	'MAMPE' & 'BOSCH' on Blue cab, Elephant design. Promotional	**£100-150**
		'FISON'S'	White body, Red interior, chassis and hubs, Grey plastic cover, 'FISON'S THE GARDEN PEOPLE' labels, 2 peat samples. Promotional	**£200-250**
941	1956-56	**Foden 14 ton Tanker 'MOBILGAS'**	**2nd type cab.** Red body and hubs, Black filler caps, Black tyres, Supertoy, (renumbered from 504)	**£350-450**
942	1955-57	**Foden 14 ton Tanker 'REGENT'**	**2nd type cab.** Dark Blue cab/chassis, Red/White/Blue tank, Black tyres, Supertoy	**£350-450**
943	1958-64	**Leyland Octopus Tanker 'ESSO'**	Dark Red body and diecast hubs, Red tinplate tank with waterslide transfers, 'ESSO PETROLEUM', spare wheel, hook, Supertoy, 1 packing piece	**£300-400**
			As previous model but with Red plastic hubs	**£300-400**
			With Red plastic hubs, logos on self-adhesive labels	**£350-450**
944	1963-70	**Leyland Octopus Tanker 'SHELL-BP'**	White/Yellow cab and body, Grey chassis and plastic hubs	**£200-300**
			White/Yellow cab and body, Grey chassis, Black plastic hubs	**£300-400**
			White/Yellow cab and body, Grey chassis, Red plastic hubs	**£300-400**
			White/Yellow cab and body, White chassis, Grey or Black plastic hubs	**£200-300**
		Export issue:	Yellow cab, White chassis, White plastic tank, Red plastic hubs. 'See-through' export box	NGPP
		NB	Each issue has 'SHELL' and 'BP' sticky labels on the front half of the plastic tank.	

Guy 4-ton Lorries with their boxes.

Back row:
511 Red/Fawn on Green box with Red/White label
431 Red/Fawn on Yellow box
Front row:
511 Dark Blue/Light Blue on Brown box with Red/White label
911 Dark Blue/Light Blue on Blu/White striped box
431 Dark Blue/Light Blue on Yellow box

Photo: Swapmeet Publications

944	1963-64	**Leyland Octopus Tanker**		
		'CORN PRODUCTS'	Only 500 of these promotionals issued White body and plastic tank, 'Sweeteners For Industry' in White on Black labels. In 944 'ESSO' box with 'CORN PRODUCTS' sticker, wrapped in Green/Grey striped gift paper	**£2,000-3,000**
945	1966-75	**A.E.C. Fuel Tanker 'ESSO'**	White cab/chassis, White tank, 'ESSO PETROLUEUM', 'Tiger in Your Tank' logo on rear, 1 PP	**£70-85**
	1975-77		As previous model but without logo at rear, card boxed or bubble-packed	**£60-75**
	1977-77	**'LUCAS OIL' Tanker**	Green cab and tank, White design on labels, promotional, bubble-packed	**£100-125**
948	1961-67	**Tractor-Trailer 'McLEAN'** ..(i):	Red cab, Light Grey trailer, Red plastic hubs, Supertoy, 2 packing pieces	**£175-225**
		(ii):	As previous model but with Black plastic hubs	**£175-225**
	19??	**'ROADWAY DOVER'** (iii):	As model (i) but with extra graphics on the front of the trailer and on the rear of the cab: 'Roadway Dover Del Express Inc.'. Black plastic hubs	**£300-500**
	1964 ?	**'BROWN SHOE Co.'** ....(iv):	As 'McLean' model but with 'Brown Shoe Co.' adhesive labels. US Promotional (75 only made)	**NGPP**
		NB	The trailer moulding is light-sensitive and varies in shade from Pale Grey to Light Grey with a Greenish tinge, through to very Pale Brown. The 'McLean' logo can be Red or Light Orange.	
950	1978-79	**Foden S20 Tanker 'BURMAH'**	Red cab, Red/White trailer, Black or Grey hatches, Red or Cream hubs	**£40-50**
950	1978	**Foden Tanker 'SHELL'**	Red cab, Red/White trailer, Cream hubs	**£60-75**
951	1954-56	**Trailer**	Grey body with hook, Red hubs, (was 551, renumbered 428)	**£20-30**
			Dark Grey body with hook, Lemon Yellow hubs	**£50-75**
958	1961-66	**Guy Warrior Snow Plough**	Yellow/Black body and plough blade, spare wheel, 1 packing piece, Supertoy	**£125-150**
			Yellow/Black body, Silver plough blade	**£125-150**
			Silver blade version in box with picture showing Silver blade	**£250-300**
959	1961-68	**Foden Dump Truck & Bulldozer**	Red or Deep Red body, Silver chassis and blade, Red hubs (plastic front; metal rear)	**£100-125**
			As previous model but with Pale Yellow plastic front hubs and Yellow metal rear hubs	**£150-175**
			All-Red body version	**£150-175**
960	1960-68	**Albion Lorry Concrete Mixer**	Orange body, Blue rotating drum with 2 Yellow triangles, Black plastic hubs, Grey tyres. Supertoy	**£90-110**
			Orange body, Grey rotating drum, Black plastic hubs, Grey tyres. Supertoy	**£90-110**
961	1954-62	**Blaw-Knox Bulldozer**	Red or Yellow body, rubber tracks, Tan driver, Supertoy, (renumbered from 561)	**£40-50**
	1962-64		Blue body, rubber tracks, Tan driver	**£40-50**
	1963-64		Red or Yellow body, rubber tracks, Blue driver	**£40-50**
	1964-64		Orange plastic body with Silver engine detail, Black diecast lifting gear, Green plastic blade and exhaust pipe, Blue driver, Light Green or Olive-Green roller wheels	**£200-250**
962	1954-66	**Muir Hill Dumper**	Yellow body, hook, Supertoy, 1 packing piece, (renumbered from 562)	**£15-20**
963	1954-58	**Blaw Knox Heavy Tractor**	Red or Orange body, Green or Black tracks. Blue/White striped box, 1 packing piece, (was 563)	**£40-50**
	1958-59		Yellow body, Green or Black tracks. Blue/White striped box, 1 packing piece	**£50-60**
963	1973-75	**Road Grader**	Yellow/Red articulated body, Silver blade, Red lower arm	**£20-30**
			White or Yellow lower arm	**£30-40**
964	1954-68	**Elevator Loader**	Yellow with Mid-Blue or Dark Blue chutes, Blue or Yellow hubs, 1 packing piece	**£45-55**
		(renumbered from 564) Boxes:	Early Blue boxes were replaced by Blue/White boxes, then by Yellow 'Supertoys' boxes.	
		Late issue:	Mid-Blue with Yellow chutes, as shown on late picture box design	**£100-150**
965	1955-61	**'EUCLID' Dump Truck**	Pale Yellow body, Yellow hubs, 'STONE - ORE - EARTH', no windows, operable tipper, 1 PP	**£65-75**
		NB	1955-56 Grey backed logo; 1959-61 Red backed logo.	
	1961-69		As previous model but with window glazing	**£75-85**
			Pale Yellow body, Military Green hubs, window glazing. In detailed picture box	**£200-250**
965	1969-70	**'TEREX' Rear Dump Truck**	Yellow body (as previous model but 'TEREX' cast under cab), 1 packing piece	**£200-250**
966	1960-64	**Marrel Multi-Bucket Unit**	Pale Yellow body, Grey skip and tyres, Black hubs, Supertoy, 1 packing piece	**£100-125**
967	1959-64	**BBC TV Control Room**	Dark Green, 'BBC Television Service', Supertoy, 1 packing piece	**£140-170**
967	1973-78	**Muir-Hill Loader/Trencher**	Yellow/Red or Orange/Black body, with driver	**£25-35**
968	1959-64	**BBC TV Roving-Eye Vehicle**	Dark Green body, BBC crest, camera, Supertoy, 1 packing piece	**£140-170**
969	1959-64	**BBC TV Extending Mast**	Dark Green body, BBC crest, dish aerial, mast, Supertoy, 2 packing pieces	**£140-170**
970	1967-71	**Jones Fleetmaster Crane**	(Bedford TK) Red cab, White roof, Red interior, Red plastic hubs, White jib, 2 packing pieces	**£80-100**
	1971-77		Metallic Red cab, White interior, and jib, chrome domed hubs, 2 packing pieces	**£80-100**
	1971-77		Pale Yellow cab, White interior, and jib, chrome domed hubs, 2 packing pieces	**£80-100**
971	1955-62	**Coles Mobile Crane** ....(was 571)	Orange/Deep Yellow body; 'Long Vehicle' signs on some, Yellow hubs, 2 drivers. Blue/White box	**£70-90**
	1962-67		Orange/Deep Yellow body; Yellow hubs, 2 drivers. Black/White diagonals warning sign. Pictorialdesign to lift-off lid on later issue Yellow/Red box	**£100-120**
	1967-69		Orange/Deep Yellow body; Yellow plastic hubs, no driver in cab. Black/White diagonals warning signs to rear and sides. Full detail end-flap picture box	**£150-175**
	1972-72		Variation with Black hubs. End-flap picture box	**£200-250**
972	1955-62	**Coles 20 ton Lorry-Mounted Crane**	Yellow/Orange (no 'Long Vehicle' signs), 2 drivers, Supertoy, 1 packing piece	**£40-50**
	1962-69		Yellow/Orange (with 'Long Vehicle' signs), 2 drivers, Supertoy	**£40-50**
	1967-69		Yellow/Black, Blue metal driver in lorry cab only, Yellow plastic hubs, Black tyres, Black/White diagonal stripes around jib, Yellow 'COLES CRANE" at rear	**£100-150**
			Variation with Black hubs. (In end-flap box)	**£100-150**
973	1954-59	**Goods Yard Crane**	Yellow operable crane on Blue base. Blue/White striped box with 1 packing piece, (was 752)	**£30-40**
973	1971-75	**Eaton 'YALE' Tractor Shovel**	Red/Yellow body with Yellow or Silver bucket exterior	**£20-30**
			Yellow/Red body, Silver wheels, no engine covers	**£25-35**
			All Yellow body, Blue wheels, engine covers	**£25-35**
974	1968-75	**A.E.C. Hoynor Car Transporter**	Bright Metallic Blue cab, White interior, Pale Orange/Dark Orange back, Grey plastic hubs, 3 PP	**£90-110**
			Dark Metallic Blue cab, Pale Orange/Dark Orange back, Grey plastic hubs, 3 PP	**£90-110**
			Dark Metallic Blue cab, Yellow and Bright Orange back, chrome domed hubs, 3 PP	**£90-110**

975	1963-67	'RUSTON-BUCYRUS' Excavator	Pale Yellow plastic body, Red jib and bucket, Black rubber tracks, with instructions	£225-275
976	1968-76	'MICHIGAN' Tractor Dozer	Yellow/Red body, driver, engine covers, Red hubs, 1 packing piece	£30-35
		Promotional:	All Yellow with Blue hubs. (100 / 200 made for Michigan Co.)	£100-150
977	1960-64	Servicing Platform Vehicle	Red and Cream body, operable platform, spare wheel, 2 packing pieces	£140-160
	NB		Version seen using 667 Missile Servicing Platform Vehicle chassis in the Red/Cream 977 livery	NGPP
977	1973-78	Shovel Dozer	Yellow/Red/Silver, Black or Silver plastic tracks, bubble-packed	£20-25
978	1964-72	Bedford TK Refuse Wagon	Diecast cab, plastic tipping body, 2 plastic dustbins.	
			Green cab, Grey tipping body, Red hubs, White (later Grey) plastic roof rack	£40-45
	1973-74		Dark Metallic Green cab, Grey tipping body, Red plastic hubs, White (later Grey) plastic roof rack	£60-70
	1975-77		Lime-Green cab, White interior, Black or Brown chassis, plastic or cast roof rack	£60-70
	1978-80		Yellow cab with Brown chassis, cast roof rack	£35-45
	NB		Over its 16-year production run, 978 came in five different types of packaging: lidded box, pictorial and non-pictorial end-flap boxes, bubble-pack, and window box.	
979	1961-64	Racehorse Transport	Grey lower body and roof, Lemon-Yellow upper body sides, 2 horses, 'Newmarket Racehorse Transport Service Ltd', Supertoy, 2 packing pieces	£250-300
980	1954-60	Horsebox (US issue) (renumbered from 581)	Maroon body (cast in aluminium), 'Hire Service', 'Express Horse Van', 'Express'. In Blue/White striped box with picture of model and 'Hudson Dobson', 2 packing pieces	£350-450
980	1972-79	Coles Hydra Truck 150T	Lemon-Yellow body, triple extension crane, handle at side and rear	£30-40
			Yellow or Orange body, 2 side handles, no rear handle	£50-60
		'SPARROWS'	Red body, 'SPARROWS CRANE HIRE', (promotional model)	£200-300
981	1954-60	Horsebox	Maroon body (cast in aluminium), 'British Railways', 2 packing pieces, (renumbered from 581)	£80-100
982	1955-63	Pullmore Car Transporter (renumbered from 582)	Bedford 'O' series cab and chassis plus aluminium trailer with 'DINKY TOYS DELIVERY SERVICE' on sides. Same logo on rear ramp but without '20' sign. Black grille/bumper, Silver trim, 1 packing piece.	
	1955-61		Blue cab and back, Mid-Blue hubs, Fawn decks	£250-300
			Dark Blue cab, Mid-Blue hubs, Light Blue back and decks, no window glazing. Blue/White striped box has picture of 994 Loading Ramp introduced in 1955	£100-120
	1961-63		As previous issue but cab has window glazing	£120-130
983	1958-63	Car Carrier and Trailer	Red/Grey, 'Dinky Auto Service', 5 packing pieces, (Supertoys 984 and 985)	£200-250
984	1958-63	Car Carrier	Red/Grey body, Grey hubs, 'Dinky Auto Service', 2 packing pieces, Supertoy	£150-200
984	1974-79	Atlas Digger	Red/Yellow body, Yellow arm/cylinders, Silver or Yellow bucket	£30-40
			Red/Yellow body, Black plastic arm, Black or Yellow cylinders, Silver bucket	£30-40
985	1958-63	Trailer for Car Carrier	Red/Grey body, 'Dinky Auto Service', 2 packing pieces, Supertoy	£50-60
986	1959-61	Mighty Antar with Propeller	Red cab (window glazing on some), Grey low-loader, Bronze propeller, 3 packing pieces	£200-250
987	1962-69	'ABC TV' Control Room	Blue/Grey/Red, 'ABC TELEVISION', camera/operator/cable	£150-180
988	1962-69	TV Transmitter Van 'ABC-TV'	Blue/Grey body, Red stripe, revolving aerial dish, Supertoy	£150-180
989	1963-65	Car Transporter 'AUTO TRANSPORTERS'	Lemon Yellow cab, Pale Grey back, Metallic Light Blue ramps, Red plastic hubs, Supertoy boxed in all-card picture box or export-only Gold 'see through' window box, 2 packing pieces	£1,000-1,500
990		Pullmore Car transporter with Four Cars	See Gift Sets section.	
991	1954-70	Large Trailer	Renumbered from 551 – see that entry for details.	
991	1954-55	A.E.C. Tanker	Red/Yellow 'SHELL CHEMICALS LIMITED', Supertoy, (renumbered from 591)	£120-140
	1955-58		Red/Yellow, 'SHELL CHEMICALS', Supertoy	£120-140

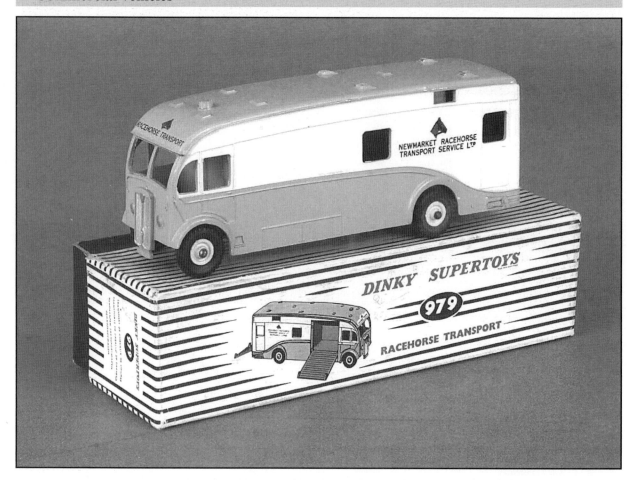

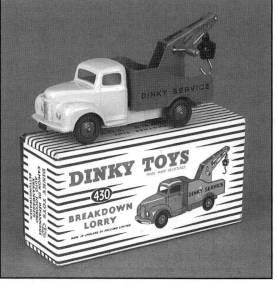

The photographs above are of Dinky Toys sold by Vectis Auctions Ltd., and are used with their kind permission

> **Type 1:** (1966-74), has sliding driver's door, opening hinged side door, and twin rear doors.
> **Type 2:** (1974-78), non-sliding driver's door, one side-hinged door, one top-hinged rear door.
> **Type 3:** (1978-80), as Type 2 but with a slightly longer bonnet (18 mm.)

Ref	Year(s)	Model name	Colours, features, details	Market Price Range
24a	1934-38	Ambulance	Types 1 or 2 criss-cross chassis, types 1, 2 or 3 grille, plated chrome or Black hubs, open windows.	
			Cream body (Red chassis), Cream body (Grey chassis)	£250-350
			Grey body (Dark Grey chassis), Grey body (Maroon chassis)	£200-250

> **Notable Auction Result**: A pre-production (lead) example of 24a was sold by Christie's in 2001 for **£470**.

Ref	Year(s)	Model name	Colours, features, details	Market Price Range
	1938-40	Ambulance	Type 2 criss-cross chassis, open windows, type 3 grille. See 30f.	
			Cream body (Red chassis), Cream body (Grey chassis)	£200-250
			Grey body (Dark Grey chassis), Grey body (Maroon chassis)	£250-300
			Black body, Black chassis (thought to be for export only)	£500-750
25h	1936-37	Streamlined Fire Engine	Red body, no tinplate chassis, tinplate ladder and bell, White tyres	£175-225
	1937-40		Red body, tinplate baseplate, ladder and bell, Black or White tyres	£125-150
25h	1948-54	(renumbered 250)	Red body and ladder, tinplate baseplate, brass bell, Black tyres	£80-100
25k	1937-39	Streamline Fire Engine	Red body, tinplate base, 6 firemen, ladder, bell, White tyres	£400-500
30f	1935-38	Ambulance	Grey body, Red wings/criss-cross chassis, plain radiator, open windows	£150-200
	1938-40		Grey body, Black moulded chassis, radiator badge, open windows	£90-110
	1938-40	South-African issue:	Grey body, Red cross, 'Bentley type' radiator	£750-950
	1946-47		Grey body, Black moulded chassis, open windows	£80-100
	1947-48		Cream body, Black moulded chassis, filled-in or open windows	£80-100
30h	1950-54	Daimler Ambulance	Cream body, Red crosses and wheels, no window glazing, (renumbered 253)	£80-90
30hm	1950-54	Daimler Military Ambulance	Military-Green body, Red crosses on White backgrounds, (US issue), (renumbered 624)	£200-300
123-P	1977	Austin Princess 'POLICE' Car	All-White, Bronze/Blue or White/Blue. (Model has not yet been seen)	NPP
195	1971-78	Fire-Chief's Range Rover	Red or Metallic Red, 'Fire Service', Speedwheels, bubble-packed	£35-40
243	1979-81	Volvo 'POLICE' Car	White body, plastic chassis. (Some made in Italy by Polistil)	£35-40
244	1977-81	Plymouth Fury Police Car	Black/White, warning lights, plastic chassis and wheels	£25-30
250	1954-62	Fire Engine	Red body and hubs, Silver tinplate ladder, bell and trim, (renumbered from 25h)	£100-120
250	1967-71	Police Mini Cooper 'S'	White body, Austin Cooper 'S' boot lid transfer, roof sign and aerial, 'POLICE' on doors	£55-65
	1971-73		As previous model but cast boot detail, no aerial	£45-55
	1973-75		As previous model but with Speedwheels	£35-45
NB			Boot casting variations: (1) 'Morris Mini-Minor' cast-in, (2) 'Austin Mini-Cooper S' cast-in.	
251	1971-72	U.S.A. 'POLICE' Car	(Pontiac Parisienne), White body, Black textured roof, Off-White interior, twin aerials, siren, rooflight	£60-75
252	1969-74	R.C.M.P. Police Car	(Pontiac Parisienne), Dark Blue body, White door panels, White interior, driver, twin aerials, Red light	£60-75
253	1954-58	Daimler Ambulance	Cream body, Red crosses and cast hubs, no window glazing, (renumbered from 30h)	£75-85
	1958-60		White body, Red crosses and cast hubs, no window glazing	£100-125
	1960-62		White body, Red crosses and cast hubs, with window glazing	£80-100
	1962-64		White body, Red plastic hubs, with window glazing	£90-110
254	1971-81	Police Range Rover	White body, Orange side stripes, 'Police', twin aerials on some, Speedwheels	£30-35
255	1955-61	Mersey Tunnel Police Van	(Land Rover), Matt Red body, smooth tyres, 'Mersey Tunnel' and 'Police', hook	£60-75
			Gloss Red body, treaded tyres, 'Mersey Tunnel' and 'Police', hook	£60-75
255	1967-71	Ford Zodiac 'POLICE' Car	White body, driver, 'POLICE' on doors and roof sign, aerial	£55-65
			As previous model but with paper labels on door and blue base	£45-55
255	1977-79	Police Mini Clubman	Blue/White body, 'POLICE', opening doors and bonnet, plastic wheels	£30-35
256	1960-64	Humber Hawk 'POLICE' Car	Black body, Cream interior, White 'POLICE' sign on roof, 'PC 49' licence plates, driver and observer, spun hubs	£80-100
257	1960-69	Canadian 'FIRE CHIEF' Car	(Nash Rambler), flashing light, suspension, window glazing	£55-65
258		U.S.A. POLICE CAR		
	1960-61	De Soto Fireflite	(192), Black body, White front doors, 'POLICE' on doors, roof and bonnet, Red roof-light	£80-100
	1961-62	Dodge Royal Sedan	(191), Black body, White front doors, 'POLICE' on doors, roof and bonnet, Red roof-light	£80-100
	1962-66	Ford Fairlane	(149), Black body, White front doors, 'POLICE' on doors, roof and bonnet, Red light, open window	£70-80
			Same but Dark Blue/White, with closed windows	£70-80
	1966-68	Cadillac 62	(147), Black/White, suspension/steering	£80-100
259	1961-69	Fire Engine (Bedford Miles)	Red body and hubs, 'FIRE BRIGADE' and crest, tinplate ladder and bell, Yellow box	£70-85
			As previous model but with 'AIRPORT FIRE TENDER' (from 276)	£70-85
			Red body, Silver cast wheels	£100-125
261	1967-77	Ford Taunus 'POLIZEI'	White and Green body, (German issue), box has card packing ring and label: 'Special contract run for Meccano Agent in W. Germany'	£200-250
263	1962-68	Superior Criterion Ambulance	Cream, 'AMBULANCE' on windows, stretcher, no beacon	£50-60
263	1978-81	E.R.F. Fire Tender	Yellow body, 'Airport Rescue', flashing light	£40-50
264	1962-65	R.C.M.P. Ford Fairlane	Dark Blue body, White doors, aerial, red beacon, 2 Mounties	£75-85
264	1965-68	R.C.M.P. Cadillac	Dark Blue body, White front doors, aerial, red beacon, 2 Mounties	£90-110
264	1978-80	Rover 3500 Police Car	White body, Yellow stripe with 'POLICE' and crest. (Some made in Hong Kong)	£20-30
266	1976-79	E.R.F. Fire Tender	Red body, 'Fire Service', White wheeled escape ladder	£50-60
	1979-80		As previous model but with Metallic Red body	£50-60
	1976-79	Danish issue:	Red body, 'FALCK'	£70-85
267	1967-71	Superior Cadillac Ambulance	Cream and Red body, 'AMBULANCE' on roof, flashing light, stretcher, patient	£50-65
267	1978-79	Paramedic Truck	Red, Yellow cylinders, 2 figures, lapel badge, (TV Series 'Emergency')	£20-30
268	1973-77	Range Rover Ambulance	White, 'AMBULANCE', stretcher, bubble-packed	£20-30

269	1962-66	Jaguar Motorway 'POLICE' Car	White or matt-White body, aerial, roof-light, 2 figures	£80-100
269	1978-79	Ford Transit 'POLICE' Van	White/Red/Blue, figures/lights/signs/cones, Type 3 casting	£35-45
270	1969-72	Ford 'POLICE' Panda Car	Turquoise body, White doors, Blue/White roof sign, cast hubs	£45-55
	1972-77		As previous model but fitted with Speedwheels	£40-50
271	1975-76	Ford Transit 'FIRE'	Red body, hose/axe/bells/plastic ladder, bubble-packed, Type 2	£55-65
		Danish issue:	As previous model but with 'FALCK' logo	£65-75
272	1975-78	'POLICE' Accident Unit	White, radar gun/beacon/aerial/cones/signs, Type 2 casting	£35-45
274	1978-79	Ford Transit Ambulance	White, 'AMBULANCE', Red crosses, beacon, Type 3 casting	£35-45
276	1962-69	Airport Fire Tender	Red body, 'AIRPORT FIRE CONTROL', bell, packing ring in box	£50-65
			As previous model but 'FIRE BRIGADE' logo (from 259), no crest	£50-65
276	1976-78	Ford Transit Ambulance	White body, 'AMBULANCE', Type 2 casting, packing ring in box	£30-40
277	1962-68	Superior Criterion Ambulance	Metallic Blue, White roof and tyres, flashing light, box has lift-off lid and 1 packing piece	£60-80
			As previous model but in Gold 'see-through' box	£80-90
277	1977-80	'POLICE' Land Rover	Blue body, White tilt, Blue beacon	£20-30
278	1964-69	Vauxhall Victor Ambulance	White, 'AMBULANCE', stretcher and patient, roof-box and light	£60-75
282	1973-79	Land Rover Fire Appliance	Red, 'Fire Service', metal ladder, bubble-packed	£30-40
	1974-78	Danish issue:	As previous model but with 'FALCK' logo	£35-45
285	1969-79	Merryweather Marquis	Metallic Dark Red body, escape ladder, working pump, 'FIRE SERVICE'	£55-65
			As previous model but (non-Metallic), Red body	£55-65
		Danish issue:	As previous model but Red or Metallic Dark Red body, 'FALCK' logo	£85-95
286	1968-74	Ford Transit 'FIRE'	Red, 'Fire Service', hose Type 1 casting, bubble-packed	£75-90
			As previous model but with Metallic Red body	£75-90
		Danish issue:	As previous model but with 'FALCK ZONEN' logo	£85-95
287	1967-71	Police Accident Unit	White body, Orange panels, roof rack and sign, radar gun, aerial, Type 1 casting	£50-65
	1971-74		White body, Red panels, roof rack and sign, radar gun, aerial, Type 1 casting	£50-65
	NB		Accessories with 287 include traffic cones and two blue 'POLICE' warning boards.	
288	1971-79	Superior Cadillac	White body with Red lower panels, 'AMBULANCE', stretcher and patient, no flashing light	£40-45
		Danish issue:	Black body/White roof, Blue interior and roof bar, 'FALCK' on roof bar and tailgate	£100-125
555	1952-54	Fire Engine (Commer)	Red body with Silver trim and ladder, no windows, (renumbered 955)	£75-85
624	1954-?	Daimler Military Ambulance	Military-Green body, Red crosses on White backgrounds, (US issue), (renumbered from 30hm)	£200-300
954	1961-64	Fire Station	Red, Yellow and 'brick' plastic, base 252 mm. x 203 mm	£200-250
955	1954-64	Fire Engine (Commer)	Red body and diecast Supertoy hubs, no window glazing, (renumbered from 555)	£75-85
	1964-70		Red body, Red diecast or plastic hubs, window glazing, Black or Grey tyres, housed in Yellow box with drawing or scene, card packing	£150-175
956	1958-60	Turntable Fire Escape Lorry	(Bedford cab). Red body and diecast hubs, no windows, Silver deck and ladder	£80-100
	1960-70		Red body, diecast then plastic hubs, window glazing, instructions, 'Tested' label, card packing	£80-100
	NB		A version of 956 has been discovered (in Norway) that has 3 ladders instead of 2.	
956	1970-74	Turntable Fire Escape Lorry	(Berliet cab). Metallic Red body and hubs, windows, 'ECHELLE INCENDIE', Silver platform	£175-225
	1974-?		As previous model but with Black platform	£150-200
		Danish issue:	Metallic Red body and hubs, windows, 'FALCK'	£175-225
2253	1974-76	Ford Capri Police Car	White/Orange, 'POLICE', Blue light, suspension. (1/25 scale)	£80-100

Photo: Vectis Auctions Ltd.

Dinky Toys Farm and Garden models

Ref	Year(s)	Model name	Colours, features, details	Market Price Range
22e	1933-40	**Farm Tractor**	'Modelled Miniature' with 'HORNBY SERIES' cast-in, no hook, Yellow/Dark Blue (lead) body, Red or Yellow (lead) wheels	£300-400
			'DINKY TOYS' cast-in, with hook, Red or Yellow wheels are lead, diecast or both, Green/Yellow, Yellow/Blue/Red, Red/Blue, Red/Red	£300-400
			Cream/Blue, Cream/Red, Blue/Cream/Red	£300-400
27a	1948-54	**'MASSEY-HARRIS' Tractor** ..	Red body, Yellow cast wheels, driver, steering wheel, hook, (renumbered 300)	£45-55
27ak	1952-54	**Tractor and Hay Rake**	27a Tractor and 27k Hay Rake, (renumbered 310)	£150-200
27b	1949-54	**Halesowen Harvest Trailer** ..	Brown body, Red racks, Yellow metal wheels, (renumbered 320)	£25-35
27c	1949-54	**M.H. Manure Spreader**	Red body with drawbar, hook, working shredders, (renumbered 321)	£30-35
27d	1950-54	**Land Rover**	Orange body, Dark Blue interior, Tan driver, Red hubs	£75-85
		(Renumbered 340)	Orange body, Dark Green interior, Tan driver, Red hubs	£65-75
			Mid-Green body, Light Brown interior, Tan driver, Green hubs	£65-75
		Promotional:	Very Dark Green body. (Ministry of Food promotional)	£1,000-1,500
	1952-53	............Gift Set model:	Dark Brown body. Only in Gift Set No.2, Commercial Vehicles Set	GSP
27f	1950-54	**Estate Car**	Pale Brown body with Dark Brown panels, rear axle pillars, Fawn hubs, small lettering on matt or gloss baseplate	£50-60
		(Renumbered 344)	Grey body with Red side panels	£100-125
27g	1949-54	**Moto-Cart**	Brown and Green body, driver, 3 metal wheels/tyres, body tips, (renumbered 342)	£40-50
27h	1951-54	**Disc Harrow**	Red/Yellow body, Silver disc blades, tinplate hook, (renumbered 322)	£20-25
27j	1952-54	**Triple Gang Mower**	Red frame, Yellow tines, Green wheels, cast-in hook, (renumbered 323)	£20-25
27k	1953-54	**Hay Rake**	Red frame, Yellow wheels, wire tines, operating lever, (renumbered 324)	£20-25
27m	1952-54	**Land Rover Trailer**	Green body and hubs, Blue body and hubs, Red body and hubs	£25-35
		(renumbered 341)	Orange body, Red, Cream or Beige hubs	£25-35
		Militarised version:	For Olive-drab version, see 'Military Vehicles' section.	
27n	1953-54	**'FIELD MARSHALL' Tractor**	Burnt Orange body and exhaust stack, Silver metal wheels, Tan driver, hook	£100-130
		(renumbered 301)	As previous model but with Green metal wheels	£150-200
30n	1950-54	**Farm Produce Wagon**	Model has stake sides to rear body; Black metal base and hook; hubs same colour as rear body.	
		(renumbered 343)	Yellow cab with Green back, or Green cab with Yellow back, or Red cab with Blue back	£60-70
105a	1948-54	**Garden Roller**	Green handle and Red roller sides, (renumbered 381)	£15-25
105b	1948-54	**Wheelbarrow**	Brown or Tan and Red body, single metal wheel, (renumbered 382)	£15-25
105c	1948-54	**4 wheeled Hand Truck**	Green/Yellow or Blue/Yellow, (renumbered 383)	£10-15
105e	1948-54	**Grass Cutter**	Yellow handle, Green metal wheels, Red blades, (renumbered 384)	£25-30
		(renumbered 384)	Yellow handle, unpainted metal wheels, Green blades	£50-75
107a	1948-54	**Sack Truck**	Blue or Pale Green body with two small Black metal wheels, (renumbered 385)	£10-15
192	1970-74	**Range Rover**	Bronze body, various interior colours, cast detailed or Speedwheels	£25-35
	1973-79		Black or Yellow body, Speedwheels	£25-35
300	1954-62	**'MASSEY-HARRIS' Tractor** ..	Red body, Yellow and Grey cast wheels, metal exhaust stack, Tan cast driver (renumbered from 27a)	£70-80
	1962-64	....	Red body, Yellow wheels (cast rear, plastic front, rubber tyres), Blue plastic driver	£100-120
	1964-66	....	Cherry Red body, Yellow/Black plastic wheels, Yellow exhaust, Blue driver, Yellow/White box	£125-150
300	1966-71	**'MASSEY-FERGUSON' Tractor**	As previous model but name changed to 'MASSEY-FERGUSON'	£70-80
301	1954-61	**'FIELD MARSHALL' Tractor**	Orange body, Green or Silver metal wheels, Tan driver, hook, (renumbered from 27n)	£150-200
			Orange body, Yellow or unpainted wheels, Tan driver, hook	£150-180
	1962-66	....	Orange body, Green wheels (plastic front, cast rear, rubber tyres), Blue driver	£300-400
			Orange body, Green plastic hubs (front and rear), Black plastic exhaust, Blue driver	£300-400
	1964-66	....	Red body, Green plastic hubs	£200-250
305	1965-67	**'DAVID BROWN' 900 Tractor**	Yellow cab and wheels, Metallic Grey engine, Red exhaust stack, 'David Brown Selectamatic 990' stickers on engine covers. In detailed picture box	£100-130
	1967-72	....	White body, wheels and exhaust stack, Metallic Grey engine, stickers as previous version	£80-100
	1972-73	....	White body and wheels, Yellow exhaust stack, Metallic Grey engine. In detailed picture box	£150-200
	1974-75	....	White body, Red engine, chassis and wheels, Black exhaust stack, unpainted front axle. Late issue with 'Case David Brown 995' on engine covers. Bubble-packed	£130-160
308	1971-72	**'LEYLAND' 384 Tractor**	Metallic Red body, Cream hubs, no driver, plastic dome box	£85-100
	1973-74	....	Metallic Red body, White hubs, driver, Yellow/Red box	£90-110
	1975-77	....	Blue body, White exhaust stack and hubs, Blue plastic driver, Yellow/Red box	£90-110
	1978	....	Orange body, White exhaust stack and hubs, Blue plastic driver, Red/Blue 'hanging' box	£80-100
	1978-79	....	Metallic Red body, White exhaust stack and hubs, Blue plastic driver, Red/Blue 'hanging' box	£75-95
		Factory error:	Blue body and plastic driver, Red hubs, White exhaust stack. Bubble-packed	£140-180
310	1954-60	**Tractor and Hay Rake**	300 Tractor and 324 Hay Rake in Blue/White box, (renumbered from 27ak)	£150-175
			Same, but late issue in Yellow box which includes a single packing piece	£200-250
319	1961-71	**Weeks Tipping Trailer**	Red/Yellow body, cast or Brown plastic wheels, plain or planked trailer bed	£25-30
320	1954-60	**Halesowen Harvest Trailer**	Red/Brown body, Red racks, drawbar, hook, cast or plastic wheels, (renumbered from 27b)	£25-35
			Red body, Yellow racks, drawbar, hook, cast or plastic wheels	£25-35
321	1954-62	**M.H. Manure Spreader**	Red body, Yellow cast wheels, 'MASSEY-HARRIS', shredders (renumbered from 27c)	£25-35
321	1962-73		Red body, Red or Yellow plastic hubs, no logo	£25-35
322	1954-67	**Disc Harrow**	Red/Yellow body, Silver disc blades, tinplate hook, (renumbered from 27h)	£25-35
322	1967-73	....	White/Red body, Silver disc blades, no hook	£25-35
			All White version	£40-50

323	1954-63	**Triple Gang Mower**	Red frame, Yellow tines, Green wheels, cast-in hook, (renumbered from 27j)	**£35-45**
324	1954-64	**Hayrake**	Red frame, Yellow wheels, wire tines, Black or Silver operating lever (renumbered from 27k)	**£25-35**
325	1967-73	**'DAVID BROWN' Tractor and Disc Harrow**	305 and 322 in White and Red. Box has inner packing piece	**£100-125**
			305 and 322 in Yellow and Red. Box has inner packing piece	**£130-150**
340	1954-66	**Land Rover**	Green body, Pale Brown interior and cast driver, Green cast hubs, (renumbered from 27d)	**£80-100**
340	1966-69		Orange body, Dark Green interior, Red or Green cast hubs, Tan driver	**£80-100**
340			Orange body, Dark Green interior, Red plastic hubs, Blue cast or plastic driver	**£110-130**
	1969-71		Red body, Red plastic hubs, Yellow interior, Blue plastic driver	**£125-150**
			Red body, Yellow plastic hubs and interior, Blue plastic driver	**£125-150**
	1971		Red body, Green plastic hubs, Yellow interior, Blue plastic driver	**£125-150**
	NB		The last three issues were supplied in the late Lighter Yellow boxes.	
341	1954-66	**Land Rover Trailer**	Orange, Green or Red, drawbar and hook, cast or plastic hubs, (renumbered from 27m)	**£25-30**
	Militarised version:		For Olive-drab version, see 'Military Vehicles' section.	
342	1954-61	**Moto-Cart**	Light or Dark Green with Tan back and driver, Red hubs, (renumbered from 27g)	**£65-75**
343	1954-64	**Farm Produce Wagon**	Mid-Green cab and chassis with Yellow back and hubs	**£80-100**
		(renumbered from 30n)	Yellow cab with Green back and hubs	**£80-100**
			Dark Red cab with Mid-Blue back and hubs	**£100-125**
			Cherry Red cab with Mid-Blue back and hubs	**£100-125**
			Late issues with plastic hubs and boxed in the late lighter Yellow box	**£125-150**
344	1954-61	**Estate Car**	Fawn with Brown or Red panels, Cream diecast hubs, treaded tyres, large print on base	**£130-160**
		(renumbered from 27f)	Fawn with Brown panels, spun hubs	**£130-160**
344	1970-72	**Land Rover Pick-Up**	Metallic Blue body, White back, cast hubs, bubble-packed	**£20-30**
	1973-78		Metallic Red body, White back, cast hubs, bubble-packed	**£20-30**
381	1954-58	**Garden Roller**	Green and Red, (renumbered from 105a)	**£15-25**
381	1977-80	**Convoy Farm Truck**	Yellow cab, Brown plastic high-sided truck body	**£15-20**
382	1954-58	**Wheelbarrow**	Brown and Red body, single metal wheel, (renumbered from 105b)	**£15-25**
383	1954-58	**4 wheeled Hand Truck**	Green or Blue body, (renumbered from 105c)	**£10-15**
384	1954-58	**Grass Cutter**	Renumbered from 105e. See 105e for variations.	
385	1954-58	**Sack Truck**	Blue with two small metal wheels, (renumbered from 107a)	**£10-15**
386	1954-58	**Lawn Mower**	Green/Red, separate grassbox, 'Dinky Toys' cast-in, (renumbered from 751)	**£80-90**
399	1969-75	**Tractor and Trailer**	300 combined with 428.	**£200-250**
428	1955-71	**Large Trailer**	See 'Commercial Vehicles' section for variations.	
561	1949-54	**Blaw Knox Bulldozer**	Red body, Green or Black rubber tracks, driver, lifting blade, Supertoy.	
		(renumbered 961)	Blue box with Orange/White label, or 'natural' card box with Red/White label, 1 PP	**£40-50**
563	1948-54	**Blaw Knox Heavy Tractor**	Red, Orange or Blue 561 without the dozer blade.	
		(renumbered 963)	Brown cardboard box has Red/White label and includes a single packing piece	**£60-70**
			Dark Blue body, Mid-Blue rollers, Green rubber tracks, driver. Brown box, Black/White picture label	**£175-200**
564	1952-54	**Elevator Loader**	Renumbered 964 – see that entry (below) for details.	
751	1949-54	**Lawn Mower**	Green/Red, separate grassbox, 'Dinky Supertoys' cast-in, (renumbered to 386)	**£80-90**
961	1954-62	**Blaw-Knox Bulldozer**	Red or Yellow body, rubber tracks, Tan driver, Supertoy, (renumbered from 561)	**£40-50**
	1962-64		Blue body, rubber tracks, Tan driver	**£40-50**
	1963-64		Red or Yellow body, rubber tracks, Blue driver	**£40-50**
	1964-64		Orange plastic body with Silver engine detail, Black diecast lifting gear, Green plastic blade and exhaust pipe, Blue driver, Light Green or Olive-Green roller wheels	**£200-250**
963	1954-58	**Blaw Knox Heavy Tractor**	Red or Orange body, Green or Black tracks. Blue/White striped box, 1 PP, (renumbered from 563)	**£40-50**
	1958-59		Yellow body, Green or Black tracks. Blue/White striped box, 1 PP	**£40-50**
964	1954-68	**Elevator Loader**	Yellow with Mid-Blue or Dark Blue chutes, Blue or Yellow hubs, 1 PP	**£45-55**
	(renumbered from 564)	Boxes:	Early Blue boxes were replaced by Blue/White boxes, then by Yellow 'Supertoys' boxes.	
	Late issue:		Mid-Blue with Yellow chutes, as shown on late picture box design	**£100-150**

Collectors notes

Dinky Toys Motor Cycles

See also Accessories and Gift Sets sections.

SWRW = solid White rubber wheels, SBRW = solid Black rubber wheels (both are of a larger diameter than those used on the small cars).

Ref	Year(s)	Model name	Colours, features, details	Market Price Range
041	1952-54	**Police Motor Cyclist**	Post-war reissue for US market of 37a	NGPP
042	1952-54	**Civilian Motor Cyclist**	Post-war reissue for US market of 37b	NGPP
043	1952-54	**Police Motorcycle Patrol**	Post-war reissue for US market of 42b	NGPP
044	1952-54	**R.A.C. Motorcycle Patrol**	Post-war reissue for US market of 43b	NGPP
045	1952-54	**A.A. Motorcycle Patrol**	Post-war reissue for US market of 44b	NGPP
14z	1938-40	**'Triporteur'**	Three-wheel delivery van with Green, Red, Grey, Blue or Yellow body, Black hubs, White tyres, rider is always a different colour from van, French model	£200-300
37a	1937-40	**Civilian Motor Cyclist**	Black motor cycle with Silver engine/exhaust detail, Blue, Maroon, Green or Black rider, SWRW or thick SBRW	£40-50
	1946-49		Black motor cycle without Silver detail, Green or Grey rider, thin SBRW	£40-50
37a	1950-54		Black motor cycle without Silver detail, Green or Grey rider, thin SBRW, export only (renumbered 041)	£40-50
37b	1937-40	**Police Motor Cyclist**	Black motor cycle with Silver engine/exhaust detail, Dark Blue rider, SWRW or thick SBRW	£75-85
	1946-49		Black motor cycle without Silver engine/exhaust detail, Dark Blue rider, thick SBRW	£40-50
37b	1950-54		As previous model, export only (renumbered 042)	£40-50
37c	1937-39	**Signals Despatch Rider**	Green motor cycle, Silver engine/exhaust detail, Khaki rider, SWRW or thick SBRW	£125-175
42b	1935-40	**Police Motorcycle Patrol**	Black motor cycle, Silver engine/exhaust detail, Dark Green/Black sidecar, Dark Blue figures, SWRW or thick SBRW	£75-95
	1946-49		As previous model but without Silver detailing and with thin SBRW	£45-55
42b	1950-55		Blue/Green, Blue figures, little detailing, SBRW, export only (renumbered 043)	£40-50
43b	1935-40	**R.A.C. Motorcycle Patrol**	Blue/Black motor cycle/sidecar, Silver engine/exhaust detail, Blue/Black rider with Red sash, SWRW or thick SBRW	£75-95
	1946-49		As previous model but no Silver detailing, thin SBRW. **NB** - two shades of Blue used post-war	£45-55
44b	1935-40	**A.A. Motorcycle Patrol**	Black/Yellow, Brown rider, more detailing, 5mm 'AA' badge, SWRW	£100-125
	1946-50		Black/Yellow, Tan rider, little detailing, 7mm 'AA' badge, SBRW (renumbered 270)	£50-60
	1950-55		As previous model but made for export only (renumbered 045)	£50-60
270	1959-62	**A.A. Motorcycle Patrol** (renumbered from 44b)	Black/Yellow, Tan rider, 'AA' sign, solid Grey plastic wheels	£40-50
			Black/Yellow, Tan rider, 'AA' sign, solid knobbly Black plastic wheels	£100-150
271	1959-62	**T.S. Motorcycle Patrol**	Yellow motorcycle combination, Belgian equivalent of the A.A.	£150-200
272	1959-62	**A.N.W.B. Motorcycle Patrol**	Yellow motorcycle combination, Dutch equivalent of the A.A.	£250-300

Photo: Vectis Auctions Ltd.

Dinky Toys Military Vehicles

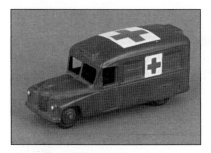

624 US issue
Daimler Military Ambulance

625 US issue
Austin Covered Wagon

640 US issue
Bedford Military Truck

Pre-war 161 Mobile Anti-Aircraft Unit
plus 603 12 Army Personnel (seated)

667 Missile Servicing Platform

620 Berliet Missile Launcher

651 Centurion Tank and
689 Medium Artillery Tractor

674 'UN' Austin Champ

660 Tank Transporter

675 US issue
Army Staff Car

669 US issue
Army Jeep (unboxed)

699 Military Vehicles Gift Set No.1

The photographs above are of Dinky Toys sold by Vectis Auctions Ltd., and are used by their kind permission.

Dinky Toys Military models

See also Action Kits, Aircraft, Ships, Gift Sets

Identification
Models issued **1933 - 1940**:.....Gloss or Matt Green or Camouflage finish with smooth diecast wheel hubs on thin axles.
Models issued **circa 1946**:.......Matt Green finish with smooth hubs and early tyres (black smooth, or thick black treaded, or thin white tyres).
Models issued **1947 - 1949**:....Matt Green finish with ridged hubs.
Models issued **circa 1950**:.......Finished in a glossy Olive Drab with ridged diecast hubs and black thin treaded tyres.

Ref	Year(s)	Model name	Colours, features, details	Market Price Range
1	1954-55	**Military Vehicles (1) Set**	See 'Gift Sets' section.	
22f	1933-34	**Army Tank**	'Modelled Miniature' with 'HORNBY SERIES' cast-in.	
			Green lead body, Orange revolving turret, Red, White or Green rubber tracks	**£250-350**
	1935-40		Green/Orange lead body, 'DINKY TOYS' cast-in, Red or Green tracks	**£250-300**
			Khaki lead body, 'DINKY TOYS' cast-in, Green tracks	**£250-300**
			Grey drab lead body, 'DINKY TOYS' cast-in, Red or Green tracks	**£250-300**
22s	1939-41	**Searchlight Lorry**	Green body, (22c casting)	**£250-300**
25b	19??-??	**Army Covered Wagon**	Military-Green body and hubs. South-African issue	**£1,200-1,500**
25wm	1952-54	**Bedford Military Truck**	Olive-Drab body, (made for export to the USA only) (renumbered 640)	**£200-250**
27m	1952-54	**Land Rover Trailer**	Olive-Drab body, (to accompany 25wm) (renumbered 341)	**£300-400**
28	19??-??	**Army Delivery Van**	Military-Green body and hubs, Type 3. South-African issue	**£750-1,000**
30hm	1950-54	**Daimler Military Ambulance**	Olive-Drab body, Red crosses on White backgrounds, (US issue) (renumbered 624)	**£200-250**
30sm	1952-54	**Austin Covered Wagon**	Olive-Drab body, made for export to USA only), (renumbered 625)	**£200-250**
37c	1937-41	**Signal Dispatch Rider**	Green body, Khaki rider, White or Black rubber wheels	**£150-175**
139am	1950-54	**US Army Staff Car**	Ford Fordor in Olive drab with White stars on roof and doors, (renumbered 170m)	**£175-250**
		....................Canadian issue:	As previous model but without stars	NGPP
150	1937-41	**Royal Tank Corps Set**	See Gift Sets section.	
	1952-55	**Royal Tank Corps Set**	See Gift Sets section.	
150a	1937-41	**Royal Tank Corps Officer**	Khaki uniformed figure with Black beret, and binoculars in hand (also in Set 150). Renumbered 600	**£25-30**
	1952-54		Khaki uniform; in 150 Set or in box of 12 x 150a	**£100-120**
150b	1938-41	**Royal Tank Corps Private**	Black overalls, seated. Box of 12	**£50-70**
	1952-54		Khaki uniform, seated; in 150 Set or in box of 12 x 150b, (renumbered 604)	**£100-120**
150c	1937-41	**Royal Tank Corps Private**	Die-cast figure in Black overalls, standing, (also in sets 151 and 152)	**£25-30**
150d	1937-41	**Royal Tank Corps Driver**	Die-cast figure in Black overalls, sitting, (also in sets 151 and 152)	**£25-30**
150e	1937-41	**Royal Tank Corps NCO**	Die-cast figure in Black uniform, walking, (also in set 150)	**£10-15**
151	1937-41	**Medium Tank Set**	See Gift Sets section.	
151a	1937-41	**Medium Tank**	Gloss or Matt-Green body/base, White markings, chain tracks, aerial	**£125-150**
			As previous model but with Black rubber wheels instead of tracks	NGPP
	1947-49		(Matt) Green body, Black base, no markings, made for export only	**£150-200**
151b	1937-41	**6-wheel Covered Wagon**	Gloss Olive-Green body, tinplate canopy, seat holes, spare wheel	**£150-200**
	1937-41	....................Lead issue:	Gloss Olive-Green body, Black ribbed tyres	**£150-200**
	1940		Camouflage body	**£150-200**
	1946		Matt Olive-Green with smooth hubs and early tyres	**£150-200**
	1947-49		Matt Olive-Green with ridged hubs	**£150-200**
	1950-54		Gloss Olive-Green, no seat holes, smooth tyres	**£150-200**
	1950-54		Matt-Green or Greenish-Brown body, 'Export only' from 1950 (renumbered 620)	**£200-250**
151c	1937-48	**Cooker Trailer**	Gloss or Matt-Green trailer, wire stand, hole in seat but no figure	**£50-70**
		NB	Two styles of baseplate lettering are known for 151c.	
151d	1937-48	**Water Tank Trailer**	Gloss Green	**£50-70**
152	1937-41	**Light Tank Set**	See Gift Sets section.	
152a	1937-41	**Light Tank**	Gloss or Matt Olive-Green body/base, White markings, chain tracks, aerial	**£100-150**
			As previous model but with Black rubber wheels instead of tracks	**£125-175**
	1947-50		Matt Olive-Green body, Black base, no markings, chain tracks, aerial	**£150-200**
	1950-54		Gloss Olive-Green body, Black base, no markings, made for export only (renumbered 650)	**£150-200**
			Mid (Chocolate) Brown variation	NGPP
152b	1937-41	**Reconnaissance Car**	Gloss Olive-Green body/base, six wheels	**£100-150**
	1946		Matt Olive-Green with smooth hubs and early tyres	**£150-200**
	1947-49		Matt Olive-Green with ridged hubs	**£125-175**
	1950-54		Gloss Olive-Green body, Black base, made for export only (renumbered 671)	**£125-175**
152c	1937-41	**Austin Seven**	Matt Green body, wire windscreen frame, hole in seat	**£125-150**
	1937-41	....................Camouflage issue:	Matt Green body	**£100-125**
	1940-41	....................Lead issue:	Matt Green body	**£100-150**
153a	1946-47	**Jeep**	Gloss Dark Green, US White star on flat bonnet and left rear side, smooth hubs, solid steering wheel, no round hole in base	**£150-200**
	1947		As previous model but with open spoked steering wheel	**£60-75**
			As previous model but with Brown body	**£150-200**
	1948-52		Matt or Gloss Green body, raised 'domed' bonnet, round hole in base	**£60-75**
	1952-54		Matt Olive-Green body, some have rounded axle ends, US export only (renumbered 672)	**£150-200**
160	1939-41	**Royal Artillery Personnel Set**	See Gift Sets section.	
160a	1939-41	**Royal Artillery NCO**	Khaki uniform; part of 160 Set	**£20-30**
160b	1939-54	**Royal Artillery Gunner**	Khaki uniform, seated, hands on knees; part of 160 Set, (renumbered 608)	**£20-30**
	1952-55	....................US only issue:	Khaki uniform, seated, hands on knees, Green box of 12	**£150-200**
160c	1939-41	**Royal Artillery Gunlayer**	Khaki uniform, seated, hands held out; part of 160 Set	**£20-30**
	1952-55	....................US only issue:	Khaki uniform, seated, hands held out, Green box of 12	**£150-200**
160d	1939-41	**Royal Artillery Gunner**	Khaki uniform, standing; part of 160 Set	**£20-30**
	1952-55	....................US only issue:	Khaki uniform, standing, Green box of 12	**£150-200**

No.	Years	Name	Description	Price
161	1939-41	Mobile Anti-Aircraft Set	See Gift Sets section.	
161a	1939-41	Searchlight on Lorry	Gloss Green body, 151b casting plus diecast or lead searchlight	£200-250
161b	1939-41	Anti-Aircraft Gun on Trailer	Gloss Green, gun elevates, figure holes, cast drawbar and hook	£40-50
	1946-50		Matt Green or Dark Brown	£80-100
	1950-54		Glossy Olive-Green, US export issue (renumbered 690)	£125-175
162	1939-54	18-pounder Field Gun Set	See Gift Sets section.	
162a	1939-41	Light Dragon Tractor	Gloss Green body, holes in seats, chain tracks	£100-125
			As previous model but Black rubber wheels instead of tracks	£250-350
	1946-55		Matt Green body (holes in some), chain tracks	£100-150
162b	1939-41	Ammunition Trailer	Gloss Green body and baseplate, drawbar and hook	£20-25
	1946-55		Matt Green body, Black baseplate	£20-25
162c	1939-41	18 pounder Gun	Gloss Green body, drawbar cast-in, tinplate shield	£20-25
	1946-55	18 pounder Gun	Matt Green body and shield	£20-25
170m	1954-54	Ford US Army Staff Car	Ford Fordor Sedan in Matt Olive, US issue. (Renumbered from 139am; renumbered to 675)	£200-250
	NB		See also 'Factory samples' listing at the end of this section.	
281	1973-76	Military Hovercraft	Olive-Drab body, Gunner, aerial, 'Army'	£25-35
341	1960	Land Rover Trailer	Olive-Drab body with drawbar and hook, (renumbered from 27m)	£300-400
600	1952-55	Royal Tank Corps Officer	US only re-issue (renumbered from 150)	£8-12
601	1966-76	Austin Paramoke	Olive-Drab, Tan hood, spun hubs, parachute	£40-50
	1976-78		Olive-Drab, Tan hood, Speedwheels	£30-40
602	1976-77	Armoured Command Car	Green or Blue-Green body with US star	£35-45
603	1957-68	Army Private (seated)	Diecast figure in Khaki uniform, Black beret, seated, box of 12	£40-50
	1968-71		Plastic figure in Khaki uniform, Black beret, seated, box of 12	£40-50
603a	1957-68	Army Personnel Set	Six diecast figures (Khaki uniforms, Black berets, seated)	£20-30
	1968-71		Six plastic figures (Khaki uniforms, Black berets, seated)	£20-30
604	1954-60	Royal Tank Corps Private	Die-cast, Khaki uniform, sitting, export only (to USA), box of 12 (renumbered from 150b)	£50-70
604	1960-72	Army Personnel	Six army driver figures (Khaki uniforms)	£20-30
604	1976-77	Land Rover Bomb Disposal	Olive-Drab/Orange, 'Explosive Disposal', robot de-fuser	£55-65
608	1954-55	Royal Artillery Gunner	Khaki uniform, seated, hands on knees. (US export issue) (renumbered from 160b)	£10-15
609	1974-77	105 mm. Howitzer and Crew	Olive-Drab body, three soldiers, Green metal wheels or Grey plastic wheels, bubble-packed	£30-40
612	1973-80	Commando Jeep	Army-Green or Camouflage, driver, two guns, jerricans, aerial	£25-35
615	1968-77	US Jeep and 105 mm. Gun	Olive-Drab body with US Army markings, driver, display box with pull-out tray	£65-85
616	1968-77	AEC with Chieftain Tank	AEC articulated Transporter 'ARMY' with 683 Tank	£90-110
617	1967-77	VW KDF and 50 mm. Gun	Grey, German markings, Green metal or Grey plastic wheels, long display box or bubble-pack	£75-85
618	1976-80	AEC with Helicopter	AEC articulated Transporter 'RESCUE', 724 Helicopter and net	£90-110
619	1976-77	Bren Gun Carrier and AT Gun	Khaki, plastic tracks, figures, gun/shells, White '57' on red shield	£35-40
	NB		Two variations exist: (i) '2035703 4', (ii) 'T2272616' plus star.	
620	1954-55	6-wheel Covered Wagon	Matt-Green or Greenish-Brown body, blued axles, export only (to USA) (renumbered from 151b)	£200-250
620	1971-73	Berliet Missile Launcher	Military-Green launcher body with White/Red 'NORD R20' missile	£100-120
621	1954-60	3 ton Army Wagon	(Bedford 'RL') tin tilt, no windows, driver in some	£60-70
	1960-63	late issue:	(Bedford 'RL') tin tilt, with window glazing, driver in some	£60-70
622	1954-64	10 ton Army Truck	(Foden) Olive-Drab, driver, tin tilt, Supertoys box	£70-80
	1954-64		(Foden) Olive-Drab, driver, tin tilt, Dinky Toys striped box	£70-80
		late issue:	As previous model but in a Yellow lidded picture box	£200-300
622	1975-78	Bren Gun Carrier	Green body, White star, driver, passenger, plastic tracks	£20-30
623	1954-63	Army Covered Wagon	(Bedford 'QL') Military-Green body with or without driver	£35-45
624	1954-?	Daimler Military Ambulance	Olive-Drab body, Red crosses on White backgrounds, (US issue) (renumbered from 30hm)	£250-350
625	1952-54	Austin Covered Wagon	Olive-Drab body, made for export only (to USA) (renumbered from 30sm)	£250-350
625	1975-77	Six-pounder Gun	Green anti-tank gun	£15-20
626	1956-61	Military Ambulance (Fordson)	Olive-Drab, Red crosses cast-in, driver on some, no windows	£60-75
	1961-62		Olive-Drab, Red crosses cast-in, driver on some, with window glazing	£80-100
630	1973-78	Ferret Armoured Car	Olive-Drab body, plastic wheels, spare wheel	£15-20
640	1954-?	Bedford Military Truck	Olive-Drab body, made for export only (to the USA) (renumbered from 25wm)	£250-350
641	1954-61	Army 1 ton Cargo Truck	Olive-Drab, tin tilt, with or without driver, no windows	£35-40
	1961-62		As previous model but with window glazing, with or without driver	£40-50
642	1957-62	R.A.F. Pressure Refueller	RAF Blue, French roundel, with or without driver, Supertoys box	£100-130
	1957-62		RAF Blue, French roundel, with or without driver, Dinky Toys box	£110-140
643	1958-61	Army Water Tanker	Olive-Drab body, no windows, with or without driver	£30-35
	1961-64		Olive-Drab body with window glazing, with or without driver	£30-35
650	1954-55	Light Tank	Matt Green body, Black base, no markings, export only (to USA) (renumbered from 152a)	£100-125
651	1954-70	Centurion Tank	Matt or Gloss Olive-Drab body, metal rollers, rubber tracks, Supertoy. Blue/White box	£80-90
		Export issue:	Version housed in U.S. Gold 'see through' box	£150-175
		late issue:	Matt Green, plastic rollers, Yellow picture box with end flap	£130-160
654	1973-79	155 mm. Mobile Gun	Olive-Drab body with star, operable gun, plastic shells	£15-20
656	1975-79	88 mm. Gun	German Grey, fires plastic shells. Black metal or Black plastic gun supports	£15-20
660	1956-61	Tank Transporter	Thornycroft Mighty Antar, Matt Olive-Green, no windows, driver in some	£70-80
		rare early issue:	'DINKY TOYS' marked on base. In Yellow box overprinted 'Dinky Supertoys'	£100-150
	1961-64	late issue:	With window glazing, Yellow box with 2 packing pieces	£100-125
	1964	trailer change:	Late issue with 908 detachable trailer (with transformer locating tabs on upper deck)	£150-200
660a	1978-80	Anti-Aircraft Gun with Crew	Olive-Drab, 3 soldiers. (Bubble-packed model)	£15-20
661	1957-65	Recovery Tractor	Army Green, six diecast wheels, driver, operable crane, Supertoy, 1 packing piece	£80-100
			As previous model but with plastic wheels, in Yellow 'picture' box	£150-200
662	1975-77	88 mm. Gun with Crew	German Grey gun (656 without wheels), 3 crew, shells, bubble-packed	£15-20
665	1964-75	Honest John Missile Launcher	Military Green body, Black platform, Green plastic hubs. All-card box	£140-160
			Military Green body, Green platform, Green plastic hubs. 'Lift-off lid' box	£90-110
			Military Green body, Green platform, Green plastic hubs. Yellow/White 'end-flap' box or bubble-pack	£70-90

666	1959-64	**Missile Erector Vehicle and**		
		Corporal Missile Launcher	Olive-Drab body, metal erector gears, White missile with Black fins, 1 packing piece	£200-250
			Olive-Drab body, Black plastic erector gears, all-White missile, 1 packing piece	£125-150
667	1960-64	**Missile Servicing Platform**	Olive-Drab, windows, spare wheel, platform lifts, Supertoy, 1 PP	£125-150
667	1976-78	**Armoured Patrol Car**	Olive-Drab body, aerial, spare wheel	£15-20
668	1976-79	**Foden Army Truck**	Olive-Drab body, windows, plastic tilt and wheels	£25-35
669	1955-57	**U.S.A. Army Jeep**	Olive-Drab body with White star, (US issue in 'plain' box)	£200-300
670	1954-64	**Armoured Car**	Olive-Drab body, turret rotates, diecast wheels	£20-25
	1964-70		Olive-Drab body, turret rotates, plastic hubs	£20-25
671	1954-55	**Reconnaissance Car**	(Matt) Green body, Black base, made for export only (renumbered from 152b)	£125-175
672	1954-55	**US Army Jeep**	Matt Olive-Green body, some have rounded axle-ends, US export only (renumbered from 153a)	£150-200
673	1953-61	**Scout Car** (Daimler)	Olive-Drab body, squadron markings, holes for personnel	£15-20
674	1954-66	**Austin Champ**	Olive-Drab body, driver fixed in position, 3 holes for personnel, tinplate windscreen frame	£35-45
	1966-71		Military-Green body, driver, tinplate windscreen frame, plastic hubs	£20-25
674	1958-70	**'U.N.' Austin Champ**	White body, no holes for personnel, tinplate windscreen frame. Made for export only	£300-400
675	1954-59	**Ford US Army Staff Car**	Matt Olive body with cross-hatching cast inside roof, sheer-cut star transfers on doors,	
			White circled star on roof. US issue in 'plain' printed box. (renumbered from 170m)	£200-250
676	1955-62	**Armoured Personnel Carrier**	Olive-Drab, squadron markings, 6 wheels, revolving turret	£25-30
676a	1973-76	**Daimler Armoured Car**	Army-Green body, Speedwheels, 73 mm. (new version of 670)	£15-20
	1973-74	...French made version:	With camouflage net ('Made in England' on base)	NGPP
677	1957-62	**Armoured Command Vehicle**	Olive-Drab body, 6 wheels, (based on an A.E.C. vehicle)	£60-70
680	1972-78	**Ferret Armoured Car**	Sand or Army-Green, Speedwheels, spare wheel, bubble-packed	£10-15
681	1972-78	**DUKW Amphibious Vehicle**	RAF Blue or Army-Green body, Speedwheels, bubble-packed	£10-15
682	1972-78	**Stalwart Load Carrier**	Olive-Drab body, 6 Speedwheels, bubble-packed	£10-15
683	1972-80	**Chieftain Tank**	Olive-Drab body, Black plastic tracks, fires shells. End-flap 'window' box, polystyrene inner	£25-35
686	1957-71	**25-pounder Field Gun**	Olive-Drab, cast drawbar, (cast hubs, plastic from 1968)	£10-15
687	1957-67	**25-pounder Trailer**	Olive-Drab, cast drawbar, (cast hubs, plastic from 1968)	£10-15
687	1978-79	**Convoy Army Truck**	Green/Black body	£10-15
688	1957-61	**Field Artillery Tractor**	Olive-Drab, driver in some, no windows, cast hubs	£30-40
	1961-70		Olive-Drab, driver in some, windows, (plastic hubs from 1968)	£30-40
689	1957-65	**Medium Artillery Tractor**	Olive-Drab, driver in some, holes, 6 wheels, tin tilt, Supertoy	£80-100
			In Yellow picture box, with plastic driver and windows	£150-200
690	1954-55	**Anti-Aircraft Gun on Trailer**	Matt Green, made for export only (renumbered from 161b)	£80-100
690	1974-80	**Scorpion Tank**	Olive-Drab, Brown or Green camouflage net, working gun. End-flap 'hanging' box or bubble-packed	£15-20
691	1974-80	**Striker Anti-Tank**	Olive-Drab, plastic tracks, aerials, 5 firing rockets	£15-20
692	1955-62	**5.5 Medium Gun**	Olive-Drab body, twin cast drawbar	£15-20
692	1974-80	**Leopard Tank**	Grey with German markings, plastic tracks, bubble-packed	£40-50
693	1958-67	**7.2 inch Howitzer Gun**	Olive-Drab body, cast drawbar, elevating barrel	£30-40
694	1974-80	**Hanomag Tank Destroyer**	Grey, German markings, plastic tracks/wheels, bubble-packed	£40-50
696	1975-80	**Leopard Anti-Aircraft Tank**	Grey-Green, German markings, plastic tracks, bubble-packed	£40-50
698	1957-64	**Tank Transporter Set**	Mighty Antar plus Centurion Tank	GSP
699	1955-58	**Military Vehicles (1) Set**	See Gift Sets section.	
699	1975-77	**Leopard Recovery Tank**	Grey-Green, German markings, dozer blade/jib, aerial, bubble-packed	£40-50
815	1962-64	**Panhard Armoured Tank**	Military-Green with French flag, (French issue)	£75-100
816	1969-71	**Berliet Missile Launcher**	Military-Green body, (French issue)	£150-200
817	1962-64	**AMX 13-ton Tank**	Green body with French flag, (French issue)	£75-100
822	1962-64	**Half-Track M3**	Green body, rubber tracks, (French issue)	£75-100
884	1962-64	**Brockway Bridge Truck**	Military-Green, 10 wheels, bridge parts, inflatables. French issue	£200-250

**620 Berliet Missile Launcher
with 'Nord R20' Missile**

This model was made between
1971 and 1973.
Its pictorial end-flap box is
representative of many
from that period.

Photo: Swapmeet Publications

See also Gift Sets section.

Ref	Year(s)	Model name	Colours, features, details	Market Price Range
60a	1934-36	Imperial Airways Liner	Cast body, tinplate wings, 4 x 2-blade propellers. Various colours, in three different patterns:	
		(Armstrong-Whitworth Atalanta) 1:	'Sunray' main colour with contrasting radial stripes on wings: Silver/Blue, Gold/Blue, Yellow/Blue, Blue/Yellow, Red/Cream, Cream/Red, Cream/Green, White/Blue, White/Blue/Green.	
		2:	'Two-tone' main colour with contrasting tail and wingtips: Gold/Blue, Yellow/Blue, Cream/Green, Gold/Blue, Yellow/Blue, Cream/Green, Cream/Red.	
		3:	'Striped' main colour with contrasting chordwise stripes and tail: Cream/Green, White/Blue.	
			Other variations on these themes may exist, all without registration marks	£200-300
	1936-39	....	Blue, Pale Blue, Cream, Gold, Red, Silver or White; all with Black 'G-ABTI' marking....................	£200-300
	1939-41	....	Gold, Green or Silver, 'G-ABTI', 'Imperial Airways Liner' under wing, (reissued as 66a)...........	£200-300
60b	1934-36	De Havilland 'Leopard Moth'...	Cast fuselage, tinplate wings, single 2-blade propeller.	
			Green with Yellow tail and wingtips or Dark Blue/Orange, Silver/Green, Blue/Yellow, Blue/Red, Gold/Red, no markings, open windows	£100-150
	1936-39	....	All-over Light Green, Dark Green, Gold, Silver, Beige, Blue, Pale Blue or Red, 'G-ACPT', open windows	£100-150
	1939-39	....	As previous model, but with 'DH Leopard Moth' under wing. Green, Gold or Silver, 'G-ACPT'	£200-300
	1939-41	....	As previous model, but blank side windows. Green, Gold or Silver, 'G-ACPT', (reissued as 66b)	£200-300
60c	1934-36	Percival 'Gull' Monoplane	Cast fuselage, tinplate wings, large 2-blade propeller. Reissued as 60k.	
			Blue with Red tail and wingtips, Red/Blue, Buff/White, Buff/Blue, Buff/Red, Gold/Green, Red/White, Silver/Green, White/Green, White/Blue, open windows, no registration markings	£100-150
	1936-39	....	White, Red, Yellow, Light Blue, Blue, Silver, Buff, 'G-ADZO' in Black, open windows, (Silver version renumbered as 60k)	£100-150
	1939-39	....	As 1936-39 version above, but with underwing stamped 'PERCIVAL GULL'. White, Red, Silver, 'G-ADZO' in Black	£200-300
	1939-41	....	Same but blank or open side windows, 'Percival Gull' under wing, (reissued as 66c)	£200-300
60c	1936-36	'Lewis's' 'Amy Mollinson' Souvenir Issue.............................	Mid-Blue with Silver wings and a Blue 'G-ADZO' marking. Sold at Lewis's of Liverpool department store in special 'LEWIS' yellow box. (Renumbered 60k when sold in normal yellow box)	£400-500
60d	1934-36	Low Wing Monoplane................ (Vickers Jockey)	Cast body, tinplate wings, 2-blade propeller. Red with Cream tail and wingtips, Orange/Cream, Blue/Yellow, Silver/Red or Gold/Blue, no markings, no pilot	£100-150
	1936-41	....	Red, Orange, Blue, Gold, Silver, Black or Yellow, 'G-AVYP', pilot's head cast-in, (reissued as 66d)..........	£100-150
			Red with cream tail and wingtips, no pilot, with 'G-AVPY' marking	NGPP
			As previous but with pilot	NGPP
60e	1934-36	General 'Monospar'	Two-piece diecasting, 2 x 2-blade propellers.	
			Pale Blue with White tail and wingtips, Cream/Red, Gold/Red, Red/Cream, Salmon/Blue or Silver/Blue, no markings..	£100-150
	1936-41	....	Silver, Lilac or Gold, 'G-ABVP' in Black, (reissued as 66e)...................................	£100-150
			Same but with 'General Monospar', Cream, Gold, Lilac, Silver or Blue	£100-150
60f	1934-36	Cierva 'Autogiro'......................	Gold body with Blue rotors and trim, no pilot	£200-300
	1936-41	....	Gold body with Blue trim, unpainted rotors, pilot cast-in, (reissued as 66f)	£150-200
	1936-41	....	Red body with Cream trim, Cream or Silver rotors, pilot cast-in	£150-200
60g	1935-36	De Havilland 'Comet'	Cast fuselage and wings, enclosed wheels, 2 x 2-blade propellers.	
			Silver, Red or Gold with Black registration 'G-ACSR' (no underwing description)	£100-125
	1936-41	....	Silver, Red or Gold with Black registration 'G-ACSR' ('DH COMET' underwing).................	£100-125
60g	1945-49	Light Racer (DH 'Comet')..........	Yellow, Red or Silver, 'G-RACE', 'Light Racer' under wing, 2 x 3-blade propellers	£175-225
60h	1936-36	'Singapore' Flying Boat	Cast fuselage (126 mm.), tinplate wings, 4 x 2-blade propellers (early hulls lead).	
			Fully-moulded bow, no roller, Silver with painted RAF roundels	£250-350
	1936-37	....	As previous model but with Red or Green plastic roller	£250-350
	1937-39	....	As previous model (with Red or Green plastic roller) and with 'Gliding Game' hole	£250-350
	1939-40	....	With Red or Green plastic roller, 'Gliding Game' hole and waterslide transfer RAF roundels	£250-350
	1940-40	....	Hollowed bow, wooden roller, no 'Gliding Game' hole, painted or transfer roundels..................	£250-350
	1940-41	....	As previous model, but in Pale Grey with transfer roundels	£250-350
	1941 ?	....	As previous model but with name under wing	£250-350
60k	1936-41	Percival 'Gull' (Amy Mollison).	Blue/Silver version of 60c, 'G-ADZO' in Blue, special box...............................	£300-400
60k	1936-41	Percival 'Gull' (H. L. Brook)	Blue/Silver version of 60c, 'G-ADZO' in Black, special box................................	£300-400
60k	1945-48	Light Tourer (Percival 'Gull') ..	Red, Silver or Dark or Light Green, 'Light Tourer' or 'Percival Tourer' under wing, no markings, small or large 2-blade propeller, (renumbered from 60c)	£150-200
60m	1936-41	Four Engined Flying Boat	Red, Pale Blue, Light Blue, Mid Blue, Dark Blue, Light Green, Mid-Green, Dark Green, Gold, Cream or Silver. 'Civilian' version of 60h with 'G-EUTC', 'G-EUTG', 'G-EVCU', 'G-EXCF', 'G-EXGF', 'G-EXFE', 'G-EYCE' or 'G-EYTV'	£175-225
		NB	With or without bow hollow, wood or plastic roller or gliding hole.	
60n	1937-40	Fairey 'Battle' Bomber	Silver or Grey, RAF roundels, 1 x 3-blade propeller, undercarriage................................	£90-120
	1938-41	....	Silver or Grey, RAF roundels, 1 x 3-blade propeller, without undercarriage, (reissued as 60s)..........	£120-150
		NB	Early issues did not have name of plane cast in.	
60p	1936-39	Gloster 'Gladiator'	Silver, stencilled roundels, Red 1 x 2-blade propeller, no name under wing	£100-140
	1939-41	....	Silver or Grey, transfer roundels, 'Gloster Gladiator' under wing	£100-140
60r	1937-40	Empire Flying Boat	Silver, 4 x 3-blade propellers, Red plastic roller, hole, own box. Liveries:	
			'CALEDONIA' ('G-ADHM'), 'CANOPUS' ('G-ADHL'), 'CORSAIR' ('G-ADVB'), 'CHALLENGER' ('G-ADVD'), 'CLIO' ('G-AETY'), 'CALYPSO' ('G-AEUA'), 'CENTURION' ('G-ADVE'), 'CAPELLA' ('G-ADUY'), 'CERES' ('G-AETX'), 'CALPURNIA' ('G-AETW'), 'CAMILLA' ('G-AEUB'), 'CORINNA' ('G-AEUC'), 'CAMBRIA' ('G-ADUV'), 'CHEVIOT' ('G-AEUG'), 'CORDELIA' ('G-AEUD').............	£250-350
	1940-49	....	As previous models but plastic, wood or brass roller, no hole. 'CALEDONIA', ('G-ADHM'), or 'CAMBRIA', ('G-ADUV'), (reissued as 60x)...................	£200-250
		NB	Camouflage issues: Early issues have Red/White/Blue roundels with a Yellow outer ring. The later (rarer) issues have a darker camouflage with just Blue/Red roundels.	

Ref	Year	Name	Description	Price
60s	1938-40	Medium Bomber	Camouflaged 60n with undercarriage, single roundel has Yellow ring, (reissue of 60n)	£100-150
60s	1940-41	Fairy 'Battle' Bomber	Camouflaged body, two Blue/Red roundels, no undercarriage, 1 x 3 PB	£150-200
	NB		Early issues did not have name of plane cast in.	
60t	1938-41	Douglas DC3 Air Liner	Silver, 'PH-ALI' 2 x 3-blade propellers, 'Gliding Game' hole, tail wheel on some, own box	£200-300
60v	1937-41	Armstrong Whitworth Bomber	Silver body, 'Gliding Game' hole in some, RAF roundels, 2 x 3-blade propellers, (reissued as 62t)	£200-300
60w	1938-40	Flying Boat 'Clipper III'	Silver body, 'USA NC16736', 4 x 3-blade propellers, plastic roller, 'Gliding Game' hole	£150-200
	(Sikorsky S32) US issue:		Silver body, 'NC 16736' markings, 'gliding' hole, Red plastic roller, leaflet	£250-350
60w	1945-48	Flying Boat	Silver, Blue or Green, no markings, 4 x 3 PB, brass roller	£150-200
60x	1937-41	Atlantic Flying Boat	Blue/Cream, 'DAUNTLESS' ('G-AZBP'), 4 x 3 PB, name under wing	£500-750
	(reissue of 60r)		Green/Cream, 'WHIRLWIND' ('G-AZBT)'	£500-750
			Black/White, 'DREADNOUGHT' ('G-AZBV')	£500-750
			Orange/Cream 'SWIFTSURE' ('G-AZBU') and Blue/Cream 'ENTERPRISE' ('G-AZBR') and Black/White 'ENDEAVOUR' ('G-AZBQ'), Red/Cream 'VALORIUS' ('G-AZBS')	£500-750
62a	1939-41	Vickers-Supermarine 'Spitfire'.	Silver body (short nose), RAF roundels, 1 x 3-blade propeller	£100-130
	1940-41	'Meccano Spitfire Fund'	Model 62a in special souvenir box (at 2/6 each). Brass ring through fin allows use as badge or pendant. Proceeds went to Spitfire Fund.	
			Blue, Green, Grey, Magenta, Red, Yellow, or Camouflage	£500-750
			Chromium plated version (originally 10/6)	£1,000-1,200
62a	1945-49	'Spitfire'	Silver, (long nose, bubble cockpit) RAF roundels, 1 x 3-blade propeller	£100-150
62b	1939-41	Bristol 'Blenheim' Bomber	Silver body, RAF roundels, Red 2 x 3-blade propellers, name under wing	£100-150
62b	1945-49	Medium Bomber	Silver body, RAF roundels, Red 2 x 3-blade propellers, name under wing	£60-80
62d	1940-41	Bristol 'Blenheim' Bomber	62b in Camouflage/Black/White, RAF roundels, 2 x 3-blade propellers	£100-150
62e	1940-41	Vickers-Supermarine 'Spitfire'.	62a in Camouflage/Black/White, RAF roundels, 1 x 3-blade propeller	£100-150
62f	1939 ?	D.H. Flamingo Airliner	Not issued (some unofficial non-Meccano 'Flamingos' cast in white-metal may be found)	NPP
62g	1939-41	Boeing 'Flying Fortress'	Silver, 4 x 3-blade propellers, 'Gliding Game' hole, name under wing, 'U.S.A.A.C.'/stars, own box	£140-160
			Pale Grey version without 'Gliding Game' hole	NGPP
62g	1945-48	Long Range Bomber	Silver body, Red 4 x 3-blade propellers, no 'Gliding Game' hole, not boxed	£90-120
62h	1938-41	Hawker Hurricane Fighter	Camouflaged body, RAF roundels, 1 x 3-blade propeller, undercarriage on some	£100-130
62k	1938-41	The King's Aeroplane	Airspeed 'Envoy', Silver/Red/Blue, 'G-AEXX', 2 x 2-blade propellers, own box	£300-400
62m	1938-41	Airspeed 'Envoy' Monoplane	Red ('G-ABDA' or 'G-ACVJ'), Silver ('G-ACVI' or 'G-ADCB'), Blue ('G-ADAZ' or 'G-ADCA'), Pale Green ('GADCA' or 'G-AENA'), Mid-Green ('G-AENA'), Gold ('G-AMTC'), Yellow ('G-ACMJ', 'G-ACMT' or 'G-ACVJ')	£120-150
62m	1945-48	Light Transport Plane	Red, Yellow, Silver or Blue, 'G-ATMH', 2 x 2-blade propellers, name under wing	£100-125
62n	1938-41	Junkers 'Ju90' Air Liner	Silver, ('D-AALU', 'D-AIVI', 'D-AURE', or 'D-ADLH'), 4 x 3-blade propellers, own box	£250-350
62p	1938-41	'Ensign' Air Liner	Silver, Red 4 x 3-blade propellers, gliding hole in some, own box. Liveries: 'ENSIGN' ('G-ADSR'), 'ELSINORE' ('G-ADST'), 'EXPLORER' ('G-ADSV'), 'ECHO' ('G-ADTB'), 'ETTRICK' ('G-ADSX'), 'ELYSIAN' ('G-ADSZ')	£150-200
62p	1945-49	Armstrong Whitworth Air Liner	As previous casting but no 'Gliding Game' hole, name under wing, 4 x 3-blade propellers, no box, Silver, Blue, Green, with Silver or Grey/Green trim, 'EXPLORER' ('G-ADSV') or 'ECHO' ('G-ADTB')	£150-200
62r	1939-41	D.H. 'Albatross' Mail Liner	Silver, 'G-AEVV', 4 x 3-blade Red propellers, 'Gliding Game' hole, name under wing, own box	£300-400
62r	1945-49	Four Engined Liner	Grey, Light Blue (Red trim) or Silver (Red trim), no markings, no hole, not boxed	£100-130
			Grey, Fawn, Light Blue or Silver, 'G-ATPV', 4 x 3-blade Red propellers	£100-130
62s	1939-41	Hawker 'Hurricane' Fighter	Silver body, RAF roundels, with or without undercarriage, 1 x 2 or 3-blade propeller	£90-120
	1945-49		Silver body, RAF roundels, no undercarriage, 1 x 3-blade propeller	£60-70
62t	1939-41	Armstrong Whitley Bomber	Light Green/Brown camouflage, Yellow ring roundels, 2 x 3-blade propellers, box	£200-300
	(reissue of 60v)		Dark camouflage version, Yellow roundels	£200-300
			Dark camouflage, Red and Blue roundels	£200-300
62w	1939-41	'Frobisher' Class Air Liner	Silver (casting as 62r), 4 x 3-blade propellers, 'Gliding Game' hole, own box, 3 liveries: 'FROBISHER' ('G-AFDI'), 'FALCON' ('G-AFDJ'), 'FORTUNA' ('G-AFDK'), (renumbered 68b)	£250-350
62x	1939-41	British 40 Seat Airliner	Grey/Green, Red/Maroon, Two-tone Green, Two-tone Blue, Blue/Silver, Yellow/Maroon, 'G-AZCA', not boxed, with or without 'Gliding Game' hole, (renumbered 68a)	£200-250
62y	1939-40	Giant High Speed Monoplane	Blue/Brown, Silver/Cream, Olive/Green, Blue/Cream, Yellow/Maroon, Red/Maroon, Two-tone Blue or Two-tone Green, 'D-AZBK', 'Gliding Game' hole, not boxed	£300-400
	1945-49		Light/Dark Green, Grey/Green or Silver, no hole or box, 'G-ATBK'	£100-125
63	1939-41	Mayo Composite Aircraft	Models 63a (fitted with special tinplate clip) and 63b together in special box (see below)	£200-300
63a	1939-41	Flying Boat 'MAIA'	Silver, 'G-ADHK', 'Mayo Composite' under wing, own box	£100-150
63b	1939-41	Seaplane 'MERCURY'	Silver, 'G-ADHJ', 'Mercury Seaplane' under wing, 'Gliding Game' hole in some	£75-100
63b	1945-49	Seaplane	Silver, 'G-AVKW', no 'Gliding Game' hole, 'Seaplane' under wing	£90-120
	1952-57		Reissue of 63b Seaplane, same as previous model, (renumbered 700)	£90-120
66a	1940-41	Heavy Bomber	Camouflaged, RAF roundels, 4 x 2-blade propellers, no name under wing, (reissue of 60a)	£250-300
66b	1940-41	Dive Bomber Fighter	Camouflaged, RAF roundels, 1 x 2-blade propeller, (reissue of 60b)	£150-200
66c	1940-41	Two Seater Fighter	Camouflaged, RAF roundels, 1 x 2-blade propeller, (reissue of 60c)	£150-200
66d	1940-41	Torpedo Dive Bomber	Camouflaged, RAF roundels, 1 x 2-blade propeller, (reissue of 60d)	£150-200
66e	1940-41	Medium Bomber	Camouflaged, RAF roundels, 2 x 2-blade propellers, 'General Monospar' under, (reissue of 60e)	£150-200
66f	1940-41	Army Co-operation Autogiro	Silver body and blades, Red/White/Blue roundels, (reissue of 60f)	£150-200
67a	1940-41	Junkers Ju89 Heavy Bomber	Matt-Black with Light Blue underside, Red propellers, Silver cockpit area, Luftwaffe insignia, with or without 'Gliding Game' hole	£750-1,000
68a	1940-41	'Ensign' Air Liner	Camouflaged, RAF roundels, no 'Gliding Game' hole, 4 x 3-blade propellers	£150-200
68b	1940-41	'Frobisher' Class Air Liner	Light or Dark Camouflage, RAF roundels, 4 x 3-blade propellers, 'Gliding Game' hole in some, (renumbered from 62w)	£150-200
70a	1946-49	Avro 'York' Airliner	Silver body, 'G-AGJC', Red 4 x 3-blade propellers. Early version has Silver propeller pins, tinplate base and blued cockpit, (renumbered 704)	£125-150
70b	1946-49	Tempest II Fighter	Silver with blued canopy, Yellow band on fuselage roundels, pointed spinner, (renumbered 730)	£35-45
70c	1947-49	Viking Air Liner	Silver or Grey body, 'G-AGOL', Red 2 x 4-blade propellers, large pointed spinners, (reissued as 705)	£55-65

70d	1946-49	**Twin-Engined Fighter**	Silver body with blued canopy, (reissued as 731)..	**£35-45**
		variation:	As previous model but 'N' in 'MECCANO' is reversed	NGPP
70e	1946-49	**Gloster 'Meteor'**	Silver body with blued canopy, Black engine intakes, large roundels, (renumbered 732)...................	**£35-45**
70f	1947-49	**Lockheed 'Shooting Star'**	Silver body with blued canopy, Black air intakes, USAF star on port wing, (renumbered 733)...........	**£35-45**
700	1954-57	**Seaplane**...............................	Silver body with 'G-AVKW' marking, (renumbered from 63b)	**£75-100**
			Silver body, 'G-AVKW', no 'Gliding Game' hole, 'Seaplane' under wing	**£75-100**
700	1979	**Spitfire Mark II ('Jubilee')**........	Plated model on plinth, 1 x 3-blade propeller, 'Diamond Jubilee of the RAF', Blue card display box	**£150-175**
701	1947-49	**Short 'Shetland' Flying Boat**.....	Silver, 'G-AGVD', 4 x 4-blade Black propellers, first Supertoys aircraft, own box	**£600-800**
702	1954-55	**DH 'Comet' Jet Airliner 'BOAC'**	White/Blue body, Silver wings and tail, 'G-ALYV', Gold wheels, (renumbered 999)..................	**£110-130**
704	1954-59	**Avro 'York' Airliner**	Silver body, 'G-AGJC', 4 x 3-blade Red propellers, ('704' beneath wing), (renumbered from 70a).........	**£125-150**
705	1952-62	**'Viking' Air Liner**	Silver body with 'G-AGOL' marking, flat head spinners, (renumbered 70c)	**£60-75**
			Silver or Grey body, 'G-AGOL', 2 x 4-blade Red propellers	**£60-75**
706	1956-57	**Vickers 'Viscount' Airliner**	Silver/Blue/White, 'AIR FRANCE', 'F-BGNL', 4 x 4-blade Red propellers.........................	**£100-125**
708	1957-65	**Vickers 'Viscount' Airliner**	Silver/White or Metallic Grey/White, 'B.E.A.', 'G-AOJA'	**£100-125**
710	1965-76	**Beechcraft S35 'Bonanza'**........	Red/White, Bronze/Yellow, or Red/Blue/White body, 1 x 2-blade propeller	**£40-50**
		German Promotional:	Green/White, 'GLUCK MIT WICKULER' on towing pennant and box	**£400-500**
712	1972-77	**US Army T.42A**	Military Green (715), Beechcraft plus wing-tip tanks, 2 x 2-blade propellers.	**£60-75**
715	1956-62	**Bristol 173 Helicopter**	Turquoise body with Red stripe and Red rotors, 'G-AUXR'	**£40-50**
715	1968-76	**Beechcraft C55 'Baron'**	White/Yellow or Red/Yellow body, Yellow 2 x 2-blade propellers	**£40-50**
716	1957-62	**Westland Sikorsky S-51**	Red and Cream helicopter body, 2 x 3-blade rotors	**£40-50**
717	1970-75	**Boeing '737'**	White/Blue body, White or Blue engine pods, 'LUFTHANSA'	**£55-65**
718	1972-75	**Hawker 'Hurricane' Mk.IIc**.....	Camouflaged body, RAF roundels, Black 1 x 3-blade propeller, guns	**£65-75**
719	1969-77	**Spitfire Mk.II**	Camouflaged, RAF roundels, Black 1 x 3-blade propeller (battery-operated), (renumbered 741)........	**£55-70**
			Early issues in 'Battle of Britain' pictorial card box	**£50-60**
721	1969-80	**Junkers Ju87b Stuka**...............	Camouflage/Yellow, German markings, 1 x 3-blade propeller, cap-firing bomb	**£90-110**
			Early issues in 'Battle of Britain' pictorial card box	**£90-110**
722	1970-80	**Hawker 'Harrier'**	Metallic Blue/Olive Camouflage, RAF markings, pilot, aerial	**£65-80**
723	1970-73	**Hawker Siddeley HS 125**	Yellow/White/Blue or Metallic Blue/White, drop-down door/steps	**£35-45**
	1973-73	**Hawker Executive Jet**	Yellow/White/Blue. In bubble-pack with English and French text. Possibly a promotional sample	**£400-600**
724	1971-79	**'Sea King' Helicopter**	Metallic Blue/White, 5-blade rotors, with 'Apollo' space capsule	**£50-60**
			Early issues in card picture box with pictorial inner stand	**£40-50**
725	1972-77	**Royal Navy 'Phantom II'**.........	Dark Blue body, Black nose, roundels, decals in bubble-pack	**£80-90**
726	1972-74	**Messerschmitt Bf-109E**	Desert camouflage, 1 x 3 PB, decals in bubble-pack	**£150-200**
	1974-76		Grey/Green camouflage, Yellow wing-tips/nose, decals in bubble-pack	**£300-400**
727	1976-77	**U.S.A.F. Phantom F4 Mark II** ..	Brown/Olive camouflage, 2 missiles, 2 figures, (no transfers issued), US market	**£500-750**
728	1972-75	**R.A.F. 'Dominie'**	Metallic Blue and camouflage, roundels, retractable wheels, bubble-pack	**£40-50**
729	1974-76	**Multi-Role Combat Aircraft**.....	Grey/Camouflage, swing-wings, decals in bubble-pack	**£40-50**
730	1952-55	**Tempest II Fighter**	Same as 70b but without blued canopy and with flat spinner, (renumbered from 70b).............	**£30-40**
730	1972-76	**US Navy 'Phantom II'**.............	Grey/Red, 'NAVY', 'USS Saratoga', fires missiles, retractable wheels	**£80-90**
731	1952-55	**Twin-Engined Fighter**	Silver body, no blued canopy, (reissue of 70d)	**£25-35**
731	1973-76	**S.E.P.E.C.A.T. 'Jaguar'**	Metallic Blue and camouflage body, Orange pilot, opening cockpit	**£40-50**
732	1952-62	**Gloster 'Meteor'**	Silver body without blued canopy, small roundels, (reissue of 70e)	**£25-35**
			Shiny Silver body finish with large roundels	NGPP
732	1974-80	**Bell 'POLICE' Helicopter**	Orange/Blue/White or Red body, sign boards and cones	**£35-45**
732	1979	**'M.A.S.H.' Helicopter**	Green body with 'M.A.S.H.' stickers	NGPP
733	1952-62	**Lockheed 'Shooting Star'**	Silver body with blued canopy, (reissue of 70f)	**£25-35**
			Variant with 'in' of 'Made in England by Meccano Ltd' missing	NGPP
733	1973-76	**German 'Phantom II'**	Grey/Green camouflage body, 'Bundesluftwaffe', two white	
			missiles, instructions and transfers, (German/Austrian market)............................	**£200-300**
733	1976-77	**US F-4K 'Phantom II'**...............	Brown camouflage, retractable wheels, fires missiles, (US market only)	**£80-90**
734	1955-62	**Supermarine 'Swift'**	Grey/Green camouflaged body, RAF markings	**£30-40**
734	1975-78	**P47 'Thunderbolt'**	Metallic Silver/Black, Red 1 x 4-blade propeller, retractable wheels, 'U.S.A.F.'	**£150-200**
735	1956-66	**Gloster 'Javelin'**......................	Camouflaged 'delta-wing' body, RAF markings, smooth (later treaded) wheels.................	**£35-45**
736	1955-63	**Hawker 'Hunter'**	Camouflaged body, RAF markings	**£30-40**
736	1973-78	**Bundesmarine 'Sea King'**	Grey/Orange helicopter, German markings, decals in bubble-pack	**£25-35**
737	1959-68	**P.1B 'Lightning' Fighter**...........	Silver (metal wheels) or Metallic Grey (Black plastic wheels)	**£60-80**
738	1960-65	**DH 110 'Sea Vixen' Fighter**	Grey/White body, Black nose, RAF roundels, 'ROYAL NAVY'	**£60-80**
739	1975-78	**A6M5 'Zero Sen'**	Metallic Green/Black, Japanese markings, decals in bubble-pack	**£60-80**
741	1978-80	**Spitfire Mk.II**	Camouflaged body, (non-motorised version of 719)	**£60-80**
749 (992)	1955-56	**RAF Avro 'Vulcan' Bomber**	Silver body (aluminium), only 500 models were made (for Canadian market). 992 is the catalogue (and box) number, '749' is cast into the model, (renumbered 992) Two castings exist; one has pointed wingtips, the other more rounded....................	**£1,500-2,000**
997	1962-65	**Caravelle SE 210 Airliner**.........	Silver/White/Blue, 'AIR FRANCE', 'F-BGNY', metal or plastic wheels, Yellow lidded picture box with card support	**£100-150**
998	1959-64	**Bristol 'Britannia'**	Silver with 'CANADIAN PACIFIC' livery in Blue/White, 'CF-CZA' in Blue on wing, striped picture box with card support..	**£250-275**
	1964-65		As previous but with Silver-Grey wings. Yellow lidded picture box with card support.............	**£200-250**
999	1955-65	**DH 'Comet' Jet Airliner**	White body, Blue fin, Silver wings, 'G-ALYV', 'No. 999' cast in underwing, (reissue of 702)	**£100-125**
			As above, but registration 'G-ALYX'	**£100-125**
			As previous model but with Silver-Grey wings	**£100-125**

BOX TYPES: Many 1970-79 issues were 'vacuform' packed and these include model nos: 710,712, 715, 717, 718, 721 to 734 inclusive, plus 736 and 739.

Recommended reading:
'Dinky Toys Aeroplanes - A Collectors Guide and Checklist'. Contact D.C. Barratt, 230 Earlham Road, Norwich, Norfolk, NR2 3RH. (Tel: 01603-453650).

Ref	Year(s)	Model name	Colours, features, details	Market Price Range
16	1936-37	Silver Jubilee Set	Locomotive and two interlocking coaches, 'LNER' and '2590' cast-in, open windows, smooth hubs with White tyres, special box.	
			Silver loco and coaches, Grey, Mid-Blue, Dark Blue, Red or Orange trim	£200-250
			Silver loco and coaches with Dark Blue trim	£200-250
			Cream loco and coaches with Red trim	£250-275
			Blue loco and coaches with Dark Blue trim	£250-275
			Green loco and coaches with Dark Green trim	£250-275
16	1937-40	Streamlined Train Set	As previous models but with a change of name and box	£200-250
	1946-52		Blue/Black loco, 'LNER', Brown/Grey coaches, closed windows, Black tyres. Individually boxed in buff box with divisions and yellow label on end of lid.	£125-150
	1952-54	(renumbered 798)	As previous model but with 'BR' crest on tender	£100-125
16z	1935-40	Articulated Train	Two-tone Blue, or Gold/Red, or Cream with Red, Blue or Orange. French issue sold in UK	£200-250
17	1935-40	Passenger Train Set	Black/Maroon loco 17a, Maroon tender 17b, Maroon/Cream coaches 20a/20b	£200-300
			Black/Green loco 17a, Green tender 17b, 2 Green/Cream coaches 20a/20b	£200-300
			Lead and mazak set in 2nd type box with correct colour spot	£400-500
17a	1934-40	Locomotive	Black/Maroon or Black/Green, diecast cab/boiler, lead chassis	£100-125
17b	1934-40	Tender	Maroon or Green diecast body	£40-50
18	1935-40	Tank Goods Train Set	Green/Black loco (21a), and 3 Green/Black open wagons (21b)	£200-300
19	1935-40	Mixed Goods Train	Maroon/Black loco (21a), Green/Red open wagon (21b), Red/Blue 'SHELL' tanker wagon (21d), Yellow/Red/Green lumber wagon (21e)	£400-500
		rare box version:	Set in 3rd type pictorial landscape box	£800-1,000
20	1935-40	Tank Passenger Set	Green/Black loco (21a), 2 Brown/Green coaches (20a), Guard's van (20b)	£300-400
20a	1935-40	Coach	Brown/Cream or Green/White roof, diecast body, lead chassis	£40-60
20b	1935-40	Guard's Van	Brown/Cream or Green/White roof, diecast body, lead chassis	£40-60
21	1932-33	Hornby Train Set	Blue/Red loco (21a), Green open wagon (21b), Green/Blue crane wagon (21c), Red/Blue 'SHELL' tank wagon (21d), Yellow/Red/Green lumber wagon (21e), 'HORNBY SERIES' cast into lead body. Red card box.	£500-600
	1934-35	Modelled Miniatures Train Set	Contents as previous set, in Red card box	£400-500
21a	1932-34	Tank Locomotive	Red/Blue 0-6-0 tank loco, 'HORNBY SERIES' cast into lead body	£50-75
	1934-41		Maroon/Black or Green/Black, 'DINKY TOYS' cast into lead body	£50-75
21b	1932-34	Open Wagon	Green/Red, Green/Blue, Green/Black, Maroon/Black, 'HORNBY SERIES' cast into lead body	£40-50
	1934-41		Colours as previous model, 'DINKY TOYS' cast into lead body	£40-50
21c	1932-34	Crane Wagon	Green body, Blue chassis, 'HORNBY SERIES' cast-in, lead	NGPP
21d	1932-34	Tanker Wagon	Red tank, Blue or Black chassis, 'HORNBY SERIES' cast-in, lead	£35-45
	1934-41		Red tank, Blue or Black chassis, 'DINKY TOYS' cast-in, lead	£35-45
21e	1932-34	Lumber Wagon	Brown/Blue, Yellow/Red or Yellow/Black, 'HORNBY SERIES' in lead	£35-45
	1934-41		Brown/Blue, Yellow/Red or Yellow/Black, 'DINKY TOYS', lead	£35-45
26	1934-40	G.W.R. Rail Car	Early issues are lead, later issues are mazak, plastic rollers.	
			Cream roof, Brown, Green, Yellow or Red body	£100-125
			Green body with Red roof	£125-150
26z	1937-40	Diesel Road Car	Cream roof, Red, Green, Orange, Yellow or Blue body. (French)	£100-125
27	1934-38	Tram Car	Plastic or metal wheels, Red 'OVALTINE' or 'LIPTONS TEA' or no logo.	
			Red, Orange, Green, Yellow or Light or Dark Blue body, Cream upper windows and roof	£200-250
			Light Blue or Dark Blue body, Cream lower/upper windows and roof	£200-250
29	1934-38	Motor Bus	Plastic or metal wheels, no logo, or Silver or Red 'MARMITE'.	
	(renumbered 29a)		Blue, Green, Maroon, Yellow or Red body, Cream or Silver roof	£200-250
29b	1936-46	Streamlined Bus	Green, Orange or Red coach body, all with Cream wheel covers, Black or White tyres, smooth hubs	£100-125
			Two-tone Blue, Yellow/Orange, Red/Maroon, Two-tone Green, or Turquoise/Red, smooth Black hubs, open rear window	£100-125
	1946-47		Cream and Dark Blue, smooth hubs, open windows	£100-125
	1947-50		Grass Green/Light Green, Light Green/Dark Green, Grey/Blue or Two-tone Blue body, Black tyres on ridged hubs, filled-in rear window	£100-125
29c		Double Decker Bus	The different casting types are shown in the adjacent diagrams.	
	1938-40	'DUNLOP TYRES'	1st Type AEC/STL, cutaway wings, stairs cast-in, smooth hubs, White tyres, crimped axle ends. Advertisement in Black on Yellow rectangle.	
		regular issues:	Cream upper deck and roof with Red, Light Blue, Maroon, Green or Orange lower deck	£300-400
	1938	early Grey roof issues:	As previous but with Grey roof	£300-400
			Cream upper body, Grey roof, Mid-Green lower body, Black smooth hubs	£600-800
		late issue:	Dark Blue lower deck, Cream upper deck and roof	£300-400
	1938-40	without advertisements:	As above but without advertisements	£200-300
		Baseplates:	1st issue 'Made in England', 29 mm x 2 mm	
			2nd issue 'Made in England', 28 mm x 1.5 mm	
	1946	without advertisements:	1st type AEC/STL grille, cutaway wings, no staircase, six vertical inside body ribs, smooth Black hubs.	
		colours:	Green lower deck with Cream or Grey upper-deck, Green hubs	£150-200
			Red lower deck with Cream or Grey upper deck, Red hubs	£150-200
	1947-48	without advertisements:	As previous model but with post-war Black ridged hubs	£85-95
			As previous model but with Two-tone Green body	£160-190
	1948-49	without advertisements:	3rd type, Leyland or AEC grille, straight-across wings, Black ridged hubs. Early issues had 6 vertical inside body ribs, later issues had 5 (3 on n/s, 2 on o/s)	
		colours:	Red or Green lower deck, Cream upper deck	£90-110
	1949-53	without advertisements:	2nd type, AEC/Regent grille, straight-across wings, lengthwise chassis strengthener with hole in chassis centre, or (1952) eight vertical inside body ribs, ridged hubs, plus in (1953) '29c' cast in chassis.	
		colours:	Red or Green lower deck, Cream or White upper deck, hubs match the lower deck colour	£90-110

29c	54-54	**'DUNLOP'**................................. (renumbered 290)	3rd type Leyland Titan grille and straight across wings, early issues have recessed stop lights, late issues (1959) protrude. Logo 'DUNLOP -The World's Master Tyre' in Black and Red. Sloping and upright designs exist.	
		colours:	Red or Green lower deck, Cream upper deck, hubs match lower deck colour................................	£80-100
29dz	39-40	**Autobus**....................................	Green or White body, metal wheels, (French issue sold in UK)	£80-90
29e	48-52	**Single Deck Bus**	Mid-Blue body, Dark Blue flashes, Black hubs................................	£80-90
			Mid-Blue body and hubs, Dark Blue flashes................................	£90-110
			Cream body and hubs, Red flashes................................	£60-80
			Cream body, Blue flashes, Blue or Black hubs................................	£60-80
			Light Green body, Dark Green flashes, Black hubs................................	£80-90
			Light Green body and hubs, Dark Green flashes................................	£140-160
29f	50-54	**Observation Coach** .... (renumbered 280)	Grey body and hubs, Red flashes and hubs................................	£70-80
			Cream body and hubs, Red flashes, Red or Maroon hubs................................	£80-90
29g	51-54	**Luxury Coach** .... (renumbered 281)	Maroon, Cream flashes and hubs................................	£65-75
			Orange body with Cream flashes and hubs................................	£80-100
			Fawn body with Orange flashes, Cream or Green hubs	£80-100
			Fawn body with Cream flashes and hubs................................	£100-130
			Blue body with Cream flashes, Yellow hubs................................	£130-160
			Cream body with Blue flashes and hubs................................	£80-100
			Cream body with Red flashes and hubs................................	£100-130
			Cream body, Orange flashes, Green hubs................................	£100-130
	NB		Market Price Ranges for models 29f, g and h are based on their being unboxed as compared to prices for the boxed renumbered issues 280, 281 and 282.	
29h	52-54	**Duple Roadmaster Coach** .... (renumbered 282)	Dark Blue body, Light Blue hubs, Silver coachlines................................	£80-100
			Red body and hubs, Silver coachlines................................	£80-100
			Green lower body, Cream upper body and hubs................................	£150-200
	NB		Early issue had a flat roof underside. Later issues have a rib front to back.	
36g		**Taxi with Driver**	'TAXI' cast into Black roof, driver cast into chassis.	
	36-46	....	Grey, Dark Blue, Green, Maroon or Red body, Black roof, open rear window	£150-200
			Yellow body, Black roof, open rear window	£700-900
	47-50	....	Dark Blue, Green, Light Green, Red, Maroon or Brown body, Black roof on all, some open rear windows (usually filled-in)	£80-100
40h	1952-54	**Austin Taxi (FX3)**..........Chassis: (Renumbered 254)	Diecast chassis with cast-in driver and model number.	
			Yellow body and hubs, Black chassis ('40H'), interior and driver................................	£90-110
			Dark Blue body, Light Blue hubs, Black chassis ('40H'), interior and driver	£90-110
			Yellow body and hubs, Brown chassis ('40H'), interior and driver................................	£250-350
			Mid-Blue body, Light Blue hubs, Black chassis ('40H'), interior and driver	£400-600
067	59-64	**Austin Taxi** (FX3)	See ref. 067 in the 'Dublo Dinky' section.	
115	79-79	**United Biscuits Taxi**	Yellow/Blue/Black, casting as 120, promotional	£45-55
120	79-80	**Happy Cab**	White/Yellow/Blue, solid wheels, 'flower-power' stickers................................	£45-55

1st Type 1938-47
AEC/STL grille, large 'V' shape
Cutaway wings, smooth hubs
No model number on base

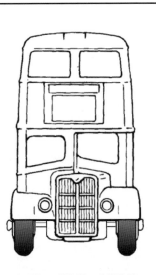

2nd Type 1949-53 and 1957-59
AEC/Regent grille, small 'V' shape
Straight across wings, ridged hubs
No model number or
'29c' cast into base

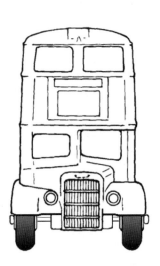

3rd Type 1948-49 and 1954-63
Leyland grille, undivided shape
Straight across wings, ridged hubs
'29c', '290' or '291' on base

241	77-77	**'SILVER JUBILEE TAXI'**	Silver body and hubs, Union Jack on bootlid, 284 casting	£30-35
254	1956-59	**Austin Taxi** (FX3)	Dark Blue body, Mid-Blue hubs	£125-150
			Dark Blue body, Light Blue hubs	£500-750
		Two-tone:	Yellow upper body and hubs, Dark Green lower body, Black chassis ('254'), interior and driver	£100-125
		Spun hubs:	Black body, spun hubs, Grey chassis ('254'), interior and driver	£110-130
265	60-64	**Plymouth U.S.A. Taxi**	Yellow/Red, '25c First 1/5 Mile, 5c Additional', windows	£80-90
266	60-66	**Plymouth Canadian Taxi**	Yellow/Red body with 'Taxi' and '450 Metro Cab'	£100-125
268	62-67	**Renault Dauphine Mini Cab**	Red body with 'Meccano', 'Kenwood', and 'Britax Safety Belts' adverts	£110-140
278	78-80	**Plymouth Yellow Cab**	Yellow body, 'Yellow Cab Co', plastic chassis and wheels	£20-30
280	54-60	**Observation Coach**	Grey body, Red flashes and hubs	£110-140
		(renumbered from 29f)	Cream body and hubs, Red flashes	£110-140
			Cream body, Red flashes, Red or Maroon hubs	£130-160
281	54-59	**Luxury Coach**	Cream body, Blue flashes and hubs	£125-150
		(renumbered from 29g)	Cream body, Red flashes and hubs	£175-225
			Cream body, Orange flashes, Green hubs	£200-250
			Cream body, Orange flashes, Cream hubs	£150-175
			Maroon body, Cream flashes and hubs	£90-120
			Mid-Blue body, Cream flashes, Yellow hubs	£200-250
			Fawn body, Orange flashes and hubs	£125-150
			Fawn body, Cream flashes and hubs	£125-150
		NB	Prices shown assume that models are in boxes with correct colour spot.	
282	54-60	**Duple Roadmaster Coach**	Dark Blue body, Light Blue hubs, Silver coachlines	£80-100
		(renumbered from 29h)	Red body and hubs, Silver coachlines	£80-100
			Light Blue body and hubs, Silver coachlines	£80-100
			Yellow body, Red coachlines and hubs	£125-150
		US issue:	Dark Green lower body, Cream upper body and hubs	£150-200
		US issue:	As previous model but with Red hubs	£150-200
282	1967-69	**Austin 1800 Taxi**	Blue/White body, Red/White 'TAXI' labels on doors and roof	£65-75
283	1956-63	**B.O.A.C. Coach**	Dark Blue/White, *British Overseas Airways Corporation*, White tyres after 1960	£125-150
283	1971-77	**Single Deck Bus**	Metallic Red body, Blue interior, 'RED ARROW'. Card box with instructions and packing	£40-50
			As previous model but in bubble pack with unused decal sheet	£35-45
			Metallic Red body, Yellow interior. Bubble pack	£45-55
		NB	Also available in kit form with 'GREEN LINE' decals. See 1023 in the Dinky Action Kits section.	
284	1972-79	**London Taxi** (FX4)	Black (or very Dark Blue) body, detailed boot on some, Speedwheels, driver, 'TAXI'	£30-40
289		**Routemaster Bus**	'London Transport', Route '221', 'KINGS CROSS', driver/conductor, cast hubs, spun hubs or Speedwheels.	
	1964-65	'TERN SHIRTS'	Red body, 'FOR 8am CRISPNESS' transfers	£80-100
	1966-69	'SSSCHWEPPES'	Red body, Blue-Green logo on White transfers, spun hubs	£80-100
	1969-80	'ESSO'	Red body, White label, 'ESSO SAFETY-GRIP TYRES'	£50-60
			Same as previous issue but with transfers	£100-150
		'ESSO' variant:	Deep Purple body, 'London Transport' and 'ESSO SAFETY-GRIP TYRES' logos, Blue driver and clippie	£300-400
	1968-68	'LONDON STORES'	Red body, Black/Gold logo 'Festival of London Stores', promotional	£100-150
	1970	'INGERSOLL RAND'	Red body, promotional	£100-125
	1974-74	'MECCANO'	Gold body, 'MECCANO - DINKY TOYS'. (Very few issued to Press only)	NGPP
	1977-79	'MADAME TUSSAUDS'	Red body, driver/conductor, White lower deck seating, Blue on White advert., cast wheels	£80-100
			Red body, driver/conductor, Dark Blue lower deck seating, White on Blue ad., plastic wheels	£80-100
			Red body, with figures, packed in 'SCHWEPPES' picture box	£100-120
	1977-77	'WOOLWORTHS'	Silver body, (Silver Jubilee limited issue) figures in some	£25-30
	1977-77	'EVER READY'	Silver body, (New Zealand Silver Jubilee issue) no figures	NGPP
	1979	'THOLLENBEEK & FILS'	Gold body, Pale Blue upper deck interior, Darker Blue lower deck interior, 'Thollenbeek 1929-79', Belgian promo	£80-90
		'FORDATH'	Red body, Light Blue upper deck seating, Deep Blue lower deck seating. Issued in plain White box with 'WITH THE COMPLIMENTS OF FORDATH LIMITED' labels to box ends. Promotional	£175-225
	1979	'GREENLINE JUBILEE'	All-Green body, 'GREENLINE GOLDEN JUBILEE'	£70-80
		'VISIT BLACKPOOL ZOO'	Cream body, plastic wheels, 'BLACKPOOL TRANSPORT' promotional	£90-110
	19??	'NEW ZEALAND CLUB'	Red body, Blue/White interior, 'CAR CLUB'S 10th ANNIVERSARY'	£90-110
290		**Double Decker Bus**	Type 2 (AEC grille), 'DUNLOP - The World's Master Tyre' advert may be	
		(renumbered from 29c)	upright or sloping, '290' cast on base, diecast hubs match lower deck.	
	1954-59	'DUNLOP'	Green lower deck, Cream upper deck	£80-100
			Red lower deck, Cream upper deck	£80-100
	1959-61	'DUNLOP'	Type 3 (Leyland grille), diecast hubs match lower deck colour, roof route box added, Mid Green or Dark Green lower deck, Cream upper deck	£100-125
			Red lower deck, Cream upper deck	£100-125
	1961-63		Same colours as previous with sloping lettering but with spun hubs	£125-150
	1963		Same body colours but with Green or Red plastic hubs	£175-200
	1963	'EXIDE BATTERIES'	Red or Green lower deck, Cream upper deck with '290' cast into base	NGPP
291		**London Bus**	Type 3 (Leyland grille) with route '73' on destination board.	
	1961-62	'EXIDE BATTERIES'	Red body with Red diecast hubs, logo in Black and Yellow	£125-150
		Factory error:	As previous model, but with 'CORPORATION TRANSPORT' transfers on sides, crimped axles	NGPP
		Promotional:	Red body and ridged hubs, White treaded tyres, no route number, Exide dealer promotional leaflet	NGPP
	1962-63		Same body colours as previous model but with spun aluminium hubs. Plain Yellow box	£150-175
	1963		Same body colours as previous but with Red plastic hubs. Box has alternating Red and Yellow panels	£175-225

291 - 293		**Atlantean City Bus**	A Leyland double-decker bus available in several versions:	
291	1974-77	'KENNINGS'	Orange body, White engine cover and interior, 'VAN & TRUCK HIRE'	£40-45
			As previous model but with Pale Blue engine cover and interior	£40-45
			As previous model but as seen with 'Yellow Pages' stickers	NGPP
			White body and lower deck interior, Pale Blue upper deck interior. Bubble pack	£40-50
			Light Blue body and interior. Bubble pack	£40-50
	1977	'LONDON & MANCHESTER ASSURANCE'	White model on plinth. 'Your Best Man For Life'. (500 issued to agents)	£400-500
292	1962-65	'RIBBLE'	Red and White body with or without 'REGENT' advertisement	£80-100
			Red and Cream body with 'CORPORATION TRANSPORT' fleetname	£80-100
			As previous model but no fleetname or logo	£80-100
292	1977	'LONDON COUNTRY'	Green body, shown in 1977 catalogue, but never issued.	
293	1963-65	'BP'	Green/Cream body, Yellow logo and smooth roof, 'BP IS THE KEY'	£80-100
			As previous model but ribbed roof	£100-120
293	1973-78	**Swiss Postal Bus 'PTT'**	Yellow body with Cream roof, clear or tinted windows, (296 casting)	£25-35
295	1963-69	**Atlas Kenebrake Bus**	Light Blue/Grey body, suspension, windows	£50-70
			As previous model but all Blue body, Red interior	£70-90
295	1973-74	**Atlantean Bus** 'YELLOW PAGES'	Yellow body, 'Let Your Fingers Do The Walking'	£40-50
295	1974-76		As previous model but deeper shade of Yellow	£40-50
			As previous model but finished in Silver, no front or rear destination blinds	NGPP
296	1972-75	**Duple Viceroy 37 Coach**	Metallic Blue body, clear or tinted windows, bubble-packed	£25-35
			As previous model but Yellow and Cream body (see also 293)	£30-40
297	1977-77	**Silver Jubilee Bus**	Leyland Atlantean (291) Silver/Black body, 'National'	£30-35
		'WOOLWORTHS'	Silver Jubilee Bus (Leyland Atlantean) Silver body, promotional	£30-35
784	1972-74	**Dinky Goods Train Set**	Blue loco 'GER', one Red Truck, one Yellow Truck	£30-40
798	1954-59	**Express Passenger Train Set** (renumbered from 16)	Green/Black loco, BR crest, Cream/Maroon coaches (Grey roofs), Black hubs/tyres	£125-150
			Green/Black loco, BR crest, Cream/Maroon coaches/roofs/hubs, Black tyres	£125-150
			Green/Black loco, BR crest, Cream/Maroon coaches/roofs, Red hubs, White tyres	£125-150
949	1961-66	**Wayne 'SCHOOL BUS'**	Deep Yellow body, Red body lines and interior, windows, Red plastic hubs. Supertoy	£160-190
			As previous model but with Black lines on sides	£100-125
952	1964-71	**Vega Major Luxury Coach**	Pale Grey body, Cream interior, Maroon side flash, cast hubs, flashing indicators	£80-100
			Off-White body, Deep Blue interior, Maroon side flash, flashing indicators	£80-100
			Late issues with Red interior, clear indicators, cast hubs	£70-90
953	1963-65	**Continental Touring Coach**	Pale Blue body, White roof, *Dinky Continental Tours*, Supertoy	£200-250
954	1972-77	**Vega Major Luxury Coach**	White body, Mid-Blue interior, Lemon-Yellow base, cast hubs	£70-90
			White body, Yellow interior, Black base, cast hubs	£90-110
			White body, Red interior, Black base, later cast hubs	£90-110
961	1973-77	**Vega Major Coach 'PTT'**	Orange body, Cream roof, Blue interior, 'P.T.T.' and emblem, Swiss model (in normal box)	£100-125
		Swiss Postal Bus variant:	Swiss box (Red/White/Yellow, 'Autocar Postal', 'Postauto', etc), plus label: 'Special contract run 1973 Swiss Post Office Bus'; also 'Specially boxed for Swiss Meccano Agent for sale under their name'	£200-250

Photo: Vectis Auctions Ltd.

'Dublo Dinky' models

'Dublo Dinky' models were made in a scale of 1:76. All their wheels are plastic: smooth wheels are fairly soft and treaded wheels are hard.

The late issues with black treaded wheels are rare and may attract a premium. These versions should all be housed in the later issue lighter yellow boxes.

Ref	Year(s)	Model name	Colours, features, details	Market Price Range
061	1958-59	Ford Prefect	Fawn or Grey body, Silver trim, Grey smooth wheels	**£50-60**
			As previous but with Grey wheels	**£65-75**
062	1958-60	Singer Roadster	Orange or Fawn body, Red interior, Grey smooth or knobbly wheels	**£75-85**
			Yellow body, Grey knobbly wheels	**£85-95**
063	1958-60	Commer Van	Blue body, Silver trim, Grey smooth or knobbly wheels	**£100-125**
064	1957-62	Austin Lorry	Green body, Black or Grey smooth or knobbly wheels	**£55-65**
065	1957-60	Morris Pick-up	Red body, Silver trim, Grey smooth or knobbly wheels	**£60-80**
066	1959-66	Bedford Flat Truck	Grey body, Silver trim, Grey smooth or knobbly wheels, hook on some	**£45-55**
067	1959-64	Austin 'TAXI'	Blue lower body, Cream upper body, Black or Grey knobbly wheels	**£65-75**
068	1959-64	'ROYAL MAIL' Morris Van	Red body, 'E II R' crest, Grey knobbly wheels	**£120-150**
			Red body, 'E II R' crest, Black knobbly wheels	**£80-100**
069	1959-64	Massey Harris Tractor	Blue body, Silver trim, Grey knobbly wheels, hole for driver	**£55-65**
			With Grey knobbly wheels on front and very Light Tan rear wheels	**£85-95**
070	1959-64	A.E.C. Mercury Tanker	Green cab (glazing in some), Red tank, Black or Grey knobbly wheels, 'SHELL-BP'	**£90-110**
071	1960-64	Volkswagen Delivery Van	Yellow body with Red 'HORNBY DUBLO' logo, Black or Grey knobbly wheels	**£60-70**
072	1959-64	Bedford Articulated Truck	Yellow cab, Red semi-trailer, Black or Grey smooth or knobbly wheels	**£50-60**
073	1960-64	Land Rover/Trailer/Horse	Green car (Grey or Black knobbly wheels), Tan or White horse. Trailers:	
			with Bright Green trailer (Green ramp, smooth Grey wheels)	**£100-125**
			with Green trailer (Brown ramp, knobbly Grey wheels)	**£100-125**
			with Bright Green trailer (Black ramp, knobbly Black wheels)	**£100-125**
			with Orange trailer (Black or Grey plastic wheels and ramp)	**£100-125**
076	1960-64	Lansing Bagnall Tractor & Trailer	Maroon tractor/trailer, Blue driver/seat, Black smooth or knobbly wheels	**£50-60**
078	1960-64	Lansing Bagnall Trailer	Maroon body, Black smooth or knobbly wheels, hook, wire drawbar	**£40-50**
-	c1959	Shop Display Stand	Pale Yellow with Red logo and wording 'NEW SERIES / DUBLO DINKY', etc. 28 x 19cm overall	**£300-500**

Photo: Vectis Auctions Ltd.

Ref	Year(s)	Model name	Colours, features, details	Market Price Range
50a	1934-41	Battle Cruiser 'HMS Hood'	Battleship Grey, (without name cast underneath 1939-41) 146 mm	£30-35
50b	1934-41	Battleship 'Nelson' Class	Battleship Grey, 'HMS Nelson' underneath (no name 1939-41) 117 mm	£30-35
50b	1934-41	Battleship 'Nelson' Class	Battleship Grey, 'HMS Rodney' underneath (no name 1939-41) 117 mm	£30-35
50c	1934-41	Cruiser 'HMS Effingham'	Battleship Grey, (without name cast underneath 1939-41) 100 mm	£30-35
50d	1934-41	Cruiser 'HMS York'	Battleship Grey, (without name cast underneath 1939-41) 98 mm	£30-35
50e	1934-41	Cruiser 'HMS Delhi'	Battleship Grey, (without name cast underneath 1939-41) 81 mm	£30-35
50f	1934-41	Destroyer 'Broke' Class	Battleship Grey, no wording underneath, 57 mm	£15-20
50g	1935-41	Submarine 'K' Class	Battleship Grey, wire mast, no wording underneath, 57 mm	£15-20
50h	1935-41	Destroyer 'Amazon' Class	Battleship Grey, no wording underneath, 52 mm	£15-20
50k	1935-41	Submarine 'X' Class	Battleship Grey, wire mast, no wording underneath, 61 mm	£15-20
51b	1934-40	Norddeutscher-Lloyd 'Europa'	Black hull, White superstructure, Brown funnels, name under, 165 mm	£35-45
51c	1934-40	Italia Line 'Rex'	Black hull, White decks, Red/White/Green funnels, name under, 152 mm	£35-45
51d	1934-40	CPR 'Empress of Britain'	Canadian Pacific Railway colours – White hull, Cream funnels, 130 mm	£30-35
51e	1935-40	P & O 'Strathaird'	White hull, Cream funnels, name underneath, 114 mm	£30-35
51f	1934-40	'Queen of Bermuda'	Furness-Withy Line, Grey/White hull, Red/Black funnels, 99 mm	£30-35
51g	1934-40	Cunard 'Britannic'	'White-Star' Liner, Black/White/Brown hull, Black/Tan funnels, 121 mm	£30-35
52	1934-35	Cunard White-Star Liner 'No. 534'	Black/White/Red, '534' cast underneath, boxed, no rollers, 175 mm	£70-80
			Same model but '534 Queen Mary' cast underneath	£60-75
52	1935-35	(renumbered 52b)	As previous model with 'Queen Mary' cast underneath, but without '534'	£60-75
52a	1935-41	Cunard White-Star Liner 'Queen Mary'	Black/White/Red, boxed, with plastic rollers, 175 mm	£60-75
	1946-49		Black/White/Red, boxed, with brass rollers	£60-75
52b	1935-36	Cunard 'Queen Mary'	Black/White/Red, boxed, without rollers, (renumbered from 52)	£60-75
52c	1935-40	'La Normandie'	Black/White, Red/Black funnels, boxed, made in France, pictorial insert	£60-75
52c	1939	Cunard 'Queen Elizabeth'	Announced in 1939 catalogue but never produced	NPP
52m	1936-40	Cunard 'Queen Mary'	Renumbered from 52b, without rollers, supplied unboxed	£20-30
53az	1938-39	Battleship 'Dunkerque'	Battleship Grey, with or without plastic rollers, boxed French issue	£40-60
281	1973-76	Military Hovercraft	Olive Drab body, Gunner, aerial, 'ARMY'	£25-30
290	1970-76	SRN-6 Hovercraft	Red or Metallic Red body, Blue or Black skirt	£20-25
671	1976-78	Mk.1 Corvette	White/Grey/Brown/Black plastic body, fires missiles	£20-25
672	1976-77	OSA-2 Missile Boat	Grey/Whit/Black, fires missiles	£20-25
673	1977-78	Submarine Chaser	Grey/White/Black, fires depth charges	£20-25
674	1977-78	Coastguard Missile Launch	White/Blue/Red/Yellow, 'Coastguard', fires missiles	£20-25
675	1973-77	Motor Patrol Boat	Grey hull with Cream/Black/Red	£20-25
678	1974-77	Air-Sea Rescue Launch	Grey/Black/Yellow, Orange dinghy, pilot/launch	£20-25
796	1960-62	Healey Sports Boat on Trailer	Mid-Green body, Cream hull, Orange cast trailer	£25-30
			Dark Green body, Deep Cream hull, Orange cast trailer	£25-30
			Red body, Deep Cream hull, Orange cast trailer	£50-65
			Yellow body, Cream hull, Orange cast trailer	£70-75
797	1966	Healey Sports Boat	Sold without trailer from trade box of 6. See entry above (796).	

Photo: Swapmeet Publications

Ref	Year(s)	Model name	Colours, features, details	Market Price Range

100 1967-75 **Lady Penelope's 'FAB 1'** .... (non-fluorescent) Pink body, clear or tinted sliding roof (Pink stripes on early issues), rockets/harpoons, Lady Penelope and Parker figures (TV series 'Thunderbirds').
With ridged cast wheels. Card picture box with pictorial inner stand **£200-250**
With ridged cast wheels. Supplied in a bubble pack **£175-225**
With Fluorescent Pink body **£250-350**
NB Rare White version reported (but not seen) sold at auction. Details welcomed, please.

101 1967-73 **Thunderbirds II and IV** .... Metallic Green (including loading door), Red thrusters, Yellow legs. Separate plastic Yellow/Red
Thunderbird IV model inside. Card box with pictorial inner stand **£225-275**
Metallic Green body, Black door, Red thrusters, Yellow legs. Bubble-packed **£175-225**
Metallic Sea-Blue body, Red thrusters, Yellow legs. Bubble-packed **£175-225**
Metallic Blue body and base, Red thrusters, Yellow legs. Bubble-packed **£125-150**
Metallic Blue body, Black base, Red thrusters, Yellow legs. Bubble-packed **£175-225**
Metallic Blue body, Yellow base, Red thrusters and legs. Bubble-packed **£175-225**
Metallic Blue body, White base, Red thrusters and legs. Bubble-packed **£125-150**
Bubble-packed issues: have card bases with Dark Blue sides and (usually) a Light Blue top. Rarer issues have a Yellow top.

102 1969-75 **Joe's Car** .... Metallic Green, driver, battery powered. (TV series 'Joe 90'). Card picture box, pictorial inner stand **£150-200**
NB Blue, Silver, Grey version reported (but not seen) sold at auction. Details welcomed, please.

103 1968-75 **Spectrum Patrol Car** .... TV series 'Captain Scarlet', shaped hubs, 'screaming motor', Red body with Yellow base,
Yellow or Cream plastic interior. Card picture box with pictorial inner stand **£125-150**
Metallic Red body with White base, Yellow or Cream plastic interior **£100-125**
Metallic Gold body, Blue tinted windows, Yellow or Cream interior **£150-175**
Pre-production prototype: Yellow body, Lemon interior, aerial, cast wheels, (resin body) **£400-500**
NB Metallic Blue and Silver versions reported (but not seen) sold at auction. Details welcomed, please.

104 1968-75 **Spectrum Pursuit Vehicle** .... Metallic Blue, Black base, Black or White front bumper, 'SPV'. Card box has inner pictorial stand **£150-175**
Metallic Blue body, Black base, White front bumper. Bubble-packed **£110-140**
Blue body, Light Green base, White front bumper. Bubble-packed **£110-140**
Blue body and base, White front bumper. Bubble-packed **£100-125**

105 1968-75 **Maximum Security Vehicle** .... White body, Red base, Red or Blue interior, 'RADIOACTIVE' crate, ('Captain Scarlet') **£150-175**
Late issue without Red body stripe **£150-175**
NB All issues should include a complete and unused decal sheet.
NB Grey version reported (but not seen) sold at auction. Details welcomed, please.

106 1967-70 **'The Prisoner' Mini-Moke** .... White body, Red/White canopy, 'bicycle' decal on bonnet, card box.
With Black windscreen frame **£250-300**
With Silver windscreen frame and Brown side panels **£200-250**

106 1974-77 **Thunderbirds II and IV** .... Metallic Blue body, Black metal base, Yellow legs. Vacuum-packed **£150-200**
Metallic Blue body, White plastic base, Yellow legs. **£150-200**
1977-79 .... Metallic Blue body, Black plastic base, Red legs **£150-200**

107 1967-68 **'Stripey the Magic Mini'** .... White/Red/Yellow/Blue stripes, with Candy, Andy and the Bearandas.
Card picture box with pictorial inner stand.. **£250-350**

108 1969-71 **Sam's Car** ('Joe 90') .... Card box with tray, pictorial backing, 'WIN' badge, instructions.
Chrome body, Lemon interior **£120-140**
Gold body, Lemon interior **£120-140**
1971-75 .... Pale (Powder) Blue body, Lemon interior, Red engine cover **£140-160**
Metallic Red body, Red or Silver trim, Lemon interior.. **£140-160**
Wine Red body, Lemon interior **£150-175**

109 1969-71 **Gabriel's Model 'T' Ford** .... Yellow/Black, (TV series 'The Secret Service'). Card picture box with pictorial inner stand **£75-85**
111 1976-78 **Cinderella's Coach** .... Pink/Gold, plastic figures and horses. ('The Slipper & The Rose') **£20-25**

112 1978-80 **Purdey's TR7** .... Yellow body, Black 'P' logo, Speedwheels. ('The New Avengers') **£55-65**
As previous model but with Yellow 'P' in Black logo on bonnet **£100-125**
As previous model but with Silver 'P' logo on bonnet.. **£35-45**
113 **John Steed's Jaguar XJC** .... Metallic Dark Blue, Gold pinstripes, rubbery 'Steed' inside. Officially not issued.................... **NGPP**

115 1979-79 **United Biscuits Taxi** .... Yellow/Blue/Black, casting as 120, promotional **£50-60**
120 1979-80 **Happy Cab** .... White/Yellow/Blue, solid wheels, 'flower-power' stickers **£50-60**

281 1968-70 **'PATHE NEWS' Camera Car** .. Black body, Red interior, cast wheels, cameraman with Brown trousers, camera and stand, (Fiat 2300) **£150-175**
As previous model but cameraman has Dark Grey trousers.. **£175-225**
350 1970-71 **Tiny's Mini Moke** .... Red body, White/Yellow striped top. ('The Enchanted House').. **£120-150**

351 1971-79 **U.F.O. Interceptor** .... From Gerry Anderson's TV series 'U.F.O.'. 'S.H.A.D.O.' labels on Light Metallic Green body.
Initially packed in card box with pictorial inner mount (prices 20% higher), later bubble-packed.
with Black missile holder, White missile, clear canopy, Red legs/skids **£150-175**
with Black missile holder, White missile, Blue canopy, Red legs/skids **£150-175**
with Red missile holder, Yellow missile, clear canopy, Orange legs/skids. Bubble packed only **£150-175**
with Red missile holder, Yellow missile, Blue canopy, Orange legs/skids. Bubble packed only **£150-175**

352	1971-75	Ed Straker's Car	Gold plated body, Blue interior, keyless motor, (TV series 'U.F.O.')	£80-100
			Yellow body, White interior, Black engine covers	£150-200
			Red body, Silver trim	£70-80
353	1971-79	'SHADO 2 Mobile'	Green body, White interior, Brown rollers, Silver tracks. Light Green base. All card box	£100-125
		(TV series 'U.F.O.')	Green body, White interior, Dark Green rollers, Black tracks. Bubble-packed	£100-125
			Green body, Yellow interior, Light Green rollers and base, Silver tracks	£100-125
			Metallic Blue body, White interior, Black base, rollers, tracks & roof. Window box, internal card base	£250-300
354	1972-77	Pink Panther	Pink car and Panther, flywheel drive, card endflap box	£35-45
	1977-79		Similar to previous model but without flywheel, bubble-packed	£35-45
			N.B. A single experimental Green diecast version exists (Christie's sale 4/95).	
355	1972-75	Lunar Roving Vehicle	Metallic Blue, White astronauts, front/rear steering	£35-45
357	1977-80	Klingon Battle Cruiser	Metallic Blue, fires 'photon torpedoes', (from 'Star Trek')	£45-55
358	1976-80	'USS Enterprise' ('NCC 1701')	White body, Yellow or White 'photon torpedoes', shuttlecraft	£60-70
359	1975-79	Eagle Transporter	White/Green body, Red rear and side thrusters, clear windows. (From 'Space 1999')	£100-125
			White/Green body, Chrome rear thrusters, Yellow side thrusters, Orange windows	£100-125
			White/Green body, Chrome rear thrusters, Yellow side thrusters, Red windows	£100-125
			White/Green body, Red rear thrusters, side thrusters and windows	£100-125
		NB	All issues should include a complete and unused decal sheet.	
360	1975-79	Eagle Freighter	White/Red, including rear and side thrusters, 'RADIOACTIVE' drums..(From 'Space 1999')	£100-125
			White/blue, Red rear and side thrusters	£100-125
		NB	All issues should include a complete and unused decal sheet.	
361	1978-80	Zygon War Chariot	Mid-Green body, two Red spacemen and rocket motor	£35-45
361	1978-80	Galactic War Chariot	Metallic Green body, two White/Yellow spacemen, Silver rocket motor	£35-45
		NB	Light Yellow-Green version reported (but not seen) sold at auction. Details welcomed, please.	
361	1978-80	Missile-firing War Chariot	Metallic Blue body, two Red spacemen/rocket motor, blister card	£35-45
362	1978-79	Trident Star Fighter	Black/Orange, fires rockets, drop-down stairway	£35-45
			Metallic Gold body. 500 only issued to guests at a special Meccano Dinner in 1979	£100-150
363	1979-79	Cosmic Interceptor	Metallic Silver/Blue, 2 pilots, Marks & Spencer model ('St.Michael' box)	£45-55
363	1979-80	Zygon Patroller	Metallic Silver/Blue, 2 pilots, ('368' in some catalogues, '363' on box)	£35-45
			Yellow/Red/Blue version in 'U.S.S. Enterprise' box	NGPP
364	1979	NASA Space Shuttle	White booster and shuttle, decals, instructions, plastic Orange satellite. Pictorial window box	£100-150
366	1979	Space Shuttle	unboxed version of 364 without booster, with plastic or cardboard load	£35-45
367	1979-80	Space Battle Cruiser	White/Red body, pilot, plastic weapons	£35-45
368	1979-79	Cosmic Cruiser	Blue body, Marks & Spencer model (in 'St.Michael' box)	£35-45
368	1979-80	Zygon Marauder	Red/White, 4 spacemen, ('363' in some catalogues, '368' on box)	£30-35
371	1980	Pocket-size 'USS Enterprise'	Small version of 358, bubble-packed, released after factory closure, (renumbered 801)	£45-55
372	1980	Pocket-size Klingon Cruiser	Small version of 357, bubble-packed, released after factory closure, (renumbered 802)	£45-55
477	1970-72	Parsley's Car	Green/Black/Yellow, head swivels, ('The Adventures of Parsley').	
			Card picture box with pictorial inner stand.	£80-90
485	1964-67	Santa Special Model 'T' Ford	Red/White body, Santa Claus, Xmas tree/toys/decals	£75-95
486	1965-69	'Dinky Beats' Morris Oxford	Pink/Green, 'Da gear', 3 beat-group figures	£75-95
602	1976-77	Armoured Command Car	Green or later Blue-Green body, White star, driver, scanner, fires sparks, (TV series 'The Investigator')	£35-45
801	1980	Pocket-size 'USS Enterprise'	Small version of 358, bubble-packed, released after factory closure, (renumbered from 371)	£45-55
802	1980	Pocket-size Klingon Cruiser	Small version of 357, bubble-packed, released after factory closure, (renumbered from 372)	£45-55

Dinky Toys Collector Information

Collectors of Dinky Toys may like to know of the following sources of further information.

DTCA – Dinky Toys Collectors Association

President David Cooke. Contact address: D.T.C.A., PO Box 60, Norwich, NR4 7WB, England.

Dinky News – Australia

Editor: Bruce Hoy. Contact address: PO Box 249 Aspley, Queensland 4034, Australia.
Tel/Fax: +61-7-3264-4227. E-mail: dinkynews@yahoo.com.au

Dinky Toys 'Action Kits'

These Action Kits were issued in the 1970s. Screws were usually included to attach their bases (which have no model numbers).
Paint supplied with the kit is not always the same colour or shade as on the relative model when supplied built and finished.

Ref	Year(s)	Model name	Colours, features, details	Market Price Range
1001	1971-77	Rolls-Royce Phantom V	Various colours (usually Blue), casting as 152	£30-35
1002	1971-75	Volvo 1800s Coupé	Yellow paint, 116 casting	£30-35
1003	1971-75	Volkswagen 1300	Red and White paint supplied, casting as 129	£30-35
1004	1971-77	Ford Escort Police Car	Blue and White paint, 'POLICE' transfers, casting as 270	£30-35
1006	1973-77	Ford Escort Mexico	Red paint and 'MEXICO' transfers, casting as model 168	£30-35
1007	1971-75	Jensen FF	Various colours of paint (usually Blue), casting as 188	£30-35
1008	1973-77	Mercedes-Benz 600	Red, Yellow or Green paint supplied, casting as model 128	£30-35
1009	1971-75	Lotus F1 Racing Car	Green paint and 'gold leaf'' transfers, casting as 225	£30-35
1012	1973-75	Ferrari 312-B2	Red paint and 'SHELL' transfers supplied, casting as 226	£30-35
1013		Matra Sports M530	Not issued	NPP
1014	1975-77	Beach Buggy	Blue paint, casting as 227	£20-30
1017	1971-77	Routemaster Bus	Red paint and 'ESSO Safety-Grip Tyres' transfers, 289 casting	£30-40
1018	1974-77	Leyland Atlantean Bus	Various (mostly White), usually 'NATIONAL' transfers, as 295	£30-40
?		Leyland Atlantean Bus	'YELLOW PAGES'. There are three variations of this:	
			1) With Mid-Blue interior, reversed front 'Yellow Pages'	£40-50
			2) White interior, reversed front 'Yellow Pages' sign	£40-50
			3) White interior, correct reading front 'Yellow Pages'	£40-50
1023	1972-77	A.E.C. Single Decker Bus	Green paint and 'GREEN LINE' transfers, casting as 283	£30-35
1025	1971-75	Ford Transit Van	Red paint and 'Avis Truck Rental' transfers supplied, casting as 407	£30-35
1027	1972-75	Lunar Roving Vehicle	Blue/White paint, casting as model 355	£30-35
1029	1971-77	Ford D800 Tipper Truck	Green or Yellow paint supplied, casting as model 438	£30-35
1030	1974-77	Land Rover Breakdown Truck	Red or White paint in kit, casting as 442	£30-35
1032	1975-77	Army Land Rover	Military-Green paint and various 'ARMY' transfers in kit, casting as 344	£30-35
1033	1971-77	U.S.A. Army Jeep	Military-Green paint and military transfers supplied, casting as 615	£30-35
1034	1975-77	Mobile Gun	Military-Green paint, 654 casting	£30-35
1035	1975-77	Striker Anti-Tank Vehicle	Military-Green paint and transfer supplied, casting as 691	£30-35
1036	1975-77	Leopard Tank	Military-Green paint and transfers supplied, casting as 692	£30-35
1037	1974-77	Chieftain Tank	Military-Green paint and transfers, casting as 683	£30-35
1038	1975-77	Scorpion Tank	Military-Green paint and transfers, casting as 690	£30-35
1039		Leopard Recovery Tank	Not issued	NPP
1040	1971-77	Sea King Helicopter	White with Blue or Orange paint plus 'USAF' transfers, casting as 724	£30-35
1041	1973-76	Hawker Hurricane Mk.IIc	Camouflage paints and RAF roundels in kit, casting as 718	£50-75
1042	1971-77	Spitfire Mk.II	Camouflage paints and RAF roundels in kit, casting as 719	£50-75
1043	1974-76	S.E.P.E.C.A.T. Plane	Blue and Green paints and transfers supplied, casting as 731	£40-60
1044	1972-75	Messerschmitt BF-109e	Brown paint and Luftwaffe transfers in kit, casting as 726	£80-100
1045	1975-76	Multi-Role Combat Aircraft	Camouflage paints and transfers supplied, casting as 729	£40-60
1050	1975-77	Motor Patrol Boat	Black/Blue/White paints and stickers, casting as model 675	£20-30

Collectors notes

Dinky Toys 124 'Holidays' Gift Set (1964-66), containing 952 Vega Luxury Coach, 137 Plymouth, 142 Jaguar and 796 Healey Sports Boat. A stepped insert holds the models in the closed box and helps to display them when open.

Dinky Toys 399 Massey-Harris Farm Tractor and Large Trailer (Produced between 1969 and 1973).

Photographs: Swapmeet Publications

BOX TYPES

Sets 001-006: Housed in Green card boxes with plain Yellow inserts.
Sets 1, 2, 3, 4, 5, 6: Oblong boxes with Yellow insert card and train picture on lid.
c 1932   Purple marbled 'Modelled Miniatures' box
c 1936   Blue patterned 'MECCANO DINKY TOYS' box, pictorial insert card
c 1939   Green box with plain insert, 'DINKY TOYS' label
1952-56   Green box with Yellow insert, stripe lid label
Train sets 17, 18, 19 and 20 box sequence:
'Modelled Miniatures' : 'Meccano Dinky Toys' : 'Dinky Toys'.

Sets 24, 25 and 30 series:
c 1934   Purple marbled 'Modelled Miniatures' box.
c 1935   Purple marbled 'MECCANO DINKY TOYS' box with
          Yellow/Red label picturing eight assorted cars and lorries.
          Purple insert with Gold script on two central lines
          'MECCANO DINKY TOYS No '24', '25' or '30'.
NB The 24 Series and 30 series sets also contained a purple packing
card stating 'PLEASE REMOVE THIS PACKING CARD
TO DISPLAY CONTENTS'.

c 1936   Blue patterned box lid with Yellow/Red label picturing eight
          assorted cars and lorries. Purple insert with no Gold Script on
          25 series (no details available on 24 and 30 series).

Sets 12, 42, 43, 44 and 49 (Pre-war issue):
Blue landscape boxes with inner Blue/Green pictorial inserts.

Sets 151, 152, 156, 161, 162:
Grey/Blue or Blue (152) display boxes with inner pictorial
scenic backdrop and packing boards.

Early Post-war USA Special Sets: Sets for the US market were distributed by
H. Hudson Dobson of New York. They are housed in flat boxes with a mottled
greenish-blue lid. The picture label on the lid depicts a boy's face plus line
drawings of various models. The lid often still retains a red 'H. Hudson Dobson'
label. The Set number and type are shown on the main label, e.g. 'No. 6
Commercial Vehicles'. Sets 1, 2, 3 and 6 are listed – the Editor would welcome
any new information on the contents of these, and of Sets 4 and 5.

Ref	Year(s)	Set name	Contents	Market Price Range
			Pre-war sets without 'fatigue' and with pristine boxes attract a premium, as do early Accessory Sets in 'Modelled Miniatures' boxes.	
001	1954-56	Station Staff ('0' gauge) (renumbered from 1)	(35mm). 1b Guard (flag in right hand), 1c Ticket Collector (right arm extended), 1d Driver, 1e Porter (with oblong bags), 1f Porter (standing)	£90-120
002	1954-56	Farmyard Animals (6)	2 x 2a horses, 2 x 2b cows, 1 x 2c pig, 1 x 2d sheep, simplified painting, (renumbered 2)	£200-300
003	1954-56	Passengers ('0' gauge) (renumbered from 3)	(35mm). 3a Woman (with child on left), 3b Businessman (Brown suit and case), 3c Male hiker (no stick), 3d Female hiker (Blue shirt), 3e Newsboy (Grey tray), 3f Woman (Light Red coat, round case)	£90-120
004	1954-56	Engineering Staff ('0' gauge) (renumbered 4)	(35mm). 2 x 4b Fitter (all-Blue and all-Brown), 4c Storekeeper (all-Brown), 4d Greaser, 4e Engine-Room attendant	£80-100
005	1954-56	Train and Hotel Staff ('0' gauge)	(35mm). 5a Conductor, 2 x 5b waiters, 2 x 5c Porter (both Brown or Blue), (renumbered from 5)	£90-120
006	1954-56	Shepherd Set	6a Shepherd (Green hat), 6b sheepdog (all-Black), 4 x 2b sheep, (renumbered from 6)	£200-300
007	1960-67	Petrol Pump Attendants	1 male (White overalls), 1 female (White coat), plastic, 35 mm. tall	£30-40
008	1961-67	Fire Station Personnel	Set of 6 fire-fighters in Blue uniforms plus hose, plastic, 35 mm. tall	£30-40
009	1962-66	Service Station Personnel	Set of 8 plastic figures in various colours and stances, 35 mm. tall	£30-40
010	1962-66	Road Maintenance Personnel	Set of 6 workmen using pick, barrow, shovels, drill etc, plus hut, brazier, barrier, and 4 lamps. Plastic, figures are 35 mm. tall	£60-70
050	1961-68	Railway Staff ('00' gauge)	12 Blue plastic figures in a clear plastic box. Early issues contained a Policeman, later ones a Shunter	£40-50
051	1954-59	Station Staff ('00' gauge)	6 plastic figures in a green card box (re-issue of pre-war Hornby-Dublo Set D1), (renumbered 1001)	£35-45
052	1961-69	Railway Passengers ('00')	11 plastic figures in a clear plastic box	£35-45
053	1954-59	Passengers ('00' gauge)	6 coloured plastic figures (re-issue of pre-war Hornby-Dublo Set D2), (renumbered 1003)	£35-45
054	1962-70	Railway Station Personnel	4 plastic figures plus 8 pieces of furniture in a clear plastic box, ('OO' gauge)	£35-45
1	1931-39	Station Staff (6) (large)	(40mm). 1a Station Master, 1b Guard (flag in left hand), 1c Ticket Collector (with open arms), 1d Driver, 1e Porter (round/oblong bags), 1f Porter (walking). 'HORNBY SERIES' (early issues), 'DINKY TOYS' (later)	£150-200
1	1939-41	Station Staff (6) (small)	(35mm). As previous but with smaller figures	£100-125
1	1939-41	Station Staff (6)	(35mm). 1a and 1d as above, 1b Guard (flag in right hand), 1c Ticket Collector (right arm extended), 1e Porter (oblong bags), 1f Porter (standing)	£150-200
1	1946-54	Station Staff (5) (renumbered 001)	(35mm). 1b Guard (flag in right hand), 1c Ticket Collector (right arm extended), 1d Driver, 1e Porter (with oblong bags), 1f Porter (standing)	£90-120
1	1954-55	Military Vehicles (1) Set (renumbered 699)	621 3-ton Wagon, 641 1-ton Truck, 674 Austin Champ, 676 Armoured Car. Blue/White box with Blue cut-out base plus packing piece on top	£300-400
No.1	1934-39	Railway Accessories Set	'Miniature Luggage and Truck'. A Porter's truck and 4 pieces of luggage (tinplate and cast), items not available separately	£100-125
No.1	1946-48	Commercial Vehicles Set	29c Bus, 25b Wagon, 25d Tanker, 25e Tipper and 25f Market Gardeners Lorry. In mottled Green, Blue and Fawn box with inner Green card cut-out base. Box lid has Light Green and Blue silhouette label	£2,000-2,500
No.1	1952-54	Farm Gear Gift Set (renumbered 398)	27a Massey-Harris Tractor, 27b Harvest Trailer, 27c Manure Spreader, 27h Disc Harrow, 27k Hay Rake. In Blue/White box with inner cut-out base plus packing piece on top	£1,000-1,500
2	1934-35	Farmyard Animals	2 x 2a horses, 2 x 2b cows, 1 x 2c pig, 1 x 2d sheep, in 'Modelled Miniatures' box	£750-1,000
2	1935-40	Farmyard Animals	Six items as previous set but displayed in 'Dinky Toys' box	£500-600
2	1946-54	Farmyard Animals	Six items as previous set but simplified (less detailed) painting, (renumbered 002)	£200-300
No.2	1934-?	Railway Accessories Set	'Milk Cans and Truck'. A 4-wheel barrow and 6 milk churns, not available separately	NGPP
No.2	1946-48	Private Automobiles Set	39a Packard, 39b Oldsmobile, 39c Lincoln, 39d Buick, 39e Chrysler. Inner Green card base in Green, Blue and Orange mottled box, Green and Blue silhouette lid label (export only issue)	£2,000-2,500
No.2	1952-53	Commercials Vehicles Set	25m Bedford End Tipper, 27d Land Rover (Dark Brown), 30n Farm Produce Wagon, 30p 'Mobilgas' Tanker, 30s Austin Covered Wagon. In Blue/White box with inner cut-out base plus packing piece on top	£2,000-2,500
3	1932-39	Railway Passengers (large)	(40mm). 3a Woman (with child on right), 3b Businessman (left hand on chest), 3c Male hiker (with stick), 3d Female hiker (White shirt), 3e Newsboy (running), 3f Woman (Red jacket, oblong case). 'HORNBY SERIES' (early issues), 'DINKY TOYS' (later)	£225-275
3	1932-39	Railway Passengers (small)	(35mm). As previous set but smaller figures. Oblong Green box with scenic background	£150-175
3	1939-41	Railway Passengers	3a Woman (with child on left), 3b Businessman (case in left hand), 3c Male hiker (no stick), 3d Female hiker (White shirt), 3e Newsboy (standing), 3f Woman (Red coat, round case)	£125-175

No.	Years	Name	Description	Price
3	1946-54	**Railway Passengers** (renumbered 003)	3a Woman (with child on left), 3b Businessman (Brown suit and case), 3c Male hiker (no stick), 3d Female hiker (with Blue shirt), 3e Newsboy (Grey tray), 3f Woman (Light Red coat, round case)	£90-120
No.3	1934-?	**Railway Accessories Set**	'Platform Machines Etc'. A posting box, ticket machine, label machine and two benches, not available separately	NGPP
No.3	1947-52	**Private Automobiles Set** (i) (export only issue)	30d Vauxhall, 36a Armstrong, 36b Bentley, 38a Frazer-Nash, 39b Oldsmobile. Inner Green card cut-out base in Green, Blue and Orange mottled box, Green and Blue silhouette lid label	£1,500-2,000
No.3	1947-52	**Private Automobiles Set** (ii) (export only issue)	30d Vauxhall, 36b Bentley, 36d Rover, 38a Fraser Nash, 38c Lagonda. Inner Green card cut-out base in Green, Blue and Orange mottled box, Green and Blue silhouette lid label	£2,500-3,000
No.3	1952-54	**Passenger Cars Set**	27f Estate Car, 30h Daimler Ambulance, 40e Standard Vanguard, 40g Morris Oxford, 40h Austin Taxi, 140b Rover 75. Blue/White box with cut-out tray plus packing piece on top	£3,000-4,000
4	1932-41	**Engineering Staff (6) (large)**	(40mm). 4a Electrician, 2 x 4b Fitter (Blue/White and Brown/White), 4c Storekeeper (Brown/Black), 4d Greaser, 4e Engine-Room attendant 'HORNBY SERIES' (early issues), 'DINKY TOYS' (later)	£150-200
4	1932-41	**Engineering Staff (6) (small)**	As previous set but smaller figures	£150-175
4	1946-54	**Engineering Staff (5)** (renumbered 004)	2 x 4b Fitter (all-Blue and all-Brown), 4c Storekeeper (all-Brown), 4d Greaser, 4e Engine-Room attendant	£125-175
No.4	1934-?	**Railway Accessories Set**	A combination of No.1 ('Miniature Luggage & Truck'), No.2 ('Milk Cans & Truck'), and No.3 ('Platform Machines Etc.'). Individual items were not available separately	NGPP
No.4	1953-54	**Racing Cars Set** (renumbered 249)	23f Alfa-Romeo, 23g Cooper-Bristol, 23h Ferrari, 23j HWM and 23n Maserati. Blue/White striped box with one packing piece	£750-1,000
No.4	1948-48	**Commercial Vehicles Set**	Contains 25d, 25f, 25w, 29c and 30e. Brown/Green box with silhouette lid label. (US export)	£2,000-2,500
5	1932-39	**Train and Hotel Staff (large)**	(40mm). 5a Conductor, 2 x 5b waiters, 2 x 5c Porter (1 Red, 1 Green), 'HORNBY SERIES' (early issues), 'DINKY TOYS' (later)	£300-350
	NB		Also sold in USA – boxes often display 'H. Hudson Dobson' label.	
5	1932-39	**Train and Hotel Staff (small)**	As previous set but smaller figures	£150-175
5	1939-41	**Train and Hotel Staff**	5a Conductor, 2 x 5b waiters, 2 x 5c Porter (both Brown or Blue)	£125-175
5	1946-54	**Train and Hotel Staff**	5a Conductor, 2 x 5b Waiter, 2 x 5c Porter (Brown or Blue) less detail, (renumbered 005)	£90-120
5	c1950	**Military Vehicles Set**	153a (672) US Army Jeep, 161b (690) Mobile AA Gun, 151a Medium Tank, 151b (620) Transport Wagon, and 152b (671) Reconnaissance Car. Green box, inner Green card base and card cut-out packing piece,. Blue, Light Green and Red mottled lid has Purple and Yellow label	£2,000-2,500
6	1934-36	**Shepherd Set**	6a Shepherd (Dark Brown smock, hat and leggings, Black boots, lamb under arm), 6b Collie dog (Black/White), 4 x 2b sheep (Beige, 'Hornby Series' cast-in), set presented in 'Modelled Miniatures' box	£500-750
6	1936-40	**Shepherd Set**	As previous set but in 'Dinky Toys' box	£250-350
6	1946-54	**Shepherd Set** (renumbered 006)	6a Shepherd (all Brown below neck, Green hat), 6b Collie dog (all Black), 4 x 2b sheep (without 'Hornby Series')	£150-200
No.6	1946-48	**Commercial Vehicles Set** (US export issue)	29c Bus, 29b Streamline Bus, 25h Fire Engine, 30e Breakdown Car and 30f Ambulance. Mottled Purple-Blue box with inner Purple cut-out card base, Yellow/Maroon silhouette lid label	£2,000-2,500
12	1937-41	**Postal Set**	12a GPO Pillar Box, 12b Air Mail Pillar Box, 12c Telephone Call Box, 12d Telegraph Messenger, 12e Postman, 34b Royal Mail Van. Blue box with Yellow insert	£500-600
13	1931-40	**'HALL'S DISTEMPER'**	Advertisement board. White figures (one with Green brush, the other with Blue brush). Box (A898)	£300-400
15	1937-41	**Railway Signals Set**	1 x 15a 'Home' and 1 x 15a 'Distant' (single-arm signals), 2 x 15b 'Home/Distant' (double-arm signals), 1 x 15c 'Home' and 1 x 15c 'Distant' (double-arm signals). Yellow box with Purple insert, 'DINKY TOYS' on lid	£150-175
16	1936-37	**Silver Jubilee Train Set**	Locomotive and two interlocking coaches, 'LNER' and '2590' cast-in, open windows, smooth hubs with White tyres, special box, 300 mm.	
			1: Silver loco / coaches, Grey, Mid-Blue, Dark Blue, Red or Orange trim	£200-250
			2: Silver loco and coaches with Dark Blue trim	£200-250
			3: Cream loco and coaches with Red trim	£250-275
			4: Blue loco and coaches with Dark Blue trim	£250-275
			5: Green loco and coaches with Dark Green trim	£250-275
16	1937-40	**Streamlined Train Set**	As previous models but with a change of name and box	£200-250
16	1946-52	**Streamlined Train Set**	Blue/Black loco, 'LNER', Brown/Grey coaches, solid windows, Black tyres	£125-150
16	1952-54	**Streamlined Train Set**	As previous model but with 'BR' crest on tender, (renumbered 798). Long portrait 'ladder' box with train picture	£125-145
17	1934-40	**Passenger Train Set**	Black/Maroon loco 17a, Maroon tender 17b, Maroon/Cream coaches 20a/20b. Long portrait 'ladder' box with train picture	£300-400
			Black/Green loco 17a, Green tender 17b, two Green/Cream coaches 20a/20b Long portrait 'ladder' box with train picture	£300-400
			Lead and Mazak set in 2nd type box with correct colour spot	£400-500
18	1934-40	**Tank Goods Train Set**	Green/Black loco (21a), and 3 Green/Black open wagons (21b). Long portrait 'ladder' box with train picture	£300-400
19	1935-40	**Mixed Goods Train**	Maroon/Black loco (21a), Green/Red open wagon (21b), Red/Blue 'SHELL' tanker wagon (21d), Yellow/Red/Green lumber wagon (21e). Long portrait 'ladder' box with train picture	£400-500
		rare box version:	Set in 3rd type pictorial landscape box	£800-1,000
20	1934-40	**Tank Passenger Set**	Green/Black loco (21a), 2 Brown/Green coaches (20a), Guard's van (20b)	£300-400
21	1932-33	**Hornby Train Set**	Blue/Red loco (21a), Green open wagon (21b), Green/Blue crane wagon (21c), Red/Blue 'SHELL' tank wagon (21d), Blue/Red/Black lumber wagon (21e). Contained in plain Red 'Hornby Series' box	£500-600
21	1934-35	**Modelled Miniatures Train Set**	As previous set, but in 'Modelled Miniatures' Red card box	£400-500
22	1933-35	**Motor Vehicles Set**	22a and 22b Cars, 22c Motor Truck, 22d Delivery Van, 22e Tractor, 22f Tank, with 'Hornby Series' or 'Dinky Toys' cast-in. 'Modelled Miniatures' box, Purple lid, full-size full-colour label with pictures of models	£2,000-2,500

23	1936-40	**Racing Cars Set**	Three models: 23c Mercedes-Benz, 23d Auto-Union, 23e 'Speed of the Wind'. Blue box (A2144)	£500-750
24	1934-40	**Motor Cars Set** .... 1st issue:	24a Ambulance, 24b Limousine, 24c Town Sedan, 24d Vogue Saloon, 24e Super Streamlined Saloon, 24f Sportsman's Coupé, 24g Sports Tourer (2 seater), 24h Sports Tourer (4 seater). Purple and Gold marbled box, lid has colour top label and Yellow/Red end label with code 'DT24'	£6,000-8,000
		later issue:	Blue box lid (with colour label), Purple inner (A2205)	£5,000-6,000
25	1934-37	**Commercial Motor Vehicles**	25a Wagon, 25b Covered Wagon, 25c Flat Truck, 25d Tank Wagon, 25e Tipper, 25f Market Gardener's Lorry. Mauve 'grained' box lid (colour label) (A1052)	£2,000-2,500
		revised set:	Contains 25b, d, e, f, g and h	£1,700-1,900
27ak	1952-54	**'MASSEY-HARRIS' Tractor and Hayrake**	27a Tractor and 27k Hayrake. Renumbered 310	£150-200
28/1	1934-40	**Delivery Vans Set in Trade Box**	(1st type) 28a Hornby, 28b Pickfords, 28c Manchester Guardian, 28d Oxo, 28e Ensign Lukos, 28f Palethorpes Sausages (A1008)	£6,000-8,000
		revised set:	28a Hornby, 28b Pickfords, 28c Manchester Guardian, 28e Firestone, 28f Palethorpes, 28n Atco Mowers	£6,000-8,000
28/2	1934-40	**Delivery Vans Set in Trade Box**	(1st type) 28g Kodak, 28h Sharps Toffees, 28k Marsh's, 28L Crawfords Biscuits, 28m Wakefield Castrol, 28n Meccano (A1008)	£6,000-8,000
		revised set:	28d Oxo, 28g Kodak, 28h Dunlop Tyres, 28k Marsh's, 28m Wakefield Castrol, 28h Crawfords	£6,000-8,000
28/3	1936-40	**Delivery Vans Set in Trade Box**	(2nd type) 28r Swan Pens, 28s Frys Chocolate, 28t Ovaltine, 28w Osram Lamps, 28x Hovis, 28y Exide Batteries	£2,500-3,000
30	1935-37	**Motor Vehicles**	30a Chrysler Airflow, 30b Rolls-Royce, 30c Daimler, 30d Vauxhall, 30e Breakdown Car (22c 2nd casting), 30f Ambulance	£3,000-4,000
	1937-41		As previous set but 30g Caravan replaces 30f Ambulance	£2,500-3,500
33/1	1935-37	**Mechanical Horse and Five Assorted Trailers**	33a Mechanical Horse, 33b Flat Truck, 33c Open Wagon, 33d Box Van, 33e Dust Wagon, 33f Petrol Tank with 'WAKEFIELD CASTROL' logo. Blue 'grained' box lid, large colour label	£600-800
33/2	1935-37	**Mechanical Horse and Four Assorted Trailers**	33a Mechanical Horse, 33b Flat Truck, 33c Open Wagon and 33e Dust Wagon. In Green display box (code A2036) with Yellow inner tray	£400-600
35	1935-41	**Small Cars Set**	35a Saloon Car, 35b Racer and 35c MG Sports Car. In display type box (A2222) with tuck in flap and scenic backdrop	£600-800
36	1936-41	**Motor Cars with Drivers, Passengers and Footmen**	36a Armstrong-Siddeley, 36b Bentley, 36c Humber, 36d Rover, 36e British Salmson 2-seater, 36f British Salmson 4-seater, all with figures. Set housed in Blue landscape box with Yellow tray with Purple inner and Brown board top packing piece. Box code A2205, dated 6-38	£4,000-6,000
37a	1937-41	**Motor Cycles Set**	Six of 37a civilian Motor Cyclists in various colours, hand-painted detail, solid White rubber tyres. Blue box with Green and White pictorial inner	£400-600
37	1938-40	**Motor Cycles Set**	Contains 37a (civilian), 37b (Police), 37c (Signals Despatch)	£400-600
39	1939-41	**USA Saloon Cars Set**	39a Packard, 39b Oldsmobile, 39c Lincoln, 39d Buick, 39e Chrysler, 39f Studebaker. Mauve box with full colour label on lid	£1,500-2,000
42	1935-40	**Police Set**	42a Police Box, 42b Motor Cycle Patrol, 42c Point-Duty Policeman (White coat), 42d Point-Duty Policeman (Blue uniform), in Blue box with pictorial inner (A2114)	£350-450
43	1935-41	**'R.A.C.' Set**	43a RAC Box, 43b RAC Motor Cycle Patrol, 43c RAC Guide directing traffic, 43d RAC Guide saluting. Blue box, pictorial inner part, (A2064)	£400-600
44	1935-41	**'A.A.' Set**	44a AA Box, 44b AA Motor Cycle Patrol, 44c AA Guide directing traffic, 44d AA Guide saluting. Blue box, pictorial inner part, (A2065)	£300-400
46	1937-41	**Pavement Set**	Dark Grey 'stone' effect (cardboard) pavement pieces in a box	£100-150
47	1935-41	**Road Signs Set**	12 road signs, 47e to 47t, (White under base, triangles usually filled-in) Yellow box and inner, box code A2073	£175-225
47	1948-54	.... US issue:	12 road signs, 47e to 47t, (Black under base, open triangles), (renumbered 770). Plain card box with Yellow label on end of lift up lid	£100-125
		US issue:	White under bases, filled-in triangles, in a plain box marked 'Made in England'. Made for sale by H. Hudson Dobson, 200 5th Avenue, New York	NGPP
49	1935-41	**Petrol Pumps Set** .... 'Pratts':	49a, 49b, 49c, 49d, 49e. White rubber hoses, Blue box	£150-200
49	1946-50	**Petrol Pumps Set** .... plain:	49a, 49b, 49c, 49d, 49e. Yellow plastic hoses, Yellow box	£90-110
		(renumbered 780) 'Pratts':	49, 49b, 49c, 49d, 49e. White rubber hoses, Yellow box	£150-200
		plain:	49, 49b, 49c, 49d, 49e. White plastic hoses, Yellow box	£100-140
50	1934-42	**Ships of the British Navy**	50a 'Hood', 50b 'Nelson', 50b 'Rodney', 50c 'Effingham', 50d 'York', 50e 'Delhi', 3 x 50f 'Broke', 50g 'X'-class Submarine, 3 x 50h 'Amazon', 50k 'K'-class Submarine. Blue box with Green/Blue label on lid	£200-300
51	1934-40	**Great Liners Set**	51b 'Europa', 51c 'Rex', 51d 'Empress of Britain', 51e 'Strathaird', 51f 'Queen of Bermuda', 51g 'Britannic'	£200-250
60	1934-35	**Aeroplanes Set** .... (1st issue)	60a Imperial Airways, 60b Leopard Moth, 60c Percival Gull, 60d Low-Wing Monoplane, 60e General Monospar, 60f Autogiro, no registration letters. Dark Blue box with Green, Blue and White 'Atlanta' airliner on lid label, Yellow/Green side label dated '5-34'	£1,200-1,500
60	1936-41	**British Aeroplanes Set** .... (2nd issue)	60a Imperial Airways, 60b Leopard Moth, 60c Percival Gull, 60d Low-Wing Monoplane, 60e General Monospar, 60f Autogiro. All the planes in this set (except 60f) have 'GA-' markings.	£1,000-1,250
		Box Type i)	Blue box with multicoloured label plus '150 varieties' slogan	
		Box Types ii) and iii)	Same as previous but with '200' or '300 varieties' slogans (code A1040).	

60p	1938-41	**Gloster Gladiator Set**	Six planes in Silver livery with RAF roundels	**£400-600**
60s	1938-41	**'Medium Bomber' Set**	Two renumbered 62n Fairey 'Battle' Bombers with camouflage finish. In Stone-colour box	**£250-350**
60z	1937-41	**'Avions' Set**	French Aeroplanes Set with 60az 'Arc-en-Ciel', Potez 58, Hanriot 180t, 61az DeWetoine 500, Breguet Corsair, 60f Cierva Autogiro. Blue box	**£900-1,200**
61	1937-41	**R.A.F. Aeroplanes Set**	60h 'Singapore' Flying Boat, 2 x 60n Fairey 'Battle' Bombers, 2 x 60p Gloster 'Gladiator' Biplanes. Contained in Blue box with full colour label on lid	**£300-500**
61z	1937-40	**'Avions' Set**	French Aeroplanes Set with DeWoitine D338, Potez 56, Potez 58, 61az DeWetoine 500d, Farman F360, 60f Cierva Autogiro. Blue box	**£900-1,200**
62h	1939	**Hawker Hurricane Set**	Six planes, camouflaged tops, Black undersides, mounted on card base with 'DINKY TOYS No.62h HAWKER HURRICANE SINGLE SEATER FIGHTER'. Green box dated 7-39	**£400-600**
62d	1939	**Bristol Blenheim Bomber Set**	Six planes, camouflaged, mounted on card base with 'BRISTOL BLENHEIM BOMBER MARK IV - DINKY TOYS 62d'. Green box	**£400-600**
62s	1939-41	**Hurricane Fighters Set**	Six Fighters, Silver fuselages, RAF roundels, undercarriages, Blue box	**£300-400**
64	1939-41	**Aeroplane Set**	60g Light Racer, 62h 'Hurricane' (Camouflaged), 62k 'Kings Aeroplane', 62m Light Transport, 62s 'Hurricane' (Silver), 63b Seaplane 'Mercury'. (In 1940 either 62a 'Spitfire' or 62s were substituted for 62h and 62s)	**£750-1,000**
64z	193?-4?	**'Avions' Set**	French Aeroplanes Set with 61az Dewoitine 'F-ADBF', 64a Amiot 370, 64b Bloch 220 'F-AOHJ', 64c Potez 63, 64d Potez 662 'F-ARAY'. Blue box, Yellow inner	**£2,000-2,500**
65	1939-41	**Aeroplane Set**	60r Flying Boat, 60t 'DC3', 60v 'Whitely' Bomber, 60w 'Clipper III', 62n Junkers, 62p 'Ensign', 62r 'Albatross', 62w 'Frobisher'. Blue box, illustrated leaflet enclosed	**£1,750-2,000**
66	1940-41	**Camouflaged Aeroplanes Set**	66a Heavy Bomber, 66b Dive Bomber Fighter, 66c Fighter, 66d Torpedo, 66e Medium Bomber, 66f Army Autogiro (Silver). Yellow-Brown box	**£2,000-3,000**
68	1940-41	**Camouflaged Aeroplanes Set**	2 x 60s 'Battle' Bombers, 2 x 62d 'Blenheim', 3 x 62h 'Hurricane' (Camouflage), 3 x 62s 'Hurricane' (Silver), 62t 'Whitely', 68a 'Ensign', 68b 'Frobisher'. Blue or Yellow box, light or dark camouflage. Models display two roundels: Red inside Blue on the wings, and White/Blue/Red on the fuselage sides	**£2,500-3,500**
	1940-41	US issue:	Camouflaged version of 60s, 62d, 62e, 62h, 62t, 68a and 68b. Box picture shows civilian aircraft. Red label states 'Sold by Meccano Company of America Inc., 200 5th Avenue, New York'	**£2,500-3,500**
101	1936-40	**Dining-Room Furniture**	101a Table, 101b Sideboard, 2 x 101c Carver Chair, 4 x 101d Chair	**£250-350**
102	1936-40	**Bedroom Furniture**	102a Bed, 102b Wardrobe, 102c Dressing Table, 102d Dressing Chest, 102e Dressing Table Stool, 102f Chair. Brown or Pink. Green box	**£250-350**
103	1936-40	**Kitchen Furniture**	103a Refrigerator, 103b Kitchen Cabinet, 103c Electric Cooker, 103d Table, 103e Chair. Light Blue/White or Light Green/Cream	**£250-350**
104	1936-40	**Bathroom Furniture**	104a Bath, 104b Bath Mat, 104c Pedestal Basin, 104d Stool, 104e Linen Basket, 104f Toilet. Brown or Pink. Green box	**£250-350**
118	1965-69	**Towaway Glider Set**	135 Triumph 2000 (Cream/Blue), Cream/Red trailer, Yellow glider	**£150-200**
121	1963-66	**Goodwood Racing Set**	112 Austin-Healey Sprite, 113 MGB, 120 Jaguar, 182 Porsche, 9 Service Station (009) plastic figures plus seated and standing drivers. In Buff/Red display box with stepped insert	**£1,000-1,250**
122	1963-65	**Touring Gift Set**	188 Caravan, 193 Station Wagon, 195 Jaguar, 270 'AA' Patrol, 295 Atlas Kenebrake, 796 Healey Sports Boat on Trailer. In Buff/Red display box with stepped insert	**£1,000-1,250**
123	1963-65	**Mayfair Gift Set**	142 Jaguar, 150 Rolls-Royce, 186 Mercedes-Benz, 194 Bentley, 198 Rolls-Royce, 199 Austin Mini Countryman, plastic figures (3 male, 1 female). Buff/Red display box with stepped insert	**£1,250-1,500**
124	1964-66	**Holidays Gift Set**	952 Vega Luxury Coach, 137 Plymouth, 142 Jaguar, 796 Healey Sports Boat. In Buff/Red display box with stepped insert	**£750-1,000**
125	1964-66	**Fun Ahoy! Set**	130 Ford Corsair with driver, 796 Healey Sports Boat with pilot. Window box	**£350-450**
126	1967-68	**Motor Show Set**	127 Rolls-Royce, 133 Cortina, 151 Vauxhall Victor, 171 Austin 1800. In Buff/Red display box with stepped insert	**£1,000-1,250**
	1968-69		127 Rolls-Royce, 159 Cortina, 151 Vauxhall Victor, 171 Austin 1800. In Buff/Red display box with stepped insert	**£1,000-1,250**
149	1958-61	**Sports Cars Set**	107 Sunbeam Alpine, 108 MG Midget, 109 Austin-Healey, 110 Aston-Martin, 111 Triumph TR2, all in 'competition finish'. Blue/White striped box	**£1,000-1,200**
150	1937-41	**Royal Tank Corps Personnel**	150a Officer, 2 x 150b Private, 2 x 150c Private, 150e N.C.O. Attached by cord to Yellow card in Yellow box or Grey/Blue box with Yellow inner, code A2187	**£200-300**
	1946-50	US export only Set:	Post-war issue of pre-war figures in original Green box with 'H. Hudson Dobson' label	**£200-300**
	1952-55	reissue, US only:	Contains 1 x 150a, 2 x 150b, 2 x 150c, 1 x 150e. Green box with one packing piece	**£200-300**
151	1937-41	**Medium Tank Set**	151a Tank, 151b 6-wheel Wagon, 151c Cooker Trailer, 151d Water Tank Trailer, 150d Royal Tank Corps Driver. Drop-front Blue box with pictorial inner, one packing piece with cut-outs	**£250-350**
152	1937-41	**Light Tank Set**	152a Tank, 152b Reconnaissance Car, 152c Austin 7 Car with 150d Royal Tank Corps Driver. Drop-front Blue box with pictorial inner, one packing piece with cut-outs	**£250-350**
156	1939-41	**Mechanised Army Set**	151a Tank, 151b 6-wheel Wagon, 151c Cooker Trailer, 151d Water Tank Trailer, 152a Tank, 152b Reconnaissance Car, 152c Austin 7 Car with 150d Royal Tank Corps Driver, 161a Lorry with Searchlight, 161b AA Gun on Trailer, 162a Light Dragon Tractor, 162b Ammunition Trailer, and 162c 18-pounder Gun. Drop-front Grey-Blue box (codes: '11-39', 'A2308') with contents shown on lid, four packing pieces.	**£2,500-3,000**
160	1939-41	**Royal Artillery Personnel** (reissued as 606 in 1954)	160a N.C.O., 2 x 160b Private, 160c Gunlayer, 2 x 160d Gunner (standing). Grey-Blue box (code: A2308) dated 11-39, Yellow box (code: A2303) and inner box dated 12-39. Production of this set continued post-war but only for export (to USA)	**£200-300**
	1952-55	reissue, US only:	Contains 1 x 160a, 3 x 160b, 2 x 160d, 1 x 150e. Green box with inner card stand	**£200-300**
161	1939-41	**Mobile Anti-Aircraft Unit**	161a Lorry with Searchlight and 161b A.A. Gun on Trailer. Blue or Green box ('A2257' on some), 1 packing piece with cut-outs	**£400-500**
162	1939-54	**18-pounder Field Gun Unit**	162a Light Dragon Tractor, 162b Trailer, 162c Gun. Blue box, 1 packing piece with cut-outs	**£150-200**

201	1965-68	**Racing Cars Set**	240 Cooper, 241 Lotus, 242 Ferrari, 243 B.R.M.	**£350-450**
237	1978-79	**Dinky Way Set**	Contains: 178 Mini Clubman, 211 Triumph TR7, 382 Convoy Truck, 412 Bedford 'AA' Van. **N.B.** Export only version of Set 240.	**£80-100**
240	1978-80	**Dinky Way Set**	211 Triumph TR7, 255 Police Mini, 382 Dump Truck, 412 Bedford Van, 20ft of 'roadway', 20 road signs, decal sheet	**£60-80**
245	1969-73	**Superfast Gift Set**	131 Jaguar 'E'-type, 153 Aston-Martin DB6, 188 Jensen FF	**£100-125**
246	1969-73	**International Gift Set**	187 De Tomaso Mangusta, 215 Ford GT, 216 Ferrari Dino	**£100-125**
249	1962-63	**World Famous Racing Cars**	230 Talbot-Lago, 231 Maserati, 232 Alfa-Romeo, 233 Cooper-Bristol, 234 Ferrari, 239 Vanwall. Bubble-packed onto large display card	**£1,000-1,500**
249	1955-58	**Racing Cars Set**	Contains 231, 232, 233, 234, 235, (renumbered from 4)	**£700-900**
294	1973-77	**Police Vehicles Gift Set**	250 Mini-Cooper, 254 Range-Rover, 287 Accident Unit. (Replaces Set 297)	**£175-200**
297	1963-73	**Police Vehicles Gift Set**	250 Mini-Cooper, 255 Ford Zodiac, 287 Accident Unit. (Replaced by Set 294)	**£175-200**
298	1963-66	**Emergency Services Set**	258 Ford Fairlane, 263 Ambulance, 276 Fire Tender, 277 Ambulance, with Ambulance-man, Ambulance-woman and Policeman	**£400-500**
299	1957-59	**Post Office Services**	260 'Royal Mail' Morris Van, 261 'GPO Telephones' Van, 750 Call Box, 011 Messenger, 012 Postman (but no Pillar Box!). Blue and White striped box	**£350-450**
299	1963-66	**Motorway Services Set**	434 Bedford Crash Truck, 269 Motorway Police Car, 257 Fire Chief's Car, 276 Airport Fire Tender, 263 (later 277) Criterion Ambulance	**£800-1,100**
299	1978-79	**'Crash Squad' Action Set**	244 Plymouth Police Car and 732 Bell Helicopter	**£45-55**
300	1973-77	**London Scene Set**	Contains 289 Routemaster Bus 'ESSO' and 284 London Taxi	**£65-75**
302	1979-?	**Emergency Squad Gift Pack**	Paramedic Truck and Plymouth Fire Chief Car plus figures of Gage and DeSoto. Not issued	NPP
303	1978-80	**Commando Squad Gift Set**	687 Convoy Army Truck, 667 Armoured Car, 732 Army helicopter	**£75-100**
304	1978-79	**Fire Rescue Gift Set**	195 Fire Chief Range Rover, 282 Land Rover, 384 Convoy Fire Truck	**£70-90**
306	1979-?	**'Space' Gift Pack**	358 'USS Enterprise', 357 Klingon Battle Cruiser, plus Galactic War Chariot. Not issued	NPP
307	1979-?	**'New Avengers' Gift Pack**	Purdey's TR7, John Steed's Special Leyland Jaguar, plus a 'fly-off' assailant! Not issued	NPP
309	1978-80	**Star Trek Gift Set**	357 Klingon Battle Cruiser and 358 'USS Enterprise'	**£125-150**
310	1954-60	**Tractor and Hayrake** ..1st issue:	Red 300 Tractor and 310 Hayrake. Blue/White striped box	**£150-200**
		2nd issue:	Cherry Red 300 Tractor with Yellow hubs. In late issue Yellow box with lift-off lid.	**£200-250**
325	19??-??	**'DAVID BROWN' Gift Set**	White 305 Tractor and Red 322 Disc Harrow	**£100-150**
			Yellow 305 Tractor and Red 322 Disc Harrow	**£125-175**
398	1964-65	**Farm Equipment Gift Set** (reissue of Set No.1)	300 Massey-Harris Tractor, 320 Harvest Trailer, 321 Manure Spreader, 322 Disc Harrow, 324 Hay Rake. Grey box with hinged lid	**£1,000-1,250**
399	1969-73	**Farm Tractor and Trailer**	300 Massey-Harris Tractor and 428 Large Trailer (Red/Silver). Yellow window box	**£200-250**
399	1977-79	**'Convoy' Gift Set**	380 Skip Truck, 381 Farm Truck, 382 Dumper Truck. 'Window' box	**£35-45**
606	1954-55	**Royal Artillery Personnel**	1 x 160a, 2 x 160b, 1 x 160c, 2 x 160d. Export only (to USA), (reissue of 160)	**£150-200**
616	1976-78	**AEC Transporter and Tank**	Militarised version of 974 with 683 Chieftain Tank and camouflage net	**£65-80**
618	1976-79	**Transporter and Helicopter**	Militarised versions of 974 and 724 with camouflage netting	**£70-80**
619	1976-78	**Bren-Gun Carrier Set**	622 Bren-Gun and 625 6-pounder Anti-Tank Gun	**£35-45**
677	1972-75	**Task Force Set**	680 Ferret Armoured Car, 681 D.U.K.W., 682 Stalwart Load Carrier	**£35-45**
695	1962-66	**Howitzer and Tractor**	689 Medium Artillery Tractor and 693 7.2in. Howitzer	**£250-350**
697	1957-71	**Field Gun Set**	688 Field Artillery Tractor, 687 Trailer, 686 25-pounder Field Gun	**£80-100**
698	1957-65	**Tank Transporter Set**	660 Mighty Antar Tank Transporter and 651 Centurion Tank. One packing piece in box	**£160-190**
699	1955-58	**Military Vehicles (1) Set** (renumbered from No.1)	621 3-ton Wagon, 641 1-ton Truck, 674 Austin Champ, 676 Armoured Car. Blue/White Striped box with inner lining and stand	**£250-350**
754	1958-62	**Pavement Set**	Twenty various Grey cardboard pieces representing paving	**£30-40**
766	1959-64	**British Road Signs**	Country Set 'A'. Six signs of the times, mostly 55 mm high. Yellow box	**£70-80**
767	1959-64	**British Road Signs**	Country Set 'B'. Six signs of the times, mostly 55 mm high. Yellow box	**£70-80**
768	1959-64	**British Road Signs**	Town Set 'A'. Six signs of the times, mostly 55 mm high. Yellow box	**£70-80**
769	1959-64	**British Road Signs**	Town Set 'B'. Six signs of the times, mostly 55 mm high. Yellow box	**£70-80**
770	1950-54	**Road Signs Set**	12 road signs, 47e to 47t, (Black under base, open triangles) US export only, (renumbered 47)	**£125-175**
771	1953-65	**International Road Signs**	Set of 12 various road signs with Silver posts and bases	**£100-125**
772	1959-63	**British Road Signs**	(Sets 766, 767, 768 and 769). 24 various road signs in a Red/Yellow box	**£150-200**
780	1950-54	**Petrol Pumps Set** (renumbered 49)	49a, 49b, 49c, 49d, 49e (plain). Yellow plastic hoses, export only	**£90-110**
			Version issued in picture box	**£100-150**
784	1972-74	**Dinky Goods Train Set**	Blue loco 'GER', one Red Truck, one Yellow Truck	**£30-40**
798	1954-59	**Express Passenger Train Set** (renumbered from 16)	Green/Black loco, 'BR' crest, Cream coaches (Grey roofs), Black tyres	**£100-125**
			Green/Black loco, 'BR' crest, Cream coaches/roofs, Black tyres	**£100-125**
			Green/Black loco, 'BR', Cream coaches/roofs, Red hubs, White tyres	**£100-125**
851	1961-	**Sets of vehicle 'Loads'**	2 each of 846 Oil Drums, 847 Barrels, 849 Packing Cases and 850 Crates	**£30-40**
900	1964-70	**'Site Building' Gift Set**	437 Muir-Hill Loader, 960 Albion Concrete Mixer, 961 Blaw-Knox Bulldozer, 962 Muir-Hill Dumper, 965 Euclid Rear Dump Truck. Grey/Red/Yellow box	**£700-900**
950	1969-70	**Car Transporter Set**	974 AEC Car Transporter with 136 Vauxhall Viva, 138 Hillman Imp, 162 Triumph 1300, 168 Ford Escort, 342 Austin Mini-Moke. Not issued	NPP
957	1959-65	**Fire Services Gift Set**	257 Fire Chief's Car, 955 Fire Engine, 956 Turntable Fire Escape	**£250-350**
990	1956-58	**Car Transporter Set**	Contains 982 Pullmore Car Transporter, one packing piece, and these cars: 154 Hillman Minx (Light Green/Cream), 156 Rover 75 (Cream/Blue), 161 Austin Somerset (Red/Yellow), 162 Ford Zephyr (Green/White)	**£1,500-2,000**
1001	1952-54	**Station Staff ('00' gauge)**	Set of 6 Blue figures (re-issue of pre-war Hornby-Dublo Set D1), (renumbered 051). Green card box	**£45-55**
1003	1952-54	**Passengers ('00' gauge)**	Set of 6 coloured figures (re-issue of pre-war Hornby-Dublo Set D2), (renumbered 053). Green card box	**£45-55**
49N2269	1965	**'Road Racers' Set**	Contains: 113 MGB, 114 Triumph Spitfire, 120 Jaguar E-type, 237 Mercedes-Benz, 238 Jaguar D-type, 242 Ferrari Racing Car, 243 BRM Racing Car. Special set for US mail-order company Sears-Roebuck	NGPP

TOYS OF QUALITY MADE BY MECCANO LTD.

DINKY Toys
200 VARIETIES

STREAMLINE SALOON
Dinky Toys No. 22h
Assorted colours. Fitted with rubber tyres.
Price 6d. each.

A FASCINATING COLLECTING HOBBY

Dinky Toys are the most realistic and the most attractive models in miniature ever produced. They are unique in their perfection of finish, and their range is so wide as to appeal to all tastes. Start now to collect these delightful little models.

ROYAL AIR MAIL SERVICE CAR
Dinky Toys No. 34
In correct colours. Fitted with rubber tyres.
Price 6d. each.

33A 33C 33F

33E 33B 33D

MECHANICAL HORSE AND FIVE ASSORTED TRAILERS
Dinky Toys No. 33
Fitted with rubber tyres

No. 33a	Mechanical Horse	...	each 6d.
No. 33b	Flat Truck	... ...	,, 6d.
No. 33c	Open Wagon	... ...	,, 6d.
No. 33d	Box Van ...	... ...	,, 8d.
No. 33e	Dust Wagon	... ...	,, 8d.
No. 33f	Petrol Tank	... ...	,, 8d.

Price of complete set 3/6

30A 30B 30C

30D 30E 30F

MOTOR VEHICLES
Dinky Toys No. 30
Fitted with rubber tyres and silver-plated radiators.

No. 30a	Chrysler Airflow Saloon	... each 9d.
No. 30b	Rolls-Royce Car	... ... ,, 9d.
No. 30c	Daimler Car...	... ... ,, 9d.
No. 30d	Vauxhall Car	... ... ,, 9d.
No. 30e	Breakdown Car	... ... ,, 9d.
No. 30f	Ambulance ...	... ... ,, 9d.

Price of complete set 4/6

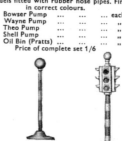

49D 49A 49E 49B 49C

PETROL PUMPS
Dinky Toys No. 49
Scale models fitted with rubber hose pipes. Finished in correct colours.

No. 49a	Bowser Pump	...	... each 4d.
No. 49b	Wayne Pump	...	... ,, 4d.
No. 49c	Theo Pump	...	... ,, 4d.
No. 49d	Shell Pump	...	... ,, 4d.
No. 49e	Oil Bin (Pratts)	...	... ,, 3d.

Price of complete set 1/6

DELIVERY VANS
Dinky Toys No. 28/1

No. 28a	Hornby Train Van	... each 6d.
No. 28b	Seccotine Van	... ... ,, 6d.
No. 28c	Manchester Guardian Van	... ,, 6d.
No. 28e	Firestone Tyres Van	... ,, 6d.
No. 28f	Palethorpe's Sausage Van	... ,, 6d.
No. 28n	Atco Lawn Mowers Van	... ,, 6d.

Price of complete set 3/-

RAILWAY MECHANICAL HORSE AND TRAILER VAN
Dinky Toys No. 33R
Price complete, L.M.S.R., L.N.E.R., G.W.R. or S.R., 1/6

DELIVERY VANS
Dinky Toys No. 28/2

No. 28d	Oxo Van	... each 6d.
No. 28g	Kodak Cameras Van	... ,, 6d.
No. 28h	Dunlop Tyres Van	... ,, 6d.
No. 28k	Marsh and Baxter's Sausage Van...	... ,, 6d.
No. 28m	Wakefield's Castrol Oil Van,,	... 6d.
No. 28p	Crawford's Biscuit Van	... 6d.

Price of complete set 3/-

PILLAR LETTER BOX AIR MAIL
Dinky Toys No. 12b
Price 3d. each

PILLAR LETTER BOX G.P.O.
Dinky Toys No. 12a
Price 3d. each.

BEACON
Dinky Toys No. 47d
(Realistic models of the Belisha Safety Beacons).
Price 1d. each.

ROBOT TRAFFIC SIGNAL
Dinky Toys No. 47a
(Four-face)
Price 3d. each

ROBOT TRAFFIC SIGNAL
Dinky Toys No. 47b
(Three-face)
Price 3d. each

ROBOT TRAFFIC SIGNAL
Dinky Toys No. 47c
(Two-face)
Right-angle or Back-to-back.
Price 3d. each

HOTCHKISS RACING CAR
Dinky Toys No. 23b
Assorted colours. Fitted with rubber tyres.
Price 6d. each

TRAILER
Dinky Toys No. 25g
For use with Dinky Toys (Commercial Motor Vehicles) No. 25. Fitted with rubber tyres.
Price 7d. each.

R.A.C. HUT, MOTOR CYCLE PATROL AND GUIDES
Dinky Toys No. 43
This set is representative of the familiar personnel and road hut of the R.A.C. Each item is finished in correct colours.

No. 43a	R.A.C. Hut ...	... ... each 6d.
No. 43b	R.A.C. Motor Cycle Patrol	... ,, 9d.
No. 43c	R.A.C. Guide directing traffic	,, 3d.
No. 43d	R.A.C. Guide at the salute	,, 3d.

Price of complete set 1/9

A.A. HUT, MOTOR CYCLE PATROL AND GUIDES
Dinky Toys No. 44
Every collector of Dinky Toys will find this new addition to the range of particular interest. Each item is finished in correct colours.

No. 44a	A.A. Hut ...	... each 8d.
No. 44b	A.A. Motor Cycle Patrol	... ,, 9d.
No. 44c	A.A. Guide directing traffic,	,, 3d.
No. 44d	A.A. Guide at the salute	,, 3d.

Price of complete set 1/11

PRODUCT OF MECCANO LIMITED LIVERPOOL

STREAMLINE TOURER
Dinky Toys No. 23g
Assorted colours. Fitted with rubber tyres.
Price 6d. each

RACING CAR
Dinky Toys No. 23a
Assorted colours. Fitted with rubber tyres. Price 4d. each

Ask your dealer for a complete illustrated list of Dinky Toys

MECCANO LIMITED — BINNS ROAD — LIVERPOOL 13

A page from the December 1935 'Meccano Magazine'.

Dinky Toys Accessories (Pre-War)

See also: Public Transport Models, Ships, Motor Cycles and Gift Sets sections.
Approximate size of figures: large 40mm (scale 1:42); small 35mm (scale 1:48).
Pre-war box sequence: 'Modelled Miniatures'; 'Meccano Dinky Toys'; 'Dinky Toys'.

Ref	Year(s)	Model name	Colours, features, details	Market Price Range
1	1939-41	**Station Staff** (large)	see Gift Sets section.	
1	1939-41	**Station Staff** (small)	see Gift Sets section.	
1a	1932-41	**Station Master** (large)	Dark Blue uniform with Gold or Silver buttons on long coat	£30-35
1a	1932-41	**Station Master** (small)	As previous version but smaller	£20-25
1b	1932-39	**Guard** (large)	Dark Blue coat (Gold or Silver buttons), blowing whistle, flag in left hand	£30-35
1b	1932-39	**Guard** (small)	As previous version but smaller	£20-25
1b	1939-41	**Guard** (large)	Dark Blue coat (Gold or Silver buttons), blowing whistle, flag in right hand	£30-35
1b	1939-41	**Guard** (small)	As previous version but smaller	£20-25
1c	1932-41	**Ticket Collector** (large)	Dark Blue uniform (Gold or Silver buttons), slightly open arms	£30-35
1c	1932-41	**Ticket Collector** (large)	As previous model but with only right arm extended	£30-35
1c	1932-41	**Ticket Collector** (small)	As previous version but smaller	£20-25
1d	1932-39	**Driver** (large)	Mid-Blue uniform (Gold or Silver buttons) holding oil-can	£30-35
1d	1939-41	**Driver** (small)	As previous version but smaller	£20-25
1e	1932-39	**Porter with Bags** (large)	Dark Blue uniform, oblong case in right hand, round hat-box in left	£30-35
1e	1939-41	**Porter with Bags** (small)	Dark Blue, oblong case in each hand. (Smaller than previous model)	£20-25
1f	1932-39	**Porter** (large)	Dark Blue uniform, walking, no luggage	£30-35
1f	1939-41	**Porter** (small)	Dark Blue, standing, no luggage. (Smaller than previous model)	£20-25
2a	1932-41	**Horses**	One Light Brown or Dark Brown horse, one White horse	£20-30
2b	1932-41	**Cow**	3 versions were available; Light Brown, Dark Brown, or Black and White	£20-25
2c	1932-41	**Pig**	A Pink porker	£15-20
2d	1932-41	**Sheep**	White sheep with Black hand-painted detail	£15-20
3a	1932-39	**Woman and Child** (large)	Woman in Green coat, child (in Red) is on woman's right	£30-35
3a	1939-41	**Woman and Child** (small)	Woman in Green suit with Grey scarf and Red hat, child on woman's left	£20-25
3b	1932-39	**Business Man** (large)	Dark Blue suit/hat, walking stick in right hand, left hand holds lapels	£30-35
3b	1939-41	**Business Man** (small)	Grey suit, left hand holds attach case	£20-25
3c	1932-39	**Male Hiker** (large)	Brown clothing, Khaki rucksack, walking stick in right hand	£30-35
3c	1939-41	**Male Hiker** (small)	Brown clothing, Khaki rucksack, no walking stick	£20-25
3d	1932-41	**Female Hiker** (large)	Blue skirt, White blouse, walking stick in right hand	£30-35
3d	1932-41	**Female Hiker** (small)	All Blue clothing, or Dark Blue skirt, White blouse	£20-25
3e	1932-39	**Newsboy** (large)	Brown or Blue clothing, running, papers in right hand and under left arm	£30-35
3e	1939-41	**Newsboy** (small)	Dark Blue clothing, standing, papers in Cream tray	£20-25
3f	1932-39	**Woman**	Red jacket, White skirt, coat over left arm, oblong case in right hand	£25-30
3f	1939-41	**Woman**	Dark Red coat, Black collar, round case in right hand	£25-30
4	1932-39	**Engineering Staff**	See the Gift Sets section.	
4a	1932-41	**Electrician** (large)	Blue overalls, White sleeves, carrying equipment	£30-35
4a	1932-41	**Electrician** (small)	Blue overalls, White sleeves, carrying equipment	£20-25
4b	1932-41	**Fitter** (large)	All-Blue overalls, or Brown overalls /White sleeves, carrying equipment	£30-35
4b	1932-41	**Fitter** (small)	As previous model but smaller	£20-25
4c	1932-41	**Storekeeper** (large)	Brown coat, Black trousers, holding forms in right hand, casting as 1a	£30-35
4c	1932-41	**Storekeeper** (small)	Brown coat, Black trousers, holding forms in right hand, casting as 1a	£20-25
4d	1932-41	**Greaser** (large)	Brown overalls, holding oil-can in right hand, casting based on 1d	£30-35
4d	1932-41	**Greaser** (small)	Brown overalls, holding oil-can in right hand, casting based on 1d	£20-25
4e	1932-41	**Engine-Room Attendant** (large).	Blue overalls, with or without White sleeves	£30-35
4e	1932-41	**Engine-Room Attendant** (small)	Blue overalls, with or without White sleeves	£20-25
5	1932-39	**Train and Hotel Staff**	See the Gift Sets section.	
5a	1932-41	**Pullman Car Conductor** (large)	White jacket, Blue trousers, slightly open arms, casting as 1c	£30-35
5a	1932-41	**Pullman Car Conductor** (small)	White jacket, Blue trousers, slightly open arms, casting as 1c	£20-25
5b	1932-41	**Pullman Car Waiter** (large)	White jacket, Blue trousers, two slightly different poses were available	£30-35
5b	1932-41	**Pullman Car Waiter** (small)	White jacket, Blue trousers, two slightly different poses were available	£20-25
5c	1932-41	**Hotel Porter** (large)	Red jacket/Brown trousers, or Green jacket/Blue trousers, casting as 1e	£30-35
5c	1932-41	**Hotel Porter** (small)	Red jacket/Brown trousers, or Green jacket/Blue trousers, casting as 1e	£20-25
6	1933-40	**Shepherd Set**	See the Gift Sets section.	
6a	1932-41	**Shepherd**	Brown with Dark Brown hat	£50-75
6b	1932-41	**Sheep-dog**	Black and White sheep-dog	£20-30
12	1937-41	**Postal Set**	See the Gift Sets section.	
12a	1935-40	**GPO Pillar Box 'GR'**	Red, with or without Red/Yellow 'Post Office' sign on top, White panel	£25-30
12b	1935-40	**Air Mail Pillar Box**	Blue body, 'Air Mail', White panel, casting as 12a	£35-40
12c	1936-40	**Telephone Box**	Cream with Silver windows	£20-30
12d	1938-40	**Telegraph Messenger**	Dark Blue body, picked out detail in darker Blue, Brown pouch, 35 mm	£20-25
12e	1938-40	**Postman**	Dark Blue body, darker Blue detail, Brown post bag and badge, 35 mm	£20-25
13	1931-40	**'HALLS DISTEMPER'**	Figures (lead) usually White, Cream (cardboard) panel, Red lettering	£250-300
15	1937-41	**Railway Signals Set**	See the Gift Sets section.	
15a	1937-41	**Single Arm Signal**	One Red 'Home' signal, or Yellow 'Distant' signal	£30-40
15b	1937-41	**Double Arm Signal**	One Red 'Home' signal and one Yellow 'Distant' signal on single pole	£40-50
15c	1937-41	**Junction Signal**	Two Red 'Home' signals, OR two Yellow 'Distant' signals on single pole	£65-75
30g	1936-39	**Caravan Trailer**	2 wheels, drawbar, body length 81 mm. open roof windows,	
			Blue/Cream, Red/Cream, Green/Cream, Orange/Cream, Two tone-Green	£90-120
			Chocolate and Beige, Blue hubs	£150-175
	1939-40		As previous models but with filled-in roof windows	£80-110

42	1935-41	Police Set	See the Gift Sets section.	
42a	1936-40	Police Box	Dark Blue box, 'POLICE' in Silver	£25-35
42c	1936-40	Point Duty Policeman	(cast in lead), White coat, Black helmet, 42 mm tall	£25-35
42d	1936-40	Point Duty Policeman	(cast in lead), Dark Blue uniform, White gauntlets, 40 mm tall	£25-35
43	1935-41	'RAC' Set	See the Gift Sets section.	
43a	1935-40	'RAC' Box	Blue and White (tinplate) call-box with 'RAC' emblem	£100-125
43c	1935-40	'RAC' Guide	(cast in lead), Blue uniform, Red sash, directing traffic, 37 mm tall	£25-35
43d	1935-40	'RAC' Guide (saluting)	(cast in lead), Blue uniform with Red sash, 36 mm tall	£25-35
44	1935-41	'AA' Set	See the Gift Sets section.	
44a	1935-40	'AA' Box	Black/Yellow tinplate box with 'AA' badge and 3 signs	£100-125
44c	1935-40	'AA' Guide	(cast in lead), Tan uniform, Blue sash, directing traffic, 37 mm tall	£20-25
44d	1935-40	'AA' Guide (saluting)	(cast in lead), Tan uniform, Blue sash, 36 mm tall	£20-25
45	1935-40	Garage	Cream/Orange (tinplate), Green opening doors, boxed, 127 x 90 mm	£300-400
46	1937-40	Pavement Set	Dark Grey 'stone' effect (cardboard) pavement pieces in a box	£80-100
47	1935-41	Road Signs Set	See the Gift Sets section.	
47a	1935-41	4-face Traffic Lights	Black on White post, Yellow beacon, White base, 62 mm high	£15-20
47b	1935-41	3-face Traffic Lights	Black on White post, Yellow beacon, White base, 62 mm high	£15-20
47c	1935-41	2-face Traffic Lights	Back-to-back lights, Black on White post, Yellow beacon, White base	£15-20
47c	1935-41	2-face Traffic Lights	Lights at 90 degrees, Black on White post, Yellow beacon, White base	£15-20
47d	1935-41	Belisha Beacon	Black on White post, Orange globe, White base, 51 mm high	£15-20
47e	1935-41	'30 MPH' Limit Sign	Black on White post, Red top '30', 52 mm high	£15-20
47f	1935-41	De-restriction Sign	Black on White post, diagonal Black bar on White circle, 52 mm high	£15-20
47g	1935-41	'School' Sign	Black on White post, Red top, Black 'beacon' design, 51 mm high	£15-20
47h	1935-41	'Steep Hill' Sign	Black on White post, Red top, Black 'incline' design, 51 mm high	£15-20
47k	1935-41	'S-Bend' Sign	Black on White post, Red top, Black 'S-Bend' design, 51 mm high	£15-20
47m	1935-41	'Left-Hand Bend' Sign	Black on White post, Red top, Black 'curve' design, 51 mm high	£15-20
47n	1935-41	'Right-Hand Bend' Sign	Black on White post, Red top, Black 'curve' design, 51 mm high	£15-20
47p	1935-41	'T-Junction' Sign	Black on White post, Red top, Black 'T' design, 51 mm high	£15-20
47q	1935-41	'No Entry' Sign	Black on White post, Red 'bar' design, 48 mm high	£15-20
47r	1935-41	'Major Road Ahead' Sign	Black on White post, Red top, Black lettering, 54 mm high	£15-20
47s	1935-41	'Crossing No Gates' Sign	Black on White post, Red top, Black 'loco' design, 51 mm high	£15-20
47t	1935-41	'Roundabout' Sign	Black on White post, Red top, Black 'arrows' design, 51 mm high	£15-20
		NB	Pre-war issues have filled in triangles.	
48	1935-41	Filling and Service Station	Tinplate construction with 'FILLING AND SERVICE STATION' logo. Orange box.	
			Green roof and base	£350-500
			Turquoise roof and base	£350-500
			Yellow roof, Green base	£350-500
49	1935-41	Petrol Pumps Set	See the Gift Sets section.	
49a	1935-40	Bowser Petrol Pump	Green pump body, White rubber hose, 46 mm	£35-45
	1946-53		Green pump body, Yellow plastic hose, 46 mm	£25-35
49b	1935-40	Wayne Petrol Pump	Turquoise pump body, White rubber hose, 39 mm	£35-45
	1946-53		Pale Blue pump body, Yellow plastic hose, 39 mm	£25-35
49c	1935-40	Theo Petrol Pump	Blue pump, White rubber hose, 58 mm	£35-45
	1946-53		Brown pump body, Yellow plastic hose, 58 mm	£25-35
49d	1935-40	'SHELL' Petrol Pump	Red pump body, White rubber hose, 53 mm	£35-45
	1946-53		Red pump body, Yellow plastic hose, 53 mm	£25-35
49e	1935-40	'Pratts' Oil Bin	Yellow bin body and opening tinplate lid, 'Pratts Motor Oil', 32 mm	£40-50
			Post-war, 49e was only available in Set 49 (without 'Pratts' logo)	GSP
101	1935-40	Dining Room Set	See the Gift Sets section.	
101a	1935-40	Dining Table	'Wood' effect dining-room table, 64 mm	£30-35
101b	1935-40	Sideboard	'Wood' effect sideboard with opening doors, tinplate back, 63 mm	£30-35
101c	1935-40	Carver Chair	'Wood' effect chair with armrests, 33 mm high	£15-20
101d	1935-40	Dining Chair	'Wood' effect chair without armrests, raised 'leather' cushion	£10-15
102	1935-40	Bedroom Set	See the Gift Sets section.	
102a	1935-40	Bed	Brown or Pink double bed	£30-35
102b	1935-40	Wardrobe	Brown or Pink wardrobe with opening door, tinplate back, 63 mm	£30-35
102c	1935-40	Dressing Table	Brown or Pink, opening drawers, tinplate mirror, 51 mm	£30-35
102d	1935-40	Dressing Chest	Brown or Pink, opening drawer, tinplate back, 40 mm high	£30-35
102e	1935-40	Dressing Table Stool	Brown or Pink stool, 13 mm high	£15-20
102f	1935-40	Chair	Brown or Pink	£10-15
103	1935-40	Kitchen Set	See the Gift Sets section.	
103a	1935-40	Refrigerator	Light Blue/White or Light Green/Cream, door, tinplate back and food tray	£35-45
103b	1935-40	Kitchen Cabinet	Light Blue/White or Light Green/Cream, opening doors/drawer, tin back	£35-45
103c	1935-40	Electric Cooker	Light Blue/White or Light Green/Cream, opening door, tinplate back	£35-45
103d	1935-40	Kitchen Table	Light Blue/White or Light Green/Cream, 34 mm high	£30-35
103e	1935-40	Kitchen Chair	Light Blue/White or Light Green/Cream, casting as 102f	£10-15
104	1935-40	Bathroom Set	See the Gift Sets section.	
104a	1935-40	Bath	Pink/White or Light Green/White, Gold taps, 69 mm	£35-45
104b	1935-40	Bath Mat	Mottled Green (rubber) mat, 50 x 37 mm	£10-15
104c	1935-40	Pedestal Hand Basin	Pink/White or Light Green/White, Gold taps, tinplate mirror, 63 mm	£30-35
104d	1935-40	Bathroom Stool	Pink/White or Light Green/White, 15 mm high	£15-20
104e	1935-40	Linen Basket	Pink/White or Light Green/White, hinged lid, 22 mm high	£15-20
104f	1935-40	Toilet	Pink/White or Light Green/White, hinged lid, 34 mm high	£35-45
	1935-40	'Dolly Varden' Dolls House	Not given a reference number, made of 'leather board' (heavy reinforced cardboard), and supplied packed flat. Cream/Brown upper storey, Red brick ground floor, Red roof, 476 x 260 mm base, 476 mm high	£500-750
		NB	It is not really possible to give individual prices for single 'Dolly Varden' items as they are very rarely available in collectable condition. Boxed sets sell for £200-300, for example. See Gift Sets section for more price information.	

Dinky Toys Accessories (Post-War)

See also: Public Transport Models, Ships, Motor Cycles and Gift Sets sections.

Ref	Year(s)	Model name	Colours, features, details	Market Price Range
001	1954-56	Station Staff ('0' gauge)	1b Guard (flag in right hand), 1c Ticket Collector (right arm extended), 1d Driver, 1e Porter (with oblong bags), 1f Porter (standing), (renumbered from 1)	£90-120
001	1979-80	'Space War Station'	Dinky Builda card (54001)	£15-20
002	1954-56	Farmyard Animals (6)	2 x 2a horses, 2 x 2b cows, 1 x 2c pig, 1 x 2d sheep, simplified painting, (renumbered from 2)	£200-300
002	1979-80	'Blazing Inferno'	Dinky Builda card (54002)	£15-20
003	1954-56	Passengers ('0' gauge)	3a Woman (with child on left), 3b Businessman (Brown suit and case), 3c Male hiker (no stick), 3d Female hiker (Blue blouse), 3e Newsboy (Grey tray), 3f Woman (Light Red coat, round case), (renumbered from 3)	£90-120
004	1946-54	Engineering Staff ('0' gauge)	2 x 4b Fitter (all-Blue and all-Brown), 4c Storekeeper (all-Brown), 4d Greaser, 4e Engine-Room attendant, (renumbered from 4)	£90-120
005	1954-56	Train and Hotel Staff	('0' gauge), 5a Conductor, 2 x 5b waiters, 2 x 5c Porter (Brown or Blue), (renumbered from 5)	£90-120
006	1954-56	Shepherd Set	6a Shepherd (Green hat), 6b sheepdog (all-Black), 4 x 2b sheep, (renumbered from 6)	£150-200
007	1960-67	Petrol Pump Attendants	1 male (White overalls), 1 female (White coat), plastic	£15-20
008	1961-67	Fire Station Personnel	Set of 6 plastic fire-fighters in Blue uniforms plus hose, supplied in a bag. (Also present in GS 298)	£65-75
009	1962-66	Service Station Personnel	Set of 8 plastic figures in various colours and stances. Supplied in a bag or a Yellow box	£65-75
010	1962-66	Road Maintenance Personnel	Set of 6 workmen using pick, barrow, shovels, drill etc, plus hut, brazier, barrier, and 4 lamps Plastic, figures are 35 mm tall. Supplied in a bag or a Yellow box	£65-75
011	1954-56	Telegraph Messenger	Mid-Blue uniform, detailing in darker Blue, Brown pouch, 35 mm, (renumbered from 12d)	£10-15
012	1954-56	Postman	Mid-Blue body, darker Blue detail, Brown post bag and badge, 35 mm, (renumbered from 12e)	£15-20
013	1954-56	Cook's Man	(Agent for the Thomas Cook travel company), Dark Blue coat, 40 mm high, (renumbered from 13a)	£20-30
050	1961-68	Railway Staff ('0' gauge)	12 Blue plastic figures in a clear plastic box. Early issues contained a Policeman, later ones a Shunter	£40-50
051	1954-59	Station Staff ('00' gauge)	6 plastic figures in a clear plastic box (re-issue of pre-war Hornby-Dublo Set D1), (renumbered 1001)	£35-45
052	1961-69	Railway Passengers ('00')	11 plastic figures plus a seat, in a clear plastic box	£35-45
053	1954-59	Passengers ('00' gauge)	6 Blue plastic figures (re-issue of pre-war Hornby-Dublo Set D2), (renumbered 1003)	£35-45
	US issue:		6 metal figures in 'Dark Red' box marked 'Made in England, For sale in the United States by H.Hudson Dobson, P.O. Box 254 - 26th Street and Jefferson Avenue, Kenilworth, New Jersey	NGPP
054	1962-70	Railway Station Personnel	4 plastic figures plus 8 pieces of furniture in a clear plastic box, ('OO' gauge)	£35-45
1	1946-54	Station Staff	See the Gift Sets section.	
1a	1946-54	Station Master	Dark Blue uniform (cap, long coat), (in Set 001 till 1956)	£20-25
1b	1946-54	Guard	Dark Blue uniform, blowing whistle, flag in right hand (see Set 001)	£15-20
1c	1946-54	Ticket Collector	Blue uniform, only right arm is extended (in Set 001 till 1956)	£15-20
1e	1946-54	Porter with Bags	Blue uniform, oblong case in each hand (in Set 001 till 1956)	£15-20
1f	1946-54	Porter	Dark Blue uniform, standing, no luggage (in Set 001 till 1956)	£15-20
2	1946-54	Farmyard Animals	See the Gift Sets section.	
2a	1946-54	Horses	3 versions; Dark Brown horse (Black tail and mane), Light Brown horse (Light Brown tail and mane), White horse (2 in Set 002 till 1956)	£20-25
2b	1946-54	Cows	Light Brown, Dark Brown, or Black/White (2 in Set 002 till 1956)	£20-25
2c	1946-54	Pig	Cream body (in Set 002 till 1956)	£15-20
2d	1946-54	Sheep	White body with Black hand-painted detail (in Set 002 till 1956)	£15-20
3	1946-54	Passengers	See the Gift Sets section.	
3a	1946-54	Woman and Child	Woman in Green suit and hat (Brown scarf), child on left (see Set 003)	£20-25
3b	1946-54	Business Man	Brown suit, left hand holds attache case (in Set 003 till 1956)	£20-25
3c	1946-54	Male Hiker	Brown clothing, Khaki rucksack, no stick (in Set 003 till 1956)	£20-25
3d	1946-54	Female Hiker	Blue or Dark Blue skirt and shirt, stick in right hand (see Set 003)	£20-25
3e	1946-54	Newsboy	Dark Blue clothing, standing, papers in Grey tray (in Set 003 till 1956)	£20-25
3f	1946-54	Woman	Light Red coat, round case in right hand (in Set 003 till 1956)	£20-25
4	1946-54	Engineering Staff	See the Gift Sets section.	
4a	1946-54	Electrician	Blue overalls, White sleeves, carrying equipment (in Set 004 till 1956)	£15-20
4b	1946-56	Fitters	2 versions; one in Blue, the other Brown, carrying equipment (Set 004)	£15-20
4c	1946-56	Storekeeper	Brown coat, Black trousers, holding forms in right hand	£15-20
4d	1946-56	Greaser	Brown overalls, holding oil-can in right hand	£15-20
4e	1946-56	Engine-Room Attendant	Blue overalls, Blue sleeves	£10-15
5	1946-54	Train and Hotel Staff	See the Gift Sets section.	
5a	1946-54	Pullman Car Conductor	White jacket, Blue trousers, slightly open arms, casting as 1c	£20-25
5b	1946-56	Pullman Car Waiter	White jacket, Blue trousers, two slightly different poses are known	£20-25
5c	1946-56	Hotel Porter	Red jacket/Brown trousers, or Green jacket/Blue trousers, casting as 1e	£20-25
6	1946-54	Shepherd Set	See the Gift Sets section.	
6a	1946-56	Shepherd	Brown with Green hat	£40-50
6b	1946-56	Sheep-dog	All-Black sheep-dog	£20-30
12c	1946-54	Telephone Box	Red call-box with Black window frames, 58 mm high, (renumbered 750)	£20-30
12d	1946-54	Telegraph Messenger	Dark Blue body, picked out detail in darker Blue, Brown pouch, 35 mm, (renumbered 011)	£15-20
12e	1946-54	Postman	Mid-Blue body, darker Blue detail, Brown post bag and badge, 35 mm, (renumbered 012)	£15-20
13a	1952-54	Cook's Man	(An Agent for the Thomas Cook travel company), Blue coat, 40 mm high, (renumbered 013)	£20-30
30g	1948-50	Caravan	Orange/Cream body, 'Caravan Club', drawbar	£45-55
42a	1954-60	Police Hut	Dark Blue hut, 'POLICE' in Silver, 66 mm high, (renumbered 751)	£20-30
47	1946-50	Road Signs Set	See the Gift Sets section.	
49	1946-50	Petrol Pumps Set	See the Gift Sets section.	
49e	194?-?	Oil Bin	As pre-war 'Pratt's' Oil Bin but only available post-war in Set 49 and without 'Pratts' logo	£25-35
117	1963-69	Four Berth Caravan	Blue/Cream, clear roof, Fawn plastic interior and door	£25-35
			Primrose Yellow/Cream, Red plastic interior, Yellow plastic door	£25-35
			Primrose Yellow/Cream, Red plastic interior, Grey plastic door	£25-35
188	1961-63	Four Berth Caravan	Green/Cream or Blue/Cream, windows, detailed interior	£25-35
	1963-63		As previous model but larger windows, (this model replaced by 117)	£25-35

190	1956-62	Streamline Caravan	Mid-Blue lower body, Deep Cream upper body, Cream hubs, drawbar, metal jockey wheel	£25-35
			Yellow lower body, Cream upper body, Cream hubs, drawbar, metal jockey wheel	£25-35
	1962-64		As previous models but with knobbly Grey or Black plastic jockey wheel. 2 packing rings also in box	£25-35
386	1954-??	Lawn Mower	Green and Red, 140mm. Renumbered from 751	£50-75
502	1961-63	Garage	Blue/Grey plastic garage, opening door, 272 mm (French issue)	£90-110
750	1954-62	Telephone Box	Red call-box with Red window frames, 58 mm high, (renumbered from 12c)	£25-35
751	1949-54	Lawn Mower	Green and Red, 140mm. Renumbered 386	£50-75
751	1954-60	Police Box	Dark Blue hut, 'POLICE' in Silver, 66 mm high, (renumbered from 42a)	£25-35
752	1953-54	Goods Yard Crane	Yellow with Blue or Dark Blue, mazak or cast-iron base, (renumbered 973)	£40-50
753	1962-67	Police Crossing	Black/White box on traffic island with policeman directing traffic	£80-100
754	1958-62	Pavement Set	Grey cardboard paving slabs (20 items in box)	£50-60
755	1960-64	Lamp Standard (Single)	Grey/Fawn/Orange, plastic single-arm lamp on metal base	£20-30
756	1960-64	Lamp Standard (Double)	Grey/Fawn/Orange, plastic double-arm lamp on metal base	£30-40
760	1954-60	Pillar Box	Red and Black pillar box with 'E II R' cast-in	£25-35
763	1959-64	Posters for Hoarding	Six different coloured poster advertisements (on paper)	£25-35
764	1959-64	Posters for Hoarding	Six different coloured poster advertisements (on paper)	£25-35
765	1959-64	Road Hoardings (6 Posters)	Green plastic hoarding, 'David Allen and Sons Ltd'	£50-60
766-772		Road Sign Sets	See the Gift Sets section.	
773	1958-63	4 face Traffic Lights	Black/White, Black base, similar to 47a but without beacon, 62 mm	£15-20
777	1958-63	Belisha Beacon	Black/White post on Black base, Orange globe, casting as 47d, 51 mm	£10-15
778	1962-66	Road Repair Boards	Green and Red plastic warning signs, 6 different	£30-40
780	1950-54	Petrol Pumps Set	See the Gift Sets section.	
781	1955-62	'ESSO' Petrol Station	'ESSO' sign, no kiosk, 2 pumps ('ESSO' and 'ESSO EXTRA')	£60-75
782	1960-70	'SHELL' Petrol Station	'SHELL' sign, Green/Cream kiosk, 4 Red/Yellow 'SHELL' pumps	£60-75
783	1960-70	'BP' Petrol Station	'BP' sign, Green/Cream kiosk, 4 Green/White 'BP' pumps.	£60-75
785	1960-64	'SERVICE STATION'	Fawn and Red plastic, with 'BP' sign, 335 x 185 mm (unbuilt kit, boxed)	£175-225
786	1960-66	Tyre Rack with tyres	Green tyre rack with 21 assorted tyres and 'DUNLOP' on board.	£35-45
787	1960-64	Lighting Kit	Bulb and wire lighting kit for model buildings	£20-25
788	1960-68	Spare Bucket for 966	Grey bucket for use with 966 Marrel Multi-Bucket Unit	£10-15
790	1960-64	Granite Chippings	Plastic bag of imitation granite chippings (50790)	£15-20
791	1960-64	Imitation Coal	in a plastic bag.	£15-20
792	1960-64	Packing Cases (3)	White/Cream plastic packing cases, 'Hornby Dublo', 38 x 28 x 19 mm	£15-20
793	1960-64	Pallets	Orange, Black, Pale Green, Yellow and Lemon-Yellow. For 930 Pallet-Jekta Van and 404 Conveyancer	£15-20
794	1954-64	Loading Ramp	Blue loading ramp for use with 582/982 Carrimore Transporter, (renumbered from 994)	£15-20
846	1961-	Oil Drums	Pack of 6 oil drums. French issue	£15-20
847	1961-	Barrels	Pack of 6 barrels. French issue	£15-20
849	1961-	Packing Cases	Pack of 6 packing cases. French issue	£15-20
850	1961-	Crates of Bottles	Pack of 6 crates. French issue	£15-20
851	1961-	Sets of vehicle 'Loads'	Two each of 846 Oil Drums, 847 Barrels, 849 Packing Cases and 850 Crates	£50-60
954		Fire Station Plastic Kit	Red doors, Cream roof, Grey floor, clear roof, 'FIRE STATION'. 'DINKY TOYS' in Red	£200-250
994	1954-55	Loading Ramp	Renumbered from 794 to 994 then back to 794 after only a year!	£15-20
973	1954-59	Goods Yard Crane	Yellow with Blue or Dark Blue mazak or cast-iron base, steps in early issues, (renumbered from 752)	£40-50
1001	1952-54	Station Staff	See the Gift Sets section.	
1003	1952-54	Station Staff	See the Gift Sets section.	

Spare tyres, batteries, bulbs, etc.

020	1968-75	Spare tyre...	Black tyre, 16 mm. dia. YB (12)	£15-20
021	1970-75	Spare tyre...	Black tyre, 20 mm. dia. YB (12)	£15-20
022	1971-76	Spare tyre...	Black tyre, 16 mm. dia. YB (12)	£15-20
023	1971-76	Spare tyre...	Black tyre, 16 mm. dia. YB (12)	£15-20
024	1971-76	Spare tyre...	Black tyre, 23 mm. dia. YB (12)	£15-20
025	1976 only	Spare tyre...	Black tyre, 17 mm. dia. YB (12)	£15-20
026	1976 only	Spare tyre...	Black tyre, 21 mm. dia. YB (12)	£15-20
027	1976 only	Spare tyre...	Black tyre, 27 mm. dia. YB (12)	£15-20
028		Spare tyre...	Not issued	NPP
029	1976 only	Track	Black Track. Box of 6	£15-20
030	1968-76	Track	Black Track. Box of 6	£15-20
031	1976-78	Track	Black Track. Box of 6	£15-20
032	1973-76	Track	Black Track. Box of 6	£15-20
033	1973-76	Track	Black Track. Box of 6	£15-20
034	1971-72	Battery	1.5 volt battery	NGPP
035	1970-76	Battery	1.5 volt battery	NGPP
034	1964-76	Battery	1.5 volt battery	NGPP
036		Battery	1.5 volt battery for use with 276 Fire Tender and 277 Ambulance	NGPP
037		Lamp	Red light-bulb for use with 277	NGPP
038		Lamp	Blue (or Orange) light-bulb for use with model 276 Airport Fire Tender	NGPP
039		Lamp	Clear light-bulb for 952 Vega Coach	NGPP
081		Spare tyre...	White fine tread tyre, 14 mm. dia.	NGPP
082		Spare tyre...	Black narrow tread tyre, 20 mm. dia.	NGPP
083 (as 099)		Spare tyre...	Grey tyre, 20 mm. in diameter	NGPP
084		Spare tyre...	Black 'recessed' tyre, 18 mm. dia.	NGPP
085 (as 092)		Spare tyre...	White tyre, 15 mm. in diameter	NGPP
086		Spare tyre...	Black fine tread tyre, 16 mm. dia.	NGPP

087 (as 60687)	Spare tyre...	Black big 'tractor' tyre, 35 mm. dia.	NGPP
089 (as 60689)	Spare tyre...	Black 'tractor front tyre', 19 mm. dia.	NGPP
090 (as 60790)	Spare tyre...	Black fine tread tyre, 14 mm. dia.	NGPP
090 (as 60791)	Spare tyre...	White fine tread tyre, 14 mm. dia.	NGPP
091 (as 60036)	Spare tyre...	Black block tread tyre, 13 mm. dia.	NGPP
092 (as 14094)	Spare tyre...	Black block tread tyre, 15 mm. dia.	NGPP
092 (as 14095)	Spare tyre...	White block tread tyre, 15 mm. dia.	NGPP
093 (as 13978)	Spare tyre...	Black medium tractor tyre, 27mm dia.	NGPP
094 (as 6676)	Spare tyre...	Black smooth tyre, 18 mm. diameter	NGPP
095 (as 6677)	Spare tyre...	Black block tread tyre, 18 mm. dia.	NGPP
096 (as 7067)	Spare tyre...	Tyre, 15 mm. in diameter	NGPP
097 (as 7383)	Spare wheel	Solid rubber wheel, 12 mm. dia.	NGPP
098 (as 10118)	Spare wheel	Solid rubber wheel, 12 mm. dia.	NGPP
099 (as 10253)	Spare tyre...	Black block tread tyre, 20 mm. dia.	NGPP
099 (as 10253)	Spare tyre...	Grey block tread tyre, 20 mm. dia.	NGPP
6676 (as 094)	Spare tyre...	Black smooth tyre, 18 mm. diameter	NGPP
6677 (as 095)	Spare tyre...	Black block tread tyre, 18 mm. dia.	NGPP
7067 (as 095)	Spare tyre...	Tyre, 15 mm. in diameter	NGPP
7383 (as 097)	Spare wheel	Solid rubber wheel, 12 mm. dia.	NGPP
10118 (as 098)	Spare wheel	Solid rubber wheel, 12 mm. dia.	NGPP
10253 (as 099)	Spare tyre...	Black block tread tyre, 20 mm. dia.	NGPP
13978 (as 093)	Spare tyre...	Black medium tractor tyre, 27mm dia.	NGPP
14094 (as 092)	Spare tyre...	Black block tread tyre, 15 mm. dia.	NGPP
14095 (as 092)	Spare tyre...	White block tread tyre, 15 mm. dia.	NGPP
60036 (as 091)	Spare tyre...	Black block tread tyre, 13 mm. dia.	NGPP
606087 (as 087)	Spare tyre...	Black big 'tractor' tyre, 35 mm. dia.	NGPP
606089 (as 089)	Spare tyre...	Black 'tractor front tyre', 19 mm. dia.	NGPP
607090 (as 090)	Spare tyre...	Black fine tread tyre, 14 mm. dia.	NGPP
607091 (as 090)	Spare tyre...	White fine tread tyre, 14 mm. dia.	NGPP

For French Dinky Toys Catalogues, please see the Catalogues listing at the end of the French Meccano Dinky Toys section.

Ref	Year(s)	Publication	Cover features, details	Market Price Range

Pre-war Catalogues, leaflets and listings

Hornby 'Modelled Miniatures' were introduced in 1931 as model railway accessories. The first catalogue listings appeared in Hornby Train catalogues, Meccano catalogues and in the 'Meccano Magazine'.

Ref	Year(s)	Publication	Cover features, details	Market Price Range
-	1932-33	Hornby 'Book of Trains'	First 'Modelled Miniatures' listed as 'Railway Accessories'	£40-50
-	1932	Meccano trade catalogue	First 'Modelled Miniatures' listed as 'Railway Accessories'	£40-50
-	1933	'Meccano Magazine'	42 Hornby 'Modelled Miniatures' listed in December issue	£20-25
-	1933-34	Hornby 'Book of Trains'	Accessories are depicted in full colour	£40-50
-	1934	Meccano trade catalogue	'Modelled Miniatures' briefly renamed 'Meccano Miniatures'	£70-90
-	1934	'Meccano Magazine'	February issue contained the last published 'Modelled Miniatures' listing	£30-40
-	1934	'Meccano Magazine'	April issue contained the first 'Meccano Dinky Toys' listing	£30-40
-	1934	'Meccano Magazine'	The May, June, July, August, September and November issues each reflected the increasing number of varieties of 'Dinky Toys'	£15-20
-	1934	'Meccano Magazine'	'150 varieties of Dinky Toys' on double pages in October and December issues	£15-20
-	1934-35	Hornby 'Book of Trains'	Catalogue shows 150 'Dinky Toys' in full colour on a double page	£50-75
13/834/900	1934-35	Meccano Catalogue	Boat plane and model plus boy on cover, 3 pages of Dinky Toys	£40-50
13/834/900	1934-35	'Halford's Toys of Interest'	Includes all Dinky, Hornby, Meccano, etc.	£200-300
16/934/100	1934-35	'Hornby Trains/Meccano' Catalogue	Blue cover, full colour design of 'The World', lists 150 models of Dinky Toys	£70-90
-	1934-35	Meccano Book	Cover depicts viaduct over river, complete Dinky Toys range is listed	£70-90
-	1935	'Meccano Magazine'	January to November issues have various Dinky Toys listings	£15-20
-	1935	'Meccano Magazine'	December issue shows 200 varieties of Dinky Toys in Black and White	£15-20
7/835/65	1935-36	Hornby 'Book of Trains'	Catalogue features 200 varieties of Dinky Toys in full colour	£40-50
-	1935-36	Hornby/Meccano	Catalogue with the same cover as the 1934-35 issue	£70-90
-	1936	'Meccano Magazine'	The February and August issues featured a road layout and a competition; the May issue introduced the 'Queen Mary' model	£15-20
-	1936-37	Hornby 'Book of Trains'	The catalogue features full colour pictures of the Dinky Toys range	£40-50
-	1937	Hornby/Meccano	Catalogue with 1934-35 'World' cover again. Seven pages of listings	£50-70
-	1937	'Meccano Magazines'	Details given in the monthly listings of the superb new 'Army' range	£15-20
13/637/25	1937	8-page Leaflet	8 page fold-out buff leaflet. Front page depicts the 1937 Army models	£35-45
13/638/1150	1938	Hornby/Meccano	74 page Catalogue, full Dinky Toys listings. Numerous b/w pictures	£30-40
13/638/1150/UK	1938	'Wonder Book of Toys'	Two boys with Meccano models plus 11 pages with Dinky Toys	£30-40
8/1238/25	1938	'DINKY TOYS' Catalogue	(Booklet). Cover shows boy and 6 models including 29c Bus, 151a Tank, and 63 Mayo Composite Aircraft. Brown print on pale-yellow paper	£100-125
-	1938	'Meccano Magazine'	Details of the full range (with pictures) are published each month	£25-35
1/439/10	1939	'DINKY TOYS' leaflet	'New Products' leaflet detailing items such as the Presentation Aeroplane Sets Nos 64 and 65. Black printing on pinkish paper	£40-50
-	1939	'MECCANO' booklets	with complete Dinky Toys listings, various	NGPP
13/639/1	1939	Hornby/Meccano	74 page Catalogue, full Dinky Toys listings and Black/White pictures	£100-125
13/639/11500 UK	1939	'A Wonder Book of Toys'	Green and Yellow cover depicts two boys with their Meccano models. The booklet includes 13 pages of Dinky Toys information	£100-125
2/739/10 (1P)	1939	'DINKY TOYS' Catalogue	Famous Red/Yellow cover picture of schoolboy with outstretched arm and 17 models. Contains 14 black and white pages	£300-400
-		'Toys Of Quality'	Maroon Express train features on cover plus 'The Hornby Railway Co' logo. 13 pages of Dinky Toys listings are included	£40-50
-	1939	Trade catalogue	Cover depicts boy with Dinky Toys and Hornby pictures with 'MECCANO TOYS OF QUALITY' logo	£40-50
2/939/20	1939	'Halford's Toys of Interest'	Includes all Dinky, Hornby, Meccano, etc.	£300-400
2/1139/20(3P) UK	1939	'DINKY TOYS' Catalogue	Superb Red and Yellow cover picture of schoolboy with outstretched arm and 17 models. Contains 10 Black/White pages of listings and pictures	£300-400
-	1939	'Meccano Magazine'	Each month contained Dinky Toys listings	£15-20
1/440 /100	1940	'Meccano Products'	Four page leaflet, buff paper, brown printing	£20-30
16/1040 /100	1940	'Meccano Products'	Four page leaflet, off-white paper, green printing (no pictures)	£20-30
16/1040 /200	1940	'DINKY TOYS' leaflet	Listing of models with pictures	£20-30
-	1940	'Meccano Magazine'	Wartime Dinky aircraft and the Meccano 'Spitfire Fund' are featured	£20-30
16/541/25 UK	1941	'DINKY TOYS' leaflet	Wartime camouflaged aircraft feature in this leaflet	£20-30
16/641/20 UK	1941	'DINKY TOYS' leaflet	Similar to previous leaflet, military models listed	£20-30
16/1141/20 UK	1941	'DINKY TOYS' leaflet	Listing of models and retail prices	£20-30

Full Dinky Toys listings also appeared in the toy catalogues of major retailers such as Gamages and Bentalls. These catalogues are difficult to find. Each: £30-40

Post-War Catalogues, leaflets and listings
Early Post-War period, 1945 – 1954

There were at least two editions per annum so the following listings are not complete. The 'leaflet' approach reflects the shortage of paper in early post-war years.

Ref	Year	Type	Description	Price
16/1145/75 UK	1945	Meccano leaflet	leaflet lists the models to be reintroduced after the War and features pictures of 23e, 29c, 39a, 62s, 62p. Sepia print on cream paper	£15-25
16/546/30 UK	1946	Meccano leaflet	Sepia printed listing on cream paper featuring pictures of models 70a, 38c, 29c, 23e	£15-25
16/1146/65 UK	1946	Meccano leaflet	Blue/Black print on cream paper, featuring models 70a, 38c, 70b, 38e	£15-25
16/347/50 UK	1947	Meccano leaflet	Brown print on light cream paper. Models depicted are 70a, 70b, 70c, 70e, 38c, 38e, 38f, and 153a Jeep	£15-25
16/448/30	1948	Meccano General Products	booklet with green printing on light cream paper	£15-25
16/948/200	1948		Same as previous issue but with mauve print on light cream paper	£15-25
16/1248/5	1948	'Dinky Toys Tyre Sizes'	Simple Leaflet giving information on Dinky Toys spare tyres	£15-25
16/449/100	1949	Meccano General Products	booklet with brown printing on light cream paper	£15-25
13/1049/150	1949	Meccano General Products	8 pp, cover has boys looking at globe circled by Hornby Trains, Meccano and Dinky Toys	£15-25
	1949	Independent shop listings	Full Dinky Toys listings and pictures featured in the catalogues published by the larger toy shops such as Bentalls, Gamages, etc	£15-25
16/250/100	1950	Meccano Leaflet	A leaflet of two pages, printed in purple with drawings of 22 models	£15-25
16/450/150	1950	Meccano General Products	booklet with pale Blue/Black printing on light cream paper	£15-25
16/550/75	1950	Meccano Leaflet	A leaflet folded into three 'pages', with listings all Meccano items including Dinky Builder	£15-25
13/1050/80 UK	1950	Dinky Toys Leaflet	A 12-page catalogue, printed on cream paper with sepia pictures, 5"x3" approximately	£25-35
-	1950	Independent shop listings	Full Dinky Toys listings and pictures featured in the catalogues of larger toy shops such as Gamages, Bentalls, etc	£15-25
16/251/33	1951	Meccano General Products	booklet with brown printing on light cream paper	£10-15
-	1951	Independent shop listings	Full Dinky Toys listings and pictures featured in the catalogues of larger toy shops such as Bentalls, Gamages, etc	£15-20
16/352/120	1952	Price List	A single sheet printed both sides in dark blue, listing 66 models with 23 model drawings	£10-15
13/952/250	1952	Price List	Beige leaflet with pictures and prices	£10-15
13/953/678	1953	Meccano Catalogue	Includes Dinky Toys, Meccano and Hornby Dublo	£15-20
16/453/500	1953	4-page Leaflet	Buff leaflet; front page shows date '15th April 1953' and boy shouting 'DINKY TOYS'	£15-25
16/753/75 (2P)	1953	4-page Leaflet	Printed in dark brown, with numerous illustrations	£15-20
16/853/25	1953	Price List	Beige leaflet with pictures and prices	£15-20
16/953/200	1953	Price List	no details at present	£10-15
16/454/50 (7P)	1954	4-page Leaflet	Printed in dark brown, with numerous illustrations	£10-15
16/854/25	1954	Price List	Beige leaflet with pictures and prices	£10-15
16/255/100 (1P)	1955	4-page Leaflet	Dinky Toys and Dinky Supertoys listed; sepia printing	£10-15

UK Catalogue editions, 1952 – 1965

The series included fourteen editions although not all issues were given an edition number. More than one catalogue was issued in some years. It was common for catalogues to be overprinted with the name and address of the toy retailer. In addition to issuing Dinky Toys catalogues, Meccano Ltd continued to issue 'Meccano Toys Of Quality' leaflets which provided a full listing of Dinky Toys with their retail prices plus details of their 'Hornby', 'Hornby-Dublo' and 'Meccano' products. As many as five printings per annum were produced using green, pink, blue or buff paper. When in perfect condition these leaflets sell for £5-8 each.

Ref	Year	Type	Description	Price
16/152/50	1952	(February) 16 pages	Cover features unknown 'C6321'	£55-65
16/452/50	1952	(April) 16 pages	As previous issue	£55-65
15/852/165	1952	(September) 16 pages	Cover shows hands holding 27f Estate Car, 'Dinky Toys' logo	£55-65
?	1953	24 page catalogue	Cover shows boy wearing green sweater, 'Dinky Toys' and 'Price 3d'	£55-65
7/953/150	1953	24 page catalogue	As next item: 7/953/360.	
7/953/360	1953	(1st October) 24 pages	(1) Cover features 555 Fire Engine, 522 Big Bedford Lorry and 25x Breakdown Lorry, price '2d'	£55-65
13/953/678	1953	(1st October)	(2) Cover shows 'Meccano Magic Carpet', two boys plus globe with flag	£55-65
7/754/600	1954	(1st September) 24 pages	Cover features 157 Jaguar, 480 'Kodak' Van, 641 Army Truck, 'Dinky Toys' logo, price '2d'	£40-50
7/455/250	1955	(May) 8 page leaflet	251, 641, 170 and 401 on cover, 'Dinky Toys' and 'Dinky Supertoys'	£20-30
7/755/515	1955	24 page catalogue	'Dinky Toys','Supertoys', 481 'Ovaltine' Van on cover, ('2d')	£40-50
7/456/800	1956	(June) 32 pages	Cover has 942 'REGENT' Tanker, 255 Mersey Tunnel 'Police' Land Rover, 157 Jaguar XK120, 'Dinky Toys' & 'Dinky Supertoys', '2d'	£40-50
71056/125 (2P)	1956	(October) 32 pages	Same as previous issue, 2nd printing	£30-40
7/657/820	1957	(August) 28 pages	Cover shows 290 'DUNLOP' Double Decker Bus etc, 'Dinky Toys', and 'Dinky Supertoys', price '2d UK'	£40-50
7/458/856	1958	28 page catalogue	Houses of Parliament shown on front cover with 'Dinky Toys' and 'Dinky Supertoys', price '2d UK'	£40-50
7/559/900	1959	28 page catalogue	Red Jaguar XK120 Coupe (157) on front cover with 'Dinky Toys' and 'UK Seventh Edition', price '3d'	£40-50
7/3/800	1960	32 page catalogue	Motorway bridge on cover, 'Dinky Toys' and 'UK Eighth Edition'	£40-50
7/561/700	1961	32 page catalogue	Black/Yellow cover with 6 models, 'Dinky Toys', 'UK 9th Edition'	£40-50
7/562/600	1962	32 page catalogue	Cover features 120 Jaguar 'E' type, 'Dinky Toys', price '2d'	£40-50
7/263/400	1963	?	No details available for this reference number	£25-35
13/163/200	1963	32 page catalogue	Motor Show stands featured on cover, '11th Edition', 'UK', '2d'	£25-35
13/763/400	1963	32 page catalogue	11th Edition, 2nd impression	£25-35
7/164/450	1964	8 page catalogue	'Widest Range & Best Value In The World' and 'Dinky Toys' logos Price '3d'	£25-35
7/764/450 (2nd.Ptg.)	1964	8 page catalogue	(2nd printing). As 7/164/450 except that page 8 shows Bedford TK instead of accessories	£25-35
7/265/200	1965	16 page catalogue	Rolls-Royce (127) on cover with 'Dinky Toys by Meccano' Price '3d'	£25-35
7/865/135 (2 ptg)	1965	16 page catalogue	(2nd printing). Cover features cars 127, 128, 133, 151 and 178	£25-35

UK Catalogue editions, 1966 – 1978

Ref	Year	Description	Details	Price
72561/2	1966	106 page catalogue	'1st Edition', '6d', 'Always Something New From Dinky' on the cover. Bound-in (pink) price list.	£25-30
72561/2	1966	(after 21st July)	2nd edition, same cover as 1st, 104 pages plus (buff) price list	£20-25
72571	1967	104 page catalogue	'No.3', '6d' 12 models on cover, same logo as 72561/2. Price list (green paper) included	£20-25
			Same as previous entry, but '2nd Printing' appears on the first page of the price list	£20-25
72580	1968	104 page catalogue	'No.4', '6d', Spectrum Pursuit Vehicle (104) on cover. Logo as 72561/2. Buff price list	£20-25
72585	1969	(May) 24 pages	'No.5', '3d'. 102 'Joe's Car', and same logo as 72561/2. '1st Printing 1st May 1969'	£15-20
		(Sept) 24 pages	2nd printing of 72585	£15-20
165000	1970	(May) 24 page catalogue	'No.6', '3d', many models on cover. Same logo as 72561/2.	£15-20
	1971	(Feb) 24 page catalogue	'2nd Printing, 1st February 1971' of 165000	£15-20
100103	1971	24 page catalogue	'No.7', '2p', '1971 Meccano Tri-ang Ltd' on rear cover. Same logo as on 72561/2. (Note the change to Decimal Currency in 1971)	£10-15
100107	1972	(June) 28 pages	'No.8', '2p', 683 Chieftain Tank. '1st Printing, June 1972'	£10-15
			2nd printing of 100107	£15-20
100108	1972	28 pages	'No.8', 725 Phantom, 784 Goods Train etc. on cover, but no date or price. No price list	£10-15
100109	1973	40 pages	'No.9', '3p', '1st Printing'. Shows 924 'Centaur', 'Dinky Toys'	£10-15
		(October) 40 pages	2nd printing of 100109	£15-20
100113	1974	(May) 48 pages	'No.10', '4p', cover shows 731 S.E.P.E.C.A.T. and 'Dinky Toys'	£10-15
100115 UK	1975	(June) 48 pages	'No.11', '5p', 'Dinky Toys' and 675 Motor Patrol Boat on cover	£10-15
100118 UK	1976	48 page catalogue	'No.12', '5p', 'Dinky Toys' and 358 'USS Enterprise' on cover	£10-15
100122 (UK)	1977	44 page catalogue	'No.13' and '5p'. Cover features 357 Klingon Battle Cruiser	£5-10
100100	1978	44 page catalogue	'No.14', '5p', 180 Rover 3500 on front cover. 'Airfix Group' logo on rear.	£5-10

Leaflets and Price Lists, 1954 – 1978

Further information. It is known that other leaflets, literature and price lists were published. The Editor would welcome more information to add to these listings.

Ref	Year	Type	Details	Price
16/854/25	1954	**Price List**	no details	£30-40
16/155/100	1955	**Leaflet / Price List**	no details	£30-40
7/455/250	1955	**Leaflet**	no details	£30-40
16/655/25	1955	**'Hamley's' Leaflet**	no details	£30-40
16/156/225	1956	**Leaflet**	no details	£30-40
16/556/500	1956	**Leaflet / Price List**	no details	£30-40
16/656/525	1956	**Leaflet / Price List**	no details	£30-40
no ref	1957	**Booklet**	Yellow cover, 'A NEW SERIES' and 'DUBLO DINKY TOYS' in red	£30-40
DT/CF/3 16/257/250 (1P)	1957	**Leaflet and Price List**	Yellow front leaflet '1st January 1957', pictures of 716, 162, 626, and 250 Fire Engine, 'Dinky Toys' and 'Dinky Supertoys' in Red	£30-40
DT/CF/4 UK 16/757/250 (2P)	1957	**Leaflet and (8-page) Price List**	Yellow front folding leaflet. 'July 1957'. Pictures of 418 Leyland Comet, 923 'Heinz' Van, and 164 Vauxhall + 190 Caravan. 'Dinky Toys' and 'Dinky Supertoys' in Red	£30-40
16/857/500	1957	**Leaflet / Price List**	no details	£30-40
DT/CL/20 16/1157/100 UK	1957	**Two-sided Leaflet**	'Dublo Dinky Toys' in Red on Yellow. Pictures of first 3 issues: 064, 065, 066	£30-40
16/958/100	1958	**Leaflet**	Car Carrier and Trailer leaflet	£30-40
10/758/450	1958	**Leaflet / Price List**	no details	£30-40
DT/CF/5 16/159/100	1959	**Illustrated Price List**	Colour cover showing 983 Transporter and cars, etc.	£30-40
DT/CF/6 16/759/100 2ndP	1959	**Price List with colour pictures**	Leaflet cover shows nos. 998, 967, 968 and 986. Dated '1959/UK' on front	£30-40
10/1259/50	1959	**Price List**	no details	£30-40
DT/CF/7 16/160/100 (3P)	1960	**Illustrated Price List**	Colour cover with 666 Missile Vehicle and 785 Service Station, etc.	£30-40
DT/CF/8 16/160/100 (4P)	1960	**Illustrated Price List**	Colour cover with 930 Pallet-Jekta plus GS 951 Fire Service, etc.	£30-40
DT/CF/11 8/561/100	1961	**Illustrated Price List**	(72535/02) Colour cover with 4 cars and 'Purchase Tax Surcharges 26th July 1961'	£30-40
72557/02	1965	**Leaflet**	Cover with 133, 127, 128, 151 and 171, with price list	£30-40
16/766/50M	1966	**Leaflet / Price List**	no details	£30-40
72579	1967	**Leaflet**	Trade Fair leaflet, 'THUNDERBIRDS'	£30-40
72939	1967	**Leaflet / Price List**	no details	£30-40
72569	1968	**Leaflet**	Features 103-105 'Captain Scarlet' vehicles	£30-40
100217	1971	**Leaflet**	Four page 'Action Kits' leaflet	£20-30
100261	1971	**Single sheet**	Full-colour flyer featuring 'All Action Fighting Vehicles'	£20-30
no ref.	72-75	**Dinky Driver's Diary**	6 models shown on the cover; descriptions and diagrams of 1970s models inside	£20-30
no ref.	1979	**Trade Catalogue 1979**	'Fifty New Models', 11fi x 8⁄ inches	£20-30

Catalogues

Meccano Trade Catalogues listing Dinky Toys

These were issued for many years but little information has been recorded (please send any information that you may have). For example: Ref. 100126 – **1978 Trade Catalogue** with 'Todays World', 'Todays Meccano',

Todays Dinky Toys' on the cover plus colour design of late 1970s models on Motorway with 'Meccano' buildings in background. Ref. 100102 – **1979 Trade Catalogue** 'Today's Meccano & Dinky'.

Meccano Catalogues 1954 - 1958

with colour 'Dinky Toys' and 'Hornby-Dublo' listing. Details known to the compiler relate solely to issues in the mid-1950's period. 'MECCANO TOYS OF QUALITY' logo on each cover.

13/654/995UK	1954-55	**24 pages, price '2d'** ....Cover depicts 4 boys on a desert island. Black/White pictures	**£20-25**
13/655/797UK	1955-56	**28 pages, price '2d'** ....Cover shows boys looking in toyshop window Black/White pictures	**£20-25**
13/756/525UK	1956	**32 pages, price '4d'** ....Cover depicts Dinky Toys, Hornby-Dublo, and a Meccano helicopter. This is a large catalogue with colour printing........................	**£30-35**
13/757/500UK	1957	**32 pages, price '4d'** ....Famous cover showing Meccano Tower, Hornby-Dublo train crossing a viaduct and Dinky Toys passing beneath. Large, with colour pictures........	**£50-75**
13/758/450UK	1958	**20 pages, price '4d'** ....Cover depicts boy, Hornby-Dublo train, 8 Dinky Toys and a Meccano model. Includes some superb engine pictures........................	**£30-35**

Meccano Magazines, 1942 - 1952

During the latter part of the war and especially during the early post-war years when Dinky Toys catalogues were not issued, the Meccano Magazine was the main source of new information for collectors. It advised on the reintroduction of models after the war and of the forthcoming new releases. Consequently the Magazines of this period are highly collectable in their own right.

1942 - September 1943. No Dinky Toys adverts or listings appeared.
September 1943 - December 1944. Back page adverts for Meccano incorporated listing and pictures of De Havilland Flamingo Aircraft and Buick 'Viceroy' Saloon.
January - November 1945. Back page adverts said 'Sorry, not available but will be ready after the war'.
December 1945. Advert on back page announced 'Ready during December'.
1946. Virtually every month a new model was added to the listing printed on the inside front cover. A picture of each model was shown.
January - September 1947. New models added regularly each month.
October 1947. First advert appears of Dinky Supertoys with pictures of 501 Foden Diesel Wagon, 502 Foden Flat Truck, 503 Foden Flat Truck with Tailboard, 511 Guy 4 ton Lorry, 512 Guy Flat Truck, 513 Guy Flat Truck with Tailboard, and 701 Short 'Shetland' Flying Boat.
1948. Single page advert every month, new models continually introduced.
1949, 1950, 1951. Double page advert each month listing new models.
1952. Double page adverts each month. The December issue shows Gift Sets No.1 Farm Gear and No.2 Commercial Vehicles.
Prices for Meccano Magazines of this period range between **£10-15** each.

Meccano Magazines 1952 - 1975

With the introduction of yearly Dinky Toys catalogues from 1952 the Meccano Magazine lost its somewhat unique role as a combined magazine/catalogue. However, with the help of 'The Toyman' and his monthly articles plus superb colour advertising of new models, the Magazine continued to provide a valuable service for collectors. Meccano Magazines of this period are in the price range of **£5-10**.

Dinky Toys Club Licences, Newsletters, etc.

no ref.	19??-??	**Dinky Toys Club Certificate** ....(unused) **£100-125**
no ref	1955-??	**Dinky Toys Club Enamel Badge**....................**£35-45**
no ref	1955-??	**Dinky Toys Club 'Welcome' Letter** ....NGPP

Dinky Toys Club Newsletters

?	195?	**Dinky Toys Club Newsletter No.1**, '3d', 'Greetings from Australia' on cover......................NGPP
19/759/35	1959?	**Newsletter No.2**, '3d'. Stirling Moss on cover, 150 Rolls-Royce in centre-fold..........**£100-125**
?	19??	**Newsletter No.3**, 'M1' on cover...........................NGPP

DTC/L/1	1958-59	**Collector's Licence**, Brown cover, 16 pages ..**£125-150**
DTC/L/2	1959-60	**Collector's Licence**, Red cover, 16 pages........**£125-150**
DTC/L/3	1960-61	**Collector's Licence**, Green cover, 16 pages **£125-150**
DTC/L/4	1961-62	**Collector's Licence**, Yellow cover, 16 pages ...**£125-150**

Factory drawings

UNISSUED MODELS
A number of models were planned but not actually produced by Meccano. This is list of known factory drawings and plans for such models.
Austin A40 Van 'OMNISPORT' drawing dated 31-8-57. **Guy Warrior Van 'GOLDEN SHRED'** drawing dated 26-3-57, Job No. 14794. **Leyland Fuel Tanker** drawing dated 30-9-65, Job No. 62520. **Single-Deck Bus** drawing dated 14-5-34, Job No. 6763. **Jowett Javelin Saloon** drawing dated 10-10-47, Job No. 12886. **Renault Fregate** drawing dated 4-7-57, Job No. 20106. **Triumph Dolomite** (intended 38e) drawing dated 1939. **Vampire Jet** drawing dated 27-11-45, Job No. 12157. **Firebrand Aircraft** drawing dated 18-12-45, Job No. 12159.

PRODUCTION MODELS
In October 2000, Christie's South Kensington sold part of the Mike and Sue Richardson collection of Meccano General Assembly Drawings for the Dinky Toys range. The following is a small selection of items from that sale. The reference numbers are 'Job Numbers'.

Drawings – English Saloon Cars. 13866/7 **Jaguar XK120 and Base**, 20335 **Base XK150**, 20329 **Spring XK150**, 13381/3 **Austin Atlantic Body and**

Base, 20121/2 and 20118/9 **Rolls-Royce Silver Wraith** (various parts), 62035/6/7 **Chauffeur and Passengers**, 13360/1/2 **Rover 75**, 14844/5 **Spring and Base for Humber Hawk**, 14982/4 **Singer Gazelle Body and Base**, 14088/9 **Austin A30 Body and Base**, 14721/3 **Sunbeam Rapier Body and Base**, 14721/3 **Sunbeam Rapier Body and Base**, 14745/7 **Hillman Minx Body and Base**, 7889 **Ford Zephyr Body**, 14097/8 **Vauxhall Cresta Body and Base**, 14937/8 **Fiat 600 Body and Base**, 14847/8 **Austin A105 Body and Base**. (*All 1950s*). In all, 33 items sold in one lot for **£750**

Drawings – Buses. 10897/8 **Double Deck Omnibus Body and Base** (both with dyeline copies), Memo 15954 about 17693 **'Dunlop' Transfers**, 13480/2 **Luxury Coach and Base**, 13750/2 **Duple Roadmaster Coach and Base**, 13424/6 **Observation Coach and Base**. 12 items in one lot sold for **£420**

Drawings – Fodens. 12163/6 and 12822 **Cab and Chassis, Body and Tanker Body**, 12164/5/9 **Bogie, Clip and Washer for Spare Wheel** + 7 drawings for **Chains, Stanchions, Tank parts**, etc. 13 items sold for **£550**

Drawings – Leyland Octopus. 7874 **Cab and Chassis**, 7875 **Front Bogie**, and Memo 20649 **Label for 'ESSO'**. 3 items sold as one lot for **£120**

Overseas Catalogues

Catalogues were often adapted so that they could be switched for use in most countries in the world irrespective of the language or the currency used. An example of this is the 1965 catalogue:

72257/02UK 1965	**UK catalogue** ....16 pages. Cover depicts 5 cars namely Nos.127, 128, 133 and 171 plus a description of various model features **£25-35**
72557 1965	**Overseas edition** ....16 pages. The cover is the same but replacing the features listing is a panel with 'Precision Diecast Scale Models' printed in English, German, French, Spanish, Italian and Swedish. The catalogue pages contain only the basic English model name and number - all the English text having been removed. The models are the same as 72257/02 ....**£25-35**
72559 1965	**Overseas edition** ....24 pages. Whilst the cover is the same as 72557, the listings are entirely different for they feature both English and French Dinky Toys, including the French issues sold in the UK **£40-50**

Price lists. Prior to the overseas editions being despatched, price lists in the correct language and currency would be inserted.
The Editor would like to express his thanks to the many collectors around the world who have contributed to this listing. New information would be welcomed.

For French Dinky Toys Catalogues, please see the Catalogues listing at the end of the French Meccano Dinky Toys section.

Africa   (Distributor unknown)

KENYA
1961 **Illustrated List** **£75-100**
RHODESIA
1953 **Illustrated Price List** **£75-100**
1954 **Illustrated Price List** **£75-100**
SOUTH AFRICA
1955 **Catalogue '7/655/20'**, Ovaltine Van + 7 others, 24 pages **£50-75**
TANGANYIKA & UGANDA, Combined Catalogue (year unknown)...**£75-100**

Australia   Agents (in 1952): E. G. Page & Co. (Sales) Pty., Ltd., Danks Building, 324 Pitt Street, Sydney, Australia.

1950 **Meccano General Products Catalogue '13/550/68'**, as 1949 UK Catalogue, 'Meccano World-Famous Toys'...........................NGPP
1952 **Catalogue '5/352/37.5'**, Cover has sepia drawings of hands holding 27f, with 139b, 25x and 532 ....NGPP
1952 **Catalogue '13/852/12'**, Cover shows boy with green sweater. An example sold at auction in 1998 for **£250**
1955 **Catalogue '7/655/30'**, 282, 591, 290, 961, 430, 251, 962 and 481 on cover..NGPP
1956 **Leaflet '16/456/15'**, 8 page folded leaflet with coloured drawings and price list. Cover has 132, 255 and 781 ....NGPP
1957 **Leaflet '16/357/7.5 (1P)'**, folded colour leaflet with 716, 162, 626 and 955 on the front............................NGPP
1957 **Leaflet '16/757/15 (2P)'**, folded colour leaflet with 932, 923, 164, 190 and 'Dinky Toys and Dinky Supertoys' on billboard......NGPP
1957 **Catalogue '7/757/30'**, Piccadilly Circus, colour, vertical, no prices, 28 pages **£75-100**
1958 **Catalogue '7/658/40'**, Cover as UK issue ....NGPP
1959 **Catalogue '7/559/40'**, Cover as UK issue ....NGPP
1960 **Catalogue '23/560/40'**, Cover as UK issue ....NGPP
1961 **Catalogue '7/61/40'**, Cover as UK issue ....NGPP
1962 **Catalogue '7/662/40'**, Cover as UK issue ....NGPP
1963 **Catalogue '13/163/100'**, Cover as UK issue ....NGPP
1964 **Catalogue '7/364/100'**, Cover as UK issue ....NGPP
1969 **Catalogue '72585'**, Cover as UK issue ....NGPP
1971 **Catalogue '100103'**, Cover as UK issue ....NGPP
1978 **Catalogue '100100'** ('No.14'), '20c' on cover, 44 pages. 'Liberty Trading Pty Ltd, Surrey Hills, Marshall St. NSW' on checklist........NGPP

Belgium and Luxembourg (French printing)

Agents: P FREMINEUR et Fils, Rue des Bogards 1, Bruxelles 1

1936 **Meccano Catalogue '13/736/265'** **£200-300**
1954 **Catalogue '16/1053 /10'**, Same cover as 1953 UK issue **£30-40**
1954 **Catalogue '16/1054 /2'**, Same cover as 1954 UK issue **£30-40**
1956 **Catalogue '16/656/156'** (DT/CL/5). Cover as 1956 UK issue **£30-40**
1958 **Leaflet '16/1258/12.5 Belgium'** ('DT/CL/32' on cover). Printed in England. 168 Singer and 178 Plymouth on cover. Text in French and Flemish. **£30-40**
1959 **Catalogue '7/539/-'**, Red Jaguar XK140 on cover...........................**£30-40**
1960 **Catalogue** (no ref.). English and French models in one catalogue, 48 pages. Printed and issued only in Belgium and Luxembourg. Cover depicts Land Rover plus two French Dinky Toys cars. 'Frs 3-'.......................**£75-100**

Belgium (Flemish printing)

1954 **Illustrated price list '16/1054 /2'** **£40-50**
1966 **1st Edition price list '72551'**, in French and Flemish, 164 pages ...**£40-50**

Canada   Agents: Meccano Limited, 675 King Street West, Toronto and 187 - 189 Church Street, Toronto.

1934 **Leaflet '10/34'**, Yellow leaflet with 'LOCKE BROS. OF MONTREAL' stamp **£150-200**
1937 **Leaflet '13/637/5'**, Eight page leaflet....................**£150-200**
1938 **Leaflet '7/38'**, Ten page fold-out leaflet with full range .**£150-200**
1940 **Leaflet '13/840/5'**, 12 black and white pages, 8.75" x 5.875". Cover shows boy with outstretched arms plus 62h, 151a, 36g, 43a, and 33r. 'The Fascinating Collecting Hobby'....**£150-200**
1941 **Leaflet '6/41'**, 12 page fold-out leaflet showing full range.......**£150-200**
1951 **Catalogue '16/351/25'**, 16 pages, boy + 3 models, blue pictures **£60-70**
1953 **Catalogue '7/953/150'**, 555 Fire Engine, 522 Big Bedford, 25x Breakdown Truck, 28 pages **£50-60**
1955 **Illustrated price list: '16/355/90'**, Off-White leaflet..............**£30-35**
1955 **Catalogue '7/655/90'**, Illustration of Bedford 'Ovaltine' Van plus seven other models.....................................**£50-60**
1956 **Catalogue '7/556/90'**, Regent Tanker/Tunnel, 1st June 1956 in colour, 32 pages **£50-60**
1956 **Illustrated price leaflet '16/656/18c'**, (DT/CL/4) in colour, featuring 131 Cadillac and 660 Tank Transporter **£15-20**
1956 **Illustrated price leaflet '16/756/18'**, in colour, featuring 706 Vickers 'Air France' Airliner **£15-20**
1957 **Catalogue '7/757/90'**, Piccadilly Circus, vertical, in colour, with prices, 28 pages **£50-60**
1959 **Catalogue '7/559/90'**, Red Jaguar + 6 models on cover, in colour, 28 pages **£50-60**
1960 **Catalogue '7/560/90'**, cover as UK issue **£40-50**
1961 **Catalogue '3/41/25 7252 3/42'**, Black with 7 models and '9th' on cover, Canada/English, 32 pages **£40-50**
1963 **Catalogue '13/163/100 7254 2/42'**, ...Motor Show 11th, Canada/English, 32 pages **£40-50**
1963 **Catalogue '13/1063 /50 7254 8/42'**, Flyer 8in x 10¼in. 10 models on cover, 'Canada 1963', 8 pages **£10-15**
1964 **Trade Catalogue '7/364/150'**, 8 page catalogue plus 4 page trade price list (half catalogue width, in centre)...............NGPP
1964 **Catalogue '7/464/150 72550/42'**, '12th', 8in x 11in, Canada/English, 8 pages **£10-15**
1964 **Catalogue** (no ref.). Flyer, 5fi x 3fi, shows 6 Hong Kong models, 12 pages **£10-15**
1965 **Catalogue** (no ref.) 1st Ed. 8fi x 5fi, 5 models on cover, 16 pp **£20-25**
1966 **Catalogue '72561'**, 1st Edition, 108 pages **£30-40**
1966 **Catalogue '72561'**, 2nd Edition, 106 pages **£30-40**
1967 **Catalogue '72571'**, 3rd Edition, 106 pages **£30-40**
1968 **Catalogue '72580'**, 4th Edition, 106 pages **£30-40**
1969 **Catalogue '72585'**, 5th Edition, 24 pages **£20-30**
1970 **Catalogue '165000'**, cover as UK issue **£15-25**
1971 **Catalogue '100103'**, cover as UK issue **£15-25**

Cyprus   1969 **Catalogue** (no ref.), Same as UK issue **£50-75**

Egypt   1952 **Catalogue '5/652/2'**, Different p.9 from UK issue with pictures of US 39 Series cars and British cars **£100-150**

Eire and Channel Islands

Agents: S.J. Gearey, 1 St Stephens Green, Dublin. (Ceased trading 1968).
Agents from 1969: Kilroy Bros Ltd, Shanowen Road, Whitehall, Dublin 9.

1955 **Catalogue '7/755/20'**. 'Eire' and 'C.I.' on cover.................**£40-50**
1959 **Catalogue '7/659/75'**, 'Eire' on cover.............................**£40-50**
1964 **Catalogue '7/364/7'**, 'Eire' on cover.............................**£30-40**
1969 **Catalogue 'No.5'**, 'Irish' on cover, (agents: Kilroy Bros Ltd).........**£30-40**

Catalogues

Hong Kong

Representatives: W.R.Loxley & Co. Ltd., Jardine House, 11th Floor, 20 Pedder Street, Hong Kong.

1959 **Illustrated price list 'DT/CF/5'**, same cover as UK issue.............**£50-75**

Italy

Agents: Alfredo Parodi, Piazza 8, Marcellino 6, Genova.

1957 **Leaflet '16/657/5'**, with 101-105 ....**£30-35**
1957 **Leaflet '16/3/57/5'**, showing 677 and 472 'Raleigh' **£30-35**
1957 **Leaflet '16/357/5'**, 642 and 455 'Brooke Bond Tea' **£30-35**
1957 **Leaflet '16/857/5'**, 237 Mercedes front, 136, 236, 238 back **£30-35**
1957 **Leaflet '16/457/5'**, 697 Military Set **£30-35**
1957 **Leaflet '16/457/5'**, 661 and 919 'Golden Shred' **£30-35**
1957 **Leaflet** (no ref.), with 163, 236 and 238 on racing circuit **£30-35**
1957 **Leaflet** (no ref.), with 237, 661, and 919 'Golden Shred' **£30-35**
1957 **Illustrated price list '16/357/5'**, 'Italy' printed after the ref. no. **£30-35**
1957 **Leaflet '12/757/50'** (DT/CL/15) 642 and 455 'Brooke Bond' **£30-35**
1957 **Catalogue '7/857/50'**, Same cover as UK issue 7/657/820 ....**£30-35**
1957 **Leaflet 'DT/CL/12'**, with 677 and 472 on cover..........................**£30-35**
1958 **Catalogue '7/758/50'**, Same cover as UK issue 7/458/856 ....**£30-35**
1964 **Catalogue '7/364/40 7225 0/37'**, 12th, 8in x 11in, includes
       four pages of French Dinky, 12 pages in total **£30-35**

Malaya and Singapore

Agents: King & Co, Singapore.

1957 **Catalogue '16/557/25 (1P)'** (DT/CF/3), 8 pages, cover depicts 170,
       626, 716, 955, other pictures within, price list in $ **£40-50**
1958 **Catalogue '7/958/10'**, cover as UK, 4 pages with prices in $ **£40-50**

Netherlands/Holland

Agents: Hausemann & Hotte NV, Kromboomsloot 57-61, Amsterdam.

Pre-War Editions
1936 **'1/736/5'**   Yellow paper with Black printing.....................**£100-150**
1937 **'13/637/75'**   Yellow paper with Black printing.....................**£100-150**
1938 **'13/738/22'**   Yellow paper with Black printing.....................**£100-150**

Post-War Editions - Some black/white, later coloured as per UK issues.
1954 **Illustrated price list '16/954/108'**, Printed in French **£15-20**
1955 **'8/1255/50'** (DT/L/7), no details.......................................**£30-35**
1956 **'16/256/30n'** (DT/CL/2), no details....................................**£20-25**
1956 **'16/256/30n'** (DT/L/9), no details.....................................**£20-25**
1958 **'16/1158 /20'**, 'Nederland Frs 3-'. Cover same as 1958 UK issue...**£30-35**
1962 **'16/256/30 (72538/29)'**, no details....................................**£20-25**
1967 **Catalogue '72571'**, 3rd Ed., price list in Dutch florins, 162 pages..**£40-50**
1970 **Catalogue** (no ref.), 6th Edition includes 8 pages of French Dinky,
       32 pages in total **£20-30**

Portugal

1956 **Illustrated Catalogue** (no ref.), no details....................................**£40-50**
1957 **Illustrated Leaflet, 'DT/CF/4'**, no details....................................**£50-70**
1958 **Illustrated Catalogue '7/858/5'**, Houses of Parliament on cover ...**£30-40**
1959 **Illustrated Catalogue** (no ref.), no details.................................**£40-50**
1961 **Illustrated Catalogue '5/261/25'**, 9th edition **£30-40**
1963 **Illustrated Catalogue** (no ref.), no details.................................**£30-40**
1960s **Illustrated Catalogue '7255049'**, group of 1960s cars on cover ...**£30-40**
1969 **'No.5' Catalogue '72585'**, cover features 'Joe 90's Car' **£30-40**

Spain

1957 **Illustrated Leaflet 'DT/CL15 SP 16/457/5'**, Similar to Italian leaflet with 697 on colour front of single sheet, unpriced list on reverse..**£10-15**

Sweden

Agents: Ludvig Wigart & Cos, AB Helsingborg.

1954 **'7/654/14'**, 4 pages, 3 pages colour pictures plus price list
       in Kroner with Swedish text..**£40-50**
1957 **Leaflet '16/357/15'**, Leaflet depicts 455 'Brooke Bond' Trojan
       plus 642 RAF Tanker. Price list in Kroner; Swedish text **£15-20**
1961 **Catalogue '14/561/60'**, as 1961 UK issue, text in Swedish **£20-30**
1968 **Catalogue '72580'**, 162 pp, as UK 1968 edition, but in Swedish ..**£20-30**

Switzerland

Agents: Riva & Kunzmann SA Basel 2, Switzerland. From 1965 address changed to Prattela, Switzerland.

1956 **Catalogue '7/356/20'**, Ovaltine + 7 others, prices in francs, 24 pp..**£40-50**
1958 **Catalogue '7/858/80'**, cover as UK version..................................**£40-50**
1962 **Catalogue '72537/25'**, 10th Edition, 48 pages, same as
       UK issue 72537/02 plus French Dinky **£40-50**
1963 **Catalogue '13/163/175'**, 11th Edition, 48 pages, same as
       UK issue 13/163/20 plus French Dinky **£40-50**
1965 **Catalogue '72559'**, 24 pp, cover as UK 72557 + French Dinky **£40-50**

United States of America

Agents: H. Hudson Dobson, PO Box 254, 26th St and Jefferson Avenue, Kenilworth, NJ.
In 1952 the address was: PO Box 254, 906 Westfield Avenue, Elizabeth, NJ.

From 1957 the address changed to 627 Boulevard, Kenilworth. New York showroom: 200, Fifth Avenue, PO Box 255. Models sold by this distributor will often be found with an 'H.Hudson Dobson' label
From 1963: Lines Bros Inc, 1107 Broadway, New York. From ?: AVA International, Box 7611, Waco, Texas 76710.

War-Time Issue
1941 **Large leaflet** (no ref.), no details available ....NGPP

Post-War Editions
1951 **Catalogue** (no ref.), boy's side face, 5 models, black and white,
       green printing, 16 pages **£80-100**
1952 **Catalogue** (no ref.), hands holding 27f (139b and 25x in picture).
       Unlike the UK edition, 39b, 39c and 39e are shown in
       two-tone colours..**£80-100**
1953 **Catalogue '7/753/150'**, same cover as 1953 UK issue 7/953/360....**£50-75**
1954 **Catalogue '7/954/150'**, same cover as 1954 UK issue 7/754/600....**£50-75**
1954 **Catalogue '7/753/150'**, 157 Jaguar, 480 Kodak, 641 Army,
       separate price list, 28 pages...**£50-75**
1955 **Catalogue** (no ref.), 20 models on cover, 5 French, black and
       white, prices in $, 32 pages **£50-75**
1956 **Catalogue** (no ref.), ...'Ever-Ready' + 11 others, Feb 57,
       black/white, prices in $, 32 pages **£50-75**
1957 **Catalogue** (no ref.), Yellow/Red cover shows model 697 plus Red
       lined sections displaying English and French models. Red
       panel with US address of H.Hudson Dobson. 36 black/white
       pages of English and French models............................**£75-100**
1957 **Catalogue** (no ref.), Yellow, Red lines, black/white, 9-30-57,
       prices in $, 36 pages **£50-75**
1958 **Catalogue '7/958/250'**, Houses of Parliament, prices in $, 32pp....**£50-75**
1959 **Leaflet '7/7/125'**, Colour, English and French, prices in $..........**£20-30**
1959 **USA Catalogue '7/559/250'**, Cover depicts Red Jaguar XK140 etc
       26 pages English models, 6 pages French **£50-75**
1959 **Leaflet '7/8/125'**, 3 pp of colour pictures + price list. English and
       French items on cover, (195 Jaguar 3.4, 265 Taxi) ....NGPP

1960 **Leaflet** (no ref.), 6 pages introducing 'Mini-Dinky' **£40-45**
1960 **Catalogue '7/3/30 NP'**, no details.......................................NGPP
1961 **Catalogue '16/161/100 72529/22'**, 4 pages..............................**£20-30**
1961 **Catalogue '14/561/200'**, Black with 7 models, USA 1961, 48 pp ...**£50-75**
1962 **Leaflet '9/762/50'**, '72542/22' and 'D.T./CL 14'....................**£10-15**
1962 **Catalogue '725377/22'**, 10th Ed., 8 pp, UK 7253702 + French **£20-30**
1962 **Catalogue '72537/22'**, 120 Jaguar 'E'-type, 10th Ed. '5c',
       16 pages of French Dinky, 48 pages in total **£50-75**
1963 **Catalogue '13/763/60'**, 11th Ed., 48 pp, UK 13/763/400 + French ..NGPP
1963 **Leaflet '16/163/50 7254 7/22'**, illustrated flyer price list, b/w **£20-30**
1963 **Catalogue '13/763/10 7254 5/22'**, Motor Show 11th USA,
       16 pages of French Dinky, 48 pages in total **£25-35**
1965 **Leaflet** (no ref. no.) Lines Bros flyer 8in x 11in,
       Hong Kong on cover **£20-30**
1965 **'Lines Bros' leaflet** (no ref. no.), 4 pages, Yellow/Red cover
       with 113 MGB..**£30-35**
1967 **Leaflet '72577/3'**, 10in x 12¾in includes 5 Hong Kong Dinky **£15-20**

1971 **Catalogue '100103'**, 7th Edition, same as UK, 24 pages **£10-15**
1972 **Catalogue '100108'**, 8th Edition, same as UK, 28 pages **£10-15**
1973 **Catalogue '100110'**, 9th Edition, same as UK, 40 pages **£10-15**
1973 **Leaflet '100265'**, 4 pages Dinky Action Kits Catalogue **£10-15**
1974 **Catalogue '100114'**, 10th Edition, same as UK, 48 pages **£10-15**
1975 **Catalogue '100/117'**, 11th Ed., 40 pages, same as UK 100115 ......**£10-15**
1976 **Catalogue '100/120'**, 12th Ed., 40 pages, same as UK 100118 ......**£10-15**
1977 **Catalogue '100/135'**, 13th Ed., 40 pages, same as UK 100122,
       but background on cover is Blue not Red.........................**£10-15**
1978 **Catalogue '100/101'**, 14th Ed., 64 pages, same as UK 100/100 ....**£10-15**

West Germany

Agents: Bienngraeber of Hamburg.

1969 **Catalogue '72585'**, 32 pages, No.5 features 'Joe's Car' on cover,
       Catalogue in English, price list in German **£40-50**

Dinky Toys Trade Boxes

Virtually all Dinky Toys models were supplied in their own individual boxes from around 1954. Before then, most small models were supplied to shopkeepers in 'Trade Boxes' containing 3, 4, 6 or 12 identical models separated by strips of card. (Some aircraft and ship models were an exception to this general rule). A single item would be sold without further packaging except perhaps for a paper bag.

These Trade Boxes have become collectors items in their own right whether full or empty (the latter selling for between £20 and £50 depending on its rarity and that of its original contents. Most of these boxes that come to

auction are full and the listing below derives mostly from the survey of such items undertaken for the 8th and 9th Editions. We are grateful to David Cooke for updating and enhancing the listing for this Edition. The boxes listed here are only those observed or reported. It is known that other trade packaging of this type exists and the Editor would welcome any additional information on the subject.

Expect Trade Boxes containing rare colour variations to attract a corresponding premium. NB See also Gift Sets for 62h and 62d pre-war Aeroplane Trade Box items. **NGPP=No guide price at present.**

Ref	Models, number in box, details	Market Price Range
Type 1 Pre-Second World War. Card boxes that have a four-digit reference code number preceded by the letter 'A'. Most have a covering of yellow paper. (The few exceptions that have orange-brown, blue or green paper coverings are noted in the list). Wording: 'Dinky Toys Made in England by Meccano Limited'. Printed information consists of model name and number, often with a date and quantity. The date code is usually a month number and year number separated by a full stop thus: '3.40', in this case indicating March 1940.		

Ref	Models, number in box, details	Market Price Range
22e	Tractor, 6, A966B	NGPP
22g	Streamline Tourer, 6, A2018	£1,500-1,750
23	Racing Car, 6, A1002	£1,500-2,000
24g	Sports Tourer, 6, A1017	£1,500-2,000
24h	Sports Tourer, 6, A1018	NGPP
25d	Petrol Wagon, 6, A1022	NGPP
25e	Tipping Wagon, 6, A1023	NGPP
25f	Market Gardener's Lorry, 6, A1024	NGPP
26	Rail Autocar, 6, A1001	NGPP
27	Tram Car, 6	£900-1,200
28/1	Delivery Vans, 1st Type, 6, A1008	£5,000-7,500
29a	('Q' type) Motor Bus, 6	£1,000-1,500
29c	Double-Decker Bus, 6, A2226	£1,200-1,600
30e	Breakdown Car, 6, A2060	£150-200
30g	Caravan, 6, A2106	£100-150
32	Chrysler Airflow, 6, orange-brown, A2032	£2,000-3,000
33a	Mechanical Horse, 6, orange-brown, A2037	NGPP
37c	RCS Dispatch Rider, 6, green, A2237	£150-200
37c	RCS Dispatch Rider, 6, blue, A2237	£150-200
39e	Chrysler Royal Sedan, 6, A2290	£1,000-1,500
47d	Beacon,12, orange-brown, A2058	NGPP
50a	Battle Cruiser HMS 'Hood', 12, A1030	NGPP
50f	Destroyer, 'Broke' Class, 12, A1035	NGPP
50f/50h	Destroyers 'Broke' and 'Amazon' Class, 2, A1035	NGPP
50g	Submarines 'K'-class, 12, A1036	NGPP
50g/50k	Submarines 'K' and 'X' Class, 12, A1036	NGPP
62d	Bristol Blenheim Bombers, 6, green box	£400-600
62h	Hawker Hurricane Fighters, 6, green box, '7-39'	£400-600
62m	Airspeed Envoy Monoplane, 6, A2234	NGPP
62s	Hurricane Fighters, 6, blue	£300-400
63b	Seaplane 'Mercury', 6 A2253	NGPP
151a	Medium Tank, 6	£1,500-2,000
152c	RTC Austin Seven, 6, A2196	£400-500
160b	Royal Artillery Gunners, 12	£200-250
160g	R.A. Personnel, (quantity not stated), A2303	NGPP

Ref	Models, number in box, details	Market Price Range
Type 2 The first of the post-war trade boxes. Brown card box with yellow contents label affixed to one end (occasionally, both ends) No box reference code in the main, but exceptions are noted below.		

Ref	Models, number in box, details	Market Price Range
14a	B.E.V. Electric Truck, 6	£90-110
23a	Racing Car, 6	£500-750
23d	Racing Car, 6	NGPP
25b	Covered Wagon, 6	£200-300
25d	Petrol Wagon, 6	£200-300
25e	Tipping Wagon, 6	£250-350
25f	Market Gardeners Lorry, 6, 'VK29'	£250-350
25f	Market Gardeners Lorry, 6, 'AS39'	£250-350
25g	Trailer, 6	NGPP
25h	Fire Engine, 6	£300-400
25j	Jeep, 6, 'M26'	£250-350
25p	Aveling Barford Diesel Roller, 4, 'M__'	£150-200
25r	Forward Control Lorry, 6, 'M23'	£200-250
25t	Flat Truck and Trailer, 3	NGPP
25v	Bedford Refuse Wagon, 4	£200-300
27a	Massey-Harris Tractor, 6	£150-200
29b	Streamlined Bus, 6, 'M24'	NGPP
29c	Double Deck Bus, 6 (packed vertically)	£200-300

Ref	Models, number in box, details	Market Price Range
29c	Double Deck Bus, 6 (laid flat)	£200-300
29e	Single Deck Bus, 6	NGPP
30b	Rolls-Royce, 6	£300-400
30d	Vauxhall, 6	£300-400
30f	Ambulance, 6, 'M28'	£300-400
30f	Ambulance, 6, 'M35'	£300-400
33w	Mechanical Horse and Open Wagon, 3	£110-150
34b	Royal Mail Van, 6	£300-400
34c	Loudspeaker Van, 6, 'VK49'	£150-180
36a	Armstrong-Siddeley Limousine, 6	£400-500
38c	Lagonda Sports Coupé, 6	NGPP
39a	Packard Super 8 Touring Sedan, 6	£400-500
39d	Buick Viceroy Sedan, 6, '(M24)'	£400-500
40a	Riley, 6, '(M__)'	£350-450
40b	Triumph 1800, 6	£350-450
40e	Standard Vanguard, 6	£350-450
40e	Standard Vanguard, 6, '(M50)'	£350-450
105a	Garden Roller, 6	£80-90
152b	Reconnaissance Car, 6	£400-500
161b	Mobile Anti-Aircraft Gun, 6	£300-400
270	'AA' Motor Cycle, 6	£200-300
272	'ANWB' Motor Cycle, 6	£250-350

Ref	Models, number in box, details	Market Price Range
Type 3 Second design of post-war box. All-yellow with direct printing (no label). Exceptions here are with 675, 677 and 994 which are grey rather than yellow. No box reference code.		

Ref	Models, number in box, details	Market Price Range
23b	Small Closed Racing Car, 6	£200-300
23c	Large Open Racing Car, 6	£200-300
23e	'Speed of the Wind' Racing Car, 6	£200-300
25l	Fire Engine, 6	NGPP
25m	Bedford End Tipper, 4	£150-200
25t	Flat Truck and Trailer, 3	£300-325
25v	Bedford Refuse Wagon, 4	£200-300
25w	Bedford Truck, 4	£200-300
25y	Universal Jeep, 4	£150-225
27a	Massey-Harris Tractor, 3	£150-200
27b	Harvest Trailer, 3	£75-85
27c	MH Manure Spreader, 3	£85-100
27d	Land Rover, 4	£150-200
27f	Estate Car, 4	£150-200
27g	Motocart, 3	£100-150
27h	Disc Harrow, 4	£60-80
29f	Observation Coach, 6	£300-400
30h	Daimler Ambulance, 4	£200-300
30j	Austin Wagon, 6	£250-300
30m	Rear Tipping Wagon, 6	£150-200
30r	Thames Flat Truck, 6	£130-160
30s	Austin Covered Wagon, 6	£150-200
30v	Electric Dairy Van, 6	£250-300
30v	Electric Dairy Van NCB, 6	£250-300
31a	Trojan Esso Van, 6	NGPP
31b	Trojan 'Dunlop' Van, 6	£500-600
35c	MG Sports Car, 6	£250-300
36a	Armstrong-Siddeley Limousine, 6	£400-500
37b	Police Motor Cyclist, 6	£150-200
38b	Sunbeam-Talbot, 6	£400-500
38e	Armstrong-Siddeley, 6	£450-550
39e	Chrysler Royal Sedan, 6	NGPP
40b	Triumph 1800 Saloon, 6	£350-450
40d	Austin Devon, 6	£350-450
40f	Hillman Minx Saloon, 6	£250-350
40g	Morris Oxford Saloon, 6	£350-450
40j	Austin Somerset, 6	£350-450
42a	Police Box, 6	£140-170
47c	Two-face Traffic Lights, 12	£40-70
70d	Twin Engined Fighter, 6	£110-130

70e	Gloster Meteor, 6	£40-60
70f	Shooting Star, 6	£100-150
105a	Garden Roller, 6	£80-90
105b	Wheelbarrow, 6	£80-90
105c	4-wheeled Hand Truck, 6	£40-60
105e	Grass Cutter, 6,	£90-110
106	Austin A90 Atlantic, 6	NGPP
107a	Sack Truck, 6	£90-110
139a	Ford Fordor, 6	£350-450
139b	Hudson Commodore, 6	£500-700
140a	Austin Atlantic, 6	£500-700
152b	Reconnaissance Car, 6	£400-500
161b	Mobile AA Gun, 6	£300-400
253	Daimler Ambulance, 4	£150-200
603a	Army Personnel (metal), 12.	
	NB early boxes long, later issues square	£80-110
603a	Army Personnel (plastic), 12	£40-50
673	Scout Car, 6	£65-85
675	Ford US Army Staff Car, 6, grey	NGPP
677	Armoured Command Vehicle, 6, grey	£150-200
687	Field Gun Trailer, 6	£65-85
705	Viking Airliner, 6	£200-300
750	Telephone Call Box, 6	£200-300
751	Police Hut, 6	£150-180
755	Lamp Standard, single-arm, 6	£30-40
756	Lamp Standard, double-arm, 6	£30-40
760	Pillar Box, 6	£150-200
768	Racks with Tyres, 6	£75-100
773	Traffic Lights, 12	£150-175
777	Belisha Beacon, 12	£65-90
786	Tyre Rack, 6	£120-160
788	Spare Bucket for 966, 6	£175-225
797	Healey Raceboats, 6	£150-200
994	Loading Ramp, 3, grey	£55-80
10253	Tyres, 12	£10-15
14095	Tyres, 12	£10-15

Type 4 As Type 3, but with the addition of a five-digit box reference code.

23f	Alfa Romeo Racing Car, 6, 50189	£250-300
23s	Streamlined Racing Car, 4, 50012	£300-400
25h	Fire Engine, 6, 50019	£300-400
25m	Bedford Truck, 4, 50021	£150-200
25p	Aveling-Barford Diesel Roller, 4, 50022	£150-200
25y	Universal Jeep, 4, 50159	£150-225
27a	Massey-Harris Tractor, 3, 50029	NGPP
27h	Disc Harrow, 4, 50035	£60-80
27j	Triple-Gang Mower, 3, 50156	£150-200
27m	Land-Rover Trailer, 4, 50161	£75-100
29g	Luxury Coach, 6, 50042	£400-500
29h	Duple Roadmaster Coach, 6, 50163	£300-400
30h	Daimler Ambulance, 4, 50049	£200-300
30j	Austin Wagon, 6, 50050	NGPP
30m	Rear Tipping Wagon, 6, 50052	£150-200
30p	Mobilgas Tanker, 6, 50051	£500-600
30pa	Castrol Tanker, 6, 50146	£500-700
30pb	Esso Tanker, 6, 50147	£500-700
30w	Electric Articulated Lorry, 3, 50059	£300-400
31a	Trojan Esso Van, 6, 50149 on some	£500-600
31c	Trojan Chivers Van, 6, 50151	£600-800
33w	Mechanical Horse and Open Wagon, 3, 50060	NGPP
34c	Loudspeaker Van, 6, 50062	£150-180
35a	Saloon Car, 6, 50063. ('Slide-tray' type box)	£290-330
35b	Racer, 6, '(CZ35)'. ('Slide-tray' type box)	£280-330
40f	Hillman Minx, 6, (number ?)	£250-350
40g	Morris Oxford, 6, (number ?)	£350-450
40h	Austin Taxi, 6, 50097	£350-450
70a	Avro York Air-Liner, 1, 50123	NGPP

70b	Hawker Tempest Fighter, 6, 50124	NGPP
70c	Viking Air-Liner, 6, 50125	NGPP
70f	Shooting Star Jet Fighter, 6, 50128	NGPP
105e	Grass Cutter, 6, 50132	£90-110
139b	Hudson Commodore, 6, 50135	£
140a	Austin Atlantic, 6, 50136	£500-700
140b	Rover 75, 6, 50137	£350-450

Type 5 As Type 3 (all-yellow, direct printed, no reference code), but these display the 'dual numbering' of the models contained. They generally date from around 1954 when Meccano renumbered most of the Dinky Toys. They are listed here in the order of the earlier model numbering system.

12c/750	Telephone Call Box, 6	£80-120
23a/220	Racing Car, 6	£200-300
23e/221	'Speed of the Wind' Racing Car, 6	£100-140
23s/222	Streamlined Racing Car, 4	£75-100
25g/429	Trailer, 6	£80-120
25h/250	Fire Engine, 6	NGPP
25r/420	Forward Control Lorry, 6	£200-250
25w/411	Bedford Truck, 4	£80-120
25y/405	Universal Jeep, 4	£80-120
27a/300	Massey-Harris Tractor, 3	£65-95
27d/340	Land-Rover, 4	£150-200
27g/342	Motocart, 3	£80-120
27m/341	Land-Rover Trailer, 4	£80-120
29g/281	Luxury Coach, 6	£150-200
30r/422	Fordson Thames Flat Truck, 6	£70-100
30s/413	Austin Covered Wagon, 6	£150-200
30v/490	Electric Dairy Van 'Express Dairy', 6	£120-160
30v/491	Electric Dairy Van 'N.C.B.', 6	£120-160
30w/421	Electric Articulated Lorry, 3	£60-90
31b/451	Trojan Van 'Dunlop', 6	£160-200
31c/452	Trojan Van 'Chivers', 6	£160-200
35b/200	Midget Racer, 6, '(CZ35)'	NGPP
40b/151	Triumph 1800 Saloon, 6	£200-250
40j/161	Austin Somerset Saloon, 6	£200-250
12c/750	Telephone Call Box, 6	£150-200
42a/751	Police Hut, 6	£50-80
63b/700	Seaplane, 6	£250-350
70c/705	Viking Airliner, 6	NGPP
70d/731	Twin Engined Fighter, 6	NGPP
70e/732	Meteor Jet Fighter, 6	NGPP
70f/733	Shooting Star Jet Fighter, 6	£80-100
105a/381	Garden Roller, 6	£80-120
105b/382	Wheelbarrow, 6	£60-80
105c/383	4-wheeled Hand Truck, 6	£80-120
105e/384	Grass Cutter, 6	£80-120
107a/385	Sack Truck, 6	£50-70
140a/106	Austin Atlantic Convertible, 6	
140b/156	Rover 75, 6	£200-250

Type 6 Post 1953-54, all-yellow printed box. These contain the newly-introduced (or re-introduced) models having just a single three-digit reference number.

270	'A. A.' Motorcyclist, 6	NGPP
272	'A.N.W.B.' Motorcyclist, 6	NGPP
603	Army Personnel - Private (seated), 12	NGPP
673	Scout Car, 6	NGPP
687	Trailer for 25lb Gun	NGPP
755	Lamp Standards, 6	NGPP
773	Robot Traffic Signal, 12	NGPP
777	Beacons, 6	NGPP
786	Tyre Racks with Tyres, 6	NGPP
788	Buckets for Marrel Multi-Bucket Unit, 6	NGPP
797	Healey Sports Boat, 6	NGPP

Type 7 (Post-war). Small boxes, covered in green paper; with 'flap' ends.

12d	**Telegraph Messenger**, 6, '50175' on some	£60-70
12e	**Postman**, 6, '50176' on some	£80-90
13a	**Cook's Man**, 6, '50174' on some	£50-60
43b	**'RAC' Motorcycle Patrol**, 6	£200-300
44b	**'AA' Motorcycle Patrol**, 6	£200-300
760	**Pillar Box**, 2	NGPP

Type 8 (Post-war). A box specially designed for 551 Large Trailer.

551	**Large Trailer**, 3. 'Dinky Toys', brown, yellow label	£45-65
551	**Large Trailer**, 3. 'Dinky Toys', blue card, '50551'	£65-85
551	**Large Trailer**, 3. 'Supertoys', brown, '50551'	£65-85
551	**Large Trailer**, 3. 'Supertoys', green, '(M49)'	£65-85
551	**Large Trailer**, 3. 'Supertoys', green, '(IH89)'	£65-85
551	**Large Trailer**, 3. 'Supertoys', blue card, '50551'	£65-85
551	**Large Trailer**, 3. 'Supertoys' yellow card '(M44)'	£45-65

Type 9 These began appearing from the early 1950s. They are 'trade packs' rather than trade boxes as they contain quantities of individually boxed models. Thin grey (or brownish-grey) card construction with flap ends or tuck-in ends; direct printing mostly in black. The printing on outer boxes for Dublo Dinkys 067 and 069 is in red. The major exception here is 078 which has an outer box of similar design to the individual Dublo boxes inside.

067	**Austin Taxi**, 6	NGPP
069	**Massey-Harris Tractor**, 6	£150-200
078	**Lansing-Bagnall Trailers**, 6	£140-170

27d	**Land-Rover**, 6	£225-275
106	**'The Prisoner' Mini-Moke**, 6	£600-800
159	**Morris Oxford**, 6	£250-350
161	**Austin Somerset**, 6	£600-800
188	**Jensen FF**, 6	£150-200
188	**4-berth Caravan**, 6	£175-200
195	**Jaguar 3.4 Saloon**, 6	£400-500
292	**Leyland Atlantean Bus**, 6	£350-450
471	**Austin Van 'NESTLE'**, 6	£300-400
491	**Electric Dairy Van 'N.C.B.'**, 6	£300-400
252/25v	**Refuse Wagon**, 4	NGPP
260	**Royal Mail Van**, 6	NGPP
260	**VW 'Deutsche Bundespost'**, 6	£150-200
344/27f	**Estate Car**, 4	NGPP
492/34c	**Loudspeaker Van**, 6	NGPP
675	**Army Staff Car**, 2	NGPP
677	**Armoured Command Vehicle**, 3	NGPP
755/6	**Lamp Standards**, 6	NGPP
994	**Loading Ramp** (for 982), 3	NGPP

Type 10 Later 1950s trade packs without printing. A small yellow label is attached that shows the model number only. 432 is an exception, being shrink-wrapped with no label.

305	**David Brown Tractor**, 6	NGPP
308	**Leyland 384 Tractor**, 6	NGPP
432	**Foden Tipping Lorry**, factory shrink-wrapped pack, 6	£80-100

The 'A' List. Before the War, most trade boxes (and some Set boxes) carried a box reference number preceded by the letter 'A'. Those that have been observed (or reported and confirmed) are listed here, in numerical order, along with the month/year (where known) of introduction and description of contents.

Box no.	Year	Model ref. and name
A 830	-	7 Set, 'Hornby Series' Watchman's Hut
A 873	-	MM 1, Station Staff
A 898	-	13 Set, Halls Distemper Set
A 899	-	21 Set, Train Set
A 930	-	1 Set, Station Staff
A 953	-	4 Set, Engineering Staff
A 966	12-33	22c, Motor Truck
A 966B	12-33	22e, Tractor
A 1001	5-34	26, Rail Autocar
A 1002	5-34	23, Racing Car
A 1005	5-34	6 Set, Shepherd Set
A 1008	5-34	28/1, Delivery Vans
A 1009	5-34	28/2, Delivery Vans
A 1017	5-34	24g, Sports Tourer (4 seater)
A 1018	5-34	24h, Sports Tourer (2 seater)
A 1019	5-34	25a, Wagon
A 1020	5-34	25b, Covered Van
A 1021	5-34	25c, Flat Truck
A 1022	5-34	25d, Petrol Tank Wagon
A 1023	5-34	25e, Tipping Wagon
A 1024	5-34	25f, Market Gardeners Van
A 1025	12-34	29a, Motor Bus
A 1026	12-34	27, Tram Car
A 1029	12-34	50, Ships of British Navy Set
A 1030	12-34	50a, Battle Cruiser 'Hood'
A 1032	12-34	50c, Cruiser 'Effingham'
A 1034	12-34	50e, Cruiser 'Delhi'
A 1035	12-34	50f/50h, Torpedo-Boat Destroyer
A 1036	12-34	50g/50k, Submarine 'K' Class
A 1037	12-34	51, Famous Liners Set
A 1040	12-34	60, Aeroplanes Set
A 1043	12-34	17, Passenger Train Set
A 1044	5-34	18, Goods Train Set
A 1045	5-34	19, Mixed Goods Train Set
A 1046	5-34	20, Passenger Train Set
A 1051	-	24, Motor Cars Gift Set

		(blue box, 2nd chassis)
A 1052	-	25, Commercial Motors Gift Set (blue box, type 2)
A 1053	-	2, Farmyard Animals Set
A 1054	-	3, Railway Passengers Set
A 2009	11-35	28/1, Delivery Vans (type 2)
A 2013	12-35	60f, Aeroplane Cierva 'Autogiro'
A 2018	4-35	22, Streamline Tourer
A 2032	-	23c, Mercedes Benz Racing Car
A 2032	6-35	30a/32, Airflow (see previous ref.)
A2034	6-35	49, Petrol Pumps Set
A 2035	12-34	52a, 'Queen Mary' (with rollers)
A 2036	6-37	33, Mechanical Horse and 4 Trailers Set
A 2037	6-35	33a, Mechanical Horse
A 2041	6-35	25g, Trailer
A 2042	6-35	48, Petrol Station
A 2047	6-35	D.H. 'Comet' Aeroplane
A 2052	6-35	12b, Pillar Letter Box Airmail
A 2058	11-35	47d, Beacon
A 2060	11-35	30e, Breakdown Car
A 2061	11-35	30, Motor Vehicles Set
A 2062	2-36	45, Garage
A 2064	11-35	43, 'RAC' Hut, Motorcycle Patrol and Guides
A 2065	11-35	44, 'AA' Hut, Motorcycle Patrol and Guides
A 2073	-	47, Road Signs Set (12)
A 2099	-	28/3, Delivery Vans
A 2106	5-36	30g, Caravan Trailer
A 2108	-	16, Streamline Train Set
A 2110	5-36	23c, Mercedes-Benz Racing Car
A 2111	5-36	23d, Auto-Union Racing Car
A 2113	12-38	60h, Singapore Flying Boat
A 2114	10-37	42, Police Hut, Motorcycle Patrol and Policemen
A 2144	12-36	23, Racing Cars Set
A2146	12-37	60n, Fairey Battle Bomber
A 2149	12-37	60k, Percival 'Gull' Monoplane
A 2172	10-37	15, Railway Signals Set
A 2177	12-37	60p, Gloster Gladiator
A 2185	10-37	61, RAF Aeroplanes Set
A 2187	10-37	150, Royal Tank Corps Pers'l. Set
A 2188	10-37	151, RTC Medium Tank Set
A 2189	10-37	152, RTC Light Tank Set
A 2190	12-37	151a, Medium Tank
A 2194	10-37	152a, Light Tank
A 2196	10-37	152c, Austin Seven Car

A 2205	10-37	Motor Cars w. Drivers/Passengers
A 2216	12-37	12, Postal Set
A 2220	12-37	60r, Empire Flying Boats
A 2222	5-36	35, Small Cars Set
A 2223	12-38	60s, Medium Bomber
A 2225	12-38	60t, Douglas DC3 Air Liner
A 2226	12-38	29c, Double Deck Bus
A 2227	12-38	60v, Armstrong Whitworth 'Whitley'
A 2229	12-37	37a, Civilian Motor Cyclist
A 2230	12-37	37b, Police Motor Cyclist
A 2231	12-38	60w, Flying Boat 'Clipper III'
A 2233	12-38	62k, Airspeed 'Envoy' King's Aeroplane
A 2234	12-38	62m, Airspeed 'Envoy' Monoplane
A 2235	7-40	66d, Torpedo Dive Bomber
A 2237	12-37	37c, Royal Corps of Signals Despatch
A 2245	12-38	25s, Six Wheel Wagon
A 2246	12-38	62n, Junkers Ju90 Air liner
A 2247	12-38	23m, 'Thunderbolt' Speed Car
A 2250	12-38	62p, Armstrong Whitworth 'Ensign' Liner
A 2251	4-39	63, Mayo Composite Aircraft
A 2252	4-39	63a, Flying Boat 'Maia'
A 2253	4-39	63b, Seaplane 'Mercury'
A 2257	3-39	161, Mobile Anti-Aircraft Unit Set
A 2260	3-39	162, 18-lb Quick-Firing Gun Unit
A 2265	4-39	62r, DH 'Albatross' Mail Liner
A 2268	6-39	62s, Hawker 'Hurricane'
A 2269	12-40	60t, A-W 'Whitley' (Camouflaged)
A 2276	4-39	62w, Imp. Airways 'Frobisher' Liner
A 2277	4-39	62x, 40-Seat Airliner
A 2281	7-40	66, Camouflaged Aeroplanes Set
A 2284	4-39	62h, H. 'Hurricane' Camouflaged
A 2285	-	62g, Boeing Flying Fortress
A 2288	5-39	64, Presentation Aeroplane Set
A 2289	5-39	65, Presentation Aeroplane Set
A 2290	6-39	39e, Chrysler 'Royal' Sedan
A 2291	6-39	39f, Studebaker
A 2298	9-39	23p, Gardner's MG Record Car
A 2303	7-40	160, Royal Artillery Personnel
A 2308	7-40	156, Mechanised Army Set
A 2327	-	62e, Spitfire (Camouflaged)
A 2328	-	62d, Blenheim Bomber (Camouflaged)
A 2343	7-40	67a, Junkers Ju89 Heavy Bomber
A 2349	7-40	68, Camouflaged Aeroplanes Set

Trade Display Unit packed in plain cardboard box. Black wooden case with 'Property of Meccano Ltd Liverpool' in black on gold; three shelves in light blue/white/yellow; four gold supports with two yellow and two red supports; four red tin flags 'DINKY TOYS'; three tin flags 'ASK FOR BOOKLET', 'OVER 200 MODELS', and 'ALWAYS SOMETHING NEW'; plus two red and two yellow balls **£400-500**

Glass Display Case. Oak frame with three glass shelves. Size approximately 32" (80 cm.) wide, 24" (60 cm.) high, 9" (22 cm.) deep. With 'DINKY TOYS' in green lettering on glass front...**£300-400**

Trade Display Stand Large yellow folding cardboard stand which non-erected measures approximately 28" (70 cm.) x 14" (35 cm.); three display levels with 'DINKY TOYS' logo in green plus 'MECCANO PRODUCT' in red on top header board. Outer corrugated cardboard packing has green printed instruction leaflet..**£200-300**

Trade Display Stand Small yellow and red folding cardboard stand which non-erected measures approximately 12" (31 cm.) x 7" (15 cm.); with one 'DINKY TOYS' and two 'DINKY SUPERTOYS' logos in red plus yellow 'MASTERPIECES IN MINIATURE' logo on red background..........**£100-125**

Display Stand (circa 1950 - 1960) Large metal stand which measures approximately 36" x 21" x 22" (91.5 x 53 x 56 cm.); with nine display shelves covered in black plastic track. Metal advertisement affixed to top states in yellow/red/black 'A MOTOR SHOW FOR GIRLS AND BOYS', 'PRECISION DIE-CAST MODELS BY MECCANO', 'BEST RANGE', and 'BEST VALUE IN THE WORLD'. Lower large transfer also in yellow/red/black repeats the message...**£400-500**

Window Sign (plastic), Top half is dark blue with white 'MECCANO' logo, bottom half is yellow with red 'Dinky Toys' logo. Approximately 18" x 6"..**£100-125**

Counter Display (cardboard), Small display stand suitable for a single new model, 'ALWAYS NEW MODELS' logo in white on red background, header states 'DINKY TOYS' in red on yellow. **£100-125**

Counter Display (cardboard) 'BATTLE OF BRITAIN' Blue/yellow displaying 719 Spitfire MkII and 721 Junkens JU 87b Stuka. **£100-150**

Shop Display Carousel with tripod base supporting four stacks of clear plastic...**£200-300**

Illuminated Shop Display Sign with 'DINKY TOYS' in large wooden letters above a glass panel lettered either 'Made by Meccano Ltd' or 'British and Guaranteed'..**£300-400**

Shelf Display Card in 'landscape' format, featuring the Hesketh 308'E Racing Car with 'OLYMPUS' advertising...**£100-150**

Illuminated Counter or Window display unit 13" x 9"" with perspex front 'DINKY TOYS' and 'NEW MODELS EVERY MONTH' logo........**£100-1500**

Counter Carousel Unit with 'Always Something New from Dinky' around its edge. Red/Yellow 'DINKY TOYS BY MECCANO' sign on top, 26" high overall..**£200-250**

Metal Counter Display Sign, triangular in shape with red 'DINKY TOYS' on yellow background, approximately 8" x 1" x 1".............................**£30-40**

Electric Revolving 'Meccano' Wooden Display Stand 'DINKY TOYS - LOOK FOR THE NAME ON THE BASE' logo, (28" square and 10" high) **£250-350**

Pre-War 'Meccano Dinky Toys' Advertising Sign. An example of this double-sided hanging sign was sold by Christie's', South Kensington for £632. It shows pictures and details of 22, 24, 25 and 28 series models available in 'Season 1934'. Date code: '16/734/1'. Size: 11in x 9in (28cm x 23cm)...**£500-600**

- c.1959 'Dublo Dinky' Shop Display Stand. Pale Yellow with Red logo and wording 'NEW SERIES / DUBLO DINKY', etc. Stand dimensions: 28cm x 19cm overall...**£300-500**

Dinky Toys Price Tickets. Aluminium tags to place on toys plus sheet of 200 self-adhesive labels showing model number and price **£200-250**

Wall Chart. 1963 Dinky Toys and Dinky Supertoys Wall Chart listing all tyre sizes for vehicles...**£100-125**

c1960 Electric 'Dinky Toys' Perspex Hanging Sign. Yellow sides with red letters, 1,300mm long **£250-350**

c1970s Electric 'Dinky Toys' Perspex Hanging Sign. Yellow sides with red letters, 1,270mm long **£175-225**

Note: This section is far from complete and the Editor would welcome details of other trade stands, posters, display cards, promotional material and advertising signs.

1960s Window leaflets / posters / stickers

72569	Lady Penelope's 'FAB 1'	£50-60
72579	Captain Scarlett and Thunderbirds	£50-60
?	486 'Dinky Beats' Morris Oxford	£30-40
?	107 'Stripey, the Magic Mini'	£30-40
?	101 Thunderbirds	£30-40
?	153 Aston-Martin DB6	£30-40
?	970 Jones Fleetmaster Crane	£20-30
?	281 Pathe News Camera Car	£30-40
?	158 Rolls-Royce Silver Shadow	£20-30
?	131 Ford 40-RV	£20-30
?	282 Austin 1800	£20-30
?	280 Midland Mobile Bank	£20-30
?	129 Volkswagen Beetle	£20-30
?	163 Volkswagen 1600TL	£20-30
?	166 Renault R16	£20-30
?	135 Triumph 2000 and 240 Cooper Racing Car	£20-30
?	141 Vauxhall Victor Estate Car	£20-30

1970s Shop window self-adhesive posters

100362	1972 Double-sided poster featuring 'All Action Fighting Vehicles' and '10 Great Fighting Vehicles'	£20-30
100367	1973 Double-sided poster featuring 'Highway Action Models'	£20-30
100482	1971 Single-sided poster advertising '451 Road Sweeper'	£20-30
100524	Single-sided poster advertising 'No 410 Bedford Van'	£20-30
100537	Single-sided poster with 'No 654 155mm Mobile Gun'	£20-30
100595	Single-sided poster advertising 'No 694 Hanomag Tank Destroyer'	£20-30
100602	Single-sided poster advertising 'No 293 Swiss PTT Bus'	£20-30
100604	Single-sided poster advertising 'No 656 88mm Gun'	£20-30
100734	Single-sided poster advertising 'No 668 Foden Army Truck'	£20-30
100741	Single-sided poster advertising 'No 432 Foden Tipper Truck'	£20-30
100742	Single-sided, advertising 'No 430 Johnson 2-ton Dumper'	£20-30
100523	Single-sided, advertising 'No 682 Stalwart Load Carrier'	£20-30
100531	Single-sided poster advertising 'No 683 Chieftain Tank'	£20-30
100496	Single-sided poster advertising 'No 725 F-4K Phantom II'	£20-30
?	Poster advertising '442 Land-Rover Breakdown Crane'	£20-30
?	Poster advertising '967 Muir-Hill Loader and Trencher'	£20-30
?	Poster advertising '915 AEC with Flat Trailer'	£20-30
?	Poster advertising 1/25th scale Ford Capri and Police Car	£30-40
?	Poster advertising 1/25th scale Saloon Car	£30-40
?	Poster advertising 724 Sea King Helicopter	£20-25
?	Poster advertising 984 Atlas Digger	£20-25
?	Poster advertising 977 Shovel Dozer	£20-25
?	Poster advertising 963 Road Grader	£20-25
?	Poster advertising 726 Messerschmitt BF109E	£20-25
?	Poster advertising 730 US Navy Phantom	£20-25
?	Poster advertising 731 S.E.P.E.C.A.T. Jaguar and 728 RAF Dominie	£20-25
?	Poster advertising 734 P47 Thunderbolt	£20-25
?	Poster advertising 739 Zero Sen	£20-25

All other late issued leaflets not listed ....each: **£20-25**

Retailer's aluminuim price tickets for attachment to Dinky Toys boxes.   Photo: Vectis Auctions Ltd.

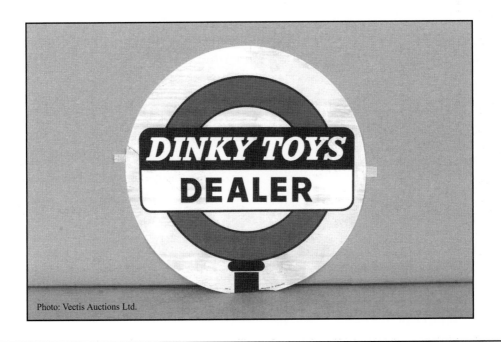

Photo: Vectis Auctions Ltd.

DINKY TOYS and NICKY TOYS
sold by Vectis Model Auctions,
Fleck Way, Thornaby, Stockton-on-Tees. TS17 9JZ

Condition abbreviations appearing in Vectis Auctions catalogues:
M = Mint, **NM** = Near Mint, **NMB** = Near Mint Boxed,
EP = Excellent Plus, **E** = Excellent, **EB** = Excellent Boxed,
GP = Good Plus, **VG** = Very Good, **G** = Good,
GB = Good Box, **F** = Fair, **FB** = Fair Box, **P** = Poor.

DINKY TOYS

CARS

22a Sports Car, red/cream, G	£370
22b Sports Coupé, yellow/green, G	£380
23m Thunderbolt Racing Car, E in GP Box	£140
24b Limousine, maroon, F	£120
24d Vogue, TT Blue, plated hubs	£190
24h Sports Tourer, yellow, criss-cross chassis, GP overall	£520
30a Chrysler Airflow, Light Blue, chrome hubs, GP	£260
30b Rolls-Royce, violet blue, G	£120
36a Armstrong-Siddeley, mid blue (PWI) E	£150
36b Bentley Coupé, dark green (PWI), E	£160
36d Rover, mid green (PWI), E	£120
36e British Salmson, greyish blue (PWI), E	£170
36f British Salmson, bright green (PWI), E	£160
38a Frazer-Nash Sports, grey, red hubs, E	£220
38d Alvis Sports Car, green, E	£170
39bu Chrysler Royale, TT Green, GB	£700
39cu Oldsmobile Sedan (US issue), TT Brown	£620
101 Sunbeam Alpine, pale blue E in E, box	£130
104 Aston Martin DB3S, pale blue, NM in G	£140
105 Triumph TR2 Sports, light grey, NM in G box	£100
106 Austin Atlantic, pale blue, E in E	£150
108 MG Midget, red, RN '24', E in NM box	£180
109 Austin-Healey 'Competition', yellow/blue, E in E box	£130
110 Aston-Martin DB3S 'Competition', green RN '22', NM in GP box	£100
111 Triumph TR2, pink/blue RN '29', NM in E box	£200
113 MG Sports Car, off-white, GP in E	£125
114 Triumph Spitfire, metallic purple, spun hubs, NM in E box	£140
129 MG Midget Sports (US Issue), red with tan interior, red hubs, NM in GP box	£560
131 Cadillac Tourer, pale yellow, GP in E box	£50
Same model in salmon pink livery, NM in E box	£140
132 Packard Convertible, pale green, E in G box	£50
Same model in pale green, spun hubs, EP in E	£140
138 Hillman Imp, metallic red, NMB	£100
Same model, metallic blue, spun cast hubs, rare late issue white faced box, NM	£250
140 Morris 1100, pale blue, E in E	£60
142 Jaguar Mk. X, Metallic light blue, NM in E box	£80
148 Ford Fairlane, light green, NM boxed	£110
152 Austin Devon, pink/green, E/UB	£120
153 Standard Vanguard, cream, closed arches, EP in GP box	£140
Same in mid blue, NM in E box	£200
155 Ford Anglia, turquoise blue, pale blue interior, spun hubs, E in E box	£80
Same as previous item but with red interior, E in E box	£110
157 Jaguar XK120, sage green, fawn hubs, E in E box	£150
Same model, red, spun hubs, E in E	£200
157 Jaguar XK120, turquoise/cerise, E in E box	£280
158 Riley Saloon, light green, E in E box	£140
161 Austin Somerset, pale blue, GP in GP box	£120
Same model, red/yellow, NM in EP box	£260
162 Ford Zephyr, TT blue, EP in NM box	£90
163 Bristol 450 Coupé, dark green, NM in GP box	£110
164 Vauxhall Cresta, maroon/cream, NM in EP box	£100
165 Humber Hawk, maroon/cream, NM in F box	£80
Same again, black/green, NM in EP box	£110
166 Sunbeam Rapier, orange/cream, E in E box	£90
Same, blue/turquoise, E in E late issue box	£140
167 AC Aceca, cream/bronze, E in E box	£110
170 Ford Fordor 'Lowline', red/cream, GP in E box	£120
173 Nash Rambler, turquoise/blue, EP in E box	£90
Same model in salmon pink, M in NM box	£120
174 Hudson Hornet, yellow/grey, E in E box	£100
Same model, red/cream, E inE box	£60
175 Hillman Minx, grey/blue, E in E box	£100

175 Austin A105, cream, dark blue flash, EP in F	£100
176 Austin A105, cream, mid blue flash, EP in F box	£130
Same, grey, red side flash, E in E	£140
178 Plymouth, TT blue, spun hubs, NMB	£130
179 Studebaker, yellow/blue flash, NM in E box	£80
180 Packard, cream/cerise, NM in EP box	£80
180 Packard, orange/grey, NM in E box	£120
181 VW, RAF Blue, blue hubs, M in NM box	£200
Same in pale blue, spun hubs, NM in E box	£100
181 VW, light grey, blue hubs, M in NM box	£120
Same in lime green, green hubs, NM in GP box	£80
182 Porsche 356A, cream, blue hubs, M in GP box	£100
Same in pale blue, cream hubs, M in E box	£140

COMMERCIAL VEHICLES, PRE-WAR

22c Motor Truck, blue/red G	£410
22d Delivery Van, orange/blue GP	£480
25b Covered Wagon, 2nd type, 'Carter Patterson', F	£240
25d Petrol Tank Wagon, red, 'Mobiloil', F	£160
28c Delivery Van, 1st Type, 'Manchester Guardian', gold wash wheels, GP	£1,050
28d Delivery Van, 1st Type, 'Oxo', blue wash wheels, GP	£1,040
28e Delivery Van, 1st Type, 'Ensign Cameras', blue wash wheels	£2,300
28l Delivery Van, 1st Type, 'Crawfords Biscuits', gold wash wheels, E	£1,100
280b Delivery Van, 2nd Type, 'Lyons Tea', E	£290
280d Delivery Van, 2nd Type, 'Bisto', GP	£255
31 Holland Coachcraft Van, orange, (fatigued), F	£240
33r Mechanical Horse 'LMS', G	£140

COMMERCIAL VEHICLES, POST-WAR

343 Farm Produce Wagon, green cab/chassis, yellow back/plastic hubs, E in late issue GP box	£160
410 Bedford End Tipper, red cab/chassis/hubs, cream back, EP, E box	£250
430 Breakdown Lorry, cream cab, mid blue back, red hubs, E in E box	£580
Another: red cab, light grey back, mid blue hubs, E in GP box	£520
448 Chevrolet/Trailers, cream/turquoise, spun hub E in GP box	£260
470 Austin Van 'Shell', E in G box	£100
490 Van 'Express Dairies', grey/blue NM in E box	£100
501 Foden Diesel Wagon, 1st Type, dark blue cab, mid blue back/flash, GP in G buff box	£480
502 Foden Flat Truck, 1st Type, orange, mid green back/flash, large hook, E in G blue box	£410
502 Foden Flat Truck, 2nd Type, orange, mid green back and Supertoy wheels, E in E blue box	£400
503 Foden Flat Truck with Tailboard, 2nd Type, TT green body, G in GP blue box	£2,000
504 Foden Tanker, 2nd Type, violet blue cab, mid blue back and hubs, G in F blue box	£1,400
505 Foden Truck with Chains, 1st Type, green cab/chassis/back, mid-green flash/hubs, EP in GP box	£4,400
505 Foden Truck with Chains, 1st Type, maroon body, silver side flash, N in NM box	**(Record) £10,200**
901 Foden Diesel Wagon, 2nd Type, red/fawn, EP in E box	£200
902 Foden Flat Truck, 2nd Type, burnt orange/mid green, NM in G box	£380
903 Foden with Tailboard, 2nd Type, yellow cab/chassis/back, mid green hubs, E in E	£2,500
903 Foden with Tailboard, 2nd Type, mid blue cab/chassis, fawn back, riveted spare wheel, E in E	£560
905 Foden Truck with Chains, 2nd Type, maroon, red hubs, NM in E box	£460
511 Guy 4 ton Lorry, fawn cab/back, red mudguards/chassis, GP in GP buff box	£200
512 Guy Flat Truck, yellow cab/back, black chassis/mudguards, red hubs, E in G box	£360
513 Guy Truck with Tailboard, 1st Type, dark green cab/chassis, mid green back/hubs, E in F box	£400
514 Guy Van 'Weetabix', E in GP box	£1,900
514 Guy Van 'Lyons', GP in G box	£360
514 Guy Van 'Slumberland', GP in GP box	£140
917 Guy Van ' Spratts', E in F box	£300
581 Horsebox, US Issue, GP in E box with Hudson Dobson label	£440
918 Guy Van 'Ever Ready', EP in F box	£220
919 Guy Van 'Golden Shred', GP in GP box	£300
920 Guy Warrior Van 'Heinz', 'Tomato Sauce', E in G box	£620
923 Big Bedford Van 'Heinz', 'Tomato Sauce', GP in G box	£380
923 Big Bedford Van 'Heinz', 'Baked Beans', EP in GP box	£200
934 Leyland Wagon, yellow cab/chassis, green band around cab, yellow above radiator, E in E box	£260
943 Leyland Octopus Tanker 'Esso', EP in G box	£200

AIRCRAFT

60c Percival Gull in 'Amy Mollinson' **box**......£440
60k Percival Gull 'Amy Mollinson', E in G......£340
60r Empire Flying Boat 'Challenger', 'G-A DVD', Mint, GP box......£360
60s pair of Medium Bombers, G-E in GP box......£240
60s pair of Medium Bombers in camouflage finish, E in E box......£320
60t Douglas DC3, 'PH-ALI', M in E box......£320
60w Clipper III, M in E box......£270
60x 'Dauntless' Flying Boat, turquoise blue/cream, E/UB......£700
62a Meccano Spitfire Fund Badge, F in F box......£460
62g Boeing Flying Fortress, E/UB......£70
62k The King's Airplane, E in E box......£360
62n Junkers JU 90, 'D-A URE', fatigue, E in E box......£270
62p Armstrong 'Explorer', grey/green, E/UB......£190
62r 'Albatross', 'G-A EVV', E in E box......£380
62t Whitley Bomber, camouflage, gliding pin and leaflet, G in G box......£260
62w Imperial Airways 'Frobisher', silver 'Fortuna', E in E box......£350
62x 40 seat Airliner, GP/UB......£250
62y Giant Highspeed Monoplane, blue/brown 'D-A ZBK'......£420
63 Mayo composite, slight fatigue, GP in G box......£300
67a Junkers JU 89 Bomber, NM in E box......£920
700 Spitfire MK. II Diamond Jubilee, plated model on plinth, NM in E box......£160
701 Shetland Flying Boat, E in G box......£680
721 JU87B Stuka, khaki green/yellow, M in rare blue/red/yellow window box......£100
726 Messerschmitt BF109E, grey green, yellow wing tips and nose, NM with instructions and unapplied decals in E blister pack......£420
734 P47 Thunderbolt, EP in E blister pack......£110
734 P47 Thunderbolt, silver/black, Mint, NM blister pack with unapplied decals......£180
902 Avro Vulcan Bomber, G in F box......£620
998 Bristol Britannia Airliner, E in E box......£270

NOVELTY, FILM and TV-RELATED MODELS

100 Lady Penelope's 'Fab-1', pink, E including carded bubble pack......£220
103 Spectrum Patrol Car, gold, E in bubble pack......£170
Same model in red, NM in GP box......£120
104 Spectrum Pursuit Vehicle, blue including base, E in E bubble pack..£130
106 Thunderbirds II & IV, metallic blue/yellow base, red thrusters/legs, NM in E box......£190
107 'Stripey the Magic Mini', E in G box......£320
108 Sam's Car, powder blue, E in G box......£120
108 Sam's Car, chrome, E in G box......£110
108 Sam's Car, red version, E in G......£110
350 Tiny's Mini Moke, E in GP box......£140
351 'UFO' Shado Interceptor, NM in E box......£130
353 'UFO' Shado 2, metallic blue, E in G box......£290
353 'UFO' Shado 2, green version, E in G box......£110

GIFT SETS

No. 2 Commercial Vehicles Set, all E-NM in GP box......£1,900
39 Series US Saloon Cars Set, G-GP in G box......£1,600
60 Aeroplanes Set, all GP-E in G box......£900
61 'RAF' Aeroplanes Set, all F-G in GP box......£280
118 Towaway Glider Set, E on E inner plinth, GP outer box......£150
125 Fun A'Hoy Set, E in E box......£420
240 'Dinky Way' Set, E in G box......£40
245 Superfast Set, E, NM in GP box......£7
246 International GT Set, E-NM in G box......£60
294 Police Vehicle Set, E in NM box......£190
297 Police Vehicles Set, all E -NM on E plinth, E outer carded box......£190
201 Racing Car Set, E-NM on G plinth......£380
126 Motor Show Set, E-NM on E plinth, box F......£515
121 Goodwood Set, all GP-E in G box......£1,200
122 Touring Set, all E-NM in E box......£1,350
123 Mayfair Set, all E-NM in GP box......£860
124 Holidays Set, all GP-E in GP box......£860
298 Emergency Set, all E-NM in G box......£400
149 Sports Car Set, GP-E inGP box......£880
299 Post Office Set, all G-GP in F box......£217
990 Pullmore Transporter Set, all G-E in P box......£380

FARM and GARDEN MODELS

27a Massey Harris. Trade Box for 3 with 2 models GP in E pack......£120
308 Leyland Tractor, blue, NM in E box......£100
384 Leyland, metallic red, white E in GP box......£90
384 Leyland Tractor, blue, red wheels, E in E (red wheels factory error).£180
Same model but with the correct white wheels, NM in G bubble pack......£90
300 Massey Harris Tractor, metal driver, exhaust stack/wheels, E in E box......£100
Same model but with plastic driver and yellow front hubs, yellow metal rear hubs E in GP box......£100
301/27n Field Marshall Tractor, burnt orange body metal wheels with silver hubs, E in F box......£130
Orange, black exhaust, green hubs, GP in G box......£180
Same model, orange, black exhaust, blue plastic driver, green plastic front hubs, green metal rear hubs, E in correct late issue GP lighter yellow box......£340
305 David Brown Tractor, white, yellow cab (repainted red), early red engine cowl, black chassis/engine, yellow exhaust stack/wheels, E in F box plus **325 David Brown Tractor with Disc Harrow**, G in F box......£160
Same model, all white body/wheels, dark brown chassis/engine, red exhaust stack, E in E card box......£120
Same model, all white body, red chassis/engine, black exhaust stack, red wheels. Late issue with 'David Brown 995' engine cover labels, E in G blister pack......£160

PUBLIC TRANSPORT MODELS, PRE-WAR

29a Motorbus, trade box of six, yellow/silver, **'Marmite'**, all GP, E......£1,400
29c Double Deck Bus, maroon/cream, grey roof, **'Dunlop Tyres'**, GP......£220
29c Double Deck Bus, red/cream, grey roof, **'Dunlop Tyres'**, G......£120
29c Double Deck Bus, light blue/cream, grey roof, **'Dunlop Tyres'**, GP..£300
29c Double Deck Bus, green/cream, grey roof, **'Dunlop Tyres'**, GP......£340

PUBLIC TRANSPORT MODELS, POST-WAR

29c Double Deck Bus, 1st type AEC, red lower body, grey upper body, GP......£190
29c Double Deck Bus, 1st type AEC, dark green lower body, lighter green upper body, GP......£190
280 Observation Coach, mid-grey/red flashes, NM in GP box......£130
281 Luxury Coach, cream/orange flashes, E in E box......£250
Same, cream/red flashes, E in P box......£170
289 Routemaster Bus 'Thollembeck & Fils', M in G window box......£60
290 Double Deck Bus, 3rd type Leyland grille, cream, mid-green lower body and ridged hubs, sloping 'Dunlop' advert, un-numbered base, E......£120
290 Double Deck Bus, 3rd type Leyland grille, cream upper body with roof box, dark green lower body, sloping 'Dunlop' advert, un-numbered base, green plastic hubs, E in P box......£120
291 London Bus 'Exide', red body, spun hubs, E in GP box......£150
291 London Bus 'Exide', red body, plastic hubs, E in F box......£160
954 Vega Major Luxury Coach, whie, red interior, black base, cast wheels, E in G bbubble pack......£100

MILITARY VEHICLES

151 Pre-war Royal Tank Corps Medium Tank Unit, G-GP in GP box..£250
155 Pre-war Mechanised Army Set, all GP in G box......£3,000
615 US Jeep with 105mm Howitzer, E overall in G box......£80
617 VW KDF with Gun, E in GP box......£60
622 10 ton Army Truck, NM in E box......£80
626 Military Ambulance, EP in E box......£100
651 Centurion Tank, E in E detail picture box......£100
665 Honest John Launcher, NM in E picture box......£130

EMERGENCY VEHICLES

250 Strealined Fire Engine, EP in E box......£110
282 Land Rover Fire Appliance 'Falk', EP in E box......£60
286 Ford Transit Appliance, E in GP box......£110
288 Superior Cadillac Ambulance 'Falk', EP in GP......£100
956 Turntable Fire Escape Echelle, met. red, white back, EP in E box....£170
956 Turntable Fire Escape Echelle, red, black back, EP in GP box......£170
956 Turntable Fire Escape, red/silver, E in E box......£90

NICKY TOYS

137 Plymouth Fury Sports, silver, blue interior, 2 figures, E in GP picture box......£100
137 Plymouth Fury Sports, red, yellow interior, black hood, 2 figures, E in GP picture box......£130
137 Plymouth Fury Sports, yellow, black interior and hood, 2 figures, E in GP picture box......£160
142 Jaguar Mk.X, metallic blue, white interior, E in G picture box......£200
142 Jaguar Mk.X, green, white interior, E in F picture box......£200
186 Mercedes-Benz 220SE, metallic blue, light grey interior, E in G picture box......£190
186 Mercedes-Benz 220SE, red, light grey interior, E in F picture box......£130
186 Mercedes-Benz 220SE, metallic light green, grey interior, E in GP picture box......£150

NICKY TOYS sold by Vectis Auctions Ltd. (continued)

194 Bentley 'S' Coupé, metallic red, with driver, E in G picture box £160
194 Bentley 'S' Coupé, silver, with driver, E in G picture box £140
194 Bentley 'S' Coupé, gold, with driver, E in G picture box £140
195 Jaguar 3.4 litre, silver, light grey interior, E in G picture box £200
195 Jaguar 3.4 litre, turquiose, light grey interior, E in G picture box £180
239 Vanwall Racing Car, metallic dark blue, blue plastic driver,
    racing number '35', E in E picture box £160
239 Vanwall Racing Car, metallic dark red, blue plastic driver,
    racing number '35', E in G plain box £140
239 Vanwall, light blue, blue driver, RN '35', GP in G picture box £140
239 Vanwall, yellow, blue driver, RN '35', E in GP picture box £180

DINKY TOYS sold by Christie's South Kensington
85 Old Brompton Road, London, SW7 3LD.
Model and Box Condition Abbreviations:
M - Mint, E - Excellent, VG - Very Good, G - Good, F - Fair, P - Poor.

22e Farm Tractor, cream and blue, G £235
24b Limousine and 24e Super Streamlined Saloon both 2nd type, G £235
25d 'Castrol' Tank Wagon, 2nd type, G-VG £822
25f Market Gardener's Van, yellow with green chassis, black hubs G ...£235
28a 'HORNBY TRAINS' Van, yellow, blue wheels, gold transfers, F £1116
29c Double Decker Bus, green and cream, F-G £235
29c Double Decker Bus, maroon and cream with 'DUNLOP' adverts,
    and red 22c Motor Truck, VG £293
29c Double Decker Bus, red and cream with 'DUNLOP' adverts F-G £176
29c Double Decker Bus, green/cream, grey roof , 'Dunlop' adverts, G £329
30b Rolls-Royce, blue with black chassis and hubs, G-VG £352
30c Daimler, green with black chassis and hubs, F £352
33a Mechanical Horse, 33f 'Castrol' Petrol Tank Wagon and
    33e Breakdown Lorry, G-VG £411
34b Royal Mail Van, 29 'Marmite' Bus and blue/tan 30g Caravan £646
36f British Salmson 4 Seater with Driver, red, maroon chassis, VG £176
45 Pre-war Garage, with matt doors and in original box, VG in G box £376

DINKY TOYS sold by Lacy Scott & Knight,
10 Risbygate Street, Bury St Edmunds, Suffolk, IP33 3AA.
Condition Grading: B = Boxed, D = Damaged, M = Mint,
NM/GM = Near Mint, G = Good, F = Fair, P = Poor, R = Repainted.

CARS
40j/161 Austin Somerset, dark blue, pale blue hubs, M in F-G box £170
105 Triumph TR2, yellow, green hubs/seats, P-G in G box £80
106 Austin Atlantic, black, red interior/hubs, M in F-G box £90
109 Austin-Healey 100 Sports, G in F-G box £80
120 Jaguar 'E'-type, G-M in G-M box £90
170 Ford Fordor Saloon, red, G in F box £80
189 Triumph Herald, pale blue/white, G-M in M box £65
231 Maserati Racing Car, red, RN '9', M in G-M box £95
239 Vanwall Racing Car, green, RN '35', M in M box £80
241 Lotus Racing Car, G-M in G-M, box £80
340 Land-Rover, green, G-M in F-G box £70

EMERGENCY VEHICLES
252 Pontiac RCMP Car, blue, M in M box £60
253 Daimler Ambulance, G-M in G box £80
255 Mersey Tunnel Police Van, M in G box £50

COMMERCIAL VEHICLES
25x Dinky Breakdown Lorry, grey/blue, G in F box £60
433 Guy Flat Truck with Tailboard, blue/orange, G-M in F box £110
503 Foden Flat Truck with Tailboard, 1st type, red/black flashes,
    F-G U/B £140
902 Foden Flat Truck, orange/green 2nd type, G-M in F-G box £170
919 Guy Van 'Golden Shred', F-G in F-G box £210
925 Leyland Dump Truck with tilt cab, G in F-G box £80
940 Mercedes-Benz Truck, white/red, grey back, M in F-G box £45
942 Foden 'Regent' Tanker, F-G in G box £180
945 'Lucas Oil' Tanker, green, M in G box £120
965 Euclid Rear Dump Truck, yellow G in F-G box £80

NOVELTY
108 Sam's Car, chrome, red grille, M in F-G box £70
351 U.F.O. Interceptor, G-M in P-F box £90

DINKY TOYS sold by Special Auction Services
The Coach House, Midgham Park, Reading, Berkshire, RG7 5UG
Abbreviations: E = Excellent, F = Fine, G = Good, M = Mint, P = Poor,
U/B = Unboxed, VG = Very Good.

CARS
23m Thunderbolt Racing Car, E slight fatigue, box VG £170
24b Limousine, pre war, turquoise and yellow, VG £480
24g 4 seater Sports Tourer, pre war, yellow and black, G-VG £100
30c Daimler, beige, black wings, E £160
30d Vauxhall, pre war with egg box grille, TT Grey, VG £650
36d Rover Streamline, pre-war, turquoise and black, G, some fatigue £130
38b Sunbeam-Talbot, red with red hubs, VG £100
38c Lagonda, green, light green hubs, E £100
113 MGB, (South African issue), blue with red interior, G-VG U/B £220
141 Vauxhall Victor (South African issue), off-white with blue interior,
    VG, Afrikaans box F-G £200
142 Jaguar Mark X (South African issue), ivory, G, Afrikaans box P £220
148 Ford Fairlane (South African issue), blue, VG-E, Afrikaans box P £300
161 Austin Somerset, blue/yellow, plain baseplate/anodized, button rivets,
    possibly a factory paint sample, G £680
165 Humber Hawk, green/black without black roof, VG-E U/B £120
177 Opel Kapitan, (South African issue), cream, red interior G-VG, U/B .£220
193 Rambler Cross Country (South African issue), lilac,
    G VG (minute chips) U/B £110
194 Bentley Coupé (South African issue), avocado, G-VG,
    Afrikaans box VG £220
155 Ford Anglia, pale green with red interior, E, U/B £360
189 Triumph Herald, lilac and white, F-G , box G-VG £130
Ford Granada Resin Prototype, silver, 'Dinky Toys' label under, G £260
254 Austin Taxi, black, VG in VG box £140

NOVELTY
100 Lady Penelope's 'Fab 1', fluorescent pink, VG U/B £150
103 Spectrum Patrol Car, E in VG box £110
107 'Stripey, the Magic Mini', complete with packing pieces,
    VG-E, box F-G £200
477 Parsley's Car, E in G box £60

GIFT SETS
118 Tow Away Glider Set, VG - E, inner plinth VG, box F - G £150

DUBLO DINKY
064 Austin Lorries, green with grey wheels and green with black wheels,
    VG - E, boxes G - VG £70
071 VW 'Hornby Dublo' Van, VG - E, box F £65
068 'Royal Mail' Van E, box VG £55
066 Bedford Flat Truck, VG, box G-VG £60
065 Morris Pick-up, VG, box G-VG £60
073 Land Rover with orange Trailer and Horse, E, box G+VG £110
067 Taxi, model and box E £50

MILITARY VEHICLES
153a Military Jeep, smooth hubs, solid steering wheel G-VG, circa 1947...£35
253 Daimler Military Ambulance, E, U/B £100
674 Austin Champ United Nations issue, white and green, E U/B £320

EMERGENCY VEHICLES
30f Ambulance, post war, cream/black, VG-E £70
256 Humber Hawk Police Car, VG, box G £65

COMMERCIAL VEHICLES
274 Mini Van 'Joseph Mason Paints', E, box F - G £320
454 Trojan 'Cydrax' Van, E in G box £110
455 Trojan 'Brooke Bond' Van, E in F-G box £120
471 Austin 'Nestles' Van, VG in F box £85
905 Foden Flat Truck with Chains (2nd type), maroon, VG-E in G box..£280
923 Big Bedford 'Heinz' Van, VG in G box £220
932 Leyland Comet Wagon, TT blue, E in F-G box £150
934 Leyland Octopus Wagon, VG in G box £170
942 Foden 'Regent' Tanker, E-M in G-VG box £340
991 AEC 'Shell Chemicals Ltd' Tanker, E in F box £130

AIRCRAFT
60r Empire Flying Boat 'Caledonia', silver, VG, box F-G £130
67a Junkers JU89 Bomber, black with crosses, E, box G £280

SHOP DISPLAY ITEMS
Electric 'DINKY TOYS' hanging sign from 1970's, oblong yellow
    perspex with red letters, 1,270 mm long £220
Large electric 'DINKY TOYS' hanging sign (1960s), with two perspex
    oblong yellow sides with red letters, 1,300mm long £320

DINKY TOYS sold by Wallis & Wallis,
West Street Auction Galleries, Lewes, Sussex, BN7 2NJ
Grades of Condition, Abbreviations:
M = Mint, **VGC** = Very Good Condition, **GC** = Good Condition,
QGC = Quite Good Condition, **FC** = Fair Condition, **TT** = Two-tone.

CARS
22g Streamline Tourer, red with dark blue wheel hubs, VGC £50
22h Streamlined Saloon, turquoise, blue wheel hubs, GC, some fatigue ...£160
36b Trade Pack for 6 Bentley two seater coupés with two examples in
  green and blue, some wear, vehicles GC....................................£350
39bu Oldsmobile, cream/tan VGC £450
106 Austin Atlantic, black, red seats/hubs, boxed, vehicle VGC - M.........£130
107 Sunbeam Alpine, deep pink/ grey seats, RN '34', boxed, VGC...........£80
108 MG Midget, cream with maroon interior RN '28', red hubs,
  box - minor wear, vehicle VGC (minor chips) £110
109 Austin-Healey Sports, cream/red, RN '23', box - minor wear,
  vehicle GC-VGC..£75
110 Aston-Martin DB3, light grey, mid blue hubs/seats, RN '20',
  box - some wear, vehicle VGC..£70
114 Triumph Spitfire, silver, red seats, boxed, VGC £80
151 Triumph 1800, mid-blue, boxed, vehicle M.................................£150
153 Standard Vanguard, mid-blue, beige hubs, boxed, vehicle M £140
156 Rover 75, TT cream/mid blue body, boxed, vehicle M £240
157 Jaguar XK 120, TT cerise and duck egg blue, boxed some wear,
  vehicle QGC...£120
158 Riley Saloon, pale green with mid green hubs, box - minor wear,
  vehicle M..£110
159 Morris Oxford, TT mid-green and cream, boxed minor wear,
  vehicle M..£170
161 Austin Somerset, light blue with dark blue hubs, boxed minor wear,
  vehicle M..£100
Ford Zephyr, TT cream and dark green, boxed, vehicle GC to VDC £50
164 Vauxhall Cresta, TT beige and maroon, boxed minor wear,
  vehicle VGC...£70
165 Humber Hawk, TT maroon roof /lower side panels, cream upper
  sides/bonnet/boot, boxed some distortion, vehicle M.................£95
165 Humber Hawk, TT black roof/lower side panels, light green upper
  sides/bonnet/boot, boxed, vehicle M....................................£80
166 Sunbeam Rapier, TT light and mid-blue with mid-blue hubs,
  boxed, vehicle VGC..£65
166 Sunbeam Rapier, TT cream and orange with beige hubs,
  boxed, vehicle VGC..£65
167 AC Aceca, TT cream and dark brown with pale brown hubs,
  boxed minor wear, vehicle M...£75
167 AC Aceca, TT grey and red with red hubs, boxed, vehicle M £80
168 Singer Gazelle, TT light brown and green with beige hubs,
  boxed, vehicle M...£100
176 Austin A105, cream with blue flash, cream hubs, boxed, vehicle M £100
176 Austin A105, grey, red flash and hubs, boxed, vehicle minor wear £75
182 Porsche 356A, mid-blue, cream hubs, boxed minor wear, vehicle M.....£95
189 Triumph Herald (South African issue), mushroom brown sides/roof,
  off white bonnet/boot/side flashes, spun hubs, GC £190
197 Morris Mini Traveller, cream/red interior, spun hubs, boxed,
  vehicle M..£85
2162 1:25 scale Ford Capri, met. blue/black roof, bubble pack, vehicle M..£70
Cars Gift Set No.4 with 231, 232, 233 , 234 and 235 complete with insert,
  age wear to box, vehicles GC...£400

TV and FILM ISSUES
100 FAB 1 'Lady Penelope's' Rolls Royce, luminous pink,
  boxed with insert, some wear, no missiles, GC - VG..................£300
106 'The Prisoner's' Mini Moke in white, example with brown tops to
  cill boxes, with white panes to sides, red/white roof plus
  spare wheel cover, boxed £235

COMMERCIAL VEHICLES
30r Fordson Thames Truck, brown with maroon hubs, GC £100
60y Thompson Aircraft Refueller, VGC, no fatigue...............................£300
33 Series Set, Mechanical Horse, 'Hornby Trains' plus 3 wagons,
  signs of ageing, otherwise GC - VGC..................................£200
409 Bedford Lorry, yellow/black, red hubs, boxed minor wear,
  vehicle VGC - M...£90
417 Leyland Comet Lorry, yellow cab/chassis, light green stake body,
  mid green hubs, boxed, VGC..£350
418 Comet Wagon, dark green, mid green hubs, bright orange rear body,
  boxed, vehicle M...£110

432 Guy Flat Truck, mid blue cab/chasis/hubs, red flatbed,
  boxed some wear, vehicle M...£115
433 Guy Flat Truck with Tailboard, dark blue cab/chassis,
  orange flatbed, mid blue hubs, boxed some wear, vehicle M £145
448 Chevrolet Pick-up & Trailers, cream/turquoise, boxed with inserts,
  vehicles M overall..£180
901 Foden Diesel 8 Wheel Wagon, red cab/chassis/hubs, fawn rear body,
  boxed minor wear, vehicle M...£260
902 Foden Flat Truck, yellow 2nd type cab/chassis, mid green flatbed,
  boxed minor wear, vehicle M...£740
903 Foden Flat Truck with Tailboard, dark blue cab/chassis, mid blue
  hubs, yellow flatbed, boxed minor wear , vehicle VGC.............£640
905 Foden Flat Truck with Chains, dark green with mid green hubs,
  boxed minor wear, vehicle VGC - M...................................£180
908 Mighty Antar with Transformer, no transformer, otherwise vehicle
  M in box with minor wear..£460
917 Guy Van 'Spratts' boxed with lid wear, vehicle M......................£460
919 Guy 'Golden Shred' Van, boxed minor wear, vehicle VGC.............£290
925 Leyland Dump Truck, white cab/chassis with bright orange rear,
  mid blue hubs, boxed minor wear to lid, vehicle M.................£130
933 Leyland Cement Wagon, yellow body, boxed minor wear,
  vehicle VGC- M...£150
934 Leyland Octopus Wagon, yellow/green, boxed minor wear,
  vehicle VGC..£190
934 Leyland Octopus Wagon, dark blue cab/chassis, yellow rear body/cab
  flash, red hubs, boxed minor wear , vehicle VGC..................£460
942 Foden 'Regent' Tanker, boxed - damp damage, vehicle VGC.........£180
948 Tractor Trailer 'McLean', boxed, vehicle M.............................£160
958 Guy Warrior Snow Plough, boxed minor wear, vehicle VGC.........£120
969 BBC TV Extending Mast Vehicle, complete with instructions,
  boxed minor wear, vehicle VG- M......................................£140
988 ABC Transmitter Van, complete with detachable dish, boxed,
  vehicle VGC - M...£140

COACHES
Continental Touring Coach, boxed minor wear, vehicle VGC.................£200
282 Duple Roadmaster Coach, yellow body, red coahlines, boxed VGC ..£140

MILITARY VEHICLES
151 Royal Tank Corps Set, contents GC - VGC some fatigue.................£190
161 Anti-Aircraft Unit Set in original 3-39 display box with travelling
  pack insert, contents VGC minor fatigue...............................£190
661 Scammell Recovery Breakdown Vehicle, boxed late example with
  plastic hubs and with windows, VGC - M..............................£130
665 Honest John Launcher with missiles/instructions, M unused.............£90
697 Field Gun Set, picture box, contents GC £100

AIRCRAFT
62k Airspeed Envoy 'The King's Aeroplane', 'G-A EXX' registration,
  complete with paperwork, boxed plane VGC.........................£260
62p Armstrong Whitworth Ensign Airliner, with rare 'Ettrick' name to
  sides, boxed, model M..£290
719 Spitfire, green/brown camouflage, bubble packed with minor wear,
  plane M condition...£130
721 Junkers JU 87B, dark green/blue livery with bomb,
  boxed with packing, plane M..£80
722 Hawker Harrier, metallic blue/green RAF camouflage,
  bubble packed, plane M..£50
726 Messerschmitt BF 109E, desert camouflage livery, M as new £90
739 A6M5 Zereo Sen Fighter, metallic green, red markings,
  minor wear to bubble pack, plane M....................................£80

MISCELLANEOUS
12 Postal Set, Royal Mail Van and accessories all complete,
  boxed models AF - VGC...£420
24 series 1930's Ambulance, 2nd type criss cross chassis,
  2nd type Bentley grille, grey body, minor fatigue £270
Dinky Toys Dealer's Display Cabinet (30" x 24") oak framed with
  green transfer wording, GC - VGC......................................£440
A2034 Pre-war Petrol Pumps Set, with 4 pumps and 'Pratt's' oil bin,
  fine display box, contents VGC..£240
43b Trade Pack, 6 'RAC' motorcycles, box minor wear, motorcycles M ..£260
17 Passenger Train Set, with engine/tender, coach, 2 guards vans,
  box GC, models GC...£160

Nicky Toys, 1968 - 1975

In the late 1960s Meccano shipped out to India obsolete model dies and tools. The objective was to overcome exporting difficulties by manufacturing toys in India itself. The Indian manufacturing company was S. Kumar & Co who traded as Atamco Private Ltd. For trade mark reasons the toys were sold as 'Nicky Toys' and the arrangement was that the words 'Meccano' and 'Dinky Toys' would be obliterated from the dies. Similarly an arrangement was agreed in respect of deleting 'Dinky Toys' from the original model boxes.

However, the removal process was not diligently implemented which resulted in Nicky Toys occasionally being sold with 'Dinky Toys' being displayed both on their baseplates and on their boxes. These models are sought after by collectors and attract a premium at auctions.

After S.Kumar & Co. had manufactured the models from the original dies, they were finished by various firms of outworkers and as a result many different paint, decal and wheel versions exist. The details of the models listed are taken from various recent auction listings so their existence is confirmed. The figures shown in the 'Market Price Range' column are based on recent auction results and reflect the prices achieved by mint models in good boxes.

Types of Nicky Toys Boxes

i) Original yellow box with 'Dinky Toys' on the front and end flaps of the box and with a single model picture on front of box. This is the type of box which should have had all references to 'Dinky Toys' removed or overstamped.

ii) A plain yellow card box with 'Nicky Toys' stamped on the box end flaps and with 'Manufactured by: ATAMCO PRIVATE LTD. CALCUTTA' printed on the box sides.

iii) A yellow box with a full colour picture on the side. 'Nicky Toys' is clearly printed on all sides of the box and on the end flaps.

Ref.	Model name	Details	MPR
050	Jaguar 'Police' Car	Metallic Red or Red/White body	£80-100
05	VW 'Police' Car	Blue body, white doors	£80-100
051	Mercedes 220E 'Taxi'	Black/Yellow, Grey or Orange body, all with a 'Taxi' headboard	£80-100
054	Standard Herald Mk.II	Metallic Green, Red, Blue, Lemon-Yellow or White/Red body	£80-100
094	Rolls-Royce	Gold body	£80-100
113	MGB Sports	Light Blue, Navy Blue, Metallic Red or Light Green body, with driver	£100-125
115	Plymouth Fury	Metallic Green, Silver or Blue body	£80-100
120	Jaguar 'E'-type	Metallic Green, Red or Grey-Green	£100-125
		Apple-Green, Blue, Silver or Yellow	£100-125
134	Standard Herald Mk.II (Triumph Vitesse)	Red or Turquoise, both with White body stripe	£80-100
		Green or Blue, both with Red body stripe	£80-100
137	Plymouth Fury Conv.	Red with Yellow interior or Yellow with Black interior	£80-100
		Apple-Green or Metallic Green	£80-100
		Red or Cream	£80-100
137	Plymouth Fury Sports	Silver with Blue interior	£80-100
		Yellow or Blue body	£80-100
		Apple-Green, Red or Turquoise body	£80-100
142	Jaguar Mk.X	Metallic Blue with White interior	£80-100
		Green with White interior	£80-100
		Metallic Red or Metallic Turquoise	£80-100
		Silver or Pale Yellow body	£80-100
144	Volkswagen 1500	Red, White, Blue or Metallic Green	£70-90
	'Police' version	Blue and White body	£80-100
146	Daimler V8 Saloon	(Jaguar 3.4 litre). No colour details	NGPP
	'Police' version	Red and White body	£80-100
170	Lincoln Continental	Blue or Silver, both with White roof	£100-150
		Pale Yellow or Cream, Black roof	£100-150
		Metallic Red with White roof	£100-150
		Metallic Turquoise with White roof	£100-150
186	Mercedes Benz 220SE	Metallic Red or Grey, both with Light Grey interiors	£80-100
		Metallic Light Green or Metallic Blue	£80-100
194	Bentley 'S' Coupé	Metallic Red, White tonneau, Black interior	£80-100
		Metallic Green, Black tonneau, Red or Yellow interior	£80-100
		Cream or Blue with Red interiors	£80-100
		Silver or Gold body	£80-100
195	Jaguar 3.4 litre	Silver body, Light Grey interior	£80-100
		Cream or Blue with Red interiors	£80-100
238	Jaguar 'D'-type (RN '35' on some)	Light Blue body, Yellow plastic hubs	£70-90
		Racing Green, Red or Silver body	£70-90
		Metallic Red or Metallic Green body	£70-90
239	Vanwall Racing Car	Dark Metallic Blue, Red or Green	£70-90
		Light Blue or Yellow body	£70-90
		(NB All issues have a blue plastic driver)	
295	Standard '20' Minibus	Metallic Red, Green or Silver body	£60-80
		Pale Blue, Red or Grey body	£60-80
	'Ambulance' version	White body, Blue rooflight, red crosses on roof/doors	£60-80
405	Universal Jeep	Gloss Brick Red body	£100-125
		Light Grey or Blue body	£100-125
	Army versions	Olive Green or Drab Green body	£100-125
		(All have black windscreen frame)	
626	Military Ambulance	Gloss Green body	£80-100
660	Mighty Antar Tank Transporter	Gloss Green body	NGPP
693	Howitzer	Gloss Green body	NGPP
705	Viscount Airliner	Red, White and Blue 'BEA' livery	NGPP
735	Gloucester Javelin	RAF and camouflage liveries	£70-90
738	Sea Vixen	RAF and camouflage liveries	£60-80
949	Wayne School Bus	No details available	NGPP
962	Dumper Truck	No details available	NGPP
999	Comet Airliner	No details available	NGPP

Nicky Toys Catalogue Cover depicts Jaguar Mk.10 at Motor Show. Range of models shown in two-tone colour | £40-60

The Editor would welcome any further information to help complete this section.

Nicky Toys 194 Bentley 'S' Coupé. Note the type iii) box, the simple tinplate baseplate, the plastic wheels and the variable spreading of the spigot heads.

Photographs: Swapmeet Publications

French Meccano Dinky Toys

The history of French Meccano Dinky Toys mirrors that of the Liverpool parent company. A table of events (on page 000) gives a chronological and comparative guide to important periods in the progress of both English and French Meccano companies.

The Meccano France subsidiary was set up by Frank Hornby at Rue Ambroise Thomas in Paris in 1912, primarily to import British-made Meccano outfits and components. Having successfully marketed Meccano in France the obvious next step was to manufacture it there and in 1921 a factory was duly established at Rue Rébéval in Paris. This was initially used as offices and warehousing until 1924 when French-made Meccano became available, the Meccano Guild having been created a year before.

Production on French soil proved even more successful and a major new factory was soon required. In 1929 building was started of the famous plant at Bobigny. In 1931, the year in which Frank Hornby became MP for Everton, French Hornby 'Lead Models' nos. 1, 2 and 3 were introduced, followed by 'Miniature Models' nos. 4 and 10 in 1932. 'Modelled Miniatures' made their appearance in England in these years. Early in 1934 'Hornby Modelled Miniatures' were announced in France. Originally intended to extend the growing range of Hornby railway accessories, they were very briefly renamed 'Meccano Miniatures'. Before the year was out they had acquired the name 'Dinky Toys' in both countries. In the same year the Bobigny factory took over all French Meccano production while the Rue Rébéval premises reverted to offices and warehousing.

In 1935, 'Dolly Varden' dolls house furniture was introduced in England and the following year in France. Military vehicles became part of the Dinky range in Britain in 1937 but plans to introduce models of this type in France came to nothing before the War. Some of the English tanks and guns were imported between 1938 and 1940 along with some aircraft and ships. A very small part of French production was imported into the Britain in the late 1930s and most of their references were given a 'z' suffix.

During the late pre-war period the names were removed from aircraft dies and the models were given vague generic titles such as 'Long Range Bomber' and 'Medium Bomber'. Some planes like the Gloster Gladiator had no name at all and models of ships were given similar anonymity. It has been said that this was done for the cause of national security – to prevent Nazi intelligence from identifying the actual planes and ships by looking at the toys!

Among resources eagerly seized by the occupying German forces was naturally any factory that could turn instantly to the production of armaments. The French Meccano factory was thus commandeered in 1940 and required to produce various industrial items to satisfy the German war effort and even some toys to be sold under the Märklin name in German-occupied parts of the Continent. Production of conventional Meccano products was of course prohibited. There were very many shortages by the time peace was declared, rubber being a particular problem in France from 1940 since Nazi activities had completely cut off supplies. When Meccano haltingly returned to production in 1946, Dinky Toys tyres were noticeable by their absence. The metal wheel castings first used in 1940 continued to be fitted right up to the beginning of 1950. Even the 49 series Petrol Pumps had to be sold without hoses for a while!

One of the most common vehicles on British and Continental roads during and after the War was the US Army Jeep. Thus in 1946 the 153a Jeep was introduced in England and the 24-M in France.

Any study of the history of Dinky Toys needs documentation from contemporary Meccano sources. Much of the required information is to be found in various catalogues and Meccano Magazines of the period but is not always reliable as an indicator of the date of introduction of models. Advertising did not always coincide with supply of models and distribution was not always even across the country. Most catalogues were generally accurate but occasionally announcements of forthcoming additions to the range could be just wishful thinking or proclamation of intent rather than actual production. Illustrations in early catalogues sometimes present problems with inaccurate line drawings and heavily retouched photographs. French catalogues suffered additional problems in having photos or drawings of English prototypes.

Many French catalogues were printed in England and some were actually English catalogues with a small amount of additional text in French plus a French currency price list. There is a marked similarity between French and English numbering systems and between actual castings, particularly before the War. However, it is important to remember that French castings are different from similar English ones, and come from French dies. All French Dinky Toys carry specific information either cast-in or stamped on a tinplate base as to the country of manufacture or assembly of the item.

In 1951, the Rue Rébéval factory closed and all French production was centralised at Bobigny. The French Meccano Magazine re-appeared in 1953 and 24-U Simca and 25-B Peugeot Van were introduced in their own individual yellow boxes. The first French Dinky Supertoy was issued in 1955.

Promotional opportunities were always being sought by Meccano and the idea of a society for young drivers of toy vehicles was welcomed by Roland Hornby who initiated the French Dinky Toys Club in 1957. 1960 saw the introduction of the French version of 'Dublo' trains ('Hornby ACHO'), production of which continued until 1974. French Hornby 'O' gauge train manufacture came to an end in 1963.

The early 1960s was a time of diversification for Meccano in both England and France with Scalextric and other toys being added to the range of products. In a decade of changing fortunes they continued to design and manufacture an interesting range of Dinky Toys. In 1970 production was moved to a factory at Calais, partly to help relieve the industrial pressure in the Paris area and also to benefit from access to a major port. To cut costs in an increasingly difficult economic climate, manufacture of French Dinky cars was undertaken by Auto-Pilen of Spain in 1975. Other production continued at Calais until 1978 when all remaining French Dinky Toys manufacturing rights were signed over to the Spanish company.

Over the years, French and English Dinkies have had remarkable similarities and some quite paradoxical differences, reflecting the independence of the two companies. 'Speedwheels', for instance, were deemed essential in England to compete with Corgi's WhizzWheels and Lesney Superfast, while in France the need seems not to have been at all apparent. The range of ship models was quite extensive in England but very limited in France. The understandable dominance of French cars in the range resulted in a stream of taxi models in France while motorcycles were completely ignored after the Triporteur was withdrawn. The excellent French idea of a diamond shaped 'viewport' in the famous yellow boxes was restricted to that country and not tried in England. We have no 'Novelty' section in the French Dinky listings since the only Dinkys that would come under that heading would be imported British ones! Indeed, the only film or television-related item that seems to have originated in France is 1406 Michel Tanguy's Renault 4L Sinpar from the French TV series 'Les Chevaliers du Ciel'.

Some interesting models exist as accessories, particularly among the railway items. All the French castings of figures differ from English ones and have distinctly French characteristics, the 'Normandy' farmer and his French countrywoman spouse, the female railway crossing keeper, and the railway Cook with his poultry dish are particularly pleasing. Road signs provide another area of interest, some of the later French versions being only available as a free addition with certain models and not sold individually.

MARKET PRICE RANGE
Please note that the prices shown refer to pristine models and boxes. Items failing to match this standard will sell for less. Note also that boxes must still contain all their original packing pieces and additional contents where appropriate.

Cars - identification and casting differences

Although French and English reference numbers (particularly pre-war) are strikingly similar, it is very important to treat them as completely different systems in order to avoid confusion. The majority of French castings are different, as are the tyres. Surprisingly, small detail differences occur, as with steering wheels for instance. Post-war French-made open sports cars such as 22-A Maserati and 546 Austin-Healey have cast steering wheels with three spokes while those fitted to English made sports cars have four spokes. Many pre-war French made tyres have 'DUNLOP' moulded into the side-wall; post-war Spanish produced tyres similarly display the name 'PIRELLI'.

The 23b Streamlined Racing Car as made and sold in England from 1935 was based on a French Hotchkiss racing car. Unlike the English version, there were two French castings with the 23b reference. One is obviously the Hotchkiss (introduced in France in 1940). The other (pre-war) one is said by some to be modelled on a Renault Nervasport or possibly a Delahaye record car.

The 23 Racing Car is generally considered to have been inspired by the MG Magic Midget though it was never actually named as such by Meccano. Many modifications were made to the actual car in the 1930s in attempts to break

various endurance and speed records, and both English and French models mirrored these changes during their production. Racing numbers on the French 23 and 23a models were never contained within a circle and were initially stencilled, later mask-sprayed. All the French 23 series castings have either 'Made in France' or 'Fab. en France' cast underneath and also have a number of other differences from the English castings.

The first French Dinky Toys car model to be sold in its own box was the 24-U Simca Aronde in 1953. Many of the French boxes had a 'viewport' or aperture (usually diamond shaped) to allow a glimpse of the model. This enabled dealers and potential buyers to establish the colour of the model without the need to open the box. At the same time it saved the cost of printing a matching colour spot on the outside.

From 1969 a free 595 Traffic Sign was included as an additional attraction with certain models and these are noted in the listings that follow. More than twenty different plastic signs were made (see the 'Accessories' listing for details). They were not sold individually, but selections were available in Gift Sets 592 and 593.

French Dinky Toys 22A Maserati Sport 2000
Photo: Vectis Auctions Ltd.

Cars

Ref	Year(s)	Model name	Colours, features, details	Market Price Range

22a 1933-37 **Sports Roadster** .... Lead two-seater open body, lead wheels, scale 1:53.
Grey body / Blue wings; Blue body / Yellow wings; Silver body / Red wings.....................**£500-750**
Green body / Yellow wings; Cream body / Red wings, Yellow body / Black wings **£500-750**

22-A 1958-58 **Maserati Sport 2000** .... Dark red body, Tan seats, plated convex hubs, white driver, 1:43. Early bases are matt; later ones shiny ...**£300-350**
1958-59 (Renumbered as 505).................... Dark red body, dark red seats, plated convex hubs, white driver **£80-100**
Bright red body and seats, plated convex hubs, white driver **£80-100**

22b 1934-37 **Sports Coupé**............................ Lead two-seater closed body, lead wheels, scale 1:53.
Cream body with black wings; Blue body with red wings; Red body with blue wings **£500-750**
Green body with yellow wings; Grey body with green wings **£500-750**
Buff body with Black wings and hubs..**£500-750**

22c 1934-37 **Sports Roadster** .... As 22a, but with white rubber tyres on smooth silvered lead hubs....................................**£500-750**
22d 1934-37 **Sports Coupé** .... As 22b, but with white rubber tyres on smooth silvered lead hubs....................................**£500-750**

23 1933-35 **Racing Car** .... Lead body with contrasting colour flash over main colour, smooth lead hubs, 'DUNLOP' tyres coloured
to match body flash. Indication of driver, 4 exhaust stubs, no exhaust pipe, scale 1:53.
Orange (with white, blue or green flash); Cream (with white, blue, green or red flash).........**£150-200**
Blue (with silver or white flash); yellow (with blue flash)..**£150-200**
1934-36 .... Lead body with contrasting colour flash, smooth lead hubs, black or white or coloured tyres matching
colour flash. Driver helmet detail, 4 exhaust stubs, no pipe.
Blue (white flash); green (orange flash); white (blue flash); silver (blue or red flash)............**£150-200**
Cream (with blue, cream, green or red flash) **£150-200**

23a 1936-37 **Racing Car** .... Diecast body and smooth hubs; black, white or coloured 'DUNLOP' tyres that match colour flash.
No driver, 4 exhaust stubs, no exhaust pipe.
Blue (white flash), green (orange flash), white (blue flash); Silver (with blue or red flash) **£200-250**
Cream (with blue, cream, green or red flash) **£200-250**
1937-39 .... Diecast body and smooth hubs; black, white or coloured 'DUNLOP' tyres that match colour flash.
Six branch exhaust pipe, driver helmet detail, scale 1:53, 90mm. Racing numbers '1' or '12'.
Blue (with silver or white flash); orange (with green or blue flash); yellow (with blue flash)....**£200-250**
Cream (with blue, green or red flash) **£200-250**
1939-40 .... As previous model but smooth diecast hubs in assorted colours, black
or white tyres, racing numbers '1' or '12'.
Blue (silver or white flash); orange (green or blue flash); **£200-250**
Yellow (blue flash); cream (blue, green or red flash) **£200-250**
1940-40 .... As 1937-39 model but with unpainted diecast wheels.
Blue (silver or white flash); orange (green or blue flash)...**£200-250**
Yellow (blue flash); cream (blue, green or red flash) **£200-250**

23b 1935-37 **Streamlined Racing Car** .... Diecast body, plated smooth hubs, 'DUNLOP' tyres in the colour of the body flash, 1:53.
Blue (red flash, '1'); yellow (red flash, '2'); orange (blue flash, '3') **£200-250**
Cream (blue flash '4'); white (green flash '5'); red (green flash, '6') **£200-250**
1937-40 .... Diecast body, plated or black smooth hubs, white 'DUNLOP' tyres, 1:53.
Blue (red flash, '1'); blue (white flash, '11' or '12'); Red (green flash, '6'); red (silver flash, '2') **£200-250**
Yellow (red flash, '2'); Cream (blue flash, '4'); White (green flash, '5') **£200-250**
Green (white flash, '7' or '8'); green (silver flash, '7' or '8')..**£200-250**
Orange (green flash, '9' or '10'); orange (blue flash, '3') **£200-250**
1940-40 .... As previous model but with metal wheels (black or unpainted) **£200-250**
NB: Many of the pre-war 23b models listed left the factory without having the racing numbers applied.
The rarity levels for these is much the same as the numbered ones, consequently prices are similar.
1949-49 .... Re-issue of 1940 model with metal wheels (black or unpainted).......................................**£130-180**
1949-49 .... As 1939 issue but cream painted smooth hubs, black tyres.
Red body, silver flash, numbers '1' to '6' on cream background **£110-140**
1952-52 .... Brief re-issue of previous model **£110-140**

23b 1940-40 **Hotchkiss Racing Car** .... Red (silver flash, RNs '1' to '6'), unpainted mazak wheels, 1:53......................................**£200-250**
1948-49 .... As previous model but with painted mazak wheels...**£200-250**
1950-51 .... As previous model but cream painted convex hubs, black tyres **£100-150**

23c 1949-49 **Mercedes-Benz W154**.............. Silver, (RNs '1' to '6'), driver, painted or unpainted metal wheels (2 sizes known), 1:43. ....**£90-120**
1949-51 .... As previous model but black or red painted convex hubs, black tyres.................................**£90-120**

23d 1950-? **Auto-Union Record Car**............ Light green, filler cap on some, RNs '1' to '6', red convex hubs, black tyres, 1:43. ....**£90-120**
As previous model but with bright green convex hubs, black tyres **£90-120**
NB: Unlike the UK version, the rear axle ends are not visible.

23-H 1953-54 **Talbot-Lago GP Car** .... Blue body, (RN's '1' to '6' in white paint), driver cast in, blue convex hubs, ribbed tyres, 1:43. ...**£100-125**
1954-55 .... Same but racing numbers '1' to '6' on yellow transfers **£100-125**
1955-59 (Renumbered in 1959 as 510) ...... Blue, (RNs '1' to '6' and '22' to '27' on yellow transfers), plated convex hubs.....................**£100-125**

23-J 1956-56 **Ferrari GP Car** .... Red body, (RN's '1' to '6'), smooth grille, driver, plated convex hubs, 1:43. ....**£120-150**
1957-59 (Renumbered in 1959 as 511) ...... Dark red body (RNs '1' to '6' and '33' to '38'), squared grille, plated convex hubs **£150-200**

24-A 1956-57 **Chrysler New Yorker**................. 'CHRYSLER NEW YORKER' on base and on box. Scale 1:48. All have plated convex hubs.
Lemon yellow body, green seats £100-130
Red body, ivory seats £80-100

1957-60 (Renumbered in 1960 as 520) ...... 'CHRYSLER NEW YORKER 1955' on base and on box. Scale 1:48. All have plated convex hubs.
Lemon Yellow or Mustard Yellow body, green seats...£300-400
Red (or orange-red) body, ivory seats £300-400
Light metallic blue body with ivory or pale grey seats £300-400

24b 1934-35 **Limousine** .... 4 doors cast-in, horizontal bonnet louvres (aligned), large headlights, no sidelights, black or white
'DUNLOP' tyres on smooth hubs, scale 1:53.
Yellow body (with black or red wings); Green body (with blue wings).....................................£300-400

1936-39 .... 4 doors cast-in, horizontal bonnet louvres (stepped), medium or small headlights, sidelights on wings,
black or white 'DUNLOP' tyres on smooth hubs.
Green body (with red wings); Grey body (with blue wings)...£300-400

1940-48 .... As previous model but unpainted mazak wheels.
Grey body (red wings); Yellow body (red wings); Red body (black wings) £300-400
Blue body (black wings); Green body (black wings) £300-400

24-B 1956-58 **Peugeot 403 8cv**........................ No window glazing, base without towing notch, plated convex hubs, smooth white tyres, 1:43.
Blue body £60-80
Black body £80-100

1958-59 (Renumbered in 1959 as 521) ...... Base has towing notch, plated convex hubs, smooth white tyres.
Blue or Light grey body £100-120
Cream body £100-150

24-C 1956-58 **Citroën DS19**............................ No window glazing, plated convex hubs, smooth white tyres, 1:43.
Green body with white or pale grey roof £80-100
Ivory body (with very dark purple roof)..£80-100

24-CP 1958-59 **Citroën DS19** .... As 24-C but with window glazing. In 24-C box with '24CP' sticker, later in own box.
(Renumbered in 1959 as 522) Green body (with white or pale grey roof); Ivory body (with very dark purple roof)..............................£125-150
Dark orange body (cream roof); Brown body (cream roof) £80-100
Yellow body, grey roof £110-130

24d 1934-35 **Vogue Saloon**............................ Spare wheel in wing, large headlights, no sidelights, smooth mazak hubs,
black or white 'DUNLOP' tyres, scale 1:53
Blue body (with black wings); Green body (with red wings) £300-400

1936-37 .... Spare wheel in wing, medium headlights, sidelights on wings,
smooth mazak hubs, black or white 'DUNLOP' tyres.
Red body (black wings); Blue body (yellow or black wings); Green body (yellow wings) £300-400

1938-39 .... No spare wheel, small headlights, sidelights on wings,
smooth mazak hubs, black or white 'DUNLOP' tyres,
Grey body (with black wings); Green body (with maroon wings)...£300-400

1940-48 .... No spare wheel, medium or small headlights, sidelights on wings, painted mazak wheels.
Yellow body (red wings); Grey body (red wings); Red body (black wings); Blue body (black wings).......£300-400

24-D 1957-59 **Plymouth Belvedere**.................... Plated convex hubs, 1:48. Some boxes have picture of model.
(Renumbered in 1959 as 523) Green body, black roof and side flash £80-100
Tan body, brown roof and side flash £200-250
Grey body, Red roof and side flash £80-100
White body, blue roof and side flash..£200-300

24e 1934-35 **Aerodynamic Saloon Car**........... Large headlights, no sidelights, smooth mazak hubs, black or white 'DUNLOP' tyres, 1:53.
Green body, blue or red wings £200-250

1936-39 .... Medium or small headlamps, sidelights in wings, smooth mazak hubs, black or white 'DUNLOP' tyres.
Blue body (with black wings); Red body (with black or yellow wings) £200-250

1940-48 .... Medium or small headlamps, sidelights in wings, metal wheels.
Blue body (black wings); green body (black wings); red body (black wings); Yellow body (red wings) £200-250

24-E 1957-59 **Renault Dauphine**..................... No window glazing, plated convex hubs, smooth black tyres, 1:43.
(Renumbered in 1959 as 524) Green or Brick-red body £100-125
Raspberry-red body...£80-100

24f 1934-35 **Sportsman's Coupé** .... Two-door body with spare wheel in wing, large headlights, no sidelights,
smooth mazak hubs, black or white 'DUNLOP' tyres, 1:53.
Green body (with yellow wings); Blue body (with black wings)...£300-400

1936-37 .... Two-door body with spare wheel in wing, medium headlights, sidelights on wings, smooth mazak
hubs, black or white 'DUNLOP' tyres.
Blue body (black or yellow wings); Green body (yellow wings); Red body (black wings) £300-400

1938-39 .... Two-door body, no spare wheel, small headlights, sidelights on wings,
smooth mazak hubs, black or white 'DUNLOP' tyres.
Red body (black wings); Yellow body (black or red wings)..£300-400
Blue body (maroon wings); Cream body (blue wings)..£300-400

1940-40 .... Two-door body, no spare wheel, medium or small headlights, sidelights on wings, painted mazak wheels.
Red body (black wings); blue (black wings); green (black wings); Yellow body (red wings)....£300-400

1947-48 ....Re-issue of 1940 versions: Red, blue, green or yellow body, black wings, metal wheels £300-400

24-F 1958-59 **Peugeot 403-U Familiale** .... Sky blue body (no windows), plated convex hubs, scale 1:43 ....£80-100
(Renumbered in 1959 as 525)
24-F 1958 .... Dark red body (no windows). Only a few made as gifts for 1958 visitors to Meccano factory ....NGPP

24g	1934-35	**4-seat Sports Car**	Spare wheel, open windscreen, large headlights, no sidelights, black or white 'DUNLOP' tyres, 1:53.	

24g 1934-35 **4-seat Sports Car** .... Spare wheel, open windscreen, large headlights, no sidelights, black or white 'DUNLOP' tyres, 1:53.
Blue body (with black wings); Green body (with red wings) **£300-400**

1936-37 .... Spare wheel, solid windscreen, medium headlights, sidelights in wings, black or white 'DUNLOP' tyres.
Yellow body (with red wings), Grey body (with blue wings) **£300-400**

1938-39 .... Spare cast-in, solid windscreen, small headlights, sidelights in wings, black or white 'DUNLOP' tyres.
Green or cream body, red wings **£300-400**

1940-40 .... Spare wheel cast-in, solid windscreen, medium or small headlights,
sidelights in wings, unpainted mazak wheels, 1:53.
Grey body (red wings); yellow body (red wings); Red body (black wings) **£200-300**

1947-48 .... Re-issue of 1940 versions with unpainted mazak wheels, 1:53.
Grey body (red wings); yellow body (red wings); Red body (black wings) **£200-300**

24h 1934-35 **2-seat Sports Car** .... Spare wheel, open windscreen, large headlights, no sidelights, black or white 'DUNLOP' tyres, 1:53.
Green body (blue wings); Black body, (blue or red wings); Red body (black wings) **£300-400**

1936-37 .... Spare wheel, solid windscreen, medium headlights, sidelights in wings, black or white 'DUNLOP' tyres.
Yellow body (black wings); Blue or green body (red wings) **£300-400**

1938-39 .... Spare cast-in, solid windscreen, small headlights, sidelights in wings, black or white 'DUNLOP' tyres.
Green body (red wings); Red or yellow body (black wings)...**£300-400**

1940-40 .... Spare cast-in, solid windscreen, medium or small headlights, sidelights in wings, unpainted mazak wheels.
Cream or yellow body (red wings); Green or red body (black wings) **£200-300**

1947-48 .... Re-issue of 1940 versions with unpainted mazak wheels, 1:53.
Cream or yellow body (with red wings); Green or red body (with black wings) **£200-300**

24-H 1958-59 **Mercedes-Benz 190sl** .... Cream body (various shades), black hard-top, scale 1:43. Picture on some boxes **£120-160**
(Renumbered in 1959 as 526) Silver body, black roof, plated convex hubs **£80-100**

24-J 1959-59 **Alfa-Romeo 1900 Sprint** .... Red or Blue body, windows, plated convex hubs, smooth black tyres, scale 1:43......................**£80-100**
(Renumbered in 1959 as 527)

24k 1939-40 **Peugeot 402**................................. No baseplate (and no base retainers cast inside body), black or white
'DUNLOP' tyres on smooth painted mazak hubs, 1:53.
Maroon, Blue, Light blue, Red or Yellow body **£300-400**

1947-48 .... No baseplate (and no retainers cast inside), unpainted mazak wheels.
Maroon, Blue, Light blue, Red or Yellow body **£500-750**

1948-48 .... With tinplate base/front bumper (and with base retainers cast inside body), unpainted mazak wheels.
Maroon, Blue, Light blue, Red or Yellow body **£500-750**

24-K 1959-59 **Simca Vedette Chambord**........... Ivory/red body, plated convex hubs, scale 1:43...**£70-90**
(Renumbered in 1959 as 528) Light green/dark green body **£70-90**

24 l 1939-40 **Peugeot 402 Taxi**....................... Royal blue/yellow or maroon/cream, smooth cast hubs, tinplate meter, no base **£500-700**
1947-47 .... Royal blue/yellow or maroon/cream, metal wheels, tinplate meter, no base **£500-700**
1948-48 .... Royal blue/yellow or maroon/cream, metal wheels, tinplate meter, with base **£500-700**

24-L 1959-59 **Vespa 400 2cv**............................ Blue/grey body, plated convex hubs, 1:43, '24L' on box **£65-75**
(Renumbered in 1959 as 529) ...... Orange/grey body, plated convex hubs. '24L' on box **£150-200**

24m 1946-48 **Military Jeep** .... US Military olive-drab body and khaki painted mazak wheels (mounted inside-out for effect), white star
on bonnet, cast star at rear, tinplate windscreen frame (bonnet castings exist with and without frame
supports), wire steering wheel, 1:43 ....**£700-900**
note: 24m was the first new French made Dinky Toys model to appear after the war. They were supplied to
shops in trade boxes of twelve units. A trailer was designed to complement the Military Jeep but was
never produced, nor did 24m ever acquire a towing hook..

24m 1948-49 **Civilian Jeep** .... Castings as military version, usually unpainted wheels (a few painted).
Red body **£200-250**
Green body **£320-370**
Blue, orange, sand, yellow, metallic grey or metallic gold body. **£425-475**

24-M 1959-59 **VW Karmann-Ghia**................... Black/red body ('pointed' bonnet), plated convex hubs, scale 1:43 ....**£80-100**
(Renumbered in 1959 as 530)

24-N 1949-58 **Citroën 11BL** ....1st version: Small rear window, small lettering on base, widely spaced grille bars, spare wheel cover, tinplate
front bumper, no direction indicators, smooth roof interior. scale 1:43.
2nd version: With 16mm wide rear window, small lettering on base, boot replaces spare wheel cover, shallow
rear axle supports, with direction indicators, smooth roof interior.
3rd version: With 17mm wide rear window, large lettering on base, boot replaces spare wheel cover, deep
rear axle supports, cast front bumper, with direction indicators, hatched roof interior.

1949-49 .... Navy blue body, black mazak wheels **£500-600**
1950-51 .... As first version but the front wheel arch casting extends below the baseplate.
Metallic gold body, black convex hubs, black tyres **£400-500**
Metallic grey body and red convex hubs, black tyres **£350-450**
Black body and yellow convex hubs, black tyres **£150-180**
1951-52 .... As first version but with large rear window.
Black body, yellow or cream hubs, black tyres **£150-180**
1953-55 .... Integral front bumper, big or small rear window, rounded boot, narrow grooves on grille,
small print on base, straight windscreen base, smooth inside roof.
Black body, cream convex hubs, black tyres **£80-100**
1955-57 .... As 1953-55 model but large print and '24N' on base. Inside of roof is cross-hatched.
Black body, cream convex hubs **£80-100**
Light grey body, yellow convex hubs...**£100-150**
1957-58 .... As 1953-55 model but large print and '24N' on base, arched base to windscreen.
Black body (cream convex hubs), or Light Grey body (Light Grey convex hubs) **£90-110**
1958-58 .... As previous model but with plated convex hubs, white tyres.
Black body **£75-85**
Light grey body **£90-110**
note: 24-N Citroën models were all supplied to shops in grey trade boxes each containing six models.

24-N 1959-59 **Fiat 1200 Grand Vue**................. Announced only in the 1959 Swiss catalogue but not made as 24-N; renumbered and produced as 531.
24-O 1949-49 **Studebaker State Commander**.. Casting same as the English 39f model but the black tinplate base is marked 'Fabriqué en France'. 1:48
                                              Cream, red or metallic blue-green body, painted mazak wheels **£400-500**
       1950-50 .... Cream or metallic blue-green body, red convex hubs, black tyres **£300-400**
                                                Cream or Red body, Black hubs..**£150-175**
                      note: 24-O Studebaker was supplied to shops in trade boxes of six units.

24-P 1949-49 **Packard Super 8 Limousine** ...... Casting as English 39a but with black tinplate base marked 'Fabriqué en France', scale 1:48
                                                Blue, Turqoise or Metallic Gold body, painted convex hubs **£750-850**
                      note: 24-P Packard was supplied to shops in trade boxes of six units.

24-Q 1950-51 **Ford Vedette**................................ Navy blue body and convex hubs, small baseprint, scale 1:43 ....**£900-1,000**
                                                Metallic blue body (red hubs); Grey body and hubs; Turquoise body and hubs; Sand body and hubs **£90-120**
       1952-55 .... Metallic blue body, red convex hubs, largebase print **£100-130**
                                                Turquoise body and hubs, or Grey body and hubs **£90-120**
                                                Sand body and hubs **£100-130**
                      note: 24-Q was supplied to shops in trade boxes of six units.

24-R 1951-52 **Peugeot 203**................................ Small rear window, smooth inside roof, round filler cap on right rear wing, scale 1:43.
                                                Maroon body, cream convex hubs **£150-200**
                                                Metallic gold body, cream or red convex hubs **£450-600**
                                                Iridescent Violet body, cream convex hubs **£750-1,000**
                                                Grey body, grey convex hubs **£75-100**
                                                Metallic blue body, cream convex hubs or Metallic green body, creamy-yellow convex hubs....................**£90-120**
       1953-55 .... Small rear window, cross-hatching inside roof, no filler cap.
                                                Grey body, grey convex hubs **£80-90**
                                                Metallic blue-green body with cream convex hubs or Grey-blue body with cream convex hubs **£90-120**
       1955-56 .... Grey or grey-blue body, spun hubs, white tyres, small rear window, no filler cap **£90-120**
       1956-57 .... Grey-blue or pale grey-green body, spun hubs, white tyres, big rear window, square filler cap **£90-120**
       1957-59 (Renumbered in 1959 as 533) ...... As previous model but with lime green body **£800-1,000**
                         Promotional: Lime green body, 'Club Dinky Toys' **£750-1,250**
                      note: 24-R was supplied to shops in trade boxes of six units.

24-S 1952-54 **Simca 8 Sport** ....1st type: Grey body, red seats, thin windscreen frame, unpainted convex hubs, white tyres, 1:43 ....**£85-95**
                                                Black body, Fawn seats **£300-400**
                                                Black body, red seats **£90-120**
       1954-56 .... Grey or black body, red seats, thin windscreen frame, spun hubs, white tyres **£75-85**
                                                Black body, red seats **£75-85**
       1956-59 (Renumbered in 1959 as 534) ...... 2nd type: Grey body, red seats, thick windscreen frame, spun hubs, white tyres **£75-85**
                                                Black body, red seats **£200-300**
                                                Ivory body, red seats **£100-120**
                                                Duck-egg Green or Duck-egg Blue body, Red seats **£125-150**
                      note: 24-S was supplied to shops in trade boxes of six units.

24-T 1952-52 **Citroën 2cv** (1951-53) .... Mid-grey or metallic grey (grey hood), grey-gold hubs, one rear lamp, rear axle ends not rounded, 1:43.
                                                Sold unboxed (supplied to shops in trade boxes of six units)...**£90-120**
       1953-54 .... Mid-grey or metallic grey (gloss or matt-grey hood), grey-gold hubs, one rear lamp, rounded rear axle ends.
                                                In box with '24T' and 'MECCANO' in large print on ends **£65-75**
                                                Dark or Light-grey body, matt-grey hood, cream convex hubs **£65-75**
       1955-59 (Renumbered in 1959 as 535) ...... Light grey body, gloss or matt-grey hood, cream hubs, three red rear lamps, rounded rear axle ends.
                                                In box with '24T' and 'MECCANO' in small print on ends **£60-70**
                                                Maroon body, matt-grey hood, cream convex hubs **£65-75**
                                                Grey-blue body, dark grey-blue hood, grey concave or convex hubs **£65-75**

24-U 1953-55 **Simca 9 Aronde** ....1st type: Olive green body, 'stepped' grille, painted convex hubs, 1:43 ....**£90-110**
                                                Light grey-green body, 'stepped' grille, painted convex hubs **£60-70**
                                                Mid grey or light grey body, 'stepped' grille, painted convex hubs **£60-70**
24-U 1956-57 **Simca Aronde Elysée** .... 2nd type: Light grey or Light Grey-Green body, 'wide' grille, spun hubs **£60-70**
                                                Sky blue body, 'wide' grille, plated convex hubs **£75-85**
       1958-59 (Renumbered in 1959 as 535) ...... 2nd type: Light grey-green body, dark green roof, 'wide' grille, spun hubs **£90-110**
                                                Blue or Sky-Blue body, White roof, 'wide' grille, spun hubs **£90-110**
                      note: 24-U Simca was the first French Dinky Toy to be supplied in its own individual box (in 1953).
24-UT 1956-58 **Simca Aronde Elysée Taxi**....... Red/blue body, meter and roof sign, painted convex hubs, second grille, 1:43 ....**£110-130**
       1958-59 (Renumbered in 1959 as 537) ...... As previous model but with plated convex hubs **£110-130**
                      note: 24-UT was supplied to shops in trade boxes of six units.

24-V 1954-56 **Buick Roadmaster** ....1st type: Blue body, dark blue roof (smooth inside), unpainted convex hubs, white tyres, 1:48............**£140-180**
                                                Yellow body, green roof (smooth inside), unpainted convex hubs, white tyres..................................**£140-180**
       1956-59 (Renumbered in 1959 as 538) ...... 2nd type: Blue body, dark blue or cream roof (cross-hatched inside), plated convex hubs, white tyres **£140-180**
                                                Yellow body, green roof (cross-hatched inside), plated convex hubs, white tyres **£140-180**
                                                Salmon-Pink body, Black roof (cross-hatched inside), spun hubs **£140-180**
                                                Ivory body, Blue roof (cross-hatched inside), spun hubs **£140-180**
                                                Ivory/metallic blue body, convex hubs **£400-500**
                                                Red/yellow with Blue roof **£1,000-1,250**

24-X 1954-56 **Ford Vedette**................................ With or without 'Made in France, Imprimé en France' on individual boxes. Scale 1:43.
                                                Dark blue body and convex hubs **£100-125**
                                                Pale grey-blue body and convex hubs **£100-125**
24-XT 1956-59 **Ford Vedette Taxi**..................... Black body, beige or cream roof, meter, taxi sign, spun hubs **£125-150**
                   (Renumbered in 1959 as 539) ...... 24-XT was supplied to shops in trade boxes of six units. It was never individually boxed.

24-Y 1955-57 **Studebaker Commander Coupé.** 1st type: Base has no towing eye, 1:48. '24Y' on box but no illustration.
Red body, Dark Cream roof, plated convex hubs, smooth tyres...£100-140
Light green body, dark green roof, plated convex hubs, smooth tyres.....................................£100-140
Ivory body, Maroon roof, plated convex hubs, smooth tyres...£150-200

1957-58 ....2nd type: Base has towing eye. '24Y' and picture of model on box.
Red body, Cream roof, plated convex hubs, smooth tyres...£90-120
Light green body, dark green roof, plated convex hubs, smooth tyres.....................................£90-120
Ivory body, dark red roof, plated convex hubs, smooth tyres...£150-200

1958-59 (Renumbered in 1959 as 537) ..... 2nd type: Base has towing eye, front wing panels match roof colour, plated
convex hubs, smooth tyres. '540-24Y' and picture of model on box.
Red body, Cream roof and wing panels £150-200
Ivory body with Maroon roof and wing panels £150-200
Pale grey body, maroon roof and wing panels £150-175

NB: The 1959 catalogue shows a two-tone blue version of 24-Y/540 but it has not been seen. Also, a photo
exists showing a 24-Y prototype of the 1953-54 Studebaker but only the 1955 car was actually modelled.

24-Z 1956-58 **Simca Vedette Versailles**........... 1st type: Base has no towing eye, picture on some boxes. Scale 1:43.
Yellow body, black roof, plated convex hubs, white tyres...£80-95
Light blue body, White roof, plated convex hubs, white tyres £80-95

1958-59 (Renumbered in 1959 as 541) ...... 2nd type: Base has towing eye, picture on box.
Yellow body, black roof, plated convex hubs, white tyres...£80-95
Light blue body, White roof, plated convex hubs, white tyres £80-95

24-ZT 1959-59 **Simca Ariane Taxi** .... Black body, red roof, plated convex hubs. '542-24ZT' on box....................£100-125
(Renumbered in 1959 as 542)

30a 1935-39 **Chrysler Airflow** .... English castings painted and assembled in France. Smooth hubs, black or white 'DUNLOP' tyres, 1:48.
Green, Blue or Red body...£150-200

35a 1939-40 **Simca 5**.. No base, black rubber wheels, scale 1:50.
Red, dark red, maroon, light blue, mid-blue, royal blue, grey,
grey-blue, green, light green, brown, silver, yellow, gold, cream £125-175

1939-40 .... Export version of 35-A with white rubber wheels.
Red, dark red, maroon, light blue, mid-blue, royal blue, grey,
grey-blue, green, light green, brown, silver, yellow, gold, cream £145-195

1940-40 .... No base, black painted mazak wheels.
Red, dark red, maroon, light blue, mid-blue, royal blue, grey,
grey-blue, green, light green, brown, silver, yellow, gold, cream £175-250

1948-50 .... No base, black rubber wheels.
Red, dark red, maroon, light blue, mid-blue, royal blue, grey,
grey-blue, light green, mid-brown, silver, yellow, gold, cream £100-125
Green, dark brown £150-200

Numbers 100 to 106 were produced as 'Dinky Juniors' - a pocket-money budget series. Most fitted with spun steel hubs or Silver hubs with 'DUNLOP'tyres. 1:43.
100 1963-68 **Renault 4L**................................ Pale-green body...£80-100
101 1963-66 **Peugeot 404** ....(553) Orange body, no frame to rear number plate £90-120
1966-69 ....(553) Orange or red-orange, rear number plate has frame £90-120
102 1963-68 **Panhard PL17** .... Grey-blue or Bright blue body..£150-200
103 1964-68 **Renault R8**.............................. Red body..£85-100
103 1969-69 **Renault R8S Gordini**................ Red body, painted headlights £350-400
104 1964-68 **Simca 1000**............................. Pale yellow or lime-green body £200-300
105 1964-68 **Citroën 2cv** .... Grey body, Light Grey concave hubs..£250-350
106 1965-69 **Opel Kadett** .... Yellow body..£300-400

500 1967-71 **Citroën 2cv** .... Beige (dark grey open top), painted concave hubs, 89mm. 'Made in France' on aperture box......................£70-80
Blue-Grey body (dark blue open top), or Pale grey body (mid-grey open top)............................£70-80
1974-75 ....Spanish issue: Beige (dark grey open top), painted hubs. 'Made in Spain' over-stamped on box, own box printed later......£70-80
1975-76 ....Spanish issue: Beige (dark grey open top), painted hubs. 'Made in Spain' and 'Meccano' on large non-aperture box £70-80
1976-78 ....Spanish issue: Orange body, 'square' headlamps, rivetted base, plated concave hubs.
'Made in Spain, impriméé en France, ref 500' on box £70-80
1978-? ....Spanish issue: Orange body, 'square' headlamps, screwed base, plated concave hubs.
'Made in Spain, impriméé en Espagne, ref 011500' on box £70-80

501 1967-70 **Citroën DS19 'POLICE' Car** .... Very dark blue/white, roof beacon, concave hubs, 1:43 ....£120-140
503 1967-69 **Porsche Carrera 6** .... White/red body, 'Carrera' in black, 1:43. Box has 'moteur...280km/h' outside of yellow lines £150-200
1969-71 .... Same model but box has 'moteur...280km/h' within yellow lines £150-200

505 1959-60 **Maserati Sport 2000** .... (previously 22a) Dark or bright red, shiny baseplate, convex chromed hubs, white driver, scale 1:43 ....£75-85
1960-61 .... Dark or bright red, shiny baseplate, concave chromed hubs, white driver £75-85
506 1960-61 **Aston-Martin DB3S**.................. Emerald green, concave hubs, driver, racing numbers '1' to '17', scale 1:43 ....£80-100
note: 506 used the English 104 body casting with 'Made in France' base and a French three-spoke steering wheel.

506 1967-72 **Ferrari 275 GTB** .... Cast base, cast detailed wheels, nylon tyres, scale 1:43.
Red body £80-100
Yellow body £120-150
Yellow body, 'hybrid' with Red doors/bonnet/boot...£70-80

507 1967-71 **Simca 1500 Estate Car** .... White, Metallic Dark Grey or Silver-Grey body, camping table, concave hubs, black tyres, 1:43 ....£65-75
507-P 1967-71 **Simca 1500 'POLICE' Car** .... White and Dark Blue body, Red interior, aerial at one side of roof £5,000-6,500

508 1966-71 **Daf 33** .... Dark red body, cast base, concave hubs, black tyres, female driver, 1:43 ....£50-60
Metallic bronze body, concave chromed hubs, black tyres...£100-120
Beige body, concave chromed hubs, black tyres..£50-60

509	1966-68	**Fiat 850**	Red body, white tilting seats, concave hubs, scale 1:43	**£40-50**

509 1966-68 **Fiat 850** .... Red body, white tilting seats, concave hubs, scale 1:43 .... **£40-50**
Yellow or White body, red tilting seats, concave hubs **£65-80**
1968-71 ....Spanish issue: Red, yellow or white body, 'PIRELLI' tyres, Barcelona number plate. 'DINKY-POCH' on box. **£300-350**
Turquoise-green body, white interior, 'PIRELLI' tyres, Barcelona number plate. 'DINKY-POCH' box. **£400-500**

510 1959-59 **Talbot-Lago GP Car** .... (previously 23-H) Blue body, (RN's '1' to '6' and '22' to '27' on yellow transfers), driver cast in,
plated convex hubs **£70-90**

510 1965-68 **Peugeot 204**............................... Two-part rear bumper, rivetted floor, concave hubs, scale 1:43
Metallic dark red or greenish-beige body. 'Par autorisation des automobiles PEUGEOT' on box. **£70-80**
1968-68 ....Spanish issue: Two-part rear bumper, rivetted floor, concave hubs, 'PIRELLI' tyres.
Bright Red body, 'DINKY-POCH' on box. Assembled in Spain **£500-750**
1968-71 ....Spanish issue: As previous model but White body. Made for export to Spain **£400-450**
1977-78 ....Spanish issue: One-piece rear bumper, screwed floor, Beige-pink body. Made in Spain, box printed in Spain **£40-50**
1981 'VGE'............Promotional issue: Off-White body with 'VGE' in Blue/White/Red with Presidential Election decor....................**£250-350**

511 1959-63 **Ferrari Racing Car**.................... (previously 23-J) Red body, 'cross-hatched' grille, racing numbers '1' or '22' to '27',
driver, concave hubs, radial or block tread tyres, scale 1:43 ....**£50-70**

511 1968-71 **Peugeot 204 Cabriolet** .... Cast base, aluminium concave hubs, tilting seats, 1:43.
Sky-blue open body, black interior **£100-125**
Red open body, black interior..**£120-160**

512 1962-66 **Leskokart Midjet Kart**.............. Blue body, Black plastic wheels. Plastic driver (white with red, yellow or blue jacket). Scale 1:43 ....**£70-90**

513 1966-68 **Opel Admiral** .... Metallic blue or metallic red, detailed hubs, luggage, scale 1:43 ....**£60-75**
1968-69 ....Spanish issue: Same but with 'PIRELLI' tyres. 'DINKY-POCH' on box **£170-190**

514 1966-71 **Alfa-Romeo Giulia 1600ti** .... Plated concave hubs, working windows, head and rear lights, 1:43.
Beige or White or Metallic Grey body, Red interior **£80-100**
Pale Green body, Red interior **£125-150**
Spanish export issue: Metallic Grey body, 'PIRELLI' tyres, Barcelona number plate. **£200-300**

515 1963-70 **Ferrari 250GT 2+2** .... Red body, White interior, concave hubs, black tyres, scale 1:43 ....**£100-125**
Metallic blue body, concave hubs, black tyres **£90-110**

516 1964-65 **Mercedes-Benz 230SL** .... Removable hard-top, concave hubs, 'MERCEDES 230SL' on base, French box.
Metallic grey/cream, or metallic red-orange/cream, or metallic red/cream **£100-120**
1965-66 .... Same as previous model but with 'MERCEDES-BENZ 230SL' on base. French box **£75-85**
1966-70 .... Metallic red-orange/cream as 1965-66 version but in British box for export to UK and USA **£60-70**

517 1962-64 **Renault R8**................................ Blue or Pale Yellow body, concave hubs, scale 1:43 ....**£80-100**
(Renumbered in 1964 as 1517) .... note: Model was introduced on the same day as the actual car
1968-70 ....Spanish issue: Cream body, concave hubs, 'PIRELLI' tyres, Silver rear number plate. 'DINKY-POCH' on box **£400-600**
Spanish issue: Dark blue body, concave hubs, 'PIRELLI' tyres, Silver rear number plate. 'DINKY-POCH' on box.........**£400-600**

517-P 1969 **Renault R8 Police Car**.............. Dark blue/white, 'POLICE'. Commissioned for use by Police **£400-450**

518 1961-64 **Renault R4L** .... Pale blue or light blue body, first grille, concave hubs, scale 1:43 ....**£50-60**
(Renumbered in 1964 as 1518) Brick-red or brown body **£50-60**
Grey-green body...**£95-125**
1968-70 ....Spanish export issue: Same but Violet body, 'PIRELLI' tyres. 'DINKY-POCH' on box **£400-600**
1964-64 .... Red body, 'POMPIERS de PARIS'. Commissioned by Fire Service **£1,200-1,600**
1964-64 .... Yellow body 'PTT' livery. Commissioned for use by Postal Service **£300-400**
1975-77 .... Dark blue, second grille, concave hubs. 'Made in Spain' and pink '4L' on box **£45-50**
1977-? .... Sky blue, second grille, concave hubs. 'Made in Spain' and blue '4L' on box **£40-45**
518-A 1970-71 **Renault 4L, 'AUTOROUTES'** .. Orange body, first grille, plated concave hubs. Box also contains 595r Traffic Sign 'Road Works'...........**£100-130**

519 1961 **Facel Vega Facellia** .... Announced in the 1961-62 catalogue but not produced. ....NPP

519 1962-64 **Simca 1000**................................ Light blue-grey body, Red interior, Black base, concave hubs, rubber tyres. '519' in black oval on box **£55-65**
note: The 1962-64 version of 519 was renumbered in 1964 as 1519. 519 continued as follows:
1962-63 .... .Red or Light blue-grey body, Cream interior, Black base. '519' in black oval on box **£65-75**
Lime-Green or Light yellow body, Cream interior **£220-240**
Sky-blue body, white interior **£80-90**
1963-64 .... Metallic grey body, black or green interior. Existence not confirmed ....NPP
1964-66 .... Light blue-grey body, white interior. Anodised base, concave hubs, nylon tyres. '519' in black band on box........**£70-90**
1966-68 ....South-African issue: Turquoise body, red interior, concave hubs. Assembled and painted in South Africa **£400-600**
South-African issue: Dark red body, white interior, concave hubs. Assembled and painted in South Africa....................**£400-600**
1968-70 ....Spanish export issue: Metallic blue body, Cream interior, concave hubs, 'PIRELLI' tyres. 'DINKY-POCH' on box **£300-400**
Spanish export issue: Red body, Cream interior, concave hubs, 'PIRELLI' tyres, 'DINKY-POCH' on box....................**£175-250**

520 1960-61 **Chrysler New Yorker** .... (previously 24-A) 'CHRYSLER NEW YORKER 1955' on base and on box. Concave hubs, scale 1:48.
Yellow body, green seats **£200-250**
Red body, ivory seats **£90-110**
Light metallic blue body, ivory seats **£200-250**

520 1963-64 **Fiat 600D** .... Red or Cream body, concave hubs, scale 1:43 ....**£65-75**
(Renumbered in 1964 as 1520) White body, Red interior, concave hubs..**£50-65**
1968 ....Spanish export issue: Pale yellow body, concave hubs, 'PIRELLI' tyres. 'DINKY-POCH' on box **£70-90**
Light blue body, concave hubs, 'PIRELLI' tyres. 'DINKY-POCH' on box **£200-300**
Off-White body, concave hubs, 'PIRELLI' tyres, Silver number plate. 'DINKY-POCH' on box **£150-200**

521	1959-60	**Peugeot 403 8cv**............................	(was 24-B) Light grey body, no windows, base has towing notch, plated convex hubs, smooth white tyres...**£55-65**
			Cream body, no windows, base has towing notch, plated convex hubs, smooth white tyres.....................**£100-120**
	1960-62	....	With windows and towing notch, plated concave hubs, smooth or treaded white tyres.
			Light grey body. (Light blue-grey picture and black picture on box) **£55-65**
			Cream body. (Light blue-grey picture and black picture on box)..**£100-120**
	1962-64	....	521 became individually unavailable in 1962 but was included in Gift Set 503 up to 1964.

522	1959-60	**Citroën DS19**...........(was 24-CP)	Green/white, or Ivory/very dark purple. With windows, convex hubs, white tyres, 1:43. '24CP' box........**£100-120**
			Yellow/grey, or Orange/cream. With windows, convex hubs, white tyres. '24CP' box.....................................**£85-95**
	1960-63	....	Orange/cream body, concave hubs, smooth white tyres. '522' on box...**£90-120**
			Yellow/grey body, concave hubs, smooth white tyres. '522' on box..**£85-95**
	1963-68	....	Orange body, cream roof, concave hubs, treaded white tyres. '522' on box..**£90-120**
			Yellowish-beige body, pale grey roof, concave hubs, treaded white tyres. '522' on box **£150-200**
			Pale yellow body, grey roof, concave hubs, treaded white tyres. '522' on box **£75-85**

523	1962	**Simca Driving School Car**	Announced (but not illustrated) in the 1962 price list. Not produced. ....**NPP**

523	1959-60	**Plymouth Belvedere**...................	(previously 24-D) Green body, black roof and panel, convex hubs, 1:48. Box with or without picture...........**£85-95**
			Tan body, metallic brown roof and panel, convex hubs. Box with or without picture **£80-100**
			Grey body, orange-red roof and panel, convex hubs. Box with or without picture....................................**£85-95**
			White body, blue roof and panel, convex hubs. Box with or without picture **£300-350**
	1960-61	....	Tobacco-brown body, maroon roof and panel, concave hubs..**£200-300**
			White body, blue roof and panel, concave hubs..**£350-450**

523	1963-64	**Simca 1500**............................	Light-blue body, concave hubs, scale 1:43 ....**£45-55**
		(Renumbered in 1964 as 1523)	Light blue or Metallic grey body, concave hubs **£45-55**
	1968-69	....................Spanish export issue:	Bright Blue body, plated concave hubs, 'PIRELLI' tyres. 'DINKY-POCH' on box **£400-600**

524	1959-60	**Renault Dauphine**....................	With windows (some without), convex hubs, smooth black tyres, scale 1:43. '524-24E' on box.
			Turqouise, Brick-red or Raspberry-red body...**£100-120**
			Ivory-White body **£100-120**
	1960-60	....	As previous models but box has 'DINKY TOYS' in upright lettering plus '524'.
			Turquoise body **£100-120**
			Brick-red or Raspberry-red body **£100-120**
			Ivory-White body **£120-150**
	1960-61	....	Same (box has 'DINKY TOYS' in upright lettering plus '524').
			Bright Blue-Green (special limited edition for Paris Dinky Toys Club) **£500-750**
	1960-61	....	With windows, concave chromed hubs. Box has 'DINKY TOYS' in oblique lettering plus '524'.
			Turqouise, Brick-red or Raspberry-red body, smooth or treaded black tyres...**£65-75**
	1961-64	............................note:	524 became individually unavailable in 1961 but remained in Gift Set 503 up till 1964.

French Dinky Toys 24D Plymouth Belvedere
Photo: Vectis Auctions Ltd.

524	1964-66	**Panhard 24CT**	Metallic grey body, concave chromed hubs, 'DUNLOP' tyres, scale 1:43. In French box	£60-80
			Pale yellow-green body, concave chromed hubs, 'DUNLOP' tyres, scale 1:43. In French box	£50-70
	1966-69		Metallic grey body; steel hubs, in English box (model made for export to UK and USA)	£60-80
525	1959-60	**Peugeot 403 Estate Car** ....(24-F)	Sky blue, no windows, convex hubs, rear bumper over-riders	£45-55
	1960-62		Sky blue, concave hubs, no rear bumper over-riders	£45-55
	note:		Model was originally shown in catalogues as being available in black. It was never produced in that colour.	
525	1964-70	**Peugeot 404 Commercial Traveller's Car**	Ocean blue or cream body, yellow or black rear number plate, spun hubs, windows, scale 1:43	£70-90
525	1964-64	**Peugeot 404 Fire Car**	Red body, 'Pompiers de Paris', concave chromed hubs, 'DUNLOP' plastic tyres, aerial	£1,000-1,250
526	1959-60	**Mercedes-Benz 190sl** (previously 24-H)	Cream body (various shades), no windows, black hard-top, convex hubs, 1:43. Picture on some boxes	£65-75
			Silver body, black hard-top, convex hubs	£65-75
	1960-62		Cream body (various shades), with windows, black hard-top, convex hubs. '526' and picture on box	£65-75
			Silver body, black hard-top, convex hubs	£80-100
526	1961-63	**Mercedes-Benz 190sl Hard-Top**	Cream body (various shades) with windows, black hard-top, concave hubs. '526' and picture on box	£75-85
			Silver body with windows, black hard-top, concave hubs	£75-85
527	1959-63	**Alfa-Romeo 1900 Sprint** ...(24-J)	Red or Blue body, windows, concave hubs, smooth (later treaded) black tyres, scale 1:43	£50-75
			Turquoise body	£450-550
528	1959-61	**Simca Vedette Chambord**	(24-K/2) Ivory/Red or Light/Dark Green body, convex hubs (concave from 1960), 1:43	£65-75
528	1966-71	**Peugeot 404 Cabriolet**	White or Metallic blue open body, red interior, female driver, steel hubs, scale 1:43	£90-120
			Pale grey or Light Beige open body, red interior, female driver, steel hubs	£110-150
529	1959-60	**Vespa 400 2cv**	Blue/grey body, chromed hubs, scale 1:43. '24L' on box	£70-80
	1960-63	(previously 24-L)	Blue/grey body, convex hubs, '529' on box	£60-70
			Orange/grey body, convex hubs, '529' on box	£300-400
530	1959-59	**VW Karmann-Ghia** .(was 24-M)	Black/red ('pointed' bonnet), convex hubs, 1:43	£60-75
	1960-62		Black/red body ('rounded' bonnet), convex hubs (some concave hubs from 1961)	£100-120
530	1964-66	**Citroën DS19**	Steel hubs. French '522' box with '530' labels, later in own '530' box.	
			Red/Cream body, Ivory interior, Silver base	£70-85
			Lime green/grey body, pale grey interior, Silver base	£70-85
	1966-68		Steel hubs. British box. Model made for export to UK and USA.	
			Red/Cream body, Ivory interior, Silver base	£70-85
			Lime green/grey body, pale grey interior, silver base	£70-85
	1968-70	........Spanish export issues:	Spun hubs, 'PIRELLI' tyres. 'DINKY-POCH' on box.	
			Red/Cream body, Ivory interior, Black base	£400-500
			Lime green/grey body, pale grey interior, black base	£400-500
			Bright Blue body	£600-800
			Silver-Grey body	£600-800
530	1976-78	**Citroën DS23**	Metallic red/black body, concave hubs, 1:43. Made in Spain	£75-85
	note:		530 Citroën DS23 was shown in the 1974 catalogue but production did not start until Auto-Pilen took over the die in 1976. The plastic base on this model (and some other Spanish models) was made in different colours and some are held in place by screws rather than rivets. Consequently, beware the 'rare combination' of base and body colours as they are easily interchanged.	
531	1959-60	**Fiat 1200 Grande Vue**	(previously 24-N) Metallic Bronze/Cream body, convex hubs, smooth tyres, 1:43	£70-80
			Cream/metallic blue body, convex hubs, smooth white tyres	£90-110
	note:		531 was shown in the 1959 Swiss catalogue with the reference '24N'.	
	1960-62		Metallic Bronze/Cream body, concave hubs, smooth or treaded tyres	£70-80
			Cream/metallic blue body, concave hubs	£90-110
532	1959-60	**Lincoln Premiere**	Silver body, dark red roof, convex hubs, scale 1:43. Box has no view window	£225-275
			Light blue body, silver roof	£85-95
			Metallic green body, dark green roof	£85-95
	1960-65		Bright blue body, silver roof, concave hubs, white smooth or treaded tyres. View window in box	£500-650
			Light blue body, silver roof	£85-95
			Metallic green body, dark green roof	£85-95
	196?-?	.............Export model:	Light blue body, silver roof. In gold card and cellophane box	£150-200
	note:		A wooden prototype of 532 exists. It was painted dark green.	NPP
533	1959-59	**Peugeot 203** .....(previously 24-R)	Grey-blue or Pale grey-green body, convex hubs, white tyres, big rear window, square filler cap	£80-100
533	1963-70	**Mercedes-Benz 300 SE**	Metallic blue or Metallic orange-red body, concave hubs, scale 1:43	£85-95
			Metallic green, plated concave hubs	£85-95
534	1959-59	**Simca 8 Sport** (previously 24-S)	Grey, back or Pale greenish-blue body, red seats, thick windscreen, convex hubs, scale 1:43	£65-75
			Cream body, red seats	£90-110
534	1963-68	**BMW 1500**	Red body, steel hubs, scale 1:43	£65-75
			Lime green body, plated concave hubs	£65-75
			Dark green body. Reported but not confirmed	NPP
	1968-?	..............Spanish export issue:	Metallic blue, plated concave hubs, 'PIRELLI' tyres, 'DINKY-POCH' on box	£500-700
535	1959-60	**Citroën 2cv**	Red or Brighter Red body, painted steel hubs, glossy baseplate. Box has '535-24T' printing	£70-80
			Blue body with Brighter Blue roof	£70-80
	1960-63	**Citroën 2cv**	Red or Blue body, chromed steel hubs, blued-steel baseplate. Box has '535' printing	£70-80
536	1959-59	**Simca Aronde Elysée** (previously 24-U)	Light grey-green/dark green, or pale green/dark green, second grille, convex hubs, scale 1:43	£70-80
			Blue body, ivory roof	£70-80
			Sky blue body, ivory roof	£250-350
	note:		Though renumbered from 24-U to 536, no boxes have yet been seen bearing the new number.	

536	1965-70	**Peugeot 404 and Trailer**............	Red car, concave hubs, black skis on yellow rack (or yellow skis on black rack), cream plastic single-wheel trailer (no. 812), luggage, scale 1:43 ....£140-170
537	1959-60	**Simca Aronde Elysée Taxi**........	(24-UT) Red/blue body, convex hubs, second type grille, scale 1:43 ....£65-75

537	1965-67	**Renault R16**............................	Concave hubs, black treaded rubber tyres, scale 1:43. Box has single viewport, R16 leaflet in early issues.
			Sky-Blue or Metallic grey body, gloss black base with '537'........................£55-70
	1967-70		Concave hubs, 'DUNLOP' nylon tyres. Box has single viewport, R16 leaflet discontinued in 1967.
			Light blue or Metallic grey body, matt black base with '537'..................£50-65
	1968-69	.................Spanish export issue:	Bright Blue, '537' on base, concave hubs, 'PIRELLI' tyres, 'DINKY-POCH' box £250-350
	1969-70		Sky-Blue body, matt black base without '537' reference, concave hubs, 'DUNLOP' nylon tyres. Box has single viewport £50-65
	1974-78	.................Spanish export issue:	Metallic grey body, base without '537' reference, concave hubs, 'DUNLOP' nylon tyres. 'MECCANO' and 'Made in Spain' on box (no viewport)..................£50-65

538	1959-59	**Buick Roadmaster**	Blue/dark blue body; Yellow/green body; or Blue/cream body, convex hubs, scale 1:48.........£100-150
		(previously 24-V)	Ivory/metallic blue body, convex hubs £500-600
			Orange-pink/black body, convex hubs £325-425
538	1963-70	**Ford Taunus 12M**....................	Turquoise or Brick red body, steel or spun hubs, scale 1:43 ....£80-95
538	1976-78	**Renault R16 TX**	Metallic plum, concave hubs, rear number plate on sticker. Made in Spain £50-65
		NB:	538 Renault R16 was shown in the 1974 French catalogue, but production was delayed until 1976.

539	1959-59	**Ford Vedette Taxi**....................	(previously 24-XT) Black/beige (various shades), meter, taxi sign, plated convex hubs, white tyres £65-75
		NB:	539 was never individually boxed (supplied to shops in trade boxes of six).
539	1963-66	**Citroën ID19 Estate**..................	Gold/Cream body, red or white seats, black or white steering wheel steel hubs, black or white tyres, scale 1:43 ....£75-100
			Green-Gold body, Darker Cream roof, spun hubs £100-130

540	1959-60	**Studebaker Commander** .(24-Y)	Tinplate base has towing notch. '540-24Y' and picture of model on box.
			Ivory body, Maroon roof and wing panels, convex hubs, smooth tyres £100-150
			Orange body, Dark Cream roof and wing panels, convex hubs, smooth tyres....................£100-150
	1960-61		Towing notch in base. '540-24Y' and picture on box.
			Ivory body, Maroon roof and wing panels, concave hubs, treaded tyres £100-150
			Orange body, Dark Cream roof and wing panels, concave hubs, treaded tyres. Existence not confirmed ....NPP

540	1963-64	**Opel Kadett**	Red or Pale Green body, steel hubs £75-85
		(Renumbered in 1964 as 1540)	Bright Blue body, plated steel hubs £120-150
		NB:	540 Opel was available with either the standard size hubs or smaller hubs. Both types were concave and were steel or spun aluminium with black tyres.

541	1959-60	**Simca Vedette Versailles** .(24-Z)	Yellow/black body or Light blue/ivory body, convex hubs, white tyres, towing notch. Picture on box...........£85-95
542	1959-62	**Simca Ariane Taxi** ..(was 24-ZT)	'Ariane' on base, '542-24ZT' on box, window glazing, 1:43.
			Black body, red (later Orange-Red) roof, meter, taxi sign, convex hubs (concave from 1961)...................£125-150
542	1964-69	**Opel Rekord**	Metallic blue body; Metallic gold-cream body; Metallic grey body (two doors), concave hubs, 1:43. ....£75-85
543	1960-63	**Renault Floride**	Concave hubs with smooth or treaded white tyres, scale 1:43.
			Metallic green body; Metallic green-gold body; Metallic bronze body....................£65-75
			White body, aluminium hubs, smooth white tyres £750-1,000
		NB:	A wooden prototype of 543 is known to exist. It was painted pink. ....NPP

544	1959-60	**Simca Aronde P60**	Convex hubs, scale 1:43. Box without (later with) viewport.
			Two-tone Grey body (with Silver flash), or Brick red body (with Cream or Pinky-Cream roof)..................£90-110
	1960-63		Concave hubs. Box with one viewport.
			Two-tone Grey body or Brown body (with Off-White roof and Silver flash)....................£90-110
			Cream body, red roof, concave hubs, smooth white tyres £1,000-1,250

545	1960-63	**De Soto Diplomat**	Salmon pink/black body, Silver flash, concave hubs, white tyres, scale 1:43. ....£70-90
			Metallic green body, pale cream body, concave hubs, treaded tyres £200-250
546	1960-61	**Austin-Healey 100-6**	White body (different shades of white reported), driver, 3-spoke steering wheel, concave hubs, 1:43 ....£100-125
546	1964-67	**Opel Rekord Taxi**	Black body, aluminium or steel concave hubs, white tyres, 1:43. Box has German text as this model was made only for export to Germany for this period. The taxi sign lettering may be in white or yellow ..£200-250

547	1960-64	**Panhard PL17** ....1st type:	Sidelights to front and rear of centre-hinged doors, black painted baseplate, steel hubs, rubber tyres.
		2nd type:	As 1st type but without rear sidelights.
		3rd type:	Front-hinged doors, sidelights under headlamps, black painted baseplate, steel hubs, rubber tyres.
		4th type:	As 3rd type but with blued-steel baseplate, steel or aluminium hubs.
		5th type:	Aluminium hubs with plastic 'DUNLOP' tyres.
	1960-60		1st type, Violet body....................£85-95
			1st type, Brick red body £90-110
	1960-61		2nd type, Violet body....................£85-95
			2nd type, Brick red or Orange body £90-110
	1962-63		3rd type, Violet body....................£65-75
			3rd type, Orange body £60-80
	1963-64		4th type, Violet or Brick-Red body....................£75-85
547	1964-64	(Renumbered in 1964 as 1547)	5th type, Blue-grey body....................£120-150
			5th type, Blue body £300-350

548	1960-63	**Fiat 1800 Familiale Estate Car**..	Lilac body with Black roof, or Lavender body with Black or Blue roof, concave hubs, scale 1:43 ....£55-65
			Yellow body, metallic brown roof, concave hubs....................£75-85
			Yellow body, black roof, concave hubs £55-65
	1962	South African issues:	Ivory body (with Red interior), or Lime Green body, or Green-Bronze body, concave hubs...................£500-600
		South African issue:	Yellow body, metallic maroon roof £200-250

549	1961-61	**Borgward Isabella TS**	Turquoise or Light Green body, concave hubs, black or white tyres, scale 1:43...................................**£85-95**
			Metallic grey body, concave hubs, black or white tyres **£85-95**
550	1961-65	**Chrysler Saratoga**.......................	Pale Pink with White flash, or Deep Pink with White flash, concave hubs, smooth or treaded white tyres....**£85-95**
			Violet with black flash, plated concave hubs, smooth or treaded white tyres **£200-250**
551	1959-61	**Rolls-Royce Silver Wraith**	Light grey/dark grey body, concave hubs, 1:43. ....**£60-75**
551	1965-67	**Ford Taunus 17M Police Car**....	Dark Green/white, 'POLIZEI', concave hubs, scale 1:43, German text on box **£250-300**
552	1961-64	**Chevrolet Corvair**.......................	Turquoise or Blue-Grey body, Cream interior, concave hubs, indication of filler cap on some, 1:43............**£50-60**
		(Renumbered in 1964 as 1552)	Red body, concave hubs, indication of filler cap on some **£75-100**
	1963	...................South African issues:	Silver or Light Grey-Blue body (both with Off-White interior), concave hubs, white tyres **£400-600**
			Smokey-Green body, Off-White interior, concave hubs...**£1,000-1,500**
553	1961-68	**Peugeot 404**..............................	1st type: Round 'O' on bonnet, steel hubs, smooth black or white tyres, painted baseplate.
			2nd type: Squared 'O' on bonnet, steel hubs, treaded black tyres, painted baseplate.
			3rd type: As 2nd type with reinforcement behind front number plate, revised glazing moulding common
			to 536 with opening roof, blued-steel baseplate.
			4th type: As 3rd type but with aluminium hubs and plastic 'DUNLOP' tyres.
	1961-62	...........................1st type:	Cream body, dark red interior, smooth black or white tyres **£75-85**
			Cream body, dark brown interior **£100-150**
			Pale blue body, bright red interior **£80-100**
553	1962-64	(Renumbered in 1964 as 1553)....	2nd type: Cream body, dark (later bright) red interior...**£85-95**
			Cream body, dark brown interior **£100-150**
553	1963-66	.............................3rd type:	Pale blue body, bright red interior **£70-80**
	1963	...................South African issue:	Pale green or Metallic charcoal grey body, bright red interior **£750-1,000**
			Cream body, dark red interior **£350-450**
553	1968-68	.............................4th type:	As 2nd type but 'PIRELLI' tyres, 'DINKY-POCH' on box. Assembled in Spain.
			Bright Blue body, bright red interior, Barcelona number plate **£750-1,000**
554	1961-63	**Opel Rekord**	Coral-pink/ivory body or Mustard-yellow/ivory body, concave hubs, scale 1:43. ....**£75-85**
			Beige body, white roof ....NGPP
			Turquoise/ivory body...**£300-400**
	1962	...............South African issues:	Pale Blue, Bright Blue or Dark Blue body with Light Grey interior **£650-750**
			Metallic Dark Green body, Grey interior, White tyres...**£900-1,100**
555	1961-69	**Ford Thunderbird**	1st type: Black painted baseplate, steel hubs, smooth white tyres.
			2nd type: Blued-steel baseplate, steel hubs, treaded white tyres.
			3rd type: Blued-steel baseplate, aluminium hubs, treaded white tyres.
			NB: Driver may wear bright or dark suit, steering wheel may be cream or black.
			White body (Red interior), or Red body (Sky-Blue interior), or Dark Brown body (Sky-Blue interior) **£80-110**
			Dark brown body, pale green interior **£100-150**
	1966-?	..............South African issues:	Bright blue, Metallic blue, Sand or Red open body, all with Red interior **£900-1,200**
556	1962-70	**Citroën ID19 Ambulance**...........	1st type: Steel hubs, metal steering wheel, centred transfer lettering.
			2nd type: As 1st type, but with plastic steering wheel.
			3rd type: As 2nd type, but with aluminium hubs.
			4th type: Aluminium hubs, plastic 'DUNLOP' tyres, plastic steering wheel, transfer lettering aligned to left.
	1962-67	....................1st/2nd/3rd types:	Grey/cream body. In standard box until 1964, then in 'Super detail' box **£85-95**
	1967-70	.......................4th type:	Grey/cream body. In 'Super detail' box **£100-125**
557	1962-70	**Citroën Ami 6**............................	1st type: Steel hubs, spare wheel under bonnet, black painted base.
			2nd type: Steel hubs, engine detail under bonnet, black painted base.
			3rd type: As 2nd type, but with blued-steel baseplate.
			4th type: As 3rd type, but with aluminium hubs and plastic 'DUNLOP' tyres.
	1962-62	...................................1st type	Pale green or Light blue body (either with white or pale grey roof), or Light blue body (pale blue roof) **£65-75**
	1963-64	(Renumbered in 1964 as 1557)....	2nd type. Pale green body (with white or pale grey roof), or Light blue body (with pale blue roof) **£65-75**
			Bright Blue body, white or pale grey roof **£80-95**
	1964-70	...........................3rd/4th types	Pale green or Light blue body, white or pale grey roof **£75-85**
558	1962-64	**Citroën 2cv Azam**	Yellow body, brown roof **£75-85**
		(Renumbered in 1964 as 1558)	Beige body, brown roof **£150-175**
			Green body, dark green roof; or Greyish-green body, black roof...**£75-85**
558	1968-70	**Citroën 2cv** ....Spanish issue:	Yellow/maroon or Green/dark green body, concave hubs, 'PIRELLI' tyres, 'DINKY-POCH' on box........**£200-300**
559	1962-64	**Ford Taunus 17M**......................	Steel or aluminium hubs, smooth or treaded black or white tyres, 1:43.
		(Renumbered in 1964 as 1559)	Ivory or Pale Grey body; steel or aluminium hubs, smooth or treaded black or white tyres...........................**£60-70**
			Metallic Brown or Metallic Grey-Brown body..**£60-70**
	1968-69	...............................Spanish issue:	Yellow body, concave hubs, 'PIRELLI' tyres, 'DINKY-POCH' on box..**£1,100-1,400**
1400	1967-71	**Peugeot 404 G7 Taxi**	Black body (536 casting), red top with sunroof, taxi sign and aerial, 'Ampere 28.30' and 'G7' shield
			on doors, concave hubs, black 'DUNLOP' tyres, 1:43, yellow box **£150-200**
1401	1967-70	**Alfa-Romeo Guilia 1600Ti**........	Dark red body (514 casting), Yellow stripe, concave hubs. Yellow box **£150-200**
1402	1968-71	**Ford Galaxie Sedan**	Dark Red (Cream interior) or Metallic Gold body (Red interior); detailed wheels, 1:43. Perspex box **£80-100**
1402	1968-68	**Ford Galaxie Police Car**	Black/white body, 'POLICE'. Commissioned for use by Police ....NGPP
1403	1967-71	**Matra M530**	White or Orange body, concave hubs, two-part roof can be stowed in boot. Perspex box....................**£65-75**
1404	1968-69	**Citroën ID19 Estate Car**...........	Grey/red, 'RADIO TELE LUXEMBOURG', camera/operator, concave hubs. Yellow box **£350-450**
	1969-71		Grey/red, 'RTL LUXEMBOURG', ('RTL' in black), concave hubs. Yellow box...............................**£350-450**
	1971-71		Grey/red, 'RTL LUXEMBOURG' ('T' of 'RTL' in black/white check). Yellow picture box.................**£3,500-4,500**
			Same model but with Grey/orange-red body. Yellow box...**£2,000-2,500**

1405	1968-70	**Opel Rekord 1900s**	Metallic blue body, scale 1:43. In perspex box	**£55-65**
1405E	1970-71	**Opel Rekord 1900s**	Metallic blue body, scale 1:43. Export model in card box	**£150-250**
1405P	1968-68	**Opel Rekord 1900s**	Prototypes using the 1405 casting were prepared for the 1420 Opel Commodore. '1405' on the base.	
			Silver or Red body, black 'vinyl' roof, Black interior, paper number plate	**£75-85**
1406	1968-71	**Renault 4L Sinpar Tanguy**	Khaki-green camouflage body, driver (Michel Tanguy), passenger, painted concave hubs.	
			Featured in the TV serial 'Les Chevaliers du Ciel' ('Knights of the Sky')	**£200-250**
1407	1968-71	**Simca 1100**	Metallic grey body, concave hubs. 'Made in France' yellow viewport box	**£75-85**
			Dark red body. This was the intended colour when 1407 was introduced but its existence is doubtful .... NPP
	1974-78	.... Spanish issue:	Metallic green body, concave hubs. 'Made in Spain' overprinted	
			on French box (later in Spanish box also printed 'Made in Spain')	**£50-60**
1408	1969-70	**Honda S800**	Yellow body, concave hubs, scale 1:43. Yellow box	**£70-80**
1409	1970	**Simca 1800**	A prototype for the 1409 Chrysler 180 but with 'Simca 1800' on the base. Just a few were sold - they	
			were finished in the same metallic blue-grey paint as the production version	**£200-250**
1409	1970-71	**Chrysler 180**	Metallic blue-grey body, 'Chrysler' on base, 'DUNLOP' tyres, scale 1:43. Yellow box	**£75-90**
	NB:		595w Traffic Sign 'Danger - Cyclists' included with 1409.	
1410	1968-71	**Moskvitch 408**	Red body, plated concave hubs, scale 1:43. Yellow box	**£40-50**
1411	1971-72	**Renault Alpine A310**	Bright red body, plastic hubs, scale 1:43. Yellow box	**£40-50**
1413	1968-70	**Citroën Dyane**	Off-white body, luggage, concave hubs, 1:43. Box has 'DYANE CITROËN' in white on yellow	**£40-50**
	1969-71		Same model but box has 'DYANE CITROËN' in white on green	**£40-50**
	1977-78	.... Spanish issue:	Off-white body, concave hubs.	**£40-50**
1414	1969-70	**Renault R8 Gordini**	Dinky Blue body, white stripes, driver, RN '36', jewelled lights, alumimium concave hubs	**£160-200**
1414	1969-70	**Renault R8-S**	Dinky Yellow or Dinky Mustard-Yellow body, driver in some. Promotional model	**£1,500-2,000**
1415	1969-71	**Peugeot 504**	Pale Blue body, concave hubs, scale 1:43. Clear plastic box	**£50-60**
			Dark blue body. Clear plastic box	**£500-600**
	1974-76	.... Spanish issue:	Pale yellow body, concave hubs or special wheels. Card box	**£50-60**
1416	1969-70	**Renault R6**	Bright red body, first grille (round headlamps), concave hubs. Side view of white model on box	**£50-60**
	1970-74		As previous model but with rear view of dark grey model on box	**£50-60**
	1974-76	.... Spanish issue:	Red or yellow body, second grille (square headlamps), concave hubs. Side view of white model on box	**£80-100**
1416	1974-75	**Renault Postal Car**	Code 2 model based on Spanish-made components, commissioned by the Postal Service.	
			Yellow body, second grille (square headlamps), plated concave hubs. Side view of white model on box.	**£50-60**
1416P	1970-70	**Renault R6 Fire Car**	Code 2 model based on Spanish-made components, commissioned by the Fire Service.	
			Red body and hubs, 'POMPIERS de PARIS', second grille, side view of white model on box.	**£80-100**
1417	1969-71	**Matra V12 F1**	Blue body, driver (J.P.Beltoise), no. '17' (transfer, later on label), special wheels, 1:43. Yellow box	**£50-60**
	NB:		595c Traffic Sign 'Dangerous Bend To Right' included with 1417.	
1419	1969-71	**Ford Thunderbird**	Battery in base for rear lights, special wheels, 1:43. Perspex box.	
			Metallic green body (black 'vinyl' roof on some)	**£75-85**
			A prototype exists with a Metallic Red body and Black 'vinyl' roof. (Not issued) .... NPP
			Metallic grey body, dark metallic grey roof	**£800-1,100**
	NB:		595g Traffic Sign 'Caution - Animals Crossing' included with 1419.	
1420	1970-71	**Opel Commodore GS**	Red body, black 'vinyl' roof, special wheels, 1:43. Some boxes have a printed design in a panel	**£70-80**
	NB:		The Opel Commodore had a 6-cylinder engine, but as 1420 was produced using the 1405 casting the	
			model retains a 4-cylinder engine and the 'Rekord' badges. 595o Traffic Sign 'Customs' included with 1420.	
1421	1969-71	**Opel GT 1900**	Dark blue body, detailed chromed wheels, luggage rack, 1:43. Yellow box	**£75-85**
	NB:		595f Traffic Sign 'Speed Limit' included with 1421.	
1422	1969-71	**Ferrari 3L V12 F1**	Red body, driver (Jacky Ickx), no. '26', detailed chromed wheels, scale 1:43	**£90-110**
	NB:		595e Traffic Sign 'Road Narrows' included with 1422.	
1423	1969-71	**Peugeot 504 Convertible**	Dark Blue, plastic base, plated concave hubs, scale 1:43. Yellow box	**£125-150**
	NB:		595i Traffic Sign 'Two Way Traffic' included with 1423.	
1424	1969-70	**Renault R12**	Mustard-Yellow body, opening doors, Red interior, reversed 'V' shape on grille, aluminium	
			concave hubs, sidelights. Yellow box	**£65-75**
	NB:		595h Traffic Sign 'Danger - End of Quay' included with French-made 1424.	
1424	1977-78	**Renault R12-TL** ...Spanish issue:	Yellow body, fixed doors, aluminium concave hubs, second (corrected) grille, no sidelights. Yellow box ..	**£65-75**
1424G	1971-71	**Renault R12 Gordini Rally Car** ...	Blue, white stripes, racing number '5', silver headlights, fixed doors, aluminium concave	
			hubs, second grille, sidelights. Yellow box	**£100-125**
	1974-78	.... Spanish issue:	Blue (slightly darker than 1971 model), white stripes, yellow headlights, fixed doors,	
			aluminium concave hubs, second grille, sidelights. Yellow box	**£100-125**
1425	1969-71	**Matra 630 Le Mans**	French blue body, driver (Pescarolo), no. '5', scale1:43. Plastic box	**£60-70**
1425E	1971-71	**Matra 630 Le Mans**	French blue body, driver (Pescarolo), no. '5', 1:43. Yellow card box	**£80-100**
	note:		595k Traffic Sign 'Road Narrows from Left' included with 1425.	
1426	1969-71	**Alfa-Romeo Carabo P33**	Metallic green/plain green/black/orange, special wheels, 1:43. Yellow box	**£70-80**
			Orange-yellow/green/black/orange-red, special wheels. Yellow box	**£100-125**
	NB:		595m Traffic Sign 'Danger - Loose Chippings' included with 1426.	
1428	1970-74	**Peugeot 304**	White body, concave hubs, scale 1:43. Yellow box	**£60-70**
	NB:		595p Traffic Sign 'Humpback Bridge' included with French made 1428.	
	1974-78		Metallic green, concave hubs. Made in Spain, yellow box	**£40-50**
1429	1970-71	**Peugeot 404 Police Car**	Blue/white body, 'POLICE', plastic base, concave hubs, 1:43. Yellow box	**£175-225**
	NB:		595n Traffic Sign 'Cycling Prohibited' included with 1429.	
1430	1970-71	**Fiat Abarth 2000**	Orange body, special wheels, scale 1:43. Plastic box also contains a 595u Traffic Sign 'Dangerous Bends' .**£30-40**
1431	1970	**Porsche 917**	A model planned but not actually issued .... NPP
1432	1970-71	**Ferrari 312P**	Red body, no driver, racing number '60', special wheels, 1:43.	
			Plastic box also has a 595v Traffic Sign 'All Vehicles Prohibited'	**£50-60**
1432E	1971-?	**Ferrari 312P**	Red body, no driver, racing number '60', special wheels. Card box	**£50-60**

| 1433 | 1971-74 | **Surtees TS5 V8 F1** .... | Red body, white driver, yellow helmet, racing number '5' or '14', 1:43. Yellow card box .... | **£40-50** |

| 1435 | 1970-71 | **Citroën Présidentielle** .... | Metallic grey and plain charcoal grey body, chauffeur, felt carpet, flag, electric interior light, Speedwheels, scale 1:43. Special plastic and rigid card box .... | **£350-450** |
| 1435E | 1971-71 | **Citroën Présidentielle** .... | Same model as 1435 but in blue presentation box .... | **£900-1,200** |

1450	1977-78	**Simca 1100 Police Car**	Spanish issue. Blue/white or black/white body, 'POLICE', plated concave hubs..........................	**£50-60**
1451	1978-?	**Renault R17-TS**....Spanish issue:	Orange-yellow body, plated concave hubs, scale 1:43...	**£50-60**
		NB:	1451 was announced in the 1976 French catalogue but production only took place in Spain from 1978.	

1452	1977-78	**Peugeot 504**..........Spanish issue:	Metallic copper body, fixed doors, special wheels. 'réf. 1452' on box.	**£50-60**
	1978-78	..................Spanish issue:	Metallic bronze body, fixed doors, special wheels. Box has: 'réf. 011452' and 'conformité du produit aux normes francaises'	**£50-60**
		NB:	Different registration numbers (on labels) may be found on 1452.	
1453	1977-78	**Renault R6**..........Spanish issue:	Blue-grey, fixed bonnet, square headlamps, concave hubs......................................	**£75-85**
		NB:	Although only available in blue-grey, 1453 continued to be shown in yellow in contemporary catalogues.	

1454	1978-78	**Matra Simca Bagheera S**	Spanish issue: Green body, concave hubs, 1:43	**£35-45**
1455	1978-78	**Citroën CX Pallas**..Spanish issue:	Metallic blue body, concave hubs, 1:43	**£45-55**
		NB:	1455 was announced (but not illustrated) in the 1977 catalogue but was not available before May 1978.	

1517	1964-65	**Renault R8** ....(previously 517)	Blue or yellow body, concave hubs, 1:43. In blister pack..	**£60-70**
1518	1964-65	**Renault R4L**......(previously 518)	Pale blue, light blue, Brick-red or maroon body, first grille. In blister pack.............................	**£60-70**
			Grey-green body. In blister pack	**NGPP**
1519	1964-65	**Simca 1000** ....(previously 519)	Light blue-grey, red interior, black painted base. Blister pack	**£60-70**
1520	1964-65	**Fiat 600 D**..........(previously 520)	Red or pale yellow body, concave hubs. Bister pack	**£55-65**
1523	1964-65	**Simca 1500** ....(previously 523)	Mid-blue, Light Blue or Metallic Grey body, concave hubs, 1:43. In blister pack	**£55-65**

1539	1980?	**VW Scirocco**........Spanish issue:	Metallic light green body, special wheels, scale 1:43..	**£60-70**
1540	1964-65	**Opel Kadett**......(previously 540)	Red or Pale Green body, concave hubs, sliding windows. Blister pack	**£70-80**
			Blue body, concave hubs, sliding windows. In blister pack.......................................	**£85-100**
1540	1980?	**Renault R14**........Spanish issue:	Metallic bright green body, special wheels, 1:43	**£60-70**

1541	1981?	**Ford Fiesta**...........Spanish issue:	Metallic light blue body, special wheels, 1:43..	**£60-70**
1542	1980?	**Chrysler 1308 GT**..Spanish issue:	Metallic green body, special wheels, 1:43	**£35-45**
1543	1980?	**Opel Ascona**.........Spanish issue:	Orange-yellow body, special wheels, 1:43	**£60-70**
1547	1964-66	**Panhard PL17**...(previously 547)	Violet body, anodised base, concave hubs, sidelights under headlights, 1:43.. In blister pack................	**£55-65**
			Brick red body, anodised base, concave hubs, sidelights under headlights. In blister pack.................	**£70-80**

1552	1964-66	**Chevrolet Corvair**....................	(previously 552) Turquoise blue or orange-red body, raised filler cap on some. Blister pack..............	**£60-70**
1553	1964-66	**Peugeot 404**.........(previously 553)	Ivory body, dark red interior. Blister pack	**£60-70**
1557	1964-66	**Citroën Ami 6**..(previously 557)	Green/white or blue/white, no spare wheel. Blister pack	**£40-50**
1558	1964-66	**Citroën 2cv Azam**	(previously 558) Yellow/maroon body, Grey concave hubs (black tyres), 1:43.. In blister pack.............	**£40-50**
			Light yellow/maroon body or Green/dark green body, Grey concave hubs (black tyres). In blister pack........	**£60-70**
1559	1964-69	**Ford Taunus 17M**	(was 559) Metallic gold body, Metallic grey-gold body or Ivory body, concave hubs, 1:43. Blister pack	**£50-60**

SOLIDO-COUGAR Models. Cast by Solido in France, all the models are in 1:43 scale, all have plastic wheels and 'Dinky Toys France' on the plastic base, and all were supplied in a 'Dinky Toys GB' box. Compare this list with the 'COUGAR Model Toys' list that follows it.

1401	1981	**Citroën 2cv6**	Orange-red body (beige open top) or Green body (grey open top), both with 'ducks' decal	**£25-35**
1402	1981	**Citroën 2cv6**	Orange-red body (beige closed top) or Green body (grey closed top), both with 'ducks' decal	**£25-35**
1402	1981	**Citroën Visa**	Metallic jade green (white base, tinted windows), or Metallic red, (grey base, clear windows), no decals	**£25-35**
1403	1981	**Fiat Ritmo/Strada**.....................	Metallic orange body (dark cream base), or Metallic blue body (yellow base), no decals	**£25-35**
1404	1981	**BMW 530**..............................	Metallic green with 'Cougar' decal, or Metallic purple with 'flames' decal	**£25-35**
1405	1981	**Alfa-Romeo Alfetta GTV**	Red or Yellow body, 'shamrock' decal	**£25-35**
1406	1981	**Peugeot 504**...........................	Metallic yellow with 'cougar' decal or Metallic blue with 'flames' decal	**£25-35**
	1983		Black body, 'Dinky France' decal, plastic wheels. (Lyons 1983 promotional)	**£35-45**

COUGAR Model Toys. Many of the 'Airfix Dinky Toys' appeared erratically in the early 1980s (in France then in the UK) under the name of 'Cougar Model Toys'. Every one had a plastic base marked 'Dinky Toys made in France' and the code '1/43 07 80'. They were presented in card backed blister-packs with 'Metal Cougar' and 'Fabriqué par Solido' printing. Numbers printed on card are 100 less than numbers moulded on base.

1301-1401	**Citroën 2cv6**	Orange-red body with 'ducks' decal, Grey base/interior/open top	**£15-25**
		Green body, 'ducks' decal, grey base, orange interior, tan open top	**£15-25**
1302-1402	**Citroën Visa**	Metallic jade green, no decal, white base, dark cream interior	**£15-25**
		Metallic red body, no decal, grey base and interior	**£15-25**
1303-1403	**Fiat Ritmo**.............................	Metallic orange (dark cream base/interior), or Metallic blue (yellow base/interior), no decal	**£15-25**
1304-1404	**BMW 530**	Metallic green, 'cougar' decal, grey base, black/grey interior, green tinted windows	**£15-25**
		Metallic purple, 'flames' decal, grey base, black/grey interior, yellow tinted windows	**£15-25**
1305-1405	**Alfetta GTV**...........................	Red body, 'shamrock' decal, tan base, black/tan interior, yellow tinted windows	**£15-25**
		Yellow body, 'shamrock' decal, tan base, black/tan interior, blue tinted windows	**£15-25**
1306-1406	**Peugeot 504 Berline**	Metallic yellow, 'cougar' decal, brown base and tinted windows, black/brown interior	**£15-25**
		Metallic blue body, 'flames' decal, blue base and interior, clear windows	**£15-25**

Commercial Vehicles

French Dinky commercial vehicles (in keeping with other ranges) have very similar series numbering to their English counterparts. But, like the cars, the French castings are different in many ways from the Liverpool produced versions and of course are marked 'Made in France' or 'Fab en France'.

An interesting point about the 25 Series is that although there was a range of body styles on offer at any one time, there was only one chassis casting for a particular period. This meant that the chassis dies wore out at a disproportionate rate to the body dies. Chassis castings are found that come from either a crisp new die or from one that is weary from over-use, and the appearance can be so different that some collectors have thought these to be the result of intentional design changes. The only differences however are the ones noted in this listing.

On the French 25 series the headlights are larger and more pointed than the English equivalent. They were originally silver plated, later silver painted. The size of the headlights was reduced over the years and are best classed as large,

medium and small. Modern replacement parts (radiator/grille/bumper) which are intended for the English lorries are not suitable for use on the French 25 Series. Like the cars, the lorries had 'DUNLOP' tyres, first in the colour of the body, later black or white. The problem of shortage of rubber affected the lorry production in 1940 and for four years after the war ended, so that in those periods the lorries had to be produced with all-metal wheels. Metal failure affects pre-war mazak castings whether they are of French or English origin though the commercial vehicles seem not to be so drastically affected as for instance aircraft or ship models.

The first French Dinky Toys commercial vehicle model to be issued in an individual yellow box was 25-B Peugeot D3a Van in 1953. In England the Supertoys range was introduced in 1947 but it was not till 1955 that a French Supertoys model appeared. The 'Auto-Echelle de Pompiers' (Delahaye Fire Escape) was the first French model to be presented in the famous blue and white striped Supertoys box and was given the number 32-D.

Ref	Year(s)	Model name	Colours, features, details	Market Price Range
14	1935-39	Triporteur	Tinplate base, smooth hubs (various colours), black or white 'DUNLOP' tyres, scale 1:40. The driver may be found as a solid casting or hollow-cast. His cap is usually the same colour as his jacket. His trousers and boots were black or very dark brown (hand applied paint that may vary in shade or extent). Vehicle colours: Yellow, Red, Light Blue, Navy Blue. Driver's jacket: Blue, Grey or Green	£350-450
		note:	The 1935 catalogue illustration (a drawing) shows 14 with a front bumper but the existence of this version is very much in doubt.	
14	1940-49	Triporteur	Plain cast wheels (black or unpainted), tinplate base, scale 1:40. Vehicle colours: Yellow, Red, Light Blue, Navy Blue. Driver's jacket: Blue, Grey or Green	£250-350
14	1950-52	Triporteur	Painted ridged hubs with black rubber tyres, no base. Vehicle colours: Yellow, Red, Light Blue, Navy Blue. Driver's jacket: Blue, Grey or Green	£150-250
14-C	1950-59	Coventry Climax Fork Lift Truck	Orange/green/black, painted ridged hubs, grey tyres, made in England. French box (orange-red outer, yellow inner), 1:43	£40-50
		note:	14-C was renumbered in 1959, then assembled in France and issued as 597.	
25a	1935-39	Open Lorry	Open chassis, grille/headlights casting, front bumper, cast-in tow hook, painted smooth hubs, black or white 'DUNLOP' tyres, 1:65. Green/black, blue/black, yellow/brown	£250-350
25a	1940-48	Open Lorry	Same, but with unpainted cast wheels. Green/black, red/black, red/grey, brown/grey	£250-350
25-A	1950-52	Ford Livestock Truck	Metallic grey or metallic light blue body, painted ridged hubs, 1:65	£100-150
			Silver body, red ridged hubs	£150-200
			Yellow cab, Red back and ridged hubs	£3,000-4,000
25b	1935-39	Covered Lorry	Open chassis, grille/headlights casting, front bumper, cast-in tow hook, smooth hubs, black or white 'DUNLOP' tyres, removable tilt, 1:65 Green/black (green tilt), blue/black (beige tilt), Red/brown (green tilt), blue/red (beige tilt)	£350-450
25b	1940-48	Covered Lorry	Open chassis, grille/headlights casting, front bumper, cast-in hook, unpainted cast (or Cream) wheels, removable tilt. Red/black (green tilt), blue/black (green tilt), Red/black (cream tilt), red/grey (green tilt)	£150-200
25-B	1953-53	Peugeot D3a Van	Navy blue body (cross-hatching on inside of roof), no advertising, red ridged hubs, 1:50.	£900-1,100
			Grey body (cross-hatching on inside of roof), no advertising, red ridged hubs	£900-1,100
	1953-54		Yellow and green body (smooth inside roof), 'LAMPE MAZDA' logo, painted ridged hubs	£200-300
		note:	This was the first French Dinky Toys commercial vehicle model to be issued in an individual yellow box.	
25BV	1954-59	Peugeot Post Van	Dark green body (smooth or cross-hatched inside roof), 'POSTES'	
		(Renumbered in 1959 as 560)	(thin lettering, tampo). Box print: '25BV, marque déposée' only	£130-160
			Same model, but with box print: '25BV, marque déposée, Made in France, Imprimé en France'	£130-160
25c	1935-39	Flat Truck	Open chassis, grille/headlights casting, front bumper, cast-in tow hook, smooth hubs, black or white 'DUNLOP' tyres, scale 1:65. Turquoise/black, blue/black, green/black	£225-275
			Red/brown or grey/red	£225-275
	1940-48		Open chassis, grille/headlights casting, front bumper, cast-in tow hook, unpainted mazak wheels. Blue/black, green/black, Cream/red or grey/red	£100-125
25-C	1954-57	Citroën H Van	Metallic grey and gold body (official Citroën colours), painted ridged hubs, 1:50. Yellow box (grey model shown)	£100-125
25CG	1957-59	Citroën H Van	Cream body, 'FROMAGE CH GERVAIS', in 25-C yellow box but with '25CG' sticker	£140-170
	1959-59	(Renumbered in 1959 as 561)	Turquoise body (various shades), 'CIBIE', ridged or concave hubs, box with '25C' or '25CG' printed	£200-300
25d	1935-35	Tanker Lorry	Red body (smooth inside tank), no advertising, maroon open chassis (no hook), grille/headlights casting, front bumper, smooth hubs, red 'DUNLOP' tyres, scale 1:65	£300-400
	1936-37		Red body (smooth or ridged inside tank), 'STANDARD ESSOLUBE', black open chassis, smooth hubs, black or white 'DUNLOP' tyres	£300-400
	1938-39		Red body (ridged inside tank), 'ESSOLUBE - ESSO', black or red open chassis, smooth hubs, black or white 'DUNLOP' tyres	£300-400
25d	1940-49	Tanker Lorry	Red body (ridged inside tank), 'ESSOLUBE - ESSO', black open chassis, mazak wheels	£200-300
			Maroon body (ridged inside), 'ESSO' or 'ESSOLUBE', grey or black open chassis, mazak wheels	£200-300
25-D	1959-59	Citroën 2cv Van 'BÉBÉ LORRAIN'	Grey body, cream hubs. Only 80 made of this Code-2 promotional (see 562)	£5,000-7,000

French Dinky Toys 563 Renault Estafette Pick-up and 25C Citroën 1200Kg Van

French Dinky Toys 885 Saviem Sinpar Steel Carrier

Photographs: Vectis Auctions Ltd.

25e 1935-39 **Tipping Lorry** .... Tipping rear truck body, open chassis, grille/headlights casting, front bumper, cast-in tow hook,
smooth hubs, black or white 'DUNLOP' tyres, scale 1:65
Blue cab, yellow body, black or brown chassis..**£240-300**
Green cab, blue body, black or red chassis **£240-300**
Green cab, yellow body, red, black or brown chassis **£240-300**
1940-48 .... As previous version, but with painted mazak wheels.
Cab/body/chassis colours: Blue/yellow/black, Green/yellow/brown, or Cream/green/red.........................**£130-180**

25f 1935-39 **Market Gardener's Lorry** .... Open chassis, grille/headlights casting, front bumper, cast-in tow hook,
smooth hubs, black or white 'DUNLOP' tyres, scale 1:65.
Violet body (black chassis), Cream body (black chassis), or Green body (red chassis).............**£240-300**
Grey body, Black chassis **£300-400**
1940-48 .... As previous version, but with unpainted mazak wheels.
Body/chassis colours: Cream/Red, Yellow/Red, Turquoise/Black, Light Green/Grey **£240-300**

25g 1935-39 **Flat Trailer with Headboard** ..... Blue, red or green, 4 mazak hubs, black or white tyres, 1:65. ....**£30-40**
1940-48 .... Turquoise, red or green, two axles, unpainted or black mazak wheels.....................**£30-40**
1949-50 .... Red or green, two axles, painted ridged hubs, black tyres. **£30-40**

25-H 1949-49 **Ford Beverage Truck** .... Flat truck with removable tailboard, cast-in tow hook, spare wheel, scale 1:65.
Blue, cream, turquoise, red, brown, metallic green, bright green body, painted mazak wheels **£250-350**
1950-50 .... Blue, cream, turquoise, red, brown, metallic green or bright green body and ridged hubs **£300-400**
Metallic green body, bright green hubs **£300-400**
25-I 1949-49 **Ford Open Wagon** .... Blue, red, green, dark grey, maroon, or brown body, cast-in towing hook, painted mazak wheels, 1:65 .....**£150-200**
1950-50 .... Beige or metallic grey body, cast-in hook, painted ridged hubs (colour as body).........................**£300-400**
1951-52 .... Cream, dark red or light blue body, separate rivetted hook and spare wheel, matching ridged hubs **£200-300**
25-J 1949-50 **Ford Covered Wagon** ......(plain) Tinplate tilt (no advertising), cast-in towing hook, spare wheel, painted mazak wheels or ridged hubs.
Metallic gold (green tilt), red (green or red tilt), Light blue (cream tilt), dark blue (brown tilt),
Brown (brown tilt), brown (green tilt), Cream body, brown tilt **£375-475**

25-JB 1949-50 **'SNCF'** .... Blue (dark blue tilt), 'SNCF' round logo, cast-in hook, black mazak wheels or ridged hubs.................**£800-1,000**
1951-52 **'SNCF'** .... Blue (dark blue tilt), 'SNCF' round logo, separate hook, black ridged hubs **£250-350**
25-JJ 1949-52 **'CALBERSON'** .... Wide spacing to letters, plus map of France, cast-in (later separate) hook, scale 1:65.
Yellow or Yellow Ochre body with black tilt, painted mazak wheels or Red or Black ridged hubs **£600-800**
25-JV 1953-53 **'GRAND MOULINS DE PARIS'** Grey body, black tilt, separate hook, painted ridged hubs...**£300-400**

25-K 1949-49 **Studebaker Farm Produce Truck** Short lateral bonnet mouldings, small windows, tool-box, painted mazak wheels (usually black), 1:55.
Red/blue, blue/turquoise, red/yellow, turquoise/red **£350-450**
Blue/greyish-green **£350-450**
1950-50 .... Red/blue, blue/red, blue/turquoise, red/turquoise-green, painted ridged hubs..........................**£200-250**
1951-52 **Studebaker Farm Produce Truck** Long curved bonnet mouldings, large windows, outline of tool-box only, painted ridged hubs.
Red/yellow, blue/maroon, blue/red..**£150-200**
Red cab, Blue back..**£400-500**
25-L 1949-50 **Studebaker Covered Truck** .... Short lateral bonnet mouldings, small windows, tool-box, painted mazak wheels, or ridged hubs, tinplate tilt.
Red (yellow tilt), blue (yellow or Brown tilt), Turquoise (cream or yellow tilt, Red or Cream hubs) **£350-450**
1951-52 .... Long curved bonnet mouldings, large windows, tool-box outline only, painted ridged hubs
Blue (brown tilt, blue hubs), red (yellow tilt, red hubs) **£150-200**
25-M 1949-50 **Studebaker Tipping Truck** .... Short bonnet mouldings, small windows, tool-box, painted mazak wheels or ridged hubs, 1:55.
Dark green/metallic grey, dark green/plain grey **£100-130**
1951-52 .... Long bonnet curved bonnet mouldings, large windows, tool-box outline only, painted ridged hubs.
Dark green/metallic grey, dark green/plain grey **£70-85**
Khaki/silver (cream hubs)..**£700-900**
25-M 1950-55 **Ford Tipping Truck** .... Green cab, metallic or plain grey tipper, black or Green ridged hubs, 1:65 ....**£65-75**

25-O 1949-50 **Studebaker Milk Truck** .... Blue/eggshell Cream or Blue/White, 'NESTLÉ' (transfer), short bonnet mouldings, small windows,
tool-box, painted wheels or ridged hubs, ten milk churns, 1:55. Red box with yellow interior **£350-450**
1951-54 .... Blue/white, 'NESTLÉ' advertising on some, long curved bonnet mouldings, large windows,
tool-box outline only, painted ridged hubs, ten churns. Red box with yellow inner **£300-400**

25-O 1950-50 **Ford Milk Truck**....................... Blue/white body, 'NESTLÉ' (transfer, thick lettering). Long red box with yellow inner, card spacer ...**£1,000-1,250**
1954-55 .... Blue/white body, 'NESTLÉ' (tampo, plain or open (later) lettering). Shorter (correct length) box **£1,000-1,250**
25-P 1949-49 **Studebaker Pick-Up** .... Mustard-yellow and dark red body, painted mazak wheels, short
bonnet mouldings, small windows, tool-box, 1:55. ....**£100-120**
1950-55 .... Yellow/Red, ridged hubs, short or long bonnet mouldings, small or large windows, tool-box outline only.....**£80-90**
25-Q 1949-49 **Studebaker Covered Pick-Up**.... Green cab and tilt, red body, short bonnet mouldings, small windows, tool-box, painted wheels, 1:55. .....**£140-190**
Dark grey-green cab and tilt, yellow ochre body, painted wheels **£130-160**
1950-52 .... Green/Yellow, Green hubs, short or long bonnet mouldings, small or large windows, box outline only ...**£125-150**
25-R 1949-50 **Studebaker Breakdown Truck**.. Red body, 'DINKY SERVICE' on some, short bonnet mouldings,
small windows, tool-box, painted mazak wheels or ridged hubs **£100-150**
1951-54 .... Red body, 'DINKY SERVICE', long curved bonnet mouldings,
large windows, tool-box outline only, painted ridged hubs **£100-150**

25-R 1954-54 **Ford Breakdown Truck** .... Red body, 'DINKY SERVICE', red ridged hubs, black tyres, 1:65. ....**£100-150**
1954-55 .... Red body, no logo, plated ridged hubs, white tyres. ....**NGPP**

25-S 1949-49 **Single-axle Trailer** .... Red body, concave rear lamps, painted wheels, scale 1:55..................................**£30-35**
1950-50 .... Red (Cream hubs), Yellow (Red hubs), Green (Yellow hubs). Concave or raised rear lamps......**£30-35**
25-T 1949-49 **Single-axle Covered Trailer**...... As 25-S but with tinplate tilt, concave rear lamps, painted mazak wheels.
Red body (green tilt), or yellow body (brown tilt)...**£30-35**
1950-55 **Single-axle Covered Trailer**...... Red (green tilt, green ridged hubs), yellow (brown tilt, yellow ridged hubs). Concave or raised rear lamps ..**£30-35**

French Dinky Toys 32AB Panhard Articulated Lorry 'SNCF'

French Dinky Toys Simca Cargo Vans – 33A in green and orange (no advertising) and 33AN 'BAILLY'

Photographs: Vectis Auctions Ltd.

25-U	1950-50	**Ford Tanker**	Red body, 'ESSO', painted ridged hubs, hook and spare wheel support, pierced base, 1:65.	**£400-500**
	1951-51	....	As previous model but without the support for hook/spare wheel	**£120-140**
	1952-53	....	As 1951 version but with smaller transfers and non-pierced base	**£100-125**
25-V	1950-51	**Ford Refuse Tipper**	Dark green body, Dark or Mid-green ridged hubs, smooth tailgate interior surface, 1:65	**£80-100**
	1952-55		Dark green body, dark-green ridged hubs, cross-braced tailgate interior surface	**£70-90**
27AC	1950-50	**Massey-Harris Tractor and Manure Spreader**	Red tractor and implement made in England, painted wheels, 1:43. French display box (Red).........	**£400-600**
30e	1936-39	**Breakdown Lorry**	Fitted with the (lead) crane from 21d Railway Crane Truck. , smooth hubs, 'DUNLOP' tyres. Scale 1:65.	
			Yellow body, green crane, brown or black chassis...	**£300-350**
			Red body, green crane, red or Black chassis; or Blue body, green crane, black chassis....................	**£300-350**
	1938-39		Green body, green crane, brown chassis; or Red body, red crane, black chassis	**£300-350**
	1940-40		With mazak wheels. Blue body with blue crane, or Yellow body, black chassis	**£900-1,200**
Panhard Articulated Lorries:				
32-A	1952-52	(plain).............................	Blue body, plain or silver grille, painted ridged hubs, 1:60. Sold unboxed	**£200-250**
32-AB	1952-52	**'SNCF'**	Blue body, 'SNCF' (locomotive in round logo), painted ridged hubs. Sold unboxed (3 to a trade box).....	**£200-250**
	1954-59	(Renumbered in 1959 as 575)	Blue body, 'SNCF' (pale green French map logo), painted ridged hubs.	
			Sold unboxed (three to a trade box) or later in own yellow box (add £30 to price).......................	**£150-200**
32-AJ	1952-53	**'KODAK'**	Yellow body (smooth inside cab roof), 'KODAK', painted ridged hubs,	
			1:60. Sold unboxed (supplied to shops in trade boxes of three)	**£300-400**
	1955-57		Yellow body (cross-hatching in cab roof), 'KODAK', painted ridged hubs. Sold unboxed (supplied to shops in trade boxes of three)...........	**£350-450**
	US issue:		Yellow body, (different letter shape from the French issue)	**£750-1,000**
32C	1954-55	**Panhard Titan-Coder Tanker, 'ESSO'**	Red body, 'ESSO' (large transfers), painted ridged hubs, '32C TRACTEUR PANHARD' on Yellow box........	**£160-200**
	1956-59	(Renumbered in 1959 as 576)	Red body, 'ESSO' (medium transfers), '32C TRACTEUR PANHARD' in 5 languages on Yellow box...........	**£130-160**
33A	1955-56	**Simca Cargo Van**	Indented (early) or raised (later) cab step-plate, no hook mounting, spare wheel held by screw, 1:55.	
			Olive-green/yellow (green/yellow picture on yellow box), painted ridged hubs	**£125-250**
			Olive-green/orange (green/orange picture on yellow box), painted ridged hubs	**£125-250**
33AN	1956-59	**Simca Cargo Van, 'BAILLY'** ...	Indented or raised cab step-plate, with hook and mounting, spare wheel held by screw.	
		(Renumbered in 1959 as 577)	Yellow/white body, 'BAILLY DEMENAGEMENTS' logo, painted ridged hubs, yellow box	**£180-220**
33-B	1955-59	**Simca Cargo Tipper Truck**	Indented (later raised) cab step-plate, no hook mounting, smooth or grooved tipper surface,	
		(Renumbered in 1959 as 578)	indented (later raised) tailgate central reinforcement, painted ridged hubs.	
			Dark green/grey, dark green/metallic grey, metallic dark green/metallic grey. Yellow box	**£70-80**
			As previous models, but later version with hook and mounting. Yellow box	**£70-80**
33-C	1955-59	**Simca Glazier's Truck**	Grey/dark green, indented or raised cab step-plate, hook mounting on later issues, grey ridged hubs, 1:55.	
		(Renumbered in 1959 as 579)	'MIROITIER SAINT-GOBAIN'. Yellow box has '33C MIROITIER' in French, later in 5 languages	**£100-150**
34-A	1955-59	**Berliet Quarry Truck**	No spare wheel support, ridged and concave painted hubs, 1:55.	
		(Renumbered in 1959 as 580)	Blue/black, orange tipper. Box first without then with picture and '34A'	**£80-90**
	1957-59	..............................Promotional:	Blue/black, orange tipper. In 'BERLIET' yellow box	**£350-450**
34-B	1956-57	**Berliet Container Truck**	Spare wheel screwed on, iron container-lifting eye, ridged and concave painted hubs.	
		(Renumbered in 1959 as 581)	Red/black/light grey, matt grey container. No picture on yellow box	**£80-90**
	1957-59		As previous model but with cast-in lifting eye, yellow box has picture and '34B plateau avec container'......	**£80-90**
35-A	1955-55	**Citroën U23 Breakdown Truck**	Red body, large tool-box, closed fuel tank, yellow 'DINKY TOYS' logo.1:50. '35A' on box	**£100-130**
	1956-59	(Renumbered in 1959 as 582)	Dark red body, small tool-box, open fuel tank, Yellow 'DINKY TOYS' logo. '35A' on box..............	**£100-130**
36-A	1956-59	**Willeme Log Lorry**	Orange cab, yellow semi-trailer (pierced beam), wooden logs, black painted base,	
		(Renumbered in 1959 as 897)	painted ridged and concave hubs, radial tread tyres, 1:55. '36A' on Supertoys box	**£125-165**
36-B	1958-59	**Willeme Tractor & Closed Trailer**	Red tractor, orange semi-trailer with removable green plastic tilt, painted ridged and concave hubs,	
		(Renumbered in 1959 as 896)	4 rollers on trailer prop, 1:55, '36B' on Supertoys box	**£125-165**
38-A	1957-59	**Unic Marrel Multi-Skip Truck** .	Grey and golden-yellow (or Lemon-Yellow) body (windows in some), fixed skip,	
		(Renumbered in 1959 as 895)	ridged and concave painted hubs, black radial or block tread tyres, 1:55, '38A' on Supertoys box	**£110-150**
39-A	1957-59	**Unic Boilot Car Transporter**	Silver/orange, ridged and concave hubs, black radial tread	
		(Renumbered in 1959 as 894)	tyres, 1:55, '39A' on Supertoys box	**£150-175**
			Variation with all-Red trailer and Black hubs	**£500-750**
39-B	1959-60	**Unic Sahara Pipe Transporter** ..	Beige body (various shades), white roof, 'open' trailer, painted ridged	
		(Renumbered in 1960 as 893)	and concave hubs, 6 black tubes, 1:55. '893' on Supertoys box	**£150-175**
50	1957-59	**Salev Mobile Crane**	Grey body, Red crane, Blue driver, ridged and concave painted hubs, 1:43. (Renumbered in 1959 as 595)	**£100-125**
70	1957-59	**Two-Axle Covered Trailer**	Red or yellow, green tilt, ridged or concave hubs, 1:60, '70' on yellow box. (Renumbered in 1959 as 810)...........	**£30-40**
90-A	1958-59	**Richier Diesel Roller**	Yellow body, blue driver, red roller wheels, '90A' on Yellow box. Supertoy. (Renumbered in 1959 as 830)...........	**£60-70**
560	1951-?	**Muir-Hill Dumper**	Yellow body, metal wheels. Imported from England; sold in special blue box, French printing on label......	**£55-65**
560	1959-60	**Peugeot D3A Van**	Dark or Light Grey body, painted ridged hubs, 1:50. (Renumbered from 25-BV)	**£550-625**
560	1959-60	**Peugeot Post Van, 'POSTES'** ...	Dark green body, 'POSTES' (thick letters, transfer). Box print: '25BV, marque déposée' only..............	**£150-175**
			Same model, but box print reads: '25BV, marque déposée, Made in France, Imprimé en France'	**£150-175**
	1960-61		Same model, but 'POSTES' transfer has oval or more square letter 'O'. Box reads '25BV/560'.............	**£150-175**
	1960-61		Same model (transfer with oval 'O' of 'POSTES'), concave painted hubs. '560' on box	**£175-200**
560	1960	**Peugeot D3a Van**....Promotional:	Turquoise body, 'CIBIE', yellow ridged hubs..	**£2,500-3,500**
560-P	1961	**Citroën 2cv Van** Promotional:	Yellow cab, Silver back, red 'PHILIPS' logo and design on door..	**£4,000-5,000**
560	1963-70	**Citroën 2cv Postal Service Van.**	Yellow body and concave hubs, blue 'swallow' logo. Yellow box print reads:	
			'C'est une fabrication MECCANO', or (later): 'C'est une fabrication MECCANO TRI-ANG'	**£125-150**
560-E	1968-70	**Citroën 2cv Azam Van**	Pale Green body, plated concave hubs, 'PIRELLI' tyres, 'DINKY-POCH' on box. Export to Spain....	**£1,750-2,250**
561	1951-59	**Blaw-Knox Bulldozer**	Red/black, with driver. Model made in England, Blue box made in France. (Renumbered in 1959 as 885)	**£100-125**

561	1959-59	Citroën H Van ......(was 25-CG)	Cream body, 'FROMAGE CH GERVAIS', 1:50. In own box with '25CG GERVAIS' print......................£150-200
	1959-63		Turquoise body (various shades), 'CIBIE', painted ridged hubs (concave from 1961).
			In 25CG box with '561 CIBIE' sticker over the number..£200-250
	1963-66		White/blue body, 'GLACES GERVAIS', blue concave hubs. Yellow box..........................£300-400
	1964-64	...................................Promotional:	Blue body, 'BAROCLEM', aluminium concave hubs. Code 2 promotional in special picture box......£3,500-4,500
561	1972-72	Renault 4L Van	Yellow body, 'PTT', first grille, grey security window, plastic base, chromed concave hubs, 1:43............£200-275
562	1951-?	Muir-Hill Dumper	Golden yellow, with driver, 1:43. Model made in England, Blue box made in France...................£50-60
562H	1965-68	Citroën 2cv Van,	
		'WEGENWACHT'	Yellow body, concave hubs, '25D' on black painted base or anodised base without '25D'.
			Model made for export to Netherlands. Yellow box marked 'WW' from 1968 ....£450-600
563	1960-62	Renault Estafette Pick-Up	Orange or green body, green tilt, painted concave hubs, 1:43, Yellow box without, later with, illustration.....£45-55
564	1963-65	Renault Mirror Truck	Red-orange body, 'SAINT-GOBAIN/MIROITIER', painted concave hubs, 1:43. Yellow box £100-150
			As previous model but with Brick red body. Yellow box..£100-150
565	1965-71	Renault Estafette Camper	Bluebody, Ivory or White plastic roof, chromed concave hubs, 1:43. Yellow box £150-175
566	1965-70	Citroën H Currus Van	Blue/white body, 'POLICE', painted concave hubs, working warning lights £150-200
567	1967-70	Unimog Snow Plough	Yellow/black body, brown removable top, painted concave hubs, 1:50. Yellow box £100-120
569	1967-71	Berliet Stradair Side Tipper	Light green/dark green body, painted hubs, green or black motor, 1:43. Yellow box, instruction leaflet.....£200-300

570 Peugeot J7 Taxi-Vans:

570	1967-67	'ALLO-FRET'	Blue body, blue or white roof, aluminium concave hubs, aerial, 1:43, 108mm. Yellow box £275-350
570	1968-68	'ICI'	Blue/white body, 'IMPERIAL CHEMICAL INDUSTRIES'. Code 2 promotional £750-1,000
570A	1970-71	'AUTOROUTES'	Orange body, two workmen plus equipment, 1:43. On diorama base in yellow box
			(also containing a 595s Traffic Sign 'Pedestrians Prohibited') £500-700
571	1951-57	Coles Mobile Crane	Yellow and black, painted hubs, 1:50. Model made in England, Blue box made in France (see 972)............£60-70
571	1969-71	Saviem Goelette	
		Horse Box and Sulky	Blue/'wood'/white, painted concave hubs, racehorse, Green two-wheel
			racing cart (sulky) with driver, 1:43. Yellow picture box £1,200-1,600
572	1970-71	Berliet Quarry Truck	Red body, yellow plastic tipper, plastic hubs, 1:43. 595d Traffic Sign 'No Overtaking For
			Heavy Vehicles' included in yellow box £1,000-1,300
575	1959-63	Panhard Artic. Lorry, 'SNCF' ..	Blue body, 'SNCF' on Pale (later Dark) Green French map logo, painted ridged or concave hubs.
	(previously 32-AB)		Sold unboxed (three to a trade box), later in own Yellow box (add £30 to price) £90-120
576	1959-60	Panhard Titan-Coder Tanker,	
		'ESSO'	Red body, 'ESSO' (medium lettering), painted ridged hubs.
	(previously 32-C)		'32C TRACTEUR PANHARD' in 5 languages on yellow box £160-200
	1960-61		Red or Dark Red body, 'ESSO' (smaller lettering), painted ridged hubs (concave from 1961).
			Yellow box has 'DINKY TOYS' in italics, '576' and description in 5 languages on flap...................£160-200
577	1959-61	Simca Cargo Van, 'BAILLY'	Yellow/white body, 'BAILLY DEMENAGEMENTS'. Indented or raised cab step-plate, with hook
	(previously 33-AN)		support, spare wheel held by screw (later by rivet), painted ridged hubs (later concave)...................£90-120
577	1965-71	Berliet Livestock Truck	Yellow and green, two black and white cows, painted concave hubs, 1:43. Yellow box £150-175
578	1959-70	Simca Cargo Tipper Truck	Dark or Mid-green/Metallic Grey, indented or raised cab step-plate, with hook mounting, spare wheel
	(previously 33-B)		held by screw (later by rivet), scale 1:55. Yellow box £65-75
579	1959-61	Simca Mirror Truck,	
		'SAINT-GOBAIN'	Grey/Dark Green, 'MIROITIER SAINT-GOBAIN'. Indented or raised cab step-plate, with hook mounting,
	(previously 33-C)		spare wheel screwed on, Grey or Yellow ridged hubs, scale 1:55.
			Yellow box has '33C MIROITIER' in 5 languages £100-150
	1961-67		Yellow/Dark Green, Yellow ridged hubs, spare wheel rivetted. Yellow box changed to read: '579-33C' £100-150
	196?-6?	...................................Export model:	Yellow/Dark Green or Grey/Dark Green, Grey ridged hubs or Cream concave hubs. £100-150
			Pale Grey/Pale Green, without 'SAINT-GOBAIN', Cream ridged or concave hubs. £100-150
580	1959-61	Berliet Quarry Truck	As 34-A but with spare wheel support, ridged and concave painted hubs, block tread tyres.
	(previously 34-A)		Blue/Black, Orange tipper. Picture on yellow box £80-100
	1961-70		Same model but with cast-in spare wheel location, concave painted hubs and anodised base...................£80-100
581	1959-60	Berliet Container Truck	Spare wheel held by screw, ridged and/or concave painted hubs, round (later square) section tyres.
	(previously 34-B)		Red/Black/Light Grey, Dark Grey container. Picture on yellow box £90-110
	1960-65		Same, but spare wheel rivetted on. Yellow box has picture and '34B plateau avec container' in 7 languages £90-110
582	1959-69	Citroën Breakdown Truck,	
		'DINKY TOYS'	Painted ridged hubs, smooth black tyres, small tool-box, open fuel tank, 1:50.
	(previously 34-A)		Dark red body, yellow 'DINKY TOYS' logo. '35A' on box £150-125
	1969-71		Red body and concave hubs, yellow logo, plastic hook, smooth or treaded black tyres. '582' on box £100-125
584	1961-65	Berliet Covered Lorry	Red or Yellow body (either with Green tilt), concave hubs, 1:43. Yellow box without (later with) picture......£80-100
585	1961-64	Berliet Builders Lorry	Blue/orange/grey, wide (later narrow) boards in tipping body, painted concave hubs, 1:43. Yellow box....£100-125
586	1961-65	Citroën 55 Milk Lorry	White/blue body, 30 bottle crates, painted concave hubs, 1:43. Yellow box £400-500
587	1964-70	Citroën H Display Van,	
		'PHILIPS'	Yellow/silver body, red concave hubs, household appliances, 1:43. Yellow picture box £500-700
588	1964-70	Berliet Beer Lorry	Yellow/red/brown, 'BIERES, LIMONADES, EAUX MINÉRALES',
			painted concave hubs, crates and barrels, 1:43. Yellow picture box £240-300
588K	1970-71	...................................Promotional:	Red body, 'KRONENBOURG LE GRAND NOM des BIERES d'ALSACE'. Code 1 promotional £3,500-4,500
589	1965-69	Berliet Breakdown Lorry	Red body, 'DEPANNAGE' in yellow or White, chromed concave hubs, 1:43.................£200-250
	1970-71		Orange body, 'DEPANNAGE AUTOROUTES', chromed concave
			hubs, aerial. 595t Traffic Sign 'Maximum Height 3.5 metres' included in box.................£200-250
595	1959-61	Salev Mobile Crane	As reference 50 but crane pillar not held by rivet, painted concave hubs £60-80
596	1960-63	LMV Road Sweeper/Washer	Cream and green body, rotating and pivoting brush mechanism, 1:43. Yellow box £100-125
597	1959-61	Coventry Climax	
		Fork Lift Truck	(previously 14-C) Orange/Yellow (or Green)/Black, ridged or concave hubs, 'assemblé en France' on base..£50-70
803	1967-69	Unic Articulated Lorry, 'SNCF'	Dark blue body, cream trailer roof, 'SNCF' and 'PAM-PAM', plastic hubs, 1:43. Yellow picture box £250-350
805	1966-71	Unic Multi Skip and Gas Tanker	Red/black/white, interchangeable skip and 'PROPANE-PRIMAGAZ'
			gas tank (from Hornby ACHO range), painted concave hubs, 1:55. Yellow picture box £250-300
810	1959-62	Two-Axle Covered Trailer	(previously 70) Red or Yellow, Green tilt, ridged or concave hubs, 1:60. '70' (later '810') on Yellow box £40-50
	1962-?	Two-Axle Covered Trailer,	
		'ESSO'	Red body and tilt, 'ESSO' transfers, painted concave hubs. Yellow box...................£55-65

830	1959-69	**Richier Diesel Roller**	(90-A) Yellow body, Blue driver, Red wheels, '90A-830' (later '830') on Yellow box, 1:43. Supertoy **£55-65**
881	1969-70	**GMC Circus Truck and**	
		Animal Trailer	Red/yellow/black, 'PINDER FAUVES', no hole in seat for driver, plastic animals, card supports, 'SUPER DINKY MECCANO FRANCE' on chassis, painted concave hubs, 1:43. Yellow box **£500-750**
	1970-71	....	Same model, but with hole in seat for driver, and 'DINKY-TOYS MECCANO TRI-ANG' on chassis **£500-750**
882	1969-70	**Peugeot 404 and Circus Caravan**	Red/Yellow/White Peugeot 404 (536) and Caravelair Armagnac 420 Caravan (564),
		'Le SUPER CIRQUE PINDER'	roof hoardings, chromed concave hubs. Yellow box also contains : a 595L Traffic Sign 'Maximum Width 2 metres', 'Martin' the circus bear and a leaflet **£1,000-1,250**
885	1959-61	**Blaw-Knox Bulldozer**	Orange/Grey/Black, driver, 1:43. 'assemblé en France' on base (see 561). Blue/White striped picture box.......**£150-175**
885	1966-71	**Saviem Sinpar Steel Carrier**......	Red cab, grey chassis, driver, plastic hubs, steel load held by magnets, scale 1:43. Yellow picture box (showing yellow/grey vehicle)...**£250-300**
886	1960-65	**Richier Road Profiler**.................	Yellow body, driver, plastic hubs, scale 1:43. Supertoys box **£100-125**
887	1959-61	**Muir-Hill Dumper**	Yellow-Cream body, driver, painted ridged hubs, 1:43. English components, 'assemblé en France' on base ..**£40-50**
887	1963-71	**Unic Articulated Tanker, 'BP'**..	White/green/lemon yellow, 'AIR BP', plastic hubs, hoses for filling tank, electric lights switched by spare wheel, scale 1:43. Supertoys blue/white box with full colour picture on lid **£150-200**
888	1960-66	**Berliet Sahara Pipe-Layer**	Sand body (various shades), White roof, operable crane, most with White or Beige plastic hubs (a few cast metal), most with tow hook (a few without), scale 1:50 ....**£175-225**
	1968	...............................Promotional:	As previous model but with 'Société Languedocienne de Forages Pétroliers' **£800-1,000**
889	1959-62	**Coles Mobile Crane**...................	Orange/yellow, 2 drivers, painted concave hubs, 'assemblé en France' on base. Was 972; reissued as 972 ....**£50-60**
893	1960-70	**Unic Sahara Pipe Transporter** ..	Beige body (various shades), White roof, window glazing, pierced (later solid) trailer
		(previously 39-B)	painted ridged and concave hubs, 6 tubes, 1:55. Supertoys box without (later with) '893' **£100-150**
	196?	...............................Promotional:	Beige body, White roof, window glazing, 'solid' trailer, painted concave hubs. 'DESTINATION: PETROLE DU SAHARA' on box. Code 2 promotional..NGPP
894	1959-68	**Unic Boilot Car Transporter**.....	Silver/orange, 'DINKY TOYS SERVICE LIVRAISON', painted concave hubs,
		(previously 39-A)	black block tread tyres, scale 1:55. '894' on Supertoys box...**£150-175**
895	1959-65	**Unic Marrel Multi-Body Truck**	Grey and golden-yellow body, fixed skip, ridged and concave (or all concave) painted hubs,
		(previously 38-A)	black block tread tyres, scale 1:55. '895' on Supertoys box..**£80-100**
896	1959-71	**Willeme Tractor and**	
		Covered Trailer	Red tractor, inclined (later straight) chassis members, Orange semi-trailer, Green tilt, painted ridged
		(previously 36-B)	and/or concave hubs, 4 (later 2) rollers on trailer prop. '36B-896' (later just '896') on Supertoys box **£100-150**
897	1959-71	**Willeme Log Lorry**...................	Orange tractor (chassis members on spindle), Yellow semi-trailer (pierced, later solid), black painted base,
		(previously 36-A)	painted concave hubs, radial or block tread tyres, 1:55. '897-36A' (later just '897') on Supertoys box **£100-120**
898	1961-65	**Berliet Transformer Carrier,**	
		'ALSTHOM'	Orange body, Grey transformer (loose parts within), painted ridged (later concave) hubs. Supertoys box..........**£300-450**
972	1957-62	**Coles Mobile Crane**...................	Orange and yellow, two drivers, painted concave hubs, 1:50. English parts, 'assemblé in France' on base.....**£50-60**
		(Renumbered in 1959 as 889)	
1412	1968-71	**Hotchkiss Willys Recovery Jeep**	Red and Yellow body, Orange or Black jib with lamp, painted concave hubs, scale 1:50 ....**£90-120**

French Dinky Toys 25R Studebaker Breakdown Truck 'DINKY SERVICE'

Photographs: Vectis Auctions Ltd.

Ref	Year(s)	Model name	Colours, features, details	Market Price Range

See also Accessories and Gift Sets sections.

25BR	1959	**Peugeot D3a Fire Service Van**...	A prototype exists with a light red body (cross-hatching inside roof), dark red ridged hubs and identical transfers to the 25D Citroën van	NPP
25D	1958-59	**Citroën 2cv Fire Service Van**	Red body and ridged hubs, 'Pompiers Ville de Paris', 1:43. Yellow box. Renumbered 562 in 1959	£100-125
	1959-59		Grey body, 'BÉBÉ LORRAIN', cream hubs. Only 80 were made of this code-2 promotional model ..	£2,000-2,500
32D	195-59	**Delahaye Fire Escape**	Red body, chromed ladder, painted ridged hubs, smooth White tyres (specially made for this model),	
	(Renumbered in 1959 as 899)		scale 1:55. Blue/White striped Supertoys box. (32-D was the first of the French Dinky Supertoys)	£150-200
32E	1957-59	**Berliet First-Aid Vehicle**	Bright Red (occasionally Brownish-Red) twin-cab body (no markings), detachable hose reel, painted	
	(Renumbered in 1959 as 583)		ridged (concave through 1959) hubs, white tyes, 1:55, '32E' on Supertoys box	£150-200
80F	1959-59	**Renault Military Ambulance**	Renault Goelette in Gloss or matt finish, painted ridged hubs, 1:55. Yellow box	£60-75
	(Renumbered in 1959 as 820)			
501	1967-70	**Citroën DS19 'POLICE' Car**	Very dark blue/white, roof beacon, plated concave hubs, 1:43	£125-150
507P	1967-71	**Simca 1500 'POLICE' Estate Car**	Dark blue/white body. Commissioned for use by Police	£300-350
517P	1969	**Renault R8 'POLICE' Car**	Dark blue/white. Commissioned for use by Police	£400-450
518	1964-64	**Renault 4L**	Red body, 'POMPIERS de PARIS'. Commissioned by Fire Service	£375-425
525	1964-64	**Peugeot 404 Fire Car**	Red body, 'Pompiers de Paris', concave chromed hubs. Commissioned for use by Fire Service	£395-445
551	1965-67	**Ford Taunus 17M Police Car**	Green/white, 'POLIZEI', plated concave hubs, 1:43, German text on box. Made for export	
			to Germany and Benelux countries	£250-300
556	1964-67	**Citroën ID19 Ambulance**	Same, but 'A' of 'Ambulance' and 'M' of 'Municipale' are not aligned. 'Super detail' box	£70-85
	1967-70		Grey/cream body, plated concave hubs, 'DUNLOP' nylon tyres, plastic steering wheel, without '556'	
			on base, 'A' of 'Ambulance' and 'M' of 'Municipale' are not aligned. 'Super detail' box	£100-125
562	1959-61	**Citroën 2cv Van** ....(was 25-D)	Red body and ridged hubs, 'POMPIERS VILLE de PARIS', scale 1:43	£90-120
	1961-63		Red body and concave hubs, 'POMPIERS VILLE de PARIS', smooth or treaded black tyres	£100-150
566	1965-70	**Citroën H Currus Van, 'POLICE'**	Blue/white body, painted concave hubs, working warning lights	£140-160
568	1968-70	**Berliet Gak Fire Escape**	Red twin-cab body, extending chromed ladder, painted concave hubs, 1:43. Yellow picture box	£250-300
570P	1971-72	**Peugeot J7 VSAB Fire Van**	'POMPIERS', Red body, painted hubs, 'MECCANO FRANCE SA' on diecast base. Yellow box	£175-250
	1972-		Later version, with 'MECCANO TRI-ANG' on plastic base. Yellow box	£175-250
583	1959-63	**Berliet First-Aid Vehicle**	Bright Red twin-cab body (no markings), detachable hose reel, painted	
	(Renumbered from 32-E)		concave painted hubs, white tyes, 1:55, '32E' (later '583-32E') on Supertoys box	£140-180
	1962-63	Promotional issue:	Red twin-cab body with 'POMPIERS de PARIS' shield, concave hubs. Fire Service promotional	£200-250
820	1959-70	**Renault Goelette Ambulance**	Gloss or matt finish, painted concave hubs, treaded rubber (later nylon) tyres, 1:55. Yellow box	£60-75
	(Renumbered from 80-F)			
899	1959-65	**Delahaye Fire Escape** ..(was 32-D)	Red body, black steering wheel, painted ridged hubs, smooth white tyres, 1:55. '32D' on Supertoys box..	£130-170
	1965-70		Red body, white steering wheel, painted concave hubs, treaded white tyres. '899' on Supertoys box	£130-170
1402	1968-68	**Ford Galaxie Police Car**	Black/white body, 'POLICE'. Commissioned for use by Police	NGPP
1416P	1970-70	**Renault R6 Fire Car**	Code 2 model based on Spanish-made components, commissioned by the Fire Service.	
		'POMPIERS de PARIS'	Red body, second grille (square headlamps), red concave hubs. Side view of white model on box.	£50-60
1429	1970-71	**Peugeot 404 Police Car**	Blue/white body, 'POLICE', plastic base, plated concave hubs, 1:43. Yellow box	£150-175
		note:	595n Traffic Sign 'Cycling Prohibited' included with 1429.	
1450	1977-78	**Simca 1100 Police Car**	Blue/white or black/white body, 'POLICE', plated concave hubs. Made in Spain	£25-40

**French Dinky Toys 32E
Berliet First Aid Vehicle**

Photo: Vectis Auctions Ltd.

Military Vehicles

A number of military vehicle models were designed in the late 1930s and the prototypes were shown in the June 1940 French catalogue. They were never put into production because of the Nazi Occupation. It came as no surprise that, following liberation by the Allies, the first new French Dinky Toy to be introduced was a model of the US Army Jeep so common at the time. The unavailability of rubber meant that all-metal wheels had to be used instead of hubs and tyres. The wheels used on the Jeep were mounted inside-out to give a heavy duty off-road effect.

During the 1960s and 1970s a number of military models from the English range were imported into France. These are listed in the Imports section. 681 DUKW Amphibious

Vehicle was not one of those imported as the French factory produced a much more detailed version (number 825). Note that the letters 'DUKW' are not initials nor are they an abbreviation - they are simply part of the General Motors design reference system of the time.

All the models listed are finished in various shades of military green unless otherwise stated. The paint can be found to be either gloss, semi-gloss or matt but this does not affect the price range.

Some military items are also noted in the Accessories section.

Ref	Year(s)	Model name	Colours, features, details	Market Price Range
24M	1946-48	**Military Jeep**	US Military olive-drab body and mazak wheels (mounted inside-out for effect), white star on bonnet, tinplate windscreen frame (some bonnet castings have frame supports), wire steering wheel, scale 1:43...**£700-900**	
		note:	24-M was the first French made Dinky Toy to appear after the War. Trade boxes contained twelve units.	
80A	1957-59	**Panhard EBR75 FL11**	Painted hubs, radial tread tyres, side headlamps or red lights, scale 1:55.	
	(Renumbered in 1959 as 815)		'80A' on base and box (picture on some boxes) **£50-70**	
80-B	1958-59	**Hotchkiss Willys Jeep**	No driver, no hook, convex painted hubs, smooth black tyres, scale 1:50.	
			'80B' printed on yellow box (picture on some) **£50-70**	
80-BP	1959-59	**Hotchkiss Willys Jeep**	With driver, no hook, convex painted hubs, smooth black tyres. There are two box types:	
	(Renumbered in 1959 as 816)		1 - '80B' Yellow box (with picture) has '80BP' stickers; 2 - '80BP' printed on Yellow box (with picture) **£50-70**	
80-C	1958-59	**AMX 13 Tank**	Gloss or matt finish, no aerial, rubber tracks, rear roller	
	(Renumbered in 1959 as 817)		treads indented or raised, scale 1:55. '80C' on Yellow box **£50-70**	
80-D	1958-59	**Berliet 6x6 All-Terrain Truck** ...	Tinplate tilt, black cab floor, painted hubs, 1:55. '80D' but no picture on yellow box **£50-70**	
	1959-59	(Renumbered in 1959 as 818)	Tinplate tilt, khaki cab floor, painted hubs, 1:55. '80D' and picture on yellow box **£50-70**	
80-E	1958-59	**Obusier ABS 155mm Gun**	Gloss or matt finish, painted ridged hubs, 1:55. Yellow box with or without picture **£40-50**	
	(Renumbered in 1959 as 819)			
80-F	1959-59	**Renault Goelette Ambulance**	Gloss or matt finish, painted ridged hubs, 1:55. Yellow box **£60-75**	
	(Renumbered in 1959 as 820)			
676	1972-72	**Daimler Armoured Car**	Painted concave hubs, camouflage net, 1:55. Model first made in France though 'Made in England' wrongly stated on base. 'MECCANO FRANCE' on yellow box **£150-200**	
		note:	676 was replaced after a short time by the Liverpool-made model with new reference '676L'.	
800	1974-?	**Renault 4x4 Sinpar**	(Revised and renumbered from 815). Khaki body, grey-green-khaki top, camouflage net, no gear lever, no aerial support, black plastic radio, painted concave hubs, 1:43. 'MECCANO' on base and box ('camouflage' effect on box) **£90-120**	
801	1973-75	**AMX 13 Tank**	Matt khaki body, grey nylon tracks, plastic rollers, camouflage	
	(Renumbered from 817)		net, aerial (a few shown), scale 1:55. '801' on yellow, part camouflaged box **£55-75**	
802	1974-?	**Obusier ABS 155mm Gun**	Khaki body with camouflage net, 'OBUSIER 155' replaces '80E' on base, painted concave hubs, 1:55. 'Camouflage' effect on yellow box **£40-50**	
	(Renumbered from 819)			
804	1973-?	**Mercedes-Benz Unimog**	(Revised and renumbered from 821). Khaki body and camouflage net, 'MERCEDES TOUS TERRAINS, 804' on chassis, grey-blue base without '821', painted concave hubs, ridged tyres. 'MECCANO TRI-ANG' on yellow box with 'camouflage' effect (box contains unused transfer sheet).....**£110-140**	
806	1973-?	**Berliet Recovery Truck**	(Revised and renumbered from 826). Khaki body and base, driver, plastic hook, camouflage net, without 'TOUS TERRAINS BERLIET' on chassis, painted concave hubs. 'Camouflage' effect on yellow box **£120-150**	
807	1973-?	**Renault All-Terrain Ambulance** ..	Khaki body, plastic concave hubs and base, 1:55. ....**£150-175**	
808	1971	**Dodge WC56 Command Car** ...	Announced in the 1971 catalogue but made as reference 810 from 1972.	
808	1972-74	**GMC US Army Recovery Truck** .	Sand body (hole for driver), painted concave hubs, black removable top, 1:43. Large yellow box..............**£175-250**	
	1974-?		Olive-drab body (hole for driver in some), painted concave hubs, black top. Large yellow box..............**£175-250**	
809	1970-	**GMC US Army 6x6 Truck**	Olive drab/black body (white stars), driver (white or khaki helmet), painted concave hubs, 1:43. Box has design panel..**£150-200**	
809	197?-?	**GMC 6x6 Truck**	Khaki/black (white stars), driver (grey helmet), painted concave hubs. 'MECCANO' on base but no design panel **£175-225**	
		note:	595q Traffic Sign 'Automatic Level Crossing' included with 809, plus additional 'white star' transfer sheet.	
810	1972-74	**Dodge WC56 Command Car**	Removable top, soldier, camouflage net, concave hubs, 1:43. 'Camouflage' effect on yellow box..............**£150-200**	
813	1969-71	**AMX with 155mm ABS Gun**	Gloss or matt finish, nylon tracks, 1:55, 96mm. Yellow box **£140-190**	
	1972-?		Gloss or matt finish, nylon tracks, simplified gun, camouflage net. 'Camouflage' effect on yellow box....**£140-190**	
814	1963-71	**Panhard Armoured Car**	Khaki finish, painted concave hubs, black (later Grey-Blue) base, scale 1:52. 'C'est une fabrication MECCANO' printed on plain side of Yellow box **£40-50**	
815	1959-63	**Panhard EBR75 FL11**	Gloss or matt finish, '80A' on base, painted hubs, block tread tyres, scale 1:55. Picture and '815' on box **£40-50**	
	(Renumbered from 80-A)			
815	1969-74	**Renault 4 Sinpar Gendarmerie** .	Khaki body, green-khaki top, two military policemen, gear lever, aerial, light grey plastic radio, ('Revised' in 1974 and issued as 800) painted concave hubs, 1:43. 'MECCANO TRI-ANG' on base.......**£140-170**	
816	1959-61	**Hotchkiss Willys Jeep** ......(80-BP)	Driver, no hook, painted ridged hubs, smooth black tyres, 1:50. Picture and '816-80BP' on yellow box **£50-70**	
	1962-63		Driver, cast-in hook, concave hubs, smooth or treaded black tyres. Picture and '816' on yellow box **£50-70**	
816	1969-71	**Berliet Rocket Launcher**	Khaki/grey body, white/red rocket ('NORD, R-20'), painted concave hubs, 1:55..............................**£200-250**	
817	1959-64	**AMX 13 Tank** ....(Was 80-C)	Gloss or matt khaki, no aerial, rubber tracks, rear roller treads raised, 1:55. '80C' on yellow box..............**£50-70**	
	1965-70		Same but only in gloss khaki and with aerial. With (later without) '80C' on base. '817' on yellow box **£50-70**	
	1973-75	(Renumbered in 1973 as 801)	Same but matt khaki body, grey nylon tracks on plastic rollers. Yellow box with 'camouflage' effect..........**£50-70**	
818	1959-65	**Berliet 6x6 All-Terrain Truck** ..	(Was 80-D). Tinplate tilt, khaki cab floor, painted concave hubs, 1:55. '80D' and picture on yellow box **£50-70**	

	1965-70		Same, but 'TOUS TERRAINS BERLIET' on base (a few without), '818' and picture on yellow box	**£50-70**
819	1959-65	**Obusier ABS 155mm Gun**	(Was 80-E). Khaki body, painted ridged hubs, '80E' on base, scale 1:55. Fully illustrated yellow box	**£40-50**
	1965-74		Gloss khaki body, painted concave hubs. Fully illustrated yellow box. (Revised in 1974; issued as 802)	**£40-50**
820	1959-70	**Renault Goelette Ambulance**	Gloss or matt finish, painted concave hubs, treaded rubber (later nylon) tyres, 1:55. Yellow box	**£60-75**
		(Renumbered from 80-F)		
821	1960-63	**Mercedes-Benz Unimog**	'MERCEDES-UNIMOG' on chassis, '821' on black painted base, painted concave hubs, smooth tyres. No picture on yellow box	**£50-70**
	1963-65		'MERCEDES-BENZ UNIMOG' on chassis, '821' on black painted base, painted concave hubs, smooth tyres. Picture and 'MECCANO' on yellow box	**£45-55**
	1965-66		As previous model. but with ridged tyres. Picture and 'MECCANO TRI-ANG' on yellow box	**£45-55**
	1966-70		Same model, but with grey-blue base without '821'. Picture and 'MECCANO TRI-ANG' on yellow box	**£45-55**
	1973		Revised in 1973 and issued as 804.	
822	1960-63	**White M3 Half-Track**	Matt finish, no machine gun, black painted chassis, painted concave hubs (smooth black tyres), 1:50. Picture of model on box	**£70-80**
	1963-65		Matt or gloss finish, with machine gun, anodised chassis, painted concave hubs (treaded black tyres). Picture of model plus scene and 'C'est une fabrication MECCANO' on box	**£70-80**
	1965-71		Same, but with picture of model plus scene and 'C'est une fabrication MECCANO TRI-ANG' on box	**£70-80**
823	1962-66	**Marion Mobile Kitchen**	Khaki body, black or khaki base, painted concave hubs, scale 1:50. Yellow box	**£50-60**
823	1969-70	**GMC Military Tanker**	Khaki/black, plastic tank, removable cab canopy, painted concave hubs, scale 1:43. Yellow box also contains a 595b Traffic Sign 'Maximum Weight 5.5 tonnes'	**£400-500**
824	1963-64	**Berliet Gazelle 6x6 Truck**	Removable cab canopy and tilt, painted concave hubs, 1:55. 'Cabine vitrée' ('cab window glazing') on illustrated yellow box	**£80-100**
	1964-70		Same model, but 'Cabine vitrée aménagée' ('cab window glazing fitted') on box	**£80-100**
825	1963-71	**GMC DUKW Amphibian**	Gloss or matt finish, drums and boxes, painted concave hubs, driver with later issues, 1:55. Yellow box (picture on later boxes)	**£120-140**
826	1963-70	**Berliet Recovery Truck**	Plastic driver, metal hook, black base, 'TOUS TERRAINS BERLIET' on chassis, painted concave hubs, scale 1:55. Yellow box	**£140-170**
	1973		Revised in 1973 and issued as 806.	
827	1964-71	**Panhard EBR75 FL10**	Khaki body, aerial, painted concave hubs, 1:55.	**£60-70**
828	1964-71	**Jeep SS10 Missile Launcher**	Driver, missile battery. painted concave hubs, 1:50.	**£55-70**
829	1964-71	**Jeep 106SR Gun Carrier**	Driver, plastic 106mm. gun, painted concave hubs, 1:50	**£55-70**
834	1963-70	**Mobile Bridge Pack**	Khaki plastic 6 part bridge plus inflatable boats (as supplied with 884), scale 1:55	NPP
841	1959-71	**Tank Tracks Pack**	Twelve tracks for AMX tanks.	NPP
843	1962-71	**Military Tyre Pack**	Twelve treaded black tyres (large for 818 and similar)	NPP
852	1962-71	**Tank Tracks Pack**	Ten replacement tracks for 822 White M3 Military Half-Track	NPP
856	1963-71	**Machine Gun**	Plastic armament for use on 822 White M3 Half-Track	NPP
883	1964-66	**AMX 13 Bridge Layer**	Gloss or matt finish, '13t AMX' on base, scale 1:55. Yellow box has reference on black oval	**£150-200**
	1966-71		Same, but 'Char AMX poseur de pont, réf.883' on base. Yellow box has reference on violet band	**£150-200**
884	1961-70	**Brockway Bridge Layer**	10 element bridge, 2 inflatable boats, 1:55. Supertoys box ('884' on some) also contains leaflet	**£275-325**
890	1959-63	**Berliet T6 Tank Transporter**	Gloss or matt finish, painted ridged hubs, 1:55, Supertoys box has no illustration	**£130-160**
	1963-70		Gloss or matt finish, painted ridged or concave hubs. Illustration on Supertoys box	**£130-160**

French Dinky Toys Military Vehicles

80D All-Terrain Truck

829 Jeep 106SR Gun Carrier

814 Panhard Armoured Car

828 Jeep SS10 Missile Launcher

Photo: Vectis Auctions Ltd.

Aircraft

In comparison with the English factory, Meccano France produced only a small range of model aircraft. They are nonetheless rather attractive and much sought after. Pre-war planes are especially difficult to find in good stable condition since the metal deterioration problem equally affected production on both sides of the Channel.

Some interesting models were designed at the end of the 1930s in the French 64 series (listed below). These were announced in the 1939 Meccano Magazine but with the advance of the occupying German forces production did not take place. Around this period a few small (normally silver) planes were given a camouflage finish and advertised as 'Reconnaissance' or

'Spotter' planes though it is very unlikely that serious production of these was actually undertaken.

Some of the English 60 series were imported into France before the war, and very few post-war (see the Imports section for details). Of the few new French made aircraft models to appear in the late 1950s, the Caravelle is perhaps the most desirable, particularly in the Swiss, Scandinavian or Algerian liveries with their specially printed Supertoys boxes.

As in England the French factory produced a number of boxed sets of model aircraft in the 1930s. They are fully described in the Gift Sets section.

Ref	Year(s)	Model name	Colours, features, details	Market Price Range
60a	1935-40	DeWoitine D388 Rainbow	(L'Arc en Ciel). Three engines, each with 2-blade propellers and no tinplate surrounds.	
			Silver/red, Gold/red, Cream/red, Cream/green, Gold/green, Gold/blue	£200-300
60A	1957-59	Dassault Mystere IVa Jet	Metallic grey, single jet, blue cockpit. Yellow box. (Renumbered in 1959 as 800)	£70-80
60b	1935-40	Potez 58	Tinplate main wings, 2-wheel undercarriage, 2-blade propeller, 2-part windscreen.	
			Yellow/grey	£150-250
			Red/silver	£200-300
60B	1957-59	Sud Aviation Vautour 'SNCASO'	Metallic grey, twin jet, blue cockpit. Yellow box. (Renumbered in 1959 as 801)	£80-100
60c	1935-40	Henriot H180T	Tinplate main wings, 2-wheel undercarriage, 2-blade propeller, 3-part windscreen.	
			Green/white, Green/red, Blue/white, Red/silver	£150-250
60C	1956-59	Lockheed Super G Constellation	Silver, 'AIR FRANCE', 'FB-HBX', 4 x 3-blade propellers, scale 1:190. Supertoys box	£150-200
		(Renumbered in 1959 as 892)		
60d	1935-40	Breguet Corsaire	Open two-seater fuselage with tinplate main wings and 2-blade propeller.	
			Silver/red, Red/green, Red/yellow	£200-300
60D	1957-59	Sikorsky S58 Helicopter	White/grey/blue, 'SABENA', black rotors. Yellow box	£100-125
		(Renumbered in 1959 as 802)		
60e	1935-40	DeWoitine 500 Hunter	Open cockpit, tinplate main wings, 2-wheel undercarriage, 2-blade propeller.	
			Cream/red, Light cream/green	£200-300
60E	1957-59	Vickers Viscount	White/grey/blue, 'AIR FRANCE', 'FB-GNX', 4 x 4-blade propellers, scale 1:190. Yellow box	£125-175
		(Renumbered in 1959 as 803)		
60f	1935-40	Cierva Autogiro	Cast body, with or without pilot.	
			Gold (Red rotors), Cream (red or Blue rotors), Silver (red or blue rotors), Red (Cream rotors)	£200-300
60F	1959-59	Caravelle SE210, 'AIR FRANCE'	Metallic grey/white/blue, 'FB-GNY', operable steps, scale 1:190. Supertoys box	£130-180
		(Renumbered in 1960 as 891)		
61a	1938-40	Dewoitine D338	Basic casting as 60a L'Arc en Ciel but with 3 x 3-blade propellers and tinplate engine surrounds.	
			Green/silver or Red/gold (in a different arrangement from L'Arc en Ciel)	£150-250
	1939-40		Different casting from first version of 61a and also having the reference 64. Three engines, each with 3-blade propellers and tinplate engine surrounds, gliding hole. 'FA-DBF' marking on body.	
			Silver or Light green body	£150-250
61b	1938-40	Potez 56	Blue/silver, Red/silver, Yellow/silver. 2 x 2-blade propellers	£150-250
61c	1938-40	Farman F360	Open two-seater, single 2-blade propeller.	
			Silver/blue, Silver/red, Silver/yellow, Silver with roundels	£150-250
61d	1938-40	Potez 58 Air Ambulance	Silver body with red cross on silver or White ground	£200-300
61e	1938-40	Henriot H180M	Silver wings and fuselage with roundels, 2-blade propeller	£200-300
61f	1938-40	Dewoitine 500 Hunter	Silver wings and fuselage with roundels, 2-blade propeller	£200-300
64	1939-40	Dewoitine D338	Different casting from previous version of Dewoitine with more prominent tailfin and also having the reference 61a. Three engines, each with 2-blade propellers, gliding hole. 'FA-DBF' marking.	
			Silver or Light Green body	£150-200
64a	1939-40	Amiot 370	Twin engine monoplane, 2 or 3-blade propellers, gliding hole.	
			Beige, Pink, Red or Blue; or Pale green with red circles on wings; or Silver with French roundels	£150-250
	1948-49		A small number of pre-war castings were issued in various colours	£150-250
64b	1939-40	Bloch 220	Twin engine airliner marked 'FA-OHJ', 2 x 3-blade propellers, gliding hole.	
			Silver, Dark red, Pale green or Ivory	£150-250
64c	1939-40	Potez 63	Twin engines, twin tailplanes, 3-blade propellers.	
			Beige, Red, Blue, Silver, Silver with French roundels	£150-250
	1948-49		A small number of pre-war castings were issued in various colours	£150-250
64d	1939-40	Potez 662	Four engine passenger plane marked 'FA-RAY', 3-blade propellers, twin tailplanes, gliding hole.	
			Silver, Red, Light blue, Yellow	£150-200
800	1959-64	Dassault Mystere IVa Jet	Metallic grey, single jet, blue cockpit. Yellow box. (Renumbered from 60-A)	£70-80
801	1959-64	Sud Aviation Vautour 'SNCASO'	Metallic grey, twin jet, blue cockpit. Yellow box. (Renumbered from 60-B)	£80-100
802	1959-61	Sikorsky S58 Helicopter	White/grey/blue, 'SABENA', black rotors. Yellow box	£100-125
		(Renumbered from 60-D)		
803	1959-61	Vickers Viscount, 'AIR FRANCE'	White/grey/blue, 'FB-GNX', 4 x 4-blade propellers, scale 1:190. Yellow box. (Renumbered from 60-E)	£125-175
804	1959-63	SNCAN Noratlas	Metallic grey, twin-fuselage French military plane, 2 x 4-blade propellers. Yellow box	£150-200
891		Caravelle SE210	(Renumbered from 60-F). All have 'Escalier escamotable' (operable steps) and Supertoys box. Scale 1:190.	
	1959-59	'AIR FRANCE'	Silver/white/blue, 'FB-GNY'	£200-250
	1959-68	'AIR FRANCE'	Metallic grey/white/blue. '60F' under wing of early issues (later without)	£250-350
	1960-?	'SWISSAIR'	Metallic grey/white/blue. 'HB-ICX', 'Swissair' on box	£900-1,200
	1960-?	'SAS'	('SCANDINAVIAN AIRWAYS SYSTEM'), Metallic grey/white/blue. 'SE-DAA'. 'SAS' on box	£900-1,200
	1960-?	'AIR ALGERIE'	Metallic grey/white/red. 'FO-BNH'. Supertoys 'Air Algerie' on box	£900-1,200
892	1959-62	Lockheed Super G Constellation	Silver, 'AIR FRANCE', 'FB-HBX', 4 x 3-blade propellers, scale 1:190. Supertoys box	£200-250

French Dinky Toys 29F Chausson AP521 Autocar

French Dinky Toys 29E Isobloc Autocar

Photographs: Vectis Auctions Ltd.

Buses

Ref	Year(s)	Model name	Colours, features, details	Market Price Range
29d	1939-51	Renault TN4H Paris Bus	All have Dark Green cast lower body, Cream tinplate top, scale 1:80. Variations as follows:	
	1939-40		Base on some, cast hubs, black or white 'DUNLOP' tyres	£300-400
	1940-40		No base, painted mazak wheels	£200-250
	1940-49		Base on some (may be black or silver painted), painted mazak wheels	£200-250
	1950-51		Driver set high; with base (may be black or silver painted), yellow ridged hubs	£250-300
29D	1952-54	Somua-Panhard Paris Bus	Dark green/cream, smooth inside roof, painted ridged hubs, 1:70. Supplied in trade boxes of 6 models	£100-130
	1954-59	(Renumbered in 1959 as 570)	Dark green/cream, cross-hatched inside roof, painted ridged hubs. In own Yellow box marked '29D'	£100-130
29E	1950-50	Isobloc Autocar	Blue/cream, smooth sides and roof, painted ridged hubs, scale 1:70	£250-350
			Dark green/light green, smooth sides and roof, painted ridged hubs	£250-350
			Blue/silver, smooth sides and roof, painted ridged hubs	£225-275
	1951-52		Blue/silver, smooth roof, raised side detail, painted ridged hubs	£185-225
	1953-55		Red/silver, raised roof detail, raised side detail, painted ridged hubs	£75-95
			Orange/silver, raised side detail, painted ridged hubs	£125-150
			Blue/silver, ridged roof, raised side detail, painted ridged hubs	£75-95
29F	1956-58	Chausson AP521 Autocar	Painted ridged hubs, scale 1:65. Box flap reads '29F AUTOCAR CHAUSSON' in French only.	
			Blue/cream body or Red/cream body	£100-125
	1958-59	(Renumbered in 1959 as 571)	As previous models, but concave hubs. Box flap reads '29F AUTOCAR CHAUSSON' in 4 languages	£110-135
541	1963-71	Mercedes-Benz Autocar	18 seater body, chromed concave hubs, 1:43. Yellow box.	
			Mid-red and cream, Orange-red and cream, or Deep Pink (various shades) and cream	£90-110
	1966-?	....................South African issue:	Blue/cream body, chromed concave hubs	£750-1,000
	19??	'PTT SUISSE'	Orange/Silver body, chromed concave hubs, 'PTT SUISSE'	£3,000-4,000
570	1959-61	Somua Paris Bus OP5 .....(29-D)	Dark green/cream, cross-hatched inside roof, painted ridged hubs. In Yellow box marked '29D'	£90-120
571	1959-60	Chausson AP521 Autocar	Painted concave hubs, 1:65. Box flap reads '29F AUTOCAR CHAUSSON' in 4 languages.	
		(Renumbered from 29-F)	Blue/cream or Red/cream body	£110-135
889	1965-70	Berliet Paris Autobus	Green/greenish-white, 'DUNLOP', 'PEPSI-COLA', painted concave hubs, 1:49. Supertoys blue/white box, colour picture on lid	£175-200
889U	1965-70	Berliet Urban Bus	Red/cream or Orange/Cream, 'DUNLOP', 'PEPSI-COLA', painted concave hubs. Supertoys blue/white box with colour illustration of the Place Bellecour in Lyons	£175-200
	NB		889 Paris Bus was modelled on a Berliet vehicle though the 1965-66 catalogue attributes it to Saviem.	

Trains

Ref	Year(s)	Model name	Colours, features, details	Market Price Range

See also Gift Sets and Accessories sections.

Ref	Year(s)	Model name	Colours, features, details	Market Price Range
16	1935-40	Northern Sector Railcar	An 'Autorail' with three articulated coaches cast in mazak, tinplate base, silvered or black lead hubs, white rubber tyres. Boxed. Blue-grey/dark blue; Grey/blue; Grey/red; Gold/red; Cream/red; Cream/green	£100-125
16a	1940	Two-Car Railcar	A two-part version of 16a. Advertised in the 1940 catalogue but not issued	NPP
17	1935-38	Electric Goods Train	See 'Gift Sets' section.	
18	1934-38	Steam Goods Train	See 'Gift Sets' section.	
19	1935-38	Electric Passenger Train	See 'Gift Sets' section.	
19a	1935-36	Electric Locomotive	Cast in lead. Various basic colours	£60-80
	1936-40		Cast in mazak. Silver/red; Light green/red; Green/black; Gold/blue; Two-tone blue	£50-70
20	1935-38	Steam Passenger Train	See 'Gift Sets' section.	
20a	1935-40	Passenger Coach	Red/blue or Green/blue. Cast in lead	£25-35
21	1934-38	Steam Mixed Goods Train	See 'Gift Sets' section.	
21a	1934-40	Steam Tank Locomotive	Red/blue; Green/blue; Green/black. Cast in lead	£30-45
21b	1934-40	Timber Wagon	Red/green wagon cast in lead, yellow mazak 'log'	£30-45
21c	1934-40	Coal Wagon	Green/red or Green/black wagon, cast in lead	£30-45
21d	1934-38	Crane Wagon	Blue and green; Green and blue; Red and blue; Yellow and red. Cast in lead, crane has 'open' jib	£25-35
21d	1938-40	Crane Wagon	Blue and green; Green and blue; Red and blue; Yellow and red. Cast in lead, crane has 'solid' jib	£25-35
26	1934-35	Bugatti Autorail	Cast in mazak, smooth sides, small windows. May have silvered metal cast wheels or bakelite moulded rollers in red, green or blue. Cream body with blue, yellow, green, red or orange sides	£90-120
	1934-40		As previous model, but with ridged sides and larger windows. Yellow body (with red or green sides); Green (with red sides)	£90-120

Caravans and Campers

See also Gift Sets section.

Ref	Year(s)	Model name	Colours, features, details	Market Price Range
564	1969-71	**Caravelair Armagnac 420**	Blue/white, plated concave hubs, 1:43. Yellow box includes 595a Traffic Sign 'Danger of Falling Rocks'	**£80-90**
565	1965-71	**Renault Estafette Camping Car**	Light blue body, ivory roof, floral curtains, aluminium concave hubs, scale 1:43. Yellow box	**£120-145**
811	1959-59	**Caravan** ('Henon' style)	Cream/White, smooth roof casting, window glazing in most, tinplate drawbar, chromed ridged hubs, 1:43.	**£60-70**
	1960-63		As previous model, but with ribbed body casting	**£50-60**
812	1965-69	**Camping Trailer**	Cream body with luggage, single chromed ridged hub and black tyre, 1:43. Sold only in plastic bag	**£30-40**

Ships

Most of the Dinky Toys model ships sold in France were imported English issues (see the Imports section for details). Those of French design and manufacture are listed below. No boxed sets made entirely in France appear to have been produced, though the Liverpool made castings of the British Naval Warships set were imported into France between 1938 and 1940. They were sold in a French version of the presentation box. The 'Locomotion Moderne' set was intended to contain ship models but was another of those proposals which fell victim to the outbreak of war (see the Gift Sets section for details).

Ref	Year(s)	Model name	Colours, features, details	Market Price Range
52c	1937-40	**Steamship 'Normandie'**	Black/white/red, no rollers, 175mm. Blue box has coloured picture of the ship at sea on the lid, and a picture of the ship and the port of Manhattan on the inner part	**£175-250**
	1940-40		Black/white/red, no rollers, 175mm. Blue box has no inner picture	**£120-170**
52d	1937-40	**Steamship 'Normandie'**	Black/white/red, with metal rollers, 175mm. Blue box has coloured picture of the ship at sea on the lid, and a picture of the ship and the port of Manhattan on the inner part	**£175-250**
	1940-40		Black/white/red, with metal rollers, 175mm. Blue box has no inner picture	**£120-170**
	1947-48		Black/white/red, with metal rollers, 175mm. Blue box has no inner picture	**£120-170**
53a	1937-40	**Battleship 'Dunkerque'**	Battleship grey, with metal rollers, 120mm. Light yellow one-piece illustrated box	**£100-150**
53b	1937-40	**Battleship 'Dunkerque'**	Battleship grey, no rollers, 120mm. Light yellow one-piece illustrated box	**£100-150**
870	1962-71	**Steamship 'France'**	White/black/red, scale 1:1200, 263mm.	**£150-200**

'Dolly Varden' Doll's House Furniture

Models of 'Dolly Varden' Dolls House Furniture were available in France and England. They are very similar in range and appearance but are definitely different castings with a different finish. French boxed sets generally appear to have much bigger boxes than the English equivalent. It is thought that the 'Dolly Varden Dolls House' was never advertised in France and is consequently almost impossible to find there.

Ref	Year(s)	Model name	Colours, features, details	Market Price Range
101	1936	**Dining Room Furniture Set**	See 'Gift Sets' section.	
101a	1936-40	**Dining Table**, Light or Dark mottled brown		**£10-15**
101b	1936-40	**Sideboard**, Light or Dark mottled brown		**£15-20**
101c	1936-40	**Carver**, Light or Dark mottled brown		**£10-15**
101d	1936-40	**Chair**, Light or Dark mottled brown		**£10-15**
102	1936-40	**Bedroom Furniture Set**	See 'Gift Sets' section.	
102a	1936-40	**Bed**, Mottled lilac		**£10-15**
102b	1936-40	**Wardrobe**, Mottled lilac		**£15-20**
102c	1936-40	**Dressing Table**, Mottled lilac, with mirror		**£15-20**
102d	1936-40	**Chest of Drawers**, Mottled lilac		**£15-20**
102e	1936-40	**Stool**, Mottled lilac		**£10-15**
102f	1936-40	**Chair**, Mottled lilac (casting as 101d)		**£10-15**
103	1936-40	**Kitchen Furniture Set**	See 'Gift Sets' section.	
103a	1936-40	**Refrigerator**, Pale green/cream or Blue/ivory		**£15-20**
103b	1936-40	**Sideboard**, Pale green/cream or Blue/ivory		**£15-20**
103c	1936-40	**Cooker**, Pale green/cream or Blue/ivory		**£15-20**
103d	1936-40	**Table**, Pale green/cream or Blue/ivory		**£10-15**
103e	1936-40	**Chair**, Pale green/cream (casting as 101d), or Blue/ivory (casting as 101d)		**£10-15**
104	1937-40	**Bathroom Furniture Set**	See 'Gift Sets' section.	
104a	1937-40	**Bath**, Pink		**£10-15**
104b	1937-40	**Bath Mat**, Pink rubber (prone to deteriorate)		**£10-15**
104c	1937-40	**Hand Basin**, Pink, with mirror		**£15-20**
104d	1937-40	**Stool**, Pink		**£10-15**
104e	1937-40	**Linen Basket**, Pink		**£10-15**
104f	1937-40	**Toilet**, Pink		**£10-15**

Collectors notes

Accessories

Pre-war figures 1 to 10 inclusive were hollow cast in lead and individually hand painted. The colours stated are therefore those observed but any other colours and shades are possible especially with painted detail. The bases are usually brown, beige or grey (some blue ones seen) and are usually marked 'MECCANO DINKY TOYS' though some early ones may be found with 'HORNBY' marked under them. Early boxes were blue-grey (often marked 'Série Hornby'), later ones were red (usually printed 'Dinky Toys' and with various shades and degrees of surface gloss). They vary greatly as far as the printing is concerned. After the War, Meccano-France considered most of the figures to be primarily railway accessories so they reverted to listing them in the 'Hornby Railway Accessories' range. Their boxes generally reflect this thinking after 1948, and between 1950 and 1955 most of models 1 to 10 were issued in plastic as 'Hornby unbreakable figures'.

Ref	Year(s)	Model name	Colours, features, details	Market Price Range

Ref	Year(s)	Model name / Colours, features, details
1	1934-40	**Station Staff Set**......See 'Gift Sets' section
1a	1934-40	**Station Master.** Dark blue coat, grey or grey-green trousers **£30-35**
1b	1934-40	**Porter.** Light blue uniform with red belt, no luggage.....**£30-35**
1c	1934-40	**Railway Guard.** Dark blue coat, grey or grey-green trousers **£30-35**
1d	1934-40	**Policeman.** Dark blue uniform **£30-35**
1e	1934-40	**Controller.** Dk. blue coat, grey or grey-green trousers ..**£30-35**
2	1934-40	**Railway Passengers Set** ......See 'Gift Sets' section
2a	1934-40	**Normandy Farmer.** Various rustic colours **£30-35**
2b	1934-40	**Farmers Wife.** A 'Peasant type Bécassine' with basket and umbrella, red or orange dress (later turquoise) **£30-35**
2c	1934-40	**Young Woman.** Bag under right arm, various colours...**£30-35**
2d	1934-40	**Boy Scout.** Boy in French scout uniform (all khaki or khaki shorts/green shirt)..................**£30-35**
2e	1934-40	**Boy (sitting).** Satchel under right arm, various colours ..**£30-35**
2f	1934-40	**Girl (sitting).** Bag under left arm, various colours **£30-35**
2g	1934-40	**Bench Seat.** Green or brown painted tinplate.................**£30-35**
3	1934-40	**Animals Set**......See 'Gift Sets' section
3a	1934-40	**Pig.** Pink (shades may vary)..................**£20-30**
3b	1934-40	**Sheep.** Cream, white or dark brown (shades may vary)..**£20-30**
3c	1934-40	**Horse.** Grey or reddish-brown 'mottled' finish (painted using a 'run' technique). Various shades known **£20-30**
3d	1934-40	**Bull.** White or reddish-brown 'mottled' finish (painted using a 'run' technique). Various shades known **£20-30**
4	1934-40	**Railway Personnel Set** ......See 'Gift Sets' section
4a	1934-40	**Cook.** White cook's outfit, carrying a (usually gold painted) fowl on a dish..................**£30-35**
4b	1934-40	**Engine Fireman.** Dark blue overalls, coal shovel..........**£30-35**
4c	1934-40	**Greaser.** Dark blue overalls, oilcan..................**£30-35**
4d	1934-40	**Wheel Tapper.** Dark blue overalls, sounding mallet......**£30-35**
4e	1934-40	**Gate Keeper.** Female figure (green shirt, black skirt) with red flag **£30-35**
4f	1934-40	**Porter with Luggage.** Dark blue uniform, carrying case and hat-box (various shades seen)..................**£30-35**
5	1934-40	**Railway Passengers Set** ......See 'Gift Sets' section
5a	1934-40	**Woman and Child.** Green or brown (various shades). Single hollow casting..................**£30-35**
5b	1934-40	**Businessman.** Grey or brown (shades), with briefcase ...**£30-35**
5c	1934-40	**Male Tourist.** Brown (various shades), with walking stick and camera..................**£30-35**
5d	1934-40	**Clergyman.** Black garb, with umbrella (usually red and grey)..................**£30-35**
5e	1934-40	**Newsboy.** Grey or brown (various shades known), papers under left arm..................**£30-35**
5f	1934-40	**Woman with Tennis Racket.** Green, grey or beige (various shades), tennis racket in right hand.................**£30-35**
6	1934-40	**Shepherd Set**......See 'Gift Sets' section
6a	1934-40	**Shepherd.** Light brown (various shades), with crook in right hand and lamb under left arm **£30-35**
6b	1934-40	**Sheepdog.** Black, with or without white detail **£30-35**
10	1934-40	**Assorted Figures Set.** Consists of Sets 1, 2 and 4. Box has two illustrations..................**£250-350**
	1938-40	The same set but in box with no illustration.............**£220-270**
40	1953-59	**Traffic Signs 'Town' Set** ......See 'Gift Sets' section
41	1953-59	**Traffic Signs 'Route' Set** ......See 'Gift Sets' section
49	1935-40	**Set of Fuel Pumps** ......See 'Gift Sets' section
49	1949-50	**Set of Fuel Pumps** ......See 'Gift Sets' section
49a	1935-40	**Pillar type Fuel Pump.** Blue, green, yellow, red, cream, gold or white. White rubber hose, wire crank handle, scale 1:43, 60mm. **£75-100**
	1948-53	Reissue of pre-war version (sold without the hose between 1948-50) **£30-35**

Ref	Year(s)	Model name / Colours, features, details
49b	1935-40	**'SHELL' Mobile Oil Pump.** Blue, green, yellow, red, cream, gold or white. White rubber hose, 1:43, 47mm.....**£75-100**
	1948-50	Reissue of pre-war version (but sold without hose)........**£30-35**
49c	1935-40	**Double Output Fuel Pump.** Blue, green, yellow, red, cream, gold or white. Two white rubber hoses, scale 1:43, 55mm. high **£75-100**
	1948-52	Reissue of pre-war version (without hoses 1948-50)......**£30-35**
49D	1954-59	**Pump Island, 'ESSO'.** Two pumps (red/white and blue/white), 'ESSO' sign. Yellow box. Renumbered in 1959 as 592..................**£65-75**
502	1959-66	**Garage.** Yellow/grey, sky-blue/grey or all light grey, plastic, with parking numbers '0' to '9'. Yellow box **£90-110**
590	1959-68	**Traffic Signs 'Town' Set** ......See 'Gift Sets' section
591	1959-68	**Traffic Signs 'Route' Set** ......See 'Gift Sets' section
592	1959-63	**Pump Island, 'ESSO'.** (49-D) Two pumps (red/white and blue/white), 'ESSO' sign, 1:43. 'DINKY TOYS 592-49D' on box..................**£65-75**
592	1969-71	**Traffic Signs 'Town' Set** ......See 'Gift Sets' section
593	1969-71	**Traffic Signs 'Route' Set** ......See 'Gift Sets' section
594	1969-71	**Traffic Lights (3-colour).** Battery operated grey/black plastic traffic lights, 1:43. Yellow box..................**£65-75**

TRAFFIC SIGNS. Since the messages given on road signs are often more graphical than textual, the list that follows contains literal interpretations that reflect the general meaning of the signs rather than attempting accurate translations. **Traffic Signs** 595a to 595w were not available for purchase, they were included free in the box of the model mentioned. Scale 1:43.

Ref	Year(s)	Model name / Colours, features, details
595a	1969-72	**'Danger of Falling Rocks',** (with model 564 Caravan) .....NPP
595b	1969-72	**'Maximum Weight 5.5 tonnes',** (823 GMC Tanker)........NPP
595c	1969-72	**'Dangerous Bend to Right',** (with 1417 Matra F1) ....NPP
595d	1969-72	**'No Overtaking for Heavy Vehicles',** (572 Berliet Truck).NPP
595e	1969-72	**'Road Narrows',** (with model 1422 Ferrari F1) ....NPP
595f	1969-72	**'Speed Limit',** (with model 1421 Opel GT) ....NPP
595g	1969-72	**'Caution - Animals Crossing',** (1419 Ford Thunderbird)..NPP
595h	1969-72	**'Danger - End of Quay',** (with 1424 Renault R12) ....NPP
595i	1969-72	**'Two-Way Traffic',** (with model 1423 Peugeot 504) ....NPP
595k	1969-72	**'Road Narrows from Left',** (model 1425 Matra 630).......NPP
595L	1969-72	**'Maximum Width 2 metres',** (882 Peugeot 'Pinder')......NPP
595m	1970-72	**'Danger - Loose Chippings',** (with 1426 Alfa-Romeo)....NPP
595n	1970-72	**'Cycling Prohibited',** (with 1429 Peugeot 'Police')........NPP
595o	1970-72	**'Customs',** (with model 1420 Opel Commodore) ....NPP
595p	1970-72	**'Humpback Bridge',** (with model 1428 Peugeot 304) ....NPP
595q	1970-72	**'Automatic Level Crossing',** (with 809 GMC Truck) ....NPP
595r	1970-72	**'Road Works',** (with model 518 Renault 'Autoroutes').....NPP
595s	1970-72	**'Pedestrians Crossing',** (570 Peugeot 'Autoroutes') ....NPP
595t	1970-72	**'Max. Height 3.5 metres',** (589 Berliet 'Autoroutes') ......NPP
595u	1970-72	**'Dangerous Bends',** (with model 1430 Abarth) ....NPP
595v	1970-72	**'All Vehicles Prohibited',** (with 1432 Ferrari 312P) ....NPP
595w	1970-72	**'Danger - Cyclists',** (with model 1409 Chrysler 180).......NPP
833	1962-	**Transformer.** Grey plastic 'ALSTHOM' transformer (as supplied with 898), scale 1:55. In yellow box........**£20-30**
834	1963-70	**Mobile Bridge Pack.** Khaki plastic six part bridge plus inflatable boats (as with 884) ....NGPP
835	1959-71	**Tyre Pack.** Twelve large black treaded tyres for racing cars and commercial vehicles (smooth till 1961). Was 6676 ..NGPP
836	1959-71	**Tyre Pack.** Twelve white treaded tyres (smooth till 1960). Previously 6677 ....NGPP
837	1959-71	**Tyre Pack.** Twelve black smooth tyres (small). Previously 7067 ....NGPP
837	1961-71	**Tyre Pack.** Twelve black treaded tyres (small) ....NGPP
837	1965-71	**Tyre Pack.** 12 black nylon tyres (small). .... French versions often marked 'DUNLOP', Spanish usually 'PIRELLI' ...NGPP
838	1961-71	**Tyre Pack.** Twelve white treaded tyres (small). Was 7068. 'DUNLOP' or 'PIRELLI' markings not seen ....NGPP

839	1959-63	**Tyre Pack**. Twelve tyres, round or square section (treaded version of 11190). Sold in paper (later, plastic) packet ...NGPP
839	1971-71	**Rally Pack**. Two sheets of rally transfers, scales 1:32 and 1:24 ....NGPP
840	1959-70	**Elastic Cord Pack**. Pack of 6 (later 10) elastic cords for 32D and 899 Delahaye Fire Escape. Was 11146......NGPP
841	1959-71	**Tank Tracks Pack**. Twelve black rubber tracks for AMX tanks. Was 11924......................NGPP
842	1959-64	**Tyre Pack**. Twelve tyres for 24-L Vespa. Was 12110 ......NGPP
843	1962-71	**Military Tyre Pack**. Twelve treaded black tyres (large square section for 818 and similar)....................NGPP
844	1959-70	**Pipe-Line Pack**. Six black tubes (as with 893 Sahara Pipe Transporter) ....NGPP
845	1959-70	**Barrier Pack**. Ten grey plastic barriers (Vauban-Samia), scale 1:43 ....NGPP
846	1959-70	**Oil Drum Pack**. Ten grey plastic oil drums ....NGPP
847	1959-70	**Barrel Pack**. Ten brown plastic barrels ....NGPP
848	1959-70	**Trunk Pack**. Ten brown plastic travelling trunks with hinged lids ....NGPP
849	1959-70	**Packing Case Pack**. Ten ivory plastic packing cases with lifting lids ....NGPP
850	1959-70	**Bottle Crate Pack**. Ten white or cream plastic crates with transparent or orange bottles ....NGPP
851	1959-70	**Assortment Pack**. Contains ten items - two each of 846 (barrels), 847 (barrels), 848 (trunks), 849 (packing cases) and 850 (bottle crates)....................NGPP
852	1962-71	**Half-Track Tracks Pack**. Ten replacement tracks for 822 White M3 Half-Track, (black rubber).....................NGPP
853	1962-64	**Tyre Pack**. Twelve extra large black tyres for use on 803 Unic and 888 Berliet ....NGPP
854	1962-68	**Milk Crates Pack**. Ten grey plastic milk crates with white bottles, as with 586 Citroën P55 Milk Lorry ....NGPP
855	1962-65	**Tyre Pack**. Twelve small black rubber treaded tyres for use on Renault R4, etc.....................................NGPP
855	1965-70	**Tyre Pack**. As previous, but made of black nylon ....NGPP
856	1963-71	**Machine Gun**. Black plastic (822 White Half-Track) .....NGPP

857	1970-71	**Racing Tyre Pack**. Two small tyres for use on the front wheels of Formula 1 racing cars ....NGPP
858	1970-71	**Racing Tyre Pack**. Two larger tyres for F1 rear wheels..NGPP
859	1970-70	**Tyre Pack**. Four tyres for use on 1419 Ford ....NGPP
860	1963-?	**Battery**. 1.5 volt battery for use with 276L ....NGPP
861	1964-?	**Lamp Bulb**. 1.5 volt bulb for use with 887 BP Tanker....NGPP
862	1965-?	**Lamp Bulb**. 1.5 volt bulb for use with 566 Citroën ......NGPP
863	1964-?	**Battery**. Mazda battery for use with 887 then 952L........NGPP
864	1968-?	**Lamp Bulb**. Bulb for use with 276L, 160L and 952L......NGPP
6676	1950-59	**Tyre Pack**. Twelve large black smooth or treaded tyres (racing cars, articulated commercials). With letter 'M' on sidewall till 1958. (Renumbered in 1959 as 835).......NGPP
6677	1950-59	**Tyre Pack**. Twelve large white treaded tyres (some smooth). 'M' on sidewall till 1958, renumbered 836 in 1959.........NGPP
7067	1950-59	**Tyre Pack**. Twelve smooth black tyres (small) for touring cars 25-BV, 25-CG, 25-D, 29-D and 80-BP. 'M' on sidewall till 1958, renumbered 837 in 1959...........NGPP
7068	1953-59	**Tyre Pack**. Twelve smooth white tyres (small). letter 'M' on sidewall till 1958. (Renumbered in 1959 as 837).......NGPP
11146	1958-59	**Elastic Cord Pack**. Six elastic cords for 32-D and 899 Delahaye Fire Escape. (Renumbered in 1959 as 840) .....NGPP
11190	1953-59	**Tyre Pack**. Twelve large black ribbed tyres originally for racing cars. Design was changed in 1958 to make them suitable for use with military vehicles. Paper packets marked either 'Racing Tyres' or 'Cross Country Tyres'. (Renumbered in 1959 as 839) ....NGPP
11924	1958-59	**Tank Tracks Pack**. Twelve black rubber tracks for AMX Tanks. Renumbered 841 in 1959............................NGPP
12110	1959-59	**Tyre Pack**. Twelve tyres for 24-L Vespa. Renumbered 842 in 1959 ....NGPP
---	1935-40	**Milk Churn (large)**. 2 fixing holes in base, scale 1:43 ...NGPP
---	1948-50	**Milk Churn**. Smaller churn, scale 1:43, as supplied with 25-O Studebaker and Ford 'NESTLE' Trucks ....NGPP
---	1969-?	**Driving Test Circuit**. Printed road layout with town and country elements, 1:43, boxed...NGPP

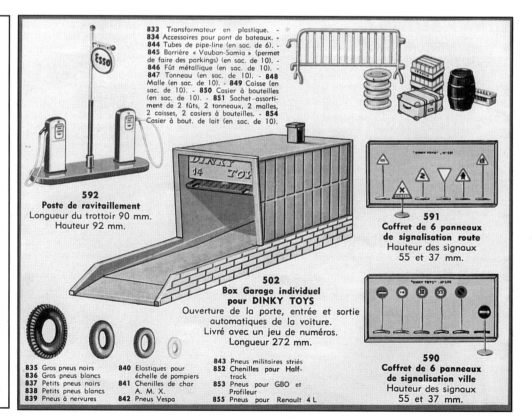

French Dinky Toys Accessories shown in the 1962 Catalogue

Photograph: Swapmeet Publications

833 Transformateur en plastique. -
834 Accessoires pour pont de bateaux. -
844 Tubes de pipe-line (en sac. de 6). -
845 Barrière « Vauban-Samia » (permet de faire des parkings) (en sac. de 10). -
846 Fût métallique (en sac. de 10). -
847 Tonneau (en sac. de 10). - 848 Malle (en sac. de 10). - 849 Caisse (en sac. de 10). - 850 Casier à bouteilles (en sac. de 10). - 851 Sachet-assortiment de 2 fûts, 2 tonneaux, 2 malles, 2 caisses, 2 casiers à bouteilles. - 854 Casier à bout. de lait (en sac. de 10).

592 Poste de ravitaillement
Longueur du trottoir 90 mm.
Hauteur 92 mm.

591 Coffret de 6 panneaux de signalisation route
Hauteur des signaux 55 et 37 mm.

502 Box Garage individuel pour DINKY TOYS
Ouverture de la porte, entrée et sortie automatiques de la voiture.
Livré avec un jeu de numéros.
Longueur 272 mm.

590 Coffret de 6 panneaux de signalisation ville
Hauteur des signaux 55 et 37 mm.

835 Gros pneus noirs
836 Gros pneus blancs
837 Petits pneus noirs
838 Petits pneus blancs
839 Pneus à nervures
840 Elastiques pour échelle de pompiers
841 Chenilles pour char A.M.X.
842 Pneus Vespa
843 Pneus militaires striés
852 Chenilles pour Half-track
853 Pneus pour GBO et Profileur
855 Pneus pour Renault 4 L

Gift Sets

Ref	Year(s)	Model name	Contents, details	Market Price Range
1	1934-40	**Station Staff Set**	Six figures: 1 x 1a Station Master, 2 x 1b Porter (no luggage), 1 x 1c Guard, 1 x 1d Policeman, 1 x 1e Inspector. Two pictures on lid of card box	**£250-300**
1	1938-40	**Station Staff Set**	Same set but in box with no illustration	**£225-275**
2	1934-40	**Railway Passengers Set**	Contains a tinplate bench (2g) and six figures: 2a Normandy Farmer, 2b Farmer's Wife, 2c Young Girl, 2d Boy Scout (with stick), 2e Boy (sitting), 2f Girl (sitting). Red box has illustrations, yellow inner	**£225-275**
	1938-40		Same set but in red box (yellow inner) with no illustration	**£200-250**
3	1934-40	**Animals Set**	Contains six animals: 3a Pig, 3b Sheep (dark brown), 3c Horse (grey), 3c Horse (brown), 3d Bull (mottled White), 3d Bull (mottled reddish-brown). Box has two pictures on lid	**£300-350**
	1938-40		Same set but in box with no illustrations	**£250-300**
4	1934-40	**Railway Personnel Set**	Six figures: 4a Cook (with fowl), 4b Engine Fireman, 4c Greaser (with oilcan), 4d Wheel Tapper (with mallet), 4e Female Gate-Keeper (with flag), 4f Porter (with luggage). Box has two illustrations	**£225-275**
	1938-40		The same set but in box without illustration	**£175-225**
5	1934-40	**Railway Passengers Set**	Contains six figures: 5a Woman and Child, 5b Businessman, 5c Male Tourist (with camera), 5d Clergyman, 5e Newsboy, 5f Female Tennis Player. Two different pictures on box	**£225-275**
	1938-40		Same set but in box without illustration	**£175-225**
6	1934-40	**Shepherd Set**	6a Shepherd (light brown), 6b Sheepdog (black), 4 x 3b Sheep (white or cream). Box has two illustrations	**£400-500**
	1938-40		Same set but box has no illustration	**£300-400**
10	1934-40	**Assorted Figures Set**	Consists of Sets 1, 2 and 4. Box has two illustrations	**£250-350**
	1938-40		The same set but in box with no illustration	**£220-270**
17	1935-38	**Electric Goods Train**	19a Electric Locomotive, 21b Timber Wagon, 21c Coal Wagon, 21d Crane Wagon. Diorama box	**£250-300**
	1938-40		As previous model, but box has no diorama	**£175-225**
18	1934-38	**Steam Goods Train**	21a Steam Tank Locomotive, 3 x 21c Coal Wagon, Diorama box	**£250-300**
	1938-40		As previous model, but box has no diorama	**£175-225**
19	1935-38	**Electric Passenger Train**	19a Electric Locomotive, 3 x 20a Coach. Diorama box	**£250-300**
20	1935-38	**Steam Passenger Train**	21a Steam Tank Locomotive, 3 x 20a Coach. Diorama box	**£250-300**
	1938-40		As previous model, but box has no diorama	**£175-225**
21	1934-38	**Steam Mixed Goods Train**	21a Tank Locomotive, 21b Timber Wagon, 21c Coal Wagon, 21d Crane Wagon. Diorama box	**£350-450**
	1938-40		As previous model, but box has no diorama	**£225-275**
24	1935-36	**Passenger Cars Set**	6 cars: 24b Limousine, 24d Vogue Saloon, 24e Aerodynamic Saloon, 24f Sportsman's Coupé, 24g 4-seat Sports Car, 24h 2-seat Sports Car. Yellow box without illustration	**£4,000-6,000**
	note:		The basic box for this set was adapted to contain the 25 series Commercial Vehicles Set.	
	1936-39		6 cars: 24b Limousine, 24d Vogue Saloon, 24e Aerodynamic Saloon, 24f Sportsman's Coupé, 24g 4-seat Sports Car, 24h 2-seat Sports Car. Purple box with picture (two different designs exist)	**£3,500-4,500**
	1940-48		The same set, but in Blue box without illustration	**£2,500-3,500**
24-55	1955-55	**Touring Cars Gift Set**	5 cars: 24-R Peugeot 203, 24-T Citroën 2cv, 24-U Simca Aronde 9, 24-V Buick Roadmaster, 24-X Ford Vedette	**£1,250-1,750**
24-56	1956-56	**Touring Cars Gift Set**	5 cars: 24-R Peugeot 203, 24-T Citroën 2cv, 24-U Simca Aronde Elysée, 24-Y Studebaker Commander, 24-Z Simca Vedette Versailles	**£1.500-2,000**
24-57	1957-57	**Touring Cars Gift Set**	5 cars: 24-A Chrysler New Yorker, 24-B Peugeot 403 8cv, 24-E Renault Dauphine, 24-Y Studebaker Commander, 24-Z Simca Vedette Versailles	**£1,250-1,750**
24-58	1958-58	**Touring Cars Gift Set**	5 cars: 24-B Peugeot 403 8cv, 24-C (or 24-CP) Citroën DS19, 24-D Plymouth Belvedere, 24-E Renault Dauphine, 24-Z Simca Vedette Versailles. Red/yellow/green/black box	**£1,250-1,750**
	note:		The annual '24 series' of Gift Sets was renumbered in 1959 ; the next issue in the series is 500.	
25	1935-37	**Commercial Vehicles Gift Set**	6 lorries: 25a Open Lorry, 25b Covered Lorry, 25c Flat Lorry, 25d Tanker Lorry, 25e Tipping Lorry, 25f Market Gardeners Lorry. Purple and gold box	**£1,800-2,200**
	note:		The basic box for this set was adapted from that used for the 24 series Passenger Cars Set.	
	1938-39		The same set, but in a long Blue box.	**£1,500-2,000**
	1940-48		Same set, but all wheels are solid metal. Long blue box with printed ends (yellow base, blue inner)	**£1,500-2,000**
25S	1948-48	**Commercial Vehicles Gift Set**	The same set, with all models having solid metal wheels, and in a Light blue box.	**£2,500-3,500**
25N	1949-49	**Commercial Vehicles Gift Set**	6 lorries: 25-H Ford Beverage Truck, 25-I Ford Open Wagon, 25-J Ford Covered Wagon, 25-K Studebaker Market Gardeners Truck, 25-L Studebaker Covered Delivery Truck, 25-M Studebaker Tipping Truck. Blue or yellow box.	**£3,500-5,000**
	1950-50		The same set, but in a Red box.	**£3,500-5,000**
40	1953-59	**Traffic Signs 'Town' Set** (Renumbered in 1959 as 590)	Six diecast signs: 'No Entry', 'No Waiting', '30km/hr', 'No Overtaking', 'Maximum Weight 5.5 tonnes', 'Right (or Left) Turn'. Scale 1:43, each 55mm. high, yellow box with 'Code de la Route' leaflet	**£65-75**
41	1953-59	**Traffic Signs 'Route' Set** (Renumbered in 1959 as 591)	Six diecast signs: 'Danger - Crossroads', 'Priority' marker, 'Dangerous Bends', 'Caution - School', 'Level Crossing with Gates'. Small signs 37mm. high; large signs 52mm., scale 1:43,. Yellow box, leaflet	**£65-75**
49	1935-40	**Set of Fuel Pumps**	Five pumps: 2 x 49a Pillar type Fuel Pump, 1 x 49b Mobile Oil Pump, 2 x 49c Double Output Pump. Blue box, later yellow	**£200-250**
49	1949-50	**Set of Fuel Pumps**	Identical to pre-war version and in yellow box	**£150-200**
50	1938-40	**British Naval Warships Set**	14 English-made models in French printed box: 50a 'Hood', 50b 'Nelson', 50b 'Rodney', 50c 'Effingham', 50d 'York', 50e 'Delhi', 3 x 50f 'Broke', 50g 'X' class Submarine, 3 x 50h 'Amazon', 50k 'K' class Submarine	**£200-300**
60	1935-37	**Aircraft Presentation Set**	6 models: 60a DeWoitine D338 Rainbow, 60b Potez 58, 60c Henriot H180T, 60d Breguet Corsaire, 60e DeWoitine 500 Hunter, 60f Cierva Autogiro. Purple and gold box (models are set out in a straight formation along the length of the box). Picture on lid	**£1,000-1,500**
	1937-39		The same 6 models but set out in a diagonal formation within a bright blue box. Picture on box lid	**£1,000-1,500**
	1939-40		The same 6 models but set out in a diagonal formation within a Dark Green box. Picture on box lid	**£1,000-1,500**
	1957-59	(Renumbered in 1959 as 501)	4 models: 60-A Dassault Mystere IVa, 60-B Sud Aviation Vautour, 60-D Sikorsky S58, 60-E Vickers Viscount. Supertoys box, picture on lid	**£300-400**

61	1938-39	**Aircraft Presentation Set**	5 models: 61a DeWoitine D338, 61b Potez 56, 61d Potez 58, 61e Henriot H180M, 61f DeWoitine 500 Hunter. Blue box	**£750-1,250**
	1939-46		6 models: 61a DeWoitine D338, 61b Potez 56, 61c Farman F360, 61d Potez 58, 61e Henriot H180M, 61f DeWoitine 500. Green box	**£750-1,250**
64	1939-48	**Aircraft Presentation Set**	Five models: 61a DeWoitine D338, 64a Amiot 370, 64b Bloch 220, 64c Potez 63, 64d Potez 662. Green box with illustration	**£750-1,250**
70	1939?	**Modern Travel Set** ('Locomotion Moderne')	Five different forms of travel represented by: 23b Racing Car, 26 Railcar, 52c Steamship 'Normandie', 53a Steamship 'Dunkerque', 60a DeWoitine Rainbow. Advertised in 1939(?) catalogue but no production known	**NPP**
101	1936	**Dining Room Furniture Set**	101a Table, 101b Sideboard, 2 x 101c Carver, 4 x 101d Dining Chair. Light or dark mottled brown	**£300-350**
102	1936-40	**Bedroom Furniture Set**	102a Bed, 102b Wardrobe, 102c Dressing Table, 102d Chest of Drawers, 102e Stool, 102f Chair. Lilac	**£300-350**
103	1936-40	**Kitchen Furniture Set**	103a Refrigerator, 103b Sideboard, 103c Cooker, 103d Table, 103e Chair. Pale Green/Cream or Blue/Ivory	**£300-350**
104	1937-40	**Bathroom Furniture Set**	104a Bath, 104b Bath Mat, 104c Hand Basin, 104d Stool, 104e Linen Basket, 104f Toilet. Pink veined	**£300-350**
500	1959-59	**Touring Cars Gift Set**	5 models: 521 Peugeot 403 8cv, 522 Citroën DS19, 523 Plymouth Belvedere, 524 Renault Dauphine, 541 Simca Vedette Versailles	**£2,000-3,000**
501	1959-62	**Aircraft Presentation Set** (Renumbered from 60)	4 models: 800 Dassault Mystere IVa, 801 Sud Aviation Vautour, 802 Sikorsky S58, 803 Vickers Viscount	**£250-350**
503	1963-64	**Touring Cars Gift Set**	5 models: 521 Peugeot 403 8cv, 522 Citroën DS19, 543 Renault Floride, 544 Simca Aronde P60, 545 DeSoto Diplomat. Blue/yellow/grey box	**£2,000-3,000**
536	1965	**Peugeot 404 and Trailer**	Red car, black skis on yellow rack or yellow skis on black rack, cream plastic trailer (no. 812), luggage	**£130-150**
590	1959-68	**Traffic Signs 'Town' Set**	(Was 40). Six diecast signs (1:43, 55mm. high): 'No Entry', 'No Parking', 'Maximum Weight 5.5 tonnes', 'Right (or Left) Turn', '30km/hr', 'No Overtaking'. Yellow box with 'Code de la Route' leaflet	**£70-80**
591	1959-68	**Traffic Signs 'Route' Set**	(Was 41). Six diecast signs: 'Danger - Crossroads', 'Priority' marker, 'Dangerous Bends', 'Caution - School', 'Level Crossing with Gates'. Small signs 37mm. high, large signs 52mm. Scale 1:43. Yellow box, leaflet	**£70-80**
592	1969-71	**Traffic Signs 'Town' Set**	Twelve plastic signs on diecast bases: 'Caution - Gyratory System', 'No Entry', 'Parking', 'No Parking', 'Caution - School', 'No U-Turn', 'Taxis', '45km/hr', 'No Overtaking', 'Do Not Use Horn', 'Blue Zone', 'No Left Turn'. Scale 1:43. In 'window' box	**£65-75**
593	1969-71	**Traffic Signs 'Route' Set**	Twelve plastic signs on diecast bases: 'Autoroute', 'End of Autoroute', 'Autoroute Toll Point', 'End of Speed Limit', 'Crossroads - Give Way', 'Dangerous Crossing', 'Priority' marker, 'Stop', 'Dangerous Bend', 'Caution', 'Gradient 10%', 'Low Flying Aircraft'. 1:43. In 'window' box	**£65-75**
1460	1969-70	**Touring Cars Gift Set**	6 models: 501 Citroën DS19 'POLICE' Car, 507 Simca 1500GLS Estate, 508 Daf 33, 509 Fiat 850, 513 Opel Admiral, 514 Alfa-Romeo 1600. Blue/yellow box	**£2,000-3,000**
1462	1969-69	**'Three Days' Gift Set**	4 models: 507 Simca 1500GLS Estate, 508 Daf 33, 509 Fiat 850, 514 Alfa-Romeo 1600. Sold in a special 'Sac-cadeau'(plastic Gift-Bag)	**£500-750**
		note:	'Galeries Lafayette' is a Paris department store with branches in several French towns. Annually '3J' sales are held in these shops. Selection 1462 was specially made for the 1969 'Trois Jours' ('Three Days') sale.	

French Dinky Toys

No.25 Commercial Vehicles Set

Photograph: Collectoys

Note that some post-war catalogues have '57B.16273' or '60B.3844' printed at the bottom of the back cover or in some inconspicuous corner. These are not catalogue reference numbers but a form of 'registered design' for publicity material. As they have no other meaning to collectors they are therefore not shown in the following list. French Dinky Toys are also mentioned in catalogues from other countries, notably Spain and Holland. We are in need of details of Meccano advertising in other countries and would welcome any help our readers could provide.

Ref	Year(s)	Publication	Contents, features, details	Market Price Range
---	1949	**Catalogue**	No details at present	£40-50
---	1949	**Catalogue**	No details at present	£40-50
---	1950	**Catalogue** (12 page booklet)	Blue on white cover shows 'Dinky Toys Miniatures' issuing from Meccano factory through arched gateway. 'Meccano 78-80 Rue Rébéval Paris (XIX)' on back cover. No price list	£40-50
---	1951	**Catalogue**	No details at present	£40-50
175-5-52	1952	**Catalogue** pages (10 page booklet)	Glossy pages fold out to twice the size of the cover. Cream cover with green and red printing. Black and white photographic illustrations, no prices, 'Imp. HENON PARIS' on last page	£40-50
---	1953	**Catalogue** (20 page booklet)	Pale grey stylized car of the period and trees on cover overprinted with 'Miniatures Dinky Toys' and 'C'est une fabrication Meccano' in red. Black and white inside illustrations; no price list	£35-45
---	1954	**Catalogue** (20 pages)	Cover simulates a Supertoys box with the famous blue/white stripes and shows Buick Roadmaster, Esso Tanker and Citroën 'H' van. Pictures inside are in black and white. No prices	£35-45
---	1954	**Leaflet**	Various, advertising new issues	£5-10
---	1955	**Catalogue** (16 page booklet)	No price list. Blue/white stripes on cover, plus Marrel truck and 32-D Delahaye fire appliance	£30-40
---	1956	**Catalogue** (April, 16 pages)	Colour printing inside, no prices. 'Supertoys look' covers with Berliet Container Truck, Autocar Chausson and Citroën car on front with Willème Log Lorry and rear view of 32-D on back cover	£30-40
---	1956	**Catalogue** (September, 20 pages)	Similar to April catalogue but cover has Log Lorry, Citroën car and Dassault plane. No price list	£30-40
---	1957	**Summer Catalogue** (16 pages)	Driverless vehicles emerging from tunnel on front cover. Printed in France	£30-40
---	1958	**Summer Catalogue** (16 pages)	Maserati and Merceds on front cover. Two to five models per page (drawn). Printed in France	£30-40
DL 1958/3	1958	**Meccano Catalogue** (32 pages)	The colourful cover shows a boy's face, an electric train at speed on a blue/gold Meccano track and three Dinky Toys. 8 pages of Dinky Toys. September price list enclosed. Printed in England	£30-40
---	1959	**Catalogue** (20 pages)	Colour booklet like 1958 issue. Cover shows Simca and lorry at an Esso station. No price list	£30-40
---	1960	**Catalogue** (24 page booklet)	Full colour with Renault Floride and Panhard on the front cover. Printed at Mulhouse in France	£25-30
---	1961	**Catalogue** (20 pages)	Full colour booklet printed in Belgium. Pictures of real vehicles plus parts of a road map of France with various Dinky Toys on it. No price list	£25-30
---	1962	**Catalogue**	Includes mention of Hornby boats and Hornby Acho trains	£25-30
---	1962	**Catalogue** (24 pages)	Cover shows Renault R4 parked on quayside next to Steamship 'France'. Printed in Belgium	£25-30
---	1963	**Catalogue** (32 pages)	'First half' catalogue. Cover shows Dinky Mercedes against photo of the actual car. February price list (on very pale green pages) stapled in. Printed in England	£25-30
---	1963	**Catalogue** (32 pages)	'Second half' catalogue (cover as 'first half'). Includes price list dated 'Juillet 1963' in centre	£25-30
---	1964	**Catalogue** (16 pages)	Full colour pages with April price list (on orange paper) stapled in. Five new models pictured and described on the cover which also has photo of car showroom interior. Printed in England	£20-25
---	1964	**Catalogue** (16 pages)	Booklet with October price list	£20-25
---	1965	**Catalogue** (20 pages)	Full colour 'first half' catalogue. Front cover shows 128L Mercedes and 537 Renault. April price list (1965/1, orange paper) stapled in. Printed in England	£20-25
---	1965	**Catalogue** (Winter 1965-66)	28 pages; includes October price list 1965/2 on red paper. Cover depicts 889 Autobuses and 510 Peugeot. The only photo within is of an actual AMX Bridge-Layer in action. Printed in England	£20-25
---	1966	**Catalogue**	'First half' catalogue	£20-25
---	1966	**'Second half' Catalogue**	(122 pages). Simca and Opel on the cover. September price list on blue paper. Printed in England	£20-25
---	1967	**'First half' Catalogue**		£20-25
---	1967	**Catalogue** (128 pages)	Porsche Carrera on cover. September price list (on pink paper) fixed in at rear. Lady Penelope's 'FAB 1' shown as newly introduced. Printed in England. '2e édition' printed inside back cover	£20-25
---	1968	**'First half' Catalogue** (130 pages)	With February price list	£20-25
---	1968	**'Second half' Catalogue**	(122 pages). Simca and fast-cornering Opel on the cover. Printed in England	£15-20
---	1969	**'First half' Catalogue** (24 pages)	Front cover shows hard-braking Ford Thunderbird avoiding errant daschund, yellow Opel GT in foreground. Rear cover advertises 'free' Traffic Signs. Printed in England	£15-20
---	1969	**'Second half' Catalogue**		£15-20
91.761	1970	**Catalogue** (24 pages)	'1970.1' printed on cover which also shows a Porsche and a Ferrari 312P racing round a banking which has 'La Marque du Connaisseur' on it in yellow. Printed in England	£15-20
91.762	1970	**Catalogue**	As previous catalogue but with '1970.2' on front cover. Printed in England	£15-20
91.786	1971	**Catalogue** (24 pages)	Cover depicts a Citroën Présidentielle and a Renault R12. Printed in England	£15-20
91.780	1971	**Meccano Tri-ang leaflet**	(full colour). Nearly A4 size; one side depicts 1971 Dinky Toys. 'Gyro-Jets' and 'Spirofoil' on reverse	£4-6
---	1976	**Meccano Catalogue** (108 pages)	Only 10 pages of Dinky Toys (English and French). Brown cover	£20-25

MAGAZINES

---	1924-38	**Meccano Magazine**	Published monthly from 1924 to 1938, large format	£4-6
---	1953-57	**Meccano Magazine**	Published monthly from October 1953 to October 1957, small format	£4-6
---	1957-59	**Meccano Magazine**	Published monthly from November 1957 to September 1959, large format	£4-6
---	1959-60	**'Actualités Meccano' Journal**	Published between October 1959 to October 1960 (5 issues), each	£4-6

Promotional Material

1957- **Membership Certificate**. 'Parchment' style 'CLUB DINKY TOYS' certificate **£35-45**

1960- **Membership Certificate**. As above, but amended **£35-45**

1960- **Subscription Reminder**. Reminder form .... NPP

1961- **Subscription Reminder**. As above, but updated .... NPP

1957- **Membership Document**. Printed details of Club membership .... NPP

1954- **Dinky Toys Driver's Licence** **£30-35**

1957- **Button Insignia**. A round metal badge, 'CLUB DINKY TOYS', screw fitting through button-hole **£30-35**

1957- **Brooch Insignia**. As above, but with 'safety pin' lapel fitting **£30-35**

1957- **Key Ring**. Round metal badge within stitched 'leather' surround **£30-35**

1957- **Key Ring**. Round metal badge encapsulated in clear plastic **£30-35**

Display Case. A small display case (no other details) **£100-150**

1961- **ESGE Display Case**. A larger display case (cream/yellow/red) with 5 shelves, 'DINKY-TOYS MECCANO' on glazing **£350-400**

Illuminated Display Case. Large display case with 6 shelves and electric lighting **£350-400**

Illuminated Curved Case. Large curved display case with 6 shelves and electric lighting **£350-400**

Counter Sign. Diecast triangular block painted red/cream, 'DINKY TOYS' **£45-55**

English Dinky Toys imported into France

The models in the following list were those manufactured in Liverpool and sent to France for sale over different periods of time. In the main they were complete English made models but some were supplied in component form for assembly in the French factory.

It is understood that the boxes were either made in England and printed "Fabriqué en Angleterre" and "Imprimé en Angleterre", or were made in France and printed "Fabriqué en Angleterre" and "Imprimé en France". In some cases the model and the box were sold just as they came from Binns Road with no modification or overprinting of any kind. It is therefore important when seeking variations to make sure whether the model was only imported fully built, imported as plain castings for assembly in France, or both (at different times). They were also on occasions supplied complete except for the baseplate which was fitted in France. The degree of painting often varied, some items being supplied fully finished while others were still "raw" from the dies.

Some models were supplied with English tyres, some without, so that French tyres could be fitted. Body colours were much the same as the UK versions though could be different shades, unique colours or a different range of colours. The 60h Singapore Flying Boat was for instance painted in a camouflage finish for the French market, and 108L Sam's Car was only available in silver or blue in France. Some renumbering also took place when models previously assembled in France (imported only as components) were later imported ready made. A couple of examples of this practice are 150/551 and 885/961. Virtually every post-war import from England carries the suffix 'L' after its reference number to indicate its Liverpool origin.

Note also that from time to time various factory items were exchanged between Liverpool and Bobigny (this included components and complete or partial dies and tools). This was done either to make up an end of run deficiency, to replace worn or broken dies, to experiment with prototypes or simply to evaluate a new idea. Consequently there may well be oddities still to be found which do not conform to the known output. If you have knowledge of any item or variation not listed, do please communicate it to the Editor so that we may share the information with others in the collecting fraternity. Thank you.

The prices you should expect to see asked for these essentially English productions are likely to be much the same as for the same items sold in British shops.

French ref.no.	Years imported	Model
14-C	1950-51	Coventry Climax Fork Lift Truck
23c	1938-39	Mercedes Racing Car
23d	1938-39	Auto-Union Record Car
23e	1938-39	'Speed of the Wind'
23m	1938-39	'Thunderbolt'
25h	1938-39	Streamlined Fire Engine
27-AC	1950-50	Tractor and Manure Spreader
29b	1939-39	Streamlined Bus
30a	1935-39	Chrysler Airflow
30b	1935-37	Rolls-Royce
30g	1938-39	Camping Trailer
50	1937-38	Battleship Gift Set
51b	1937-39	Norddeutscher-Lloyd 'Europa'
51c	1937-39	Italia Line 'Rex'
51d	1937-39	'Empress of Britain'
52a	1936-39	'Queen Mary'
60h	1938-38	Singapore Flying Boat (camouflaged)
60m	1938-38	Singapore Flying Boat (civilian)
60r	1938-39	'Empire' Flying Boat
60w	1938-39	'Clipper III' Flying Boat
62k	1938-39	'King's Aeroplane'
62n	1939-39	Junkers 'Ju90'
62p	1939-39	'Ensign' Air Liner
63	1939-39	Mayo Composite
100L	1968-71	Lady Penelope's 'FAB 1'
101L	1968-69	Thunderbirds II / IV
104L	1969-71	Spectrum Pursuit
106L	1969-70	'The Prisoner' Moke
108L	1970-71	Sam's Car
110L	1965-68	Aston-Martin DB5
114L	1964-66	Triumph Spitfire
116L	1967-71	Volvo P1800
118L	1967-70	Towaway Glider Set
127L	1965-68	R-R Silver Cloud
128L	1965-70	Mercedes 600
129L	1968-68	Volkswagen 1300
131L	1969-71	Jaguar 'E'-type 2+2
132L	1968-71	Ford RV40
142L	1963-67	Jaguar Mark 10
150L	1962-64	R-R Silver Wraith
151a	1938-38	Medium Tank
152a	1938-38	Light Tank
152L	1967-70	R-R Phantom V
153L	1968-70	Aston-Martin DB6
155L	1962-65	Ford Anglia
160L	1968-71	Mercedes-Benz 250
161	1939-40	Mobile A-A Gun
161L	1967-71	Ford Mustang
162	1939-40	Light Dragon Tractor
163L	1967-71	Volkswagen 1600TL
165L	1969-70	Ford Capri 1600
172L	1967-71	Fiat 2300 Estate
173L	1969-71	Pontiac Parisienne
174L	1969-70	Ford Mercury Cougar
175L	1969-71	Cadillac Eldorado
176L	1969-71	NSU Ro80
182L	1962-64	Porsche 356a
186L	1962-63	Mercedes-Benz 220
187L	1969-71	De Tomaso Mangusta
188L	1969-71	Jensen FF 542
189L/1	1962-64	Triumph Herald
189L/2	1969-71	Lamborghini Marzal
190L	1971-?	Monteverdi 375L
192L	1971-?	Range Rover
194L	1962-63	Bentley 'S'
195L	1962-65	Jaguar 3.4
198L	1963-66	R-R Phantom V
199L	1962-67	Austin 7 Countryman
200L	1971-?	Matra 630
202L	1971-?	Fiat Abarth 2000
204L	1971-?	Ferrari 312 P
205L	1969-71	Lotus Cortina
208L	1971-?	VW Porsche 914
210L	1971-?	Alfa-Romeo 33 LM
213L	1970-71	Ford Capri 1600 GT
215L	1965-71	Ford GT Le Mans
216L	1968-71	Ferrari Dino
217L	1969-71	Alfa-Romeo Scarabeo
218L	1970-71	Lotus Europa GT
220L	1970-71	Ferrari P5
221L	1970-71	Chevrolet Corvette
223L	1970-71	McLaren Can-Am
224L	1971-?	Mercedes-Benz C111
225L	1971-?	Lotus 49B F1
238L	1971-?	Ferrari 3L F1 (not issued)
240L	1963-70	Cooper Racing Car
241L	1963-70	Lotus Racing Car
242L	1963-70	Ferrari Racing Car
243L	1964-70	BRM Racing Car
252L	1962-64	Bedford Refuse Truck
253L	1962-62	Daimler Ambulance
258L	1962-63	De Soto USA Police
258L	1963-64	Dodge USA Police
258L	1965-66	Cadillac USA Police
258L	1967-68	Ford Fairlane USA Police Car
263L	1963-68	Super Criterion Ambulance
270L	1969-71	Ford Escort Police
276L	1963-69	Airport Fire Tender
300L	1962-70	Massey-Harris Tractor
308L	1971-?	Leyland Tractor
320L	1962-70	Halesowen Trailer
321L	1962-71	Massey-Harris Manure Spreader
324L	1962-64	Hay Rake
340L	1962-67	Land Rover
341L	1962-67	Land Rover Trailer
344L	1971-?	Land Rover Pick-up
351L	1971-?	'SHADO' Interceptor
370L	1970-71	Dragster / Launcher
401L	1962-64	Coventry Climax Fork Lift Truck
437L	1963-71	JCB Hydraulic Shovel
439L	1971-?	Ford Snow Plough
449L	1962-63	El Camino Pick-up
451L	1971-?	Ford D800 Johnston Road Sweeper
475L	1964-68	Ford Model 'T' 1908
476L	1965-69	Morris Oxford 1913
485L	1964-70	Ford Model 'T' 'Father Christmas'
601L	1967-70	Austin Para-Moke
615L	1971-?	Jeep / Field Gun
617L	1969-71	VW KDF / Field Gun
620L	1971-?	Berliet Gazelle with Missile
651L	1962-70	Centurion Tank
661L	1962-63	Recovery Tractor
665L	1965-71	Honest John Carrier
666L	1961-65	Corporal Missile
667L	1962-64	Servicing Platform
676L	1972-?	Scout Car
697L	1962-70	Artillery Set
719L	1970-71	Spitfire
721L	1970-71	Stuka Ju 87b
722L	1970-71	Hawker Harrier
724L	1971-?	Sea Rescue Helicopter
796L	1962-68	Dinghy on Trailer
930L	1961-64	Bedford 'Pallet-Jekta'
936L	1965-68	Leyland Test Chassis
952L	1964-70	Vega Major Coach
958L	1962-65	Guy Snow Plough
960L	1962-69	Albion Cement Mixer
961L	1962-63	Blaw-Knox Bulldozer
962L	1962-64	Muir-Hill Dumper
964L	1962-63	Elevator Loader
965L	1961-64	Euclid Quarry Truck
971L	1962-63	Coles Mobile Crane
972L	1962-69	Coles Lorry Crane
973L	1971-?	Yale Diesel Shovel
974L	1969-71	AEC Hoynor Car Transporter
976L	1969-71	Michigan Shovel Dozer

FRENCH DINKY TOYS sold by
Special Auction Services,
The Coach House, Midgham Park, Reading, Berkshire, RG7 5UG.
Condition abbreviations used in SAS catalogues: **E** = Excellent, **F** = Fine,
G = Good, **M** = Mint, **P** = Poor, **U/B** = Unboxed, **VG** = Very Good.

24 Series pre-war Automobiles Set, models VG, box F-G £2,800
24B Peugeot 403, black, VG-E £140
24g Four-seater Open Tourer, grey/red, F-G..............................£100
24h Two-seater Open Tourer, pre war, fatigue blisters, overall G £260
24R Peugeot 203 without rear light or petrol cap, G £100
24R Peugeot 203 special issue for Club Dinky Toys, lime green, F-G ...£650

24V Buick Roadmaster, red/yellow with blue roof, F-G...................£900
24O Studebaker State Commander, red with black hubs, G £240
    Same model, cream with black hubs, G £110
24 l Peugeot Taxi, blue/yellow, F-G.....................................£260
542 Simca Ariane Taxi, black/red, VG in F box £130

548 Fiat 1800 Station Wagon (South African issue), off-white, E in E box £550
552 Chevrolet Corvair (South African issue), pale blue, E in G box £340
553 Peugeot 504 (South African issue), cream, VG in G box..............£300
554 Opel Rekord (South African issue), blue, E in VG box..............£600
562H 'Wegenwacht' Dutch Export Citroën 2cv Van, G-VG U/B...........£140

FRENCH DINKY TOYS sold by
Vectis Model Auctions,
Fleck Way, Thornaby, Stockton-on-Tees. TS17 9JZ

Condition abbreviations appearing in Vectis Auctions catalogues:
M = Mint, **NM** = Near Mint, **NMB** = Near Mint Boxed,
EP = Excellent Plus, **E** = Excellent, **EB** = Excellent Boxed,
GP = Good Plus, **VG** = Very Good, **G** = Good,
GB = Good Box, **F** = Fair, **FB** = Fair Box, **P** = Poor.

CARS
22A Maserati Sport 2000, deep red, NM £110
24A Chrysler New Yorker, yellow/green, E in E box £80
24B Peugeot Berline, cream/green, GP overall £140
24CP Citroën DS19, yellow/grey, GR in E box £110
24D Plymouth Belvedere, white/blue flash, E in G box £250
    Same model in TT brown, chrome hubs, E in P box...........£170

23J Ferrari RC, dark red, chrome hubs, RN '1', NM in E box £220
24V Buick Roadmaster, TT blue, E in E box £210
24X Ford Vedette, dark blue, E in E box £120
24Y Studebaker State Commander, TT green, EP in EP box £120
24Y Studebaker State Commander, grey/maroon, E in GP box £200
    Same model in red/cream, E in G box £80

24Z Simca Versailles, pale yellow/black, GP in GP box £70
506 Ferrari 275 GTB, red in GP box £130
515 Ferrari Coupé 250 GTO, red in E box £100
511 Peugeot 204 Cabriolet, red, E in GP box £140
525 Peugeot 404 Estate Car Commerciale, dark blue/red, E in G box £80
532 Lincoln Premiere, blue/silver, E in E box £80
536 Peogeot 404 with Trailer, red, E in GP box £140
538 Ford Taunus 12m, turquoise, E in E box £80
544 Simca Aronde, brown / off-white, E in E box £80
548 Fiat Familiale, ivory, red interior, E in GP box £310
550 Chrysler Saratoga, lilac, black flash/stripe, E in GP box £240

1401 Alfa Romeo Giula 1699TL, red, yellow stripe, E in G box £220
1404 Citroën Estate Camera Car 'RTL', E in GP box...................£400
1414 Renault R8 Gordini, blue/white stripe, RN '36', E in GP box...........£240
1423 Peugeot 404 Cabriolet, dark green, blue £120
1435 Citroen Présidentiale, NM in E box £400

SOUTH AFRICAN ISSUES (all with spun hubs)
519 Simca 1000, turquoise, red interior, NM in GP box..................£780
552 Chevrolet Corvair, pale grey, off-white interior, EP in P box £400
552 Chevrolet Corvair, smokey green, off-white interior, white tyres,
    EP in EP box £1,300

553 Peugeot 404, metallic black, red interior, EP in E box £1,000
553 Peugeot 404, pale lime green, red interior, E unboxed £580
554 Opel Rekord, dark metallic green, grey interior, white tyres............£1,000
555 Ford Thunderbird, bright blue, red interior, white tyres, E unboxed...£660

COMMERCIAL VEHICLES
560 Citroën 2cv Van 'Postal Service', NM in E box.................£150
561 Citroën 12kg Van 'Cibie', NM in E box........................£240
565 Renault Estafette 'Camping', blue/cream NM in G box.........£140
569 Berliet 'Stradair' Wagon, turquoise/green E in E box.........£290

572 Berliet GBO Dump Truck, NM in GP box......................£220
587 Citroen Van 'Phillips', NM in EP box.........................£640
589a Berliet GAK 'Autoroutes' Breakdown Truck, E in GP box £150

803 Unic SNCF 'Pam Pam' Lorry, E in GP box..................£280
805 Unic Multi Bucket Lorry, E in GP box........................£280
881 'Pinder' Lorry/Animal Cage, NM in G box..................£420
882 Peugeot 404 & Caravan 'Pinder', E in G box................£480
887 Unic Tanker 'Air BP', E in GP box...........................£140
885 Saviem Pipe Carrying Lorry, E in GP box....................£190
1406 Renault Sinpar 4x4 'Michel Tanguy', E in P box £150

BUSES
889 Autobus Parisienne, green/grey, GP in E box £160
889u Autobus Urbain, red/cream, E in E box.....................£180

EMERGENCY VEHICLES
501 Citroën DS19 Police Car, white/dark blue, GP in GP box £130
1429 Peugeot Police Estate Car, E in GP box.....................£160
568 Berliet Fire Engine, E in P box £160

AIRCRAFT
891 Caravelle SE21 'Air France', E in E box.....................£140

MILITARY VEHICLES
806 Military Breakdown Truck, E in G box.......................£140
808 GMC Military Breakdown Truck, Sand body NM in GP box £220
809 GMC Military 6 Wheeled Wagon, NM in E box...............£190

823 GMC Tanker, E in GP box..................................£130
826 Berliet Breakdown Truck, GP in GP box.....................£140
825 DUKW, E in E box..£120

GIFT SETS
No. 24-57 Coffret Cadeau Set, GP in GP box...................£1,550
No 24-58 Coffret Cadeau Tourisme set, models E in E box.................£700

FRENCH DINKY TOYS sold by Wallis & Wallis,
West Street Auction Galleries, Lewes, Sussex, BN7 2NJ.
Condition abbreviations used by Wallis & Wallis:
M = Mint, **VGC** = Very Good Condition, **GC** = Good Condition.

MILITARY VEHICLES
808 GMC Breakdown Truck, olive green, black canopy,
    boxed minor wear, vehicle VGC, M £180
809 Military Truck, olive green, black canopy, complete with
    inner packaging and USA decal transfers.............£190
822 Military M3 Half Track, complete with machine gun and rail,
    boxed minor wear, vehicle M £65
825 DUKW Vehicle, complete with driver, hatch cover and accessories,
    boxed, vehicle M £80
826 Berliet Breakdown Wagon, olive green complete with
    instructions, minor box wear, vehicle VGC £100
823 Military GMC Tanker, olive green, black canopy, with inner
    packaging/instructions/road sign, VGC, M £310
883 Military AMX Tank, complete with paperwork, boxed, vehicle M £140
884 Brockway Bridge Vehicle, complete with 2 boats/pontoons and
    paperwork, boxed, vehicle M £190

FRENCH DINKY TOYS
sold by Collectoys, Bourges, France
and Christie's, South Kensington
See the colour section (pages xiv - xvi) for illustrations and results of
models sold by Collectoys, and Christie's, South Kensington (pages xii-xiii)

22a Sports Car
(£305)

22b Sports Coupé
(£1,057)

22c Motor Truck
(£998)

22d Delivery Van
(£2,232)

22d Delivery Van
(£1,527)

22e Farm Tractor
& Trade Box
(£470)

22f Army Tank
(£376)

22g Streamlined Tourer
(£329)

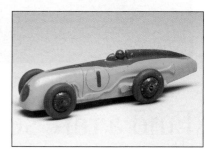

23a Pre-War Racing Car
(£190)

23a Pre-War Racing Car
(£165)

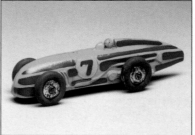

23a Racing Car, 'Humbug' pattern,
silvered hubs, blue tyres (£1,292)

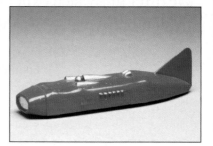

23s Streamlined Racing Car
(£282) (Post-war)

Models sold by Christie's of South Kensington, London. Pictures reproduced by their kind permission.

24a Pre-War Ambulance
(£176)

24c Town Sedan, 2nd type chassis and
grille, plated hubs (£305)

24d Vogue Saloon
2nd type chassis, 1st type grille (£493)

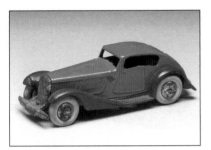

24e Super Streamlined
Saloon
(£176)

24g Sports Tourer Four Seater
2nd type chassis and body type,
with spare wheel cover (£376)

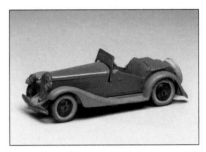

24h Two Seater
Sports Car
(£258)

36e British Salmson
2 seater with driver (£822)

36f British Salmson
4 seater with driver (£763)

36g Taxi
Rare yellow/black livery (£1,292)

Half-dozen Trade Box, code A1002, (April 1934)
With three 23 series Racing Cars without racing number or
driver, two stub exhaust manifold without pipe (£763)

Half-dozen Trade Box, code A2032 (1934/5)
With six No. 32 Airflow Saloons (£3,055)

Dinky Toys - 28 Series Delivery Vans

28b 'Pickfords Removals'
(£564)

28c 'The Manchester Guardian'
(£587)

28d 'Oxo'
(£3,760)

28e 'Ensign Cameras'
(£2,685)

28e 'Firestone Tyres'
(£1,880)

28f 'Palethorpes Royal Cambridge'
(£564)

28g 'Kodak Film'
(£4,112)

28h 'Sharps Toffee'
(£1,410)

28l 'Crawford's Biscuits'
(£1,762)

28m 'Wakefield Castrol'
(£1,410)

28n (22d)
'Meccano'
(£3,525)

Dinky Toys - Post War

23b Hotchkiss Racing Cars (£85)

30b Rolls-Royce (£180)

30f Ambulance (£110)

36a Post-War Armstrong Siddeley,
with blue hubs (£188)

36e British Salmson (£100)

38b Sunbeam-Talbot (£210)

38f Jaguar SS100 (£110)

39cu U.S. issue Lincoln Zephyr Coupé
Two tone red and maroon livery,
blued rear steel axle (£2,820)

39eu U.S. issue Chrysler Royal Sedan
Two tone yellow and red livery (£2,820)

Models sold by Christie's of South Kensington, London. Pictures reproduced by their kind permission.

39eu Chrysler Royal Sedan
US issue (£1,600)

39eu Chrysler Royal Sedan
US issue (£850)

Models sold by Vectis Auctions Ltd., Fleck Way, Thornaby, Stockton-on-Tees, TS17 9JZ. Pictures reproduced by their kind permission.

Dinky Toys - Post War

Gift Set 299
Post Office Services

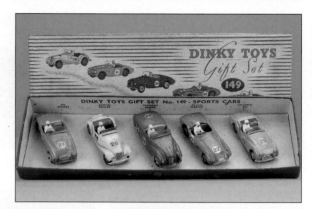

Gift Set 149
Sports Cars

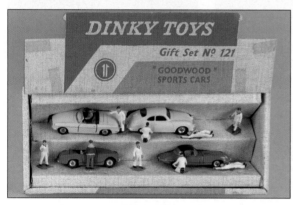

Gift Set 121
"Goodwood" Sports Cars

Gift Set 123
"Mayfair"

108 MG Midget Sports

110 Aston-Martin DB3 Sports

110 Aston-Martin DB3 Sports
Unusual Light Green

153 Standard Vanguard
Name inside roof, closed wheel arches,
large lettering.

154 Hillman Minx,
dual-numbered box

156 Rover 75 Saloon

156 Rover 75 Saloon

170 Ford Fordor Sedan
'Lowline'

170 Ford Fordor Sedan
'Highline'

171 Hudson Commodore Sedan
'Highline'

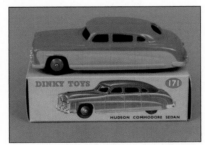

171 Hudson Commodore Sedan
'Lowline'

171 Hudson Commodore Sedan
'Highline'

171 Hudson Commodore Sedan
'Lowline'.

172 Studebaker Land Cruiser

178 Plymouth Plaza
plain Yellow/Red box

Dinky Toys - Post War

154 Hillman Minx

154 Hillman Minx

157 Jaguar XK120

157 Jaguar XK120
Lighter yellow late box

157 Jaguar XK120

159 Morris Oxford

161 Austin A40 Somerset

161 Austin A40 Somerset

165 Humber Hawk
All Green upper body variation

Gift Set No.4 – Racing Cars

234 Ferrari Racing Car
Yellow triangle on nose
Lighter Yellow late box

114 Triumph Spitfire Sports Car
Metallic Purple, Gold interior

Dinky Toys - Post War

25b Covered Wagon
Type 4 Unboxed

412 Austin Wagon

430 Commer Breakdown Lorry
Yellow box

430 Commer Breakdown Lorry
Yellow box

417 Leyland Comet Lorry
Yellow box

418 Leyland Comet Wagon
with Hinged Tailboard

431 Guy Warrior 4-ton Lorry

432 Guy Warrior Flat Truck

450 Trojan Van
dual-numbered box

455 Trojan Van

465 Morris Van

482 Bedford Van

512 Guy Flat Truck
1st type cab
Blue White Striped box

512 Guy Flat Truck
'buff' box

919 Guy Van
Blue White Striped box

920 Guy Warrior Van
'plain' striped box

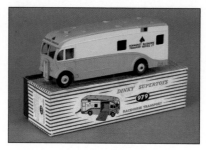

979 Racehorse Transporter

29e Single Deck Bus

281 Luxury Coach

953 Continental Touring Coach
'Picture' box

Pre-War 290 Double Decker Bus

Pre-War 37 Tram Car

505 Foden Flat Truck with Chains
1st type cab

501 Foden Diesel 8-wheel Wagon
2nd type cab - Two Tone Green (Picture
supplied by Lacy, Scott & Knight)

French Dinky Toys - Pre and Post War Issues

14a Triporteur
silvered hubs
(£400)

22a Roadster
Sport Two Seater
(£700)

22b Grand Sport
Coupé - lead cast solid wheels
(£1,500)

22d Grand Sport Coupé
silvered hubs
(£1,900)

24h Two Seat Open Tourer
(£550 for two similar models)

24 Series
Wartime Issue box
(£220)

24h Two Door Coupé -
solid zine wheels - post war
(£320 for two similar models)

23b Renault Nervasport
Record Car - Post War
(£350 for two similar models)

24n Citroën 11B2
(£600 for two similar models)

23H Talbot Lago
Trade box (£750)

503 Gift Set
(£958)

524 Renault
'Dauphine'
Trade box (£400)

French Dinky Toys - Post War Issues

24S Simca 8 Sports
convex hubs
(4 items in lot £329)

24S Simca 8 Sports
(4 items in lot £329)

24T Citroën 2cv
(£411)

24A Simca Aronde
2nd type
(3 items in lot £705)

24UT Simca
Aronde Taxi
(3 items in lot £293)

24V Buick Roadmaster
1st type smooth roof
(5 items in lot £446)

525 Pompiérs de Paris
Peugeot 404 Estate
(£1,292)

518 Renault
Pompiérs de Paris 404 Estate
(£1,880)

542/24 ZT
Simca Ariane Taxi
(£470)

24Z Simca Versailles
1st type with towing eye
(£470)

24Y Studebaker State Commander
(5 items in lot £470)

140B Renault Sinpar 4x4
'Michel Tanguy'
(£258)

French Dinky Toys

1947 24k Peugeot 402
with metal wheels
(1,296€)

1947 24l Peugeot 402
Taxi with metal wheels
(1,220€)

24R Peugeot 203
(rare violet version)
(1,601€)

32AJ Panhard Articulated Lorry
"Kodak" (USA Export Issue)
(1,068€)

507P Simca 1500
'Police' Estate Car
(9,605€)

541 Mercedes
Minibus 'PTT Suisse'
(6,403€)

25A Ford
Farm Produce Wagon
(6,098€)

560`P Citroën 2cv
Van 'Philips'
(9,147€)

561 Citroën 1200kg Van
'Baroclem' (a 'Code-2' Promotional)
(7,470€)

532 Lincoln Premiere
(1,100€)

'Touring Cars'
Gift Set No 24 (1955)
(2,287€)

25D Citroën 2cv Van
'B.B. Lorrain' Promotional
(10,672€)

Pictures kindly supplied by Collectoys, Editoys - BP22 - 18001 Bourges Cedex-France and reproduced by their kind permission.

French Dinky Toys

1404 Citroën ID19
Estate Car 'RTL'
Orange chequered 'T' variation (3,964€)

30E Breakdown
Lorry (1940)
(1,200€)

25JJ Ford Covered
Truck 'Calberson'
(1,200€)

1435E Presidential
Citroën in 1971 Presentation box
(1,800€)

588K Berliet Gak
Beer Lorry 'Kronenbourg'
(4,500€)

571 Saviem Goélette
Horse Transport and Sulky
(1,800€)

25JB Ford Covered Wagon
'SNCF' (1950)
(1,500€)

25O Ford
Milk Lorry 'Nestle'
(1,600€)

572 Berliet GBO
Quarry Tipper Truck
(2,400€)

559 Ford Taunnus 17M
A French Dinky made in Spain by
Poch, S.A. (2,000€)

891B Caravelle
'Swissair' Airliner
(1,677€)

882 'Circus Pinder'
Peugeot 404 and Caravan
(1,769€)

French Dinky Toys Gift Sets

'Tourism' Gift Set
No. 24-56 (1956)
(2,800€)

'Tourism' Gift Set
No. 24-58 (1958)
(2,440€)

'Tourism' Gift Set
No. 1460 (1968)
(4,269€)

'Aircraft' Gift Set
No.60 (1934-1939)
(1,373€)

Pictures kindly supplied by Collectoys, Editoys - BP22 - 18001 Bourges Cedex-France and reproduced by their kind permission.

Horse Transporter No.1130
complete with horses, display insert
and packing.
Performing Poodles No.511

Circus Crane No.1144
Circus Menagerie No.1139

Gift Set 23
'Chipperfields' Circus Models

N.B. All models shown are in excellent to mint condition unless shown differently.

(No.435) Karrier Bantam; (No.1110) 'S' Type Tanker 'Mobilgas'
(No.1140/1) Bedford 'TK' Tankers ('Milk' & Mobilgas')
(No.462) Commercial Van; (441) Var Van; (413) Karrier
Bantam 'Smiths'(453) Commercial Van, 'Walls'
(411) Karrier Bantam;

(459) ERF 44G Van 'Moorhouses'; (471) Karrier Bantam
'Potato Frites'; (426) Karrier Van 'Chipperfields'; (508)
Commer 'Holiday' Bus; (471) Karrier 'Snack Bar'; (428)
Karrier 'Mister Softee' Van; (474) Ford Anglia 'Walls Ice
Cream' Van

Corgi Toys

Gift Set No 4

GS 10 Marlin Rambler Set

Gift Set 12
Grand Prix Racing Set

Gift Set 20
Scammell Tri-decker
Transporter Set

Gift Set 36
"Lotus" Racing Team Set

Gift Set 48 Scammell Transporter Set

Gift Set 48 Ford Transporter Set

Shop Display Stand
With picture of Gift Set No 8

Gift Set No 1
Bedford Carrimore
Transporter Set

Gift Set No 16
'Ecurie Ecosse'

Gift Set 20
Scammell Transporter Set

Gift Set 21
"Chipperfields" Circus Set

Corgi Toys

GS No.3 1st type 'Batman'

Gift Set 3 "Batman"
Batboat is early issue with tin back,

Gift Set 40 "Batman"

Gift Set 38 "Monte-Carlo Rally"

Gift Set 15 "Silverstone"

Gift Set 40 "The Avengers"

Batmobile (1st issue)

Batboat & Trailer
(1st issue with tin back)

Green Hornet

"Saints" Volvo P1800

Rolls Royce Silver Ghost
"Hardy Boys"

Juniors "James Bond"
Ford Escort "O.H.M.S.S."

Models sold by Vectis Auctions Ltd., Fleck Way, Thornaby, Stockton-on-Tees, TS17 9JZ. Pictures reproduced by their kind permission.

Corgi Toys

201 M Austin Cambridge
Orange body

203 M Vauxhall Velox,
Orange body

204 M Rover 90
Metallic green

200 Ford Consul
Green/cream

201 Austin Cambridge
Silver over metallic green

202 Morris Cowley
Pale green/blue

214 M Ford Thunderbird
Pink/black, yellow interior

225 Austin 7 "Jensons"
Dutch Promotional issue

225 Austin 7 Mini
Primrose yellow, red interior

227 Morris Mini Cooper
"Competition" blue/white RN '1'

227 Morris Mini Cooper
"Competition" pale yellow/white RN '3'

321 Mini Cooper-S
With roof signatures

Corgi Toys

Bentley Continental Sports Saloon
Black over silver

240 Ghia Fiat 600 "Jolly"
Blue, 2 figures

242 Ghia Fiat 600
Yellow, 2 figures

328 Hillman Imp "Monte Carlo Rally"
Complete with rare advertising card

335 Jaguar 'E' Type

349 Morris Mini Minor "Popart Mostest"
Red body, lemon interior, cast wheels

Canadian issue catalogues
1. 1961 racing cars scene, 2. 1963-64 boy in blue,
3. 1963-64 boy in red

256 VW 1200
'East African Safari'

304 Mercedes Benz 300SL
Hardtop Roadster

320 Ford Mustang Fastback 2+2
Metallic deep yellow and black

322 Rover 2000 "Monte Carlo"

322 Rover 2000 "International Rally
Finish", (box has international rally
label on side)

Corgi Toys

270 "James Bond" Silver Aston Martin DB5 with tyre slashers

Group of three "James Bond" 1:36 scale. Model nos 2 x 94060, C271/1

270 "James Bond" with tyre slashers 1st issue wing flapped bubble pack

270 "James Bond" Aston Martin DB5 Silver with tyre slashers.

"James Bond" Toyota 200 GT

391 "James Bond" Ford Mustang Mach 1.

Gold plated No 272
"James Bond" Citroën 2cv.
No 8 of only 12 produced in 1981 for a special promotion.
Strada authentication certificate must be present.

Gold plated Corgi Classic 96445
"James Bond" Aston Martin DB5.
This being "0007" and signed by Shirley Eaton from "Goldfinger".

416 S Land Rover Radio Rescue "TS Radio" (Touring Secours) Belgian issue

421 Bedford Van "Evening Standard" Black body, silver roof

421 Bedford Van "Evening Standard" Black lower body, silver upper body

422 Bedford Van "Corgi Toys" Yellow with blue roof

422 Bedford Van "Corgi Toys" Blue lower body, yellow upper body

428 Smiths "Mr Softie" Ice Cream van

438 Land Rover "Lepra" variant

447 Ford Thames "Walls Ice Cream"

Mettoy "Castoys" Luxury Observation coach

433 VW Delivery Van "Vroom & Dreesman"

Window display sign
27" long x 8" high, illuminated probably Belgian issue

Matchbox Toys - 1-75 Series

5 Routemaster Bus
"Drink Peardrax" BPW

5 Routemaster Bus
"Pegram" BPW

23 Berkeley Cavalier Caravan
Metallic lime green GPW

8 Ford Mustang
Orange, red interior, chrome hubs

9 Dennis Fire Engine
Red body, gold trim with front bumper GPW,

11 ERF Road Tanker
Green, gold trim, metal wheels

20 Chevrolet Impala "Taxi", orange
yellow, cream interior, rare GPW

22 Vauxhall Cresta
Pale pink/blue green GPW

26 Foden Cement Mixer
Orange, grey barrel and plastic wheels

45 Ford Corvair with boat
white interior BPW

31 Lincoln Continental, metallic lime green,
black plastic wheels

30 Magirus Deutz Crane Lorry
Light brown, red jib and hook GPW

46 Morris Minor 1000
Pale brown, metal wheels

46 Removals Van
"Beales Bealesons"

75 Ford Thunderbird, cream-peach side
panels, black base and wheels

218
Y16-1 Maroon Spyker

231
Gift Set No 9

311
Early Lesney,
Cement Mixer

317
Early Lesney,
Coronation Coach

318 Early Lesney,
Road Roller

323 Early Lesney,
Milk Cart

491
58a AEC Coach SPW

513
26b Foden Cement Mixer
Grey barrel, GPW

345
36b Lambretta & Sidecar
4e Triumph & Sidecar

360
45a Vauxhall Victor

498
12b Land Rover, GPW

443
626 TV Service Van
L-R Radio Rentals,
2x 'Rentaset' Vans
in early & late boxes

497
465 'Pickfords'
3 & 2 line decals

500
5c Routemaster
Double-decker Bus

511
15a Diamond 'T'
Prime Mover, GPW

512
26a Cement Mixer, SPW

Matchbox - 'Models of Yesteryear'

Shop Display Stand

Y1-3 1911 Ford Model T
Y2-2 1911 Renault
Y3-2 1910 Benz
Y4-3 Opel
Y5-2 1929 Bentley
Y6-2 1935 Bugatti
Y7-2 1913 Mercer
Y8-2 1914 Sunbeam
Y9-2 1912 Simplex
Y10-2 1928 Mercedes 36/220
Y11-2 1912 Packard
Y12-2 1912 Thomas
Y13-2 1911 Daimler
Y14-2 1911 Maxwell Roadster
Y15-1 1907 Rolls Royce
Y16-1 1904 Spyker

'Moko' & Early Lesney

L-R Ruston-Bucyrus Excavator, Excavator with bucket shovel, Bulldozer,
Lesney Prime mover trailer with bulldozer, Lesney Massey Harris Tractor,
Moko Pop-Pop Scooter, Moko Builders crane.

Budgie, Timpo, Chad Valley, Benbros & Crescent

Budgie "Supercar"

Budgie 256 "Pluto" Aircraft Tanker

Timpo Toys "Pickfords"

"Chad Valley" Van

Benbros Low Loader

Crescent No 1276 Scammell Scarab

Models sold by Vectis Auctions Ltd., Fleck Way, Thornaby, Stockton-on-Tees, TS17 9JZ. Pictures reproduced by their kind permission.

Britains, Mettoy, Morestone, Charbens, Benbros
Chad Valley, Timpo & Kemlows

Britains Army Ambulance (No. 1512)
Mettoy 'BOAC' Van
Mettoy 'Post Office' Telephones Van
Morestone Gipsy Caravan
Charbens Horse Delivery Van

Benbros 'United Dairies' Van
Morestone 'Breakdown' Van
Morestone 'AA' Land Rover
Chad Valley Cable Lorry
Chad Valley Milk Tanker

Chad Valley 'Lyons' Guy Van
Charbens Van
1950's Timpo 'Smiths' Van
Kemlows 'Pickfords' Van
Timpo 'Pickfords' Van

Models sold by Wallis & Wallis, West Street Auction Galleries, Lewes, Sussex BN7 2NJ. Pictures reproduced by their kind permission.

Britains Vehicles

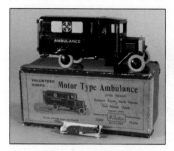

No. 1313 'Volunteer Corps'
Ambulance

No. 2045 'Clockwork Van'

No. 128F 'Fordson Major'
Tractor

No. 1335 'Army Lorry'

No. 1512 'Army Ambulance'

'Air Force Transporter'

Models sold by Special Auction Services, Kennetholme, Midgham, Near Reading, Berkshire R97 5UX. Pictures reproduced by their kind permission.

Britains Vehicles

No. 819 'St Johns' Ambulance

No. 2024 'Light Goods Van'

No. 2024 'Light Goods Van'

No. 2024 'Light Goods Van'

No. LV620
'Lilliput Series' Bedford Truck

No. LV169
'Lilliput Series' Royal Mail Van

Models sold by Vectis Auctions Ltd., Fleck Way, Thornaby, Stockton-on-Tees, TS17 9JZ. Pictures reproduced by their kind permission.

Zebra Toys No 16

Zebra Toys No 30 Routemaster Bus
"Fina Petrol"

Sundaw Products H131 Motorbus (Green)
"Transport Sevices"

Sundaw Products Motorbus (Red)
"Transport Services"

Benbros "United Dairies"

Lone Star "Gulliver County Services"
3 single deck buses

Morestone No 2 Foden 8 wheel lorry

Morestone AA Land Rover (large)

No 4 Morestone Series
Foden 14 ton Express Delivery
Diesel Wagon.

Lone Star Roadmaster cars
Trade box of 6

Crescent Toys
1293 Vanwall Racing Car

Chad Valley Humber Super Snipe

Chad Valley Tower Repair Wagon

Chad Valley Fire Engine

Lone Star

Robert Newson has provided the following information on Lone Star models.

'Lone Star' was the trade name of Die Casting Machine Tools Ltd (DCMT) who started in 1939 as manufacturers of diecasting machines. They were based at Palmers Green in North London. After the war they started making diecast toys which were distributed by The Crescent Toy Co Ltd. In the Crescent Toys section of this catalogue, the items listed as 'early post-war models' were all made by DCMT with the exception of the Locomotive and the Racing Car. From 1950 DCMT arranged their own distribution direct to wholesalers. Over the next four decades DCMT Lone Star made several ranges of diecast vehicles including

'Slikka Toys' (early 1950s), 'Modern Army Series' (mainly 1960s), 'Roadmaster Majors' (1960s and 1970s), 'Farmer's Boy' (1980s) and the well known 'Lone Star Locos' miniature railway system (later called 'Treble-O-Lectric' or 'Treble-O-Trains'). The four ranges of most interest to collectors are listed here - the original DCMT 'Roadmasters' of 1956, the 1:50 scale 'Roadmasters' (1960s), the 'Impy' and 'Flyers' series made in various forms from 1966 to the mid 1980s, and the miniature 'Tuf-Tots' (1970s). The Editor would welcome any further information on Lone Star products.

NB See the 'Miscellaneous Models' colour section for Lone Star pictures.

DCMT Lone Star Roadmasters

This was a short-lived series introduced in 1956, consisting of three sports cars and four veteran cars, all around 1:35 to 1:40 scale. The models had diecast bodies but all other components were plastic. Plastic drivers and passengers were included with the models.

-	-	**1904 Darracq 'Genevieve'**	Black or Red body, Yellow plastic chassis; Metallic Blue or Silver body, Black plastic chassis	**£200-300**
-	-	**1904 Daimler 'Windsor' Phaeton**	Red body, Yellow plastic chassis	**£60-70**
-	-	**1912 Ford Model 'T'**	Silver body, Black plastic chassis	**£60-70**
-	-	**1912 Morris Oxford 'Bullnose'**	Metallic Blue body, Black plastic chassis	**£80-100**
-	-	**Daimler Conquest Roadster**	Red, Metallic Light Blue, Pale Yellow, Pale Green or Pale Blue	**£80-100**
-	-	**Ford Thunderbird**	Red, Metallic Light Blue, Pale Yellow, Pale Green or Pale Blue	**£80-100**
-	-	**MG Midget TF**	Metallic Light Blue or Red	**£80-100**

Lone Star Roadmasters - 1:50 scale

In 1960 Lone Star produced four American cars on behalf of the US firm of Tootsietoy. These were the first four models listed below and they had 'Tootsietoy Classic Series' cast underneath. This arrangement only lasted for a couple of years, as by 1962 there were eight models available, all now marked 'Lone Star Roadmasters'. The models featured plated grilles, bumpers and wheels, and had windows but no interior detail. Around 1964 the plated parts were replaced by less attractive painted or self-coloured plastic, and vacuum-formed interiors were fitted. Later issues have yellow interiors, white wheels, plastic grille and bumpers. Five further numbers were added to the range before they were withdrawn around 1966.

1258	-	**Farm King Tractor and Trailer**	Red tractor, 'Farm King' paper label, Blue trailer, 'Farm Estates Co.' paper label. (Roadmaster Major)	**£60-70**
1470	-	**Chevrolet Corvair**	Red or Orange-Red	**£60-70**
1471	-	**Rambler Rebel Station Wagon**	Sea-Green, Metallic Blue-Green or Green with Cream roof, Metallic Brown with White roof or all Green	**£60-70**
1472	-	**Cadillac 62**	Pale Blue, Blue with Cream roof or all Blue	**£60-70**
1473	-	**Ford Sunliner Convertible**	White or Light Blue; Red interior	**£60-70**
1474	-	**Chevrolet El Camino Pick-Up**	Yellow or Orange	**£60-70**
1475	-	**Dodge Dart Phoenix**	Metallic Dark Blue or Mid Blue	**£60-70**
1476	-	**Rolls-Royce Silver Cloud II**	Grey with Black upper half or Metallic Blue	**£70-80**
1477	-	**Dodge Dart Police Car**	Black, 'POLICE PATROL' or 'POLIZEI'	**£70-80**
1478	-	**Rambler Ambulance**	White, Red Cross transfer on bonnet	**£70-80**
1479	-	**Chevrolet Corvair**	Red body, 'FIRE CHIEF', 'FEUERWEHR' or 'BRANDWEER'	**£70-80**
1480	-	**Chevrolet Corvair**	Army Staff Car (continued after 1966 as no.1273 in ``Modern Army'' series), Olive Green	**£60-70**
1481	-	**Rambler Military Ambulance**	(continued after 1966 as no.1274 in 'Modern Army' series), Olive Green	**£70-80**
1482	-	**Citroën DS19**	Turquoise	**£60-70**
-	-	**Rambler Police Car**	White body, 'POLIZEI' on bonnet	**£70-80**

Lone Star 'Tuf-Tots'

The first thirteen Tuf-Tots were introduced in 1969, and the next five followed in 1970. The remainder had appeared by 1972. They were available boxed or bubble-packed, and when bubble-packed there was an additional '2' in front of the model number to give a four-digit reference. Later, models were sold in open counter-top trays.

The trucks were based on a common US Ford chassis. Most models exist in numerous colour variations. The series was discontinued after 1980. Market Price Range is **£5** to **£10**.

601	**Ford Petrol Tanker**	'ESSO' labels
		'ESSO' cast into sides
602	**Citroën DS Convertible with Driver**	
603	**Chevrolet Corvette Stingray Convertible with Driver**	
604	**Dodge Dart Convertible with Driver**	
605	**Mercedes-Benz 280SL Convertible with Driver**	
606	**Ford 'TT' Tow Truck**	
607	**Ford 'Big L' Dumper Lorry**	
608	**Jeep and Trailer**	'Herts. Farm', scale 85:1
609	**Ford 'Autos' Flat Truck** with metal petrol pump island	
		with plastic petrol pump island
610	**Ford Tipper Lorry**	'LS Construction Co.' labels
		with ribs cast onto body instead of labels
611	**Ford Luton Van**	with 'Express Freight' labels
		with ribs cast onto body instead of labels
612	**Ford Articulated Low-Loader** 'Apache'	
613	**Chris Craft Capri Speedboat** (plastic) **on Trailer**, scale 86:1	
614	**Ford Refuse Lorry**	with 'City Refuse' labels
		with 'City Refuse' cast lettering

615	**Ford Cement Mixer**	
616	**Ford Milk Float**	'Milk, Milk, Milk' cast on each side
617	**Ford Cattle Transporter**	
618	**Ford Skip Lorry**	
619	**Citroën DS Coupé**	
620	**Chevrolet Corvette Stingray Coupé**	
621	**Dodge Dart Coupé**	
622	**Mercedes-Benz 280SL Coupé**, scale 86:1	
623	**Routemaster Bus**	with 'London Bus' advertisements
624	**ERF Fire Engine**	with ladder, 'Fire Brigade' labels
625	**Caravan**	
626	**Ford Circus Cage Lorry** with plastic lion, 'Circus' cast-in	
627	**Tractor Shovel**	

Gift Sets

2570	**Building Site Playset**	4 models plus sand hopper
2571	**Garage Playset**	4 models plus car ramp
2572	**Highway Playset**	4 models plus street and traffic lights
2573	**Travel Playset**	4 models plus 'Stop' barrier
2574	**Dutch Farm Playset**	4 models plus windmill
2575	**Bridge Playset**	4 models plus girder bridge

579	**Commercial Vehicle Set** 6 models	
580	**Car and Trailer Set**	6 models
581	**12 Vehicle Set**	12 models
582	**Highway Set**	
	3 models plus sand hopper, car ramp, street and traffic lights	
583	**Travel Set**	
	3 models plus girder bridge, windmill and 'Stop' barrier	

In the following listing the year shown is the date of introduction. Most models remained in production until 1976. **IW** = Impy wheels, **FW** = Flyers wheels, **HSW** = Hi-Speed wheels, **BPW** = black plastic wheels.

7	1971	**Vauxhall Firenza**, IW / FW, RHD and LHD	**£15-25**
8	-	**Ford Capri**, not issued	NPP
9	1970	**Maserati Mistral**, IW or FW	**£10-20**
10	1966	**Jaguar Mk.X**, IW or FW	**£10-20**
11	1966	**Chevrolet Corvette Stingray GT**, IW or FW	**£10-20**
12	1966	**Chrysler Imperial**, IW or FW	**£10-20**
13	-	**Ford Thunderbird**, not issued	NPP
13	1971	**Toyota 2000 GT**, Flyers wheels	**£10-20**
14	1966	**Ford Zodiac Mk.III Estate**, IW or FW	**£10-20**
15	1966	**Volkswagen Microbus**, IW or FW	**£10-20**
16	1966	**Ford Zodiac Mk.III Estate 'POLICE' Car**, IW or FW	**£10-20**
16	-	**Chrysler Imperia 'POLICE' Car**, IW or FW	**£10-20**
16m	-	**Mercedes-Benz 220 SE 'POLIZEI' Car**, Impy wheels	**£10-20**
17	1966	**Mercedes-Benz 220 SE**, IW or FW	**£10-20**
18	1966	**Ford Corsair**, IW or FW	**£10-20**
19	1967	**Volvo 1800 S**, IW or FW	**£10-20**
20	1967	**Volkswagen Ambulance**, IW or FW	**£10-20**
21	1967	**Fiat 2300 S Coupé**, IW or FW	**£10-20**
22	1967	**Rolls-Royce Silver Cloud III Convertible**, IW or FW	**£10-20**
23	1967	**Alfa Romeo Giulia 1600 Spider**, IW or FW	**£10-20**
24	1967	**Foden Tilt-cab 8w Tipper**, black plastic or HSW	**£10-20**
25	1967	**International Harvester Tractor Shovel**	**£10-20**
26	1967	**Foden Tilt-cab Petrol Tanker**, 'MOBIL', BPW or HSW	**£10-20**
27	1967	**Ford Taunus 12M**, IW or FW	**£10-20**
28	1967	**Peugeot 404 Saloon**, IW or FW	**£10-20**
29	-	**Cement Mixer Lorry**, not issued	NPP
29	1971	**Foden Tilt-cab Box Van**, 'LUCAS', BPW or HSW	**£15-20**
29	1972	**Foden Tilt-cab Box Van**, 'EXPRESS FREIGHT' labels, black plastic wheels	**£15-25**
30	1967	**AEC Merryweather Fire Engine**, black plastic or HSW	**£10-20**
31	1967	**Ford Transit Breakdown Lorry**, 'ESSO', BPW or HSW	**£10-20**
32	1968	**'FIRE CHIEF' Car**, Ford Corsair, red, IW or FW	**£10-20**
32		**'FEUERWEHR' Car**, Ford Corsair, red, Impy wheels.	**£10-20**
33	1968	**Austin-Western Mobile Crane**, elevating jib	**£10-20**
34	1968	**Euclid Crawler Tractor**, rubber tracks	**£10-20**
35	-	**Articulated Flat Truck**, not issued	NPP
36	1969	**Lotus Europa**, Flyers wheels	**£10-20**
37		**Ford GT**, not issued	NPP
38	1971	**Chevrolet Corvette Stingray**, Flyers wheels	**£15-25**
39	1971	**Ford Mustang**, Flyers wheels	**£15-25**
40	1973	**Cadillac Eldorado**, Flyers wheels	**£10-20**
41	1972	**Leyland Builders Supply Lorry**, 4 girders, 8 HSW	**£10-20**
41	1973	**Leyland Builders Supply Lorry**, 4 girders, 6 HSW	**£10-20**
41	1973	**Foden Half-cab Builders Supply Lorry**, 4 girders,6 HSW	**£10-20**
42	1972	**Foden Half-cab Tipper**, 'TILCON' labels, 8 HSW	**£15-25**
43	1973	**Leyland Flat Lorry with Pipes**, 6 HSW	**£10-20**
43	1973	**Foden Half-cab Flat Lorry with Pipes**, 6 HSW	**£10-20**
44	1972	**Leyland Marine Transport Lorry**, Speedboat, 8 HSW	**£10-20**
44	1973	**Leyland Marine Transport Lorry**, Speedboat, 6 HSW	**£10-20**
44	1973	**Foden Half-cab Marine Transport Lorry**, Speedboat, 6 HSW	**£10-20**
46	1973	**Leyland Dropside Lorry**, 6 Hi-Speed wheels	**£10-20**
47	1973	**Leyland High-Side Lorry**, 6 Hi-Speed wheels	**£10-20**
47	1973	**Foden High-Side Lorry**, Half-cab, 6 HSW	**£10-20**
48	1973	**Leyland Hopper Lorry**, 6 HSW	**£10-20**
48	1973	**Foden Half-cab Hopper Lorry**, 6 HSW	**£10-20**
49	1973	**Foden Half-cab Tipper**, 6 HSW	**£10-20**

IMPY GIFT SETS All are scarce, hence NGPP

301	1967	**Six-piece Gift Set**	NGPP
302	1967	**Six-piece Gift Set**	NGPP
303	1968	**'MOBIL' Gift Set**	NGPP
304	1968	**Five-piece Commercial Vehicle Gift Set**	NGPP
309	1968	**Twelve-piece Gift Set**	NGPP

IMPY ACCESSORIES

401	1967	**Car Lifting Ramp**	**£5-10**
402	1967	**Lock-Up Garage** (plastic)	**£5-10**
403	-	**Service Station** (not issued)	NPP
404	1968	**'MOBIL' Petrol Pump Island**, Canopy, Forecourt Sign	**£5-10**
406	-	**Fire House** (not issued)	NPP

IMPY TWO-PACKS

422	**VW Ambulance** (20) and **Mercedes-Benz 'Polizei'** (16M)		**£20-30**
423	**Fiat 2300S** (21) and **Breakdown Lorry** (31)		**£20-30**
424	**Foden Tanker** (26) and **Ford Taunus** (27)		**£20-30**
425	**Ford Zodiac** (14) and **Tractor** (25)		**£20-30**
427	**Alfa Romeo** (23) and **'MOBIL' Petrol Pumps** (404)		**£20-30**
431	**Chevrolet Corvette** (11) and **Fiat 2300S** (21)		**£20-30**
432	**Fire Engine** (30) and **Ford Corsair 'FEUERWEHR'** (32)		**£20-30**

IMPY series, post-1976

The Market Price Range is shown as £5 - £10 but as yet there is little collectors' interest in these recent models.

50	**Six-wheel Tipper**	**£5-10**
51	**Six-wheel High Side Lorry**	**£5-10**
52	**Six-wheel Flat Lorry with Crane**	**£5-10**
53	**Six-wheel Flat Lorry with Speedboat**	**£5-10**
54	**Six-wheel Cement Mixer**	**£5-10**
55	**Six-wheel Luton Van**	**£5-10**
56	**Six-wheel Dropside Lorry**	**£5-10**
57	**Six-wheel Flat Lorry with Water Tank**	**£5-10**
58	**Six-wheel Hopper Lorry**	**£5-10**
59	**Six-wheel Flat Lorry with Pipes**	**£5-10**
60	**Six-wheel Flat Lorry with Planks**	**£5-10**
61	**Six-wheel Petrol Tanker**	**£5-10**
71	**Range Rover**	**£5-10**
72	**Cadillac Eldorado**	**£5-10**
73	**Chevrolet Corvette Stingray**	**£5-10**
74	**Toyota 2000 GT**	**£5-10**
75	**Range Rover Police Car**	**£5-10**
76	**Chevrolet Corvette Stingray 'GT Rally'**	**£5-10**
77	**Jaguar Mk.X**	**£5-10**
78	**Maserati Mistral**	**£5-10**
79	**Ford Mustang**	**£5-10**
80	**Lotus Europa**	**£5-10**
81	**Volvo Coupé**	**£5-10**
82	**Mercedes-Benz**	**£5-10**
181	**Articulated Flat Lorry with Crane**	**£5-10**
182	**Articulated Petrol Tanker**	**£5-10**
183	**Articulated Low Loader with Tuf-Tots car**	**£5-10**
184	**Articulated Flat Lorry with water tank**	**£5-10**
185	**Cadillac Eldorado with Tuf-Tots Speedboat on trailer**	**£5-10**
185	**Range Rover with Tuf-Tots Speedboat on trailer**	**£5-10**
185	**Range Rover 'RNLI' with boat on trailer**	**£5-10**
185	**Jaguar Mk.X with Cabin Cruiser on trailer**	**£5-10**
186	**Crane Lorry (no.52) with Impy car**	**£5-10**
187	**Luton Van (no.55) with Trailer**	**£5-10**
188	**Articulated Low Loader with Cabin Cruiser**	**£5-10**
189	**Articulated Flat Lorry with Planks**	**£5-10**
190	**Petrol Tanker (no.61) with Trailer**	**£5-10**
191	**High Side Lorry (no.51) with Trailer**	**£5-10**
192	**Cement Mixer (no.54) with Flat Trailer**	**£5-10**
1251	**Articulated Car Transporter**	**£5-10**
1252	**AEC Merryweather HTTL Fire Engine** (re-packed no.30)	**£5-10**
1256	**Car Transporter (no.1251) with four Impy cars**	**£30-40**

Lone Star Sets

'International Peace Force Vehicles' Set (made 1974) contains:
1271 Small Tank, 1272 Searchlight on Trailer, 1273 Mortar Launcher, 1274 Radar Detector Unit, 1275 Ack-Ack Gun, 1276 Silver Small Canon, 1277 All Blue Military Jeep ....NGPP

'GULLIVER COUNTY' Series. Boxed set of three Coaches. White card box with scene depicting a coach, fire engine, articulated lorry and two cars.
i) Mid-Green Coach, Grey wheels, 'SCHOOL BUS' logo on sides
ii) Cream Coach, Grey wheels, 'SCHOOL BUS' logo on sides
iii) Mid-Green Coach, Grey wheels, 'GREENLINE' logo on sides **£100-150**

'War in the Desert' Set includes 3 German and 3 US military vehicles...NGPP

Miscellaneous items

1259 Routemaster Bus. Made 1972-89 from two castings which include seats and stair details. Red body, Silver trim, paper adverts on sides 'SEE LONDON BY BUS' and 'BUY LONE STAR'. Route is '29 VICTORIA', Black plastic tyres. Cast into base: 'LONE STAR' and 'MADE IN ENGLAND'............**£5-10**
RAC Land Rover and Caravan....no details..NGPP

'Aircraft of the World' Series (1:250 scale)

'Scandinavian Airlines' Caravelle **£40-50**
'Pan American' Boeing 707 ....**£50-60**

'Modern Army' Series

'Lorry', 'Bren Gun Carrier' and **'Jeep'** ....each: **£10-15**
'Small Mobile Fighting Unit' ....NGPP

'Farm' Series, 'Jeep' **£10-15**

The greatest *IMPY* yet!

No 24

FODEN Tilt-Cab TRUCK

Here's a really great model for you—with *all* the authentic details $3\frac{3}{4}$" long, this die-cast metal model has all these features :—

★ Tilting Cab
★ Windows, seats and steering wheel
★ Die-cast chassis
★ Die-cast engine
★ Non-scratch tyres
★ Tipping back with hinged loading flap

3!

LONE ★ STAR
Roadmaster **IMPY**
Super Cars
have everything

Remember, IMPYs are the die-cast models with ALL the Real-Car features! Additions to the series are coming along all the time!

Next on the list are.

★ **Ford Taunus**
★ **Tractor**
★ **Rolls Royce**
       Silver Cloud III
★ **Merryweather**
       Fire Engine

An advertisement for **Lone Star Impy** models as it appeared in the 'Eagle and Boy's World' comic of 24 June 1967.

Matchbox Toys

Introduction

The company was founded in 1947 by the unrelated Leslie and Rodney Smith who combined their names to form 'Lesney' Products Ltd. They were soon joined by Jack Odell – a recognised die-casting expert.

The most famous of the various early products was the 'Coronation Coach'. During the 1950s the company developed the highly successful Matchbox '1-75' and 'Models of Yesteryear' ranges. Today, certain models in the '1-75' series are highly sought after and fetch very high prices at auction.

Following a difficult trading period Lesney Products Ltd was bought in 1982 by the Universal Toy Co. of Hong Kong. Models issued subsequently fall outside the scope of this publication. (Collectors requiring information on the later issues should contact MICA whose details appear on the opposite page).

The Models of Yesteryear section has been completely replaced by a unique new listing specially prepared for the Catalogue by Horace Dunkley, the leading authority on Yesteryears. The Editor is indebted to Trevor Bannister and Nigel Cooper who have fully revised the '1-75' Series listings.

The Editor would also like to thank the many collectors who have contributed additional information.

'Moko' Products

'**Moko Products**' was a toy distribution firm founded by Moses Kohnstam who came to Britain from Nuremburg, Germany at the turn of the century.

Moko provided the distribution and storage facilities and, irrespective of the supplier, all toys were marketed as Moko products. The early issues after the Second World War were housed in plain cardboard boxes with 'tuck in' ends. These usually had only single colour printing that did not include a picture of the model. During the early 1950s the packaging became much more attractive with brightly coloured boxes displaying a picture of the model inside. Moko will best be remembered for their distribution of the early Matchbox '1-75' toys under the name of 'MoKo-Lesney'. Moses Kohnstam was succeeded by Richard Kohnstam in 1953.

The following listing of Moko items constitutes all the information available to publish at present. Additional information would be welcomed by the Editor.

Year(s)	Details	MPR
c1948-53	**Mechanical Tractor** Probably early Lesney. Orange body, Green rubber tracks, Black wheels, Green/Black driver, (early issue in plain box)	**£300-400**
1950-55	**Mechanical Tractor** As previous model but with Orange wheels, (later issue in picture box)	**£300-400**
1947-50	**Excavator (with open cab)** Orange body and jib, Black digger and chassis, Green rubber tracks, Orange crank handle. Early card box has 'Moko TOYS OF DISTINCTION' logo	**£300-400**
1950-55	**'RUSTON BUCYRUS' Excavator** Yellow over Red body with Black '10 RB' logo. Black or Dark Green chassis, jib, digger, crank wheel and rubber tracks. Later box with full colour picture	**£200-250**
1950-55	**Builders Crane** All Blue crane base and jib with unpainted metal hook. Later card box with full colour picture	**£175-200**
1947-50	**Crawler Bulldozer** Red body and dozer blade (possibly early Lesney). Early plain card box	**£250-300**

Year(s)	Details	MPR
1950-55	**'Pop-Pop Series' Motor Scooter** Dark Red scooter with Black seat. Female figure has blonde hair, blue sweater, red or blue trousers. Later box with full colour picture	**£450-550**
1950-55	**Drummer Boy (Mechanical)** Red body, Gold trim, Black busby. Cream/Yellow drum, Gold drumsticks	**£900-1,200**
1947-50	**Hayrick** Yellow/Green body	**£200-250**
1947-50	**Fairground Carousel** Blue/Red base and centre column, Maroon/Blue roof, 2 Red and 2 Blue seated figures. Plain card box	**£1,000-1,200**
1947-50	**Mechanical Mouse** Grey body with Red eyes plus curling tail. Early plain card box	**£175-200**
c1950	**Peregrine Puppet**	NGPP
c1950	**'Jumbo, the Walking Elephant'**. Mechanical / tinplate. With diagonal printing	**£300-400**
	With horizontal printing	**£400-500**
c1950	**0-4-0 Tank Engine** Light Metallic Green, bare metal wheels	**£125-150**

Moko 'Farmette' Series

Miniature size models packed in end-flap type boxes with colour picture of the model. The die-cast horses have dark brown bodies and white feet.
NB These are delicate models; some signs of metal deterioration have been observed.

No.	Year	Name	Details	MPR
No.1	1950-53	**Timber Trailer with two Horses**	Green body, four Red wheels, timber load	**£150-200**
No.2	1950-53	**Farm Cart with two Horses**	Mid or Dark Blue cart body, Red raves, four Red 12-spoke wheels	**£150-200**
No.3	1950-53	**Bull Wagon with two Horses**	Green wagon body, two horses in tandem, Brown metal bull, four Red 12-spoke wheels.	**£150-200**

'Treasure Chest' Series

Packed in Brown 'chests' with yellow 'strapping'.
NB These are delicate models; some signs of metal deterioration have been observed.

No.	Year	Name	Details	MPR
No.10	1950-53	**Hay Cart**	Orange body, two Green raves, two Green wheels, one horse	**£50-75**
No.11	1950-53	**Millers Cart**	Blue body, two Red wheels, three White sacks, one horse	**£50-75**
No.12	1950-53	**Water Cart**	Green/Red cart, two Red wheels, one horse	**£50-75**

The early 'Lesney' toys

Lesney Products issued their first diecast toys in 1948. Whilst production ceased during the Korean war period (1950-52), the models produced formed the basis from which the 1-75 series was launched in 1953. They were sold in boxes under the name of 'MoKo' who were ultimately to also market all the early 1-75 series models. **NB Models were sold boxed.**

Road Roller	All Green (shades) body and flywheel, unpainted wheels	**£350-400**
	As previous model but with Red roller wheels and Yellow flywheel	**£350-400**
	With a driver but without a flywheel	**£200-250**
	Without a driver and without flywheel	**£150-200**
Cement Mixer	All Green or All-Blue body, Red wheels	**£150-200**
	Pale Green body, Red or Yellow drum and wheels	**£200-250**
	Dark Green body, Red or Yellow drum and wheels	**£200-250**
	Red body, Green drum and wheels	**£200-300**
	Orange engine cover, Black drum, Yellow wheels	**£200-300**
Caterpillar Tractor	Orange or Yellow body, Red roller wheels, Black rubber tracks	**£300-400**
Caterpillar Bulldozer	Green, Orange or Red body, Black rubber tracks	**£300-400**
	Yellow body, Red dozer blade and wheels	**£175-200**
Prime Mover	Orange tractor (Green engine on some), Blue trailer, Red/Yellow dozer, 'BRITISH ROAD SERVICES'	**£900-1,200**
	As previous but with Beige trailer	**£900-1,200**
'MASSEY-HARRIS' Tractor	Red body, Cream hubs, Black rubber tyres	**£450-550**
Milk Cart	Orange body, White driver and six crates, Black or Brown horse, Black or Grey wheels, 'PASTEURISED MILK' cast into cart	**£650-750**
	As previous model but with Blue body	**£800-1,000**
Soap-Box Racer	Brown box, Grey spoked wheels (16 and 9), Brown or Dark Blue boy, Pink face	**£2,500-3,500**

Quarry Truck	Yellow body, Black tyres, 'LAING'. Only one example known to exist	**NGPP**
Covered Wagon with Barrels	Green body, White cover, two Red barrels, six Mid-Brown horses (with White tails), with postilion rider and wagon driver	**£250-300**
Covered Wagon	As previous model but with Chocolate Brown horses and **no barrels**	**£175-200**
'RAG & BONE MERCHANTS' Cart	Yellow body, Red wheels, Black horse, Brown driver, with seven pieces of 'junk': mangle-wheel, bike frame, bedhead, bath, bucket, box, cistern	**£1,200-1,500**
	Same but Green body, Red wheels	**£1,500-1,800**
Coronation Coach (large)	Gold coach with King and Queen, eight White horses, Gold/Red trappings, four Red riders. 200 issued	**£800-1,000**
Coronation Coach (large)	Gold, Silver or Gilt coach with just the Queen inside. Horses and riders as for previous model	**£225-275**
Coronation Coach (small)	Silver or Gold coach, eight White horses, Red/Gold trappings, four Red riders, 'A MOKO TOY BY LESNEY' cast into horsebar (1,000,000 sold)	**£120-140**
'Muffin The Mule'	White body, Red/Gold harness, Black trim	**£250-300**
Excavator	Digger and chassis are Dark Brown	**£250-300**
Motor Scooter	Blue Scooter	**NGPP**
Breadbait Press	1st type: Red body, unpainted 'butterfly' press	**£40-50**
	2nd type: As 1st type but with Green press	**£50-60**
	3rd type: As 2nd type but with 'MILBRO' cast onto Red body	**£60-70**

Matchbox Toys Auction Results

MATCHBOX TOYS sold by Vectis Model Auctions,
Fleck Way, Thornaby, Stockton-on-Tees. TS17 9JZ
Condition abbreviations appearing in Vectis Auctions catalogues:
M = Mint, **NM** = Near Mint, **NMB** = Near Mint Boxed, **EP** = Excellent Plus,
E = Excellent, **EB** = Excellent Boxed, **GP** = Good Plus, **VG** = Very Good,
G = Good, **GB** = Good Box, **F** = Fair, **FB** = Fair Box, **P** = Poor.
Matchbox wheel abbreviations: **GPW** = Grey Plastic Wheels,
SPW = Silver Plastic Wheels, **BPW** = Black Plastic Wheels.

REGULAR WHEELS MINIATURES
5b 'Players Please' DD Bus, 57mm, GPW, M in GP box	**£70**
8e Ford Mustang, orange, red interior, chrome hubs	**£370**
11a ERF Tanker, green, gold trim, NM in E box	**£600**
12c Land Rover Safari, met. gold, red-brown load, BPW, M in E box	**£1,050**
15a Diamond-T Prime Mover, yellow, metal wheels, EP in M box	**£1,200**
15b Super Atlantic Tractor, orange, large GPW, M in E box	**£1,800**
17a Bedford Removals Van, maroon, gold trim, NM in E box	**£160**
19b MG-MGA Sports Car, off-white, SPW	**£410**
20c Chevroleet Impala Taxi, yellow, cream interior, rare GPW	**£2,800**
21b Bedford Coach, 68mm, dark green, GPW, MB	**£200**
22b Vauxhall Cresta, metallic copper, GPW, M in E box	**£120**
22b Vauxhall Cresta, dark gold body, SPW, NM in E box	**£90**
22b Vauxhall Cresta, pale grey over lilac, GPW, NM in NM box	**£140**
23b Berkley Caravan, metallic lime-green, GPW, E/UB	**£680**
25d Ford Cortina Mk.II, blue body, silver base, BPW (new variation)	**£1,200**
26a ERF Cement Mixer, orange including barrel, SPW, M in E box	**£1,800**
26b Foden Cement Mixer, orange, grey barrel, GPW	**£950**
27c Cadillac Sixty Special, metallic lilac, pink roof, SPW	**£110**
31b Ford Station Wagon, yellow, clear windows, SPW, NM in G box	**£220**
31c Lincoln Continental, met. lime-green (Superfast colour), BPW, MB	**£1,150**
32a Jaguar XK120, red, GPW, M in NM box	**£210**
34b VW Caravette, pale green, dark green base/interior, SPW, M in E box	**£2,000**
39a Ford Zodiac Convertible, pale peach, SPW	**£220**
39b Pontiac Convertible, metallic purple, NM in NM box	**£100**
41a Jaguar 'D'-type, green, GPW	**£110**
41c Ford GT40, white, red interior, RN '6', wire wheels, NM in E box	**£2,200**
42a Bedford 'Evening News' Van, BPW, NM boxed	**£130**
43a Hillman Minx, green, metal wheels, NM in E box	**£220**
45a Vauxhall Victor, red body, MW, NM in E box	**£2,600**
46a Morris Minor 1000, blue, GPW, MB	**£160**
46a Morris Minor 1000, pale brown, metal wheels, NM in NM box	**£2,500**
55b Ford Fairlane, metallic blue, SPW, red dome light, NM in E box	**£620**
66a Citroën DS19, yellow, SPW, NM in NM box	**£510**
73a Leyland Pressure Refueller, RAF blue, BPW, NM in M box	**£3,000**
75a Ford Thunderbird, cream, peach side panels, GPW	**£140**
75b Ferrari Berlinetta, red body, chrome hubs, MB	**£240**

MOKO
Excavator, maroon cab, E in G box box	**£310**
Bulldozer, red green, rubber tracks, E in G box	**£210**
Road Roller, green including canopy, GP	**£180**
Builder's Crane, blue, E in GP box	**£180**
'Pop-Pop' Series Motor Scooter with rider, blue, GP in G box	**£400**

EARLY LESNEY
Large Scale Coronation Coach (with Queen), silver, E in GP box	**£200**
Major No. 1 Massey-Harris Tractor, red, E in GP box	**£320**

KING SIZE
K8 Tractor and Transporter 'Laing', E in GP box	**£170**

MATCHBOX TOYS sold by Christie's S. Kensington
85 Old Brompton Road, London, SW7 3LD. Abbreviations:
M - Mint, **E** - Excellent, **VG** - Very Good, **G** - Good, **F** - Fair, **P** - Poor.
Moko Lesney Matchbox PS4 Commercial Vehicle Set, 1959, grey plastic wheels, E in P box	**£763**
11a ERF Tanker, green body in original box, G-VG in G box	**£446**

MATCHBOX TOYS sold in MICA Postal Auctions
Moko Heavy Tractor in Orange with complete original rubber tracks, driver, without cast tow hook, clean picture box	**£168**
Lesney Jumbo Elephant clockwork toy, excellent unboxed	**£401**
Y2 Prince Henry Vauxhall in blue with red seats, Mint Boxed	**£591**
Y4-3 Opel Coupé pre-production colour trial, as issue 7, but (Simplex) pea green body and chassis	**£601**
Y9 Showman's Engine in dark maroon as issue 2, slight marks, line drawing box	**£121**
Y10-2 as issue 1 with black seats, boxed, virtually mint	**£1,526**
Y12-2 1909 Thomas Flyabout as issue 1, but bright red seats/grille, mint unboxed	**£238**

Matchbox Model Identification

Model Number is always cast into the base, chassis or body. Obvious exceptions are the early models which were not numbered. 'Lesney' is cast into all issues between 1953 and 1982.

'Matchbox' or **'Matchbox Series'** is shown on the base or chassis of all issues after 1965. All issues after 1957 had the model name on the base or chassis. Exceptions include those without a base (e.g., No.24 Excavator).

Suspension and **windows**. Car models were fitted with windows after 1961 and suspension after 1965. Baseplates are metal castings until the late 1970s

when plastic bases introduced. From 1983 they are marked 'Made in Macau'.

Wheels were metal castings on early models and were gradually changed to grey, silver or black plastic. **Superfast wheels** introduced in late 1960s and issues from 1968-69 may be found with either type. Novelties such as **'Laser Wheels'** introduced in the late 1980s. **'Rolamatics'** were introduced in the 1970s having working parts that were operated by pushing (see the Superfast section for these).

Model descriptions. This Catalogue tries to give original maker's description of model names and

colours but early Matchbox listings are known to be inaccurate graphically. Maker's catalogue photographs are often taken of mock-ups months before production starts while model designs become changed before release. Because of space limitations, it has been necessary to include a number of descriptive abbreviations (refer to list at the foot of this page).

Dimensions refer to the greatest overall measurement (usually the length).

Superfast issues are listed separately elsewhere in this Matchbox section.

Ref.	Intro.	Details	MPR

MB 1

1a	53	**Diesel Road Roller** (Aveling Barford). Red metal roller wheels, Tan driver cast-in, no number, crimped axles, 49mm.	
		Type 1: curved lower canopy ends and thin braces above canopy supports, **Type 2**: straight ends and thick braces above supports, brace extension.	
		Dark Green body, Type 1	**£180-220**
		Dark Green body, Type 2	**£60-70**
		Light Green body, Type 2	**£150-175**
1b	56	**Diesel Road Roller** (Aveling Barford)	
		Light Green body, Red metal roller wheels, Lt. or Dk. Tan driver, high peaked canopy, no number, hook, 57 mm	**£35-45**
1c	58	**Diesel Road Roller** (Aveling Barford)	
		Light Green body and driver, Red metal roller wheels, number cast-in, high peaked canopy, hook, 62 mm	**£80-100**
		Dark Green body	**£40-60**
1d	62	**Diesel Road Roller** (Aveling Barford)	
		Green body and driver, Red plastic rollers, 67 mm	**£25-30**
1e	67	**Mercedes Truck**	
		Turquoise body, Orange canopy, Black plastic wheels, 75 mm	**£8-12**

MB 2

2a	53	**Muir Hill Site Dumper.** Dark Green body, Red dumper,	
		Green painted MW, 42 mm	**£120-140**
		Same but with unpainted MW	**£40-50**
2b	57	**Muir Hill Site Dumper.** Same but:	
		Tan driver, metal wheels, 46 mm	**£40-50**
		Same but GPW, crimped axles	**£40-50**
		Same but GPW, rounded axles	**£40-50**
2c	62	**Muir Hill Dumper Truck**	
		Red body, Green dumper, '*LAING*', Black plastic wheels, 54 mm	**£20-30**
		Same but '*MUIR HILL*' logo and picture-box (72 only known)	**£60-80**
2d	67	**Mercedes Trailer.** Turquoise body, Orange top, BPW	**£8-12**

MB 3

3a	53	**Cement Mixer**	
		Orange MW, Blue main body	**£30-40**
		GPW, crimped axles	**£80-100**
		GPW, rounded axles	**£80-100**
3b	61	**Bedford Tipper Truck.** (All have Grey body and chassis)	
		Maroon back, GPW, 24 treads	**£160-180**
		Maroon back, GPW, 45 treads	**£400-500**
		Maroon back, BPW	**£20-30**
		Red dump, GPW	**£80-100**
		Red dump, BPW	**£25-35**
3c	67	**Mercedes Ambulance.** Cream or Off-White body	**£20-30**

MB 4

4a	54	**Massey Harris Tractor.** (with mudguards over rear wheels), Red body, Gold or Yellow rear hubs, Tan driver	**£60-80**
4b	57	**Massey Harris Tractor.** (without mudguards over rear wheels), metal wheels, Gold or Yellow rear hubs	**£50-60**
		Grey plastic wheels	**£80-90**
4c	60	**Triumph T110 Motor Cycle**	
		Steel Blue bike/sidecar, Silver spoked wheels, BPT	**£90-120**
		Same but with Copper bike	**£2,000-3,000**
4d	66	**Stake Truck** Blue stake body	**£80-100**
		Green stake body	**£12-15**

MB 5

5a	54	**London Bus** (52 mm).	
		'Buy Matchbox Series' on paper label	**£60-70**
5b	57	**1957 London Bus** (57 mm).	
		'Buy Matchbox Series' decal, metal wheels	**£40-50**
		'Buy Matchbox Series' decal, Grey plastic wheels	**£60-70**
		'Players Please' decal, GPW	**£100-120**
		'BP Visco-Static' decal, GPW	**£200-250**
5c	60	**Routemaster** (66 mm).	
		'Players Please' decal, GPW	**£110-130**
		'Peardrax', GPW or BPW	**£500-750**
		'BP Visco-Static' decal, Grey or Black plastic wheels	**£25-35**
		'Baron of Beef' decal, Grey or Black plastic wheels	**£350-450**
5d	65	**Routemaster** (70 mm).	
		'BP Longlife' decal	**£20-25**
		'BP Visco-Static' decal or label	**£15-20**
		'Baron of Beef' decal	**£350-400**
		'Pegram' label	**£350-400**

MB 6

6a	54	**Quarry Truck** 55mm.	
		Orange body, Grey tipper with six ribs, metal wheels	**£40-50**
		Same but Grey plastic wheels, domed/crimped axles	**£600-700**
6b	59	**Euclid Quarry Truck**	
		Yellow body, four ribs, decals, six BPW, '*Euclid*'	**£40-50**
		Knobbly GPW, domed axles	**£1,500-2,000**
6c	63	**Euclid Dump Truck**	
		Six Black wheels (rear double wheels are one piece)	**£15-20**
		Ten Black wheels (rear wheels are normal double wheels)	**£15-20**
6d	68	**Ford Pick Up** Red body, White canopy, chrome grille	**£18-20**
		Same but White grille	**£25-35**

MB 7

7a	54	**Horse Drawn Milk Float**	
		Dark Orange body, White driver, crates and logo, metal wheels	**£50-65**
		As previous but with GPW	**£90-110**
		Pale Orange body, metal wheels	**£50-65**
		Pale Orange body and logo, White hat and crates, GPW	**£90-110**
		Pale Orange body, Silver driver and crates, Grey plastic wheels (beware fakes)	**£450-550**
7b	61	**Ford Anglia** Light Blue, Green windows, GPW	**£70-80**
		With Silver plastic wheels	**£45-55**
		With Black plastic wheels	**£35-40**
7c	67	**Refuse Truck.** Orange-Red body, Grey and Silver dumper	**£10-15**

MB 8

8a	55	**Caterpillar Tractor** (42 mm).	
		Yellow body and rollers, Red driver, Green tracks	**£350-450**
		Same but with unpainted rollers	**£50-65**
		Orange body and driver, Gold or Silver grille, Green tracks	**£65-80**
		Yellow body/driver, Silver or Yellow grille, Green or Grey tracks	**£40-50**

Abbreviations used in this listing:	
BPT = Black plastic tyres	**MPR** = Market Price Range
BPW = Black plastic wheels	**MW** = metal wheels
GPW = Grey plastic wheels	**RN** = racing or rally number
	SPW = Silver plastic wheels

8b   58   **Caterpillar Tractor** (42 mm).
Yellow body and driver, no.'8' cast-in, Green rubber tracks £70-85
8c   61   **Caterpillar Tractor** (48 mm).
Yellow body, metal rollers, Green tracks £40-55
Same but with Silver rollers...£90-110
Same but with Black rollers...£30-35
8d   64   **Caterpillar Tractor** (51 mm).
Yellow body, no driver, Green rubber tracks, Black rollers............£20-25
8e   66   **Ford Mustang**
White body, Black wheels with Silver hubcaps........................£25-35
White body, Silver wheels with Black tyres..........................£20-30
Orange body, Silver wheels..£300-400

MB 9

9a   55   **Dennis Fire Escape** (57mm).
Red body, no front bumper, metal wheels, crimped axles...............£45-55
9b   58   **Dennis Fire Escape** (58mm).
Red body, with front bumper, MW, number cast underneath.............£70-80
Same but with GPW...£350-450
9c   59   **Merryweather Marquis Series III Fire Engine**
Red body with Tan ladder, GPW, crimped axles, 64 mm................£60-75
Same but with rounded axles.......................................£40-50
Same but with Gold ladder..£40-50
With Gold ladder and BPW...£30-40
With Silver ladder, BPW...£80-90
With Tan ladder, BPW...£65-75
9d   66   **Boat and Trailer** (76mm, 77mm).
Blue/White boat, Blue trailer, Black plastic wheels £15-20

MB 10

10a   57   **Scammell Mechanical Horse**
Red cab, Gold trim, Grey trailer, crimped axles, MW, 56mm........£70-85
10b   57   **Scammell Mechanical Horse**
Red Cab, Brown trailer, crimped axles, metal wheels, 75 mm £50-60
Red cab, Gold trim, Light Brown trailer, Grey plastic wheels........£85-95
Red cab, Silver trim, Light Brown trailer, Grey plastic wheels......£75-85
10c   60   **Foden 8-wheel Sugar Container**
Dark Blue body, with crown on rear decal, Grey wheels £80-90
Without crown, Grey wheels.......................................£70-80
Without crown, Silver wheels £120-130
Without crown, Black wheels......................................£50-60
10d   66   **Leyland Pipe Truck**
Red body, 6 or 7 Grey pipes, Silver base and grille £15-20
Same but White base and grille £60-75

MB 11

11a   55   **E.R.F. Road Tanker**. All models with metal wheels.
Green body, Gold trim £1,400-1,800
Dark Yellow body, Silver trim £150-175
Light Yellow body, Silver trim £85-100
Red body, Gold trim, small 'ESSO' decal on rear of tank £120-140
Same but large 'ESSO' decal.......................................£75-85
Same but two small 'ESSO' decals on tank sides £600-800
Same but two large 'ESSO' decals on sides £600-700
11b   58   **'ESSO' Petrol Tanker (E.R.F.)**.
All models with red body and 'ESSO' decal at rear.
Metal wheels, Gold trim £250-350
Metal wheels, Silver trim £75-85
Grey plastic wheels £60-70
Silver plastic wheels £1,000-1,100
Black plastic wheels £90-100
11c   65   **Jumbo Crane**
Yellow body and weight box £25-30
Yellow body, Red weight box £15-20
11d   69   **Mercedes Scaffolding Truck**
Silver body, Yellow plastic scaffolds, BPW £15-18

MB 12

12a   55   **Land Rover**
Green body, Silver trim on some, Tan driver, MW, 43 mm............£40-50
12b   59   **Land Rover Series II**
Green body, Black plastic wheels, crimped axles.....................£50-60
BPW, rounded axles £35-45
Grey plastic wheels £250-350
12c   65   **Land Rover Safari**
Green body, Brown luggage, BPW £25-30
Blue body, Brown or Red-Brown luggage, BPW £18-20
Metallic Gold body, Red-Brown luggage, BPW......................£800-900

MB 13

13a   55   **Wreck Truck** (51mm).
Tan body, Red crane and hook, MW on crimped axles.................£40-55
13b   58   **Wreck Truck** (54mm).
Light Brown body, Red crane and hook, '13' cast-in, MW............£40-60
Same but with GPW...£70-85
13c   60   **Thames Trader Wreck Truck**
All models with Red body and crane.
Yellow side decals, knobbly Grey MW (24 treads), Red hook........£70-80
Fine tread Grey wheels (45 treads), Grey hook.....................£85-100
BPW, Silver or Grey hook..£50-60
13d   65   **Dodge Wreck Truck**
Green cab, Yellow body, Grey hook, 'BP' decal...................£1,800-2,000
Note: Fakes from 1970 have red hooks, 'BP' labels, crimped
axles and the thick crane casting. Only the original Green cab
version (from the Lesney factory) has a thin crane. But these
fakes (only 24 were produced) are now sought after by some
collectors and thus sell for £400-500
Yellow cab, Green body, Grey hook £20-30
Same but with Red hook..£20-25

MB 14

14a   55   **Ambulance (Daimler)** (49mm). Cream body, Silver trim,
Red cross on roof, MW on crimped or domed/crimped axles,
no number, 'Ambulance' cast on sides................................£40-50
14b   58   **Daimler Ambulance** (59 mm). All have a 'Red Cross' on roof.
Cream body, metal wheels £40-50
Cream body, Grey plastic wheels...................................£70-80
Off-White body, metal wheels £140-160
Off-White body, GPW..£60-70
Off-White body, SPW..£250-275
14c   62   **Bedford Lomas Ambulance**
All models with 'Red Cross' and 'LCC Ambulance' on sides.
White body, Black wheels £125-150
White body, Silver wheels £275-300
Off-White body, Silver wheels £120-150
Off-White body, locating marks for Red Cross cast into
roof, Silver grille, Silver wheels £350-400
Off-White body, Grey wheels £200-240
Off-White body, Black wheels £30-35
14d   68   **Iso Grifo**
Metallic Blue body, Blue interior...................................£25-30
Dark Metallic Blue, Blue interior...................................£20-25

MB 15

15a   55   **Diamond T Prime Mover**
Yellow body, six MW, hook, no number, 55 mm.................£1,400-1,800
Orange body, six metal wheels £30-35
Same but with ten GPW..£400-500
15b   59   **Super Atlantic Tractor**
Orange body, Black base, hook, BPW, 67 mm.........................£50-60
Orange body, knobbly GPW......................................£1,000-1,200
15c   63   **Tippax Refuse Collector**. All models with Blue body,
Grey container and Black wheels.
With knobbly tread wheels (24 treads), decal........................£60-70
With fine tread wheels, *'Cleansing Service'* decal or label............£20-25
15d   68   **Volkswagen 1500 Saloon**
Off-White or Cream body, '137' decals on doors.....................£35-40
Same but '137' labels on doors.....................................£25-35

MB 16

16a   55   **Transporter Trailer**. Tan body, 6 MW (crimped axles or
domed <u>and</u> crimped axles)..£25-35
16b   60   **Super Atlantic Trailer**
Tan body, Grey plastic wheels £90-100
Orange body, GPW...£950-1,100
Orange, BPW, Black or Orange drawbar £35-45
16c   63   **Scammell Snow Plough**. Grey body, Orange tipper,
Red/White or Orange/White decal, GPW...........................£110-130
With Black plastic wheels £25-30
16d   69   **Case Bulldozer Tractor**
Red/Yellow body, Green rubber tracks, hook, 64 mm.................£12-15

MB 17

17a   55   **Bedford Removals Van**. All models with
'MATCHBOX REMOVALS SERVICE' decals and MW.
Light Blue body, Silver trim £200-250
Maroon body, Silver trim £450-500
Maroon body, Gold trim £225-250
Green body, Silver trim £45-60

17b 58 Bedford Removals Van
Green body, MW, decal with or without Black outline £40-50
Green body, Grey plastic wheels, decal with outline.....................£70-90
Dark Green body, GPW, decal with outline £175-200

17c 60 Austin FX3 Taxi
Maroon body, Mid-Grey interior, Tan driver, GPW......................£45-55
Same but with SPW, Mid-Grey interior £100-120
With Pale Grey interior and Silver plastic wheels £120-140

17d 64 Foden Tipper
Red chassis, Orange tipper, *'HOVERINGHAM'*, Black base.........£20-30
Same but with Red base £15-20

17e 69 Horse Box
Red cab, dark green box, grey door,
chrome base, 2 white horses on sprue...................................NGPP

MB 18

18a 55 Caterpillar Bulldozer (46 mm).
Yellow body, Red blade, Green tracks £40-50

18b 58 Caterpillar Bulldozer (50 mm).
Yellow body and blade, Green tracks £60-70
Same but with Grey tracks £70-80

18c 61 Caterpillar Bulldozer (58 mm).
Yellow body and blade, Green tracks, metal rollers £25-30
Same but Silver plastic rollers £140-160
Same but Black plastic rollers £25-230

18d 64 Caterpillar Bulldozer (62 mm). Yellow body and blade,
no driver, Green tracks, Silver plastic rollers £140-160
Black plastic rollers £20-25

18e 69 Field Car. Yellow body, Red-Brown roof, Red hubs £10-15
Same but unpainted base £10-12
Same but with Green hubs..£270-300

MB 19

19a 56 MG Midget TD
Cream body, Brown driver, Red seats, MW, no number, 51 mm £70-80
Off-White body, metal wheels £120-140

19b 58 MG 'MGA' Sports Car. All models with Off-White body,
Red seats and Tan driver.
Metal wheels, Gold trim £300-400
Metal wheels, Silver trim £120-140
Grey plastic wheels, Silver trim £120-140
Silver plastic wheels £250-300

19c 62 Aston Martin DBR5. All models with Metallic Green body,
Yellow wheels, White driver.
Number '19' £40-60
Number '41' or '52' £120-140
Number '3' or '5' £80-100

19d 65 Lotus Racing Car. Dark Green body, Yellow wheels,
White driver, racing number '3' as decal or label £10-15
Orange body, RN '3' £40-50

MB 20

20a 56 E.R.F. Stake Truck
Light Green body, Silver trim, metal wheels £2,000-3,000
Maroon body, Gold trim, MW £250-300
Maroon body, Silver trim, MW £35-45
Maroon body, Silver trim, Grey plastic wheels £200-300
Dark Red body, metal wheels £45-55
Dark Red body, GPW £200-300

20b 59 E.R.F. 68G Truck. All have Dark Blue body and 'EVER READY'
decals on sides. Early decals with Orange outline, later with Red.
GPW, crimped axles £65-75
GPW, rounded axles £50-60
Silver plastic wheels £140-160
Black plastic wheels £60-80

20c 65 Chevrolet Impala Taxi
Orange-Yellow body, Cream interior, GPW, Taxi decal........£1,800-2,000
Orange-Yellow, Cream interior, BPW, Silver base, Taxi decal £30-40
Same but with unpainted base £15-20
Same but with red interior £20-30
Yellow body, Cream interior, Taxi label £120-140
Same but with Red interior £25-30

MB 21

21a 56 Bedford Coach (57 mm).
Green body and base, *'LONDON-GLASGOW'*, MW £60-70

21b 58 Bedford Coach (68 mm).
All have Black base and *'LONDON TO GLASGOW'* decals.
Green body, metal wheels £80-100
Green body, Grey plastic wheels £90-110
Dark Green body, GPW £120-140

21c 61 Commer Bottle Float
All models with Pale Green body and Black base.
On early models the bottles are Cream, later ones are White.
Bottle on door, SPW, clear windows £100-130
Bottle on door, SPW, Green windows.....................................£70-80
Cow on door, SPW...£50-60
Cow on door, GPW...£120-150
Cow on door, BPW £25-30

21d 68 Foden Concrete Truck
Yellow body, Red chassis, Black wheels.................................£15-20

MB 22

22a 56 Vauxhall Cresta. Body colours and shades from Dark
Red to Maroon, roof from White to Cream £35-45

22b 58 Vauxhall Cresta
Pale Pink or Cream body, without windows, metal wheels........£600-650
Same but with Grey plastic wheels £120-140
Same but with windows £175-200
Pale Pink body, Blue-Green side panels, GPW £2,500-3,500
Light Metallic Brown body, Blue-Green side panels, GPW.......£175-200
Light Grey body, Lilac side panels, Grey or SPW £90-120
Light Gold body, Grey or SPW £100-120
Dark Gold body, Silver wheels £100-120
Metallic Copper body, Grey, Silver or Black wheels................£140-160

22c 65 Pontiac GP Sports Coupé
Red body, Pale Grey interior, BPW, pattern no. on base £25-35
Red body, Pale Grey interior, BPW, <u>no</u> pattern no. on base £35-40

MB 23

23a 56 Berkeley Cavalier Caravan
Pale Blue, *'On Tow MBS 23'*, metal wheels, 65 mm.................£40-60

23b 57 Berkeley Cavalier Caravan. All have *'ON TOW'* rear decal.
Pale Blue, metal wheels £30-40
Lime-Green, metal wheels £110-130
Lime-Green, GPW £60-80
Metallic Lime-Green, GPW £1,200-1,500

23c 60 Bluebird Dauphine Caravan
All models without windows and with *'ON TOW'* rear decal.
Metallic Lime-Green body, Grey plastic wheels £1,000-1,200
Metallic Mauve body, Maroon base......................................£600-800
Metallic Mauve body and base, Grey plastic wheels £40-50
Metallic Mauve body and base, Silver wheels £30-40
Metallic Mauve body and base, Black wheels £400-500
NB A few issues of 23c are known with plastic windows...............NGPP

23d 65 Trailer Caravan
Yellow body, knobbly-tread wheels £12-15
Yellow body, fine-tread wheels £30-40
Pink body, knobbly-tread wheels £30-40
Pink body, fine-tread wheels £12-15

MB 24

24a 56 'Hydraulic' Excavator
Orange-Yellow body, metal wheels, *'WEATHERILL'*, 58 mm.......£30-40
Same but Yellow body, metal wheels, *'WEATHERILL'* £50-70

24b 59 'Hydraulic' Excavator
Yellow body, Grey plastic wheels, crimped axles £35-45
Yellow body, Grey plastic wheels, rounded axles £25-30
Yellow body, Black plastic wheels £15-20

24c 67 Rolls-Royce Silver Shadow
All models with Metallic Red body and Black base.
Black wheels with Silver hubcaps £20-25
Silver wheels with Black tyres...£15-18

MB 25

25a 56 Bedford 12 cwt Van
Dark Blue body, Black base, *'DUNLOP'* decals, MW £40-45
Grey plastic wheels £45-55
Black plastic wheels £1,200-1,500

25b 60 Volkswagen 1200
Metallic Steel-Blue body, GPW, clear windows, 62 mm...........£45-55
As previous model but with Green tinted windows......................£60-70
Same but with SPW £50-60

25c 64 Bedford Petrol Tanker
Yellow cab, Green chassis, White tank, *'BP'*, BPW..................£20-25
Same but Grey plastic wheels £600-800

64 German issue: Dark Blue cab and chassis,
White tank, *'ARAL'*, Black plastic wheels............................£200-250

25d 68 Ford Cortina Mk.II
Metallic Light Brown body, Black plastic wheels £20-25
Gift Set issue: Same but with Yellow roof rack £40-60
Blue body, Silver base, Black plastic wheels........................£800-1,100

MB 26

26a 56 E.R.F. Cement Mixer
Orange body, Gold trim, MW, crimped axles, 45 mm..............**£275-300**
Same but with Silver trim **£40-45**
With GPW, Silver trim..**£70-80**
With SPW, Silver trim..**£600-800**

26b 61 Foden Cement Mixer (66mm)
Orange body, Lt or Dk Grey barrel, small knobbly GPW **£600-800**
Orange body, Orange barrel, Grey or Black plastic wheels **£20-25**
Orange body, Orange barrel, Silver plastic wheels....................**£800-900**

26c 68 G.M.C. Tipper Truck
Red cab, Green chassis, Silver tipper, BPW, 67 mm.....................**£10-12**

MB 27

27a 56 Bedford Low Loader (78mm)
Pale Blue cab, Dark Blue trailer, six MW, crimped axles **£600-700**
Pale Green cab, Tan trailer..**£60-70**

27b 58 Bedford Low Loader (95mm)
Pale Green cab, Tan trailer, metal wheels **£80-90**
Same but with GPW..**£100-120**
Dark Green cab, Light Brown trailer, Grey plastic wheels.........**£140-160**

27c 60 Cadillac Sixty Special
Metallic Pale Green/White, Crimson base, SPW **£350-400**
Silver-Grey body, Off-White roof, SPW **£110-130**
Metallic Lilac body, Pink roof, Crimson base, GPW or SPW **£70-80**
Same model but with Black base...**£90-110**
Same but Black base and BPW **£120-130**

27d 66 Mercedes 230 SL
White body, Red interior **£18-20**

MB 28

28a 56 Bedford Compressor
Orange/Yellow body, Silver trim, metal wheels, 47 mm **£25-35**
Yellow body, Silver trim, MW, domed/crimped axles **£50-60**

28b 59 Ford Thames Compressor Truck
Yellow body, Black wheels, crimped axles **£40-50**
Yellow body, Black wheels, rounded axles **£20-25**
Yellow body, Grey wheels...**£900-1,100**

28c 64 Jaguar Mk.10
Pale Metallic Brown, Cream seats, BPW, 74 mm.........................**£20-30**
With 'Matchbox' lapel badge..**£50-60**
With GPW and without 'Matchbox Series' on base **£800-900**

28d 68 Mack Dump Truck
Orange body, Red wheels..**£15-20**
Orange body, Yellow wheels **£20-25**

MB 29

29a 56 Bedford Milk Delivery Van
Light Brown body, White bottle load, metal wheels, 57 mm **£30-35**
Same but GPW, White or Cream bottles......................................**£40-50**

29b 61 Austin A55 Cambridge
Two-tone Green body, Green tinted windows, GPW.....................**£30-35**
Same but SPW, clear or tinted windows **£20-25**
Same but with BPW **£20-25**

29c 66 Fire Pumper Truck
Red body, with or without 'Denver' decal....................................**£15-20**

MB 30

30a 56 Ford Prefect
Grey-Brown body, Red and Silver trim, MW, 58 mm **£30-35**
Same but with GPW..**£40-50**
Same but Light Blue body, Grey plastic wheels, 58 mm **£200-220**

30b 61 Magirus-Deutz Crane Lorry
Light Brown body, Red or Orange crane, GPW **£3,000-4,000**
Silver body, Orange jib and hook, Grey or Silver wheels **£60-70**
Silver body, Orange jib, Grey or Silver hook, Grey or BPW **£30-35**

30c 65 8 Wheel Crane Truck
Green body, Orange jib **£15-20**
Turquoise body, Orange jib **£600-700**

MB 31

31a 57 Ford Station Wagon
Yellow body, metal wheels, 66 mm **£40-45**
Yellow body, Grey plastic wheels **£45-55**

31b 60 Ford Station Wagon
Yellow body, Black base, Grey wheels **£300-350**
Yellow body, Black base, Silver wheels.....................................**£250-300**
Yellow body, Crimson base, clear or Green windows, SPW **£200-250**
Metallic Green body, Pink roof, Crimson base, GPW or SPW **£40-50**
Same but with Black base, SPW **£60-70**
Same but with Black base, GPW...**£80-90**
Same but with Black base, BPW...**£100-120**

31c 64 Lincoln Continental
Metallic Blue body, BPW **£18-20**
Sea Green body **£15-18**
Metallic Lime Green body **£1,400-1,600**

MB 32

32a 57 Jaguar XK-140
Off-White body, Black base, metal wheels, 60 mm **£40-50**
Same but with GPW..**£50-65**
Bright Orange-Red body, GPW...**£130-160**
Dark Red, Black base, GPW **£130-160**

32b 62 Jaguar 'E'-type
Metallic Red body, Green windows, Grey tyres, 66 mm..........**£180-200**
Metallic Red body, clear windows, grey tyres **£45-55**
Metallic Red body, clear windows, Black tyres **£40-50**

32c 68 Leyland Tanker All have a White tank.
Green chassis, Silver base and grille, 'BP' decal **£40-50**
Green chassis, Silver base and grille, 'BP' label **£15-20**
Green chassis, White base and grille, 'BP' label **£60-70**
Blue chassis, Silver base and grille, 'ARAL' label **£150-175**

Matchbox Motor Cycles and Sidecars
66b Harley-Davidson   36b Lambretta Motor Scooter   4c Triumph T110

MB 33

33a 57 Ford Zodiac
Dark Green body, hook, no windows, MW, 68 mm £30-40
58 Dark Blue body, hook, no windows, metal wheels........**£700-800**
58 Sea-Green body, hook, no windows, metal wheels £100-120
Same but with GPW...£60-75
59 Metallic Mauve body, Orange panels, no windows, GPW ..**£110-130**
60 Same but with Green tinted windows, GPW or SPW £70-90
33b 63 Ford Zephyr 6. Sea-Green body, GPW, 67 mm £40-50
same but with SPW £25-30
same but with BPW..£20-25
33c 68 Lamborghini Miura
Yellow body, White interior, 71 mm. Black plastic wheels...£15-20
Yellow body, White interior, Chrome hubs.......................**£300-400**
Metallic Gold body, White interior, Chrome hubs...........£250-300

MB 34

34a 57 Volkswagen 15cwt Van. All have Blue body; 'MATCHBOX' decals.
Metal wheels..£35-45
Grey plastic wheels..£35-45
Silver plastic wheels..**£400-600**
34b 62 Volkswagen Caravette. All have Pale Green body; Green interior.
Silver wheels..£250-300
Knobbly-tread Grey wheels (24 treads) £40-50
Fine-tread Grey wheels (45 treads)................................£50-60
Black wheels..£35-45
34c 67 Volkswagen Camper
Silver body, with high roof (7 windows) £25-30
same but lower roof (1 window) £20-25
Pale Green body, Dark Green base/interior, SPW **£1,500-1,750**

MB 35

35a 57 E.R.F. Marshall Horse Box
Red cab, Light Brown box, metal wheels, 52 mm............£30-35
Same but with GPW..£30-40
With Silver plastic wheels...175-200
With Black plastic wheels..£75-90
35b 64 Snow-Trac. Red body, Silver base, Snow tracks.
'Snow Trac' cast on sides...£25-30
same but with 'Snow Trac' decals on sides £15-20
same but without 'Snow Trac' £15-20

MB 36

36a 57 Austin A50 Cambridge
Blue-Green body, Black base, metal wheels, 60 mm........£30-35
Same but with GPW..£30-40
Pale Blue body, GPW...£50-60
36b 61 Lambretta and Sidecar
Pale Metallic Green Scooter and side-car, BPW, 49 mm ..£60-80
36c 66 Opel Diplomat
Metallic Gold body, Silver engine £10-15
Metallic Gold body, Grey engine...................................£35-45

MB 37

37a 57 Karrier Bantam Lorry
All models with 'COCA-COLA' side and rear decals.
Orange-Yellow body, uneven load, metal wheels.............£180-200
Yellow body, uneven load, metal wheels.......................£180-200
Orange-Yellow body, even load, metal wheels.................£45-55
Orange-Yellow body, even load, grey plastic wheels.......£180-220
Yellow body, even load, metal wheels...........................£60-80
Yellow body, even load, Grey plastic wheels..................£220-240
37b 60 Karrier Bantam Lorry
All models with 'COCA-COLA' side and rear decals.
GPW, crimped axles...£100-120
GPW, rounded axles...£35-45
Silver plastic wheels..£750-850
Black plastic wheels...£70-80
37c 66 (Dodge) Cattle Truck. Yellow body, Grey cattle box,
2 White bulls, Silver plastic base £15-20
Unpainted metal base £10-15

MB 38

38a 57 Karrier Refuse Collector
All models with 'Cleansing Department' side decals.
Grey-Brown body, MW..£350-400
Grey body, metal wheels..£40-50
Grey body, GPW, crimped axles £65-75
Grey body, GPW, rounded axles £40-50
Silver body, GPW...£50-60
Silver body, SPW..£500-550

38b 63 Vauxhall Victor Estate
Yellow body, Red interior, Grey wheels..........................£175-200
same but with Silver wheels...£25-30
same but with Black wheels..£20-25
Yellow body, Green interior, GPW.................................£60-70
same but with Silver wheels...£30-35
same but with Black wheels..£20-25
38c Honda Motorcycle and Trailer
Metallic Green bike, Orange trailer without decals..........£30-40
Same, but Orange trailer with 'Honda' decals.................**£80-120**
Same, but Yellow trailer with 'Honda' decals or labels....£20-25

MB 39

39a 57 Ford Zodiac Convertible
Pale Peach body, Light Brown base/interior/driver, MW ..£300-325
Same but with Light Green base and interior, metal wheels....£50-60
Same but with Light Green base, Grey plastic wheels......£60-70
Pale Peach body, Silver plastic wheels £175-200
Dark Peach body, Blue-Green base and interior, GPW £60-70
Dark Peach body, Blue-Green base and interior, GPW £100-120
Dark Peach body with Sea-Green base, Grey plastic wheels....£75-85
39b 62 Pontiac Convertible.
Metallic Purple body, Crimson base, Red steering wheel, SPW..£100-120
Same but with Grey wheels..£450-500
Lemon body, Crimson base, Red steering wheel, SPW or GPW....£65-75
Same but Cream steering wheel....................................£25-35
Lemon body, Black base, SPW......................................£80-90
Same but with Grey wheels..£50-60
Same but with Black wheels...£30-35
39c 67 Ford Tractor
Blue body, Yellow engine cover, Black plastic tyres, 55 mm..£15-20
Blue body and engine cover..£20-25
All-Orange body, Yellow hubs.......................................£50-60

MB 40

40a 57 Bedford 7 Ton Tipper
Red body, Brown tipper, metal wheels, 53 mm...............£35-45
Same but with Grey plastic wheels, domed crimped axles ...£35-45
Same but with Grey plastic wheels on rivetted axles.......£30-35
40b 61 Leyland Tiger Coach
Steel Blue body, GPW..£90-110
Silver plastic wheels..£25-35
Black plastic wheels...£20-25
40c 67 Hay Trailer. Blue body, Yellow plastic hay racks
and wheels, Black plastic tyres £12-15
NB No. 40c deleted in 1972 but appeared in Two-Packs between 1976-1981.

MB 41

41a 57 Jaguar 'D'-Type (55 mm)
Green body, MW, No '41'...£50-60
Green body, MW, No '52'...£400-500
Green body, GPW, No '41' £90-120
41b 60 Jaguar 'D'-Type (62 mm). All have Green body and Black base.
GPW, crimped axles, No '41' £70-80
same but with rounded axles..£60-70
Wire hubs with Black tyres, No '41' £60-80
same but with No '5' or '6' £110-130
Red hubs with Black tyres...£350-450
41c 65 Ford GT Racer. All models with racing number '6'.
White body, Red hubs, BPT...£275-300
White body, Yellow hubs, Black tyres.............................£20-25
Yellow body, Yellow hubs, black tyres (US set)...............£175-200
White body, spoked wheels, Black tyres **£2,000-2,200**

MB 42

42a 57 Evening News Van
Yellow body, 'EVENING NEWS' decals, MW, 57 mm..............£35-40
GPW with 24 treads..£50-60
GPW or BPW with 45 treads..£120-150
BPW with 24 treads..£100-125
42b 65 Studebaker Lark Wagonaire (with hunter and dog figures),
Blue body, sliding rear roof painted as body £70-80
same but rear roof painted Light Blue £25-30
42c 69 Iron Fairy Crane. Red body, Yellow boom, BPW £15-18

MB 43

43a 58 Hillman Minx
Light Green body, Silver/Red trim, metal wheels, hook £350-375
Blue/Grey body, Pale Grey roof, metal wheels £40-45
Same but with GPW..£60-70
Turquoise body, Cream roof, Grey plastic wheels £50-60

43b 62 A.B. Tractor Shovel
Yellow body, driver and shovel £110-130
Yellow body and shovel, Red driver and base £20-25
Yellow body, driver and base, Red shovel............................£40-45
Yellow body, Red driver, base and shovel £200-250
43c 68 Pony Trailer
Yellow body, Grey ramp, Light Brown base, BPW £15-20
same but with Dark Green base......................................£10-15

MB 44

44a 58 Rolls-Royce Silver Cloud
Metallic Silver-Blue body, Red trim, metal wheels, 67 mm £30-35
  60 As previous but with GPW £30-40
Same but with SPW £50-60
44b 64 Rolls-Royce Phantom V
Metallic Mauve body, Black wheels £25-30
Same but with Grey wheels £120-140
Same but with Silver wheels £220-240
Metallic Silver-Grey body, BPW £90-110
Same but with Silver wheels £400-600
44c 67 GMC Refrigerator Truck
Red body, Sea-Green container, Black wheels, 76 mm £10-15

MB 45

45a 58 Vauxhall Victor
Red body, MW, 61 mm £2,000-3,000
Yellow or Lemon body, MW £35-40
Yellow body, metal wheels, no dashboard casting bar.............£350-375
Yellow or Lemon body, GPW, no window glazing £40-45
same but with clear windows £70-80
same but with Green windows £50-60
Lemon, Green windows, SPW £80-90
Yellow body, SPW or BPW £80-90
45b 65 Ford Corsair with Boat
Cream body, Red interior, Black wheels, Silver painted base £40-45
Same but with unpainted base £25-30
Same but with Grey wheels £75-80
Models with white interior are pre-productions £600-800

MB 46

46a 58 Morris Minor 1000
Pale Brown body, no windows, metal wheels, 53 mm £2,000-3,000
Dark Green body, Black base, MW, domed crimped axles £60-70
Dark Blue/Green body, MW £70-80
Same but with GPW £100-125
Blue body, GPW £150-175
46b 60 'PICKFORDS' Removals Van
Dark Blue body, Grey wheels, three line decal....................£90-120
Dark Blue body, Silver wheels, three line decal.................£140-160
Dark Blue body, Grey wheels, two line decal.....................£110-130
Dark Blue body, Silver wheels, two line decal...................£200-240
Green body, Grey wheels £60-70
Green body, Silver wheels £120-140
Green body, Black wheels £40-50
'BEALES BEALESONS' Van. Light Brown body,
'*Beales Bealesons*' decal, BPW, without box £500-700
Same but in special White box with 'sun' and
'*It's A Pleasure*' decal £850-1,000
46c 68 Mercedes-Benz 300 SE. Green body £20-25
  69 Metallic Blue body...£15-20

MB 47

47a 58 Trojan Van
Red body, '*BROOKE BOND TEA*' decals, MW, 58 mm..................£35-45
Same but with GPW £40-50
47b 63 Commer Ice Cream Van '*LYONS MAID*',
Metallic Blue body, BPW £100-120
Same but with Blue body £30-40
Blue body, Grey wheels £300-350
Blue body, Black wheels, White side decals........................£40-50
Cream body, '*LYONS MAID*' £200-230
Cream body, White side decals £60-70
'*LORD NIELSENS ICE CREAM*',
Cream body, Red/White labels £80-90
Blue body, Black plastic wheels £100-130
47c 68 DAF Container Truck
Sea Green body, Grey roof, Yellow container, BPW £50-60
Silver body, Grey or Silver roof, Yellow container, BPW £12-15

MB 48

48a 58 Meteor Sports Boat and Trailer
Black trailer, Light Brown boat, Blue hull, metal wheels £30-40
With Grey plastic wheels £50-60
With Silver plastic wheels £175-200
48b 61 Sports Boat and Trailer. Boat with Cream or White deck and
Red hull or with Red deck and Cream or white hull.
Dark Blue trailer, Black wheels £20-25
Dark Blue trailer, Grey wheels £80-100
Light Blue trailer, Black wheels £40-50
48c 66 (Dodge) Dumper Truck
Red body, Silver trim, wide or narrow BPW, 76 mm.................£10-15

MB 49

49a 58 M3 Personnel Carrier
Military Green, White bonnet star on some, MW and rollers........£25-30
Grey plastic wheels, metal rollers £30-35
Grey plastic wheels and rollers £350-400
Grey plastic wheels, Silver rollers £60-80
BPW and rollers, Grey tracks £30-40
BPW and rollers, Green tracks £30-40
49b 67 (Mercedes) Unimog
Light Brown body, Sea-Green base, 61 mm £20-25
Light Brown body, Red base (factory error?) £700-800
Light Blue body, Red base £15-20

MB 50

50a 58 Commer Pick-Up
Pale Brown body, MW, 64 mm £30-40
Pale or Light Brown body, GPW £35-45
Light Brown body, SPW £150-180
Red and White body, SPW £400-500
Red and Grey body, SPW £180-200
Red and Grey body, GPW £140-160
Red and Grey body, BPW £130-150
50b 64 John Deere Lanz Tractor
Green body, Yellow hubs, Grey tyres, 50 mm £20-25
Same but Black tyres £10-15
50c 69 Ford Kennel Truck
Metallic Green body, White grille, smooth kennel floor £20-25
Same but textured kennel floor and/or Silver grille £15-20

MB 51

51a 58 Albion Chieftain
All models with Yellow body, Tan or Light Beige load,
'*PORTLAND CEMENT*' decals, metal wheels £40-55
'*BLUE CIRCLE PORTLAND CEMENT*' decals, MW.......................£50-60
Same but with GPW £40-55
Same but with SPW £180-200
Same but with knobbly BPW £200-250
51b 64 Tipping Trailer
Green body, three Yellow barrels, Yellow hubs, Grey tyres £10-15
With Yellow hubs, Black tyres £12-15
51c 69 AEC Mammoth Major 8 Wheel Tipper
Orange body, Silver tipper, '*DOUGLAS*', White base grille........£70-80
Same but chrome base £20-25
Yellow body, Silver tipper, '*DOUGLAS*' £40-50
Yellow body, Silver tipper, '*POINTER*'...........................£12-18

MB 52

52a 58 1948 Maserati 4 CLT
Red body, Cream driver, no decal, BPW, 61 mm £40-50
Same with racing number '52'......................................£35-45
Red body, racing number '52', wire wheels, BPT..................£300-350
Lemon body, wire wheels, '30' or '52' £40-50
Same but number '3' or '5'......................................£120-140
52b 65 B.R.M. Racing Car
Blue body, Yellow hubs, BPT, '5' £15-20
Same but with racing number '3' £60-80
Dark Blue (Ultramarine) body, racing number '5' £75-85
Gift Set model: Red body, Yellow hubs with Black tyres...........£70-80
Dark Cherry Red body, Yellow hubs, racing number '5'...........£100-120

MB 53

53a 58 Aston Martin DB2-4 Mk.I
Metallic Green body, MW, 65 mm £30-40
Same but with GPW. £40-50
Metallic Red, knobbly GPW £250-300
Metallic Red, knobbly BPW £200-240
53b 63 Mercedes-Benz 220SE
Maroon body, Silver wheels £25-30
Maroon body, Grey wheels £30-40

Maroon body, Black wheels...£60-80
Dark Red body, Grey wheels...£60-80
Dark Red body, Black wheels...£20-25

53c 68 **Ford Zodiac Mk.IV**
Light Metallic Blue body, BPW...£20-25
Light Metallic Green body, Black plastic wheels....................£700-900

MB 54

54a 58 **Saracen Personnel Carrier**
Olive Green body, six BPW, crimped axles, 57 mm.............£25-35
Same but with rounded axles...£20-25

54b 65 **Cadillac Ambulance**
White, Red cross label or decal and roof lights, BPW..........£20-25

MB 55

55a 58 **DUKW Amphibian**
Olive Green body, MW, 71 mm...£20-25
Same but GPW or BPW...£25-35
In box with Green model picture (normally Red picture)..........£180-200

55b 63 **Ford Fairlane 'POLICE' Car**
Non-metallic Dark Blue, BPW...£280-320
Metallic Blue, knobbly BPW...£120-130
Metallic Blue, BPW...£45-55
Metallic Blue, GPW...£900-1,200
Metallic Blue, SPW...£450-500

55c 66 **Ford Galaxy 'POLICE' Car**
White body, 'Police & Shield' decal, Blue roof light...........£130-150
same but with Red roof light...£18-20

55d 68 **Mercury 'POLICE' Car**
White body, 'Police & Shield' labels, Red roof light..........£350-380
Same but with Blue roof light...£25-35

MB 56

56a 58 **London Trolley Bus.** All models with Red body,
'DRINK PEARDRAX' and destination decals.
Black poles, metal wheels, (beware fakes).......................£175-200
Black poles, GPW, (beware fakes).............................£250-300
Red poles, metal wheels...£45-55
Red poles, GPW or BPW...£35-45
Red poles, SPW...£150-180

56b 65 **Fiat 1500** (all have Black plastic wheels)
Sea-Green body, Brown luggage...£15-20
Same but with Red-Brown luggage...£10-15
Gift Set version: Red body, Red-Brown luggage...................£70-80

MB 57

57a 58 **Wolseley 1500**
Pale Green body, GPW, Gold trim, 55 mm.......................£220-250
Same but with Silver trim...£35-45

57b 61 **Chevrolet Impala**
All versions have Metallic Blue body and Pale Blue roof.
Clear windows, Black base, SPW...£110-130
Clear windows, Dark Blue base, SPW..............................£70-80
Green windows, Dark Blue base, SPW..............................£25-30
Green windows, Dark Blue base, GPW..............................£50-60
Green windows, Pale or Light Blue base, SPW.................£120-140
Black base, GPW...£75-85
Black base, SPW...£70-80
Black base, BPW...£60-70

57c 66 **Land Rover Fire Truck**
Red body, 'KENT FIRE BRIGADE', BPW, 64 mm.................£25-30
Same but with GPW...£750-850

MB 58

58a 58 **AEC 'BEA' Coach**
Dark Blue body, White letters, Grey wheels, 65 mm..........£50-60
Dark Blue body, Black letters on White ground, Grey wheels..£40-50
Same but with Silver wheels...£150-170
Same but with Black wheels...£180-200

58b 62 **Drott Excavator**
Red body, Silver base, Black rollers, Green tracks...........£20-25
Same but with Silver rollers...£100-120
Orange body, Silver base, Black rollers......................£25-30
Orange body and base, Black rollers......................£15-20

58c 68 **DAF Girder Truck**
White body, Red base and 12 girders, 6 BPW, 75 mm..........£10-15

MB 59

59a 58 **Ford Thames Van 'SINGER'**
Pale Green body, GPW...£60-75
Same but SPW, rivetted axles...£200-250
Dark Green body and Grey plastic wheels, rivetted axles....£190-220
Dark Green body, Silver plastic wheels, rivetted axles.....£230-260

59b 63 **Ford Fairlane Fire Chief**
All models with Red body and 'FIRE CHIEF' decals on
doors and bonnet, Black wheels...£40-50
With Grey wheels...£180-200
With Silver wheels...£800-900
With shield decals on doors (pre-production trial)............£200-250

59c 66 **Ford Galaxie Fire Chief**
Red body, Blue dome light, 'FIRE CHIEF', BPW.................£20-25
Same but with Red dome light...£250-350

MB 60

60a 58 **Morris J2 Pick Up**
All with Light Blue body and 'BUILDERS SUPPLY COMPANY'
decals. 'Supply Company' in Black, Grey plastic wheels........£50-60
'SUPPLY COMPANY' in White, with rear window,
GPW or BPW...£30-35
Same but with SPW...£40-50
Without rear window, GPW...£180-200
Without rear window, BPW...£30-40

60b 66 **Site Hut Truck**
Blue body, Yellow and Green plastic building, Black wheels...£12-18

MB 61

61a 59 **Ferret Scout Car**
Olive Green body, Tan driver, Black plastic wheels, 57 mm...£25-30

61b 66 **Alvis Stalwart 'BP'**
White body, Green wheels with BPT, smooth carrier bed......£30-40
Same but with ribbed carrier bed...£15-20
White body, Yellow wheels with Black tyres......................£60-80
Two-Pack version: Military Olive Green body, Black wheels....£20-30

MB 62

62a 59 **AEC General Service Lorry**
Olive Green body, tow hook, six BPT, 68 mm.................£30-35

62b 63 **Commer TV Service Van**
All have Cream body, Red plastic ladder, aerial and 3 TV's.
'RENTASET', knobbly Grey wheels (24 treads)..............£250-300
'RENTASET', Black wheels...£40-50
'RENTASET', fine-tread Grey wheels (45 treads)..............£300-350
'RADIO RENTALS', BPW...£50-60
'RADIO RENTALS', fine-tread Grey wheels......................£450-550

62c 68 **Mercury Cougar**
Cream body, White interior, Chrome hubs...................£2,000-2,500
Metallic Lime Green body, Red interior......................£10-15

MB 63

63a 59 **Service Ambulance (Ford)**
Olive Green body, Red crosses, BPW, crimped axles............£35-40
Same but with rounded axles...£25-30

63b 63 **Alvis Foamite Crash Tender**
Red body, Silver hose nozzle, six BPW, 63 mm.................£85-100
With Gold hose nozzle...£20-30

63c 68 **Dodge Crane Truck**
Yellow body, Red hook, 76 mm...£10-15
Yellow body, Yellow hook...£15-18

MB 64

64a 59 **Scammell Breakdown Truck**
Olive Green body, metal or plastic hook, BPW, 64 mm..........£35-45

64b 66 **MG 1100**
Green body, White seats, driver, dog, BPT, 67 mm............£15-20

MB 65

65a 59 **Jaguar 3.4 litre**
Dark Blue body, Silver rear number-plate, GPW, 62 mm.......£40-50
As previous but with Blue rear number plate......................£35-45
Metallic Blue body and number plate, Grey plastic wheels....£100-130

65b 62 **Jaguar 3.8 Sedan**
Metallic Red body, Silver base, Red plastic wheels, 68 mm....£80-90
Red body, Silver plastic wheels...£150-200
Red body, Grey plastic wheels...£50-60
Red body, Black plastic wheels...£30-35

65c 67 **Claas Combine Harvester**
Red body, Yellow blades and front hubs, no hole in base......£150-250
As previous but with hole in base......................£10-12

MB 66

66a 59 **Citroën DS 19**
Yellow body, Silver trim, GPW...£50-60
Same but with SPW...£100-120

66b 62 **Harley-Davidson Motor Cycle**
Metallic Bronze bike and sidecar, spoked wheels, BPT..........£90-110

66c 66 'GREYHOUND' Coach
Silver-Grey body, clear windows, Black plastic wheels **£90-110**
Silver-Grey body, Amber windows, Black plastic wheels **£10-15**

MB 67

67a 59 Saladin Armoured Car
Olive Green body, six BPW, crimped axles, 61 mm......................**£30-35**
Same but with rounded axles **£25-30**

67b 67 Volkswagen 1600 TL
Red body, Black wheels with Silver hubcaps **£25-30**
Red body, Silver wheels with black tyres **£18-20**
Gift Set version: Red body with Maroon plastic roof rack **£80-90**
Metallic Purple body, Chrome hubs with Black tyres..............**£300-400**

MB 68

68a 59 Austin Radio Truck Mk.II
Olive Green body and base, BPW, crimped axles **£30-35**
Same but with rounded axles **£25-30**

68b 65 Mercedes Coach (all have BPW)
Turquoise/White body, US issue **£180-200**
Orange/White body, BPW..**£15-20**

MB 69

69a 59 Commer Van 'NESTLES'
Maroon body, driver, Yellow logo, GPW, 56 mm **£45-55**
Red body, GPW with 20 treads..**£60-70**
Red body, GPW with 36 treads...**£90-100**

69b 65 Hatra Tractor Shovel
Orange body, Orange wheels, Grey tyres, 78 mm **£65-75**
With Red hubs, Grey tyres **£30-40**
With Red hubs, Black tyres **£25-30**
With Yellow hubs, Black tyres **£20-25**
Yellow body, Yellow hubs..**£20-25**
Yellow body, Red hubs..**£100-120**
Orange body, Yellow shovel **£500-600**

MB 70

70a 59 Ford Thames Estate Car
Turquoise and Yellow body, Grey wheels, no windows **£40-45**
Grey wheels, clear windows...**£40-50**
Grey wheels, Green windows...**£25-30**
Silver wheels, clear windows **£40-50**
Silver or Black wheels, Green windows **£35-40**

70b 66 Ford Grit Spreader
Red body, Pale Lemon container, BPW, 68 mm **£15-20**
Red body, Dark Yellow container, Black or Grey slide, BPW........**£60-70**

MB 71

71a 59 200 gallon Water Truck
Olive Green body, BPW...**£30-40**
Same model with first *'Matchbox Collectors'* badge.....................**£55-65**

71b 64 Jeep Gladiator Pick-Up
Red body, Green interior, Black plastic wheels, 66 mm................**£50-60**
Red body, White interior...**£20-25**

71c 69 Ford Heavy Wreck Truck (all BPW)
Red and White body, Amber windows, smooth loadbed............**£400-500**
Same but with ribbed loadbed **£400-500**
Same but with Green windows **£20-25**
Military Green body...**£20-25**

MB 72

72a 59 Fordson Major Tractor. All models with Blue body.
Grey front wheels, Orange rear hubs with Grey tyres, 50 mm.......**£40-45**
Black front wheels, Orange rear hubs with Black tyres **£35-40**
Orange hubs front and rear, Grey tyres...**£40-45**
Orange hubs front and rear, BPT **£30-35**
Yellow hubs front and rear, Grey or Black tyres.....................**£900-1,000**

72b 66 Jeep CJ5
Orange-Yellow body, Yellow hubs, White interior...................**£800-1,000**
Yellow body, Yellow hubs, Red interior **£15-20**

MB 73

73a 59 Leyland R.A.F. 10 ton Refueller
Airforce-Blue body, roundel, six GPW, 66 mm............................**£50-60**
Same but with BPW...**£1,500-1,800**

73b 62 Ferrari F1 Racing Car. Red body, Grey or White driver,
RN '73', 'spoked' metal hubs, Black plastic tyres.........................**£30-35**

73c 68 Mercury Commuter Station Wagon
Metallic Lime Green body, Silver hubs, Black plastic tyres **£12-15**

MB 74

74a 59 Mobile 'REFRESHMENTS' Bar
White body, Pale Blue base, Blue interior, GPW **£120-140**
Cream body, Light Blue base, Grey plastic wheels **£100-120**
Pinkish Cream body, Light Blue base, Grey plastic wheels.......**£500-600**
Silver body, Light Blue base, Grey plastic wheels **£30-40**
Silver body, Light Blue base, Silver plastic wheels.......................**£40-45**
Silver body, Light Blue base, Black plastic wheels.................**£800-1,000**
Silver body, Sea Green or Dark Blue base **£100-120**

74b 66 Daimler Fleetline Bus
Cream body, *'ESSO'* decals..**£15-20**
Cream body, *'ESSO'* labels...**£30-35**
Green body, *'ESSO'* labels...**£15-20**
Red body, *'ESSO'* labels..**£30-35**

MB 75

75a 60 Ford Thunderbird All have Cream body and Peach side panels.
Blue base, Silver wheels..**£40-50**
Blue-Green base, Silver wheels **£180-200**
Black base, Silver wheels...**£70-80**
Black base, Grey wheels...**£85-100**
Black base, Black wheels..**£350-400**

75b 65 Ferrari Berlinetta
Metallic Green body, wire wheels, Silver painted base **£50-60**
Metallic Green body, wire wheels, unpainted base **£20-25**
Metallic Green body, Silver wheels with Black tyres....................**£15-20**
Red body, Chrome hubs with Black tyres **£280-320**
Red body, wire wheels..**£600-650**

'Matchbox Series' Miniature Metal Vehicles by Lincoln Industries, New Zealand
See opposite page for details.   Photo: Vectis Auctions Ltd.

A1a	1957	**'ESSO' Petrol Pump Set** .... Red pumps, White figure	**£30-40**
A1b	1963	**'BP' Petrol Pump Set** .... White pumps, Yellow/White decal	**£25-35**

A2 1957 **Car Transporter** .... Box type 1: Dark Blue/Yellow front and back 'MOKO - LESNEY' line-drawing box.
Box type 2: Yellow front/back, Blue end tabs, 'LESNEY MATCHBOX SERIES' logo.
1: Pale blue body, Dark Blue logo 'MATCHBOX CAR TRANSPORTER', metal wheels on tractor and trailer, 1st type box **£50-60**
2: Pale Blue body, Red 'CAR COLLECTION Ltd CAR TRANSPORTER', GPW (tractor), BPW (trailer), 1st box **£150-200**
3: Pale Blue body, Red 'CAR COLLECTION Ltd CAR TRANSPORTER', Black plastic wheels on tractor and trailer, 1st type box **£60-70**
4: Pale Blue body, Red 'CAR COLLECTION Ltd CAR TRANSPORTER', Grey plastic wheels on tractor and trailer, 1st type box **£40-50**
5: Red cab and lower deck, Grey upper deck and sides, BPW, Red logo: 'CAR COLLECTION Ltd' on Pale Yellow background, 2nd box **£220-240**

A3	1957	**Garage** .... Yellow/Green/Red, opening doors, all metal with metal connecting clip	**£30-40**
A4	1960	**Road Signs Set** .... Eight Red/White/Black signs 'Lesney' on base	**£30-40**
A5	1960	**'HOME STORES' Shop** .... Food shop with window display and opening door	**£40-45**
MG1a	1959	**Service Station and Showroom** ...... 'MATCHBOX', Red plastic building with Yellow base and roof sign	**£70-80**
		Same but Yellow plastic building with Red base and roof sign	**£60-75**
MG1b	1961	**Service Station and Showroom** ...... 'MATCHBOX', Yellow plastic building and ramp, Red sign 'MATCHBOX', 'ESSO'	**£180-200**
		Same but White plastic building with Green base and Yellow sign 'BP'	**£120-150**
MG1c	1968	**Service Station** .... Green and Yellow plastic building and card forecourt 'BP'	**£65-75**
MF1a	1963	**Fire Station** .... White building with Green roof, 'MATCHBOX FIRE STATION' on a Brown or Red background	**£200-250**
		White building with Red roof, 'MATCHBOX FIRE STATION' on a Brown or Red background	**£160-190**

'Matchbox' Series Painting Books

Four different types of cover and contents numbered 1 to 4.
Mint unused set of books **£2,000-3,000**

Major Packs Series

Ref.		Details	MPR	Ref..		Details	MPR
M1	58	**Caterpillar Earthmover** Yellow body, MW, crimped or rounded axles, 99mm............ **£40-50**		M6	60	**Scammell Transporter 'PICKFORDS'** Dark Blue tractor, Maroon low-loader, BPW, 279mm **£75-90**	
M1	63	**'BP' Petrol Tanker** Green/Yellow/White body, knobbly or fine tread BPW **£25-35**				Blue tractor, Bright Red low-loader, BPW **£120-140**	
M2	58	**Bedford Articulated Truck 'WALLS ICE CREAM'** All versions have a Light Blue tractor cab, 101mm. Cream trailer, metal wheels **£50-60**		M6	66	**Racing Car Transporter 'BP'** Green body, Silver ramp/rear door, Red hubs with BPT, 'Monza/Le Mans/Sebring/Nurburgring' on sides **£300-350**	
	59	Cream trailer, Grey plastic wheels............................. **£50-60**				With 'Le Mans/Sebring/Silverstone/Nurburgring' on sides ... **£40-50**	
	59-61	White trailer, Grey plastic wheels..................... **£75-85**		M7	60	**Thames Trader Cattle Truck 'JENNINGS'**, Dark Red cab, Light Tan box trailer, knobbly GPW **£60-70**	
M2	61	**Bedford Tractor and York Trailer 'DAVIES TYRES'** Orange cab, Silver trailer, clear windows, knobbly BPW **£65-75**				With Dark Tan trailer, Red rear lamp, knobbly GPW............ **£70-80**	
		With Green tinted windows, knobbly BPW **£55-65**				As previous model but with knobbly BPW **£85-100**	
		With Grey knobbly tread wheels........................ **£95-110**				Same but with Grey fine-tread wheels (45 treads)............ **£130-150**	
		With Black fine tread wheels (45 treads) **£60-80**				Same but with Black fine-tread wheels (45 treads)........... **£120-140**	
		With Grey fine tread wheels (45 treads) **£160-180**				Light Blue cab, base and rear ramp, Metallic Copper back, Grey plastic wheels **£2,000-3,000**	
		Silver cab, Dark Red trailer, Black base **£200-220**		M8	61	**'MOBILGAS' Petrol Tanker** Red body, White 'MOBILGAS' logo, knobbly GPW **£70-85**	
M2	64	**Bedford Tractor and York Trailer 'LEP INTERNATIONAL'** Silver cab, Dark Red trailer, Dark Red base............ **£130-150**				With Black knobbly-tread wheels (24 treads).................. **£130-150**	
		Silver cab, Dark Red trailer, Black base **£60-70**				With Black fine-tread wheels (45 treads) **£180-200**	
M3	59	**Mighty Antar Tank Transporter and Centurion Tank** Both models in Military Olive Green, Transporter always has Black wheels. Tank with metal rollers **£45-55**		M8	64	**Guy Warrior Car Transporter** Blue-Green cab, Orange trailer, Orange wheels with Grey tyres, 209 mm. 'FARNBOROUGH-MEASHAM' in Black, White outline....... **£120-140**	
		Tank with Grey plastic rollers......................... **£220-250**				'FARNBOROUGH-MEASHAM' in White, Black outline....... **£50-60**	
		Tank with Black plastic rollers **£140-160**		M9	62	**Inter-State Double Freighter 'COOPER-JARRETT'**. All versions have a Dark Blue cab.	
M4	59	**Ruston Bucyrus Excavator** Maroon cab, Yellow shovel arms, Black base, Green tracks .. **£50-70**				Silver trailers, one-piece double wheels, Yellow lettering **£70-80**	
M4	65	**'FREUHOF' Hopper Train** Maroon tractor, two Silver trailers, Red wheels, BPT........... **£60-70**				Same but double wheels are two separate wheels **£60-70**	
						Same but Orange lettering **£130-150**	
M5	59	**'MASSEY FERGUSON 780' Combine Harvester** Red body, Yellow blades, Silver front wheels, Black rear **£40-50**				Grey trailers, Yellow lettering **£100-120**	
		Orange front wheels, Black rear wheels **£70-80**		M10	62	**Whitlock Dinkum Dumper** Yellow body, 'DD-70', unpainted metal wheels, 108 mm..... **£50-60**	
		Yellow front wheels, Black rear wheels.............................. **£85-100**				Same but Red plastic hubs with Black tyres **£60-70**	
		Orange front and rear wheels with Black tyres **£120-140**					
		Yellow front and rear wheels with Black tyres **£140-160**					

Lincoln Industries 'Matchbox Series'

Collectors should be aware that a range of models exists which were made in New Zealand and which at first sight appear to be Matchbox Miniatures. The packaging in particular is strikingly similar to early Lesney Matchbox boxes, even to the extent of having 'MATCHBOX SERIES' printed in a banner as on the Lesney boxes.

It seems that the makers, Lincoln Industries, were so taken with the Lesney idea of 'a model in a matchbox' that they were tempted to capitalise on it by adopting it themselves. 'Lincoln Industries Ltd' and 'Made in New Zealand' are also clearly marked on the boxes so confusion should be avoidable. The

models are a little cruder than genuine Matchbox products and all seem to have metal wheels. They are nevertheless collectable and include: a Utility Truck, Breakdown Truck, Large Parcels Van, Ambulance, and a sports car resembling a Jaguar XK120. See illustration on opposite page.

These auction results were achieved by Vectis Auctions Ltd. in July 2000:
4506 Coach .... Green body **£170**
4509 Ambulance .... Red cross on roof **£140**
4510 Jaguar XK120 .... Cream, with driver **£560**
The Editor would welcome more details of these products.

Matchbox Presentation and Gift Sets

Presentation Sets

The first presentation set was sold in the USA in 1957 and consisted of an enlarged normal 'Matchbox' containing eight of the sixty-four models that Lesney manufactured at that time. The first sets were not sold in the UK until 1959.

Ref	Year(s)	Set name	Contents, features, details	Market Price Range
PS 1	1957	Matchbox Presentation Set	Contains models 1 - 8 (only available in USA)	£2,000-3,000
PS 2	1957	Matchbox Presentation Set	Contains models 9 - 16 (only available in USA)	£2,000-3,000
PS 3	1957	Matchbox Presentation Set	Contains models 17 - 24 (only available in USA)	£2,000-3,000
PS 4	1957	Matchbox Presentation Set	Contains models 25 - 32 (only available in USA)	£2,000-3,000
PS 5	1957	Matchbox Presentation Set	Contains models 33 - 40 (only available in USA)	£2,000-3,000
PS 6	1957	Matchbox Presentation Set	Contains models 41 - 48 (only available in USA)	£2,000-3,000
PS 7	1957	Matchbox Presentation Set	Contains models 49 - 56 (only available in USA)	£2,000-3,000
PS 8	1957	Matchbox Presentation Set	Contains models 57 - 64 (only available in USA)	£2,000-3,000
PS 1	1959	Private Owner Set	Contains 19 MGA, 43 Hillman Minx, 45 Vauxhall Victor, A-3 Garage	£400-600
PS 2	1959	Transporter and 4 Cars Set	Contains 30 Ford, 31 Ford Station Wagon, 33 Ford Zodiac, 36 Austin A50, and an A-2 Transporter	£300-400
PS 3	1959	Transporter and 6 Cars Set	Contains 22 Vauxhall Cresta, 32 Jaguar XK, 33 Ford Zodiac, 43 Hillman Minx, 44 Rolls-Royce Silver Cloud, 45 Vauxhall Victor and an A-2 Transporter	£400-600
PS 4	1959	Commercial Vehicle Set	Contains No.5 Bus, 11 Petrol Tanker, 21 'Dunlop' Van, 35 Horse Box, 40 Bedford Tipper, 47 'Brooke Bond' Van and 60 Morris Pickup	£500-600
PS 5	1959	Army Personnel Carrier Set	Contains M3 Personnel Carrier, 54 Saracen, 55 DUKW, 61 Ferret, 62 General Service Lorry, 63 Ambulance, M-3 Tank Transporter	£350-400

Gift Sets

The packaging for the first UK issued sets consisted of a frail blue box with a yellow lid panel on which were displayed (in red) the models making up the set. Sets in similar packaging were issued for the German market. Note however that contents may vary within the same type of box (the G4 Farm set listed below is an example). Please advise us of any other different model combinations you may have.

Ref	Year(s)	Set name	Contents, features, details	Market Price Range
GS 1	c1960	Garage Set 'C'	'MATCHBOX' Sales and Service Station (Red/Yellow), Roadway Layout, Accessories Pack No.1 (Esso petrol pumps), Accessory Pack No.2 (Car Transporter, Blue/Red lettering), Major Pack No.6 ('Pickfords' Transporter), 1-75 series models (5c, 29b, 31b, 42a, 45a, 46b, 57b, 74a). All models are individually boxed and housed in larger display box printed with 'MATCHBOX SERIES' and pictures of the garage and models, etc.	£1,800-2,000
G 1	1960-61	Commercial Motor Set	Contains: 5b 'Players Please', 20b, 37a (even load), 47a, 51a, 59a, 60a and 69a. (All models in G 1 had Grey plastic wheels)	£550-600
G 1	1962-63	Commercial Vehicle Set	Contains 5c 'Visco-Static', 10c, 12b, 13c, 14c, 21c, 46b, 74a	£550-600
G 1	1965	Motorway Set	Contains 6, 10, 13, 33, 34, 38, 48, 55, 71 and R-1 layout	£400-500
G 1	1967	Service Station Set	A1 Service Station and 'BP' Pump Set, 31c or 32c, 13d and 64b in pictorial display case	£200-240
G 2	1960-61	Car Transporter Set	A-2 Transporter (metal wheels) and cars 22b, 25b, 33b, 39a, 57b and 75a	£500-700
G 2	1960-61	2nd issue:	A-2 Transporter (with Grey plastic wheels to tractor and Black plastic wheels to trailer), plus cars 7b, 22b, 25c, 27c, 57b and 75a	£500-700
G 2	1962-63	Car Transporter Set	Contains models 25b, 30b, 31b, 39b, 48b, 65b and Accessory Pack No.2	£500-700
G 2	1965	Car Transporter Set	Contains 22c, 28c, 36c, 75b and Major Pack 8b	£300-350
G 2	1967	Transporter Set	Contains K8 Transporter, 14d, 24c, 31c and 53c	£180-200
G 3	1960-61	Building Constructors Set	Contains 2, 6, 15, 16, 18, 24, 28 and M-1	£240-280
G 3	1962-63	Constructional Plant Set	Contains 2, 6, 15, 16, 18, 24, 28 and M-1	£240-280
G 3	1963-64	Farm and Agricultural Set	Contains K8, K11, M5 and M7	£270-300
G 3	1965	Vacation Set	Contains 12c, 23d, 27d, 42b, 45b, 56b, 68b, and Sports Boat on Trailer	£250-300
G 3	1968	Farm Set	Contains 4d, 12c, 37d, 40c, 39c, 43c, 65c and 72b	£120-150
G 4	1960-61	Farm Set (1st issue)	M-7 Cattle Truck (GPW), 12b Land Rover (BPW), 23b Berkeley Caravan (Lime Green, GPW), 31b Ford (Met.Green/Pink/Maroon, SPW), 35a Horse Box (MW), 50a Commer (Lt.Brown, SPW), 72a Fordson (Orange rear hubs, GPW)	£340-380
		(2nd issue)	M-7 Cattle Truck (GPW), 12b Land Rover (BPW), 23c Bluebird Dauphine Caravan (Metallic Mauve, SPW), 31b Ford (Yellow, Maroon base, clear windows, SPW), 35a Horse Box (SPW), 50a Commer (SPW), 72a Fordson (Orange rear hubs, GPW)	£300-350
G 4	1963	Grand Prix Set	Contains 13c, 14c, 19c, 41b, 47b, 52a, 32b, 73b and Major Pack No.1, R-4 Racetrack, instructions	£600-650
G 4	1965	Racetrack Set	13d, 19d Green, 19d Orange, 41c White, 41c Yellow, 52b Blue, 52b Red, 54b, Major Pack M-6 29c	£300-350
G 4	1968	Race 'n' Rally Set	19d Orange, 19d Green, 52b Blue, 52b Red, 29d, 3c, 41c, 67b, 25d, 8e	£200-250
G 5	1960-61	Military Vehicles	Contains 54, 62, 63, 64, 67, 68 and M-3	£200-250
G 5	1963	Army Gift Set	Contains 54a, 62a, 63a, 67a, 68a, 64a and Major Pack No.3	£220-250
G 5	1965	Army Gift Set	Contains 12, 49, 54, 61, 64, 67 and M-3 (picture box)	£220-250
G 5	1965	Fire Station Set	Contains Fire Station, 29c, 54b and 59c	£250-300
G 6	1965	Commercial Trucks Set	Contains 6, 15, 16, 17, 26, 30, 58 and 62	£250-300
G 6	1966	Truck Set	Contains 16c, 17d, 25c, 26b, 30c, 69b, 70b, 71b	£200-250
G 9	1963	Major Series Set	Contains Major Packs 1, 2, 4 and 6	£250-350
G 9	1965	Service Station Set	Contains 13, 33, 71, A-1, MG-1	£220-250
G 10	1963	Service Station Set	Contains Service Station, 13c, 25b, 31b, and Accessory Pack No.1	£250-300
G 10	1965	Fire Station Set	Contains MF-1, 14, 59, 2 of No.9	£250-300
FB 5	1969	Matchbox Traffic Game	Contains two cars (No.45 Ford Corsair and No.56 Fiat 1500) plus game board, etc	£175-200
?	?	'GAF' Racing Car Game	Belgian game set contains four 24d 'TEAM MATCHBOX' racing cars including the rare Metallic Blue and Yellow variants. Set issued by 'GAF', not by Matchbox.	£300-400

Following successful sales of Major Models, Lesney Products decided to further develop the range by introducing a larger scale toy. The name chosen was 'King-Size'. In 1966 the popular Major Models were discontinued in name but were themselves built into the King-Size range.

K1-1	60	**Hydraulic Shovel**	
		All Yellow body, Grey plastic wheels, 'WEATHERILL' **£40-45**	
K1-2	63	**Tipper Truck**	
		Red cab and chassis, Orange tipper, 'HOVERINGHAM' ..**£30-40**	
	NB	'HOVERINGHAM GRAVELS LTD' issued models in	
		their own outer box to their customers **£120-150**	
K1-3	71	**'O & K' Excavator**	
		Red body, Silver shovel, tinted windows, BPT **£30-40**	
K2-1	60	**Dumper Truck**	
		Red body, 'MUIR HILL 14B', Black or Green MW **£30-40**	
K2-2	64	**Dumper Truck**	
		Yellow body, 'KW DART' logo, 6 Red wheels, BPT.........**£30-40**	
K2-3	68	**Scammell Wreck Truck**	
		White body, Red jib and wheels, Grey hook, 'ESSO' **£40-45**	
	71	Gold body version...**£40-50**	
K3-1	60	**Caterpillar Bulldozer**	
		Yellow body, Red engine, Grey metal rollers.....................**£40-50**	
		As previous model but with Red metal rollers...............**£40-50**	
		As previous model but with Yellow metal rollers.............**£40-50**	
K3-2	65	**'HATRA' Tractor Shovel** Orange body, Red wheels **£30-35**	
K3-3	70	**'MASSEY FERGUSON' Tractor and Trailer**	
		Red body, Yellow trim...**£35-40**	
K4-1	60	**'McCORMICK INTERNATIONAL' Tractor**	
		Red body, Green wheels **£35-45**	
		As previous model with Orange or Red wheel hubs..........**£30-40**	
K4-2	67	**GMC Tractor and Hoppers**	
		Dark Red cab, 2 Silver hoppers, 'FREUHOF' logo **£60-70**	
K4-3	69	**Leyland Tipper**	
		Dark Red cab and chassis, Silver tipper 'W. WATES' **£25-30**	
		As above but with Yellow/Green body colours................**£500-600**	
		With Red cab and chassis, Green tipper........................**£50-60**	
		With Blue cab and chassis, Silver tipper 'Miner' label......**£60-70**	
		With Silver tipper and 'LE TRANSPORT' logo **£30-40**	
K5-1	61	**Tipper Truck**	
		Yellow body and tipper, Red wheels, 'FODEN' logo..**£35-45**	
K5-2	67	**Racing Car Transporter**	
		Green body, Silver drop down rear door, Red wheels........**£35-40**	
K5-3	70	**Tractor and Trailer**	
		Yellow body, Red chassis, 'MUIR HILL' **£35-40**	
K6-1	61	**Earth Scraper**	
		Orange body, Red engine, 'ALLIS CHALMERS' **£35-45**	
K6-2	67	**Mercedes Ambulance**	
		White body, Red badge, ambulance-man, stretcher **£25-30**	
K7-1	61	**Rear Dumper**	
		Yellow body, Red engine, 'CURTISS-WRIGHT' **£35-40**	
K7-2	67	**Refuse Truck**	
		Red body and wheels 'CLEANSING DEPARTMENT' **£25-30**	
	72	Blue body version...**£60-70**	
K8-1	62	**Prime Mover and Transporter with Crawler Tractor**	
		Orange bodies, Yellow tractor, 'LAING', unpainted or	
		Red plastic wheels, Green tracks................................**£140-180**	

K8-2	67	**Guy Warrior Transporter** 'FARNBOROUGH - MEASHAM'	
		Blue cab, Yellow car transporter **£60-70**	
		Orange cab, Orange or Yellow transporter.....................**£50-60**	
K8-3	70	**'CATERPILLAR TRAXCAVATOR'**	
		Yellow body and shovel, Blue or White driver.................**£30-35**	
	72	Silver body **£50-60**	
K9-1		**'AVELING BARFORD' Diesel Road Roller**	
		Green body, Red wheels and driver......................................**£40-45**	
K9-2	67	**'CLAAS' Combine Harvester**	
		Red body, Yellow blades and wheels, ...**£40-50**	
		Green body, Red blades and wheels **£40-50**	
K10-1	63	**'AVELING BARFORD' Tractor Shovel**	
		Blue-Green body, Red seat and wheels **£40-50**	
K10-2	66	**Pipe Truck.** Yellow body, Red wheels, 6 Grey pipes **£45-50**	
		('Super-Kings' issue) Purple body, Grey or Yellow pipes ...**£25-30**	
K11-1	63	**'FORDSON SUPER MAJOR' Tractor and Trailer**	
		Blue tractor, Grey/Blue trailer **£50-60**	
K11-2	69	**DAF Car Transporter** Yellow body, Yellow/Red decks ...**£40-50**	
		Metallic Blue body, Gold trailer decks................................**£60-70**	
K12-1	63	**Breakdown Truck** 'MATCHBOX SERVICE STATION',	
		Green body, Yellow jib...**£50-60**	
K12-2	69	**Scammell Crane Truck**	
		Yellow body and chassis, 'LAING' on crane **£35-40**	
	71	Silver body..**£50-60**	
K13-1	63	**Concrete Truck**	
		Orange body and barrel, 'READYMIX' logo **£40-50**	
		As previous model but with 'RMC' logo.............................**£50-60**	
K14-1	64	**Jumbo Crane**	
		Yellow body and crane, 'TAYLOR JUMBO CRANE' **£30-35**	
K15-1	64	**Merryweather Fire Engine**	
		Red body, Silver ladder, 'KENT FIRE BRIGADE'...........**£35-45**	
K16-1	66	**Tractor and Twin Tippers**	
		Green cab, Yellow tippers, 'DODGE TRUCKS' in Red......**£80-90**	
		Yellow cab, Blue tippers same logo (Superfast) **£60-65**	
K17-1	67	**Low Loader and Bulldozer**	
		Green cab and loader, Red/Yellow Bulldozer.....................**£80-90**	
	71	Red cab **£60-70**	
K18-1	66	**Articulated Horse Box** 'ASCOT STABLES',	
		Red cab, Brown box, 4 White horses **£40-55**	
K19-1	67	**Scammell Tipper** Red body, Yellow tipper, Silver trim **£25-30**	
K20-1	68	**Tractor Transporter (Ford)**	
		Red body, Yellow rack, 3 Blue/Yellow tractors (MB39c)...**£70-80**	
		As previous model but with Orange tractors **£120-150**	
	71	Blue cab **£180-200**	
K21-1	69	**Mercury Cougar** Gold body, Cream or Red seats.........**£25-30**	
K22-1	69	**Dodge Charger** Blue body, Yellow or Pale Blue seats......**£50-60**	
K23-1	69	**Mercury 'POLICE' Car**	
		White body with 'HIGHWAY PATROL' logo **£30-35**	
K24-1	69	**Lamborghini Miura** Red body, Cream seats...................**£30-35**	

'Battle-Kings' issued 1974

Models packed in 'window' boxes. Each has a 'military' theme and includes three plastic soldiers. Expect to pay **£20-25** for any of these items.

K101 Sherman Tank....	**K111** Missile Launcher	
K102 M48 AS Tank.....	**K112** DAF Ambulance	
K103 Chieftain Tank....	**K113** Crane Truck	
K104 King Tiger Tank	**K114** Army Aircraft	
K105 Hover Raider......	Transporter	
K106 Tank Transporter	**K115** Petrol Tanker	
K107 155mm Gun	**K116** Troop Carrier	
K108 Half Track	and Howitzer	
K109 Sheridan Tank....	**K117** Rocket Launcher	
K110 Recovery Vehicle	**K118** Army Helicopter	

'Sea-Kings' issued 1976

These models were packed in 'window' boxes. Expect a Market Price of **£12-18** for any of these 'Sea-Kings'.

K301 Frigate 'F109' ....
K302 Corvette 'C70'.......................................
K303 Battleship '110'......................................
K304 Aircraft Carrier with 4 aircraft '36' ....
K305 Submarine Chaser 'C17'.......................
K306 Convoy Escort 'F101'............................
K307 Helicopter Carrier with 2 Helicopters .
K308 Guided Missile Destroyer ....
K309 Submarine '117'.....................................
K310 Anti Aircraft Carrier ....

'Big MX' models 1972 - 1974

Special packaging contained models and accessories powered by an 'Activator Gun' which plugged into them and operated the mechanisms.

MX1 Incinerator Site + K7 Refuse Truck..**£50-70**
BM2 Mechanised Tractor Plant and
Winch Transporter (K20-1 Ford),
with Blue/Yellow MB39c Tractors...**£70-80**
with Orange MB39c Tractors **£120-150**
BM3 Mechanised (K12 Scammell) Crane
Truck and Building Site................**£50-70**
BM4 Mechanised Coal Delivery Hopper
and (K4 Leyland) Tipper................**£50-70**
BM5 Mechanised Quarry Site and
(K8, silver/red) Traxcavator **£40-50**
BM6 Fire Rescue Scene with mechanised
(K15 Merryweather) Fire Engine
plus 4 figures and scenery **£120-140**

'King-Size' Gift Sets

---	1963	**King-Size Set** ....Contains K1-1, K2-1, K3-1, K5-1, K6-1...**£200-250**
---	1965	**Construction Set** ....Contains K16-1, K7-1, K10-1, K13-1, K14-1...**£180-200**
---	1966	**King-Size Set** ....Contains K16-1, K11-1, K12-1, K15-1...**£180-200**

'Super-Kings' and 'Speed-Kings' 1971 – 1980

After 1970 the 'King Size' range developed into the larger 'Super-Kings' Series. They were fitted with extra wide speed slick tyres.

During the period 1971-79 certain issues were sold as 'SPEED KINGS' and retailed in different coloured packaging. These have been identified in the listings by the abbreviation (SPK).

Market Price Range. In general 'Super-Kings' are not very collectable and most models may be purchased for **under £15**. However, a little more price information on some of the rarer items has been received since the previous Edition and this is shown where appropriate. We regret we are unable to provide more specific price information on the remainder at this time.
Further information on the rare issues and price levels would be welcomed.

K2	77	**'24 HOUR' Car Recovery** ....
K3	74	Mod Tractor and Trailer..............................
	74	**Grain Transporter**, Green
		cab (German)...........................**£60-70**
	74	Red, 'KELLOGGS'.....................**£20-25**
K4	74	**Big Tipper**, blue/silver **£60-70**
K5	72	**Muir Hill Tractor and Trailer,**
		Yellow....................................**£25-30**
		Blue (German)........................**£60-70**
K6	76	**Cement Mixer**, blue **£20-25**
K6	74	**Motor Cycle Transporter**, 'HONDA' ....
K7	73	**Transporter**, 'TEAM MATCHBOX' ....
	74	With 'Martini' labels **£45-50**
K9	73	**Fire Tender** 'DENVER' ....
K10	76	**Transporter**, 'AUTO TRANSPORT' ....
K11	76	**Recovery Truck**, 'SHELL RECOVERY'........
	76	Recovery Truck in Red............**£70-80**
K12	75	**Hercules** 'LAING' Crane ....
K13	71	**Building Transporter**, 'DAF' ....
K13	76	**Aircraft Transporter** ....
K14	71	**Scammell Freight** 'LEP' ....
K14	77	**Breakdown Truck**, 'SHELL' ....
K15	71	**Merryweather Fire Engine**, 'KENT' ....

K15	73	**Londoner Bus issues**.
		'HARRODS - ENTER A
		DIFFERENT WORLD' ....
		'CARNABY STREET' ....
		'SILVER JUBILEE', ...
		'HARRODS - MORE
		THAN MONEY' ....
		'LONDON DUNGEON' ....
		'HAMLEYS' ....
		'ROYAL WEDDING 1981' ....
		'LONDON WIDE TOUR' ....
		'TELEGRAPH & ARGUS' ....
		'MACLEANS' ....
		'HERITAGE OF ENGLAND' ....
		'BUTTERKIST' ....
		'TOURIST LONDON' ....
		'FIRESTONE' ....
		'CHESTERFIELD 1984' ....
		'LONDON PLANETARIUM' ....
		'PETTICOAT LANE' ....
		'NESTLES MILKY BAR' ....

K16	74	**Ford LTS Tanker**,
		'TEXACO', 'CHEMCO',
		'LEP', 'ARAL'
		'SHELL', 'EXXON', TOTAL'
		'U.S. MATCHBOX CLUB',
		'QUAKER STATE' ....
	75	With 'BP' labels **£200-300**
K17		**Container Trucks**
		'DBP', 'PENGUIN',
		'7 UP', 'GENTRANSCO' ....
K18	74	**Tipper Truck**
		'TARMAC', 'US STEEL',
		'HOCH & TIEF' ....
K19	79	**Security Truck**

		'GROUP 4', 'FORT KNOX' ....
K20	73	**Cargo Hauler** ....
	79	Peterbilt 'HEAVY DUTY' ....
K21	71	**Cougar Dragster** (SPK) ....
	74	**Tractor Transporter** ....
	79	**Ford Transcontinental**
		'CONTINENTAL',
		'POLARA', 'SUNKIST' ....
K22	71	**Dodge Dragster** (SPK) ....
K22	74	**Hovercraft**, 'SEASPEED' ....
		'HOVERLLOYD' ....
		All-white....................................**£40-50**
K23	71	**Mercury 'POLICE' Car**, (SPK).............
	74	**Low Loader**, 'HOCH & TIEF' ....
K24	71	**Lamborghini Muira** ....
	77	**Scammel Truck**
		'LONDON TO GENEVA'...............
		'MICHELIN' ....
		'GENTRANSCO' ....
		'BAUKNECT' ....
K25	77	**Powerboat and Trailer**
		'SEABURST' ....
		'CHRYSLER' ....
	78	Digger, 'MUIRHILL' ....
K26	71	**Mercedes Ambulance** (SPK) ....
K26	78	**Bedford Cement Truck**
		'McALPINE'
		'HOCH & TIEF' ....
K27	71	**Camping Cruiser** ....
	78	**Powerboat Transporter**
		'EMBASSY' ....
		'MISS SOLO' ....
K28	71	**Drag Pack** (SPK) ....
	78	**Bedford Skip Truck**
		'HOCH & TIEF' ....
		'HALES' ....
K29	71	**Muira 'SEABURST'** Set, (SPK)............
	77	**Ford Delivery Van**, 'U-HAUL', 'AVIS',
		'MR SOFTY', 'BASSETTS', 'TAA' ....
K30	72	**Mercedes C111** ....
	78	**Unimog/Compressor** ....
K31	72	**Bertone Runabout** (SPK) ....
K31	78	**Peterbilt Refrigeration Truck**
		'CHRISTIAN SALVESON', 'PEPSI', 'IGLOO',
		'GERVAIS GLACE', 'DR KOCH'S TRINK',
		'Dura PENTA' (S. African), 'BURGER
		KING'
K32	71	**Shovel Nose** ....
K33	78	**Cargo Hauler** ....
K34	72	**Thunderclap** (SPK) ....
	79	**Pallet Truck** ....
K35	72	**Lightning** (SPK) ....
	79	**Massey Ferguson Tractor and Trailer** ....
K36	72	**Bandolero** (SPK) ....
	78	**'LAING' Transporter** ....
K37	73	**Sandcat** (SPK) ....
	79	**Leyland Tipper 'LAING'** ....
K38	74	**Gus's Gulpher** (SPK) ....
K39	73	**'MILLIGANS MILL'** (SPK) ....

K40	73	**Blaze Trailer** 'FIRE CHIEF' (SPK) ....
K41	73	**Fuzz Buggy** 'POLICE' (SPK) ....
	78	**Brabham F1** (SPK) ....
K42	73	**Nissan 270X** (SPK) ....
	79	**Traxcavator Road Ripper** ....
K43	73	**'CAMBUSTER'** (SPK) ....
K44	73	**'BAZOOKA'** (SPK) ....
	78	**Surtees F1** ....
K45	73	**Marauder** (SPK) ....
K46	73	**Racing Car pack** with K34 and K35 ....
K47	73	**Easy Rider Tricycle** (SPK) ....
K48	74	**Mercedes 350 SLC**, Bronze or White (SPK)..
K49	73	**Ambulance** (SPK) ....
	74	**'MALTESER' Truck** ....
K50	74	**Street Rod** (SPK) ....
K51	73	**Barracuda** (SPK) ....
K52	76	**Datsun Rally Car** (SPK) ....
K53	76	**Hot Fire Engine** (SPK) ....
K54	76	**AMX Javelin** (SPK) ....
K55	76	**Corvette** 'CAPER CART' (SPK) ....
K56	76	**Maserati Bora** (SPK) ....
K57	76	**Javelin Drag Racing Set**,
		K38 & K39 (SPK) ....
K58	76	**Corvette Power Boat Set**,
		K45 etc. (SPK) ....
K59	76	**Ford Capri Mk.II** (SPK) ....
K60	76	**Ford Mustang** (SPK) ....
K61	76	**Mercedes 'POLICE'** (SPK) ....
	78	**Mercedes 'POLIZEI'** (SPK) ....
K62	77	**Doctors Car** (SPK) ....
K63	77	**Mercedes 'Binz'** 'AMBULANCE' (SPK).......
K64	78	**'FIRE CONTROL'** Range Rover (SPK).......
K65	78	**Plymouth Mountain Rescue**
		'EMERGENCY RESUCE' ....
		'BERGRETTUNG WACHT' ....
K66	79	**Jaguar XJ12 'POLICE'** Set ....
K67	78	**Dodge Monaco** (SPK) ....
		i) 'FIRE CHIEF' ....
		ii) 'HACKENSACK' ....
K68	78	**Dodge Monaco and Trailer** (SPK) ....
K69	78	**Jaguar XJ12 and Caravan** (SPK) ....
K70	79	**Porsche Turbo** ....
K71	79	**Porsche 'POLIZEI'** Set ....
K72	79	**Brabham F1**, Red or Green..................
K73	79	**Surtees F1**, White or Tan ....
K74	79	**Volvo Estate** ....
K75	79	**Airport 'FIRE' Rescue**
		'AIRPORT FIRE TENDER' ....
		'FLUGHAFEN-FEURWEHR'..............
		'SECURITE AEROPORT' ....
K76	79	**Volvo Rally Set** 'CIBIE' ....
K77	79	**Rescue Vehicle**
		'STRASSEN SERVICE' ....
		'SECOURS ROUTIER' ....
		'HIGHWAY RESCUE' ....
K78	79	**US Police Car**
		'POLICE', 'POLIZEI' or 'CITY POLICE' .....
K79	79	**US Taxi**

'Convoy' Series

The 'Convoy' model range was launched in 1982 and early issues were made in England before manufacture was transferred to Macau. Many variations exist particularly in the USA where they have been used as promotionals linked to NASCAR truck racing. For a listing of the many variations available contact:
Carr Collectables, Central House, High Street, Ongar, Essex, CM5 9AA. Tel: (01277-366144).

Matchbox Catalogues

1957	**Folded Leaflet**	Yellow cover has Blue edging and depicts No.1 Diesel Roller. Colour pictures of nos. 1 - 42 of '1-75'series **£140-180**

1957 **Folded Leaflet** ....Blue/Yellow cover featuring MOY No.1 Allchin 7nhp Traction Engine 1st series box. Contents list first nine Yesteryears **£180-200**

1958 **16-page catalogue** .Cover shows Rolls-Royce (44), emerging from box. Models 1 - 60 in colour inside, early 'Major Packs' and Accessory Packs...**£80-90**

1959 **Leaflet** ....'Everyone buys MATCHBOX TOYS by LESNEY'. Blue with line drawings. Gives details of Presentation and Gift Sets **£200-300**

1959 **Folded Leaflet** ....Features first 14 Yesteryears in colour **£85-100**

1959 **16-page catalogue** .Same cover as 1958 catalogue with '1959 Edition'. Lists 1-75's, Major Packs and accessories. Colour pictures **£85-100**

1959 **24-page catalogue** .'UK' and '2d' on cover with MOY No.9, 1-75 series, No.'43', and Accessory No.'2'. Colour contents show MB 1 - 72 and MOY 1 - 14 plus Accessories and Major Packs..**£85-100**

1960 **32-page catalogue** .'UK' and '3d' on cover featuring logo *'ALL THE MATCHBOX POCKET TOYS BY LESNEY'* plus semi-circle picture of MOY and 1-75's. Contents illustrate all ranges.....**£75-90**

1961 **32-page catalogue** .*'International Pocket Catalogue'* on cover with picture of 1-75 model No.5 Bus. New style smaller catalogue listing all issues in colour plus International price list **£60-70**

1962 **20-page catalogue** .'2d', *'International Pocket Catalogue'* and *'1962 Edition'* on cover. All issues listed, European price list included......................**£40-50**

1963 **20-page catalogue** .No.53 Mercedes-Benz printed on cover with '2d' and *'1963 Edition'*. Contents include good Gift Set pictures and listings .**£25-35**

1964 **32-page catalogue** .'3d' on cover depicting Blue Mk.10 Jaguar (No.28). *'1964 Matchbox Prices'* on back cover. Contents include superb Gift Set pictures and listings......................**£25-35**

1965 **32-page catalogue** .Cover features Motor Racing Cars. *'1965 Matchbox Prices'* on back cover. Excellent full colour Gift Set pictures. (Price 3d)......**£20-25**

1966 **40-page catalogue** .London scene and *'Price 3d'*. Excellent pictures of mid-sixties Gift Sets plus history of Matchbox............................**£20-25**

1967 **40-page catalogue** .Cover shows flags and 1-75 issues, *'Price 3d'*. Contents list and depict Veteran Car Gifts. **£20-25**

1968 **40-page catalogue** .1968 car picture and *'Price 3d'* on cover. Inc. details of manufacturing processes **£20-25**

1969 **48-page catalogue** .Cover features Motorway scene. Contents include detailed history of the real cars making up the MOY range **£12-15**

2nd edition: ....The 2nd edition of the 1969 catalogue inc. first reference to *'Superfast'* issues......**£12-15**

1970 **64-page catalogue** .Only drawings of models (no photographs) throughout. Superfast track featured. '6d', *'MATCHBOX SUPERFAST'* and a collage of models on cover...........................**£8-10**

1971 **64-page catalogue** .'24p' on Blue/Red cover with scorpion design. 'Speed Kings' listed plus pictures of first Superfast Gift Sets..**£8-10**

1972 **72-page catalogue** .Yellow *'MATCHBOX'* and '3p' on cover. Contents feature launch of 'Scream'n Demon' bikes and excellent Gift Set pictures.............**£8-10**

1973 **80-page catalogue** .'5p' and '1973' on cover of the largest Matchbox catalogue produced. Contents include good 'Super Kings' and Aircraft Kit listing..**£8-10**

1974 **64-page catalogue** .'2p' and '1974' on cover. Includes first 'SKYBUSTERS' listing **£5-8**

1975 **64-page catalogue** .'2p' and '1975' on cover. Contents feature 'Rolamatics' and 'Battle Kings' **£5-8**

1976 **64-page catalogue** .'1976' on cover. Contents feature 'Sea Kings' plus 'Baby Dolls' and 'Disco Girl Dolls'........**£5-8**

1977 **80-page catalogue** .'1977' on cover. Contents list the 'Two Pack' (TP) range of 1-75's. Good Gift Set pictures and listings of 1-75's...**£5-8**

1978 **64-page catalogue** .'1978' on cover. Includes good 'SKYBUSTERS' and 1-75 Gift Set pictures ..**£5-8**

79-80 **80-page catalogue** .'5p' and '1979-80' on cover. The contents feature good pictures of Gift Sets G1 - G8. '900' TP series introduced.............................**£5-8**

80-81 **80-page catalogue** .'5p' on cover. All ranges listed including 'Walt Disney' and 'Power Track' equipment...**£4-6**

81-82 **64-page catalogue** .'5p' and '1981-82' on cover. 'Adventure 2000' space models pictured. 'Playtrack', 'Popeye' and 'Streak Sets' listed **£4-6**

82-83 **64-page catalogue** .'1982-83' on cover. 'Convoy' series introduced, good MOY pictures **£2-4**

1984 **64-page catalogue** .'1984' on cover. 'MATCHBOX SPECIALS' introduced, good Gift Set pictures, 'Burnin' Key Cars', 'Rough Riders' and 'Lock Ups' **£2-4**

1985 **48-page catalogue** .'1985' and 'chequered flag' design on cover. All ranges listed plus introduction of 'Trickshifters', 'Power Blasters', 'Matchmates' and 'Carry Cases'. (Printed in Italy).............**£2-4**

1986 **48-page catalogue** .'1986' on cover. 'High Riders', 'Twin-Pack', 'Action Packs' listed inside. 'Motor City'....**£2-4**

1987 **72-page catalogue** .'1987' on cover. Listing includes 'Superfast Lasers', 'Pocket Rockets', 'Speed Riders', 'Streak Racing', 'Hot Rod Racers', 'Turbo 2', 'Turbo Specials' and 'Demolition Cars'..........**£2-4**

1988 **88-page catalogue** .'1988' on cover. Listing includes Miniatures Gift Sets pictures, 'Lasers', 'Super GT Sport' and 'Super Miniatures', 'Team Convoy', 'Road Blasters', 'Motor City' and 'Action Matchbox'. Also includes 'MICA' and 'Junior Matchbox Club' membership details.............**£2-4**

1989 **80-page catalogue** .'1989' on cover. Listings include 'Miniatures', 'Twin-Pack', 'Motor City' Gift Sets, 'Dinky Collection', 'World Class', 'Conn-Nect-Ables', 'Flashbacks', 'Super ColourChangers' and 'Skybusters ColourChangers' ....**£2-4£2-4**

Overseas Catalogue Editions

During the 1960s there were normally six editions of each catalogue: British, International, U.S.A., German, French and French-Canadian. The catalogues were usually of the same format as the UK editions but with the appropriate language and currency. 'INTERNATIONAL CATALOGUE' was shown on the front cover together with the edition, e.g. 'EDITION FRANCAISE', 'INTERNATIONAL' or 'U.S.A. EDITION'.
The 1960 'International Pocket Catalogue' listed the national prices for every product in Australia, Austria, Belgium, Spain, Denmark, Eire, France, Germany, Great Britain, Holland, Hong Kong, Italy, Kenya and East Africa, Singapore and Malaysia, South Africa, Sweden and Switzerland. From 1972 the country-specific editions only listed the model range available in that country.

Market Price Range Prices are equivalent to those asked for UK editions.

Other Matchbox literature

'**Mike and The Modelman**' (1st edition 1970), was a childrens' book issued by Lesney telling the Matchbox story.
A copy in perfect condition should cost between **£25 - £30**.

Trade Catalogues have been published for many years and occasionally become available for sale. Those before 1970 are scarce and no price information is possible at present. Those from the 1970-80 period tend to be in the region of £10-15 while post-1980 editions sell for £2-5 depending on content and condition.

This listing refers to Superfast models produced between 1969 and 1983. In this period, most models in the range were presented in picture boxes with some variations being sold in Twin Packs and carded 'bubble packs'. The 'cut-off point' for many collectors of these Matchbox Miniatures is 1983 when picture boxes ceased. 'See-through' window boxes sealed at both ends were then introduced.

All the models listed have 'Made in England' bases. Those with 'Macau', 'China', 'Thailand' or elsewhere are too numerous to mention and are outside the scope of this listing. There are also many wheel variations for the models listed, such as 5-spoke, 4-spoke, 'dot-dash' etc., but again, only specific wheel variations such as hub colour are noted. Due to limitations of space, it has been necessary to introduce the use of the following abbreviations into the listing. These have been mainly restricted to indicate colour of bases and window glazing.

MB 1e   Mercedes Truck

Windows	Base colour
AG = amber glass	BB = black base
BG = blue glass	GB = grey base
CG = clear glass	PB = purple base
GG = green glass	SB = silver base
OG = orange glass	UB = unpainted base
PG = purple glass	WB = white base
	YB = yellow base

Wheels	General
BW = black wheels	BE = black engine
NW = narrow wheels	CE = chrome engine
UW = unpainted	LE = limited edition
WW = wide wheels	SE = silver engine
	TP = Twin Pack

70-70 Metallic gold body, yellow or orange canopy, green glass, narrow wheels.....**£18-20**
76 Military olive drab green body, tan canopy, purple glass, WW, '4TS702K', (TP) ...**£35-40**
76-80 Same but military olive green...............**£8-12**
76-80 Red body, yellow or orange canopy, PG, wide wheels, 'Transcontinental' (TP)....**£8-10**
80-82 Light blue body, light orange canopy, purple glass, WW, 'IMS' (TP) **£12-15**

MB 1f   Mod Rod

71 Yellow body, OG, SE, red wheels, UB or SB, 'spotted cat's head' label...........**£20-30**
71-75 Same but with black wheels **£10-12**
Black wheels and silver base **£18-20**
71-75 Same but with 'Wildcat' label **£10-12**
73 Same but with 'Flower' label............**£20-25**
74 Same but with 'Scorpion' label **£35-40**
78 Striped silver body, BW, UB. (U.S.A. 'Roman Numeral' LE)..........**£25-30**

MB 1g   Dodge Challenger

76-79 Red body, white roof, silver interior........**£6-8**
76-79 Same but with white interior **£10-15**
76-79 Same but with red interior...............**£15-18**
80-82 Blue body, white roof, red interior **£6-8**
82-83 Orange body, blue roof, black interior, UB or SB, 'Revin Rebel' **£10-12**
82 Same but with white roof **£15-20**

MB 2d   Mercedes Trailer

70 Metallic gold body, yellow or orange canopy, green glass, narrow wheels.....**£15-18**
76 Military olive drab green body, tan canopy, WW, '4TS702K' (TP)'...........**£30-35**
76-80 Same but military olive green.............**£10-12**
76-80 Red body, WW, yellow or orange canopy, 'Transcontinental' (TP)............**£8-10**

MB 2e   Jeep Hot Rod

71-75 Pink body, white or cream seats,

---

light or dark green base **£10-15**
Same but white base **£45-50**
75-76 Red body, white or cream seats, WB....**£12-18**
Same but green base **£45-50**

MB 2f   Rescue Hovercraft

76-78 Light or dark lime green body, fawn or light brown skirt, red or silver air intakes, amber or red windows, 'Rescue' **£6-8**
76-79 With Metallic light or dark green body ...**£6-8**
Same but with red windows..................**£7-10**
78 Same but black skirt.....................**£7-10**
Black skirt, red or purple windows **£10-12**
78-80 Pale green body, black skirt, purple or AG, '2000' or 'Rescue' **£15-20**

MB 2g   S-2 Jet

81-82 Black/yellow, yellow or red glass **£6-8**
82-83 Metallic light blue and white or grey, clear glass, 'Viper' on some.................**£7-10**

MB 3c Mercedes 'Binz' Ambulance

70-73 Cream or off-white body, light blue glass, NW, opening rear door.............**£15-20**
Same but with dark blue glass **£15-20**
77-80 Cream body, dark blue glass, red cross on doors, rear door cast shut (TP) **£10-12**
78-80 Military olive-green body, WW with silver hubs, rear door cast shut (TP)...**£15-25**
Same but with black hubs.................**£12-15**

MB 3d   Montiverdi Hai

73-78 Orange body, pale yellow interior, black or UB, '3' on bonnet **£7-10**
Same but '6' on bonnet....................**£12-15**

MB 3e   Porsche Turbo

78-79 Metallic brown body, cream interior, clear glass, black base ...**£7-10**
79-80 Metallic brown body, UB...................**£10-12**
Silver body, CG, cream or red interior, black or dark grey base..................**£5-7**
Tan interior, black or dark grey base ..**£12-15**
Tan interior, brown base.......................**£18-20**
Red interior, brown base.....................**£8-10**
80-82 Metallic green body, cream interior, clear glass, black or dark grey base........**£6-8**
With light or dark yellow interior **£6-8**
Same but with unpainted base **£10-12**
Red interior, dark GB or BB...............**£12-15**
Red body, tan interior, opaque glass, black base, 'Porsche Turbo 90'................**£10-18**
82-83 Red body, tan or white interior, CG, black or dark grey base, 'Porsche Turbo 90' on some......................**£5-8**

MB 4d   Stake Truck

70-72 Orange-yellow cab, green stake body, green glass.................................**£20-25**
Same but bright yellow cab **£50-60**

MB 4e   Gruesome Twosome

71-75 Gold body, SB or UB, cream interior, purple glass **£7-10**
With white or black interior...............**£12-15**
Gold body, SB, cream interior, AG......**£60-70**
75 Red body, SB or UB, yellow interior, purple glass **£12-15**
Same but with cream interior **£12-15**
Orange-red body, SB or UB, cream interior, purple glass **£25-30**

MB 4f   Pontiac Firebird

75-77 Metallic light blue body, UB, AG **£8-10**
78-80 Same but metallic dark blue **£12-15**

MB 4g   '57 Chevy

80-81 Purple body, silver interior, UB, CG **£8-10**

82-83 Red, 'Cherry bomb', SB or UB, CG **£7-10**
Same but with black base **£20-25**

MB 5e   Lotus Europa

69-70 Dark metallic blue body, ivory interior, UB, NW.........................**£12-15**
Same, no 'Superfast' cast on base ...**£140-160**
Dark metallic blue with '20' and stripe labels from G3 racing set....................**£25-30**
70-75 Pink body, ivory interior, silver base, NW or WW...............................**£25-30**
Same but with unpainted base **£10-12**
Same, but with UB, NW, '20', and stripe decals...............................**£25-30**
77-78 Black body, ivory interior, UB, NW, 'JPS' (Japanese issue).................**£20-25**
Same but without 'JPS' (TP) **£12-15**

MB 5f   Seafire Boat

75-79 White deck, blue hull, orange-yellow, blue or lemon man, black or red exh'ts ..**£4-6**
79-82 Red deck, white hull, orange-yellow or lemon man, red exhausts, black trailer (TP).........................**£7-10**
81 Red deck, blue hull, lemon man, red exhausts, black trailer (TP)...........**£55-65**
81 White deck, brown hull, lemon or orange-yellow man, red exhausts........**£45-50**
82 Black deck, yellow hull, red man, red exhausts, black trailer (TP)...........**£30-35**
83 Red deck, yellow hull, red man, red exhausts, black trailer (TP)...........**£35-40**

MB 5g   US Mail Truck

78-82 Dark or light blue body, white roof (small or large windows), WB, BW, black or silver hubs, 'US Mail' on some **£6-8**
Same but with black base **£7-10**
78 Pale blue body, white roof, 'sleet and snow' base, 'US Mail'. US LE **£10-12**

MB 5h   4x4 Jeep Off-Road

82-83 Metallic light or dark bronze body, black base, 'Golden eagle' **£7-10**

MB 6d   Ford Pick-up

70-71 Red body, white roof, white or chrome grille, NW or WW, black base **£18-20**
Metallic green or UB **£30-35**
Green or Grey base **£18-20**

MB 6e   Mercedes 350sl

74-75 Orange body, black roof, UB, ivory or pale yellow interior, amber or CG **£7-10**
75-79 Yellow body, black roof, UB, pale yellow interior, amber or CG.................**£7-10**
77 Silver body, black roof, UB, pale yellow interior, CG, 'Rennservice' (German issue) **£40-50**
Same but without 'Rennservice' **£25-35**
79 Metallic bronze body, black roof, UB, pale yellow interior, amber glass **£12-18**
79-81 Metallic bronze, white roof, AG, UB, pale yellow or cream interior **£7-10**
81-82 Metallic red body, white roof, UB, pale yellow interior, AG or CG...............**£6-8**

MB 6f   Mercedes Convertible

82-83 Metallic blue body, white interior, UB or SB, silver side stripe on some **£8-10**
83-84 Maroon body, BB, SB or UB..............**£8-10**

MB 7c   Ford Refuse Truck

70-72 Orange or orange-red cab, grey back ..**£18-20**

MB 7d   Hairy Hustler

71-74 Metallic bronze body, AG, '5' on yellow

side stripe and bonnet, GB or BB..........**£8-10**
Same but purple glass.........................**£55-60**
Metallic bronze body, AG, '5' on blue
side stripe and bonnet, UB or BB..........**£8-10**
Same but green base **£12-15**
Same but green base, plain sides........**£12-15**
Same but black base, plain sides.........**£10-12**
Metallic bronze body, AG, '3' on
side labels, '5' on bonnet, BB.............**£25-30**
Metallic bronze, AG, '3' or '137' on sides,
'Scorpion' on bonnet, GB or BB **£40-50**
75-77 White 'Streakers' version, AG, red stripes
with black/white check, GB or BB.......**£7-10**
Same but with black base **£7-10**
78 White body, AG, grey base **£25-35**
78-79 Yellow body, AG, 'flames', BB,
US 'Roman Numeral' Ltd. Edition......**£18-20**

MB 7e Volkswagen Golf

76-77 Metallic lime green body, yellow interior,
AG, BB, roof-rack, black surfboards....**£8-10**
77-81 Same but metallic light green body.......**£8-10**
77-81 Metallic dark green body, yellow or
lemon interior, AG, BB or GB.............**£8-10**
Same but with orange glass **£8-10**
Red interior, grey base **£20-30**
77 Yellow body and interior, matt black
base, 'ADAC' , (German issue)............**£25-30**
79-80 Red body, yellow interior, CG or AG,
BB, roof rack, surfboards, (TP) **£12-15**
Same but red interior, CG, (TP)...........**£35-40**
81-82 Yellow body, red interior, CG, BB or
GB, roof rack and black surfboards........**£4-6**
82-83 Silver body, red interior, CG, BB or GB,
green stripes and 'Golf' **£4-6**
Same but with tan interior **£15-20**

MB 8e Ford Mustang

70 White body, red interior, BB, CG **£80-90**
70-71 Red body, red interior, BB, CG **£200-250**
Same but with ivory interior...........**£120-140**
Orange-red body, red interior **£80-90**
Same but with ivory interior **£60-80**

MB 8f Wildcat Dragster

71 Pink body, yellow interior, black
and orange 'Wildcat' labels, BB.........**£12-15**
71-75 Same but Orange body, BB **£12-15**
Same but with UB or orange base........**£20-25**
With dark or bright yellow base...........**£20-25**
Same but with grey base **£18-20**
Orange body, yellow interior, yellow/
orange 'Wildcat' labels on some, BB ..**£12-15**
Same but grey base **£10-12**
Same but with UB or green base........**£30-35**
Orange body, yellow interior,
black base, 'Rat Rod' labels **£30-40**
Same but with 'Sailboat' labels **£50-60**

MB 8g De Tomaso Pantera

75-81 White body, red interior, blue base,
'8' and 'Pantera' labels on some.........**£10-12**
Same but orange interior.........................**£6-8**
With unpainted base...............................**£6-8**
White body, orange interior, '9' or
yellow 'Sun' in black or green circle
bonnet label, blue base.......................**£12-15**
81-82 Blue body, black interior, '8' and
'Pantera' labels on some, BB, US issue ..**£6-8**
NB MB8g can be found with the larger rear
wheels swapped with the smaller front.

MB 8h Rover 3500

81 Yellow body, red interior, sunroof,
black base, (G1 Gift set) **£225-250**
Metallic bronze body, white interior,
sunroof, black base **£15-20**
Same but dark or light tan interior **£8-10**

MB 9d Boat and Trailer

70-72 White hull, light turquoise deck,
dark blue trailer **£15-20**
76-83 White hull, light blue deck,

light blue trailer (TP).........................**£15-20**
82 White hull, black deck,
light or dark blue trailer (TP)............**£40-50**
Same but with black trailer **£20-25**

MB 9e AMX Javelin

72-78 Metallic lime green body, opening doors,
yellow interior, AG, black air intake,
UB or SB...**£10-12**
Same but with silver air intake **£20-25**
Metallic lime green body, orange interior,
AG, black air intake, UB or SB **£10-12**
Same but white interior, UB **£25-30**
Same but blue interior **£40-50**
76-78 Metallic light blue body, yellow or
orange-yellow interior, AG, UB or SB **£4-6**
78-81 Metallic dark blue body, cast-in doors,
orange-yellow interior, AG, UB
or SB, (TP)..**£4-6**
80-81 Blue body, cast-in doors, UB or SB,
orange-yellow interior, AG, black
air intake, white '1', (US Ltd.Ed.).......**£12-15**
81-83 Metallic dark green body, cast-in
doors, orange-yellow interior, AG,
UB or SB, black air intake, (TP) **£4-6**
82 Red body, cast-in doors, UB or SB,
orange-yellow interior, AG, (TP) **£20-25**

MB 9f Ford Escort RS2000

78-82 White body, tan interior, BB, CG, '9',
'Ford', 'Shell', and 'Dunlop' decals ...**£10-12**
Same but with grey base.....................**£10-12**
Same but red interior, black base.......**£90-100**
White body, tan interior, BB, CG,
'Phantom' decals, (TP)........................**£18-20**
80-82 Blue body, tan interior, BB or GB,
CG, 'Phantom' decals, (TP)................**£10-12**
Same but with blue-grey base.............**£20-25**
82-84 Green body, tan interior, BB or GB,
CG, 'Phantom' decals (TP) **£10-12**
Green body, white interior, BB, CG,
'Phantom' decals, (TP) **£20-30**
Same but with red interior **£90-100**

MB 10d Pipe Truck

70 Red body, silver base and grille,
6 grey pipes on sprue.........................**£60-70**
70-73 Same but orange-red body **£20-25**
Orange body, silver base and grille,
6 grey or yellow pipes on sprue...........**£12-15**
Same but grey base and grille **£30-35**

MB 10e Piston Popper

73-80 Metallic blue body, yellow interior,
AG, 'Superfast' on UB.......................**£80-100**
Same but 'Rola-Matic' on UB **£8-10**
Same but with silver base **£18-20**
With CG, 'Rola-Matic' on UB or SB ..**£18-20**
80 White body, yellow interior, AG,
'Rola-Matic' on UB (German
multi-pack issue)............................**£200-225**
80-81 Yellow body (red flames) and interior,
AG, 'Rola-Matic' on UB. US LE. **£15-20**

MB 10f Plymouth Gran Fury Police Car

79-81 White body, black panels, blue or pale
or dark yellow glass, UB, 'Police' **£8-10**
82-83 Same but with 'Metro Police Traffic
Control', shield and '012', UB or SB......**£6-8**
Same but 'Mercury' base from no 55....**£8-10**

MB 11d Scaffolding Truck

70-72 Silver body, red base and grille, green
glass, yellow scaffolding, NW,
'Builders Supply Company' **£20-25**

MB 11e Flying Bug

72-77 Red body, SB or UB, grey glass, yellow
exhausts, silver helmet, square cut or
heart-shape bonnet decal **£12-15**
Heart-shape decal, UB, blue glass......**£25-30**

78 Orange body, UB, black glass and
exhausts, flying beetle bonnet decal,
US Ltd. Ed. **£18-20**

MB 11f Car Transporter

NB Usually comes with 1 red, 1 blue and
1 yellow car. Other combinations are
common (e.g., 1 blue and 2 yellow)
but this does not affect the price.
77-80 Orange cab, white or beige back, BB
or UB, blue, purple or green glass.........**£5-8**
80-83 Red (later Dark Orange) cab, beige or
grey back, BB, SB or UB, blue or
purple glass..**£5-8**

MB 12c Safari Land-Rover

70 Metallic blue body, white interior,
UB, NW, brown luggage...........**£1,500-2,000**
70-71 Metallic gold body, white interior,
UB, NW, brown luggage **£20-25**

MB 12d Setra Coach

71 Metallic gold, grey roof, UB, CG **£20-25**
Same but with white roof **£18-20**
72-73 Yellow body, white roof, UB, CG **£18-20**
Same but with green glass **£150-200**
73-74 Metallic crimson, UB, CG or GG........**£12-15**
74-75 Met. purple, UB or PB, CG or GG........**£12-15**

MB 12e Big Bull

75-79 Orange, green shovel, black rollers **£30-40**
Same but with yellow rollers **£12-15**
Same but with orange rollers **£5-7**

MB 12f Citroën CX

79-82 Light or dark metallic blue body, pale
yellow or cream or ivory interior, SB or
GB or BB or UB, clear or blue glass......**£8-10**
Light metallic blue, tan interior.........**£10-12**
Dark metallic blue, red interior...........**£80-90**
82-83 Yellow body, red interior, black base,
dark blue glass, (TP) **£10-12**
With clear glass, BB, GB or SB, (TP)...**£8-10**
Yellow, red interior, BB, CG, 'Team
Matchbox' in black or blue, (TP)........**£12-15**
83 White body, red interior, BB or UB,
blue glass/lights, 'Ambulance', (TP) **£8-10**
Same but 'Police', 'Marine Division'
and '8' prints, blue stripes, (TP).............**£8-10**

MB 13d Dodge Wreck Truck

70-71 Yellow (or lighter yellow) cab, green
back, yellow crane, red hook 'B.P.'......**£25-30**

MB 13e Baja Buggy

71-78 Metallic light green body, orange interior,
UB, black or red exhausts, red or
orange bonnet flower label......................**£6-8**
With red exhausts, no bonnet label........**£8-10**
With red exhausts, 'Police' bonnet
label from 55d...................................**£35-40**
Same but with red interior **£30-35**
Metallic light green body, orange interior
from 47c, UB, red exhausts,
orange bonnet flower label.............**£150-200**
78 Metallic dark green body, orange interior,
UB, red exhausts, orange flower label **£6-8**
Same but 'Sun' label from 47c **£18-20**

MB 13f Simon Snorkel

78-80 Light red body, SB or UB, blue glass,
blue lights, yellow crane and man **£6-8**
Same but amber glass and lights **£25-30**
80-82 Dark red body, SB or UB, blue glass,
blue lights, yellow crane and man **£6-8**
82 Same but white crane and man **£8-10**

MB 14d Iso Grifo

69-71 Metallic dark blue body, pale or dark
blue interior, UB, NW..........................**£18-20**
Same but with white interior **£200-250**
71-75 Lighter metallic blue body, white

interior, UB or SB, NW **£18-20**
Sky blue, white interior, UB, NW **£18-20**
77-78 Lighter powder blue, white interior,
UB, WW, (Japanese issue)..................**£25-30**

MB 14e   Mini Ha Ha

75-82 Red body, dark blue glass, UB, 'flesh'
coloured man, brown helmet,
4 circle side labels...............................**£15-20**
Same but with purple man..................**£20-25**
'Flesh' man, light blue glass **£10-12**
Purple man, light blue glass **£12-15**
Pink man, light blue glass...................**£10-12**
Red body, light blue glass, 'flesh' or
pink man, 2 circle side labels..............**£10-12**

MB 14f   Leyland Petrol Tanker

82-83 Red cab, white tank, 'ELF' with red/blue
stripes or orange/turquoise stripes **£4-6**

MB 15d   Volkswagen 1500

69-70 Off white or cream body, cream interior,
'137', 'Monte Carlo'............................**£25-35**
70-72 Metallic red body, cream interior,
'137', 'Monte Carlo' on some **£25-30**
77-78 Off white body, cream interior, '137',
no bumper decal (Japanese issue)........**£25-30**

MB 15e   Forklift Truck

72-77 Red body, yellow hoist, grey forks, UB,
black steering wheel, 'horse' and
'Lansing Bagnall' labels **£5-7**
Same but with green or black base.........**£6-8**
77-82 Red body, unpainted hoist, yellow forks,
UB, black steering wheel, 'horse' and
'Lansing Bagnall' labels **£5-7**
Same but with green or black base.........**£6-8**
Same but no steering wheel **£5-7**
Same but with black or grey forks.........**£5-7**
With red forks, no steering wheel.......**£12-15**
82-83 Orange body, unpainted hoist, yellow
forks and roof, UB or SB or BB, no
steering wheel, 'Hi-Lift' labels **£10-12**
NB   Models can be found with 'horse' label
facing forwards or backwards and
before or after 'Lansing Bagnall'.

MB 16d   Case Bulldozer

69-74 Red body, yellow cab, shovel, engine and
base, green rubber tracks **£8-10**
Same but with black tracks.................**£10-12**
77 .   Military olive drab green body, black
shovel, BB, black tracks (TP) **£55-60**
Same but olive green body (TP).........**£20-25**

MB 16e   Badger

74-80 Metallic bronze body, SB, silver radar,
green glass (Rola-Matic) **£10-12**
Same but BB or SB, cream radar **£8-10**
Same but with light or dark grey base...**£8-10**
Dark grey or black base, black radar **£8-10**
Same but with purple glass.................**£10-12**
Black base, white radar, green glass.....**£8-10**
Same but with dark grey base...............**£8-10**
76   Military olive drab green body, light grey
base, cream radar, green glass(TP) **£35-40**
76-78 Same but olive green body (TP)..........**£18-20**

MB 16f   Pontiac Firebird

80-81 Metallic light brown body, red interior,
UB, 'Eagle' bonnet label on most.........**£8-10**
81-82 Same but metallic light gold body.........**£8-10**
Same but metallic dark gold body........**£8-10**
82-83 White body, red interior **£6-8**

MB 17e   Horse box

70   Red cab, dark green box, grey door,
chrome base, 2 white horses on sprue .**£55-60**
70-71 Same but orange-red cab **£20-25**
Orange-red cab, light grey-white box,
mustard door **£20-25**

Same but orange cab............................**£15-18**
Mustard-yellow cab, dark green
box, grey door.....................................**£15-18**

MB 17f   'Londoner' Buses

Unless otherwise stated all buses have red bodies and
white interiors. Most have metal bases in gloss or
matt black, grey, brown or unpainted. Before
changing to the Titan bus some were fitted with
plastic bases. Factory issued models are listed first,
then Lesney issued promotional models.

72-74 'Swinging London', 'Carnaby Street' ...**£8-10**
73   Silver plated Gift Ware version **£70-80**
73   Gold plated Gift Ware version **£70-80**
73-80 'Berger Paints'. (Brushes may be at
front or rear of label...............................**£5-7**
73   Same but silver body...........................**£70-80**
73   Same but gold body **£90-100**
Same but orange body **£45-50**
73   Same but cream body, brown roof......**£60-65**
75   'Esso Extra Petrol' **£65-70**
77   'Silver Jubilee 1952-77'. Silver body
with red interior, special issue box **£12-15**
Same but red body, white interior........**£70-80**
78   'Matchbox 1953-78'.................................**£4-6**
Same but orange body **£65-70**
Same but blue body **£45-50**
72   'Preston Guild Merchant' **£75-80**
73   'Impel 73' Trade Fair **£35-40**
'London and Kensington Hilton'.........**£75-80**
'The Baron of Beef' **£100-120**
'Sellotape Selbstklebebander'.........**£250-300**
'Sellotape Packaging Systems'........**£125-150**
'Sellotape Electrical Tapes' **£125-150**
'Barclays Bank' **£80-90**
'Chambourcy Yogurt'.........................**£65-70**
'Interchemicals and Plastics' **£200-250**
74   'Typhoo puts the 'T' in Britain'..........**£80-90**
76   'Impel 76' Trade Fair. Cream body
with brown roof, white interior...........**£25-30**
'British Airways Busch Gardens' **£60-70**
'Ilford HP5 Film' **£150-180**
'A.I.M. Building Fund 1976' **£35-40**
'Selfridges' **£15-20**
'Santa Claus, Aviemore Centre'..........**£35-40**
'Amcel takes you places' **£65-75**
'Eduscho Kaffee'............................**£140-160**
77   'New! The Museum of London' **£18-20**
'Army and Navy' **£18-20**
'Jacob's the Biscuit Makers'
Red body with white interior.............**£35-40**
Orange body with white interior.........**£18-20**
78   'Aral-Deutschlands Autopartner'
Blue body with white interior.............**£45-50**
Same but red body **£90-100**
79   'Impel 79' Trade Fair **£25-30**
80   'You can't kid a Bisto kid'....................**£8-10**
'Borregaard Paper'............................**£90-100**

MB 17g   Leyland Titan Bus

82   'Berger Paints' **£3-5**
'Laker Skytrain'.....................................**£3-5**
82   'Chesterfield Transport Centenary' **£3-5**
'Matchbox No.1, Montepna'
Pale blue/white (Greek issue) **£18-20**
Same but red body **£20-25**
'I.C.P. Interchemicals'.........................**£70-80**

MB 18e   Field Car

70-75 Light yellow body, light brown roof,
white interior, SB, NW or WW **£18-20**
Same but WW, UB................................**£15-18**
Black roof, UB, WW.............................**£30-40**
76   Military olive drab green body, tan roof,
black interior, BB, 'A' square door
labels, black wide wheels (TP) **£35-45**
76-80 Same but olive green body (TP)..........**£18-20**
Same but 'RA391' bonnet label **£18-20**
With circled star bonnet label (TP).....**£20-25**

77-78 White body, black roof, black interior,
BB, Black/white checked bonnet label,
black wide wheels (TP) **£200-300**
Same but silver wheel hubs (TP) **£200-300**
Orange body, black roof, black interior,
BB, black/white checked bonnet label,
black wide wheels (TP) **£12-15**
Same but silver wheel hubs (TP)........**£12-15**
Orange body, black roof, black interior,
SB, black/white checked bonnet label,
black wide wheels (TP) **£20-25**
78-80 Metallic ruby-red body, tan roof, black
interior, SB or BB, '44', 'Champion' and
'Goodyear' bonnet label (TP) **£8-10**
80   Dark orange body, black roof, black
interior, BB or SB, 'AC Filters' and '179
Scout Racing' labels, US Ltd. Ed. **£20-25**
Same but no labels, US Ltd. Ed. **£20-25**
82-83 Dark yellow body, black or tan roof,
black interior, SB, black/white
checked bonnet label, (TP) **£25-30**
Orange, black roof and interior, BB,
black/white checked bonnet, (TP) **£18-20**
Orange body, black or tan roof, white
interior, BB, '44', 'Champion' and
'Goodyear' bonnet label, (TP) **£25-30**

MB 18f   Hondarora

74-75 Red body, chrome forks, SE, black
seat, 'Honda' tank labels, WW **£18-20**
75-80 Same but no labels or with BW............**£8-10**
Red body, black forks, SE, white
seat, 'Honda' tank labels, WW **£85-95**
Same but with black seat **£10-12**
76   Orange body, black forks, SE, black seat,
'Honda' labels, (King Size set 6).........**£20-25**
76   Military olive drab green, black forks,
BE, black seat, no labels, WW (TP)....**£25-30**
76-78 Same but military olive green (TP) **£15-18**
81-82 Metallic green body, black forks,
BE or SE, black seat, no labels, BW **£6-8**
82-83 Yellow body, black forks, SE, black
seat, no tank labels, black wheels.........**£8-10**
Same but with brown or tan rider........**£8-10**

MB 19d   Lotus Racing Car

70   Metallic purple body, UB, SE, white
driver, round No.'3' side labels............**£35-40**

MB 19e   Road Dragster

70-75 Light red body, UB or SB, off-white
interior, '8' labels normal or sideways...**£8-10**
Same but with 'Scorpion' labels..........**£40-50**
72   Metallic pink body, UB, off-white
interior, 'Wynns' labels. Promotional ..**£60-70**
Same but smaller 'Wynns' labels.........**£60-70**
75   Metallic purple body, UB, off-white
interior, 'Scorpion' labels **£40-50**
Same but with '8' labels or no labels **£8-10**
Metallic red body, UB, off-white
interior, '8' labels as normal **£200-250**

MB 19f   Cement Truck

76-81 Red body, yellow barrel with red stripes,
unpainted base, green glass **£5-7**
Same but black stripes or no stripes **£5-7**
79   Same but grey barrel with red stripes.....**£5-7**
Same but with purple glass.................**£10-12**
81-82 Red body, lemon barrel with red stripes
unpainted base, green glass **£5-7**
Same but black stripes or no stripes **£5-7**
Same but with purple glass...................**£8-10**

MB 19g   Peterbilt Cement Truck

82-83 Metallic green body, orange barrel,
yellow or white 'Big Pete' **£7-9**

MB 20d   Lamborghini Marzal

69   Metallic red body, white interior, UB..**£15-18**
70   Same but with 'Avon' and '2' labels
from G3 Racing Specials set **£20-25**
71   Bright pink body, white interior, UB ..**£10-12**
Bright pink, silver base **£20-30**

Same but with 'Avon' and '2' labels
from G3 Racing Specials set **£20-25**

71-75 Orange or orange-pink body, white
interior, unpainted base **£10-12**

72 Yellow body, white interior, UB,
('Brroom Stick' blister pack issue)......**£40-50**

MB 20e Police Patrol

75-80 White, UB, orange or red 'Police' stripe,
orange light and interior (Rola-Matic) ..**£7-10**
White body, UB or SB, orange 'Police'
stripe, blue or yellow light and interior ..**£6-8**
Same but with black base **£8-10**
White body, UB, 'Ambulance' and Red
Cross, orange light and interior **£15-18**

76-78 White body, UB, orange 'Site Engineer'
stripes, orange light and interior,
(G3 Consruction Set)..........................**£30-35**
Same but with orange body **£25-30**
Orange body and 'Police' stripe, orange
light and interior, UB, (G3 Set)........**£25-30**

76 Military olive drab green body, UB,
yellow and red 'Police' arrow, orange
light and interior (TP) **£40-50**
Same but 'Ambulance' labels **£40-50**

76-77 Military olive green body, UB, yellow
and red 'Police' arrow, orange light
and interior (TP) **£18-20**
Same but with 'Ambulance' labels **£18-20**

80 Blue body, UB, yellow 'Paris-Dakar 81'
stripe, (French issue blister pack)........**£40-45**

81 White body, UB, blue 'County Sheriff'
labels, blue light and interior **£12-15**
Same but '017', 'Sheriff', blue roof....**£15-18**

81-83 White body, UB, yellow 'Police' and
'shield' stripe above chequered stripe ..**£8-10**
Same but with black base **£8-12**
White body, UB, black 'Police' on
sides, yellow light and interior **£12-15**

83 Light brown or beige body, UB, yellow
'Securite-Rallye Paris-Dakar 83'........**£12-15**

MB 21d Foden Concrete Truck

70-73 Dark yellow cab, yellow barrel, red
body and shute, green base................**£18-20**
Same but bright yellow cab,
green or dark green base....................**£25-30**

MB 21e Rod Roller

73-78 Yellow body, black wheels with
metallic red hubs, GB, 'flame' label..**£18-20**
Same but with matt red hubs **£15-18**
Yellow or darker yellow body, black
wheels, GB or BB, 'flame' or no label ..**£8-10**

MB 21f Renault 5TL

78-79 Metallic blue, red interior, BB or SB ..**£15-20**
Metallic blue body, tan interior,
black, dark grey or silver base............**£8-10**
Yellow body, red interior, BB or SB,
'Le Car' and stripe prints **£12-15**
Yellow body, tan interior, BB or SB
or dark grey base, 'Le Car' prints........**£8-10**

79-81 Silver body, red interior, BB or SB,
'A5' and stripe prints **£12-15**
Same but no tampo prints **£8-10**
Silver body, tan interior, BB or SB **£15-20**

81-82 Silver body, red interior, dark grey or
BB or SB, 'Le Car' and stripe prints **£8-10**

82-83 White body, tan interior, BB, 'Renault'
and '4' on green prints **£8-10**
Same but 'Renault' roof prints **£8-10**
White body, white interior, BB, 'Renault'
and '4' on green prints **£8-10**
White body, tan interior, BB, 'Roloil'
and '21' on yellow prints **£8-10**
Same but with orange base **£20-25**
White body, white interior, BB, 'Roloil'
and '21' on yellow prints **£8-10**

MB 22c Pontiac GP Sports Coupé

70 Red body, grey interior, BB..........**£800-1,000**
Light purple, grey interior, BB **£30-40**

Dark purple, grey interior, BB............**£30-40**

MB 22d Freeman Intercity

70-71 Metallic purple body, off-white interior,
UB, yellow arrow labels on some..........**£8-10**

71-72 Metallic gold body, off-white interior,
UB, yellow arrow labels **£15-18**

72-75 Metallic red body, off-white interior,
UB or SB, arrow labels on some **£8-10**

MB 22e Blaze Buster

75-80 Red body, silver interior, UB,
yellow ladder, 'Fire' labels....................**£6-8**
Same but with black ladder **£20-30**
Same but with white ladder **£130-150**
Red body, silver or white interior,
black or dark grey base, yellow ladder....**£6-8**

80-82 Dark red body, white interior, grey or
BB, yellow ladder, 'Fire' labels **£6-8**

83 Light red body, white interior, BB, dark
yellow ladder, 'Fire' labels....................**£6-8**
Same but 'No.32' on yellow labels.....**£12-15**

MB 23e Volkswagen Camper

70-72 Blue body, orange interior and hinged
roof, UB, CG, rear sailboat side labels
on some, petrol filler cap, NW **£55-60**
Same but no filler cap........................**£20-25**

72-75 Orange body, orange interior and hinged
roof, UB, CG, sailboat labels, NW ..**£100-120**
Light or dark orange body, white interior,
orange hinged roof, UB, CG, sailboat
labels on some, NW............................**£18-20**

77-80 Military olive green, no interior, cast roof,
BB, BG, Red Cross labels, WW (TP) ..**£15-18**

80 White body, no interior, cast roof, BB,
GG, 'PizzaVan', WW. US LE **£30-35**

MB 23f Atlas Truck

75-81 Metallic blue body, orange tipper with
yellow and red arrow labels, chrome
interior, AG, UB **£10-12**
Same but without tipper labels **£6-8**
Same but grey interior, CG, UB **£4-6**
Same but grey interior, AG, SB or UB....**£6-8**
With grey interior, CG and SB **£8-10**

81 Metallic blue body, silver tipper, grey
interior, CG, SB **£8-10**

81-82 Same but red body..............................**£8-10**
Same but red body, black interior......**£12-14**

MB 24c Rolls-Royce Silver Shadow

70-73 Light metallic red body, cream
interior, black base **£18-20**
Same, but Dark metallic red body **£10-15**
Same but with pink base **£20-25**
Same but SB or grey base..................**£15-18**
Same but with metallic green base **£30-40**

77-78 Light metallic dark body, cream
interior, UB, (Japanese issue) **£80-120**
Same but BB (Japanese issue)............**£25-30**

MB 24d Team Matchbox

73 Bright yellow body, white man, '4' (or '8')
and 'Team Matchbox' bonnet label .**£180-200**
Metallic blue body, white man,
'1' and 'Team Matchbox' label......**£230-250**
With '5' and 'Team Matchbox'......**£200-220**

73-75 Metallic green, white man, '5' (or '8'),
'Team Matchbox' label, (G4 set) **£30-50**

73-78 Metallic red body, white man,
'8' and 'Team Matchbox' label..............**£8-10**

78-80 Metallic ruby-red body, white man,
'44', 'Champion', 'Goodyear',
black trailer (TP)..............................**£10-12**

82-83 Same but orange body, yellow man ..**£60-70**

MB 24e Diesel Shunter

78 Metallic dark green body, light brown
control panel, 'Railfreight' **£6-8**
Same but with 'D1496-RF' labels **£4-6**

78-83 Light or dark yellow body, light brown
control panel (or none), 'D1496-RF'......**£3-5**

MB 25d Ford Cortina GT

70 Metallic light brown body, off white
interior, unpainted base..................**£90-100**

70-72 Same but metallic light blue body **£20-25**
Same but metallic dark blue body **£30-35**

MB 25e Mod Tractor

72-78 Metallic purple body, BB, yellow seat,
headlights cast on rear mudguards **£30-40**
Without lights on rear mudguards **£8-10**
Metallic purple body, BB, red seat....**£80-90**
Metallic purple, UB, yellow seat **£8-10**

76-79 Red body, BB, yellow seat (TP) **£8-10**

MB 25f Flat Car Container

78-80 Light beige container red roof, black flat
car, 'United States Lines' labels **£8-10**
Same but with 'N.Y.K.' labels **£4-5**
Same but 'Sealand' labels......................**£5-7**
Dark beige container, red roof, black
flat car, 'N.Y.K.' or 'Sealand' labels **£4-5**
Same but with 'OCL' labels **£10-12**
Dark brown container, red roof, black
flat car, 'N.Y.K.' labels **£12-15**

MB 25g Audi Quattro

82-83 White and black, 'Audi' and '20' **£10-12**

MB 26c GMC Tipper Truck

70-72 Red tipping cab, silver tipper, green
chassis, green glass, wide wheels........**£15-18**

MB 26d Big Banger

72-76 Red body, UB, 'Big Banger',
dark blue glass **£10-12**
Same but with amber glass..................**£14-18**

78 Dark brown, 'Brown Sugar', WB,
amber, black or blue glass (USA)........**£20-25**

81-83 White body, BB, 'Cosmic Blues'
clear or blue glass, (US issue) **£12-15**

MB 26e Site Dumper

76-78 Yellow body, yellow dumper,
black seats, black base **£5-7**

78-81 Same but with red dumper **£4-6**
Same but dark grey base **£8-12**
Same but brown base **£12-15**

81-82 Orange-red body, silver dumper, white
seats, black base **£4-6**
Same but wheels have yellow hubs **£7-10**
Orange-red body, silver dumper, white
seats, dark grey base..............................**£4-6**
Same but wheels have yellow hubs **£7-10**

MB 26f Cable Truck

82-83 Orange-yellow body, red base, blue
glass, two light grey cable drums **£15-18**
Same but red body or BB **£7-10**

83 Bright yellow body, BB, blue glass,
two dark grey cable drums..................**£40-50**
Same but dark red body **£12-15**

MB 27d Mercedes 230sl

70-71 White body, red interior, clear glass,
unpainted base, narrow wheels............**£25-30**

71 Same but yellow body........................**£20-25**

71-73 Yellow body, black interior,
CG, UB, NW or WW..........................**£12-15**

MB 27e Lamborghini Countach

73-75 Yellow body, BB, red glass, '3' **£6-8**
Same but with amber glass **£8-10**
Same but with purple glass **£10-12**
Yellow body, UB, red glass, '3' **£6-8**
Same but with purple glass **£10-12**

75 Orange body, UB, red glass, '3' **£20-30**
Same but with amber glass **£20-30**

75-81 **Lamborghini 'Streakers'**. All have
green/black 'Streaker' prints and a red
'8' on the bonnet.
Orange body, chrome interior, BB........**£8-10**
Same but with amber or green glass ...**£10-12**

Orange body, grey interior, BB, GG **£8-10**
Same but with purple glass **£10-12**
Orange body, grey interior, UB, green
glass, red '8' on bonnet **£8-10**
Same but with brown base **£10-12**
Orange body, yellow interior, BB or
dark grey base, green glass **£8-10**
Orange, chrome interior, UB, green
or amber glass, red '8' on bonnet **£10-12**
Orange body, grey interior, dark grey
base, green glass **£8-10**
Same but with purple glass **£10-12**
Orange body, beige interior,
dark grey base, green glass **£8-10**
Same but with purple glass **£10-12**
Orange body, beige interior, BB, GG **£8-10**

MB 27f   Swing Wing

81-83   Red/white, red glass **£6-8**
Red/white, dark yellow-orange glass **£7-9**
Red/white, red or black 'Jet Set' **£7-10**

MB 28d   Mack Dump Truck

70-73   Metallic lime green body and dumper,
UB, cab steps cast closed..................**£18-20**
Same but with steps cast open............**£18-24**
77-79   Military olive drab green body/dumper,
BB, cab steps cast closed (TP) **£40-50**
Military olive green (TP) **£20-25**

MB 28e   Stoat

73-76   Metallic gold body, UB or BB, dark
brown man, (Rola-Matic issue) **£3-6**
77   Military olive drab green body, BB,
dark brown man, (TP) **£40-50**
77-79   Military olive green body, BB, dark
brown man, (TP) **£18-20**

MB 28f   Lincoln Continental

79   Light red body, white roof,
beige interior, clear glass, UB **£8-10**
79-81   Dark red body, beige, dark brown
or grey interior, clear glass, UB............**£8-10**

MB 28g   Formula Racing Car

81-83   Metallic brown-grey body, BB or UB,
white driver, 'Exxon' and '8' prints.........**£5-7**

MB 29c   Fire Pumper Truck

70   Red body, white back and ladders,
UB, blue glass, narrow wheels............**£35-40**
81   Same but 'P1' and 'Los Angeles Fire
Dept.', wide wheels ('Code Red') **£18-20**

MB 29d   Racing Mini

70-72   Metallic bronze body, SB or UB,
off-white interior, '29' on yellow
labels (orange edges) **£15-20**
72-76   Orange body, SB or UB, cream or
off-white interior, '29' on yellow
labels (orange edges) **£12-15**
Same but with green label edges........**£12-15**
76-81   Red body, SB or UB, off-white or
cream interior, '29' on yellow
labels (green edges) (TP)....................**£10-12**
Red body, SB, cream interior, '3' on
white circle door labels (TP) **£35-40**
Same but with no labels.......................**£12-15**

MB 29e   Tractor Shovel

76-78   Light yellow body, red shovel, silver
engine and seat, yellow base.................**£8-10**
77   Lime green body, yellow shovel, silver
engine and seat, yellow base
(German PS1000 set issue).................**£60-70**
78-81   Yellow body, red shovel, silver or
black engine and seat, yellow base.........**£6-8**
Same but with cream base **£8-10**
Same but with black base **£6-8**
Yellow body, red shovel, black engine
and seat, yellow base, yellow hubs.........**£6-8**
Yellow body, black shovel, black engine
and seat, yellow base **£6-8**

Same but with cream base **£8-10**
Same but with black base **£6-8**
79   Yellow body, black shovel, black engine
and seat, BB, black stripes, ('C' prints
on some), (G5 Construction Set)............**£6-8**
81   Orange-red body, red shovel, dark grey
engine and seat, black base, ...**£20-25**
82-83   Same but with black shovel **£10-12**

MB 30c   8-wheel Crane

70   Red body, dark orange crane arm with
yellow hook, UB **£240-280**
Same but with gold crane arm............**£18-20**

MB 30d   Beach Buggy

70-76   Light metallic purple body, yellow
spots, UB, white interior **£20-25**
Same but with yellow interior...............**£8-10**
Same but dark metallic purple body......**£8-10**
NB   The yellow spots on this model can
vary from only a few spots to almost
an entire body covering.

MB 30e   Swamp Rat

76-81   Military green deck, light brown hull,
'Swamp Rat' labels on some **£6-8**

MB 30f   Articulated Truck

81-83   Metallic steel-blue cab, WB,
red glass, silver trailer...........................**£6-8**
Blue cab, WB or YB, silver trailer..........**£5-7**
83   Blue cab, pale yellow or WB, blue
trailer with 'Pauls' white labels,
(Ltd. blister-pack issue of 900)...........**£35-45**
Blue cab, WB or YB, yellow
trailer, 'International' labels..................**£8-10**
Red cab, YB, yellow trailer with
'International' labels **£8-10**
Red cab, YB, silver trailer...................**£10-12**

MB 31e   Lincoln Continental

70   Sea-green body, white interior,
unpainted base, CG, NW **£1,500-2,000**
Metallic lime-green body, white
interior, UB, CG, NW **£15-20**
Same but with wide wheels **£20-25**

MB 31d   Volksdragon

71-77   Red body, PG, UB or SB, yellow or
cream interior, 'eyes' label on some **£10-12**
Red body, purple glass, UB or SB,
yellow interior, 'flower' label...............**£15-20**
78   Black body, purple glass, UB, yellow
interior, 'bug'/ 'flames' (US issue)......**£15-20**

MB 31e   Caravan

77-83   White body, off-white or light brown
interior, UB, AG, orange or yellow door,
orange stripe with white bird labels.........**£6-8**
White body, light yellow interior, light
blue, orange or yellow door, orange
stripe with white bird labels on some **£6-8**
Same but dark blue door, blue stripe
with white bird labels on some...............**£6-8**

MB 32c   Leyland Petrol Tanker

70-73   Dark green cab and body, white tank,
SB, blue glass, 'B.P.' labels in centre
or front of tank, NW **£18-20**
Dark green cab and body, white tank,
GB, 'B.P.' labels in centre of tank........**£35-40**
Blue cab and body, white tanker, SB,
'Aral' labels in centre of tank, (German
issue in Aral Tankwagen box)............**£80-90**
Metallic purple cab and body,
silver tank, SB, no labels **£100-125**
Same but with 'N.A.M.C.' labels.....**£150-180**
Red cab and body, white tank,
SB, 'N.A.M.C.' labels **£300-400**

MB 32d   Maserati Bora

73-78   Metallic crimson body, lime green base,
yellow interior, stripe and '8' label........**£8-10**
Same but with dark green or UB........**£10-12**
Same but dark green base, '3' label.....**£15-20**
Same but with no label.........................**£6-8**
79   Metallic gold, SB, yellow interior,
no bonnet label, tow hook, (TP) **£35-40**

MB 32e   Field Gun

77-81   Military green body, light or dark brown
base, 2 soldiers and 4 shells on sprue,
black wide wheels.................................**£6-8**
Same but black wheels, silver hubs **£30-40**
78   Military olive green body, no base,
soldiers or shells, black wheels (TP) **£3-5**

MB 32f   Excavator

81-82   Orange-red body, dark grey or black
swivel base, silver-grey tracks **£6-8**
82-83   Yellow body, black swivel base, black
tracks, black stripes & 'CAT' prints **£8-10**
Same but with no 'CAT' print **£6-8**

MB 33c   Lamborghini Miura P400

69   Yellow body, red interior, UB, NW..**£100-120**
70   Light metallic bronze body,
red interior, UB, NW **£25-30**
Dark metallic bronze body,
red interior, UB, NW **£100-120**
70 -73   Light metallic gold body, off-white
interior, UB, NW **£18-20**
Same but dark metallic gold body.......**£18-20**
Dark metallic gold body, red interior,
UB, NW **£25-30**
Lt. met. gold body, off-white interior,
red or pink-red base, NW or WW **£25-30**
77-78   Light gold body, off-white interior,
UB or BB, WW (Japanese issue)........**£25-30**

MB 33d   Datsun 126X

73-75   Yellow body, orange base, AG **£6-8**
Same but with unpainted base **£30-40**
75-77   Yellow body, orange base, AG,
red/orange or red/black flame prints,
('Streakers' issue)................................**£10-12**
78   Yellow body, BB, AG, red/black flame
prints, (US Roman Numeral issue)......**£18-20**
Gold plated body, BB, black glass,
green prints, (US Roman Numeral).....**£18-20**

MB 33e   Police Motorcycle

77-79   White frame, chrome or black engine,
white bars, UW, blue man, white or
black seat and panniers, 'Police' **£5-7**
79   White frame, chrome engine, white bars,
UW, green man, seat and panniers,
'Polizei' (German) **£15-18**
79   Same but cream frame, man has white
helmet and gloves (King Size 71
German Polizei Patrol set)................**£15-18**
79   All black bike and wheels, dark blue
man, white helmet, 3 stripes and shield,
white seat and panniers, 'Police',
gold star tank labels (KS 66 set)........**£20-25**
79   White frame, black engine and wheels,
white bars, blue man, white helmet
and gloves, white seat and panniers,
'Police' labels **£8-10**
79-81   White frame, black engine, white bars,
black wheels, green man, seat and
panniers, 'Polizei' labels (German) **£10-12**
79   Same but white helmet and gloves **£12-15**
79-81   Same but white helmet and gloves,
UW, (KS 66 Police Patrol set) **£20-25**
81   White frame, black engine white bars,
black wheels, green man, white
seat and panniers, 'LAPD' labels **£20-25**
81   White frame, chrome engine, black
bars, black wheels, no man, white
seat and panniers, 'Police' labels........**£10-12**
81-82   Black frame, chrome engine, white

bars, black wheels, blue man, white
seat/panniers, 'LAPD' (Code Red)......**£12-15**

MB 34d   Formula I Racing Car

71-72   Metallic purple body, UB, CG, yellow
or blue stripe, '16' label, 4 NW **£12-15**

71   Same but yellow stripe, 'Wynns'
labels (Promotional issue)...................**£60-70**

72-75   Yellow body, UB, CG, blue bonnet
stripe, '16' label, 4 NW or WW **£6-8**
Same but front NW, rear WW **£8-10**
Yellow body, UB, CG, yellow stripe,
'16' label, 4 NW **£8-10**
Yellow body, UB, AG, blue or yellow
stripe, '16' label, 4 NW **£12-15**

73-75   Metallic blue body, UB, CG, yellow
or blue stripe, '15' label, 4 WW (or
front NW, rear WW) (G4 set) **£35-40**
Orange body, UB, CG, blue or
yellow stripe, '16', 4 WW (or front
NW, rear WW) (G4 set) **£30-35**
Orange-yellow body, UB, CG, blue
stripe, '16' label, 2 NW, 2 WW **£15-18**

MB 34e   Vantastic

75-78   Orange body, WB, GG, white interior,
rear stripes labels **£6-8**
Same but motif instead of stripes **£8-10**
Same but with stripes and UB **£100-150**

78   Orange body, WB, GG, white interior,
'Jaffa Mobile', (Promotional)......**£200-230**

78   Orange body, WB, GG or CG, white
interior, bonnet 'Sun' label **£25-30**

78-81   Orange body, WB, GG, white interior,
'34', rear stripes labels on some **£6-8**

MB 34f   Chevy Pro-Stocker

81-83   White body, UB, blue '34' prints.............**£6-8**
Same but with no tampo prints **£6-8**
White body, red base, blue '34' **£10-12**

MB 35c   Merryweather Fire Engine

69-71   Metallic red body, GB, white ladder,
'London Fire Service', NW **£18-20**

71-75   Red body, GB, white ladder, 'London
Fire Service', NW or WW **£12-15**
Red, GB, 'Flame-Proof Wool' **£70-80**
Same but in promotional box **£150-200**
Red body, BB, ladder, 'London
Fire Service', wide wheels...............**£20-25**
Same but with tan base **£25-30**
Red body, GB, different style ladder,
'London Fire Service', WW, (TP) **£12-15**

81   Red body, GB, white ladder and man
from 13f, 'Los Angeles City Fire
Dept.' prints, WW, (Code Red) **£18-20**

MB 35d   Fandango

75-77   White body, red interior, red base,
red or silver rear disc, arrow and '35'
bonnet label (Rola-Matic)......................**£6-8**
White body, red interior, UB, red rear
disc, arrow and '35' bonnet label **£25-30**
White body, red interior and base,
silver rear disc, stripe and '6' bonnet
label from 41c **£15-20**

77-82   Red body, red interior, red base,
blue arrow and '35' bonnet label,
blue or silver rear disc **£85-100**
Red body, off-white interior, WB,
blue arrow and '35' label, blue, silver
or red rear disc **£6-8**
Red body, off-white or white interior,
UB, blue rear disc, arrow and '35' **£10-12**
Red body, white interior, UB, blue rear
disc, 'Sun' bonnet label from 47d....**£18-20**

MB 35e   Zoo Truck

82   Red body, blue cage, light brown lions,
blue glass, black base........................**£5-7**
Same but with red base....................**£25-30**
Same but with grey base....................**£10-12**

83   Red body, silver cage, light or dark

---

brown lions, blue glass, black base.........**£5-7**

MB 36c   Opel Diplomat

70   Metallic light or dark gold body,
silver grille, white interior, BB **£20-25**
Same but without silver grille...............**£18-20**

MB 36d   Hot Rod Draguar

70-73   Metallic dark red body, off-white or
light yellow interior, silver 'Draguar'
label.......................................**£12-15**
Same but with orange interior **£18-20**
Same but lemon or white interior **£8-10**

73-75   Metallic pink body, light yellow
interior, silver 'Draguar' label...........**£12-15**
Metallic pink body, cream interior,
no boot label **£8-10**
Metallic pink body, light or dark
yellow interior, no boot label **£8-10**
Same but with amber glass.................**£8-10**

MB 36e   Formula 5000

75-77   Orange body, blue or yellow man,
'Formula 5000' and orange or yellow
'3', '5000' on rear spoiler **£6-8**

77   Same but red body, yellow man.............**£6-8**

77-78   Red body, yellow man, 'Texaco 11' on
bonnet, no spoiler label or 'Marlboro' **£6-8**

78-80   Same but 'Champion' on rear spoiler **£8-10**

MB 36f   Refuse Truck

80-82   Metallic red cab, all-yellow container,
red load, no labels **£6-8**
Same but without 'Collectomatic'
on container...**£50-75**

82-83   Blue cab, all-yellow or all-orange
container, black or red load,
'Metro DPW66' on side labels **£5-7**
Same but orange container with
yellow opening back, red load **£8-10**

MB 37c   Cattle Truck

70-71   Orange-yellow cab and body, grey
back and 2 white cattle **£15-20**

71   Same but orange cab and body...........**£30-40**
Orange cab and body, silver back......**£80-90**

72   Bright-yellow cab/body, grey back **£70-80**

MB 37d   Soopa Coopa

72-75   Metallic light blue body, yellow interior,
AG, unpainted or silver base **£6-8**

75-76   Metallic light purple body, yellow
interior, AG, UB, 'flower' label **£12-15**
Same but with red base...................**£150-200**

77   Orange body, yellow interior, AG,
SB, 'Jaffa Mobile' (Promotional) **£100-120**

MB 37e   Skip Truck

76-81   Red cab/body, yellow skip, chrome
interior, AG, BB **£6-8**
Same but grey interior, clear glass **£5-7**
Same but with brown base.....................**£6-8**
Red cab/body, yellow skip,
orange interior, CG, BB **£8-10**
Red cab/body, blue skip,
grey interior, CG, BB...........................**£90-100**

77   Orange cab/body, yellow skip, grey
interior, CG, BB (German issue).......**£90-100**
Red skip (German PS1000 set)........**£90-100**

81-82   Metallic blue cab/body, yellow skip,
grey interior, CG, gloss or matt BB........**£6-8**
Same but with silver base **£10-12**

MB 37f   Matra Rancho

82   Blue body, blue base, black interior......**£8-10**

83   Yellow body, yellow base, black
interior, red side stripe prints **£15-20**

MB 38c   Honda Motorcycle and Trailer

70-71   Metallic blue-green bike,
yellow trailer, 'Honda' labels...............**£20-25**

71   Same but metallic pink bike **£25-30**

72-73   Same but metallic purple bike **£25-30**

77   Metallic green bike, orange trailer
with 'Honda' labels on some (TP)......**£18-20**

82   Same but yellow trailer (TP)...............**£15-18**

MB 38d   Stingeroo

73-76   Metallic purple body, purple forks
white horse's head.............................**£10-12**
Same but with pale blue forks **£35-40**
Same but with chrome forks...........**£250-300**

MB 38e   Jeep

76-80   Military green body, gun, BB/seats,
'21*11' or 'star' label..........................**£8-10**

77   Military olive drab green body,
no gun, BB/seats, 'star' label, (TP)......**£55-65**
Same but military olive green body **£25-30**
Same but with '21*11' label (TP).......**£20-25**
Yellow body, BB/seats, 'Gliding Club',
(TP with yellow glider trailer)..........**£15-20**
Same but with white base,
(TP with yellow glider trailer) **£35-40**
Red body, BB/seats, 'Gliding Club',
(TP with red glider trailer)..........**£450-550**

MB 38f   Ford Camper

80-82   Orange-red body, green glass, cream
back with AG, UB with no.'35'........**£90-110**
Same but camper back with no glass **£7-10**

MB 38g   Ford Model 'A' Van

The 'collectable cut-off point' for this Catalogue is
generally 1983. However, the MB38g casting was
used well into the 1990s and proved popular as a
promotional item. This section therefore includes
issues up to the end of 1989 but excludes items likely
to be priced below £5.

84   'TOY FAIR 84' (US), roof label **£70-85**
Same but without roof label **£40-50**

84   'PEPSI COLA', 'COME ALIVE'..........**£5-8**
Same but without 'COME ALIVE' **£8-10**
'PEPSI COLA', 'Matchmates'..............**£6-9**

84   'BEN FRANKLIN'.....................**£250-350**

84   'MATCHBOX USA'............................**£15-20**

86   'WEET-BIX'/'SANITARIUM'..............**£6-8**

86   'H.H. BRAIN'.......................................**£6-8**

87   'W.H.SMITH & SON Ltd', Red.........**£7-10**

87   'MICA' 2nd CONVENTION..........**£100-125**

87   'SILVO 1912-1987`.............................**£8-10**

87   'This Van Delivers', with phone no.......**£8-10**
without phone no.........................**£250-350**

87   'RICE KRISPIES', Dark Blue, (US)....**£8-10**

88   'MICA 3rd CONVENTION'....................**£7-9**

88   'MICA 1st N.A. CONVENTION'........**£5-8**
with black 'island' **£18-22**

88   'W.H. SMITH & SON Ltd', Yellow....**£7-10**

88   'UNIROYAL' (Canada).........................**£8-10**

89   'MB US COLLECTORS CLUB'........**£18-22**

89   'JACKY MAEDER' (Swiss)..................**£6-9**

89   'SWARFEGA'..

89   'CAMPERDOWN' (Australia) ....NGPP

MB 39d   Clipper

73-79   Metallic crimson body, yellow interior,
AG, unpainted base, chrome or white
exhausts, (Rola-Matic)........................**£15-20**
With green base and amber glass **£8-10**
With green base and clear glass **£10-12**

MB 39e   Rolls-Royce Silver Shadow

79-81   Silver body, Red interior, SB or UB....**£10-12**

81-82   Metallic red body, off-white or yellow
interior, silver or unpainted base **£8-12**

82-83   Metallic gold-brown body, white

---

interior, silver or unpainted base **£8-10**
83   Ruby red body, white interior, matt
black or matt silver base **£8-12**

MB 40c   Hay Trailer

67-70   Dark blue body, yellow sides,
BPT with yellow hubs............................**£8-10**
79-79   Lt. yellow body, no sides, BPT (TP) **£4-6**
Same but with black fixed sides (TP).....**£4-6**
Orange-yellow body, black fixed sides,
black wheels (TP) **£8-10**
79   Same but with light blue body, (TP)....**£10-12**
80   Same but with red body, (TP).............**£10-12**
81   Same but with beige body, (TP) **£50-60**

MB 40d   Vauxhall Guildsman

71-74   Pink body, GG, cream interior, UB,
blue circle flame bonnet label...............**£8-12**
Same but with silver base **£15-20**
With UB, black circle flame label **£8-12**
Same but with silver base **£15-20**
75   Pink body, GG, cream interior, UB,
blue '40' print (Streakers issue)......**£100-120**
75-76   Red body, AG or GG, cream interior,
UB or SB, blue '40' (Streakers)........**£12-15**
76   Red body, GG or AG, cream interior,
unpainted base, Blue circle flame bonnet
label, (TP) **£12-15**
Red body, AG, UB, cream interior,
no bonnet label, (TP) **£12-15**

MB 40e   Horse Box

77-80   Orange cab, cream box, light or dark
brown door, BB, SB, GB or UB **£10-12**
80-83   Light metallic green cab, cream box,
dark brown door, unpainted base **£8-10**
Same but with white door......................**£8-10**
Dark metallic green cab, cream box,
dark brown door, UB, SB or BB............**£8-10**
Same but lime green door, SB or BB ..**£12-15**
83   Dark metallic green cab, dark brown
box, white door, unpainted base **£12-15**
Yellow cab, dark brown box, lime
green door, black base **£20-25**
Same but with white door...................**£18-20**
Orange cab, dark brown box, lime
green door, BB, SB or UB **£10-12**
Same but with white door....................**£8-10**

MB 41c   Ford GT

69-70   White body, light or dark green or BB,
red interior, '6' on bonnet, NW **£20-25**
71-72   Metallic bronze body, dark green or
BB, red interior, '6', NW or WW.......**£15-18**
Same but WW, cream base **£30-35**
Same but WW, grey base **£18-20**
WW, light or dark yellow base...........**£30-35**
Blue body, Yellow interior...................**£40-45**
77   White body, red interior, 'Wildcat'
or '6' label, BB, (Japanese issue) **£30-35**
79   Yellow body, red interior, BB, no
bonnet label, MP1 Italian issue ....**£1,000+**

MB 41d   Siva Spyder

72-75   Metallic red body, cream interior, black
band, unpainted base, clear glass..........**£8-10**
Same but with chrome band **£15-18**
Metallic red body, white interior, black
band, unpainted base, clear glass..........**£8-10**
75-78   Metallic dark blue body, white or cream
interior, black band, UB, CG, stars &
stripes, '8', (Streakers issue)..............**£15-20**
77   Light blue body, off-white interior, black
band, UB, black glass or CG, 'Spider'
print, (US Roman Numeral issue) **£20-25**

MB 41e   Ambulance

78-81   White body, grey interior, side stripe
with 'Ambulance', red cross labels....**£7-10**
Same but with yellow interior.............**£10-12**
White body, grey interior, side stripe

---

with 'Emergency Medical Services'......**£7-10**
Same but with yellow interior.............**£10-12**
White body, grey interior, no stripe -
only 'Ambulance' in grey letters.......**£12-15**
80   Silver body, grey interior, 'Paris-Dakar
81' (French blistercard issue)............**£35-40**
Same but with white rear doors..........**£35-40**
81   Red body, grey interior, 'Notarzt' and
red cross prints, (German issue)........**£25-30**
White body, grey interior, side stripe
with 'Ambulance', Blue Cross labels **£7-10**
Same but with 'Pacific Ambulance,
Emergency, 101' prints (Code Red).....**£25-30**

MB 42c   Iron Fairy Crane

70   Red body, yellow boom/hook/base......**£80-90**
Light or dark orange-red body, lime
boom, yellow hook, yellow base.........**£20-25**

MB 42d   Tyre Fryer

72-77   Metallic light blue body,
yellow interior, unpainted base **£20-25**
Same but with black base **£8-12**
Metallic dark blue body,
orange-yellow interior, black base......**£18-20**
77   Orange body, yellow interior, BB,
'Jaffa Mobile' (Promotional) **£100-120**

MB 42e   Mercedes Container Truck

77   All-yellow body, BG, BB, 'Deutsche
Bundespost' labels (German issue)......**£20-25**
77-80   Red cab/body, cream container with
red doors and roof, BG, UB,
'Sealand' or 'NYK' labels **£5-7**
Same but with black base **£7-10**
Same but with UB, 'OCL' labels............**£7-10**
81   Same but with 'Confern Mobeltransport-
betriebe' labels, PG (German issue) **£18-20**
Dark blue cab and body, blue container
BG, UB, 'Karstadt'(German issue) **£20-25**
81-82   Red/white, 'Matchbox', BG or PG......**£6-8**
Metallic green/yellow, BG or PG,
'Mayflower' and ship labels.................**£6-8**
Same but with red glass.........................**£8-10**
Same but red/white body, BG or PG **£6-8**

MB 42   '57 Thunderbird

82-83   Red body, white interior, UB or SB....**£7-10**

MB 43c   Pony Trailer

70-71   Yellow body, grey door, light green
base, 2 white horses, NW **£25-30**
Same but with dark green base **£20-25**
76-79   Orange body, brown door, BB or GB,
2 horses, 'horse head' labels (TP).......**£10-15**
79-83   Same but light brown body..................**£10-15**
83   Light brown body, brown door, BB,
2 horses, 'Silver Shoes' or
no labels (TP)......................................**£10-15**

MB 43d   Dragon Wheels

72-77   Dark green, BB, 'Dragon Wheels' **£12-18**
Same but with unpainted base **£18-20**
Light green, BB, 'Dragon Wheels'......**£18-20**

MB 43e   Steam Locomotive

78-82   Red cab/sides, black engine, '4345' **£4-5**
Same but with 'NP' labels **£5-7**
'81   Green cab/sides, black engine, '4345' **£8-10**
81-83   Same but with side 'NP' labels (TP).......**£7-9**

MB 44c   Refrigerator Truck

70   Red cab and body, green back, grey
rear door, green glass, UB, NW.......**£100-120**
70-71   Yellow cab and body, red back, grey
rear door, green glass, UB, WW.........**£10-15**

MB 44d   Boss Mustang

72   Yellow body, black bonnet, UB, WW ..**£10-15**
Same but with silver base **£20-30**
80   Green, UB, 'Cobra', (US Ltd. Ed.)......**£10-15**
82-83   Dark or light orange body, off-white

---

interior, UB, 'The Boss' and '5' **£10-12**

MB 44e   Passenger Coach / Caboose

78-83   Red/black, off-white roof, green glass,
red '431 432' side labels.........................**£6-8**
Same but with clear glass **£8-10**
Same but with no glass **£6-8**
Red/black, off-white roof, no glass,
red '5810 6102' side labels.....................**£6-8**
Same but with cream or tan roof............**£6-8**
Red/black, off-white roof, no glass,
green '5810 6102' side labels.................**£6-8**
Red/black, off-white or cream roof,
no glass, green 'GWR' side labels........**£8-10**
81-83   Green/black, off-white raised roof, no
glass, green '5810 6102' labels (TP)......**£6-8**
Red/black, off-white raised roof, no
glass, red '431 432' labels (TP)..............**£6-8**
Same but red '5810 6102' labels (TP)....**£6-8**

MB 45c   Ford Group 6

70   Non-metallic green body, white interior
CE, CG, UB, '7' label, NW **£250-300**
70-71   Dark metallic green body, CE,
CG, UB or BB, '7' label, NW **£25-30**
Same but 'Burmah' labels (G3 set) **£25-30**
Dark metallic green body, CE,
CG, BB or GB,'45' label, NW **£12-15**
Same but with pink body **£18-20**
71-73   Metallic lime green body, CE,
AG, BB, '45' label, WW.....................**£10-15**
Same + 'Burmah' labels, (G3 set) **£15-18**
Metallic lime green body,
grey engine, AG, BB, '45', NW **£10-15**
Same but grey or CE, GB, WW **£10-15**
73-76   Metallic dark or light purple body,
grey or CE, AG, BB, '45', WW...........**£10-12**
Metallic dark purple body, CE, AG,
BB, 'eyes' label from 31d, WW.........**£30-35**

MB 45d   BMW 3.0 CSL

76-81   Light or dark orange body, cream
interior, GG, 'BMW' label on some **£10-12**
Same but with clear glass **£12-15**
77   White body, cream interior, GG,
'BMW' and 'Manhalter' signature
label, (Austrian 50,000 issue) **£30-35**
White body, GG, 'Polizei 123', blue
or yellow light, (German issue) **£50-60**
Same but no light or 'Polizei 123'.......**£50-60**
82   Red body, GG, 'BMW' (G15) **£80-100**

MB 45e   Kenworth Cabover

82-83   White body, AG, blue/brown stripes......**£7-10**

MB 46c   Mercedes 300se Coupé

70   Metallic blue body, white interior, UB,
opening doors and boot, NW **£100-120**
70-71   Metallic light or dark gold body,
opening doors and boot, NW..............**£45-50**
Metallic light gold body, opening boot
but doors cast shut, NW.....................**£20-25**
77   Military olive green body, boot and
doors cast shut, 'Staff' labels (TP).....**£18-20**
81   Silver body, WW, (Multi Pack).........**£70-80**

MB 46d   Stretcha Fetcha

72-77   All-white body, red base, BG,
'Ambulance', large Red Cross labels **£6-8**
Same but no 'Amulance', small RC **£15-18**
All-white body, UB, BG, 'Ambulance'
and large Red Cross labels.....................**£8-10**
All-white body, red base, 'Ambulance',
large Red Cross labels, AG **£15-20**
Same but no 'Amulance', small RC **£20-25**
77   All-red body, red base, BG, 'Unfall
Rettung' labels (German issue)...........**£40-50**
80   Lime green/white, WB or BB, AG,
'Viper Van' prints (US Ltd. Ed.).........**£20-25**

MB 46e Ford Tractor and Harrow

78-81 Blue body, yellow interior, UB, black
wheels, yellow plastic harrow **£5-7**
Same but black wheels, yellow hubs **£6-8**
Blue body, white interior, UB, black
wheels, yellow hubs, yellow harrow **£6-8**
79 Blue body, yellow interior, UB, black
wheels, no harrow (TP)...........................**£5-7**
81 Metallic lime green, yellow interior,
BW, yellow hubs, no harrow (TP) **£6-8**
81-83 Metallic green body, yellow interior,
BW, yellow hubs, yellow harrow **£5-7**
83 Blue body, yellow interior, GB, BW
with gold hubs, no harrow (TP)...............**£6-8**

MB 47c DAF Container Truck

70-72 Silver cab/body, yellow tipper **£12-15**

MB 47d Beach Hopper

73-78 Blue body with paint spots, light or
dark pink base, orange interior, light
brown man, clear or no windscreen,
'Sun' label, wide WW (Rola-Matic)......**£8-10**
Same but UB, no windscreen **£15-18**
With light pink base, yellow interior,
no windscreen, dark brown man.........**£30-35**

MB 47e Pannier Locomotive

79-82 Dark green and black, BB, 'G.W.R.' **£3-5**
Same but with unpainted base **£8-10**
Same but with brown or grey base **£10-12**

MB 47f Jaguar SS100

82-83 Red body, light brown interior, BB.......**£8-10**
Same but with grey base **£10-12**

MB 48c Dodge Dumper Truck

69-71 Blue cab and body, yellow tipper,
chrome base, NW or WW..................**£12-15**

MB 48d Pie-Eyed Piper

72-77 Metallic blue body, silver engine and
exhausts, BG, UB, '8' and stars...........**£8-128**
Same but with amber glass **£12-15**
Red body, 'Big Banger', CE and
exhausts, BG, UB **£150-200**
78 White body, silver/black engine, black
exhausts, glass and base, orange
prints, (US Roman Numeral issue)......**£12-15**
81-83 Red body, SE, black exhausts, AG,
BB, 'Red Rider' prints (USA) **£12-15**

MB 48e Sambron Jack Lift

77-81 Yellow body, BB, red 'Sambron'......**£80-100**
Same but with no tampo prints...............**£5-7**
Yellow body, BB, yellow hubs **£5-8**
Same but with grey or brown base **£7-10**
81-83 Yellow body, black forks, BB or GB **£6-8**

MB 49b Unimog

70 Blue body, red base, green glass,
silver or plain grille........................**£25-30**
70-71 Same but metallic steel-blue body **£20-25**
71-72 Same but sky blue body, plain grille ...**£18-20**
78 Military olive green body, BB, GG,
tan load, 'A' label in square (TP) **£35-40**
Same but 'star' circle label, tan load
on some, (TP)...............................**£35-40**

MB 49c Chop Suey

73-76 Metallic red-purple frame, chrome
forks, CE, 'bull's head' **£250-300**
Same but with red forks.....................**£8-10**
With black or orange forks **£35-40**

MB 49d Crane Truck

76-79 Yellow body and crane arm, red hook,
black base, green glass...................**£6-8**
77 Red body, yellow crane arm, red hook,

BB, CG (German PS1000 set)............**£70-80**
Same but GG (German PS1000 set)....**£60-70**
80-82 Yellow body, black crane arm, red
hook, black base, purple or red glass ..**£10-12**
Same but green glass **£6-8**
82-83 Same but 'A1 Crane Service' on arm
+ 'Safety First', 'C', 'Cat' on some.....**£10-12**

MB 50c Kennel Truck

70-71 Dark or light metallic green body, BB,
silver grille, 4 white dogs, NW...........**£18-20**
Dark Metallic Green body, Grey base,
silver grille, 4 white dogs, NW...........**£15-18**
Same but with yellow base **£25-30**
72-73 Lime Green body, BB or GB,
silver grille, 4 white dogs, WW **£20-25**
Same but white grille, BB or GB **£30-35**
Same but with unpainted base **£35-40**

MB 50d Articulated Truck

73-79 Yellow cab/body, BB, light blue trailer
with yellow chevron side labels, yellow
or orange trailer body, red or PG **£7-10**
Same but no labels **£6-8**
80 Red cab/body, BB, light blue trailer, no
labels, red trailer body, PG **£35-40**
Yellow cab/ body, light blue trailer, no
labels, yellow trailer body, white tow
hook, purple glass (TP)......................**£6-8**
Red cab/body, silver trailer (red body),
white hook on some, PG (TP) **£35-40**
80 **Articulated Trailer** Light blue
trailer (yellow body) (TP) **£6-8**
Silver trailer, red trailer body (TP) **£35-40**

MB 50e Harley-Davidson

80-82 Light gold frame, black handlebars **£10-12**
82-83 Dark bronze frame, black bars............**£10-15**

MB 51c 8-wheel Tipper

70-71 Yellow cab and body, silver tipper, BG,
SB, 'POINTER' labels on some **£20-25**
Same but with grey base....................**£75-80**

MB 51d Citroën SM

72-74 Metallic bronze body, cream interior,
unpainted base, NW **£12-15**
Same but with orange interior **£60-70**
Same but with yellow interior **£20-25**
With cream interior, silver base **£12-15**
75 Metallic blue body, yellow interior,
unpainted base, WW **£25-30**
75-78 Same plus '8', UB (Streakers issue)....**£12-14**
With '8', UB and off-white or orange
interior (Streakers issue)....................**£15-18**
79 Metallic blue body, orange interior, UB,
roof rack, 'Yamaha Shell STP' (TP)....**£15-18**

MB 51e Combine Harvester

78-81 Red body, yellow blades/arm, BB,
black 'regular wheels' **£6-8**
Same but with black Superfast wheels **£8-10**
Same but with yellow hubs **£8-10**
Red body, yellow blades/arm,
no base, black Superfast wheels **£8-10**
Same but with yellow hubs **£12-14**
Yellow body, red blades/arm, no base,
'2' print, Superfast wheels (Gift Set).....**£8-10**

MB 51f Pontiac Firebird SE

82-83 Red body, tan interior, silver base **£8-10**

MB 51i Motorcycle Trailer

79-82 Metallic blue body, 3 orange-yellow or
yellow bikes (TP)................................**£7-10**
Same but with 3 red bikes (TP)...........**£10-12**
82-83 Red body, 3 yellow bikes (TP)...........**£12-15**

MB 52c Dodge Charger Mk.III

70-71 Metallic light or dark red body,
black interior **£8-12**
Same but with '5' labels (G3 set) **£25-30**

71 Metallic purple body, black interior **£8-12**
71-75 Metallic lime green, black interior **£8-12**
Same but with '5' labels (G3 set) **£25-30**
Same but with UB (G3 set) **£25-30**

MB 52d Police Launch

76-80 White deck, light blue hull, light or dark BG,
orange stripes, 'Police', 2 light blue
men, 2 horns **£8-10**
81 Same but with no roof horns **£6-8**
White deck, red hull, roof and rear,
BG, 'Los Angeles Fire Department',
2 light blue men (Code Red issue) **£25-30**
Same but 2 yellow men (Code Red)....**£18-20**

MB 52e BMW M1

81-83 Silver body, red interior, BB, CG, black
stripes and '52' tampo prints **£7-10**
Same but blue-grey base....................**£10-12**
With BB, amber glass **£25-30**
With BB, CG, no tampo prints **£7-10**

MB 53c Ford Zodiac Mk.IV

70 Metallic light blue body, NW **£450-500**
70-71 Metallic light green body, NW **£20-25**
Metallic dark green body, NW **£20-25**
Metallic emerald green body **£25-30**
72 Lime green body, wide wheels **£40-55**

MB 53d Tanzara

72-74 Orange body, SE, silver interior,
UB, AG...**£7-10**
Same but with green glass **£10-15**
75-76 White body, SE, silver interior, UB,
AG, blue/orange stripes/stars, '53' **£12-15**
Same but with no tampo prints **£18-20**
With blue/red stripes/stars, '53' **£12-15**
Same but with green glass **£18-20**
White body, red engine, red interior,
UB, AG, blue/red stripes/stars, '53'.....**£80-90**

MB 53e CJ6 Jeep

77-80 Red body, yellow interior, light brown
roof, UB, WW **£5-8**
Same but with black interior................**£8-10**
With yellow interior, silver base **£5-8**
81-82 Metallic green body, yellow interior,
light brown roof, UB, WW **£5-8**
Same but with black interior................**£8-10**
With yellow interior, silver base **£5-8**
Pale yellow body, dark brown roof, black
interior, BB or GB, 'CJ6' print **£12-15**

MB 53f Flareside Pick-up

82-83 Blue body, '326' and 'Baja Bouncer' **£8-10**
Same but with some or prints or none...**£8-10**

MB 54b Cadillac Ambulance

70 White body, silver grille, red roof lights,
BB, small Red Cross door labels.......**£20-30**
Off-white body, plain grille, red roof
lights, BlB, large Red Cross labels.....**£20-25**

MB 54c Ford Capri

71 Pink or orange body, black bonnet,
UB, wide wheels **£18-20**
72-75 Metallic crimson body UB or SB **£18-20**
76 Orange body, UB, (TP)....................**£18-20**

MB 54d Personnel Carrier

76-79 Military green body, black base, green
glass, light brown soldiers on some......**£8-10**

MB 54e Mobile Home

80-82 Cream or white body, brown door,
side stripes on some, BB **£6-8**
Same but with grey or brown base **£7-9**

MB 54f NASA Tracking Vehicle

82-83 White/red/black, BB, 'US Space
Shuttle Command Centre', 'NASA' **£7-10**
Same but with grey base....................**£10-12**

MB 55d Mercury Police Car

70	White body, 2 men, blue roof light, shields and 'Police' label **£40-50**
	Same but with red roof light.............**£25-30**

MB 55e Mercury Estate Police Car

71-74	White body, off-white interior, no men, UB, 2 red roof lights, bonnet shield and 'Police' label and side shield labels.....**£25-30**
	Same but UB or SB, bonnet and side 'Police' arrow labels **£12-15**
	Same but UB or SB, bonnet 'Police' arrow label, plain sides **£15-18**

MB 55f Hellraiser

75-76	White body, red interior, UB, 'Stars and Stripes' bonnet label **£8-10**
77-78	Metallic blue body, red interior, SB, 'Stars and Stripes' bonnet label **£10-12**
	Metallic blue body, off-white interior, UB or SB, 'Stars and Stripes'................**£8-10**
	Metallic blue body, off-white interior, SB, bonnet stripe and '3' label...........**£20-25**
	Same but with no label **£8-10**

MB 55g Ford Cortina

79-80	Metallic green body, red interior, UB, clear glass, opening doors **£8-10**
	Same but with light yellow interior **£12-15**
81	Metallic red body, light yellow interior, UB, opening doors **£8-10**
82-83	Metallic light brown body, white interior, UB or SB, opening doors, black stripe ..**£8-10**
	Light red body, white interior, UB or SB, doors cast shut.....................**£8-10**
	Same but with gloss black base **£18-20**
	Bright red body, white interior, UB or SB, opaque glass, doors cast shut (Gift Set issue) **£20-25**
83	Light red body, light brown interior, UB or SB, doors cast shut, black side stripe prints (TP) **£20-25**
	Same but white interior (TP) **£8-10**

MB 56c BMC 1800 Pinifarina

69-70	Metallic gold body, UB, NW **£12-15**
	Same, with '17', 'Gulf' (G3 set) **£20-25**
71-73	Peach body, UB, NW **£25-30**
	Orange body, UB, NW or WW...........**£10-12**
	With '17' and 'Gulf' (G3 set) **£20-25**

MB 56d Hi-Tailer

74-78	White body, orange/blue stripes, UB, 'MB5 Team Matchbox', yellow man **£8-10**
	Same but with silver or red base **£12-14**
	Same but with blue man **£8-10**
79	Red base, 'Martini 7' (Gift Set)..........**£12-14**

MB 56e Mercedes 450 SEL

79-80	Metallic blue body, red interior **£10-12**
	Same but with light brown interior **£7-10**
81-83	Light brown body, light or dark brown interior, red 'Taxi' sign, UB or SB **£7-10**

MB 57c Land-Rover Fire Truck

70	Red body, 'Kent Fire Brigade' labels...**£60-70**
	Same but with 'Kent Fire Brigade' labels cut around words **£60-70**

MB 57d Eccles Trailer Caravan

70-71	Cream body, orange roof, green interior, maroon side stripe labels **£12-15**
	Same but brown side stripe labels **£15-18**
	With brown stripe and flower labels **£12-15**
72	Pale Yellow body, orange roof, green interior, brown stripe, flower labels **£18-20**
76-78	Yellow body, red-orange roof, white interior, black stripe, flowers (TP) **£12-15**
	Same but with side red dots label from K-27 Camping Cruiser set (TP) **£25-30**
79-81	Light brown, red-orange roof, white

interior, black stripe, flowers (TP) **£10-12**
| | Same but 'white bird' label (TP) ....**£20-25** |
| 82 | White body, red-orange roof, white interior, 'Sunset', palm tree (TP) ....**£15-18** |

MB 57e Wildlife Truck

73-80	Yellow body, clear back, red glass, 'Ranger' (Rola-Matic version)..............**£8-10**
	Same but with amber back **£10-12**
81	White body, clear back, red glass, light brown lion, black/white camouflage prints, (Rola-Matic version)..................**£8-10**
	Same but with amber glass **£10-12**
	Same but with purple glass **£12-15**
	Same but tinted detachable back **£12-15**

MB 57f Carmichael Rescue Vehicle

82	White body, 'Police Rescue'................**£12-15**
83	Red body, 'Fire' **£15-20**

MB 58c DAF Girder Truck

70	Cream or off-white cab and body, red base (with 'Pat App' on some) **£80-100**
70-71	Metallic lime green cab and body **£18-20**

MB 58d Woosh 'n' Push

72-75	Yellow body, red interior, '2' label **£7-9**
	Same but pale yellow interior **£25-30**
	With red interior, 'flower' label **£12-15**
76	Metallic red body, pale yellow interior, '2' label on roof **£8-10**
	Same but '8' and stars label...............**£12-15**

MB 58e Faun Dump Truck

76-81	Yellow body, yellow tipper.....................**£6-9**
79	Yellow body, red tipper (G5 set).........**£25-30**
82-83	Yellow body, yellow tipper, 'CAT' **£10-12**

MB 59e Ford Galaxie Fire Chief

70	Red body, white interior, 'Fire Chief' and side shield labels **£25-30**

MB 59d Mercury Fire Chief

71-74	Red body, '59' or '73', 2 men, yellow 'Fire Chief' on bonnet, 'shield' labels on sides **£20-25**
	Same but 'helmet & axes' on sides......**£12-15**
	Same but yellow bonnet 'helmet and axes' labels, plain sides **£10-12**
	Same but yellow 'helmet and axes' labels on bonnet and sides **£10-12**
	With nothing or just '59' on base **£10-12**
78	Same but with no men (TP) **£10-12**
	Red body, CG, 'Fire', shield (TP) **£10-12**
	Same but with purple glass (TP) **£15-20**
79	White, CG, 'Police', shield (TP) **£20-25**
81	Red body, 'Los Angeles Fire Dept' tampo prints (Code Red).....................**£18-20**
	White body, CG or BG, 'Los Angeles Police' tampo prints, (Code Red) **£18-20**
82	White body, CG, PG or BG, 'Police' and shield label, black wing panel prints......**£15-18**
	White body, CG or BG, 'Metro Police', black wing tampo prints as 10f............**£8-10**
	Same but with white wing panels........**£10-12**

MB 59e Planet Scout

75-77	Metallic green and lime green **£5-7**
78-80	Metallic red and light brown **£8-10**
77	Avocado/black, PG or AG (Adventure 2000 K2005 Command Force set)......**£25-30**
80	Metallic blue/black, PG, (Adventure 2000 set)..**£50-60**

MB 59f Porsche 928

80-81	Light metallic brown body, brown interior, black base, clear glass **£8-10**
	Same but cream or off-white interior ..**£10-12**
	With brown interior, amber glass........**£10-12**
	Dark metallic brown body, brown interior, black base **£8-10**
	Same but with amber glass **£10-12**
	Same but with brown glass **£10-12**

With clear glass, brown or grey base....**£8-10**
	With AG, brown or grey base **£12-15**
81-82	Metallic blue body, brown interior, clear glass, black base........................**£7-9**
	Same but with grey or silver base **£8-10**
82-83	Black body, brown interior, 'Porsche' ..**£9-12**
	Same but with red interior **£10-12**

MB 60b Truck with Site Office

70	Blue truck, yellow/green office **£18-20**

MB 60c Lotus Super 7

71-75	Orange body, black interior and boot, bonnet 'flame' label **£8-12**
	Same but with Yellow body **£12-15**
75-76	Same but blue stripe and check design + bonnet '60' prints, (Streakers).........**£12-15**

MB 60d Holden Pick-up

77	Metallic ruby red body, yellow interior, AG, yellow bikes, '500' label **£10-12**
77-80	Bright red body, yellow interior, AG, yellow bikes, '500' label **£10-12**
	Same but with orange glass **£10-12**
	Bright red body, red interior, orange or AG, olive green bikes, '500' label **£12-14**
	Bright red body, red interior, orange or AG, olive green bikes, 'Sun' label......**£20-25**
	Bright red body, yellow interior, AG, yellow bikes, 'striped' bonnet label ...**£15-18**
80	Metallic blue body, yellow interior, orange or amber glass, yellow bikes, 'Paris-Dakar 81' (French issue) **£20-25**
81-83	Cream body, red interior, orange or AG, red bikes, stripes and Superbike! ...**£8-10**
	Same but with yellow bikes.................**£8-10**
	Cream body, red interior, AG, red bikes, 'Honda' labels **£25-30**

MB 61b Alvis Stalwart

66-71	White body, yellow detachable top, clear glass, 'BP Exploration' labels, regular black wheels, yellow hubs.......**£35-40**
78	Metallic olive green body, fixed top, GG, black wide wheels (TP)...............**£20-25**

MB 61c Blue Shark

71-77	Metallic blue, UB or SB, CG, '86' **£8-10**
	Same but '69' label from 69d **£12-14**
	Metallic blue body, SB, CG or AG, 'Scorpion' label on bonnet...............**£35-40**
	Metallic blue body, UB or SB, AG, bonnet arrows and '86' label **£12-14**
	Same but '69' label from 69d......**£12-15**

MB 61d Wreck Truck

78-80	Red body, white arms, red hooks, BB or GB, AG and 2 roof lights **£5-7**
	With red or white arms, black hooks......**£5-7**
	Red body, red arms, red hooks, BB, black glass and 2 roof lights...........**£25-30**
81	Red body, off-white arms, red hooks, BB, AG, 'Radio Despatches 24 Hour Towing' tampo prints (TP)...................**£12-14**
81-82	Light yellow body, red arms, black hooks, AG, black or grey base **£5-7**
	Same but with brown base....................**£8-10**
	Same but with silver base **£8-10**
	With red arms & hooks, BB or GB **£5-7**
	Light yellow body, white arms, red hooks, BB or GB, AG and lights **£20-25**
	Light yellow body, green arms, red or black hooks, BB or GB, AG lights ..**£10-12**
	Dark yellow body, red arms, black hooks, BB, AG **£7-9**
	Same but with brown base....................**£8-10**
	Dark yellow body, red arms, red hooks, BB or GB, AG and lights......................**£7-9**

Dark yellow body, white arms, red
hooks, BB, AG and lights **£20-25**
Dark yellow body, green arms, red
or black hooks, BB, AG and lights **£12-15**
Same but with grey base **£15-20**

MB 61e   Peterbilt Wreck Truck

82-83   Red-orange, white 'Eddies Wrecker' **£6-8**
        Same but with black tampo prints **£8-10**
        Blue body, no tampo print, from
        'Highway Express' Gift Set) **£20-25**

MB 62c   Mercury Cougar

70   Light metallic gold or gold-green body
        red interior **£20-25**

MB 62d   Mercury Cougar Dragster

70   Light green body, red interior, UB,
        'Rat Rod' labels **£20-25**
70-73   Same but lime green body **£10-12**
        Same but silver base **£25-35**
        Same but UB, 'Wild Cat' labels **£25-30**

MB 62e   Renault 17TL

74-78   Red body, white interior, '9' label **£8-10**
        Red-orange body, white interior, '9' **£8-10**
        Same but label reversed to read '6' **£10-12**
76   Red body, white interior, 'Fire'
        labels, (from G12 Rescue set) **£20-25**

MB 62f   Chevrolet Corvette

79-81   Metallic ruby red body, grey interior,
        UB, CG, white bonnet prints **£8-10**
        Same but with black interior **£10-12**
        Same but white interior **£12-15**
        Same but with black interior **£8-10**
        Same but with grey interior **£8-10**
81-83   Black body, grey interior, UB, CG,
        orange/yellow bonnet stripes **£7-9**
        Same but with silver base **£8-10**
83   Same but UB, opaque glass, (from
        Streak Racing set) **£12-15**

MB 63c   Dodge Crane Truck

70-72   Yellow body, yellow crane, arm
        and hook (orange hook on some) **£15-18**

MB 63d   Freeway Gas Tanker

73   Red/black/white, 'Castrol' labels **£60-70**
73-77   Red/black/white, 'Burmah' labels **£5-7**
        Same but with tow hook hole in rear **£6-8**
76   Military olive drab green and black,
        'Canadian' flag labels (TP) **£300-400**
        Same but with 'French' flag (TP) **£70-80**
76-77   Military olive green cab black base,
        '95 High Octane' labels (TP) **£18-20**
77   Light blue/black/white, 'Aral'
        labels (German issue) **£30-35**
78-79   Red/black/white, 'Chevron' labels,
        tow hook hole in rear of tanker **£6-8**
        Same but with white tow hook (TP) **£8-10**
        Red/black/white, 'Burmah' labels,
        cream tow hook (TP) **£8-10**
79-80   White/yellow, 'Shell' labels, PG **£8-10**
        Same but with red glass **£10-12**
        Yellow/black/white, 'Shell', PG **£15-18**
80-81   White/yellow, 'Exxon' labels **£15-18**
        White/black, 'Exxon' labels **£15-18**
        White/yellow, 'Shell' labels,
        cream tow hook (TP) **£8-10**
        White/yellow, 'Exxon' labels,
        cream tow hook (TP) **£15-18**
81-82   White/black/green, 'BP Super' **£8-10**
        White/yellow, 'BP Super' (TP) **£20-25**

MB 63dx   Freeway Gas Trailer

78-79   White/red, 'Chevron' labels (TP) **£8-10**
        Same but with 'Burmah' labels (TP) **£8-10**
80-81   White/yellow, 'Shell' labels (TP) **£6-8**
        White/yellow, 'Exxon' labels (TP) **£15-18**
81-82   White/yellow, 'BP Super' (TP) **£20-25**

MB 63e   4x4 Open Back Truck

82-83   Orange or light orange body, '24' and
        'FWD' or '4x4' prints **£6-8**

MB 64b   MG 1100

70   Green body, white interior with man and
        dog, unpainted base, clear glass **£220-240**
70-71   Same but metallic light blue body **£18-20**
        Same but metallic dark blue body **£25-30**

MB 64c   Slingshot Dragster

71-72   Metallic pink body, BB, black exhausts,
        bonnet flame and '9' labels **£10-12**
73   Orange body, BB, black exhausts,
        bonnet flame and '9' label **£100-120**
        Same but red exhausts **£150-200**
73-75   Metallic blue-green body, UB, red
        exhausts, bonnet flame, '9' label **£15-18**
        Same but BB, front NW or WW **£6-8**
        Same but with '3' **£18-20**

MB 64d   Fire Chief Car

76-79   Red body, 'Fire', some yellow shield
        labels have black edging **£6-8**
        Same but with orange body **£8-10**

MB 64e   Caterpillar D-9 Tractor

79-81   Yellow body, brown roof, yellow shovel,
        black tracks, orange or yellow rollers **£7-10**
82   Yellow body, black roof, yellow shovel,
        'C' on cab, black tracks, yellow rollers ..**£8-10**
82-83   Same but black shovel, black or silver
        tow hook, 'C' on cab **£7-10**
        Same plus 'CAT' print, (black hook) **£8-10**

MB 65c   Claas Combine Harvester

67-72   Red body, yellow cutters, black base,
        black wheels with yellow hubs **£8-10**

MB 65d   Saab Sonnet III

73-76   Metallic blue body, yellow interior,
        UB, AG, grey rear door **£8-10**
79   White body, yellow interior, UB, AG,
        grey rear door, (Multi Pack) **£200-220**

MB 65e   Airport Coach

NB All Airport Coach models have white roofs

77-81   Metallic blue body, off-white or
        pale yellow interior, AG or CG, UB,
        'British Airways' **£7-9**
        Same but with labels reversed **£10-12**
        Metallic blue body, off-white interior,
        UB, AG, 'American Airlines' labels **£8-10**
        Same but with clear glass **£12-15**
        Same but pale yellow interior, AG **£8-10**
        Same but with clear glass **£12-15**
        Metallic blue body, off-white or pale yellow
        interior, AG, 'Lufthansa' (German) **£8-10**
        Same but with clear glass **£12-15**
81   Orange body, pale yellow interior, UB,
        AG, 'Schulbus' (German issue) **£25-35**
81-83   Red body, 'TWA' **£7-9**
        Red body, 'Qantas' **£7-9**
82   Red body, 'Fly Braniff' **£25-35**
        White body, 'Stork SB'(Australian) **£18-20**
        Metallic Blue body, 'Girobank'
        (Promotional issue) **£18-20**
83   Metallic Blue body, UB or SB, AG,
        'British' labels **£7-9**
        Metallic Blue body, UB or SB, AG,
        'Australian' labels **£12-14**
        White body, UB or SB, 'Alitalia' **£15-20**
        White body, UB or SB, 'Lufthansa' **£25-30**

MB 66c   Greyhound Coach

70   Silver body, yellow interior, AG, matt
        or gloss BB, 'Greyhound' **£18-20**
        Same but with yellow or pink base **£25-35**

MB 66d   Mazda RX500

71-74   Orange body, SE, white base, PG **£7-9**
        Same but with unpainted base **£15-20**

Orange body, SE, white base, AG **£12-15**
75-76   Red body, SE, WB, AG, white/green
        '77' and stripes(Streakers version) **£7-9**
        Same but with PG (Streakers) **£12-14**
        Same but UB, AG (Streakers) **£12-14**
        Red body, light brown engine, WB,
        AG, '77' and stripes (Streakers) **£12-14**
        Same but with PG (Streakers) **£15-18**

MB 66e   Ford Transit

77-80   Orange body, green glass, UB,
        brown load, green interior **£15-20**
        Same but light brown interior **£12-15**
        Same but light yellow interior **£7-9**
        Orange body, amber glass, UB,
        beige load, green interior **£156-20**
        Light brown or light yellow interior **£12-15**
81-82   Yellow-orange body, off-white or green
        interior, AG, brown load, green glass ..**£8-10**
        Same but with beige load **£7-9**
        Yellow-orange body, green interior, GB,
        brown or beige load, green glass **£8-10**
        Same but with black base **£15-20**

MB 66f   Tyrone Malone Superboss

82-83   White body, blue/red stripes on some,
        'Tyrone Malone' on white aerofoil **£8-10**
        With plain white or cream aerofoil **£6-8**

MB 67b   Volkswagen 1600TL

70   Dark or light red body,
        white interior, UB, CG, NW **£90-100**
70-71   Metallic purple body (may be dark,
        mid or light), white interior, UB, CG,
        narrow or wide wheels **£18-20**
71-72   Metallic pink body, white interior,
        UB, CG, NW or WW **£15-18**

MB 67c   Hot Rocker

73-74   Metallic green-gold body, white interior,
        UB, CG (Rola-Matic version) **£12-15**
        Same but with silver base **£20-30**
        Same but metallic green body, UB **£12-15**
        Same but with silver base **£20-30**
75-77   Red body, UB, (Rola-Matic version) **£9-12**
        Same but with silver base **£20-30**

MB 67d   Datsun 260Z 2+2

78-80   Metallic crimson body, white interior,
        clear glass, black base **£6-8**
        Same but with grey base **£8-10**
79   Metallic blue body, pale yellow
        interior, matt black base (TP) **£15-20**
        Same but with red interior (TP) **£30-40**
        Metallic blue body, red interior,
        brown base (TP) **£40-50**
80   Metallic red body, pale yellow
        interior, black base **£8-10**
81-83   Silver body, red interior, black base **£6-8**
        Same but grey or blue-grey base **£8-10**
        Same but with brown base **£8-10**
        Silver body, white interior, GB or BB,
        red stripes, black 'Datsun 2+2' (TP) **£8-10**
        Silver body, white interior, BB, blue
        stripes, black 'Datsun 2+2' (TP) **£10-12**
83   Black body and interior, BB (TP) **£20-30**

MB 68c   Porsche 910

70-74   Metallic red body, pale yellow interior,
        UB, AG, '68' label on bonnet, NW **£8-10**
        Same + '68' side labels (G3 set) **£25-35**
        Metallic red body, pale yellow interior,
        UB, AG, bonnet '68' label, WW **£8-10**
        Same but with '45' label from 45c **£25-30**
        Silver body, White interior, UB **£140-160**
72   White body, pale yellow interior, UB,
        AG, WW ('Brroom Stick' issue) **£35-40**

MB 68d   Cosmobile

75-78   Metallic light blue body, yellow under,
        white or silver interior, AG **£5-7**

77	Avocado body, black under, white interior, AG, (Adventure 2000 set) **£20-25**
	Same but with purple glass (set) **£15-20**
	Same but with silver interior (set) **£25-30**
78-79	Metallic red body, beige under, white or silver interior, AG **£8-10**
80	Metallic dark blue, black under, silver interior, PG (Adventure 2000 set) **£50-65**

MB 68e   Chevy Van

79-80	Orange body, UB, BG, blue/red or blue/white stripes **£8-10**
	Same but CG, blue/red stripes **£10-12**
	Same but BG, red/black stripes **£8-10**
	Same but with green or red glass **£8-10**
80-81	Orange body, 'Matchbox Collectors Club' labels, BG (Ltd. Edition) **£15-18**
81-82	White body, 'Adidas' (German) **£25-30**
	White body, 'USA-1' (US issue) **£12-15**
	Green body, 'Chevy' with brown or yellow segmented stripes **£7-9**
82-83	Yellow body, 'Collect Exciting Matchbox' (Australian issue)................**£20-25**
	Silver body, blue glass, 'Vanpire' **£8-10**

MB 69c   Rolls-Royce Silver Shadow

69-70	Metallic blue body, brown interior, tan folded top, BB, AG, NW **£12-15**
	Same but dark or light yellow base **£20-25**
71-72	Metallic light gold body, brown interior, tan folded top, BB, AG, WW **£12-15**
	Same but dark or light yellow base **£20-25**
	Same but with silver base **£12-15**
	With black folded top, BB **£10-12**
	Same but with light yellow base **£20-25**
	Same but with silver or grey base **£12-15**
	With off-white interior, black folded top, black base, AG, WW **£12-15**
	Same but with grey base **£15-20**
	Metallic dark gold, AG, off-white interior, black folded top, BB, WW **£12-15**
	Same but with grey or silver base **£18-20**
	Metallic dark gold body, brown interior, black folded top, BB, AG, WW **£12-15**
	Same but with grey or silver base **£18-20**
72-73	Metallic lime gold body, off-white or brown interior, BB, AG, WW **£12-15**
	Same but with grey or silver base **£18-20**

MB 69d   Turbo Fury

73-77	Metallic red body, CG, '69' and arrows label, (Rola-Matic version) **£8-10**
	Same but AG (Rola-Matic version) **£10-12**
	Metallic red body, '86' and arrows label, (Rola-Matic version) **£15-18**
	Same but 'Scorpion' (Rola-Matic) **£40-45**

MB 69e   Security Truck

78-83	Dark red body, cream roof, UB or SB, BG, '732 2031', 'Wells Fargo' **£8-10**
	Light red body, white roof, SB, CG, '732 2031' and 'Wells Fargo' **£12-15**
	Same but BG, UB or SB.......................**£5-7**
	Light red body, white roof, SB, BG, 'QZ 2031' and 'Wells Fargo' **£8-10**
81	Metallic dark green body, SB, BG, 'Dresdner Bank' (German promo)......**£20-25**

MB 70b   Grit Spreading Truck

70	Red cab and body, dark or pale yellow grit spreader, UB, GG, NW **£12-5**

MB 70c   Dodge Dragster

71-75	Dark pink body, BB, 'snake' labels **£10-12**
	With purple, cream, light green, light yellow, dark yellow or grey base **£20-25**
	With brown or unpainted base **£35-40**
	Dark pink body, BB, 'Wild Cat' **£40-50**
	Dark pink body, 'Rat Rod' labels **£40-50**

	Light pink body, BB, 'snake' labels.....**£15-18**
	Bright pink body,BB, 'snake' labels ...**£15-18**
78	Yellow body, red glass, GB or BB, side prints, (US Roman Numeral) **£18-20**

MB 70d   S.P. Gun

76-80	Military green body, black or brown tracks, (Rola-Matic version) **£8-10**

MB 70e   Ferrari 308 GTB

81-83	Red body and base, black stripe, CG.....**£8-10**
	Red body and base, CG, 'Ferrari'..........**£8-10**
	Same but with AG...............................**£10-12**
83	Red body, silver base, no 'Ferrari' **£8-10**

MB 71c   Ford Heavy Wreck Truck

70-72	Red cab, white body, red crane and hook, BB, GG, 'Esso' **£18-20**
	Same but with yellow hook **£18-20**
79	Military olive green, black hook, BB, GG, '3LGS64' labels (TP)..........**£20-25**
81	Dark blue, blue crane, black hook, BB, GG, no labels (Multi Pack) **£80-90**

MB 71d   Jumbo Jet

73-75	Metallic blue frame, red elephant head, dark blue handlebars, black wheels **£8-10**
	Same but light blue handlebars...........**£20-25**

MB 71e   Cattle Truck

76-81	Metallic orange-red cab, dark yellow back, UB or SB, GG or BG, 2 black cattle **£8-10**
	With AG, PG or orange glass, SB **£8-10**
79-83	Dark red cab, off-white back, SB, BG, 2 black cattle (TP) **£8-10**
	Same but with red or PG (TP)................**£8-10**
	Dark red cab, dark or light yellow back, SB, PG, 2 black cattle (TP)..................**£8-10**
81-83	Metallic light green cab, off-white back, SB, OG, 2 brown cattle **£6-8**
	Metallic light or dark green cab, yellow back, SB, red or OG, 2 brown cattle **£6-8**
	Metallic dark green cab, dark brown back, SB, red or AG, 2 brown cattle **£6-8**
83	Yellow cab, brown back, BB, UB or SB, red or AG, 2 light brown cattle **£6-8**
	Same but with black tow hook (TP)........**£6-8**

MB 71ex   Cattle Truck Trailer

79-83	Dark red body, off-white or light or dark yellow back, SB, 2 black cattle (TP) **£5-7**
83	Yellow body, dark yellow back, SB, 2 light brown cattle (TP).........................**£5-7**

MB 72b   Standard Jeep

70-71	Dull yellow body, red interior, UB **£18-20**
	Bright yellow body, red interior.........**£50-60**
	Orange body...................................**£20-24**

MB 72c   SRN Hovercraft

72-78	White body, BB, BG, 'R.N.L.I.' **£6-8**

MB 72d   Bomag Road Roller

79-82	Yellow/red, black roller, 2 wheels **£6-8**
	Same but 2 wheels have yellow hubs **£7-9**

MB 72e   Dodge Delivery Truck

82-83	Red cab, white back, 'Pepsi'....................**£6-8**
	Red cab, white back, 'Kelloggs'...............**£6-8**
	Either of the above with gold hubs **£7-9**
	Red cab, white back, 'Smiths Crisps' (Promotional offer)..............................**£6-8**
	Same but with gold hubs (Promo)...........**£7-9**

MB 73c   Mercury Commuter

70-71	Metallic lime green body, UB with '59', '55' or '73', NW or WW **£20-25**
71-73	Red body, UB, 'Bull head' label on bonnet of some, wide wheels..............**£10-12**

MB 73d   Weasel

74-76	Metallic green body, metallic green and green base, (Rola-Matic) **£8-10**
76	Military olive drab green body, metallic green and green base, (Rola-Matic) (TP) **£35-40**
76-79	Same but with military olive green body (Rola-Matic) (TP) **£12-15**
	Military olive green body, olive green and green base, (Rola-Matic) (TP) ...**£12-15**
	Same but olive green and black base, (Rola-Matic) (TP) **£12-15**

MB 73e   Ford Model 'A' Car

79-80	Cream body, dark green wings, GG **£8-10**
	Same but no spare wheel or glass.........**£7-9**
80	White body, dark green wings, GG **£10-12**
80-82	Metallic green body, dark green wings, GG or no glass **£5-7**
82-83	Light brown body, dark brown wings, amber glass **£5-7**
	Same but with clear glass **£6-8**

MB 74b   Daimler Bus

70-72	Red body, white interior, 'Esso' **£18-20**
	Same but 'dayglo' pink body...............**£20-25**
72	Red body, 'Inn on the Park' labels **£130-150**
	Red body, 'The Baron of Beef' **£140-160**
	Red body, 'Big T Scotch Whiskey' labels (Promotional)......................**£150-200**
	Red body, 'NAMC', 'The Miniature Vehicle' labels (Promotional) **£160-180**
	Red body, 'Swinging London'..........**£85-100**
	Red body, 'Beefeater Gin' **£100-120**
	Red body, 'Fly Cyprus Airways' **£100-120**
	Red body, 'Barclays Bank' **£100-120**
	Red body, 'Kensington Hilton'.......**£100-120**
	Red body, 'I.C.P. Interchemicals' ...**£100-120**

MB 74e   Tow Joe

72-77	Metallic green-gold body, UB, AG and roof light, green arms, Red hooks **£10-12**
	Same but with BB or SB **£10-12**
	With UB and black hooks **£12-15**
	Metallic green body, BB, AG and roof light, green arms, red hooks..........**£8-10**
76-81	Yellow body, BB, SB or UB, AG, red arms, black hooks (TP)..........................**£8-10**
	With matt base, red or black hooks ...**£75-100**
	Metallic green body, BB, AG, red arms, black hooks (TP)..................**£25-30**
	Same, BB or SB, white arms (TP).....**£90-100**
	Red body, BB, AG, red or green arms, red or black hooks (TP) **£150-170**
82	Yellow body, UB, AG, red arms, black hooks, 'Hitch Hiker' labels (TP)......**£100-120**

MB 74d   Cougar Villager

78-81	Metallic light or dark green body, yellow interior, UB, AG **£10-12**
81-82	Metallic blue body, yellow or orange-yellow interior, UB, AG **£15-20**

MB 74e   Fiat Arbath

82-83	White body, red interior, 'Matchbox' ..**£10-12**
	Same but with black interior...............**£40-60**

MB 75b   Ferrari Berlinetta

70	Metallic green body, off-white interior, unpainted base, clear glass...............**£150-200**
70-71	Red body, off-white interior, UB, CG, silver grille on some.....................**£45-55**

MB 75c   Alfa Carabo

71-75	Metallic Purple body, YB, NW **£8-10**
	Same but with unpainted base **£10-12**
75	Metallic light pink body, YB, WW **£15-20**
75-76	Metallic light pink or red body, WW, (Streakers) yellow/black/green prints ..**£10-12**

MB 75d   Seasprite Helicopter

77-81   White body, Red underside, BG or GG,
black rotors, blue 'Rescue' labels **£8-10**
Same but with red glass **£12-15**
Same but with purple glass.................**£15-18**

MB 75e   Helicopter

82-83   White/orange, black interior, black skids,
AG, 'MBTV News' tampo prints **£6-8**
White/black, black or grey interior, black
skids, AG or CG, 'Police' and '36'.........**£6-8**
White/black, black or grey interior,
black or grey skids, AG, 'Rescue' **£8-10**

ABBREVIATIONS

Windows	Wheels	Base colour	General
AG = amber glass	BW = black wheels	BB = black base	BE = black engine
BG = blue glass	NW = narrow wheels	GB = grey base	CE = chrome engine
CG = clear glass	UW = unpainted	SB = silver base	LE = limited edition
GG = green glass	WW = wide wheels	UB = unpainted base	SE = silver engine
OG = orange glass		WB = white base	TP = Twin Pack
PG = purple glass		YB = yellow base	

Matchbox Superfast and Miscellaneous Sets

G 1	1968	**Service Station Set** Contains 13d, 56b, 32c, and 'BP' Service Station **£150-180**
G 1	1970	**Service Station Set** Contains 13d, 15d, 32c, and 'BP' Service Station **£150-180**
G 1-8	1981	**Transporter Set** Contains Transporter and 5 Superfast Cars **£50-60**
G 1-9	1984	**Transporter Set** Contains K10 plus 4 cars **£40-50**
G 2-7	1970	**Transporter Set** Contains Transporter and 5 Superfast models **£85-100**
G 2-8	1973	**Transporter Set** Contains Transporter and 5 Superfast models **£85-100**
G 2-11	1981	**Railway Set** Contains 43e, 2 x 44e, 25f.............**£25-30**
G 3-7	1970	**Racing Specials Set** Contains 5e, 20c, 45c, 56c, 52c and 68c **£120-150**
G 3-8	1973	**'WILD ONES' Set.** Contains 5 Superfast Cars **£70-80**
G 3-9	1981	**Racing Car Set** Transporter and 4 Racing Cars........**£40-50**
G 4-7	1970	**Truck SuperSet** Contains 47c, 63c, 58c, 49b, 16d, 21d, 11d and 51c **£80-90**
G 4-8	1973	**Team Matchbox Set** Contains Racing Car Transporter and 4 Racing Cars....**£60-70**
G 4-9	1981	**Military Assault** Landing Craft + 6 military models ...**£50-60**
G 5-9	1981	**Construction Set** Contains 5 construction models.....**£30-40**
G 6-6	1970	**Truck Set** Contains 1e, 10d, 21d, 26c, 30c, 60b, 70b and 49b ...**£100-120**
G 6-7	1973	**Drag Race Set** Contains 6 Superfast Cars **£60-70**
G 6-8	1981	**Farm Set** Contains 6 farming models......................**£35-40**
G 7-5	1973	**Ferry Boat** With Plastic Boat and 4 Superfast Cars....**£45-50**
G 7-8	1978	**Car Ferry Set** Contains 3 Cars and Sports Boat........**£40-50**
G 7-6	1981	**Emergency Set** Contains 5 Rescue models **£40-50**
G 7-7	1984	**Emergency Set** With models 8, 12, 22, 57 and 75 .....**£40-50**
G 8-5	1984	**Turbo Charged Set** Contains Turbo Charger plus 7, 9, 52, 60 and 68 ....**£35-40**
G 10-5	1986	**'PAN-AM' Set** Contains 10, 54, 64, 65 and 'Sky-Buster' Boeing **£40-45**
G 11-1	1978	**Strike Force Set** Contains 6 Army Vehicles...............**£45-50**
G 11-2	1986	**'LUFTHANSA' Set** Contains 30, 54, 59, 65 and 'Sky-Buster' Airbus **£50-60**
G 12	1978	**Rescue Set** Contains 6 Rescue Vehicles.....................**£40-45**
G 13	1978	**Construction Set** Contains 6 Construction Vehicles ..**£35-40**
G 14	1978	**Grand Prix Set** Transporter and 4 Racing Cars.........**£35-40**
G 15	1978	**Transporter Set** Transporter and 5 Superfast Cars.....**£35-40**
G 40	1988	**40 years Set** ('Made in China' cast under models). Aveling-Barford Road Roller, London Bus, Horse Drawn Milk Float, M-H Tractor, Dennis Fire Engine **£20-25**
C 6		**Emergency Gift Set** All Japanese Set **£25-30**
C 11		**Airport Gift Set** Japanese Foam Pump, Ikarus Coach and Aircraft **£30-35**
---	1971	**Matchbox Crash Game** With 4 assorted cars, racetrack, dice and instructions ...**£50-60**
---		**Multi-Pack Gift Set** Contains 5 Superfast models......**£20-25**
A1	70-73	**Service Ramp** 'CASTROL'.................................**£30-35**
A2	1970	**'Superfast Auto Sales'** Plastic kit includes 'MATCHBOX SALES OFFICE', 'STAR VALUE' stand, 3 'M' flagpoles and 4 lamp posts, plus pink card base, signs and advert. stickers. 25 items in total..............**£150-200**
A2	71-73	**'Matchbox' Sales Park** Pink card sales park with four lampposts.....................**£35-40**
A3	c1971	**'Brroooom Stick'** Blister-packed car with steering control. Contains No.20 Lamborghini Marzal in Yellow and No.68 Porsche in White **£60-70**

We regret that it has not been possible to continue listing the Miniatures models produced from 1983 (with the exception of the important 'Londoner Bus' issues). We would suggest that collectors requiring more information should contact: Nigel Cooper, 46 Thyme Close, Chineham, Basingstoke, RG24 8XG, Telephone: (01256) 356455. E-mail: coopertoys@hotmail.com. Also see MICA details at the end of the book.

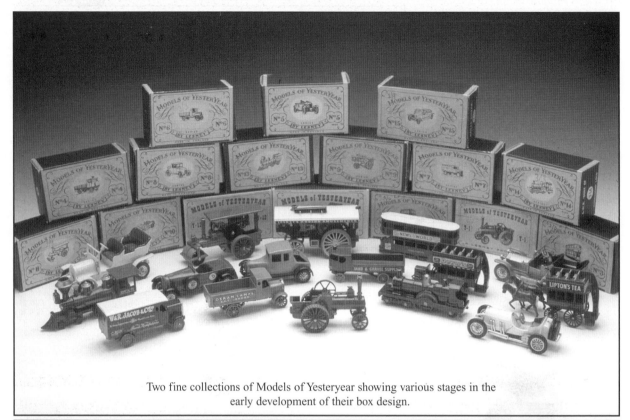

Two fine collections of Models of Yesteryear showing various stages in the
early development of their box design.

Many variants of Yesteryears have resulted from long production runs which often required renewal or modification of worn dies. Considerable numbers of model variations have thus been issued over the years, some of them quite minor. The objective of this listing is to identify for the Yesteryear collector all those price-significant variations which really do matter. Collectors requiring details of the all the variations issued should contact:
The Matchbox International Collectors Association (M.I.C.A.)
PO Box 120, Deeside, CH5 3HE, UK.

This new listing has been extensively updated by Yesteryear authority Horace Dunkley.

Identification

Common features. Many models have common identifying features and these are shown below to avoid unnecessary repetition in the Features column.

Model name and number. Both **'Models of Yesteryear'** and **'Made in England by Lesney'** are cast underneath all models issued up to the end of 1982. With the change of ownership this was replaced by **'Matchbox Intl Ltd.'** From 1987 **'Made in Macau'** appears on the base. All models have their 'Y' number shown underneath.

Wheels. All the wheels prior to 1970 were of metal construction. From 1972 (approximately), plastic wheels were used on all models. Nevertheless the models issued at this changeover period are to be found with either metal or plastic wheels.

Scale of models ranges from 1:34 to 1:130. The scale of each model is usually shown on its box.

Logos and designs. The early models had waterslide transfers. Labels have also been used and currently models are tampo printed.

Catalogue listings. Do not place too much reliance on the model colours shown in catalogues. Very often the pictures shown are from mock-ups in colours never actually issued. For example, the 1969 catalogue showed a picture of a blue Y-5 Peugeot that was issued in yellow. Similarly the 1973 catalogue showed a silver Hispano Suiza which was then issued in red.
Bumpers, dashboards, headlights, radiator shells and windscreens. All assumed to be of metal construction prior to 1974 (approx.), after which plastic was increasingly used.
Base plate and chassis are usually of metal construction.
Tyres are of treaded black plastic unless otherwise indicated.
Seats are all made of plastic unless otherwise indicated.

Boxes

1956-57	All card box with just a plain black number shown on box ends. Line drawing of model on the front of box.
1957-60	All card box with line drawing of model used for first 15 models issued, blue number shown on white circle on endflap.
1960-61	As first box but with a red number. All card box with coloured picture of the model (3 varieties of this box exist). All card box with model pictures on the box endflaps.
1968-69	Pink and yellow box with clear window.
1968-70	As previous box with hanging display card (developed in the US market and led to blister-pack design).
1969-70	Mauve and yellow box with window.
1974-78	'Woodgrain' window box in various colours
1979-83	'Straw' (light cream), window box.
1984-90	'Red' (maroon), window box.

MPR = Market Price Range   **GSP** = Gift Set price

Years of production; scale; other details	MPR

Y1-1 Allchin Traction Engine

1956-1965. Scale 1:80. Early issues have rear wheel treads with a straight-across pattern, second type are diagonal; third type has a smooth tread.

With straight-across treads to rear wheels	**£75-125**
Rear wheel treads in Red (as per spokes)	**£55-85**
Rear wheels with no tread pattern (smooth)	**£450-650**
Smoke box door in green (as per body)	**£150-200**
Other versions	**£35-55**

Y1-2 1911 Ford Model 'T'

1964-1984. Scale 1:42. All Y1-3 models have 'brass effect' finish wheels.

With twin brake lever (Dark Red models only)	**£55-75**
Black textured roof (Dark Red or White/Red models)	**£55-75**
Bright Red textured roof (White/Red models only)	**£75-100**
Other versions	**£2-15**

Y1-3 1936 Jaguar SS100

1977-1994. Scale 1:38.

With small sidelights (Off-White model only)	**£85-125**
Steel-Grey body and chassis	**£150-175**
Other versions	**£2-15**

Y2-1 1911 'B'-type London Bus

1956-1961. Scale 1:100. The diecast driver may be found in any shade of mid or dark blue, sometimes black.

With 4 over 4 side windows	**£75-100**
With Black wheels	**£50-75**
Other versions	**£35-55**

Y2-2 1911 Renault Two-Seater

1963-1968. Scale 1:40. Note that the red pigment used in the plastic seats is prone to fading in bright light.

All versions	**£10-15**

Y2-3 1914 'Prince Henry' Vauxhall

1970-1979. Scale 1:47.

With Copper petrol tank (Red and Silver issue only)	**£200-225**
Bright Red seats (Blue and Silver issue only)	**£500-650**
Other versions	**£2-8**

Y3-1 1907 'E'-class Tramcar

1956-1965. Scale 1:130. All versions have a bright Red body with Yellow **'LONDON TRANSPORT'** fleetname and **'NEWS OF THE WORLD'** decals.

With thin (Grey) cow-catchers	**£100-125**
Grey base (with thin or thick cowcatchers)	**£125-150**
Other versions	**£35-55**

Y3-2 1910 Benz Limousine

1965-1984. Scale 1:54.

With Cream body and chassis, Light Yellow roof	**£150-200**
Light Green body and chassis, Dark Green roof	**£150-200**
Light Green body and chassis, Light Yellow roof, separate rear wing supports	**£175-225**
Light Green body and chassis, Black roof	**£75-100**
Dark Metallic Green body and chassis, Light Yellow roof	**£200-250**
As previous model, but without holes in base	**£300-350**
Other versions	**£10-15**

Y3-3 1934 Riley MPH

1974-1979. Scale 1:35.

With Dark Purple body and chassis, Black seats and grille................£125-175
Ruby Red body and chassis, Black seats and grille £125-175
Other versions £2-6

Y3-4 1912 Ford Model 'T' Tanker

1981-1989. Scale 1:35.

'BP', Green body, Red tank, with 'No. Y12' cast on base....................£75-125
'BP', other versions £2-4
'ZEROLENE', with 'No. Y12' cast on base £20-25
'ZEROLENE', other versions £2-4
'EXPRESS DAIRY', all versions..£2-6

Y4-1 1928 Sentinel Steam Wagon

1956 only. Scale 1:100. Blue body, **'SAND & GRAVEL SUPPLIES'**.

With Black plastic wheels..£85-100
With Grey metal wheels...£35-55

Y4-2 1905 Shand-Mason Fire Engine

1960-1965. Scale 1:63. Red metal body, two horses, three plastic firemen.

'KENT' Fire Brigade, Pale Grey Horses £300-400
'KENT' Fire Brigade, White Horses £85-125
'LONDON' Fire Brigade, Bronze horses £100-150
'LONDON' Fire Brigade, White or Black horses £80-120

Y4-3 1909 Opel Coupé

1967-1984. Scale 1:38.

With Tan textured hood with rear window £125-175
Other versions £2-8

Y4-4 1930 Duesenberg 'J' Town Car

1976-1997. Scale 1:43.

White body, Orange-Red or Red chassis, Yellow hood and seats ..£1,250-1,750
White body, Orange-red or Red chassis, Black hood and seats £1,500-2,000
Dark Red body and chassis, Maroon hood and seats £175-200
Dark Red body and chassis, Dark Green hood and seats....................£75-100
Dark Red body and chassis, Dark Green hood, Light Brown seats £100-125
Light Green body and chassis, Lime Green side and rear body panels...£45-65
Other versions £2-5

Y5-1 1929 Le Mans Bentley

1958-1961. Scale 1:55. All are finished in British Racing Green.

With Grey folded hood, Silver radiator £75-100
With Grey folded hood, Gold radiator..£85-110
Other versions £35-55

Y5-2 1929 4½ litre Bentley

1962-1968. Scale 1:52. Model has Union Jacks and racing numbers on its
sides, folded windscreen and silver 24-spoke wheels, (spare on nearside).

With Apple Green body, Dark Green or Dark Red seats £100-150
British Racing Green body, Red racing number '6' £65-85
Other versions £10-15

Y5-3 1907 Peugeot

1969-1977. Scale 1:43. Except where noted, the model has 12-spoke wheels.

Yellow body and chassis, Black roof, no rib on rear edge of
    front seat side panels..£40-50
Yellow body and chassis, Black roof, clear windows.........................£80-100
Yellow body and chassis, Gold roof..£100-150
Orange-Gold, or Light-Gold body, Black chassis and roof..................£65-85
Light-Gold body and roof, Black chassis,
    Chrome 12 or 24 spoke wheels, clear windows..........................£85-125
Other versions £6-8

Y5-4 1927 Talbot Van

1978-1988. Scale 1:47.

'LIPTONS TEA' (1978), all versions..£2-5
'CHOCOLAT MENIER' (1978-1979), all versions £2-5
'TAYSTEE BREAD' (1980), all versions...£2-5
'NESTLES' (1981), with Matt Black roof...£175-225
    With Gloss Black roof..£200-250
    All other versions..£2-5
'CHIVERS' (1982), all versions...£2-5
'WRIGHTS' (1982), with Dark Brown roof...£125-175
    All other versions..£2-5
'EVER READY' (1983), all versions £2-5

Y6-1 1916 AEC 'Y' type Lorry

1957-1961. Scale 1:100. **'OSRAM LAMPS'**

Pale Blue or Mid Blue body, Grey metal wheels £1,250-1,750
Light Grey body, Grey metal wheels...£40-60
Dark Grey body, Grey metal wheels...£50-70
Dark Grey body, Black plastic wheels..£1,250-1,500

Y6-2 1935 Type 35 Bugatti

1961-1965. Scale1:48. Model has a black baseplate and gold 8-spoke wheels
with a spare on the nearside. Racing number '6' may be upside-down and
appear as '9'.

Blue body, Grey tyres £45-65
Blue body, Blue radiator...£80-100
Blue body, White dashboard £275-350
Red body, Red radiator...£80-100
Red body, Black dashboard £300-375
Other versions £15-25

Y6-3 1913 Cadillac

1968-1975. Scale 1:48.

Gold body, Dark Red textured roof £75-100
All other Gold body versions...£6-12
Green body, thin spare tyre carrier £45-65
All other Green body versions £2-6

Y6-4 1920 Rolls-Royce Fire Engine

1977-1984. Scale 1:48.

Without locating lugs for side label...£75-100
With red front seats £250-300
All other versions...£2-8

Y7-1 1918 Leyland 4-ton Van

1957-1960. Scale 1:100. **'W. & R. Jacob & Co. Ltd.'**

Dark Brown body..£55-75
Dark Brown body with centre line of transfer omitted £500-750
Reddish Brown body £40-60
Reddish Brown body, Black plastic wheels.......................................£750-1,000

258	1991	**Daimler Ambulance Kit**	Re-issued as a kit of unpainted castings (by Autocraft)	**£10-20**
260	1962	**Ruston-Bucyrus Excavator**	Yellow / Red cab, '10-RB', Beige or Olive-Green base and jib, 73 mm	**£100-125**
262	1962-64	**Racing Motorcycle**	No maker's name. Unpainted cycle, tinplate fairing in Metallic Blue, Metallic Lilac, Metallic Brown or Lime Green, Black plastic rider, 104 mm	**£75-100**
264	1962-64	**Racing Motorcycle and Sidecar**	Cycle as 262, sidecar and fairing in Metallic Blue, Metallic Pinkish-Red, Metallic Green, Metallic Lilac, Metallic Brown or Lime Green. Black plastic rider / passenger, no maker's name, 104 mm	**£75-100**
266	1962-64	**Motorcycle and Delivery Sidecar**	Blue cycle as 262, Red sidecar, 'EXPRESS DELIVERY' cast-in, no maker's name, Black plastic rider. 108 mm	**£75-100**
268	1962-64	**A.A. Land Rover**	Different from Morestone AA Land Rovers. Yellow body, Black roof, windows, opening rear doors, 'AA ROAD SERVICE' transfers, 97 mm	**£125-150**
270	1962-66	**Leyland Articulated Tanker**	Red, windows, 'ESSO PETROLEUM COMPANY LTD' labels, 132 mm	**£60-75**
272	1962-64	**Supercar**	From TV series. Red / Silver body, Red wings (or colours reversed), clear plastic canopy, 'SUPERCAR' transfers, 122 mm	**£175-225**
274	1962-66	**Ford Thames Refuse Lorry**	Blue cab / Silver body, or Yellow cab / Metallic blue body, windows	**£45-55**
276	1962-66	**Bedford LWB Tipper**	Red cab with windows, Yellow tipper, 'HAM RIVER GRIT', 128 mm	**£40-80**
278	1963-64	**RAC Land Rover**	Casting as 268, Blue, windows, 'RAC RADIO RESCUE' transfers, 97 mm	**£125-150**
280	1963-64	**AEC Super Fueller Tanker**	White cab and trailer, windows, Green base and canopy, 'AIR BP', 219 mm	**£300-400**
282	1963-66	**Euclid Scraper**	Yellow or Lime Green, windscreen, 'EUCLID', Black plastic wheels, 163 mm	**£35-45**
284	1962	**Euclid Crawler Tractor**	Not issued	NPP
286	1962	**Euclid Bulldozer**	Not issued	NPP
288	1963-66	**Leyland Bulk Flour Tanker**	Red cab, windows, Off-White silos, Yellow hopppers, 'BULK FLOUR', 107 mm	**£45-55**
290	1963-64	**Bedford Ice Cream Van**	No maker's name on model. Blue body and base, windows, 'Tonibell' transfers, Pink plastic cow on roof, 103 mm	**£85-110**
292	1963-66	**Leyland Bulk Milk Tanker**	Blue or Red cab, windows, White tank, 'MILK', 107 mm	**£45-55**
294	1963-66	**Bedford TK Horse Box**	Off-White cab, windows, Brown body, Light Brown doors. two Brown plastic horses. 'EPSOM STABLE' transfer, 109 mm	**£60-70**
296	1963-66	**Motorway Express Coach**	Midland Red livery: Red body, Black roof, 'BIRMINGHAM-LONDON MOTORWAY EXPRESS' transfers, windows, 121 mm	**£70-85**
		USA livery:	Light Blue body, Cream roof, 'WASHINGTON D.C.' and 'BLUE LINE SIGHTSEEING CO.' transfers, phone number 'LA9-7755' at rear	**£300-400**
298	1963-66	**Alvis Salamander Crash Tender**	Red body, windows, Silver plastic ladder, Yellow engine cover at rear, Black plastic wheels. 'FIRE SERVICE' transfers, 92 mm.	**£100-125**
300	1963-65	**Lewin Sweepmaster**	Blue / Silver, windows, Black plastic wheels, Black sweeping brush	**£60-75**
302	1963-66	**Commer Cabin Service Lift Truck**	Blue cab, windows, Silver body, 'BOAC CABIN SERVICES', 104 mm	**£60-75**
304	1964-66	**Bedford TK Glass Transporter**	Off-white cab and chassis, windows, Green body. 'TOWER GLASS CO.' transfers. Four clear plastic 'glass' sheets, 108 mm	**£45-55**
306	1964-66	**Fiat Tractor with Shovel**	Orange tractor, Metallic Blue shovel, 108 mm	**£75-100**
308	1964-66	**Seddon Pitt Alligator Low Loader**	Green cab, windows, Yellow trailer with Black ramp, 163 mm	**£45-55**
310	1964-66	**Leyland Cement Mixer**	Orange cab, windows, Silver mixer, 'INVICTA Construction Co.', 98 mm	**£45-55**
312	1964-66	**Bedford Super Tipmaster**	Dark Green cab, windows, Silver tipper. 'SUPER TIP-MASTER', 127mm	**£45-55**
314	1965-66	**Fiat Tractor with Dozer Blade**	As 306 but enclosed cab, Orange tractor, Metallic Blue blade, 81 mm	**£45-55**
316	1965-66	**Albion Overhead Maintenance Vehicle**	Green body, windows, Silver / Black boom assembly, 107 mm	**£40-50**
318	1965-66	**Euclid Mammoth Articulated Dumper**	Modified from no.242. Green cab, Yellow chassis, Orange tipper, 201 mm	**£75-95**
322	1965-66	**Scammell Routeman Pneumajector Transporter**	Light Blue cab, Cream or White tank, 'THE ATLAS CARRIER CO.', 111 mm	**£50-60**
324	1965-66	**Douglas Prospector Duomatic Tipper**	Tips in two directions. Blue cab and chassis, windows, Grey tipper, 112 mm	**£55-65**
326	1965-66	**Scammell Highwayman Gas Transporter**	Green cab, windows, Dark Green trailer, 6 White / Red gas cylinders, 146 mm	**£125-150**
328	1966	**Scammell Handyman Artic**	Planned but not issued	NPP
330	1966	**Land Rover**	Modified 268, planned but not issued	NPP
332	1966	**'Kenning' Breakdown Lorry**	Planned but not issued	NPP
334	1966	**Austin Gipsy Fire Tender**	Planned but not issued	NPP
404	1960-61	**Horse Drawn Covered Wagon**	with Four Horses. For details see Morestone and Modern Products entry.	
410	1961	**Stage Coach with Four Horses**	Blue or 'Gold' plated coach, no lettering cast on sides but 'WELLS FARGO STAGE COACH' and 'A BUDGIE TOY' cast underneath, plastic horses and driver, bubble-packed, 118 mm	**£70-90**
430	1960-61	**Wagon Train Set**	Contains 3 of no. 432 plus two more horses with riders, bubble-packed	**£100-150**
432	1960-61	**Horse Drawn Covered Wagon with Two Horses**	Red wagon, ('A BUDGIE TOY' on floor), Grey, White or Lemon metal canopy, 2 barrels, plastic horses, driver, passenger, bubble packed, 82 mm	**£35-45**
434	1961	**Stage Coach with Four Horses**	'WELLS FARGO' above windows, 'STAGE LINES' on doors, luggage cast on roof, Red or Blue, plastic horses and driver, 189 mm	**£70-90**
452	1958-63	**A.A. Motorcycle and Sidecar**	Initially in Morestone box. Windscreen, plastic rider, integral rails and hinged lid on sidecar, steerable, rubber tyres, plain number plates, 82 mm	**£75-100**
452	1964-66	**A.A. Motorcycle and Sidecar**	New design. Sidecar with transfers and 'BUDGIE' underneath, plastic rider, windscreen and leg guards, plain number plates, 84 mm	**£75-100**
454	1958-63	**RAC Motorcycle and Sidecar**	Initially in Morestone box. Windscreen, plastic rider, integral rails and hinged lid on sidecar, steerable, rubber tyres, plain number plates, 82 mm	**£75-100**
454	1964-66	**RAC Motorcycle and Sidecar**	New design. Sidecar with transfers and 'BUDGIE' underneath, plastic rider, windscreen and leg guards, plain number plates, 84 mm	**£75-100**

Budgie Toys and Models

456	1958-66	**Solo Motorcycle** ....Initially in Morestone boxes. Two casting versions as 452 and 454 but

456 1958-66 **Solo Motorcycle** ....Initially in Morestone boxes. Two casting versions as 452 and 454 but
'Silver plated'. Plastic riders:
Police Patrol (Blue uniform) **£40-50**
Despatch Rider (Light Brown uniform) **£40-50**
GPO Messenger (Light Blue uniform) **£40-50**
'Tourist Trophy' Rider (White racing overalls) **£40-50**

701 1983 **Aveling-Barford Road Roller**...............Re-issued Modern Products model. Dark Green body, Silver / Red wheels,
Dark Blue driver **£10-15**

702 1984-85 **Scammell Scarab Vans** ....Re-issue of 238. Very Dark Blue cab and trailer, White 'RN' on doors,
'ROYAL NAVY' on tilt **£15-20**
Very Dark Blue cab and trailer, 'HALLS MENTHO-LYPTUS' labels.....................**£15-20**
Maroon cab and trailer, 'LMS LIVERPOOL ROAD' transfers..............................**£15-20**
Maroon cab and trailer, 'SPRATTS BONIO' transfers......................................**£15-20**
Maroon cab and trailer, 'REA EXPRESS' transfers...**£15-20**

703 1984 **Austin FX4 Taxi** ....As no.101 but in window box. Black, Silver, Met.Dk.Pink, Gold,
Dark Green, Grey or White **£15-20**

704 1984 **AEC Routemaster Bus**.........................Yellow / Red body with windows, 'SHOP LINKER' labels, casting as 236............**£15-20**
705 1984 **AEC Routemaster Bus**.........................Silver body with windows, '25 FAITHFUL YEARS' labels, casting as 236 ....**£15-20**
706 1984 **AEC Routemaster Bus**.........................Yellow / Red with windows, 'Watford FA Cup Final 84' labels, 236 casting **£15-20**

Budgie Gift Sets

No. 4 1961 **Gift Set No.4**...Contains four models. Price depends on contents which vary **£125-165**
No. 5 1961 **Gift Set No.5**...Contains five models. Price depends on contents which vary........................**£150-200**

Seerol Models

- 1985 **Austin FX4 Taxi** ....Re-issue of Budgie no.101 with amended base lettering and low friction wheels.
Black body, 106mm. Still available **£5-10**

- 1985 **Rolls-Royce Silver Cloud** ....Re-issued Budgie 102, amended lettering, low friction wheels. Black, Silver,
White, Yellow, Dark Blue, Pink or Maroon, 107 mm. Still available **£5-10**

- 1985 **AEC Routemaster Bus**.....................New design, 1:76 scale, 108 mm. Was available from London souvenir outlets till the late 1990s.
- Red, Light Green or Dark Green, 'Houses of Parliament Tower Bridge' labels **£10-15**
- Red, 'The Original London Transport Sightseeing Tour' labels................................**£10-15**
- Red, 'Greetings from London' tampo print **£5-10**
- Red, 'Tower of London' tampo print **£5-10**
- Red, 'Petticoat Lane' tampo print **£5-10**
- Red, 'Buckingham Palace' tampo print **£5-10**

Budgie Leaflets and Catalogues

A leaflet was included in the box with most Budgie Toys. Dates are not shown on any except the 1963 and 1964 catalogues.

- 1959 **Leaflet**..Printed on one side only. 'Budgie Toys Speak for Themselves' at top.
1st version:.................................Includes the Six-horse Covered Wagon **£10-20**
2nd version: ....Timber Transporter replaces the Covered Wagon **£10-20**
- 1960 **Leaflet**..'Budgie Toys Speak for Themselves' on front, 'Budgie Toys for Girls and Boys' on reverse **£10-20**
- 1961 **Leaflet**..'Budgie Toys Speak for Themselves' on Black background.........................**£10-15**
1961 **Trade catalogue** ....Fold-out leaflet showing Noddy items, Wagon Train and Budgie miniatures as well
as the main Budgie range. Separate price list marked 'Price List 1961' showing
wholesale and retail prices...**£30-40**
- 1962 **Leaflet**..'Die-Cast Models by Budgie They Speak for Themselves' on Black background.
1st version:.................................268 AA Land Rover on front, 258 Daimler Ambulance on reverse................**£10-15**
2nd version: ....214 Mobile Crane on front, 266 Express Delivery Motorcycle on reverse **£10-15**
- 1963 **Leaflet**..'Die-Cast Models by Budgie They Speak for Themselves' on Black background.
1st version:.................................278 RAC Land Rover on front, 258 Daimler Ambulance on reverse **£10-15**
2nd version: ....278 RAC Land Rover on front, 266 Express Delivery Motorcycle on reverse....**£10-15**
- 1963 **Trade Catalogue** (8 pages)............Landscape format, includes retail price list...**£30-40**
- 1964 **Trade Catalogue** (8 pages)............'Budgie Models' on cover (portrait format). Includes retail price list **£30-40**

Collectors notes

The 'River Series'

A trademark owned by M/s Jordan and Lewden of Homerton, London E9. Note that, while 'River Series' models were cast using tools supplied by DCMT, they had no other connection with DCMT. The Jordan and Lewden company started to offer diecast toys to the toy trade from about 1953 and continued to do so for only a few years. Dies were eventually sold to the Habonim firm in Israel and models subsequently appeared in the 'Gamda' series of toys. Some examples are known to have been produced in New Zealand by Lincoln Industries (who were also responsible for some 'lookalike' Matchbox models). Only 'Made in England' and the car name appear on the diecast base of each model. None of the models acquired window glazing while made as 'River Series' – some did when produced as 'Gamda' toys.

These car models came in various colours and had cast hubs / rubber tyres where friction-motor fitted, otherwise one-piece rubber wheels.

Ford Prefect ....NGPP
American Buick ....NGPP
Daimler Conquest...NGPP
Austin Somerset ....NGPP
Standard Vanguard II Saloon ....NGPP
Standard Vanguard Estate..............................NGPP

These larger items were also available in various colours, some have clockwork motor, most have one-piece cast wheels, and some were boxed.

Cattle Truck ....NGPP
Car Carrier...NGPP
Excavator Truck..NGPP
Tower Wagon..NGPP
Cattle Truck ....NGPP

The Editor would welcome any additional information on the 'River Series'.

'River Series'
American Buick

'River Series'
Austin Somerset

Scamold Racing Cars

Manufactured between 1939 and 1950 by Scale Models Ltd from whose title the model name was obtained. The models are extremely accurate 1/35 diecast scale models, with their original measurements being taken from the real racing cars at the famous Brooklands race track. Pre-war boxes state 'MANUFACTURED BY SCALE MODELS LTD, BROOKLANDS TRACK, WEYBRIDGE, ENG.'. This was dropped after the war. The proprietor of Scale Models Ltd was a Mr Tilley who wound up the business in the 1960s.

The model detail and castings are outstanding, with features such as removeable exhausts, spring suspension, steering wheels and dashboards. In addition the back axle could be exchanged for one containing a clockwork motor which was

wound up by a long starting handle. The wheel axles were crimped and the hubs were either brass (early) or aluminium (later) with black treaded rubber tyres.

Scamold kits were also available. The kit models had detailed features similar to the production issues including a working differential gear. In addition, it was also possible to fit a flywheel type motor which was activated by turning a 'starting handle'.

This information on Scamold models and kits has been kindly provided by Mr R.N. Eason-Gibson. The Editor would welcome additional information on this small but fascinating range.

PRODUCTION MODELS

101	1939-50	**ERA Racing Car**...................Blue (Light or Dark), Green (Light or Dark), Yellow, White or Black body	....	**£90-120**
103	1939-50	**Maserati Racing Car**...........Red, Blue, Green (Mid or Dark), Silver body	....	**£90-120**
105	1939-50	**Alta Racing Car**...................Green (Mid or Dark), Silver, White or Blue	....	**£90-120**

SCAMOLD KITS

Austin 7 Single-seater 750cc, Bugatti Type 35, 'E'-type E.R.A. (prototype only), Brooklands Riley, MG (planned type not known), Bentley LeMans Tourer and Maserati Racing Car.

Mobil Midget Fun-Ho! Series

Manufactured and distributed by the Underwood Engineering Co. Ltd, Mamaku Street, Inglewood, New Zealand.

Market Price Range. Most small cars and trucks etc. **£20-30**. Exceptions: No.7 BOAC Observation Coach **£40-50**, No.9 VW Beetle **£40-50**, No.11 Morris Mini Minor **£80-90**, No.2 Vauxhall Velox **£30-40**, No.? Morris 1100 **£40-50**, No.17 Austin Mini **£80-90**, No.23 Mark 10 Jaguar **£80-90**, No.25 MG Sports **£80-100**; No.43 E Type Jaguar **£80-90**.
Larger Commercials/Emergency vehicles etc.:
Nos.18, 21, 22, 27, 31, 35, 36, 40 **£30-40**.

Technical Information. Models from No.10 are 1:80 scale. Early models 1-32 1963-66 were all either chrome or copper plated. Painted finishes were introduced in 1966. Boxed models 1-18 include a folded leaflet in black and white giving details of the first 18 models and all have Black plastic wheels. Similarly the later issues contained leaflets showing the complete 1-46 model range as per the above leaflet.

'Fun Ho!' Mighty Mover Sets
1 Army Construction Battalion Kit Set: Contains six Military models, Bulldozer, Cement Mixer, Road Roller, Earth Mover, JCB, Land Rover, Brown display box **£50-60**
2 Civilian Road Construction Set: Yellow/Silver Bulldozer, Red/Silver Bedford Lorry, Green Aveling Road Roller, Blue Earth Mover, Red/Blue Ford Sand Dumper, Yellow JCB, Red window display box **£50-60**
3 Fire Service Kit Set: Contains six Red models, 21 Fire Engine, Jeep, Pick Up, Artic Lorry, Rescue Truck, Fire Van with Blue light, Red window display box **£50-60**

Later issues (c.1965?) Window Boxes
48 Ford, Brown/Green, Two-tone Green or Maroon White body **£10-15**, 49 Ford Sand Dumper, Red/Blue body **£10-15**, 50 Ford Dumper **£10-15**, 51 Ford Articulated Truck **£15-20**, 52 Sand Dumper Trailer **£5-10**

Shackleton Models

The company was formed by Maurice Shackleton and traded as James Shackleton & Sons Ltd. from 1939 to 1952. They had premises in Cheshire and originally produced wooden toys such as lorries and dolls houses. The toy lorries were only made pre-war and had four wheels, a simple wooden chassis and body with a green name badge on the rear of the cab, and were fitted with a highly detailed aluminium radiator grille. Known models are a Chain Lorry, Breakdown Lorry and a Sided Wagon. Their price today is around £100 each. In 1948 having expanded its staff to nearly 40 people, the company started to produce diecast constructional models based on the Foden FG six-wheel platform lorry. The models consisted of separate parts all of which were, incredibly, made 'in house', including the clockwork motor, its key, and the

wheels and tyres. The models were advertised in the 'Meccano Magazine' with the slogan 'You can dismantle it - Just like the real thing', and they were originally priced at £2/19/6. Eventually the range was extended to include a Dyson Drawbar Trailer and a Foden Tipper. Each model was packed in its own distinctive box which displayed a black and white picture of the model inside.

In 1952, whilst in the midst of producing the David Brown Trackmaster 30, Tractor, a shortage of materials coupled with difficult trading conditions brought about the end of the company. Some remaining models from this period were acquired and distributed by Chad Valley. The unique models produced by the Shackleton company are now highly collectable and difficult to find.

---	1948-52	**Foden FG 6-wheel Platform Lorry** ....Yellow, Blue, Grey or Green body with Red wings, Grey chassis and Red or Grey fuel tanks, 12fi inches (305 mm.) long, initially in Blue/Yellow box, later in mottled Green box, (20,000 made)	**£200-300**
		Same colours as above but with Grey or Black wings and Red chassis	**£300-400**
		Same casting but with Red, Orange or Brown cab	**£300-400**
		NB Box difficult to find: ....Blue box with paper label having picture of chassis.	
---	1949-52	**Dyson 8-ton Drawbar Trailer** ....Yellow, Blue, Grey or Green body, packed in Red and Yellow box, (15,000)	**£100-150**
---	1950-52	**Foden FG 6-wheel Tipper Lorry** ....Yellow, Blue, Grey or Green body with Red wings, Grey chassis and Red or Grey fuel tanks, Silver wheels, (5,000)	**£300-400**
		As previous models but with Grey wings and Red chassis	**£300-400**
		As previous models but with Blue wings, Grey chassis, Grey wheels	**£300-400**
		Orange or Red body	**£300-400**
---	1952	**David Brown Trackmaster 30 Tractor** ..Red body, Black rubber tracks, 10 inches long, boxed. Only 50 models thought to exist	**£750-950**
		Note: It is known that some prototype models were made of Ploughs and Harrows, though it is not known if any were produced for sale.	
---	1958-60	**Foden S21 8-wheel Platform Lorry** ....Dark Blue, Dark Green or Light Turquoise fibreglass cab with Red metal chassis and wheels, wooden flatbed, length overall 18fi inches (470 mm), plastic injection moulded springs and axle parts, powered by 'Minimax' electric motor. (250 made as a promotional for Foden)	**£750-950**

The information in this listing has been taken from an original article written by John Ormandy in the 'Modellers World' magazine, Volumes 12 and 13, and is used by kind permission of the Editors, Mike and Sue Richardson. Robert Taylor provided additional information. Gary Irwin contributed information on the DB Trackmaster.

Foden FG 6-wheel Platform Lorry with a **Shackleton Dyson 8-ton Drawbar Trailer**
(Models sold by Romsey Model Auctions, Romsey, Hampshire; picture used by their kind permission)

Taylor and Barrett Lead Vehicles and the Postwar Re-issues

by Mike Richardson

The firm of Taylor and Barrett dates from the early 1920s when they started producing mainly figures but with a few odd carts. The vehicles themselves were only introduced in about 1935. These were rather crude by comparison with the Dinky Toys of the day as the lead gravity casting process was incapable of working to the fine limits possible with pressure diecasting as used by Meccano Ltd. The majority of the vehicles use a basic chassis incorporating the bonnet and wings. Different bodies are attached to this base unit by tabs and a radiator is plugged into the front. Some versions have the grille cast integrally with the bonnet, and most of these use plain metal wheels instead of having rubber tyres. These vehicles have a tremendous amount of charm as toys while they are only a generic representation of the types of vans and small trucks of the time.

A wide variety of types were made including petrol tankers, a pick-up truck and a couple of mail vans. The breakdown truck is particularly attractive with a working crane on the rear. These toys were made until the production was halted in 1940 when the factory was bombed out of existence. All salvageable tools, moulds and stock was moved to a new location in North Finchley but production stopped very soon after because of the munitions requirements of the war effort.

During the war the tools were split between the Taylors and the Barretts for safe keeping but they did not join up again afterwards and two separate companies, F.G.Taylor & Sons and A.Barrett & Sons, started up in 1945. The main part of the range, the small commercial vehicles and the cars, does not seem to have survived the War, only the trolley buses, which became Barretts, and the Leyland coach which appeared in one-piece casting form as a Taylor. It is interesting to note that the trolleybus carries a route board '621 Finchley' which probably means that they went past the factory.

A range of very nice fire engines came along in the late 1930s with a super turntable ladder appliance as the top of the range. These were longer than the main range and had many parts. To mark the advent of the Home Office Fire Precautions scheme (where fire appliances were made available to local areas by central government), Taylor and Barrett painted their range in grey as well as the more traditional red. These grey models are highly sought after now. Personnel were also available to go with these fire engines. A 'Decontamination Squad'

being a particular favourite with their gas masks and chemical-proof overalls. There is also a fire engine in the short chassis range but it is not very impressive.

The trolley buses came in two sizes. The large one has a separate driver figure (and conductor as well in the T & B version but not the later Barrett), and the body is in two pieces, upper and lower decks. The small one is in one piece and has no driver. Needless to say there is a vast difference in the values of the two sizes.

There are generic cars, roadster, coupé, saloon, on the short base but there is also quite a good model of the 1935 Singer Airstream saloon. This is also the poor man's Chrysler Airflow but never really caught on, the styling made the car look too tall to be appealing. A rather crude one-piece Austin Seven racer was the final car but this was to a larger scale.

Dinky Toys were not the only factory to make a model of the Air Mail Service Car based on the Morris Commercial chassis. T & B also made one and a nice chunky toy it is too. A couple of aeroplanes, a De Havilland Comet and an air liner, completed the range of powered vehicles. A modified version of the Comet seems to have been made by Barrett later but it differs a lot from the T & B, which is a much better model.

Some of the moulds were still around a few years ago and some attempts were made to make models again. These were fairly unsuccessful as casting techniques had changed and the new metals did not have the same flow characteristics as the early lead. Some models are definitely known to have been re-made as they have been seen at a swapmeet some time back, so collectors are advised to be wary.

Editor's note: All the models are rare - any auction prices that become available will be published in subsequent editions of this Catalogue.

The following listing is of models issued by Taylor and Barrett between 1920 and 1939. Post war production was split between F. G. Taylor & Sons and A. Barrett & Sons, each firm inheriting some moulds and continuing to make some but not all of the models until about 1952.
(FGT) = produced by F. G. Taylor after 1945, **(AB)** = produced by A. Barrett after 1945, **(-)** = date and company not known for certain,
NGPP = no price grading possible at present.

14	**Trotting Pony Racer** (FGT).	£55-65
15	**Turntable Fire Escape** (AB)	£55-65
16	**Fire Engine and Escape** (FGT)	£100-150
17	**Fire Engine and Men** (FGT)	£200-300
20	**Horse Drawn Water Cart** (FGT)	£300-400
21	**Horse Drawn Brewer's Cart** (FGT)	£100-200
22	**Horse Drawn Window Cleaner's Cart** (FGT)	£100-200
23	**Horse Drawn Baker's Cart** (FGT)	£100-200
26	**Roman Chariot** (FGT)	£25-35
27	**Donkey Drawn Coster Cart with Dog and Boy** (FGT)	£50-60
28	**Donkey Drawn Coster Cart, Plants load, Walking Coster** (FGT)	£50-60
28a	**Donkey Drawn Coster Cart, Vegetable load, Walking Coster** (FGT)	£50-60
29	**Ice Cream Bicycle**, 'ICE BRICKS' (FGT)	£200-300
36	**Milk Float and Milkman**, 'EXPRESS DAIRY' (AB)	NGPP
42	**Fire Escape and Team of Firemen** (FGT)	£150-200
43	**Air and Land Postal Service Set** (-)	£150-200
49	**Street Cleaning Barrow with two Bins** (FGT)	NGPP
92	**Llama Cart** (FGT)	£20-30
92a	**Donkey Cart** (FGT)	£20-30
109	**Pony Drawn Governor's Cart** (AB)	£20-30
109a	**Pony Drawn Cart** (AB)	£20-30
111	**Saloon Car** (-)	£80-100
112	**Transport Lorry** (-)	£20-30
113	**'ROYAL MAIL' Van** (-)	£150-200
114	**'AMBULANCE'**, Grey (Wartime civilian) (-)	£150-200
114a	**'AMBULANCE'**, Khaki (Army) (-)	£150-200
115	**Sports Car** (-)	£100-200
116	**Coupé** (-)	£100-200
117	**'AMBULANCE'**, (Street, civilian) (-)	£150-200
119	**Racer** (AB)	£20-30
120	**Fire Engine** (AB)	£50-60
123	**Atlanta Touring Plane** (AB)	£50-75

124	**'AIR MAIL' Van** (AB)	£100-200
128	**Petrol Tanker** (-)	£100-200
129	**Breakdown Lorry** (-)	£100-120
137	**DH 'Comet' Aeroplane** (AB)	£50-60
138	**'AIR MAIL' Streamline Van** (-)	£100-120
139	**Saloon Car** (-)	£50-60
152	**Streamline Motor Coach** (-)	£100-200
163	**Streamline Fire Engine** (-)	£50-60
197	**Trolley Bus** (small) (AB)	£200-250
204	**Trolley Bus** (large) (AB)	£300-400
302	**Horse Drawn Covered Wagon** (-)	£50-60
304	**Sledge and Dogs** (FGT)	£50-60
306	**Aeroplane Set** (Comet, Atlanta and pilots) (FGT)	£100-120
307	**Fire Brigade Set** (-)	£300-400
310	**Rickshaw pulled by Chinese Coolie** (FGT)	£100-150
311	**Light Trailer Fire Pump in Action Set** (-)	£100-150
?	**Space Ship** (-)	NGPP
?	**Coronation Coach** (small) (AB)	£20-30
?	**State Landau Coach** (-)	£30-40
?	**Farmer's Gig** (FGT)	£30-40
?	**Farm Cart with Trotting Horse** (-)	£30-40
?	**Mobile Animal Trailer and Vet** (-)	£60-70
---	**Racing Car**, Red body with 'MG Magnette' cast into side, 110 mm. 'FGT & SONS'	£60-70
---	**Petrol Pumps**, Black/White with rubber hoses (T&B)	£25-35
---	**Village Blacksmith Set**, contains blacksmith, forge with hood, anvil, Shire horse. In 2-part card box	£120-150

The listing has been compiled from original manufacturer's records by Mr Norman Joplin to whom the Editor would like to express his grateful thanks. Thanks are also due to Mr J.R. Anderson of Queensland, Australia and Ross Kennett of Roscoes Relics, South Australia, Australia for kindly sending new model information.

Robert Newson has provided this history and listing of cast metal Timpo motor vehicles.

The name Timpo comes from 'Toy Importers Ltd'. It was only with the outbreak of war in 1939 that Timpo started to manufacture their own lines, when importing became impossible. A few vehicles were made in 1940-41, but the main Timpo range started in 1946. The models were cheap and sturdy, if somewhat crude, and many have survived. Relatively few suffer from metal deterioration. In 1949 Timpo advertised 'faithful replicas of famous delivery services' and introduced several vans with attractive advertising liveries. An AEC Monarch lorry in the livery of Vaux brewery was introduced around 1950, and this was a far better model than the earlier toys. Sadly it was not the first of a new range - the 1951-2 ban on the use of zinc meant that Timpo discontinued all their diecast vehicles. Some of the dies were subsequently sold to Benbros, including the AEC lorry.

Timpo Toys are very rarely seen in mint condition, and prices are therefore quoted for good original condition. Dates given are the approximate year of introduction.

NB See the 'Miscellaneous Models' colour section for a picture of a Timpo model.

Intro	Model name	Details	MPR
1940	**MG Record Car**	Hollow-cast lead. Red, 'TIMPO TOYS' cast on side, 98 mm.	**£40-50**
1940	**Streamlined Saloon**	Separate body and chassis. 'Timpo' in script underneath. 99 mm.	**£30-40**
1940	**Pick-Up Truck**	Separate body and chassis. 'Timpo' in script underneath. Re-issued post-war with name blanked out. 97 mm.	**£30-40**
1940	**Four-light Saloon**	Possibly re-issue of a Goody Toy	NGPP
1946	**MG Record Car**	Zinc diecast. 'TIMPO TOYS' cast at rear on offside. 97 mm.	**£40-50**
1946	**'American Star' Racer**	Star transfer on each side, 101 mm.	**£40-50**
1946	**'Timpo Saloon'**	Vaguely like a Morris 8. 93 mm.	**£40-50**
1946	**Austin 16 Saloon**	Black. 'TIMPO TOYS' underneath. 96 mm. Re-issued by Betal in four versions:	**£40-50**
		1. No name on model, brass wheel hubs	**£30-40**
		2. 'A BETAL PRODUCT' under roof, tin base with friction motor, brass wheel hubs	**£30-40**
		3. As 2. but with plastic body	**£30-40**
		4. As 3. but with clockwork motor and solid metal wheels	**£30-40**
1946	**MG Midget**	Composition wheels. 82 mm.	**£30-40**
1946	**Packard Saloon**	Fitted with aluminium baseplate and friction motor from 1948. 113 mm.	**£30-40**
1946	**'Speed of the Wind' Record Car**	Similar to the Dinky Toy. 99 mm.	**£40-50**
1946	**No.1 'Arctic' Set**	Sledge and dog team, Eskimo with whip, another with rifle, walking stick, 2 penguins, 2 seals, polar bear, snowy hedge and igloo. Boxed.	**£300-400**
1947	**Alvis 14 Saloon**	A big four-light saloon. 106 mm.	**£30-40**
1947	**Utility Van**	With aluminium baseplate and friction motor from 1948. (Early casting 102mm, later 104mm).	
		1. No transfers, plain colours, without motor	**£10-15**
	'TYRESOLES'	2. Black, 'TYRESOLES SERVICE' transfers, no motor	**£150-200**
	'HMV'	3. 'HIS MASTER'S VOICE' transfers, pale Yellow, Orange-Yellow, pale Blue or Green, with or without motor.	**£150-200**
1947	**Artic. Petrol Tanker**	No transfers. Re-issued by Benbros. 149 mm. Red/white body, 'ESSO' logo	**£70-80**
1947	**Lincoln Convertible**	Vaguely like a 1942 Lincoln. Aluminium baseplate and windscreen. Usually single colours. Late version in cream with blue seats. 115 mm.	**£30-40**
1947	**Armstrong-Siddeley Hurricane**	A coupé with top up. 105 mm.	**£30-40**
1947	**Streamlined Fire Engine**	Red, 2 yellow aluminium ladders. Aluminium baseplate + friction motor from '49. 105 mm.	**£30-40**
1947	**Artic. Box Van**	Re-issued by Benbros. 146 mm. Boxed.	
	'TIMPO'	1. Green, Blue or Red trailer with 'TIMPO TOYS' transfers	**£140-160**
	'PICKFORDS'	2. Black cab and trailer with Grey roof, Red wheel hubs, 'PICKFORDS' transfers	**£120-140**
	'UNITED DAIRIES'	3. Orange cab and trailer, Black roof, 'UNITED DAIRIES' transfers	**£120-140**
	'WALL'S'	4. Light Blue cab, Light Blue and Cream trailer, 'WALL'S ICE CREAM' transfers	**£120-140**
		5. Dark Blue cab and trailer with off-White roof, 'LYONS TEA' transfers	**£120-140**
	'BISHOPS'	6. Pale Yellow cab and trailer, transfers with 'BISHOPS MOVE' logo and 'BISHOP & SONS DEPOSITORIES LTD. 10-12 BELGRAVE ROAD LONDON, S.W.1'	**£120-140**
	'BISHOPS/LUNN'	7. Same, but transfers with 'BISHOPS MOVE' logo and 'JOHN H. LUNN LTD. 6 HOPE CRESCENT EDINBURGH'.	**£120-140**
1947	**London Taxi**	Cast in two parts. 94 mm.	**£20-25**

Intro	Model name	Details	MPR
1947	**Alvis 14 Police Car**	Police sign and loudspeakers at front of roof, wire aerial behind. Black. 106 mm.	**£50-75**
1947	**Artic. Low Loader**	Re-issued by Benbros. 168 mm.	**£10-15**
1947	**Buick Saloon**	Crude model, composition wheels. 99 mm.	**£10-15**
1947	**Pick-Up Truck**	With eight cast-in barrels. 104 mm.	**£15-20**
1947	**Forward Control Tipper Lorry**	Cream cab and chassis, Red tipper. 101 mm.	**£15-20**
1947	**Forward Control Luton Van**	Same chassis as the tipper. 97 mm. boxed.	
		1. No transfers, black lower, light blue upper	**£15-20**
	'SMITH'S'	2. Dark blue, 'SMITH'S CRISPS' transfers.	**£100-120**
	'WILLS'	3. Brown, 'W.D. & H.O. WILLS' transfers	**£100-120**
1949	**Forward Control Box Van**	Same chassis as above. Re-issued by Benbros.	
	'CHIVERS'	Dark blue, 'CHIVERS JELLIES' transfers	**£100-120**
1949	**Normal Control Box Van**	Later models with aluminium baseplate and friction motor. 105 mm. Models were boxed.	
	'EVER READY'	1. Dark Blue with White roof, 'EVER READY' transfers, motor in some	**£100-120**
	'GOLDEN SHRED'	2. Green, 'GOLDEN SHRED', with motor	**£100-120**
	'MELTONIAN'	3. Green, 'MELTONIAN SHOE CREAM' transfers, with motor	**£100-120**
1949	**Normal Control Petrol Tanker 'ESSO'**	Red, 'MOTOR OIL ESSO PETROL' on paper labels. Re-issued by Benbros. 116 mm.	**£100-120**
1950	**AEC Monarch Brewery Lorry**	Red. 'VAUX' cast on headboard behind cab, 'SUNDERLAND' cast on cab sides. Boxed. Brown hollow-cast barrels with 'VAUX' cast on ends. Re-issued by Benbros without the headboard + other changes. 129 mm.	**£100-120**
1940s	**Bomber Station Set**	3 x twin-fuselage aircraft, 2 x twin-engined, single-fuselage aircraft and a single-engined fighter. Box has a pictorial label on its lift-off lid.	**£100-150**
No.249	**Hopalong Cassidy Series Set**	Contains 7 cowboys including Hopalong Cassidy, Lucky, California, etc. Boxed	**£600-800**
	Petrol Station No.2 Set	Saloon Car and Racing Car plus 3 Personnel and 5 Pumps. Pictorial box lid states: 'THE FAMOUS TIMPO CARS'	**£100-150**
	Station Figures Set	Contains Station Master, Porter with trolley, Porter with luggage, Signalman with flag, Signalman with whistle, Railwayman with lamps, Mr Brown, boy hiker, lady with bag, girl in red coat. Boxed	**£400-500**
	Tiger Hunt Set	Contains elephant, elephant with mahouts, Maharaja, hunter, 2 tigers, 4 bears. Boxed	**£400-500**
	Gypsy Organ Grinder with Dancing Bear		**£50-70**

Timpo figures.

Knights of the Round Table and Ivanhoe figures ...... each £10-15
Policeman, Policewoman, Zoo Keeper, Farm Girls ...... each £5-10
Station Passengers (as in set), Soldier with Kitbag ...... each £5-10
Super heroes: Captain Marvel, Mary Marvel, Marvel Junior ...... each £30-40
Wild West: Seated cowboys with guitars, Indian chief, squaw with papoose ...... each £15-20

MARKET PRICE RANGE   Please note that for MPR purposes, the models have been assumed to be boxed where appropriate and in good condition.

Tri-ang Minic Ships

Minic ships are accurately detailed waterline models made between 1958 and 1964 to a scale of 1:1,200 (1in to 100ft).
Six sales catalogues were published which nowadays are quite hard to find.
No single catalogue shows the full range.
Minic ships re-introduced in 1976 were fitted with wheels and have 'Hong Kong' on the base.

Ocean Liners

Ref	Year(s)	Model name	Colours, features, details	Market Price Range
M701		RMS 'Caronia'	Green body, one plain Red/Black or detailed funnel, one mast, 178 mm. 'Painted in the correct Cunard green she is a most striking vessel'.	£45-55
M702		RMS 'Queen Elizabeth'	Black/White, 2 plain Red/Black or detailed funnels, 2 masts, 262 mm. 'The worlds largest ship and the pride of the Cunard fleet'.	£55-65
M703		RMS 'Queen Mary'	Black/White, plain Red/Black or detailed funnels, 2 masts, 259 mm. 'Her three funnels make her the most easily recognisable'.	£45-55
M704		SS 'United States'	Black/White body, two Red/White/Blue funnels, 252 mm. 'The present holder of the Blue Riband of the Atlantic'.	£45-55
M705		RMS 'Aquitania'	Black/White body, four Red/Black funnels, two masts, 231 mm.	£80-100
M706		SS 'Nieuw Amsterdam'	Grey/White body, two Yellow funnels, two masts, 192 mm.	£45-55
M707		SS 'France'	Black/White, 2 Red/Black funnels, 5 masts, 262 mm. 'The longest ship in the world – 1035ft, being 4ft longer than Queen Elizabeth'.	£80-100
M708		RMS 'Saxonia'	Black/White body, one Red/Black or detailed funnel, nine masts, cargo handling gear on stern	£40-50
M708/2		RMS 'Franconia'	Green body, one Red/Black funnel, nine Green masts, 155 mm, swimming pool on stern. 480 made	£500-550
M709		RMS 'Ivernia'	Black/White or Green body, 155mm, cargo handling gear on stern.	£40-50
M709/2		RMS 'Carmania'	Green body, one Red/Black funnel, nine Green masts, 155 mm, swimming pool on stern. 480 made	£500-550
M710		RMS 'Sylvania'	Black/White, one Red/Black funnel, nine masts, 155 mm.	£35-45
M711		RMS 'Carinthie'	Black/White, one Red/Black funnel, nine masts, 155 mm.	£35-45
M712		NS 'Savannah'	White, no funnels (nuclear powered), four masts, 149 mm.	£45-55
M713		SS 'Antilles'	Black/White, one Red/Black funnel, ten masts, 152 mm.	£45-60
			All White body, one Red/Black funnel, ten masts	£65-70
M714		'Flandre'	Black/White, one Red/Black funnel, ten masts, 152 mm.	£35-45
			All White body, one Red/Black funnel, ten masts	£45-55
M715		RMS 'Canberra'	White body, one Yellow funnel, three masts, 189 mm.	£55-65
M716		MS 'Port Brisbane'	Grey/White, one Red/Black funnel, eight masts, 140 mm.	£90-110
M717		SS 'Port Auckland'	Grey/White, one Red/Black funnel, seven masts, 140 mm.	£90-120
M718		RMS 'Amazon'	White, Yellow funnel, 19 masts, 10 lifeboats, 149 mm.	£115-130
M719		RMS 'Arlanza'	White, Yellow funnel, 19 masts, 149 mm.	£130-150
M720		RMS 'Aragon'	White, Yellow funnel, 19 masts, 149 mm.	£115-130
M721		RMS 'Britannia'	The Royal Yacht. Blue/White body, Yellow/Black funnel, 3 masts, 105 mm.	£20-25
M721/H		RMS 'Britannia'	Hospital Ship. White body, three masts, 105 mm.	£20-25

Smaller craft

CHANNEL ISLANDS STEAMERS (78mm long)
M722	'Isle of Jersey'	Black/White, 2 Yellow/Black funnels, 2 masts	£18-24
M723	'Isle of Guernsey'	Black/White, 2 Yellow/Black funnels, 2 masts	£18-24
M724	'Isle of Sark'	Black/White body, 2 Yellow/Black funnels, 2 masts	£18-24
M726	'PILOTS' Boat	Black/White/Yellow, 45 mm	£65-75
M727	Lifeboat	Blue body	£15-20

PADDLE STEAMERS (all are 78 mm long)
M728	'Britannia'	Black/White, 2 funnels (black/blue, red/black or yellow/black), 2 masts	£20-25
M729	'Bristol Queen'	Black/white, 2 funnels (black/blue, red/black or yellow/black), 2 masts	£20-25
M730	'Cardiff Queen'	Black/White, 2 funnels (Black/Blue, Red/Black or Yellow/Black), 2 masts.	£20-25

OIL TANKER
M732	SS 'Varicella'	Black/White body, Black/Yellow funnel ('SHELL' logo), 2 masts, 169 mm.	£30-40

WHALE FACTORY SHIPS
M733	TSS 'Vikingen'	Grey body, six masts, 125 mm.	£25-30
M734	Whale Chaser	Grey, Yellow/Black funnel, 39 mm.	£12-15

TUGBOATS (all except 'Turmoil' are 38mm long)
M731	Tugboat	Black/Grey/Red, Red/Black funnel	£5-7
M731	Tugboat	Black/Grey/Red, Yellow/Black funnel	£5-7
M731	Tugboat	Black/Blue/Red, Yellow/Black funnel	£5-7
M731	Tugboat	Black/Grey/Yellow, Yellow/Black funnel	£5-7
M740	Barge	Intended to match M731, but not issued	NPP
M810	Navy Tug HMS 'Turmoil'	Black/Blue or Grey, Black funnel, 50 mm.	£10-15

LIGHTSHIPS (all are 33mm long)
M735	'SUNK'	Red body, White logo/name	£10-15
M736	'SHAMBLES'	Red body, White logo/name	£10-15
M737	'CORK'	Red body, White logo/name	£10-15
M738	'VARNE'	Red body, White logo/name	£10-15
M739	'St GOWAN'	Red body, White logo/name, no number on base	£10-15

Tri-ang Minic Warships

BATTLESHIP
M741   HMS 'Vanguard' .....Grey or Blue, two masts, 206 mm...............**£30-40**

AIRCRAFT CARRIERS
M751   HMS 'Bulwark' ....Grey or Blue, one mast, 186 mm **£25-35**
M752   HMS 'Centaur' ....Grey or Blue body with one mast **£25-35**
M753   HMS 'Albion'..........Grey or Blue body with one mast **£25-35**

COMMANDO SHIP
M754   HMS 'Albion'..........Grey ship with 12 Cream or Brown plastic
helicopters. 1000 models issued and given to H.M.S. 'Albion' crew
members (Capt. Adams in command) **£400-500**

CRUISERS
M761   HMS 'Swiftsure' ......Blue or Grey, one crane jib, 145 mm **£15-18**
M762   HMS 'Superb'........Blue or Grey, one crane jib, 145 mm **£15-18**

DESTROYERS, FLEET ESCORT, 'DARING' CLASS
M771   HMS 'Daring' ....Blue or Grey, one mast, 98 mm **£10-15**
M772   HMS 'Diana' ....Blue or Grey, one mast, 98 mm **£10-15**
M773   HMS 'Dainty' ....Blue or Grey, one mast, 98 mm **£10-15**
M774   HMS 'Decoy'..........Blue or Grey, one mast, 98 mm **£10-15**

DESTROYERS, FLEET, 'BATTLE' CLASS
M779   HMS 'Alamein'........Blue or Grey, one mast, 97 mm **£10-15**
M780   HMS 'Jutland'........Blue or Grey, one mast, 97 mm **£10-15**
M781   HMS 'Anzac'..........Blue or Grey, one mast, 97 mm **£10-15**
M782   HMS 'Tobruk' ....Blue or Grey, one mast, 97 mm **£10-15**

DESTROYERS, GUIDED MISSILE, 'COUNTY' CLASS
M783   HMS 'Hampshire' ...Grey body with two masts, 136 mm **£25-35**

M784   HMS 'Kent'.............Grey body with two masts, 136 mm **£30-35**
M785   HMS 'Devonshire' ...Grey body with two masts, 136 mm **£30-35**
M786   HMS 'London'........Grey body with two masts, 136 mm **£30-35**

FRIGATES, FAST ANTI-SUBMARINE, 'V' CLASS
M787   HMS 'Vigilant' ....Blue or Grey, one mast, 92 mm...................**£10-15**
M788   HMS 'Venus'........Blue or Grey, one mast, 92 mm..........**£10-15**
M789   HMS 'Virago' ....Blue or Grey, one mast, 92 mm..........**£10-15**
M790   HMS 'Volage' ....Blue or Grey, one mast, 92 mm..........**£10-15**

FRIGATES, ANTI-SUBMARINE, 'WHITBY' CLASS
M791   HMS 'Whitby' ....Blue or Grey body, 94 mm **£10-15**
M792   HMS 'Torquay' ....Blue or Grey body, 94 mm **£10-15**
M793   HMS 'Blackpool'........Blue or Grey body, 94 mm **£10-15**
M794   HMS 'Tenby' ....Blue or Grey body, 94 mm **£10-15**

MINESWEEPERS, 'TON' CLASS
M799   HMS 'Repton' ....Blue or Grey body **£10-15**
M800   HMS 'Dufton' ....Blue or Grey body **£10-15**
M801   HMS 'Ashton' ....Blue or Grey body **£10-15**
M802   HMS 'Calton' ....Blue or Grey body **£10-15**
M803   HMS 'Picton' ....Blue or Grey body **£10-15**
M804   HMS 'Sefton' ....Blue or Grey body **£10-15**
M805   HMS 'Upton' ....Blue or Grey body **£10-15**
M806   HMS 'Weston' ....Blue or Grey body **£10-15**

SUBMARINES, 'A' CLASS
M817   Sub 'A' Class.............Blue or Grey body, 61 mm **£5-7**
M818   Sub Recon............Blue or Grey body, 61 mm **£7-10**

Accessories, Gift Sets, Hong Kong issues and Catalogues

DOCKSIDE ACCESSORIES
M827	**Breakwater Straights**, Grey	**£3-4**
M828/L	**Breakwater Angle**, Left, Grey	**50p**
M828/R	**Breakwater Angle**, Right, Grey	**50p**
M829	**Breakwater End**, Grey	**50p**
M836	**Quay Straights**,Tan	**£3-4**
M837	**Crane Units**, Tan, Brown or Green cargo	**£3-4**
M838	**Storage Tanks**, Grey/Silver and Red	**£2-3**
M839	**Customs Shed**, Green	**£3-4**
M840	**Warehouse**, Brown	**£3-4**
M841	**Ocean Terminal**, White with Black windows	**£5-6**
M842	**Swing Bridge**, Red, no description on base	**£2-3**
M843	**Terminal Extension**, White with Black windows	**£5-6**
M844	**Lock Gates** (pair), Brown	**£1-2**
M845	**Landing Stages**, Cream 'L' shaped, 1in long	**£1-2**
M846	**Lift Bridge**, Silver/Tan	**£2-3**
M847	**Pier centre section**, White	**£2-3**
M848	**Pier entrance section**, White	**£2-3**
M849	**Pier head**, White	**£12-14**
M850	**Pier Shelter**, Green, 35 mm	**£5-6**
M851	**Pier archways**	**£2-3**
M852	**Pier Building**, White/Blue/Green, Silver Cupola, 'RESTAURANT' plus 'DANCING TONIGHT'	**£2-3**
M853	**Factory Unit**, Pink and Buff, Black chimneys	**£25-30**
M854	**Tanker Wharf Straight**, Cream and Red	**£65-75**
M855	**Tanker Wharf Berth**, Red and Green or Cream and Green, Black plastic pipeline	**£2-3**
M857	**26in Sea**, Blue plastic	**£14-18**
M857	**52in Sea**, Blue plastic	**£25-30**
M861	**Lifeboat set**, Grey, Blue shed, one lifeboat	**£35-40**
M878	**Lighthouse**, White	**£1-2**
M880	**Whales**, White or plain Grey	**£12-15**
M882	**Beacon**, White/Red or Green	**£1-2**
M884	**Statue of Liberty**, Green/Grey	**£15-20**
M885	**Floating Dock**, Grey, 4 Black plastic cranes	**£20-25**
M -	**Helicopter**, Cream or Brown plastic	**£20-25**

GIFT SETS and SPECIAL PRESENTATION PACKS
M891	**'Queen Elizabeth'** Gift Set	**£75-100**
M892	**'United States'** Gift Set	**£150-175**
M893	**'Task Force'** Gift Set	**£30-40**
M894	**'Royal Yacht'** Gift Set	**£80-100**
M895	**'Nieuw Amsterdam'** Gift Set	**£600-700**
M702s	**'Queen Elizabeth'** Presentation Set	**£80-100**
M703s	**'Queen Mary'** Presentation Set	**£100-120**
M704s	**SS 'United States'** Presentation Set	**£100-120**
M705s	**RMS 'Aquitania'** Presentation Set	**£125-150**
M707s	**SS 'France'** Presentation Set	**£125-150**
M741s	**HMS 'Vanguard'** Presentation Set	**£50-60**

HONG KONG 'BLUE BOX' MODELS (1976-80)
These models are slightly larger than the original issues, e.g., Canberra is 207mm.
'Queen Mary', 'Queen Elizabeth', 'United States', 'Canberra',
HMS 'Vanguard', HMS 'Bulwark', 'Missouri', 'Bismark',
'Scharnhorst', 'Yamato'. Each, boxed **£15-20**
RMS 'Canberra, boxed **£25-30**

HONG KONG SETS of MODELS
1	**Fleet Anchorage Set**	**£25-30**
2	**Quay Set**	**£25-30**
3a	**Ocean Terminal**, lid shows stern of RMS 'Queen Mary'	**£45-50**
3b	**Ocean Terminal**, lid shows bow of RMS 'Queen Mary'	**£35-40**
4	**Naval Task Force**, with HMS 'Bulwark' and 'Vanguard'	**£35-40**
5	**Naval Task Force**, with 'Bismark' and 'Scharnhorst'	**£50-55**

MINIC CATALOGUES 1958-64
1	**Leaflet** ....with first Minic Ships listed	**£75-100**
2	**Booklet** ....with first Minic Ships listed	**£25-30**
3	**Booklet** ....with Ships and other Tri-ang products	**£60-75**
4	**Booklet** ....with Minic Ships only	**£25-30**
5	**Booklet** ....with Minic Ships only	**£25-30**
6	**Booklet** ....with Tri-ang range	**£30-35**
M862	**Leaflet** ....Minic illustrated leaflet	**£10-15**

Tri-ang
Spot-On models

Introduction

Spot-On Models were introduced in 1959 by Tri-ang Toys to gain a foothold in the diecast market dominated at the time by Dinky Toys and their recently established rivals Corgi Toys.

Tri-ang realised that they had to offer not only a range of features similar to those of their competitors' products but something more besides. They decided that collectors would appreciate models that were all made to the same precise scale right across the range.

The models would thus look right together and qualify as such rather than toys. Much of the Dinky and Corgi cars range was made to a scale of around 1:45 (with a few exceptions).

Tri-ang advertised the precise nature of their (larger) chosen scale as being 'spot-on' at 1:42.

A large modern factory was set up in Belfast, Northern Ireland to produce the models. A coloured picture of the real vehicle was included in the box of most early issues.

Well over a hundred different models were designed, the range being extended to include scale buildings and road signs. Production continued till the time that Tri-ang bought up Dinky Toys in 1967. After the cessation of UK production, some of the Spot-On dies went to New Zealand where some interesting versions were produced for a couple of years.

All Spot-On models are highly collectable today particularly commercial vehicles, buses and the Presentation and Gift Sets.

NB See the 'Miscellaneous Models' colour section for pictures.

Spot-On model identification

Makers Name and Trade Mark are clearly marked on base of the model ('SPOT-ON' and 'Models by Tri-ang'). Some New Zealand produced versions have nothing at all on the base.

Model Name is shown on the base (except some New Zealand versions) while the **Model Number** is usually shown on box but not always on the model.

Baseplates can be any of a variety of colours: black, silver, grey - even green has been observed on the base of a maroon version of No. 155 Taxi !

Scale of models is 1:42 (with very few exceptions) and is usually (but not always) shown on the base.

Wheel hubs on cars are usually turned aluminium with a raised 'hub cap'. Truck models usually have diecast and more accurate representations of real hubs. **Tyres** are mostly black rubber (occasionally plastic) on all the vehicle models. Rear twin wheels have special 'double tyres'.

Number plates are represented on most Spot-On models with the exception of those having plastic chassis (such as 266 Bull Nose Morris and 279 MG Midget). A large range of registration numbers were available to factory production staff and were applied randomly to most models. Different number plates are therefore to be expected on different examples of the same model and do not have any effect on the price.

Windscreens and windows are included in all vehicle models.

Other features include seats and steering wheel on most models, suspension on most cars, driver, other figures and lorry loads with some. Very few 'decals' or 'frills' is the norm.

Colours are all listed where known though different and previously unknown colours still come to light occasionally.

Prices shown in the 'Market Price Range' column are for mint models in pristine boxes. These models are rare, hence their high market prices. The condition of models generally encountered tends towards the average and consequently command lower prices. Similarly, rare colours or combinations of colours puts the price into the higher part of the range with common colours achieving a more moderate price level.

Spot-On Cars

Ref	Year(s)	Model name	Colours, features, details	Market Price Range

100 1959 **Ford Zodiac** (without lights) .... Red / Cream or Blue / Cream body, 107 mm £70-90
Red body £80-100
Cream body £70-90
Yellow body £110-140
Light Blue, Salmon-Pink or Green body £70-90
Bluish-Grey and Brownish-Pink body £75-100
Light Blue over Grey body, Red interior £100-120

100sl 1959 **Ford Zodiac** (with lights) .... Grey/Turquoise or Grey/Pink body £100-120
Grey/White, Grey/Light Blue, or Green/White body £100-120
Yellow/White, Grey/Green, or Two-tone Blue body £100-120

101 1959 **Armstrong Siddeley 236 Sapphire** Blue / Grey, Turquoise / Black, Blue / Black,
Pink or Mauve body £100-130
Salmon body, Black roof £150-175
Mid-Green body, Dark Green roof £150-200
Light Blue body, Dark Blue roof £150-175
Powder Green, Metallic Green / Black, or Bluish-Grey £75-100
Light Blue body £100-150
Light Blue / Black, Grey / Black £95-125
Pale Green / Metallic Charcoal, or Deep Lilac / Black roof £160-190
Cream / Metallic Charcoal or Metallic Blue / Black £75-100
Yellow body, Black roof £150-175

102 1959 **Bentley Continental 4-door Sports**. Metallic Green / Silver, or Metallic Grey / Blue. 127 mm £80-125
Metallic Maroon / Silver £150-175
Two-tone Grey, Silver / Grey or Green / Grey £95-125
Silver / Light Blue or Grey / Light Blue body £120-150

103 1959 **Rolls Royce Silver Wraith** .... Metallic Silver and Maroon body, White seats, 131 mm £200-300
Metallic Silver and Metallic Light Blue (Cream seats), or
Metallic Silver and Metallic Green body £125-150

104 1959 **M.G. 'MGA' Sports Car** .... Beige body, 95 mm £150-175
Red body (Grey seats), Mid-blue or Pale Blue body (White seats) £130-160
Turquoise or Cream body (White seats) £130-160
Salmon Pink (Grey seats) or Bluish-Green (Lemon seats) £150-200
Greenish-Grey (Turquoise seats) .... NGPP
Deep Green body (White seats) £150-175
Metallic Steel Blue body (Grey seats) £130-160

105 1959 **Austin-Healey 100/6** .... Yellow (White or Grey seats), Grey (Red seats), Beige (Grey seats) ... £140-200
Red / Cream or Metallic Blue / Cream £200-300
Blue, Green, Cream, Turquoise, Metallic Blue, Metallic Green, or Pink ... £130-170
Light Blue body (Royal Blue seats) or Turquoise (Light Grey seats) £150-180

107 1960 **Jaguar XK-SS** .... Metallic Blue body, Lemon seats, Black folded hood £150-175
Cream, Beige, Red or Light Green body £150-175
Dark Olive (Light Grey seats / hood), or
Pale Blue (Pale Grey seats / hood) £150-175
Lilac body with Grey seats, Black folded hood £150-175
Light Blue with Dark Blue seats and folded hood £150-175
Light Grey body, Pale Blue seats and folded hood £150-200
Fawn body, cast hubs have 'stick-on' wheel trims that create a
spoked wheel and white-wall tyre effect .... NGPP

108 1960 **Triumph TR3a Sports** .... Light Blue with Dark Blue seats, 88 mm £150-200
Cream body with Dark Brown seats £150-200
Light Brown (White seats), Pale Green (Off-White seats) or Apple Green (Cream seats) ... £140-170
Red or Sea Green body with Grey seats £120-150
Grey body (White seats), or Metallic Green (Lemon seats) £125-175
Pale Blue body with Pale Grey seats £125-175
Mid-Blue body with Mid-Grey seats £125-175
Note: Two baseplate castings are known with this model.
One exposes the axle ends near to the wheels, while the
other completely hides the axles.

112 1960 **Jensen 541** .... Grey, Mauve, Pink, Maroon / Black or Metallic Green body, 106 mm ... £100-125
Light Blue or Pale Green or Metallic Blue body £100-125
Lemon body (Black roof), or Yellow body (Red seats) £100-125

113 1960 **Aston-Martin DB3 Saloon** .... Light Blue, Grey, Red, Light Green, Dark Green, 104 mm £125-150
Maroon body £200-250
Very Pale Pink or Deep Pink body, Cream interior £130-160
Deep Lilac or Light Brown body £130-170
White or Metallic Dark Green body £130-160
Metallic Silver Blue body £130-160
Yellow body, Lemon interior, Red steering wheel £175-225

114 1960 **Jaguar 3.4 Mark 1 Saloon** .... Metallic Blue, Maroon, Mauve, Metallic Green, or Pink, 108 mm £125-150
Light Grey or Mid-Green body £140-180
Light Blue or Yellow body £110-150
White or Dark Red body £150-180
Very Pale Pink or Deep Pink body £150-200

276

115	1960	**Bristol 406 Saloon**	Orange or Red body, 116 mm	£100-130
			Metallic Dark Steel body	£140-160
			Yellow or Metallic Green body	£100-160
			Grey body, Black roof, Cream seats	£100-130
118	1960	**BMW Isetta Bubble Car**	Pale Blue, Beige, Grey or Turquoise, 56 mm	£75-100
			Green or Metallic Green, Red, Pink or Yellow	£75-100
			Yellow body	£120-160
119	1960	**Meadows Frisky Sport**	Orange / Grey, Blue / Grey or Turquoise / Black	£60-80
			Red / Light Grey, Red / Black, or Light Blue / White, 69 mm	£75-100
			Pale Blue / Black or Red / White	£100-125
120	1960	**Fiat Multipla Estate**	Blue (Cream seats), or Mauve (Red seats), 85 mm	£70-80
			Pink, Light Blue, Yellow, Red, Dark Red, Sea Green or Pale Green	£100-125
			White (Off-White seats)	£100-125
131	1960	**Goggomobil Super Regent**	Grey / Black, Yellow / Black, Mauve / Black, Blue / Grey, Blue, Green, or Grey	£50-75
			Metallic Green, Beige, Light Grey, Pink, Deep Salmon Pink, Red or Turquoise	£50-75
			Light Blue / Black, Red / Black, Dark Blue / Black, Green / Black	£50-75
154	1961	**Austin A40 Farina Saloon**	Green, White, Light Blue/White or Grey/Blue	£50-70
			Light Grey, Metallic Blue, Beige, Light Blue, Navy or Turquoise body	£50-75
			Pale Grey body, White interior	£100-125
			Metallic Green body, Cream interior	£80-100
			Red / Black, Blue / Black, Green / Black, Lavender / Black	£60-80
	1966	**'MAGGI' Promotional**	Red body, Cream interior, 'MAGGI' in yellow on front doors. Housed in special red / yellow box with leaflet	£200-300
157	1963	**Rover 3-litre** (without lights)	Mid Blue, Mauve, Beige or Yellow	£100-120
			Mid-Grey, Dark Grey, Pale Grey, Sea Green, Dark Green, Light Blue or Deep Pink	£90-120
			Dark Blue body	£150-175
			White body	£95-125
157sl	1963	**Rover 3-litre** (with lights)	Mid Blue, Mauve, Beige, Red or Yellow	£90-120
			Grey, Pale Grey, Sea Green, Dark Green, Light Blue	£90-120
			Dark Blue or Dark Grey	£120-150
			White body	£95-125
165/1	1961	**Vauxhall PA Cresta Saloon**	Beige, Red, Maroon, Pink, Turquoise or Yellow, 115 mm	£80-100
			Blue, Light Blue, Grey or Light Grey	£90-120
			Plum Red or Sea Green body	£100-125
165/2	1961	**Vauxhall PA Cresta with roof rack**	Beige, Red, Maroon, Pink, Turquoise or Yellow, 115 mm	£80-100
			Blue, Light Blue, Grey or Light Grey	£90-120
			Plum Red or Sea green body	£110-150
166	1962	**Renault Floride Convertible**	Blue, Green or Grey body, 101 mm	£80-100
			Dark Red, White or Yellow body	£80-100
183	1963	**Humber Super Snipe Estate**	Beige / White, Blue / White, Green / White, Blue / Black, Beige, Blue, Metallic Bronze or two-tone Blue, wing mirrors on some	£75-100
184	1963	**Austin A60** (with skis)	Beige, Green or White body, 2 figures, roof rack, 106 mm	£80-10
			Red, Light Blue or Light Grey (Grey rack)	£75-100
			Lime Green or Greyish-Blue (Black or Grey roof-rack)	£90-120
185	1963	**Fiat 500**	Light Blue, Green, Red or Grey body	£80-100
			Yellow or Dark Blue	£120-150
191	1963	**Sunbeam Alpine Convertible**	Beige, Mid-Blue, Green, Red, Mauve or Pink, 95 mm	£90-120
			Turquoise or Grey (Cream seats), or Light Blue (White seats)	£90-120
			Deep Salmon Pink or White with Red seats; or Yellow with Cream seats	£100-130
191/1	1963	**Sunbeam Alpine Hardtop**	Red / White, Turquoise / White, Blue / Black, Blue / Cream, White / Black, Beige / White, Grey / Black body and hardtop	£100-130
			Dark Green (Red seats), or Metallic Green / Black	£100-130
			Pink (Cream seats)	£90-120
			Mauve (Cream seats), or Yellow body (Cream seats)	£120-150
			Light Blue, Light Blue/White, Pale Blue/White	£80-110
193	1963	**N.S.U. Prinz**	Turquoise, Beige, Pale Blue, Light or Dark Blue, Cream, Grey or Red	£50-70
			White body	£80-90
195	1963	**Volkswagen Rally Car**	Beige, Cream, Maroon, or Orange body, roof light, flags on bonnet, racing number '9' or '23'	£150-175
			Red body, racing number '11', or Metallic Bronze	£200-300
			Light Blue ('6'), Turquoise ('9')	£150-175
210	1960	**Morris Mini Minor**	Shown in catalogue but not issued	NPP
211	1963	**Austin Seven** (Mini)	Light Blue, Grey, Red or Yellow body, 73 mm	£125-150
			Pink body	£200-250
			White body	£160-180
213	1963	**Ford Anglia Saloon**	Beige, Grey, Yellow or White body, 95 mm	£130-160
			Turquoise, Light Blue, Dark Blue, Red or Pink	£130-160
215	1961	**Daimler Dart SP250**	Beige, Green or Yellow body, 75 mm	£90-120
			White (Red seats), or Light Blue (Blue seats)	£140-160
			Turquoise (White seats), Red (Cream seats) or Grey (Cream seats)	£100-125

216	1963	**Volvo 122s**	Red, Orange, Blue or Turquoise body, sliding roof	£90-120
			Grey, Bright Yellow or Dark Green	£100-125
			Lime Green, White interior	£125-150
217	1963	**Jaguar 'E' Type**	Beige, Cream, Light or Dark Green, Red,	
			White or Yellow / Black	£90-120
			Mid-Blue or Light Grey body	£100-130
			Light Blue body	£200-250
218	1963	**Jaguar Mk.10**	Metallic Brown or Blue, 122 mm	£90-120
			Dark or Mid-Green, Bronze or White	£120-150
219	1963	**Austin-Healey Sprite Mk.III**		
		(with driver figure)	Red (White seats), Blue (Red seats), Beige (White seats)	£100-125
			Off-White or Light Blue body	£100-125
259	1963	**Ford Consul Classic**	White (Blue seats), Beige (White seats); or Blue, Light Blue,	
			Red, Grey or Green body, 105 mm	£80-100
260	1963	**Royal Rolls-Royce Phantom V**	Maroon body, Blue interior, two flags on roof, Queen and Prince	
			Philip in rear seats, driver and attendant in front	£200-300
261	1963	**Volvo P1800**	Two versions of this model exist (no price difference):	
			1: the bonnet and boot open and a spare wheel is supplied;	
			2: only the bonnet can be opened.	
			Light Blue, Mid-Blue, Red, Turquoise, Grey or Met. Bronze	£80-100
			Tan body	£100-130
			Red body, Grey interior	£125-150
262	1963	**Morris 1100**	Dark Blue or Red (Grey seats), Green or Beige (Red seats)	£70-90
			Lime Green or Light Blue body	£70-90
263	1964	**Bentley 4fi Litre** (Supercharged)	Green body, Union Jack, racing number '27', '11' or '15'	£80-100
266	1965	**'Bull Nose' Morris** 1923	Red / Black or Yellow / Black, Brown driver, (scale 1:48)	£70-80
267	1964	**M.G. 1100 Saloon**	White / Dark Green (Red seats), Red (Cream seats),	
			Green (Red seats) or Red / White (Red interior), 88mm	£100-125
			Royal Blue / White, Red interior	£350-450
268	1965	**Vauxhall PB Cresta**	Shown in catalogue but not issued under this number, see 280	NPP
270	1965	**Ford Zephyr 6 Mk.III**	Pale Blue (Red seats), Cream, Green, Greyish-Green or Grey (Red seats); or	
			Red (Grey seats), with poodle	£100-125
274	1965	**Morris 1100 and Canoe**	Green, Grey, Light Blue, Dark Blue or Red car, Brown canoe on roof	£70-80
			Light Blue or Two-tone Blue (Red canoe) or Red (Red / White canoe)	£70-80
			Light Blue car with Blue / Red canoe, Orange paddle (Set 703)	GSP
276	1964	**Jaguar 'S' type**	Metallic Bronze body, 114 mm., 2 figures	£120-150
			Metallic Blue or Metallic Green body, Red interior, 2 figures	£120-150
			Silver body, 2 figures	£180-220
			Greyish Green body, Red interior, 2 figures	£150-175
278	1965	**Mercedes-Benz 230 SL**	Metallic Red, Cream, or Maroon body, 100 mm., 2 figures	£80-100
			Metallic Blue or Metallic Bronze	£90-120
279	1965	**M.G. PB Midget** 1935 (scale 1:48)	Dark Blue or Red body, Black wings and seats	£70-80
280	1963	**Vauxhall PB Cresta**	Beige / Red, Dark Blue / White or Grey / Green body	£100-125
281	1966	**M.G. Midget Mk.II**	Blue or Red body, White interior, driver with scarf, policeman figure, 83 mm	£120-140
286	1965	**Austin 1800**	Light or Dark Blue, Cream, Green or Beige (all with Red seats); or Red (Grey seats)	£70-85
287	1965	**Hillman Minx**		
		(with Roof Rack and Luggage)	Pale Green, Beige, Cream or Green (all with Red seats),	
			Red (Grey seats) or Greyish-Green body. Two brown suitcases.	£80-100
287/1	1965	**Hillman Minx** (with Roof Rack)	Same details as 287	£80-100
289	1963	**Morris Minor 1000**	Metallic Blue or Light Blue body	£120-150
			Red or Metallic Green body	£160-200
304	1967	**VW Variant Estate Car**	Mid-Blue body and plastic opening tailgate. See also 401/1	NGPP
306	1964	**Humber Super Snipe Estate**	Same casting as 183 but with roof-rack and two suitcases.	
			Beige, Blue, Green or Red or Metallic Bronze body	£120-150
			Light Blue (White roof-rack) or Turquoise (White roof-rack)	£85-100
			White and Turquoise body, Grey roof-rack	£100-120
			Blue body, White roof	£80-95
307	1965	**Volkswagen Beetle 1200**	Metallic Blue or Metallic Dark Red body	£200-250
308	1965	**Land Rover and Trailer**	Green (Tan plastic canopy), trailer has Brown plastic body	£80-100
401/1	1967	**VW Variant Estate Car**	Dark Blue body, White plastic opening tailgate	£300-500
405	1966	**'BEA' Vauxhall Cresta**	Dark Grey body with Red 'BEA' logo	£100-125
407	1966	**Mercedes-Benz 230 SL**	Brown body, Red interior, boot rack and luggage	£70-80
408	1966	**Renault Caravelle**	Not issued	NPP
410	1966	**Austin 1800 and Rowboat** (on roof)	Green, Blue, Beige or Red car with Red or Orange boat	£80-100

'Magicar' series

501	1965	**Jaguar Mk.10**	Blue or Green body	£70-90
502	1965	**Rolls-Royce Silver Cloud Mk.III**	Blue or Red body	£100-125
503	1965	**Bentley S3 Saloon**	Blue or Red body	£80-110
504		**Ferrari Superfast**	Blue or Red	£80-110
505	1966	**Batmobile**	Black body with Batman and Robin figures	£150-175
?	?	**Tric-Trac car**	Plastic bodied racing car	£80-110
MG1	?	**Magicar**	no details	NGPP
MG2	?	**Magicar**	no details	NGPP
MG3	?	**Magicar**	no details	NGPP

Spot-On Commercial Vehicles

Ref	Year(s)	Model name	Colours, features, details	Market Price Range
106a/0c	1960	Austin Articulated Flatbed Lorry with MGA in Crate	Light Blue, Dark Blue, Red or Orange cab, 234 mm	£250-400
106a/1	1959	Austin Articulated Dropside Lorry	Light Blue, Green or Orange cab and body, 234 mm	£200-250
106a/1c	1960	Austin Articulated Flatbed Lorry with Crate Load	Light Blue, Light Green or Orange cab, seven black plastic crates	£200-250
			Turquoise or Dark Blue body	£300-350
CB106	1961-62	Four Wheel Trailer	Turquoise or Red body, for use with ERF and AEC lorries	£90-110
109/2	1960	E.R.F. 68g Flatbed Lorry	Turquoise, Light Grey or Blue body, 210 mm	£160-190
			Maroon body	£350-400
109/2p	1960	E.R.F. 68g Flatbed Lorry with Planks	Turquoise (with or without Black cab roof), 210 mm	£200-250
			Yellow body	£300-400
109/3	1960	E.R.F. 68g Dropside Lorry	Dark Blue cab with Pale Blue or Silver truck body	£300-400
			Yellow body (Metallic Grey roof), Light Green body (Green roof), Blue body or Green body (Black roof)	£160-190
			Deep Blue body, Silver chassis	£250-350
			Orange-Red body, Light Grey chassis	£350-450
			Lemon, Pale Green or Turquoise body, Silver chassis	£190-225
109/3b	1960	E.R.F. Dropside Lorry with Barrel load	Turquoise, Light Blue or Red body (Silver truck bed on some), hinged tailboard, ten Brown plastic barrels	£250-350
110/2	1960	A.E.C. Mammoth Major 8 Flatbed Lorry	Red body (with or without Black roof), 210 mm	£170-200
			Maroon or Dark Blue body	£450-500
110/2b	1960	A.E.C. Lorry 'London Brick Co Ltd'	Red body, Black cab roof, 'brick' load, 'Phorpes Bricks'	£200-250
110/3	1960	A.E.C. Lorry 'British Road Services'	Red body, with or without Black cab roof, Silver chassis and back, barrels load	£400-500
110/3d	1962	A.E.C. Lorry with Oil Drums Load	Red body, Black cab roof, Silver trim	£225-300
110/4	1961	A.E.C. Tanker 'SHELL-BP'	Green cab, Red tank, Black chassis and catwalk	£300-400
			Yellow cab, White/Yellow tank, Silver chassis / catwalk	£500-750
111/30g	1962	Ford Thames with Garage Kit	Orange cab and truck body, Silver chassis, 219 mm	£300-350
			Light Blue cab and truck body, White garage	£250-300
111/a0t	1961	Ford Thames Trader with Three Log Load	Dark Blue or Red cab and truck body, 3 logs	£275-325
			Light Blue cab and truck body	£200-275
			Light Yellow cab and truck body	£250-300
111a/1	1959	Ford Thames Trader 'British Railways'	Maroon and White body, '4884 BGM', 'M 1741 GT6'	£225-300
111a/1	1960	Ford Thames Trader 'R.Hall & Son'	Green body, logo on door. Doubtful if model issued	NPP
111a/1s	1960	Ford Thames with Sack Load	Light Blue and Silver, twelve brown plastic sacks	£250-325
			Dark Green body	£300-350
			Two-tone Blue body	£300-400
			Strawberry and Cream body	£300-400
116	1959	'CATERPILLAR' Tractor D9	Brown / Silver body, Black rubber tracks, 'CAT D9'	£500-750
117	1963	'JONES' Mobile Crane	Cream cab and jib, Red body and wheels, Black chassis, Grey base	£150-200
			Dark Red cab / body, White jib, Light Grey chassis, Silver wheels	£300-400
122	1961	'UNITED DAIRIES' Milk Float	Red / White body, chains, 'Lada and New Yoghurt'	£90-120
123	1959	Bamford Excavator	Red / Yellow, 'J.C.B.'. Intended model but not issued	NPP
137	1962	'MASSEY FERGUSON 65' Tractor	Red / Grey body, Orange engine cover, yellow wheels	£350-500
158a/2	1961	Bedford 'S' Type 2000 Gallon 'SHELL-BP' Tanker	Green cab, Red tank, Black chassis, 'P33A37' logo	£400-500
			Yellow cab, White tank, 'P33A37' logo, 202 mm	£700-1000
			Dark Metallic Green cab, Red tank, Black chassis	£500-600
158a/2C	1961	Bedford Low Loader	Red low-loader with cable drum load. Doubtful if issued	NPP
161	1961	Land Rover (long wheel base)	Grey / White, Light Grey / White or Blue / White	£65-80
210	1961	Morris Mini Van	Bright Yellow, seats / steering wheel, suspension	£90-120
210/1	1962	Morris Mini Van 'Royal Mail'	Red body, Post Office crest, 'E-II-R', suspension	£70-90
210/2	1962	Mini Van 'P.O. Telephones'	Olive-Green body, White interior, Gold crown logo and 'TELEPHONE MANAGER'	£140-160
258	1963	'R.A.C.' Land Rover	Dark Blue body, 'RADIO RESCUE', 108 mm	£100-125
265	1964	'TONIBELL' Ice Cream Van	Blue body, thick Red flash, attendant, 'Tonibell' on doors	£90-135
271	1965	'EXPRESS DAIRIES' Milk Float	Blue / White, 3 wheels, driver, 'Drink Express Milk'	£100-125
273	1965	Commer Van 'SECURITY EXPRESS'	Green / Gold, driver and seated guard, coin slot in roof	£100-130
308	1965	Land Rover and Trailer	Green (Tan plastic canopy), trailer has Brown plastic body	£80-100
315	1965	'GLASS & HOLMES' Commer Van	Blue / Yellow, ladder, figures, 'Window Cleaning Co. Est 1891'	£160-190
402	1966	Crash Service Land Rover	Orange body, 'MOTORWAYS CRASH SERVICE' in Blue	£100-120
404	1966	Morris Mini Van	Yellow body, suspension, ladder, figure, 79 mm	£300-350
404/1	1966	Morris Mini Van 'SHELL'	As previous model but without ladder and figure	£400-500
404/2	1966	Morris Mini Van 'AA'	Shown in 1966 catalogue but never seen	NGPP

Buses, Coaches and Taxis

145	1963	Routemaster Bus	Red 'London Transport' bus, route '284', 'Ovaltine - The Worlds Best Nightcap'.	
			1st type has chrome moulded radiator	**£300-400**
			2nd type has transfer print on plastic background	**£300-400**
155	1961	Austin FX4 Taxi	Maroon body, Cream steering wheel, Green base, tin-plate hubcaps	**£300-400**
			Black body, Red steering wheel, Grey base	**£65-80**
156	1961	Mulliner Luxury Coach	Pale Blue / Grey, Red flash, 'Tri-ang Tours' rear logo, 213 mm	**£200-300**
			Yellow / White body, Brown side flash	**£900-1,200**
			Sea Green / Cream, Red flash	**£800-1,000**
			Silver / Red / Dark Blue	**£250-350**
			Sky Blue / White body, Red flash	**£500-600**

Military models

415	1965	R.A.F. Land Rover	Blue/Grey, R.A.F. roundel, hose/pump/attendant, 111 mm	**£80-100**
416	1965	Leyland Army Ambulance	Olive Green body. Not issued	NPP
417	1965	Military 'FIELD KITCHEN'	Olive Green body, squadron markings, suspension, 108 mm	**£100-125**
418	1965	Leyland Military Bus	Olive Green body, 'Army Personnel'. Not issued	NPP
419	1965	Land Rover and Missile Carrier	Olive Green body, three White missiles	**£200-250**

Emergency vehicles

207	1964	Wadham Ambulance	Cream body without Red crosses, with stretcher and patient	**£200-300**
			White body with Red crosses, with stretcher and patient	**£300-400**
256	1966	Jaguar 3.4 'POLICE' Car	White or Black. Very few exist with undamaged aerial or roof sign	**£200-275**
258	1963	'R.A.C.' Land Rover	Dark Blue body, 'RADIO RESCUE', 108 mm	**£100-125**
309	1965	Police 'Z' Car	Ford Zephyr police car from the BBC-TV series 'Z-Cars'.	
			1st type with aerial and 'POLICE' sign, White body	**£130-160**
			2nd type with no aerial or police sign. Black body	**£300-400**
			2nd type (no aerial or police sign), White body	**£300-400**
316	1966	'FIRE DEPT' Land Rover	Red body, suspension, two firemen, 112 mm	**£125-150**
402	1966	Land Rover 'MOTORWAYS'	Orange / Blue body, hook, Blue 'CRASH SERVICE' logo	**£100-125**
409	1966	Leyland 'Black Maria'	Blue body, 'Police', policeman and villain. Not issued	NPP

Caravans, Boats, Motor Scooter

135	1961	14ft Sailing Dinghy and Trailer	Blue / Grey, Dark Blue / Red, Dark Blue / White, or	
			Red / White boat (with or without cover), plastic trailer	**£40-55**
135	1964	14ft GP Sailing Dinghy	Brown or Yellow boat on trailer, 128 mm	**£35-45**
139	1960	Eccles E.16 Caravan	Blue body, White roof, 146 mm	NPP
229	1966	Lambretta	Pale Grey body, Red or White side panels, Black seat	**£175-225**
264	1962	Tourist Caravan	Blue body, White roof, 152 mm	**£90-120**
			Yellow body, White roof	**£70-90**
			Tan body, White roof	**£80-125**

Garages and Equipment, Road Signs and Accessories

Garages and equipment

L146	'SHELL' lamp standard	**£10-15**
L147	'SHELL' sign	**£10-15**
L148	'SHELL' petrol pump	**£10-15**
L148	Trade pack, Blue card box of 6 of L148 pumps	**£80-100**
L149	Oil Dispenser Rack	**£10-15**
L159	'BP' Lamp Standard	**£10-15**
162	'BP' or 'SHELL' Filling Station	**£35-45**
162/1/2/3	Garages, each	**£15-20**
163	'BP' Petrol Pump	**£10-15**
164	'BP' Forecourt Sign	**£10-15**
172a	'SHELL' Garage Set	**£50-75**
172b	'BP' Garage Set	**£50-75**

Road signs and accessories

L208/B	Road Traffic Signs: 20 different signs issued, each	**£5-10**
L1271/	Road Direction Signs: /1 Portsmouth, /2 Guildford, /3 Bristol, /4 Birmingham, /5 Biggar, /6 Dumfries	**£10-15**

Bus Stops: No details available **£10-15**

Road sections: Straights, curves, T-junctions. Each **£6-8**

Plastic Figures: In groups set on a card. Figures include: Garage Personnel, Newspaperman/Milkman/Postman, Doctor/Parson/Schoolmaster, 2 Policeman and an RAC Man, 3 Schoolboys, 2 Children and a Man (in country clothes), 3 Roadmen and Brazier and 3 Roadmen and Road Drill/Planks/Walls

Per card **£5-10**

Retailer's sheet of any six cards of figures **£75-95**

Spot-On Presentation and Gift Sets

Colours of individual items are not listed. It is possible to find virtually any factory colour that was available at the time of manufacture in Spot-On Gift Sets. Early sets should contain Picture Cards, Fleet Owners leaflets and Magazine Club leaflets.

Ref	Year(s)	Set name	Contents	Market Price Range
A	1960	Presentation Set 'A'	102 Bentley, 108 Triumph TR3, 114 Jaguar 3.4, 118 BMW Isetta, 154 Austin A40	£350-450
No.0	1960	Presentation Set	106a/1 Austin Articulated Dropside Lorry, 100 Ford Zodiac, 103 Rolls-Royce Silver Wraith, 104 MGA and 113 Aston Martin	£400-500
No.1	1960	Presentation Set	100 Ford Zodiac, 101 Armstrong-Siddeley, 103 Rolls-Royce and 104 MGA	£500-600
No.2	1960	Presentation Set	109/3 ERF Dropside Lorry, 101 Armstrong-Siddeley, 102 Bentley Continental and 105 Austin-Healey 100/6	£500-600
No.3	1960	Presentation Set	Contains 111a/1 Ford Thames Trader, 101 Armstrong-Siddeley, 104 MGA, 108 Triumph TR3a, 112 Jensen 541, 113 Aston Martin, 114 Jaguar 3.4	£500-600
No.4	1960	Presentation Set	106a/1 Austin Articulated Dropside Lorry, 109/3 ERF Dropside Lorry, 100 Ford Zodiac, 107 Jaguar XK-SS, 112 Jensen 541	£500-600
No.4a	1963	Presentation Set	104 MGA, 105 Austin-Healey, 107 Jaguar XK-SS and 108 Triumph TR3a	£300-400
No.5		Presentation Set	118 BMW Isetta, 119 Meadows Frisky Sport and 131 Goggomobil Super Regent	£250-300
No.6		'Miniature' Presentation Set	131 Goggomobil, 185 Fiat 500, 193 NSU Prinz and 211 Austin Seven	£300-400
			Variation with 210/1 'ROYAL MAIL' Van instead of 193 NSU Prinz	£300-400
No.6a		'Miniature' Presentation Set	131 Goggomobil, 185 Fiat 500, 119 Meadows Frisky and 211 Austin Seven	£300-400
No.7		Rally Presentation Set	Contains 166 Renault Floride, 191 Sunbeam Alpine, 211 Austin Seven, 213 Ford Anglia, 215 Daimler Dart, 217 Jaguar 'E'-type	£500-600
No.8		Presentation Set	157 Rover, 191 Sunbeam, 213 Ford Anglia, 216 Volvo, 258 RAC Land Rover	£500-600
No.9		Presentation Set	122 Milk Float, 145 Routemaster Bus, 193 NSU Prinz, 207 Wadham Ambulance, 211 Austin Seven, 256 Jaguar Police Car	NGPP
No.10		Presentation Set	122 Austin Seven, 145 Routemaster Bus, 157 Rover 3 litre, 158a/2 Bedford Tanker, 185 Fiat 500, 165 Vauxhall Cresta, 166 Renault Floride, 211 Austin Seven, 215 Daimler Dart and 262 Morris 1100	£400-500
No.14		Presentation Set	211 Austin 7 Mini, 154 Austin A40, 156 Mulliner Coach, 191/1 Sunbeam (Hardtop), 122 'UNITED DAIRIES' Milk Float, 157sl Rover 3 Litre with lights	£500-600
173		Terrapin Building Set	A constructional set	£20-30
208/a		Road Construction Set	4 workmen, brazier, hut, poles, road sections and 18 other small items	£125-175
259		Garage Set	A constructional set	£20-30
701		'His, Her's, Junior's' Set	219 Austin-Healey Sprite, 267 MG 1100, 280 Vauxhall Cresta, in 'window' box	£200-250
702		Gift Set 702	270 Zephyr Six, 274 Morris 1100 and canoe, 286 Austin 1800 and 135 Dinghy	£200-250
702(a)		Gift Set 702	195 VW Rally, 217 Jaguar 'E' type, 261 Volvo P1800, 287 Hillman Minx	£300-350
212	1963	Car, Dinghy and Trailer Set	Contains 165 Vauxhall PA Cresta and 135 GP Dinghy	£125-150
269	1965	Ford Zephyr and Caravan	Contains 270 plus 264 Caravan	£125-175
308	1965	Land Rover and Trailer	Green bodywork, Fawn cover, 170 mm	£65-85
406	1966	Hillman Minx and Dinghy	Contains 287 Hillman Minx and 135 GP Dinghy and trailer	£70-95
MG1	1966	'Magicar Motoring' Set	501 Jaguar Mk.10 and 502 Rolls-Royce, roadway sections and traffic cones	NGPP
MG2		'Magicar Motoring' Set	503 Bentley S3 and 504 Ferrari Superfast, roadway sections and traffic cones	NGPP

'Tommy Spot' Gift Sets

All include a building kit and Tommy Spot figure.

Ref	Set name	Contents	Market Price Range
801	'Home with Tommy Spot'	287 Hillman Minx (with Mr Spot), 270 Ford Zephyr Six with driver, pictorial stand	£200-275
802	'Cops 'n' Robbers with Tommy Spot'	309 BBC-TV 'Z-Car' with driver and criminal, 276 Jaguar and driver, pictorial stand	£275-350
803	'Superville Garage with Tommy Spot'	286 Austin 1800 with driver, 279 MG Midget, two garage workers, pictorial stand	£200-275
804	'Sailing with Tommy Spot'	280 Vauxhall PB Cresta and sailing dinghy with Tommy and Mr Spot, pictorial stand	£150-225
805	'Fire with Tommy Spot'	316 Fire Dept Land Rover and trailer, two firefighters, pictorial stand	£195-260
806	'Royal Occasion with Tommy Spot'	260 Royal Rolls-Royce with chauffeur and royal passengers, 6 guardsmen, pictorial stand	£450-650
807	'Pit stop with Tommy Spot'	Mercedes-Benz 230 SL and Jaguar 'S', two racing drivers, pictorial stand	£300-400
808	'Motorway Rescue with Tommy Spot'	402 'Crash Service' Land Rover and mechanic, A.A. van and man, pictorial stand	£400-500

Catalogues, Leaflets and Pictures

Ref	Issued	Publication	Cover, features, contents	Market Price Range
---	1959	Early issue	Red cover featuring a Target plus the dividers and diagram of Rolls Royce 'LTP 103'. Wording: '1/42' and 'SPOT-ON MODELS BY TRI-ANG'. Contains 8 pages	£30-40
---	1959	'1st Edition'	Village scene with Spot-On buildings and models, 'Tri-ang' logo in bright red, '6d', 'dividers' mark, 'SCALE 1/42'. Thick numbered pages with superb pictures	£30-40
---	1960	'2nd Edition'	As 1st Edition but 'Tri-ang' logo in maroon and pages not numbered	£25-35
100M/C.P.C./6.61	1961	'3rd Edition'	Same as 2nd Edition	£20-30
5a7383/DP	1963	'4th Edition'	Royal Rolls-Royce on cover, '3d', Page 19 shows the new Presentation Sets 5-10 and 14	£20-30
---	1964	'5th Edition'	Blue Austin 1800 (286) on cover, '2d', concertina type leaflet featuring new type of Black/Red window boxes for Gift Sets and single models	£20-£30
---	1965	'6th Edition'	Cover again features 286 Austin 1800 plus 289 Morris Minor, '2d', concertina type leaflet which includes 'Tommy Spot' and 'Magicar' listings and pictures	£20-£30
---	1966	'7th Edition'	Booklet type featuring 407 Mercedes 230 SL and 287 Hillman Minx, '6d', 'Tommy Spot' featured with 'Royal Occasion' set and Car Spotters guide	£20-30

Leaflets and Model Pictures

The early 'blue boxes' for cars and small commercial vehicles and the early card boxes for the large commercial vehicles contained a model picture and a yellow / blue / white leaflet listing the models available. Prices of model picture cards can vary depending on the rarity of the model itself within a price range from £5 to £25. Spot-On 'Picture wallets' are to be found at £15-20. It should be noted that no 'blue box' model or early large commercial boxed model is complete without the model picture. Leaflets are not uncommon and may be obtained for £2-3.

Trade Display Material

Ref			Market Price Range
---	---	Electric revolving Trade Display Unit	£300-400
---	---	Glass shop-sign with 'SPOT-ON MODELS' in red/black/yellow design, 25 inches long	£150-200

Spot-On New Zealand issues

When Tri-ang took over the production of Dinky Toys in 1967 they stopped production of Spot-On Models in the United Kingdom. Fourteen models were subsequently produced by the Tri-ang Pedigree company of New Zealand from the original dies sent out from the U.K.

New Zealand production lasted just two years and ceased in 1969 / 70. The New Zealand model reference numbers were different to their UK counterparts

as listed in the Spot-On 7th Edition catalogue. Extras such as roof racks and luggage were not included with NZ issues and the models were housed in New Zealand yellow cellophane 'window' boxes. The following listing first appeared in 'Mini Cars' ('The News Sheet for Caledonian Autominologists'), dated September 1972 and was prepared by Eric Brockie in New Zealand. Thanks are due to James McLachlan (Club Secretary) for his kind permission to reproduce the listing.

UK no.	NZ no.	Model name	Difference from UK version	NZ colour	Market Price Range
289	101	Morris Minor 1000	Not manufactured in New Zealand	-	NPP
219	102	Austin-Healey Sprite	Colour only	White body, Red seats	£200-300
281	103	MG Midget	No Policeman included	Dark Green or Red, White seats	£200-300
404	104	Morris Mini Van	No 'Shell' logo, ladder or mechanism	Yellow	£100-150
267	105	MG 1100	Single colour only	Green	£100-150
262	106	Morris 1100	Same as UK issue	Blue	£100-150
287/406	107	Hillman Minx	No roof rack or dinghy	Green	£100-150
280	108	Vauxhall Cresta	Single colour only	Blue	£100-150
276	109	Jaguar 'S' type	Same as UK issue	Blue	£200-300
286	110	Austin 1800	No lady driver or schoolboy	Light Brown	£100-150
270	111	Ford Zephyr 6	Same as UK issue	White	£100-150
308	112	Land Rover	No trailer included	Olive Green body, Pale Green tilt	£100-150
407	114	Mercedes-Benz 230 SL	Not manufactured in New Zealand	-	NPP
401	115	Volkswagen Variant	No roof rack or skis	Dark Blue, Red int., White hatchback	£200-300
279	116	MG PB Midget	Same as UK issue	Blue, Black	£150-200
265	117	'TONIBELL' Ice Cream Van	Same as UK issue	Turquoise	£200-300
402	118	Crash Service Land Rover	Same as UK issue	Orange, Blue	£100-150
316	119	Fire Dept Land Rover	No Firemen	Red	£100-150
415	120	RAF Land Rover	Not manufactured in New Zealand	-	NPP

The 'Cotswold Village' series

The 'Cotswold Village' items are rare and it is suggested that larger buildings (church, shop, etc) are likely to be in the region of £100 - £150, while smaller items might be anything from £10 - £50 depending on size, complexity, etc.

These price levels can only be applied

to pristine items in perfect original boxes.

1	School	5	Antique Shop
2a	Haystack	6	General Store
3	'Cornerstones' Cottage	7	Bourton Town Hall
4	'Fourways' Cottage	8	Barn
4b	'The Cot' Cottage	9	Public House
		10	Farm House
		11	Manor House
		12	Post Office

13	Church
14	Forge
15	Memorial Stone
16	Water Well
16a	Stocks
-	Set of Trees
-	Bridge Sides

| **Illustrations on opposite page** | **Top**: Tri-ang Spot-On Models were advertised regularly in the 'Eagle' comic; this example is from the 19 March 1960 edition. **Below**: Page 109 of Gamages of Holborn 1961 'Model Book' |

Spot-on Auction Results

SPOT-ON MODELS sold by Vectis Model Auctions,
Fleck Way, Thornaby, Stockton-on-Tees. TS17 9JZ
Condition abbreviations appearing in Vectis Auctions catalogues:
M = Mint, NM = Near Mint, NMB = Near Mint Boxed, EP = Excellent Plus, E = Excellent, EB = Excellent Boxed, GP = Good Plus, VG = Very Good, G = Good, GB = Good Box, F = Fair, FB = Fair Box, P = Poor.

CARS
107 Jaguar XKSS, metallic blue, NM in E box £190
112 Jensen 541, EP in E box £110
113 Aston-Martin DB3, pale blue, E Boxed £120
114 Jaguar 3.4, beige, E boxed £160
115 Bristol 406, E in EP box £150
183 Humber Super Snipe , blue, EP in GP box £120
213 Ford Anglia, grey, EP in NM box £170
215 Daimler Dart SP250, blue, NM in E box £110
217 Jaguar 'E'-type, light blue, E in NM box £120
219 Austin-Healey Sprite, pale blue, M in GP box £100
259 Ford Consul Classic, turquoise, E Boxed £110
260 Rolls-Royce, NM in perspex case £240
276 Jaguar 'S'-type, blue, E in GP box £120
267 MG 1100 Saloon, red/white, NM in GP box £110
309 Ford Zephyr 6, white, NM in E box £190

309 Ford Zephyr 'Z Cars' E in GP box £70
316 Fire Department Land-Rover, E in G box £50
402 Crash Service Land-Rover, E in GP box £70

COMMERCIAL VEHICLES
106a/1 Austin Prime Mover, E in G box £180
106 Austin Lorry with MGA in Crate, GP in F box £150
109/3 ERF 68g with Box Float, pale yellow/black, G in G box £140
109/3b ERF 68g with Barrel Load, E in GP box £280
110/3 AEC Lorry 'British Road Services', GP in G box £350
110/3d AEC Mammoth Major 8 with oil drum load, EP in G box £400
110/4 AEC Tanker 'Shell/BP', E in E box £680
116 Caterpillar D9 Bulldozer, G in GP box £440
145 LT Routemaster Double Decker Bus, 2nd type E in GP £260
156 Mulliner Coach, blue/silver, E in E box £240
158a/2 Bedford 'S'-type Tanker 'Shell/BP', E in GP £520
207 Wadham Ambulance, GP in P box £160
210/2 Morris GPO Telephone Van, NM, boxed £110
271 Express Dairy Van, E in G box £90

SETS
No.0 Presentation Set, E in NM box £700
802 'Cops 'n' Robbers' Tommy Spot Gift Set, E in G box £260

282

EAGLE 19 *March* 1960

SPOT-ON
1/42 SCALE MODELS BY Tri-ang

NEW THIS MONTH!

FX4

AUSTIN TAXI

KL 10-10 JONES MOBILE RAPIDE

TELEPHONE BOOTH L44

All Spot-On 1/42 Scale models by Tri-ang are to scale in all dimensions. Only Spot-On offers a complete highway system—roadway sections, signs and model buildings. Ask your dealer for details.

SPOT-ON models by Tri-ang

Scale 1/42

Each model is true to scale, 1/42nd of the size of the original vehicle, and built to the same high standard. Every perfect miniature is a collectors' item and justly deserves pride of place in your collection. Many Spot-on models have Independent Suspension, Plated Radiators and Bumpers, also Windows, Number Plates, Seats, Steering Wheels and beautiful duo-tone finish.

No. 118 BMW ISETTA. Length 2¼"   2/9

No. 113 ASTON MARTIN D.B.3. Length 4⅛"   3/6

No. 115 BRISTOL 406 with independent suspension. Length 4⁹⁄₁₆"   4/9

No. 131 GOGGOMOBIL 'SUPER' Length 2⅜"   2/11

No. 154 AUSTIN A40 with independent suspension Length 3½"   3/9

No. 157 ROVER 3 Litre, with independent suspension, plated radiator, etc. Length 4¾"   5/3

No. 155 AUSTIN TAXI with independent suspension Length 4¾"   4/6

No. 117 JONES CRANE KL 10/10. Length 7⅝"   24/11

No. 110/2B AEC MAMMOTH MAJOR 8, with brick load. Finished in London Brick Co. livery. Length 8½"   14/11

No. 165 VAUXHALL CRESTA, with independent suspension, plated radiator, etc. Length 4⅜"   4/11

GAMAGES, HOLBORN, LONDON, E.C.1.   HOLborn 8484   *Gamages Convenient Payment Plan—See Page 3*

Miscellaneous and Minor Manufacturers

Many toys and models exist about which we know very little. The 1940s in particular saw a proliferation of small manufacturers (often only a one-man operation in a North London shed). In this post-wartime period the established manufacturers were engaged in an export drive that meant shortages of products at home. Not surprisingly, enterprising ex-servicemen and others turned their hands to toy production on a scale that they could manage. Their range was small (sometimes only one product) and they were often in business for only a year or two.

One outcome of this is that some toys and models discovered in attics or at swapmeets present us with a puzzle. Who made the item? When were they in production? Where was the maker's workshop? Very often there is no information at all on the product or simply a statement to the fact that it was 'Made in England'. Identification is sometimes difficult – but is it impossible?

Since the 9th Edition was published, some very interesting additional information has been obtained and we are delighted to be able to pass on the details below. However, our lists below are far from complete and we do still require your help, so if you have any information on any of the manufacturers mentioned, please write to: The Editor, Swapmeet Publications, PO Box 47, Felixstowe, Suffolk, IP11 9HE.

Arbur	Condon	John Hill & Co.	Mafwo	Tal Developments
Baxtoys	W.H.Cornelius	Jolly Roger	Millbo	Teddy Toys
Betal	Denzil Skinner	Kenbo	Millbro	Industries
BMC	Eaglewall Plastics	Kenbro	Model Toys	Toby
Bren L Toys	Empro	Kemlow	Moultoys Ltd	Toy Products
Castle Art	Gaiety	Kitmaster	Salco	Trent Products
Cherilea	Goody Toys	Knight	Slikka	Wardie
City Toys	Johillco	Louis Marx	Sundaw	

ARBUR PRODUCTS   BREN L TOYS   TOBY   JOLLY ROGER

John Hill & Co.
i) **Roman Gladiator Set**: Gold Chariot and Charioteer, 2 horses, 5 Centurion Gladiators + Officer in pale cream toga. Boxed**£125-150**
ii) **Roman Chariot**: Gold Chariot with 2 horses and Gold Charioteer..........................**£80-100**
Coronation (1935 Jubilee) **Coach Set**, 4 white horses + 2 riders, 6 'Beefeaters', 6 Footmen. The coach is 23cm long and contains figures of King George V & Queen Mary. Blue box marked 'Jubilee'..........NGPP
Jubilee Coach, King George V and Queen Mary in a 'coronation'-style coach with 4 white horses, 2 riders, 6 mounted Life Guards, 6 Beefeaters, 6 footmen, blue box..........

Brimtoy (diecast issues)
1948-50 **Vauxhall Saloon**. Yellow body, Silver trim, cast wheels, plain card box with model picture................**£100-150**

Sundaw Products (c1950)
H130 **Single-deck Motor Bus**. Red body, 'TRANSPORT SERVICES' logo, rubber wheels, Red/white end-flap box with model picture................**£250-350**
H131 **Double-deck Motor Bus**. Green body, 'TRANSPORT SERVICES' logo, rubber wheels, Green/white end-flap box with model picture................**£400-600**
NB Similar models were sold by Vectis Auctions Ltd in December 2000 for **£180** (H130) and **£600** (H131). See colour section.

True-to-Type Models (similar in size to Matchbox Miniatures; all have unpainted cast wheels)
i) **Cable-Layer Truck**. Green truck, Grey/Cream cable drum................**£25-35**

ii) **Tip Cart Truck**. Red body and tipper**£25-35**
iii) **Excavator Truck**.
Green body, Blue back................**£25-35**
NB The three models listed above were sold by Vectis Auctions Ltd in 2000 for **£800**!

Kembo
Articulated Lorry. A heavy lorry cab (tinplate base) and open semi-trailer with curved front board and 'KEMBO TRANSPORT' paper labels. Wheels are Minic-style tinplate with rubber tyres...NGPP
Saloon Car. Cast wheels, no base........**£15-20**

Kemlow
Made in the 1950s by Kemlow's Diecasting Products Ltd., Wood Green, London. Their distributors were B.J. Ward Ltd. (trading as 'Wardie Products'). Products included:
'PICKFORDS' Removal Van, 1:60 ....
Articulated Timber Truck, 1:50 ....
Farm Tractor and Trailer, 1:60 ....
Caravan. 1:43 ....
Ford Zephyr Mk.I, 1:43 ....
Thornycroft Mighty Antar, 1:43 and 1:60...
Flat Truck, 1:50 ....
Armoured Car, 1:60 ....
Field Gun, 1:60 ....

Minitoy
Racing Car. Simple one-piece body casting which includes cast stub axles for the solid cast wheels. 90mm long................NGPP

Jolly Roger
Made c1946/7 by Tremo Mouldings, Cardiff. Boxed models include:
Racing Car ....
Saloon Car (see main picture above)............

Bradcars (c1950-55)
Bradshaws Model Products. 1:75 scale. One-piece castings, no interiors. Boxed models include:
Austin A30, **Riley 1.5 litre**, **Austin 7**, **Morris 6**.

Gaiety Toys (late 1940s)
Castle Art Products Ltd., Birmingham.
Models in boxes are rare. Products known:
Morgan 3-wheel Sports Car, 4.75in. long....
Racing Car, single driver, 5in. long..............
Racing Car, driver/co-driver, 4in. long.........
Racing Car, single driver, 3.25in. long.........
Fire Engine................
Models are to be found painted in various colours, often chromed and sometimes motorised.

Sacul
'Rob Roy' Set. This film-related boxed set contains Rob Roy in full tartan with sword and an English Redcoat with sword
................**£1,000-1,250**
'Bill and Ben' Set. A television-related set containing Bill, Ben, Little Weed and 2 terracotta flower pots **£100-200**

Cherilea
Set 1001 'Spacemen'. Contains rocket, 3 robots, 6 spacemen, 2 space animals
................**£500-600**

Gilco
No. 4 Traffic Sign Set. Contains 24 items including Road Signs, Traffic Lights, Telegraph Poles and two Belisha Beacons. Pictorial card box. **£80-100**

Betal
Saloon Car. Seen with and without clockwork motor (photo opposite)......**£15-20**

The **Kembo Articulated Lorry** listed on the opposite page. Its tinplate base has 'KEMBO' impressed into it.
Photo: Peter Brighty

The **Kembo Saloon Car** shown on the left is a very similar casting to the **Betal Saloon Car** on
the right, but has detail differences. The Betal product has been observed with and without
a clockwork motor; in both cases the wheels are solid castings.   Photographs: Swapmeet Publications.

Kemlow 'PICKFORDS' Van

Set of Petrol Pumps marked
'A Wardie Product'.
Photo: Peter Brighty

MISCELLANEOUS ITEMS sold by
Lacy Scott & Knight
10, Risbygate Street, Bury St Edmunds, Suffolk, IP33 3AA.
Condition abbreviations used in their catalogues:
M = Mint, **G** = Good, **F** = Fair, **P** = Poor, **R** = Repainted, **U/B** = Unboxed.

Chad Valley Trade Van 'GUYS MOTORS Ltd.', clockwork
with key, finished in green, in G original box, M **£160**
Meccano No.1 Sports Tourer M245, red/blue with hood and
spare parts, in original box, G in F-G box **£680**
Meccano No.1 Sports Car, green/yellow with red seats, G U/B **£220**
Meccano No.2 Constructor Car, red/blue, white tyres, boat tail
with driver in cream, G-M U/B..**£380**
Meccano No 2 Constuctor Car, yellow/green with lighting
accessory set and parts, F **£650**
Wells, pre-war clockwork Rolls-Royce based on Sedanca-de-Ville,
cream/black, seated chauffeur, M.......................................**£150**
Wells, pre-war clockwork lithographed Town Car, cream/orange, F-G**£100**
Kingsbury Sunbeam 1,000hp Record Car, red, pressed steel,
clockwork, missing driver, (R) **£160**
Kingsbury 'Bluebird' Record Car, c1929 blue body, missing driver **£180**
Kingsbury Seagraves 'Golden Arrow' Record Car, gold body (R) **£130**
Chad Valley No.10045, lithographed printed aluminium **London Bus
biscuit tin** in G original plain card printed box, M **£700**
Chad Valley No.10032 Games Delivery Van with squared games
in F-G original box, M **£680**
Chad Valley No.10003 Streamlined Racing Car, lime green pressed
aluminium lithographed body in F original box, M............................**£250**

MISCELLANEOUS ITEMS sold by
Vectis Model Auctions, Stockton-on-Tees. TS17 9JZ
Condition abbreviations appearing in Vectis Auctions catalogues:
M = Mint, **NM** = Near Mint, **NMB** = Near Mint Boxed, **EP** = Excellent Plus,
E = Excellent, **EB** = Excellent Boxed, **GP** = Good Plus, **VG** = Very Good,
G = Good, **GB** = Good Box, **F** = Fair, **FB** = Fair Box, **P** = Poor.

MORESTONE
No.1 Foden Petrol Tanker 'Esso', E in E box...........................**£240**
No.2 Foden Long Distance Wagon, NM in E box..........................**£140**
No.3 Foden 14 ton Chain Lorry, NM in E box...........................**£150**
Articulated Car Transporter, orange/grey E in GP box.................**£260**
Gypsy Caravan, yellow/green/red, grey horse, Gypsy, E in G box...........**£250**
SHACKLETON
Foden FG 6 wheel Tipper, lime green, red mudguards, E in F box.........**£700**
Foden FG 6 wheel Platform Lorry, grey, red mudguards, E in F box ..**£1,150**
Dyson Trailer, dark green, E in G box **£150**
CHAD VALLEY, CLARK TOYS and CRESCENT TOYS
Chad Valley 'Guy Motors Ltd.', clockwork, green, E in G box **£190**
Chad Valley Motor Bus, National Single Decker, 'CV 10071',
'London De-Luxe Express Glasgow' on sides, E in G illustrated box **£240**
Clark Toys, 'Express Dairy' Electric Milk Float Wagon,
dark blue, E in E box **£160**
Crescent Toys 1809 Dextra Tractor (rare version), orange with
red plastic wheels, EP, unboxed **£250**
Crescent Toys very rare Dodgem Car, dark blue, child passenger.........**£130**
TRI-ANG MINIC Pre-war Issues
22m Transport Van, green cab, stone body 'Minic Transport', G **£120**
48m Breakdown Lorry, red cab, green body with transfers, G............**£160**
60m Double Decker Bus, 2nd Series, stone and red upper deck,
'Ovaltine' and 'Bovril' adverts, F-G ....Estimate £120-£150
TRI-ANG MINIC Post-war Issues
17m Vauxhall Tourer, red/black, E in F-G illustrated box.....................**£140**
18m Vauxhall Town Coupé, green/black, E in VG illustrated box **£170**
22m 'Carter Patterson & Pickfords' Van, red cab, green body, F-G.....**£100**
48m Breakdown Lorry, green/red, green crane, E in VG illustrated box...**£420**
52m Green Line Single Deck Bus, 'Green Line' to sides,
'Minic' to rear, F-G **£100**
66m 6-wheel Army Open Lorry, standard cab, camouflage, E in G box ..**£410**
71m Articulated Milk Tanker 'Minic Dairies', E in VG illustrated box .**£240**
73m Articulated Cable Lorry, red with green trailer, 2 cable drums,
VG in F-G illustrated box **£150**
103m Shutter Van, red forward control cab, 'Minic Transport' transfers,
E in VG illustrated box **£220**

Clockwork Jeep No. 2, folding windscreen, U.S. stars to bonnet,
spare wheel/jerrycan/key/leaflet, E in G-VG illustrated box **£240**
MECCANO
No.1 Constructor Car as Saloon Coupé, green/yellow, VG, G illus. box..**£280**
No.2 Constructor Car, blue with cream wings/running boards, driver E..**£580**
Two Seater Sports Car, cream with red wings and running boards,
E in G original box with illustrated label............................**£680**
HORNBY SPEED BOATS
Racer I, cream with green engine cover, 9", working order **£130**
Racer II, blue, white deck, windscreen, 12", working order, F in P box **£130**
Racer III, blue/cream deck, 2 windscreens, 16", working order (repaint)..**£100**
Venture, light green, white deck/cabin roof, 16", working order, F-G.......**£140**
SUTCLIFFE SPEED BOATS
Jupiter Ocean Pilot, red hull, white deck/cabins, E in G illustrated box.....**£90**
Racer I, red hull, white deck, blue engine cover, E in G illustrated box **£80**
Bluebird Speedboat, cream with Union Jack and 'Bluebird' transfers
to hull, 12", VG in VG illustrated box **£340**
Valiant Battleship, black hull, grey top, 12", G in VG illustrated box **£180**
METTOY
Monoplane, camouflage livery, clockwork, VG **£90**
Bomber Aircraft F19131, 19" long, camouflage livery, clockwork, VG ..**£300**
Airliner, 'Mettoy Airways', cream, blue/orange markings, 16" long, VG ..**£90**
Petrol Tanker 'Shell' and 'BP', red with yellow detail, clockwork, VG ..**£110**
Removal Lorry, grey cab with cardboard rear body 'Mettoy Removals
and Road Transport', 7.5", clockwork, VG **£200**
Refreshment Lorry with Six Wheels, red with highly detailed
lithography to sides, 9.5", VG...**£420**
Rapid Transport Lorry, red and black with yellow detail,
tipping rear body, working order, G-VG **£360**

MISCELLANEOUS ITEMS sold by
Christie's, South Kensington
Condition Abbreviations used in Christie's catalogues:
M = Mint, **E** = Excellent, **VG** = Very Good, **G** = Good, **F** = Fair, **P** = Poor.
Shackleton Foden FG6 Tipper, grey/blue, matching **Dyson Trailer**, VG **£376**
Meccano Trade Fair model of 'Titanic'-style ocean liner with
electric pitching action, VG **£1,116**
Retail display model of a **Two Tower Suspension Bridge**,
electrically operated, G-F **£528**
Meccano Outfit No.7, first type red and green, in original oak case
with hinged lid and two subsidiary drawers, with brass D-handles,
circa 1927, VG, case VG...**£3,172**
Wooden Counter-Top Retail Display Chest, red with five drawers
and contents, red and green, mid to late 1950's, many parts still
in original boxes and packing, VG overall **£3,290**
Meccano Outfit No. 10, red and green, original oak veneered case
with hinged lid, one subsidiary drawer, VG-E, case G-VG..............**£1,762**
Meccano Clockwork No. 1 Constructor Car, red and blue four seater
tourer, instructions and key, G in original G box **£352**

MISCELLANEOUS ITEMS sold by Wallis & Wallis,
West Street Auction Galleries, Lewes, Sussex, BN7 2NJ.
Condition abbreviations: **VG** = Very Good, **B** = Good.

Meccano No.6 Set dated 6-9-39, gold with blue, red wheels, blue cords,
in original two-layer box, guarantee/instructions, Mint/unused..........**£780**
Meccano 1932 Aeroplane Sets 1 and 1A, silver finish with red
components, contents G -VG for age, instructions, in G boxes..........**£430**
Hornby Clockwork Speed Boat No.1 'Martin', mid-blue hull,
white engine cover, key/instructions, VG in VG box **£320**
Tri-ang Minic 8m open Tourer, light grey, cream tonneau and wings, G..**£75**
Minic 21m Transport Van, green cab, red back, G original box **£130**
Tri-ang Minic 32m Dustcart, green cab, red back, VG.....................**£160**
Tri-ang Minic 48m Breakdown Lorry, red cab, green back with
red crane, G, in original box **£140**
Tri-ang Minic 48m Breakdown Lorry, 2nd Series, red cab, dark green
back with red crane, G, in original box................................**£300**
Tri-ang Minic 53m Single Decker Bus, TT green with black wings,
'Dorking' headboard, 'London Transport Greenline' to sides, G.........**£150**
Tri-ang Minic 60m Double Decker Bus (II version), red roof,
cream-red upper deck, all red lower deck, 'Tri-ang Toys' and
'Pedigree Dolls' adverts, 'LBL 174', G, in original box **£250**

Abbreviations

A

A.E.C.	Associated Equipment Company
AA	Anti-aircraft
A.A.	Automobile Association
ABC-TV	Associated British Cinemas (Television)
A.F.S.	Auxiliary Fire Service
AG	Amber glass
AMC	American Motor Corporation
APC	Armoured Personnel Carrier
ATV	Associated Television

B

BA	British Airways
BAC	British Airways Corporation
BB	Black base
BBC	British Broadcasting Corporation
BEA	British European Airways
BG	Blue glass
bhp	brake horsepower
BLMC	British Leyland Motor Corporation
BMC	British Motor Corporation
BMW	Bayrische Motoren-Werke
B.O.A.C.	British Overseas Airways
BP	British Petroleum
BPT	Black plastic tyres
BPW	Black plastic wheels
BR	British Railways
BRM	British Racing Motors
BRS	British Road Services
B.S.M.	British School of Motoring
BW	Black wheels

C

CG	Clear glass
CLE	Certificated Limited Edition
cv	chevaux-vapeur (a measure of power; translated into English, it literally means 'horse-steams')
C.W.S.	Co-operative Wholesale Society
cwt.	hundred-weight

D

DCMT	Die Casting Machine Tools
DH	De Havilland
Dk.	Dark (shade of colour)
DUKW	An amphibious military vehicle developed by General Motors in WWII. The letters are not initials or an abbreviation but simply part of an early drawing office reference.

E

EEC	European Economic Community
e.g.	exempli gratia (= 'for example')
EMI	Electrical & Musical Industries
ER	Elizabetha Regina, (E II R, Queen Elizabeth II)
ERF	Edwin Richard Foden
Est.	Established (or estimate/d)

F

Fiat	(or FIAT) Fabbrica Italiana Automobile Torino
fig(s)	figure(s)

G

GB	Green box, or Grey base
G.B.	Great Britain
GER	Great Eastern Railway
GG	Green glass
GMC	General Motors Corporation
GP	Grand Prix
GPO	General Post Office
GPW	Grey plastic wheels
GR	Georgius Rex
GS	Gift Set
GSP	Gift Set price
GTO	Gran Turismo Omologato
GTV	Gran Turismo Veloce
GWR	Great Western Railway

H

HM	His/Her Majesty
HMS	His/Her Majesty's Ship
H.M.V.	'His Masters Voice'
hp	horse-power
H.W.M.	Hersham & Walton Motors

I

ICI	Imperial Chemical Industries
INTER	(or INTL) International
I.O.M.	Isle of Man

J

JB	James Bond
JCB	Joseph C. Bamford

K

K.D.F.	Kraft durch Freude
K.L.G.	Kenelm Lee Guinness
K.L.M.	Koninklijke Luchtvaart Maatschappij NV (Dutch airline)

L

L.A.P.D.	Los Angeles Police Department
LE	Limited Edition
LM	Le Mans
LMS	London Midland & Scottish Railway
LNER	London & North Eastern Railway
LNWR	London & North Western Railway
Lt.	Light (shade of colour)
Ltd.	Limited Liability Company
LWB	Long wheel-base

M

MB	Matchbox
Met.	Metallic
MG	Make of car, ('Morris Garages')
M.I.C.A.	Matchbox International Collectors Association
mm.	millimetres
MOY	Models of Yesteryear
MPR	Market Price Range
MW	Metal wheels

N

N	North
NAAFI	Navy, Army & Air Force Institutes
N.A.S.A.	National Aeronautics & Space Administration
NB	nota bene ('mark well')
NCO	Non-Commissioned Officer
NGPP	No guide price at present
nhp	(or n.h.p.) nominal horsepower
No.	Number
NPP	No price possible
NS	(or n/s) Nearside

O

OG	Orange glass
OS	(or o/s) Offside

P

PB	Propeller blade(s)
PG	Purple glass
P.I.	Private Investigator
PLC	Public Limited Company
PO	Post Office
PSV	Public service vehicle
P.T.T.	Postes-Telephones-Telegraphes

R

RAC	Royal Automobile Club
RAF	Royal Air Force
R.C.M.P.	Royal Canadian Mounted Police
RHD	Right-hand drive
RM	Routemaster (bus)
RN(s)	Racing or Rally number(s)
RNLI	Royal National Life-boat Institution

S

S	South
SB	Silver base
SBRW	Solid black rubber wheels
SBX	Special box
SPW	Silver plastic wheels
SR	Southern Railway
St.	Saint or Street
SWB	Short wheel-base
SWRW	Solid white rubber wheels

T

TC	Twin carburettors
TDF	Tour de France
TK	Type of Bedford truck
TP	Twin Pack
TS	'Touring Secours'
TT	Two-tone (or Tourist Trophy)
TV	Television

U

UB	Unboxed, or Unpainted base
UK	United Kingdom
UN	United Nations
US	United States (of America)
USA	United States of America
USAAF	United States Army Air Force
USAF	United States Air Force
USS	United Space Starship
UW	Unpainted wheels

V

VW	Volkswagen

W

W	West
WB	Window box, or White base
WW	Wide wheels

Y

YB	Yellow box, or Yellow base
YMCA	Young Men's Christian Association

Official Company Acknowledgements

The names 'CORGI TOYS', 'CARS OF THE '50s', 'CORGITRONICS', 'CORGIMATICS', 'HUSKY', 'JUNIORS' and 'ROCKETS' are all acknowledged as trademarks of Corgi Classics Ltd. 'BRITAINS' is acknowledged as the trademark of Britains Ltd.
The name 'TRI-ANG' is acknowledged as a trademark of Hornby Hobbies Ltd., Margate, Kent.
The names 'MATCHBOX', 'MODELS of YESTERYEAR', 'DINKY TOYS' and 'SUPERFAST' are acknowledged as trademarks of Mattel Inc. USA.

Guide to Advertisers

MICA – The Matchbox International Collectors Association

MICA was founded in 1985 and provides its Members with a bi-monthly magazine full of useful information about past, present and future issues of Matchbox and the 'Dinky Collection' range of products. Aspects covered include such topics as new releases, variations and past issues and it has a members' advertisement section. Yearly social conventions are held providing talks, exhibitions on Matchbox and special Matchbox-only auctions. A special 'members only' model is issued to commemorate the event.

HOW TO CONTACT MICA

In the UK: Kevin McGimpsey, MICA, PO Box 120, Deeside, CH5 3HE, UK
Tel: 01244 539414, Fax: 01244 303335, E-mail: kevin@matchboxclub.com

In the US and CANADA:
Rita Schneider (Membership Secretary), MICA North America,
PO Box 28072, Waterloo, Ontario, Canada, N2L 6JB
Tel: 519 885-0529, Fax: 519 885-1902.

In AUSTRALIA, NEW ZEALAND and SOUTH PACIFIC:
Elaine Winkworth (Membership Secretary), MICA,
PO Box 26, Winston Hills, NSW 2153, Australia.
Telephone: (02) 9686-6685   Fax: (02) 9686-6970

RECOMMENDED READING

'The Yesteryear Book 1956 - 2000'. Kevin McGimpsey (Editor of the MICA Magazine) and Stewart Orr, assisted by several Club members have produced the ultimate book for MOY collectors. 250 pages packed with details of every variation plus diagrams and superb colour photos. Contact MICA for details.

'Collecting Matchbox Diecast Toys – the First Forty Years'
Published in 1989, it contains chapters on every aspect of Matchbox production since 1947. MICA members provided much of the technical input to this well-illustrated book which is now out of print. (The 'Regular Wheels' section was written by Nigel Cooper; Paul Carr wrote the Superfast section).

'Modern Diecast' information, contacts, collector clubs, etc.

CORGI CLASSICS
United Kingdom
Corgi Collector Club (Susan Pownall)
c/o Corgi Classics Ltd, Meridian East, Meridian Business Park, Leicester, LE19 1RL
E-mail: susie@collectorclubs.org.uk. Tel: 0870 607 1204.

Australia
Corgi Collector Club, Hobbyco Ltd., PO Box Q99, Queen Victoria Building Post Office, Sydney, NSW 2000.

New Zealand
Corgi Collector Club New Zealand, PO Box 63064, Papatoetoe South, Auckland, New Zealand.

USA
Corgi Collector Club, c/o Corgi Classics Inc., Suite 205, 430W. Erie Street, Chicgao IL60610.
Canada
Corgi Collector Club, 4461, Highway No.7, Unionville, Ontario, L3R 1M1.

LLEDO DAYS-GONE and VANGUARDS
Lledo Days-Gone Collectors Club
Ray Dowding, PO Box 5959, Halesowen, West Midlands, B63 3TS.
Tel: 0121 550 5959
E-mail: admin@lledocollectorsclub.com
Club website: www.lledocollectorsclub.com
Manufacturer's website: wwwlledo.com

EXCLUSIVE FIRST EDITIONS
For model information and subscriber service, please address all correspondence to:
Gilbow (Holdings) Limited, 32 Woodhall Road, Enfield, EN3 4LG

OXFORD DIE-CAST
PO Box 519, Berkhamstead, Herts., HP4 1 YR.
Tel: 01442 879996
Fax: 01442 877703
Website: www.oxforddiecast.co.uk